Det Norske Zinkkompani A/S
Eitrheim, Odda, Norway
Chapter 8, page 223

AIME World Symposium on Mining & Metallurgy of

LEAD & ZINC

Volume II

Extractive Metallurgy of Lead and Zinc

Editors

CARL H. COTTERILL

JOHN M. CIGAN

Sponsored by

Extractive Metallurgy Division

The Metallurgical Society of AIME

Mining & Exploration Division

Minerals Beneficiation Division

Society of Mining Engineers of AIME

The American Institute of Mining, Metallurgical, and Petroleum Engineers, Inc.

New York, New York 1970

Printed in the United States of America
by Port City Press, Inc., Baltimore, Maryland

Color Illustrations Printed by
Lew A. Cummings Co., Inc., Manchester, N. H.

Library of Congress Catalog Card Number 78-132404

ORGANIZATION OF AIME WORLD LEAD-ZINC SYMPOSIUM

CO-CHAIRMEN

Extractive Metallurgy Division, TMS

Carl H. Cotterill
Executive Office
American Zinc Company
St. Louis, Missouri

Mining and Exploration Division, SME

Donald O. Rausch
Tintic Division
Kennecott Copper Corporation
Eureka, Utah

Minerals Beneficiation Division, SME

Burt C. Mariacher
Colorado School of Mines Research Institute
Golden, Colorado

VICE CHAIRMEN

Extractive Metallurgy Division, TMS

John M. Cigan
Research Laboratories
St. Joe Minerals Corporation
Monaca, Pennsylvania

Mining and Exploration Division, SME

Robert L. Haffner
Bunker Hill Company
Kellogg, Idaho

Minerals Beneficiation Divisions, SME

Edward S. Frohling
Mountain States Enterprises, Inc.
Tucson, Arizona

KEYNOTE SESSION

Chairmen

H. R. Spedden
Metal Mining Division
Kennecott Copper Corporation
Salt Lake City, Utah

H. L. Young
Executive Office,
American Zinc Company
St. Louis, Missouri

PUBLICITY

Extractive Metallurgy Division, TMS

ROBERT B. MCGEORGE
American Smelting and Refining Company
New York, New York

Mining and Exploration Division, SME

J. B. ELIZONDO
American Metal Climax, Inc.
New York, New York

Minerals Beneficiation Division, SME

D. B. SMITH
American Metal Climax, Inc.
New York, New York

POST-CONVENTION TOURS

Extractive Metallurgy Division, TMS

CHARLES DEARMOND
Anaconda Company
New York, New York

Mining and Exploration Division, SME

F. H. MAIN
New Jersey Zinc Company
New York, New York

Minerals Beneficiation Division, SME

F. J. PISACANE
Parsons-Jurden Corporation
New York, New York

FREE-FORM SESSIONS

Chairman

T. I. MOORE
American Zinc Company
St. Louis, Missouri

COMMITTEES FOR THE SYMPOSIUM AND VOLUME II

ALBERT W. SCHLECHTEN
Vice President-Academic
Colorado School of Mines
Golden, Colorado

ROBERT K. WARING
Consultant
RFD 1
Palmerton, Pennsylvania

SESSION CHAIRMEN

J. V. ANDERSON
President
Canadian Electrolytic Zinc Company
Toronto, Ont., Canada

ANGUS BETHUNE
Vice President and General Manager
Matthiessen & Hegeler Zinc Company
LaSalle, Illinois

H. ROBERT BIANCO
Assistant Manager
St. Joe Minerals Corporation
Herculaneum, Missouri

ALLEN BOOTH
Manager
Blackwell Zinc Company
Blackwell, Oklahoma

W. E. MCFADDEN
Zinc Plant Superintendent
Hudson Bay Mining & Smelting Company
Flin Flon, Man., Canada

EARL R. MARBLE
Assistant to the Director of Research
American Smelting & Refining Company
South Plainfield, New Jersey

PETER R. MEAD
Technical Manager
Sulphide Corporation (Pty.), Ltd.
Boolaroo, N.S.W., Australia

HERMAN MICHAELIS
Research Director
Berzelius Metallhutten GMBH
Duisburg-Wanheim, West Germany

THOMAS I. MOORE
Consulting Engineer
American Zinc Company
St. Louis, Missouri

THOMAS J. O'KEEFE
Department of Metallurgical Engineering
University of Missouri-Rolla
Rolla, Missouri

A. C. POMMERIE
Technical Director
Royale Asturienne des Mines
Paris, France

S. TOKUNAGA
Consulting Engineer
Mitsui Mining & Smelting Company
Tokyo, Japan

H. R. WAMPLER
Vice President-Manufacturing
American Zinc Company
St. Louis, Missouri

FOREWORD

In all professions, the state-of-the-art merits formal examination periodically. No less is true of the Mining and Metallurgy of Lead and Zinc. The AIME Volume No. 121 on the metallurgy of these metals, so capably edited by Dr. C. R. Hayward in 1936, remains a remarkable landmark in its field, despite publication of individual papers of quality on the subject in the 34 years elapsed.

The Proceedings of this 1970 World Symposium on the Mining and Metallurgy of Lead and Zinc have been three years in preparation, involving Co-Chairmen from three Divisions of AIME (the Extractive Metallurgy Division of The Metallurgical Society and the Minerals Beneficiation and Mining and Exploration Divisions of the Society of Mining Engineers) and a host of committeemen and authors from around the world. The Symposium site of St. Louis was chosen principally due to its proximity to the major "New Lead Belt" of Southeast Missouri. Too, this was timely, inasmuch as the discovery and development of the early 1960's had resulted in completion by 1969 of five new lead mills, two new lead smelters, and major expansion of a third smelter.

Publication of this work was completed before oral presentation of the papers, thus the recording of discussion of the papers was precluded in exchange for timeliness of the bound two-volume set. Also unrecorded are the "Free-Form" discussion sessions covering ten narrow operating subjects for in-depth, off-the-record interchange of ideas. Seven field trips, scheduled on the day immediately preceding and the day following the Symposium, visited the nearby lead mines and mills, three lead smelters, and two zinc smelters. Finally, four one-week post-Symposium tours were conducted through some of the typical lead and/or zinc mines, mills, and smelters in the USA, Canada, and Mexico.

Lead and zinc are truly international commodities, so that developments in one part of the world inevitably and rapidly affect the industry and its technology elsewhere. Thus, professional interchange on methods of operation must transcend national boundaries in order to keep the whole industry viable in its constant struggle to wrest from Nature her ever more jealously guarded metals. Therefore we have made a special effort to invite descriptions of the most modern, yet typical, cross section of lead and zinc operating plants and processes worldwide, be they mine, mill, smelter, or refinery. It is our firm belief that the monumental effort expended in acquiring, tabulating, and publishing the comprehensive inventory of lead and zinc mines, mills, smelters, and refineries with their pertinent characteristics will prove to have been among the most worthwhile of our collective labors.

With an eye to the future, our guidelines for authors requested that the paper set forth explicit tonnages, assays, efficiencies, man-hours, and equipment descriptions at each stage in the process. We expect that many in the next generation of minerals engineers (and faculty) will be the beneficiaries of this work, even beyond the immediate value of today's practicing mining and metallurgical engineers.

Under the objective aegis of the American Institute of Mining, Metallurgical, and Petroleum Engineers' professionalism, we have gratefully found ready cooperation from authors, committee members, and their companies. Acknowledgment likewise is due the invaluable assistance of the permanent staff of the Society of Mining Engineers of AIME, and to the forbearance of our respective companies in regard to both expense and time.

CARL H. COTTERILL
BURT C. MARIACHER
DONALD O. RAUSCH

June 12, 1970
St. Louis, Missouri, USA

PREFACE TO VOLUME II

Of the some 37 papers published in this Extractive Metallurgy volume of the Proceedings, we have chosen to duplicate three chapters which are of common interest to both the miner and the metallurgist, in order that each volume will be complete unto itself, although the books are superior as a two-volume set. Without apology, we draw your attention to the decidedly multinational complexion of the entire Symposium and therefore ask you to savor the differences in expressions in their English translation as you read from paper to paper. Likewise, you will note the considerable variation in seeming depth and quality of treatment on subject matter even though the papers were prepared under the same set of stringent Guidelines from the Chairmen. For this we must ask your indulgence, as the task of asking for author revision was not compatible with the goal of timely publication. Nonetheless, we do feel that the paper quality is generally excellent throughout and the effort as a whole will prove to have been quite worthwhile for the industry and the profession.

All papers in this volume were specifically invited after a thorough questionnaire examination of all significant producers of lead and zinc in the world outside the so-called Eastern Bloc nations (invitations accepted by personnel of the USSR Ministry of Mines to present summaries of Soviet plant practice on both zinc and lead subsequently became unavailable and were then cancelled from the Symposium). Selections were then recommended by our "deans of the industry" Advisory Council based upon modern practice, keeping in mind process and geographical balance and in some cases uniqueness and innovations. Where possible, the choice favored plants or processes which had not recently appeared in the technical literature. The Chairmen desired this work to encompass an across-the-board updating of the state-of-the-art, thus considered only significantly successful operating plants or processes, avoiding pilot plant and designed plants even though extremely promising.

Regarding the latter, the Extractive Metallurgy Division, TMS, joined with the Minerals Beneficiation Division, SME, in sponsoring a process research survey-type luncheon paper which identifies areas of future promise for metals extraction. We have also endeavored to cover jointly the general economic setting for the industry, which identifies nontechnical factors affecting us; the survey of all operating lead and zinc properties which points out some of the history and changing trends in the character of economic orebodies, in types of smelting and refining processes, and the effect of geography, transportation, and national aspirations on the complexion of the industry; and finally the unique properties of the metals which account for their status in the marketplace, with a look ahead to possible fields of expanding utility to mankind.

Ten off-the-record "Free-Form" sessions each of two hours' duration enabled those most knowledgable in one of the narrow technical fields in lead and zinc smelting and refining to freely discuss their chosen topic in depth with others equally competent, in an entirely informal atmosphere. Field trips were scheduled to five of the lead and zinc smelters nearby to the Symposium city. Complete plant-description writeups on these visits are included in this volume on an equal basis with those papers actually presented during the sessions.

Particular attention is drawn to the use of the metric system of units (SI) throughout this volume, except as otherwise noted.

The Editors do wish to express their gratitude for the superb assistance rendered by the Editorial Board, the Advisory Council, the Session Chairmen, the SME Staff, and to their respective secretaries and employers, making an otherwise insuperable task possible. Naturally, we are deeply indebted to the authors for the unusually good cooperation tendered in meeting our somewhat exacting specifications.

May 23, 1970
St. Louis, Missouri, USA

CARL H. COTTERILL
JOHN M. CIGAN

TABLE OF CONTENTS

VOLUME II

TABLE OF CONTENTS

Volume I

Page

Page

LIST OF COLOR ILLUSTRATIONS

SECTION I

GENERAL

Chapter 1

ECONOMIC SETTING FOR THE WORLD LEAD AND ZINC INDUSTRY

by E. McL. Tittmann

Chairman

American Smelting & Refining Co.
New York, N.Y.

Deep-seated human instincts urge us to positively mark the passage of time. We celebrate the passage of each year. Years give way to decades, and decades to half centuries and centuries. At all these mileposts we are inclined to pause, take a look around and catch our breaths before embarking on the next leg. We are at such a point now and this meeting I am sure will give direction to the road ahead into the decade of the seventies. In looking around at this point, 1970, it is obvious to all of us that the environment in which we must mine, mill, smelt and refine lead and zinc has radically changed. These changes have, of course, occurred over a long period of time. They have, however, all been in the same general direction. They have all had the same motivation. The period of greatest contrast is probably the fifteen years just before World War II and the fifteen years following the end of that war. I thought that I might review briefly with you what seems to me to be four of the more important changes that have developed since World War II that profoundly affect our activities in the lead and zinc industry. I mentioned before that all these changes have been in the same direction; that is, they have all tended to restrict our freedom of action in pursuing our objective of producing lead and zinc on a competitive basis at a profit. Consequently, in discussing them you may think that I am merely viewing with alarm. This is not the intent. This is merely supposed to be an objective analysis. I think it appropriate before discussing these trends in detail to examine the position of lead and zinc today.

THE SETTING FOR LEAD

Lead, one of the oldest and possibly least glamorous metals in the service of man has always had an important role in industry. While it has been replaced by other metals and compounds in some cases, new uses have developed so that over the years the growth in the use of lead has averaged about 2 to 3% per year. In total tonnage used, it ranks fifth after steel, aluminum, copper and zinc in that order. The pre-war use of lead for cable sheathing has largely given way to plastics. White lead pigment has been almost entirely replaced with titanium oxide. Lead pipe has virtually been replaced be copper tubing and galvanized steel pipe.

Offsetting these three major substitutions for lead, has been rapid growth in the use of lead-acid batteries not only for automobiles but for many other industrial uses and there is every indication that lead-acid batteries will find large use in the future, particularly if efforts to perfect battery-powered vehicles for broad public use are successful.

The use of lead additives to control the burning rate of gasoline and thereby make possible the use of high compression gasoline engines has materially increased in the post-war period. This use for lead is under attack as a contribution to air pollution. However, the benefits of using lead additives I think will prove so great that ways will be found to control the emission of hydrocarbon in automobile exhaust fumes without eliminating the use of lead additives.

Other uses of lead are developing in the field of sound attenuation in the construction industry, to dampen vibration from heavy machinery and to shield nuclear power plants and radioactive wastes.

Worldwide growth of the heavy chemical industry has also increased the use of lead construction for such plants because of its acid resistant qualities. The free world production of lead in 1969 was 3,200,000 metric tons.

Economic sources of lead are widely scattered throughout the free world. Australia and the United States are the two largest producing countries. Canada, Mexico, Peru, Southwest Africa and Europe are other important producing areas. Most of the mine production is from complex ores containing zinc, silver and often copper. In a substantial proportion of these ores, the economic value of the silver, zinc and copper exceeds the value of the lead. The one notable exception are the deposits of Southeast Missouri, the largest lead-producing area in the United States.

THE SETTING FOR ZINC

Zinc carbonate was used to make brass before man discovered and learned to produce the metal. As mentioned previously, zinc is the fourth metal in tonnage used in our industrial society. Zinc was first produced as a metal in commercial quantities in the early 19th century. The low melting point of zinc and its unique characteristic of solidifying very quickly, its resistance to corrosion and its alloying properties make it particularly desirable for die castings and galvanizing. As you know, a host of different parts for all types of machinery and mechanical equipment are produced as zinc die castings. While plastics have been substituted for zinc in some cases, it is doubtful if this trend will continue provided sufficient zinc is available at reasonable prices.

Zinc is also widely used as the principal component of brass and is a minor component in other non-ferrous alloys. The use of zinc is growing a little faster than lead--3 to 4% per year. The large increase in consumer hard goods which requires numerous die cast parts and the development of a continuous process to galvanize sheet steel has materially raised the demand for zinc in the post-war period.

Economic sources of zinc occur in almost all sections of the world. The largest producers are the United States, Canada, and Australia. Peru, Mexico, Europe and Africa also have significant production. In most complex sulfide ores containing lead and zinc, zinc predominates. In the United States and Canada, a substantial tonnage of zinc is produced from almost pure zinc ores. The free world production of zinc in 1969 was 4,100,000 metric tons.

LEAD AND ZINC, INTERNATIONAL COMMODITIES

Both lead and zinc, of course, move in international commerce and, therefore, both metals are subject to worldwide economic changes. Prices of lead and zinc are determined in the international market place, although prices in some areas are influenced temporarily by quotas, tariffs, etc., that have been imposed from time to time in various countries. Over the long pull, however, such devices have not prospered and the economic exploitation of lead and zinc ore bodies must be based upon international prices.

Unlike iron ore and bauxite, the most widely used minerals, lead and zinc deposits vary widely in grade or metal content. Therefore, although these two metals are modestly priced as industrial raw materials in competition with worldwide sources, bonanza ore bodies can be developed as we have seen in several cases during the post-war period. The chance of finding better than average deposits which will return better than average profits has sparked the exploration work that has maintained an adequate supply of lead and zinc.

A complicating economic factor affecting the production of lead and zinc and the price each of these metals commands in international markets arises from the fact that the bulk of the lead and zinc are produced from complex ores containing not only these metals, but silver and often copper. Strong demand for zinc, silver and copper, for example, might make it possible to dump the lead at prices on which a strictly lead deposit could not exist. Likewise, strong demand for lead, silver and copper could so affect zinc.

Lead and zinc are scarce metals in that the prices for which they sell must reflect the cost to find new deposits to maintain reserves. They occur together for the most part in complex ores having silver and sometimes copper as co-products. They occur in economic quantities in most areas of the free world, but in none of these does production balance consumption so that lead and zinc are international commodities dependent on prices set in international markets.

NON-TECHNOLOGICAL FACTORS

This brief reference to the many forces that influence the economic welfare of the lead and zinc industry should convince you that we who are engaged in this industry have enough technical and economic problems without being subjected to political buffeting. Unfortunately, that is not the case and I will now discuss the four trends mentioned earlier.

These four trends are:

(1) the rising tide of taxation

(2) the increasing restrictions on mineral prospecting on the public domain

(3) the rising power of organized labor; and

(4) the increasing drive to prevent air and water pollution.

The problems facing successful exploitation of a lead or zinc ore body discovered prior to World War II may have been formidable, but they didn't include taxation. At that time, local and state taxes were one-tenth what they are today. Taxes on incomes were at one-third of today's rate. Also, payroll taxes, sales taxes and excise taxes, etc., were in their infancy. However, it is the heavy increase in income taxe rates, particularly the application of excess profit taxes and the application of graduated rates to personal income taxes, that has had the most profound effect on the lead and zinc industry. This is simply because during the post-war period the cost of discovering new lead or zinc reserves has been steadily rising. At the same time, on average about 60% of the disposable income from the presently operating properties has been siphoned off in taxes of various kinds. Looking for new mines is a risky poker game. If a third party in the person of local, state and federal gevernments are going to take 60% out of every pot, we have to have better cards before we can bet.

Consequently, glancing back along the tax road we have come and looking forward into the seventies, the view ahead is hazy but we are pretty sure the pressure for even higher taxes will persist. This problem of ever higher taxes is, I think, a trend that we should certainly view with alarm. The lead and zinc industry, of course, is not alone. The entire extractive industry of the world is faced with the same problem. Considering how important the extractive industry is to the welfare of society, it is indeed alarming to note that worldwide we are following tax policies that will strangle us.

Since the end of World War II, there has been a swelling volume of regulations limiting prospecting activities on the public domain. It sounds trite, but we will have no use for the vast technology mining and metallurgical engineers have developed and which is so evident in the mills, smelters, refineries and fabricating plants throughout the world if we can't find lead and zinc deposits to supply the ore. Looking back over the road we have come, ore reserves have not been too severe a problem. In fact, as a nation we have taken them for granted. That may be why prospecting activity on the public domain has been increasingly restricted. Contrary to the earlier concept that mineral exploration should be encouraged by any individual or group that had the intestinal fortitude to so risk time and money, there seems to have now developed almost universal acceptance that undiscovered mineral wealth somehow or other belongs to the people and the state should therefore dispose of this unknown mineral wealth if at all only to the highest bidder. The prospecting fees and the royalties, the time limits, etc., that could thus be imposed on yet unknown deposits of lead and zinc can very materially affect the future supply of these metals. One of the consolations in exploring for lead and zinc is the very real possibility of finding deposits too low in grade, too remote, not amenable to present technology, or for some other reason not exploitable at the present time. Obviously, the discoverer should be allowed to hold such deposits subject to a little earnest money. However, the present trend is the other way.

As we glance backwards over the period since World War II, nowhere do we see a drift toward private ownership of mineral deposits. The trend is strongly the other way toward state ownership, and at best a tennant relationship. I think we can expect this trend to continue. It will materially increase the cost of maintaining adequate reserves over the years ahead, and poses a problem for the lead-zinc industry that was unknown or of little moment before World War II.

Those actively engaged in the industry prior to World War II had only occasional problems with labor organizations. Wage and salary rates varied from one geographical area to the other. Working practices likewise were quite different from district to district. Here in the United States, passage of the Wagner Act and the organization of the C.I.O. marked the beginning of the rise in labor union political power. Elsewhere in the world this trend had already made some headway. However, since the end of World War II, the political power of labor unions has grown faster in the United States and Canada than anywhere else in the Free World, possibly because it had farther to go in these two areas. The effect on the lead and zinc industry has been more severe than in many others. There have been some offsetting advantages in that high post-war labor costs coupled with a drop in individual efficiency prompted a great many technical improvements in methods and processes, and this materially mitigated for a while the rise in wage rates and the drop in efficiency--but only for a while. As organized labor gained more political power, it succeeded in bringing all wage rates and all working conditions closer together. The wage differential that existed before World War II and which attracted competent people to lead and zinc operations was slowly eroded away. The result has been an increasing shortage of capable workmen. After the mid-sixties, operating costs were materially increased through incompetence, mostly because of laziness and an indifferent attitude nutured over the years by union organizations.

A measure of what is happening to us because of these forces is indicated by the following information published by the Bureau of Labor Statistics and the U.S. Department of Commerce. Allowing for higher prices and higher tax rates, the disposable weekly income of the average American citizen employed in the manufacturing industry on an hourly basis has declined 80 cents in purchasing power between 1965 and 1969. The net profits of all industry in the U.S. in 1966 was about 50 billion dollars; in 1969 it was the same. During the same period hundreds of millions of dollars was spent on new plants, new processes and better equipment. I don't have a specific figure for the total for the five-year outlay. Who got the benefit for all this ingenuity, effort and money plowed into new and improved facilities. It didn't show up in profits. It didn't show up in lower prices or in better products. I suppose that for the most part, it has been consumed in lower individual efficiency and lower individual production. A rather new development in labor union affairs is the growing tendency for the rank and file to reject wage contracts negotiated by the union. Unions have aquired almost sovereign powers under the Wagner Act, but it is becoming apparent they can't control the membership. The result is obvious. Only the most extreme union leadership will be tolerated. Obviously, a change in law is required, but it is equally obvious that this is presently impossible.

As we gaze ahead laborwise, there seems little change on the horizon. We face accelerating wage increases for the next few years, lower efficiency and an insufficient number of men for the harder, more demanding jobs.

The last and fourth trend that I want to discuss briefly is not new. Pollution of air and water, destruction of field and forest and the shrinking population of wild animals is something that all of us in the extractive industry have been conscious of for a long time. This is one of the problems that has always faced the lead and zinc industry in mining, in milling, in smelting and refining and in fabricating. A great deal of effort, time and money has been expended to avoid pollution of air and water and destruction of the countryside. Furthermore, a lot of progress has been made. Available statistics, which I won't take the time to quote, certainly indicate that air pollution in a great many locations is lower today than it was twenty years ago. Development of baghouses and other air filtering methods, electrostatic systems, tall stacks, production of SO_2 and H_2SO_4 from waste gases, impounding and stocking of tailings, replanting of tailings ponds and mine dumps is old hat to all of you in the lead and zinc industry.

The results accomplished to date are impressive. The future will see further improvements and similar results. As mentioned before, there is nothing new about the pollution problem to the lead-zinc industry. What is new is the emotional explosion that has occurred regarding pollution of the environment. Examples of irrational responses engendered by this emotional approach are too numerous to mention, but as an example of what I am talking about consider the two billion dollar lawsuit brought on behalf of the Citizens of Arizona against the copper smelters operating in the state. Also, consider New York City's decision to burn only non-sulphur or very low sulphur-bearing fuel oil in the power plants, but at the same time placing no restriction on particulate emission from heating furnaces, incinerators, garbage dumps, etc. I would guess that no one has ever smelled any SO_2 in New York City, but there is certainly enough dirt blowing around in the air.

Another example is the emotional frenzy generated by the announcement of a possible open-pit mining operation any place in the country. Such scars or holes in the earth's surface are generally in remote areas. They are only visible to those in close proximity or in an airplane. To judge by the number of visitors to the better known open-pit iron and copper mines, a large segment, maybe a majority of the people, of this country really admire these pits as engineering masterpieces.

As mentioned earlier, over the past several decades these four trends have become more pronounced. These drives were conceived with the idea of improving our standard of living, of making life easier and more pleasant. And with these objectives, of course, we cannot quarrel. But because responsibility for results, and authority for action in these policy matters is so far separated and not tied together as it should be, the chances of obtaining the objectives are materially reduced and some segments of industry, such as ours, are threatened with extinction.

While much of what I have said may seem remote form the subjects to be discussed at these meetings, it seems to me that in addition to developing and perfecting new methods for finding and producing lead and zinc; in addition to finding and perfecting new uses for the metals, we must accomplish this within a framework which is being more and more circumscribed as I have tried to describe. We don't have the engineering options that were available to the mining and metallurgical engineers of pre-World War II days. This only means that the engineers of today, those gathered for this meeting will have to show more ingenuity, more resourcefulness and more determination than their forbears. This I am certainly sure they are capable of doing.

Chapter 2

SURVEY OF WORLD LEAD AND ZINC PRODUCTION

Allen L. Hatch*
Vice President
American Smelting and Refining Company

K.C. Hendrick
Vice President
Noranda Sales Corporation Ltd.

W. Sies
Direktor
Metallgesellschaft A.G.

*Most people in the industry will recall with sadness the death of Allen Hatch on March 3, 1970. His participation as co-author of this paper was assumed by R.D. Mushlitz, also of the American Smelting and Refining Company.

Abstract

A survey of all phases of the world's lead and zinc production in 1968 from ore through to refined metal was conducted by sending questionnaires to individual companies and the results of this survey are tabulated at the end of the paper.

The paper goes on to review changes in the geographical distribution of the world's lead and zinc mine and metal production and in the trading patterns of raw materials, present and future utilization of metal production capacity, developments in metal smelting and refining processes and the growing importance of marketing, product development and research in the 1950's and 1960's.

As originally conceived by the Committee, this paper was to present a detailed statistical survey of all phases of lead and zinc production in the world, from ore through refined metal, in a historical year such as 1948 and in the most recent year for which complete data were available. These data were then to be used to outline the development of the industry over the period between the two base years.

Such detailed statistical data could only be obtained by contacting each producer directly for answers to extensive questionnaires and it soon became apparent to my co-authors, Allen Hatch of ASARCO and Walter Sies of Metallgesellschaft, and to me that the coverage we would be able to achieve for 1948 or even 1958, particularly in the area of mine production, would be inadequate. Many of the operations were untraceable or had ceased to exist.

Consequently, the statistical tables presented with this paper are limited to 1968, which was the last year for which complete data were available when the questionnaires were first circulated last fall.

The lack of comparative data for an earlier year eliminates the possibility for detailed trend analysis which was part of the original concept. However, the tables do present a picture of current lead and zinc production in considerably more detail than has been available previously. They also provide a reference base for future studies and we hope their value will be commensurate with the effort involved in compiling them.

At this point, we would like to record our appreciation to the following people who contributed considerable time and effort in drawing up and circulating the questionnaires, translating and compiling the data and providing background information.

D.E. Moulds	United States Bureau of Mines, Washington D.C., U.S.A.
S. Yamamoto	Mitsui Mining & Smelting Co., Ltd., Tokyo, Japan.
L.C. Woodul	Asarco Mexicana, Mexico City, Mexico.
W.T. Brown F.A. Wise	American Smelting and Refining Company, Lima, Peru.
T.S. Cree	Mt. Isa Mines Ltd., Sydney, Australia.
J. Wiessler H.B. Ferner	Metallgesellschaft A.G., Frankfurt am Main, Germany.

D.L. Bumstead Noranda Sales Corporation Ltd.,
R.G. Barham Toronto, Canada.

In total, about 650 questionnaires were mailed of which some two-thirds were completed and returned to us. My co-authors and I would like to thank those companies who responded to the questionnaires and without whose cooperation the survey would have been impossible. In some cases where no reply was received, we have included in the tables, data from other sources or our own estimates, and you will find the tables annotated accordingly

Based on the statistics published by the International Lead and Zinc Study Group, we believe the coverage achieved in our tables, including the data from sources other than the questionnaires, is equivalent to 79% and 82% respectively of world lead mine and refined metal production and 86% and 98% respectively of world zinc mine and metal production. The coverage based on the information taken from the questionnaires only is 70% and 69% for lead mine and refined metal production and 83% and 98% of zinc mine and metal production. Details of the coverage in each country are set out in Appendices 1 and 2.

Unfortunately, like the Study Group statistics, this survey does not include any figures for production in Bulgaria, China, Czechoslovakia, East Germany, Poland, Romania, North Korea and the U.S.S.R. Yugoslavia has also been omitted as no replies were received to our questionnaires from operations in that country.

While we do not have data for a historical year in the same detail as for 1968, certain developments in the world's lead and zinc production emerge from published data and our tables.

We have set out the geographic distribution of lead and zinc production since the early 1950's in Appendices 3, 4, 5 and 6. Examination of these tables indicates the dominance of a few major producing countries. Throughout the period, four producing countries, although not always the same four, accounted for 55 - 65% of total lead mine and refined metal production, while eight countries accounted for 75 - 85%. The pattern in zinc mine production was similar but zinc metal production was somewhat more concentrated with 60 - 70% coming from four countries and approximately 85% from eight countries.

In the ten years from 1958 to 1968, total production of refined lead rose by about 650,000 tons or 30%, including 285,000 tons in Western Europe. In the same period, total zinc metal production increased by 1.4 million tons or 60%, with Japan contributing 465,000 tons for an individual growth of 330%.

Lead mine production in 1968 was almost 400,000 tons or 20% higher than in 1958, mainly due to expansion in Canada and the

United States. Again, the increase in zinc mine production was greater at 1.5 million tons or 60%, almost half of which came from Canada whose mine production rose by more than 750,000 tons or close to 200%.

Although the relatively large quantity of secondary feed used in refined lead production makes precise analysis difficult, it appears that through the 1950's and early 1960's the proportion of refined metal produced from imported raw materials remained at about 20 - 25%, rising to somewhat more than 30% by 1968 as a result of increasing dependence on imports in Europe and the United Kingdom and the emergence of Japan as a substantial importer.

In contrast, the position on zinc has remained more or less constant with approximately 40% of the world's metal being produced from imported concentrate, mainly in the United States, Western Europe and, latterly, Japan.

The proportion of lead metal produced from imported concentrates should increase somewhat over the 1968 level of 30 - 40% with new metal capacity being developed in the importing countries, mainly Japan while, except for Mt. Isa, Australia, little or none is planned in concentrate exporting countries.

Overall, and in the light of the relatively satisfactory level of capacity utilization in 1968, estimated at 85 - 90%, the rate at which new lead metal capacity is planned to come on stream appears adequate to provide for growth in consumption at the historical rate of 3½ - 4%.

For zinc, the proportion of metal produced from imported concentrates is expected to remain at about the same level as in 1968 with the substantial net increase in metal capacity in the concentrate importing areas of Western Europe and Japan almost matched by the new metal capacity under development or being considered in the concentrate producing countries of Finland, South Africa, Canada, Algeria, Ireland, Mexico and Peru.

With more than enough zinc metal capacity already in place, these further expansions could result in a significant increase in the excess of capacity and threaten the balance of the zinc industry.

Based on the data in our tables, it appears that, in 1968, only 75 - 80% of the world's zinc metal capacity was utilized, leaving idle capacity in the order of one million tons. By the end of 1970, it appears that zinc metal capacity will have been increased by approximately 500,000 tons over the 1968 level, with a further 8 - 900,000 tons of new capacity in various stages of planning for the years 1971 - 3. This would bring the total additional capacity installed during the five year period to 1.3 - 1.4 million tons, which is equivalent to an annual expansion rate of 5 - 6%. Since this approximates the historical rate of increase in zinc metal consumption, there might appear to be no cause for alarm. However, since there already existed about one million tons of excess capacity in 1968, the growth in capacity is on a higher base than the growth in consumption. Consequently, we face the unpleasant prospect of an increase in idle capacity at a rate of 75 - 100,000 tons per year and total idle capacity in 1973 in the order of 1.5 million tons.

An important factor which has not been taken into account in the above assessment is the loss of capacity resulting from plant closures (except where already announced). These would moderate the net growth in capacity. However, based on the figures outlined above, it would appear that at least ten or twelve plants would have to be closed to redress the situation by 1973. It seems to be unreasonable to expect closures on this scale and hence a more restrained approach to the building of new capacity by all concerned is needed for the continued balance and well-being of the industry.

It will be recalled that in the 1950's, the artificial stimulus of the United States' stockpile programme caused the production of lead and zinc to be expanded substantially ahead of consumption. The resultant surplus led to the five year import quota restrictions which, in turn, accentuated the problem of oversupply in other countries. Not only were the arbitrary barriers to trade unsuccessful in isolating the United States from the subsequent depression in the lead and zinc industry, but the massive stockpiles continue to overhang the market. While the United States' administration is seeking to arrange for disposal without disruption to the market, it will still be some years before the impact of the policies initiated twenty years ago is overcome.

The current projected rate of increase in zinc metal capacity would not threaten to create surpluses of the same magnitude, particularly if the growth of mine production remains more closely aligned with growth in metal consumption, but it could nevertheless lead to serious imbalances and possibly encourage tariff and other restrictions to trade.

We will not attempt to comment on the relative merits of locating metal facilities near the mine in the producing country as opposed to locating them in the market of the consuming country. However, we do express the sincere hope that despite the current resurgence of economic nationalism, those in both the public domain and the private sector who influence decisions on additional capacity, will recognize the potential distortion and disruption inherent in building new smelters, refineries or reduction plants which are uneconomically located or lacking in adequate long-term supplies of raw material or without a market for the metal production.

Metallurgically, the highlight of the last 20 years has been the development of the Imperial Smelting Furnace (ISF) combining the treatment of mixed lead and zinc concentrates with the simultaneous production of lead bullion and zinc metal. At the same time, the oldest method of zinc smelting, the horizontal retort, has declined in importance. An estimate of the world's zinc metal production capacity accounted for by the processes in 1958 and 1968 is set out below.

PROCESS	YEAR OF COMMERCIAL ADAPTATION	PERCENTAGE OF TOTAL PRODUCTION	
		1958	1968
Horizontal Retort	1800	32%	15%
Electrolytic	1915	50%	56%
Vertical Retort	1930	7%	14%
Electrothermic	1936	3%	4%
ISF	1950	8%	11%

There is not the same variety of smelting and refining methods for lead but, based on the data compiled in the tables, we estimated that over 80% of the total bullion is produced in conventional furnaces with about 8% each in ISF and other types of furnaces. We also estimated that approximately 30% of the total is refined electrolytically with the remaining 70% refined by standard pyrometallurgical processes.

No review of the lead and zinc industry would be complete without some comment on price. Although not intending any deep analysis, it is readily apparent from even a cursory examination that the growth in the lead and zinc industry has been accomplished at relatively stable prices. Comparing present U.S. published levels with the average over the five years, 1947 through 1951, the price of lead has risen only 4% and the price of zinc only 14%, while copper is up 278%, nickel 304% and aluminum 82%. Considering the pace of inflation generally and in view of the depletion of high grade and surface ore deposits and the rapidly rising costs of exploration, mine development, production and marketing, lead and zinc at today's prices must be regarded as very good value.

While not apparent from statistics, some of the greatest changes in lead and zinc have occurred in the methods for marketing these traditional metals.

In the immediate post war years, there was a tremendous demand for industrial materials of all kinds for the massive rebuilding of the world's economies. Consequently, the emphasis as far as lead and zinc were concerned, was firmly on production and availability. This emphasis was maintained through the early fifties with the United States Government stockpiling programme. The market was there and the producers of lead and zinc concentrated on maximizing production.

The situation changed and changed rapidly at the end of the fifties and through the sixties. The accelerating pace of new knowledge and technology led to the development of many new alloys and other materials with improved properties and values. Combined with the greater availability of materials generally, these new products provided the consumer with much greater freedom of choice in selecting materials for a given function. The area of substitution widened and competition intensified for all primary industrial products.

No longer were lead and zinc assured of traditional markets and a definite share in the growing usage of metals and materials.

The response of the lead and zinc industry to this challenge came partly from the producers acting independently through integration toward the market and expanded company programmes on research and promotion. However, more significant was the strengthening and broadening of industry's cooperative efforts.

There are now fifteen promotional and product development associations for lead and zinc based in 10 countries--Australia, Canada, France, Germany, India, Italy, Japan, Scandinavia, the United Kingdom and the United States. The best known are the Zinc Institute and the Lead Industries Association in the United States and the Zinc and Lead Development Associations in the United Kingdom. Although independently constituted and financed, these associations operate in close cooperation and together spend over $3.5 million each year in promoting the use of lead and zinc and in providing technical service to users. Recently, in recognition of the increasing consumption and the tremendous growth potential for lead and zinc in the developing countries, a special organization called the Zinc and Lead International Service or ZALIS was set up by the Australian, Japanese, United Kingdom and United States associations to stimulate the consumption of lead and zinc in Africa, Latin America, the Middle East and the Far East. Local information centres have already been established in certain countries with financial and technical support from ZALIS.

During the difficult market period of the late fifties, it became increasingly apparent that the industry required greater research effort beyond the capability and scope of any individual company. In view of the success of the industry's cooperative market development, a research programme was launched by a group of nineteen producing companies from Australia, Canada, the United Kingdom, Mexico and the United States under the sponsorship of the Zinc Institute and the Lead Industries Association. As the programme expanded and became more international, the International Lead Zinc Research Organization or ILZRO as it became known, was incorporated as a separate organization. Today it is supported by 30 member companies in 11 countries representing approximately 75% of the world's production and has an annual budget of over $1.5 million. Dr. Radtke will be speaking to you later on the variety and scope of ILZRO's research programmes which are underway in many countries and on the market impact of their more successful developments.

Marketing of lead and zinc has also been assisted by more accurate, uniform and comprehensive statistics available from national organizations and from the International Lead and Zinc Study Group which celebrated its tenth anniversary last year. The Study Group also provides a forum for international discussion among government and industry representatives on aspects of the world industry at its annual session in the fall of each year.

The growing international character of the lead and zinc industry as a whole is apparent from the above review. This is as it should be. As metals, lead and zinc have no geographic distinction whether produced in the United States or in Australia. They move freely among world markets and respond to basic economic forces. No producer or market can long be isolated from trends in other areas of the world.

Looking forward, we believe the changes we have seen in recent years will accelerate. The international marketplace will become even more demanding.

The diversification of end use, the adaptability of new competing products and the readiness of consumers to substitute, require the lead and zinc industry to be increasingly aware of trends and increasingly responsive to developments in order to survive and grow. However, we believe the industry has demonstrated that it is alert to the changes taking place, is in close touch with its markets, is sensitive to developments and will continue to demonstrate an ability to both react and to initiate.

Therefore, provided reasonable balance can be maintained between production capability and market demand, and prices are reasonably remunerative and stable, we are confident the lead and zinc industry is in a position to take advantage of the opportunities in the changing world that lies ahead.

APPENDIX 1

World Lead Production - 1968

Country	MINE PRODUCTION (Metal Content)			METAL PRODUCTION		
	ILZSG	Survey	Coverage	ILZSG	Survey	Coverage
	'000 MT	'000 MT	%	'000 MT	'000 MT	%
AFRICA						
Algeria	5.3	5.3	100.0	-	-	-
Morocco	81.0	22.7	28.0	24.2	24.2	100.0
S. Africa	60.8	59.7	98.2	55.4	55.7	100.5
Tunisia	16.0	-	-	15.0	-	-
Zambia	22.7	9.0	39.6	22.8	22.7	99.5
Other	4.4	-	-	-	-	-
	190.2	96.7	50.8	117.4	102.6	87.4
AMERICA, N.						
Canada	329.6	308.5	93.6	183.3	183.3	100.0
U.S.A.	339.4	248.9	73.3	828.6	447.5	54.0
	669.0	557.4	83.3	1,011.9	630.8	62.3
AMERICA, C&S						
Argentina	26.0	-	-	37.8	-	-
Bolivia	20.4	22.0	107.8	-	-	-
Brazil	21.0	21.2	100.0	15.8	19.4	122.8
Mexico	161.7	126.5	78.2	172.1	185.0	107.5
Peru	164.9	160.1	97.1	86.4	86.3	99.8
Other	29.0	13.4	46.2	-	-	-
	423.0	343.2	81.1	312.1	290.7	93.1

Country	MINE PRODUCTION (Metal Content)			METAL PRODUCTION		
	ILZSG '000 MT	Survey '000 MT	Coverage %	ILZSG '000 MT	Survey '000 MT	Coverage %
ASIA						
Burma	18.0	8.8	48.9	12.0	8.0	66.7
India	3.8	2.6	68.4	2.0	1.6	80.0
Japan	63.9	35.3	55.2	164.6	164.1	99.5
Other	30.0	16.1	53.6	3.8	3.5	92.1
	115.7	62.8	54.3	182.4	177.2	97.1
EUROPE						
Austria	5.9	5.9	100.0	11.3	12.0	106.2
Belgium	-	-	-	95.3	95.3	100.0
Denmark	-	-	-	9.7	-	-
Finland	4.5	4.5	100.0	-	-	-
France	26.4	13.7	51.8	148.2	99.8	67.3
Germany W.	57.4	44.8	78.0	270.9	272.6	100.6
Greece	11.2	-	-	7.9	8.5	107.6
Ireland	62.2	60.0	96.4	-	-	-
Italy	35.9	11.3	31.5	76.1	57.9	76.1
Netherlands	-	-	-	17.5	17.5	100.0
Norway	3.9	3.7	94.8	1.3	-	-
Portugal	1.3	-	-	1.2	-	-
Spain	71.2	25.3	35.5	62.2	45.4	73.2
Sweden	70.1	70.1	100.0	61.0	43.0	70.5
Turkey	6.8	11.0	161.7	1.6	-	-
United Kingdom	-	-	-	234.2	227.5	97.1
	356.8	250.3	70.2	998.4	879.5	88.0
OCEANIA						
Australia	378.6	366.8	96.8	203.2	200.0	98.4
	378.6	366.8	96.8	203.2	200.0	98.4
TOTAL	2,133.3	1,674.2	78.5	2,825.4	2,280.8	82.1

APPENDIX 2

World Zinc Production - 1968

Country	MINE PRODUCTION (Metal Content) ILZSG '000 MT	Survey '000 MT	Coverage %	METAL PRODUCTION ILZSG '000 MT	Survey '000 MT	Coverage %
AFRICA						
Algeria	18.2	17.5	96.2	-	-	-
Congo(Leopoldville)	119.3	119.3	100.0	62.6	62.0	99.0
Morocco	33.0	12.1	36.7	-	-	-
S. Africa	23.2	23.7	102.1	-	-	-
Tunisia	7.0	-	-	-	-	-
Zambia	67.2	20.3	30.2	50.0	53.2	106.4
Other	3.8	-	-	-	-	-
	271.7	192.9	71.0	112.6	115.2	102.3
AMERICA, N.						
Canada	1,165.9	1,150.0	98.6	387.3	387.2	99.9
U.S.A.	527.8	439.6	83.3	982.7	917.5	93.4
	1,693.7	1,589.6	93.8	1,370.0	1,304.7	95.2
AMERICA, C&S						
Argentina	26.2	-	-	19.0	-	-
Bolivia	10.0	6.9	69.0	-	-	-
Mexico	238.5	192.0	80.5	82.7	84.3	101.9
Peru	303.3	312.4	103.0	67.3	65.8	97.7
Other	18.0	13.0	72.2	5.0	-	-
	596.0	524.3	88.0	174.0	150.1	86.3

Country	MINE PRODUCTION (Metal Content)			METAL PRODUCTION		
	ILZSG '000 MT	Survey '000 MT	Coverage %	ILZSG '000 MT	Survey '000 MT	Coverage %
ASIA						
Burma	6.0	3.9	65.0			
India	10.0	7.0	70.0			
Japan	264.3	146.2	55.3	605.6	608.5	100.5
Other	47.0	20.7	44.0	23.0	24.2	105.2
	327.3	177.8	54.3	628.6	632.7	100.7
EUROPE						
Austria	10.7	10.5	98.1	15.4	15.3	99.3
Belgium	-	-	-	247.3	247.3	100.0
Finland	65.4	64.9	99.2	-	-	-
France	21.8	3.8	17.4	207.5	221.0	106.6
Germany W.	134.2	134.8	100.4	203.3	202.3	99.5
Greece	10.1	-	-	-	-	-
Ireland	53.3	54.6	102.4	-	-	-
Italy	140.1	51.1	36.5	112.3	116.0	103.3
Netherlands	-	-	-	42.5	42.1	99.1
Norway	11.7	8.7	74.4	60.0	60.0	100.0
Portugal	0.5	-	-	-	-	-
Spain	75.7	63.3	83.6	75.9	75.4	99.3
Sweden	75.7	75.5	99.7	-	-	-
Turkey	14.0	4.8	34.3	-	-	-
United Kingdom	-	-	-	132.8	137.8	103.8
	613.2	472.0	77.0	1,097.0	1,117.2	106.8
OCEANIA						
Australia	383.6	386.9	100.9	208.2	201.7	96.9
	383.6	386.9	100.9	208.2	201.7	96.9
TOTAL	3,886.5	3,343.5	86.0	3,590.4	3,521.6	98.1

APPENDIX 3

Source of Lead Mine Production 1952/56-58-68 (Metal Content)

	Average 1952 - 1956			1958			1968		
	Country	Production '000 MT	% of Total	Country	Production '000 MT	% of Total	Country	Production '000 MT	% of Total
1	U.S.A.	314.7	18.8	Australia	326.3	18.7	Australia	378.6	17.7
2	Australia	274.3	16.4	U.S.A.	247.2	14.2	U.S.A.	339.4	15.9
3	Mexico	218.9	13.1	Mexico	200.0	11.5	Canada	329.6	15.5
4	Canada	177.1	10.6	Canada	176.0	10.1	Peru	164.9	7.7
		985.0	58.9		949.5	54.5		1,212.5	56.8
5	Peru	113.7	6.8	Peru	120.0	6.9	Mexico	161.7	7.6
6	Morocco	83.8	5.0	Morocco	92.9	5.3	Morocco	81.0	3.8
7	S. Africa	70.9	4.2	S. Africa	82.0	4.7	Spain	71.2	3.3
8	Germany, W.	63.4	3.8	Spain	70.2	4.0	Sweden	70.1	3.3
		1,316.8	78.9		1,314.6	75.4		1,596.5	74.8
World Total (excl. Soviet Countries)		1,670.8	100.0		1,742.7	100.0		2,133.3	100.0

Source: International Lead and Zinc Study Group

APPENDIX 4

Source of Refined Lead Metal Production 1952/56-58-68

	Average 1952 - 1956			1958			1968		
	Country	Production '000 MT	% of Total	Country	Production '000 MT	% of Total	Country	Production '000 MT	% of Total
1	U.S.A.	776.4	36.7	U.S.A.	692.2	31.9	U.S.A.	828.6	29.3
2	Mexico	205.9	9.7	Australia	203.5	9.4	Germany, W.	270.9	9.6
3	Australia	194.0	9.2	Mexico	198.0	9.1	U.K.	234.2	8.3
4	Canada	147.2	7.0	Germany, W.	172.1	7.9	Australia	203.2	7.2
		1,323.5	62.5		1,265.8	58.3		1,536.9	54.4
5	Germany, W.	146.9	6.9	U.K.	137.0	6.3	Canada	183.3	6.5
6	U.K.	124.0 (E)	5.9	Canada	120.6	5.6	Mexico	172.1	6.1
7	France	90.0 (E)	4.2	France	101.9	4.7	Japan	164.6	5.8
8	Belgium/Lux	77.8	3.7	Belgium/Lux	93.3	4.3	France	148.2	5.2
		1,762.2 (E)	83.2		1,718.6	79.2		2,204.4	78.0
World Total (excl. Soviet) Countries)		2,117.8 (E)	100.0		2,168.4	100.0		2,825.4	100.0

Source: International Lead and Zinc Study Group

APPENDIX 5

Source of Zinc Mine Production 1952/56-58-68 (Metal Content)

	Average 1952 - 1956			1958			1968		
	Country	Production '000 MT	% of Total	Country	Production '000 MT	% of Total	Country	Production '000 MT	% of Total
1	U.S.A.	497.8	21.2	U.S.A.	410.7	16.9	Canada	1,165.9	30.0
2	Canada	405.9	17.3	Canada	398.0	16.4	U.S.A.	527.8	13.6
3	Australia	248.3	10.6	Australia	267.1	11.1	Australia	383.6	9.9
4	Mexico	223.0 (E)	9.5	Mexico	243.0	10.0	Peru	303.3	7.8
		1,375.0 (E)	58.4		1,318.8	54.2		2,380.6	61.2
5	Peru	153.3	6.5	Japan	143.0	5.9	Japan	264.3	6.8
6	Germany, W.	117.1	5.0	Peru	137.0	5.6	Mexico	238.5	6.1
7	Italy	115.8	4.9	Italy	132.0	5.4	Germany, W.	140.1	3.6
8	Japan	105.0	4.5	Congo	114.0	4.7	Italy	134.2	3.4
		1,866.2	79.3		1,844.8	75.8		3,157.7	81.2
World Total (excl. Soviet Countries)		2,352.6 (E)	100.0		2,434.6	100.0		3,886.5	100.0

Source: International Lead and Zinc Study Group

APPENDIX 6

Source of Zinc Metal Production 1952/56-58-68

	Average 1952 - 1956			1958			1968		
	Country	Production '000 MT	% of Total	Country	Production '000 MT	% of Total	Country	Production '000 MT	% of Total
1	U.S.A.	888.1	41.5	U.S.A.	751.0	33.8	U.S.A.	982.7	27.4
2	Canada	217.5	10.2	Canada	228.7	10.3	Japan	605.6	16.9
3	Belgium/Lux	205.7	9.6	Belgium/Lux	213.6	9.6	Canada	387.3	10.8
4	Germany, W.	168.2	7.9	Germany, W.	179.3	8.1	Belgium/Lux	247.3	6.9
		1,479.5	69.1		1,372.6	61.8		2,222.9	62.0
5	Japan	100.0	4.7	France	148.0	6.7	Australia	208.2	5.8
6	Australia	99.2	4.6	Japan	141.0	6.3	France	207.5	5.8
7	France	96.3	4.5	Australia	116.6	5.2	Germany, W.	203.3	5.7
8	U.K.	78.3	3.7	U.K.	75.8	3.4	U.K.	132.8	3.7
		1,853.3	86.5		1,854.0	83.4		2,974.7	83.0
World Total (excl. Soviet Countries)		2,141.5	100.0		2,224.3	100.0		3,590.4	100.0

Source: International Lead and Zinc Study Group

APPENDIX 7

PLANNED AND POSSIBLE INCREASES IN ZINC METAL CAPACITY 1969 - 1975

Country	Plant	Process	Period: Jan. 1/69 -Dec. 31/70 '000 MT	Period: Jan. 1/71 -Dec. 31/75 '000 MT
AFRICA				
Algeria:	New Plant (Government)	Electrolytic		40
S. Africa:	New Plant (SWACO)	Electrolytic	35	
AMERICA (NORTH)				
Canada:	New Plant (T.G.S.)	Electrolytic		100
AMERICA (C&S)				
Mexico:	New Plant (Penoles)	Electrolytic		100
	New Plant (Asarcomex)	Electrolytic		105
Peru:	New Plant (Government)	Electrolytic		60
ASIA				
Japan:	New Plant (Dowa-Akita)	Electrolytic		70
	New Plant (Hachinohe)	I.S.F.	65	
	Expansion (Mitsubishi-Akita)	Electrolytic	15	50
	Expansion (Mitsui-Kamioka)	Electrolytic		10

Country	Plant	Process	Period Jan. 1/69 -Dec. 31/70 '000 MT	Jan. 1/71 -Dec. 31/75 '000 MT
	Expansion (Mitsui-Miike)	V. Retort	20	5
	New Plant (Mitsui-Hikoshima) (Partial Replacement of H.Retort)	Electrolytic		85
	Expansion (Nippon-Mikkaichi)	Electrothermic	25	
	Expansion (Nisso-Aizu)	Electrolytic		15
	Expansion (Toho-Anaka)	Electrolytic		55
	New Plant (Toho-Onahama)	Electrolytic		45
India:	Expansion (Cominco-Binani)	Electrolytic		20
	Expansion (Hindustan Zinc)	Electrolytic		20
	New Plant (Government)	Electrolytic		30
EUROPE Belgium:	Expansions (Miscellaneous)		25	
	New Plant (Prayon) (Partial Replacement of H.Retort)	Electrolytic		50
Finland:	New Plant (Outokumpu)	Electrolytic	90	

APPENDIX 7 -- continued

Country	Plant	Process	Period: Jan. 1/69 -Dec. 31/70 '000 MT	Period: Jan. 1/71 -Dec. 31/75 '000 MT
France:	Expansions (Miscellaneous)		15	
Germany:	Expansions (Miscellaneous)		20	
	New Plant (Preussag) (Partial Replacement of H.Retort)	Electrolytic		90
	New Plant (Ruhr Zink)	Electrolytic	135	
Ireland:	New Plant (I.B.M.)	Electrolytic		70
Italy:	Expansions (Miscellaneous)		25	
	New Plant (A.M.M.I.)	I.S.F.		65
Norway:	Expansion (D.N.Z.)	Electrolytic	10	15
Spain:	Expansion (Espanola)	Electrolytic		10
United Kingdom:	Expansions (I.S.C.)	I.S.F.	40	
OCEANIA Australia:	Expansion (E.Z.)	Electrolytic	15	35
TOTAL			535	1,145

APPENDIX 8

PLANNED AND POSSIBLE INCREASES IN LEAD SMELTER AND REFINERY CAPACITY 1969 - 1975

Country	Plant	Process	Period: Jan. 1/69 -Dec. 31/70 '000 MT	Period: Jan. 1/71 -Dec. 31/75 '000 MT
ASIA				
Japan:	Expansion (Dowa-Akita)	Electric Smelter Electrolytic Refinery	5	
	New Plant (Hachinohe)	I.S.F.	30	
	Expansion (Mitsui-Kamioka)	Conventional Smelter	5	
	Expansion (Mitsui-Takehara)	Betts Refinery	20	
	Expansion (Nippon-Saganoseki)	Conventional Smelter Betts Refinery	10	
	Expansion (Toho-Chigirishima)	Conventional Smelter Electrolytic Refinery	20	
India:	New Plant (Orissa)			10

APPENDIX 8 -- continued

Country	Plant	Process	Period Jan. 1/69 -Dec. 31/70 '000 MT	Jan. 1/71 -Dec. 31/75 '000 MT
EUROPE Italy:	New Plant (A.M.M.I.)	I.S.F.		35
	Expansion (Pertusola)	Conventional Smelter Pyro Refinery	30	
Spain:	New Plant (La Cruz & Asturiana)			25
	Expansion (Penarroya) (Partial Replacement)	Conventional Smelter Pyro Refinery	70	
TOTAL			190	70

SURVEY OF WORLD LEAD AND ZINC PRODUCTION 1968

STATISTICAL TABLES

Explanatory Notes

1. The tables are presented in three sections:

   (i) Mines and Mills (on facing pages).
   (ii) Zinc Plants.
   (iii) Lead Smelters and Refineries.

2. Each section is divided into six main geographical areas:

   (i) Africa. (iv) Asia.
   (ii) America, North. (v) Europe.
   (iii) America, South and Central. (vi) Oceania.

   Within each of these areas, countries are listed alphabetically with companies listed alphabetically in each country.

3. All quantities are in metric tons of 1,000 kilos or 2,204.6 lbs.

4. Assays are expressed as percentages except for gold and silver which are expressed as grams per metric ton (31.1035 grams = 1 troy ounce).

5. Mining Methods:
   B.C. denotes Block Caving.
   C&F denotes Cut and Fill.
   R&P denotes Room and Pillar.
   S.S. denotes Shrinkage Stoping.
   S.L.S. denotes Sub-level Stoping.
   O.S. denotes Open Stoping.
   L.H. denotes Long Hole.
   Sq.S. denotes Square Set Stoping.

6. The information contained in the tables is taken from questionnaires completed by the companies except where marked, (Est.) signifying an estimate made by the authors.

SURVEY OF WORLD LEAD AND ZINC PRODUCTION IN 1968

MINES

Country and Company Name	Name of Mine	Location of Mine	Year First Operated	Principal Metals Mined	Type of Deposit	Mining Method	Ore Production (1968)							Where Milled
							Tonnage	Analysis						
								Au	Ag	Cu	Pb	Zn	Other	
AFRICA														
Algeria														
So.Na.R.Em.	El Abed	S.W. of Tlemcen	1952	Pb,Zn	Lens	R&P/SqS	206,000		Tr		1.2	5.0		Own Mill - Oujda
"	Ain Barbar	Annaba	1883	Cu,Pb,Zn	Vein	C&F/S.S.								Own Mill - Annaba
"	Ouarsenis	Al Asnam	1890	Pb,Zn	Lens, Massive	S.S.								Own Mill - Al Asnam
"	Djebel Gustav	Setif	1904	Pb,Zn	Lens	R&P								Own Mill - Setif
"	Sidi Kamber	Constantine	1913	Pb,Zn	Vein	O.S.								Own Mill - Constantine
Congo (Leopoldville)														
Gecomin	Kipushi	Kipushi		Cu,Zn	Vein	S.L. Top Slicing								Own Mill - Kipushi
Morocco														
Soc. Min. Djebel Aouam	Djebel Aouam	Meknes	1960	Ag,Pb,Zn	Vein	Sq.S.	149,300		183		9.5	1.12		Own Mill - Meknes
Asturienne des Mines	Touissit	Oujda	1930	Ag,Pb,Zn	Lens	R&P	508,700				2.61	2.79		Own Mill - Ouida
V.M. de l'Atlas Occident	Erdouz	Erdouz	1949	Ag,Pb,Zn	Vein	C&F								Own Mill - Erdouz

SURVEY OF WORLD LEAD AND ZINC PRODUCTION IN 1968

MILLS

Country and Company Name	Name/ Location of Mill	Year First Operated	Mines Milled	Rated Daily Capacity	Milling Method	Tonnage Milled	Concentrate Produced (1968)								Other Products
							Type	Tonnage	Analysis						
									Au	Ag	Cu	Pb	Zn	Other	
AFRICA															
Algeria															
So.Na.R.Em.	Oujda	1945	One	1,200	Flotation	206,000	Lead	2,934	Tr	700	0.08	69.0	0.9		
							Zinc	17,628	Tr	150	0.08	0.77	57.0	Cd.30	
"	Annaba	1954	One	180	Flotation	40,000	Lead	240				50.0			Cu Conc.
							Zinc	1,700					50.0		
"	Al Asnam	1952	One	400	Flotation/ Calcination	110,000	Lead	2,000				68.0			
							Zinc	4,000					52.0		
							Calcines	3,000					47.0		
"	Setif	1967	One	180	Flotation	26,000	Lead	425				60.0			
							Zinc	4,800					40.0		
"	Constantine	1954	One	160	Flotation/ Gravity	27,000	Lead	2,100				76.0			
							Zinc	2,300					53.0		
Congo (Leopoldville)															
Gecomin	Kipushi		One		Flotation	1,128,242	Lead	78			5.13	39.74	6.41		
							Zinc	211,333		33	1.68		56.47	Ge27gm/t	Cu Conc.
Morocco															
Soc. Min. Djebel Aouam	Meknes	1960	One	500	Flotation	153,900	Lead	19,550		1,188		67.3			
							Zinc	1,200		262			51.8		
Comp. Royale Asturienne Des Mines	Oujda	1948	One	1,750	Flotation	503,450	Lead	14,100		693		67.52			
							Zinc	20,100		168			57.22		
V.M. de l'Atlas Occident	Erdouz	1949	One	150	Flotation	15,500	Lead								
							Zinc								

SURVEY OF WORLD LEAD AND ZINC PRODUCTION IN 1968

MINES

Country and Company Name	Name of Mine	Location of Mine	Year First Operated	Principal Metals Mined	Type of Deposit	Mining Method	Ore Production (1968)							Where Milled
							Tonnage	Analysis						
								Au	Ag	Cu	Pb	Zn	Other	
Morocco (Cont'd)														
Mines d'Aouli (Penarroya)	Aouli	Midelt		Pb	Vein	C&F/S.S.								Own Mill - Midelt
"	Mibladen	Midelt		Pb		Open Pit C&F								Own Mill - Midelt
South West Africa														
South West Africa Co.	Bergaukas	Bergaukas		Pb	Lens	LHOS/SS								Own Mill - Bergaukas
Tsumeb Corp.	Tsumeb	Tsumeb		Ag,Cu,Pb,Zn										Own Mill - Tsumeb
" "	Kombat	Kombat		Cu,Pb										Own Mill - Kombat
Zambia														
Zambia Broken Hill Dev. Co. Ltd.	Broken Hill	Kabwe	1905	Pb,Zn	Pipe	S.L.S.	267,731				13.0	27.5		Own Mill - Kabwe
AMERICA, NORTH														
Canada														
American Smelting and Refining Co., Buchans Unit	Buchans	Buchans, Nfld.	1928	Pb,Zn,Cu	Lens, Massive	C&F/Sq.S	342,900	1.0	138	1.02	6.83	12.03	Cd	Own Mill

SURVEY OF WORLD LEAD AND ZINC PRODUCTION IN 1968

MILLS

Country and Company Name	Name/ Location of Mill	Year First Operated	Mines Milled	Rated Daily Capacity	Milling Method	Tonnage Milled	Concentrate Produced (1968)								Other Products
							Type	Tonnage	Analysis						
									Au	Ag	Cu	Pb	Zn	Other	
Morocco (Cont'd)															
Mines d'Aouli	Midelt		One	1800	Flotation	387,400	Lead								
" "	Midelt		One	600	Flotation	123,490	Lead								
South West Africa															
S.W. Africa Co.	Bergaukas		One		Flot/Grav	140,000	Lead	6780				42.6	17.3	$V_2O_5$17.2	
							Zinc	28,180				1.6	48.9		
							Mixed	12,530				14.7	46.8		
Tsumeb Corp.	Tsumeb		One		Flotation	526,500		55,000	MT contained Lead (Est.)						
" "	Kombat		One		Flotation	323,500		4,000	MT contained Zinc (Est.)						
Zambia															
Zambia Broken Hill	Kabue	1946	One	523	Flot/Heavy Media	143,433	High Lead	3106				77.7	4.2		
							Low Lead	14,334				45.8	12.3		
							Zinc	36,194				2.0	56.2		
							Pyrite	5201				9.5	18.2	Fe28.7	
AMERICA, NORTH															
Canada															
American Smelting and Refining Company, Buchans Unit	Buchans/ Nfld.	1928	One	1134	Flotation	342,900	Lead	36,843	4.11	589	2.58	58.31	13.16	Fe 3.87	Cu Conc.
							Zinc	65,531	0.69	154	0.71	3.85	57.78	Cd 0.22	
														Fe 2.27	

SURVEY OF WORLD LEAD AND ZINC PRODUCTION IN 1968

MINES

Country and Company Name	Name of Mine	Location of Mine	Year First Operated	Principal Metals Mined	Type of Deposit	Mining Method	Ore Production (1968) Tonnage	Analysis Au	Ag	Cu	Pb	Zn	Other	Where Milled
Canada (Cont'd)														
Anaconda Britannia Mines Ltd.	Britannia	Britannia Beach, B.C.	early 1900's	Zn,Cu	Vein,Lens	S.S./ S.L.S./ L.H.O.S.	544,320			1.2				Own Mill
Brunswick Mining and Smelting Corp. Ltd.	Brunswick #12	Bathurst, N.B.	1962	Pb,Zn,Cu	Lens, Massive	C&F/ L.H.O.S.	1,564,435		66	0.27	3.38	8.56		Brunswick #12 Mill
"	Brunswick #6	Bathurst, N.B.	1965	Pb,Zn,Cu,Ag	Lens, Massive	Open Pit	892,940		52	0.35	2.47	5.66		Brunswick #6 Mill
Canadian Exploration Ltd.	Jersey	Salmo, BC	1949	Pb,Zn	Bedded	R&P	459,243		171		1.44	3.23		Own Mill
Canadian Jamieson Mines Ltd.	Canadian Jamieson	Timmins, Ont.	1966	Pb,Zn,Cu	Lens	S.S.	150,165			2.75		4.42		Own Mill

MILLS

Country and Company Name	Name/ Location of Mill	Year First Operated	Mines Milled	Rated Daily Capacity	Milling Method	Tonnage Milled	Concentrate Produced (1968)								Other Products
							Type	Tonnage	Analysis						
									Au	Ag	Cu	Pb	Zn	Other	
Canada (Cont'd)															
Anaconda Britannia Mines Ltd.	Britannia/ B.C.	1905	One	2,903	Flotation	544,320	Zinc	450	0.69	27	2.79		53.98	Cd 0.23 Fe 4.2 S 33.26	Cu Conc. Silica Sand
							Pyrite	13,463	0.69	8	0.30		0.50	Fe 41.1 S 47.3	
Brunswick Mining and Smelting Corp. Ltd.	Brunswick #12/N.B.	1964	One	4,080	Flotation	1,564,435	Lead	108,455		395	0.38	32.21	11.31	Cd 0.015 Fe 19.53 S 30.63	
							Zinc	200,596		66	0.27	1.73	50.68	Cd 0.69 Fe 11.26 S 32.33	
" " "	Brunswick #6/N.B.	1966	One	2,722	Flotation	892,940	Lead	35,224		452	1.73	33.83	13.50	Cd 0.015 Fe 19.5 S 30.6	
							Zinc	47,034		67	0.29	1.78	50.61	Cd 0.069 Fe 11.0 S 32.0	
							Mixed	42,030		208	0.85	11.05	32.26	Cd 0.053 Fe 14.58 S 31.52	
Canadian Exploration Ltd.	Jersey/ B.C.	1949	One	1,996	Flotation	459,243	Lead	7,627		206		74.46	5.25	Fe 3.0 S 16.0	
							Zinc	23,203		171		1.68	56.73	Cd 0.45 Fe 6.3	
Canadian Jamieson Mines Ltd.	Canadian Jamieson/ Ont.	1966	One	408	Flotation	150,165	Zinc	26,576	0.34	93	0.40	1.20	49.2	Cd 0.1	

SURVEY OF WORLD LEAD AND ZINC PRODUCTION IN 1968

MINES

Country and Company Name	Name of Mine	Location of Mine	Year First Operated	Principal Metals Mined	Type of Deposit	Mining Method	Ore Production (1968) Tonnage	Analysis Au	Ag	Cu	Pb	Zn	Other	Where Milled
Canada (Cont'd)														
Cominco Ltd.	Bluebell	Riondel, BC	1952	Pb, Zn	Limestone Replacement	C&F/R&P	226,800	Low	48	Low	4.7	5.7	Fe 21.1	Bluebell Mill
" "	Sullivan	Kimberley, B.C.	1911	Pb, Zn	Conformable Massive	R&P/ S.L.S.	1,950,480	Low	57	Low	4.4	3.6	Fe 21.5	Sullivan Mill
Cupra Mines Ltd.	Cupra	Stratford, P.Q.	1965	Cu	Lens	C&F								Solbec Mill
Dresser Minerals, Div. of Dresser Ind. Inc.	Dresser	Walton, N.S.	1960	Pb, Zn, Cu, Ag	Vein, Lens	B.C./ C&F	45,166		243	0.39	3.9	0.3		Own Mill
Ecstall Mining Ltd.	Kidd Creek	Kidd Twp., Ont.	1966	Pb, Cu, Ag, Zn	Lens, Replacement	Open Pit	3,266,000							Own Mill
Heath Steele Mines Ltd	Heath Steele	Northumber-land, N.B.	1956	Pb, Zn, Cu, Ag	Massive Strata	L.H.O.S.	355,045		69	0.93	2.3	5.6		Own Mill
Hudson Bay Mining and Smelting Co. Ltd.	Chisel Lake	Snow Lake, Man.	1960	Zn	Lens	S.L.S.	252,564				1.3	13.0		Flin Flon Mill
"	Flin Flon	Flin Flon, Man.	1930	Zn, Cu	Lens	S.L.S.	731,657	2.40	38	2.29		4.7		Flin Flon Mill
"	Osborne Lake	Snow Lake, Man.	1968	Zn, Cu	Lens	S.L.S.	160,937			4.40		1.5		Flin Flon Mill
"	Schist Lake	Flin Flon, Man.	1950	Zn, Cu	Lens	C&F/S.S.	109,771	1.54	40	4.36		8.0		Flin Flon Mill
"	Stall Lake	Snow Lake, Man.	1964	Cu	Lens	C&F	209,382			4.77				Flin Flon Mill
Kam Kotia Mines Ltd.	Kam Kotia	Timmins, Ont.	1960	Zn, Cu	Lens, Stringers	S.L.S.	607,283			1.37		3.35		Own Mill

MILLS

Country and Company Name	Name/ Location of Mill	Year First Operated	Mines Milled	Rated Daily Capacity	Milling Method	Tonnage Milled	Concentrate Produced (1968)								Other Products
							Type	Tonnage	Analysis						
									Au	Ag	Cu	Pb	Zn	Other	
Canada (Cont'd)															
Cominco Ltd.	Bluebell/ B.C.	1952	One	680	Flotation	226,800	Lead	13,699		652	1.0	68.0	2.0	Fe 7.0 S 18.0	
							Zinc	24,494		69	0.5	3.0	48.0	Cd 0.24 Fe 14.0 S 32.0	
" "	Sullivan/ B.C.	1923	Sullivan + 360,000 M.T. Pine Point	9,072	Flotation	2,268,000	Lead	181,440	low	446	low	68.0	4.0	Fe 7.0 S 18.0	Tin Conc.
							Zinc	274,882	low	69	low	6.0	50.0	Cd 0.10 Fe 9.0 S 32.0	
							Pyrite	329,950						S 51.0	
Dresser Minerals. Div. of Dresser Industries Inc.	Dresser/ N.S.	1961	One	130	Flotation	45,166	Lead	4,858		1689	3.58	36.5	2.8	Fe 16.8	8,459 tons Barite Conc.
Estall Mining Ltd.	Kidd Creek/ Ont.	1966	One	8,165	Flotation	3,266,000	Lead Zinc	93,229 530,263		3255 49	3.91 0.51	13.02 0.20	12.94 52.67	 Cd	
Heath Steele Mines Ltd.	Heath Steele /N.B.	1956	One	963 (average)	Flotation	355,045	Lead Zinc	11,632 26,576	2.06 0.34	586 93	3.90 0.40	25.90 1.20	7.70 49.2	 Cd 0.1	
Hudson Bay Mining and Smelting Co. Ltd.	Flin Flon/ Man.	1930	Chisel Lake, Flin Flon, Osborne Lake, Schist Lake, Stall Lake	6,350	Flotation	1,460,592	Lead Zinc	2,540 119,115	12.69 1.37	902 34	2.1 0.7	53.7 0.3	6.6 47.6		Cu Conc.
Kam Kotia Mines Ltd.	Kam Kotia/ Ont.	1960	One	2,450	Flotation	607,283	Zinc	28,628					49.0	Cd 0.1 Fe 10.0 S 32.8	Cu Conc. Au,Ag

SURVEY OF WORLD LEAD AND ZINC PRODUCTION IN 1968

MINES

Country and Company Name	Name of Mine	Location of Mine	Year First Operated	Principal Metals Mined	Type of Deposit	Mining Method	Ore Production (1968) Tonnage	Analysis Au	Ag	Cu	Pb	Zn	Other	Where Milled
Canada (Cont'd)														
Lake Dufault Mines Ltd.	Lake Dufault	Noranda, P.Q.	1964	Zn, Cu	Lens	S.L.S./ Open Slash	376,488							Own Mill
Manitou-Barvue Mines Ltd.	Manitou-Barvue	Val d'Or, P.Q.	1942	Pb, Zn, Cu, Ag, Au	Lens	S.S./ L.H.O.S.	422,755							Own Mill
Mastodon-Highland Bell Mines Ltd.	Highland Bell	Beaverdell, B.C.	1946	Pb, Zn, Ag	Vein	O.S.	33,034	0.45	530		0.80	0.72		Own Mill
Mattagami Lake Mines Ltd.	Mattagami Lake	Matagami, P.Q.	1963	Zn	Massive	S.L.S.	1,237,150							Own Mill
Mines de Porier Inc.	Poirier	Joutel, P.Q.	1966	Zn, Cu, Ag	Lens	C&F/ S.L.S.	513,983		5	1.52		2.10		Own Mill
New Calumet Mines Ltd.	Calumet	Calumet Island, P.Q.	1942	Pb, Zn, Ag	Lens	C&F/O.S.	77,198	0.65	143		2.06	6.64		Own Mill
New Hosco Mines Ltd.	New Hosco	Matagami, P.Q.	1964	Zn, Cu	Lens	S.L.S./ Glory Hole	297,303			1.07		2.50		Orchan Mill
Nigadoo River Mines Ltd.	Nigadoo River	Robertville N.B.	1968	Pb, Zn, Cu, Ag	Vein	C&F/S.S./ S.L.S.								Own Mill
Noranda Mines Limited (Geco Division)	Geco	Manitou-wadge, Ont.	1957	Pb, Zn, Cu, Ag	Lens	C&F/ L.H.O.S.	1,356,599							Own Mill
Normetal Mines Ltd.	Normetal	Normetal, P.Q.	1937	Zn, Cu, Ag	Vein	C&F/Sq.S.	326,948	0.93	61	1.49		7.23		Own Mill

SURVEY OF WORLD LEAD AND ZINC PRODUCTION IN 1968

MILLS

Country and Company Name	Name/ Location of Mill	Year First Operated	Mines Milled	Rated Daily Capacity	Milling Method	Tonnage Milled	Concentrate Produced (1968)								Other Products
							Type	Tonnage	Analysis						
									Au	Ag	Cu	Pb	Zn	Other	
Canada (Cont'd)															
Lake Dufault Mines Limited	Lake Dufault/ Ont.	1964	One	1,090	Flotation	376,488	Zinc	22,261					51.86	Cd 0.13	Cu Conc.
Manitou Barvue Mines Ltd.	Manitou Barvue/P.Q.	1942	One	1,180	Flotation/ Chemical	422,755	Lead	345	92.19	6262	7.4	31.5			Cu Conc.
							Zinc	5393		31			59.7		
Mastodon-Highland Bell Mines Ltd.	Highland Bell/B.C.	1950	One	109	Flotation	33,034	Mixed	2,100		8094		12.34	7.0		Au
							Zinc	264		1892		2.18	34.53	Cd 0.37	
Mattagami Lake Mines Limited	Mattagami/ P.Q.	1963	One	3,493	Flotation	1,237,150	Zinc	208,568	0.48	41	0.34	0.15	52.7	Cd 0.1 Fe 9.8 S 32.5	Cu Conc.
Mines de Poirier Inc.	Poirier/ P.Q.	1966	One	1,633	Flotation	513,983	Zinc	14,716					50.9		
New Calumet Mines Ltd.	Calumet/ P.Q.	1943	One	635	Flotation	77,198	Lead	2,596	13.92	3306	2.56	56.7	5.95		
							Zinc	9,203	0.31	90		0.35	52.85	Fe 8.76	
Nigadoo River Mines Ltd.	Nigadoo River/N.B.	1968	One	9,072	Flotation	245,452	Lead	11,279		1575	1.76	49.85	4.7	Bi 0.23	
							Zinc	9,383		139	1.25	2.34	50.6	Cd 0.72	
Noranda Mines Limited (Geco Division)	Geco/Ont.	1957	One	3,765	Flotation	1,356,599	Lead	2,235	0.86	2194	5.0	51.0	7.3	Cd tr Fe 12.0 S 24.0	
							Zinc	92,200	0.17	79	0.79	0.02	54.50	Cd 0.41 Fe 9.6 S 33.9	
Normetal Mines Limited	Normetal/ P.Q.	1937	One	9,072	Flotation	328,850	Zinc	40,629	0.41	53	0.28		52.30		Cu Conc.
							Pyrite	13,353						S 51.01	

SURVEY OF WORLD LEAD AND ZINC PRODUCTION IN 1968

MINES

Country and Company Name	Name of Mine	Location of Mine	Year First Operated	Principal Metals Mined	Type of Deposit	Mining Method	Cre Production (1968)							Where Milled
							Tonnage	Analysis						
								Au	Ag	Cu	Pb	Zn	Other	
Canada (Cont'd)														
Orchan Mines Ltd.	Orchan	Matagami, P.Q.	1964	Zn	Lens	C&F/ S.L.S.	333,052			1.34		10.50		Own Mill
Pine Point Mines Ltd.	Pine Point	Pine Point, N.W.T.	1965	Pb,Zn	Mississippi Valley	Open Pit	2,268,000	Low	Low	Low	5.7	9.2		Own Mill + 360,000 MT at Sullivan Mill, Riondel, B.C.
Quemont Mines Ltd.	Quemont	Noranda, P.Q.	1949	Zn,Cu,Ag	Lens, Replacement	C&F S.L.S.	389,469	4.11	27	0.80		2.00		Own Mill
Reeves MacDonald Mines Ltd.	Reeves MacDonald	Remac, B.C.	1949	Pb,Zn	Limestone Replacement	S.L.S.								Own Mill
Sullivan Mines Ltd.	Solbec	Stratford, P.Q.	1961	Pb,Zn,Cu,Ag	Lens	C&F								Solbec Mill
United Keno Hill Mines Ltd.	Calumet, Elsa	Elsa, Yukon	1947	Pb,Zn,Ag	Vein	C&F/Sq.S	55,158		1,162		6.5	5.6		Elsa Mill
Western Mines Ltd.	Lynx	Myra Creek, B.C.	1967	Zn,Cu,Ag	Lens	C&F 35%/ Open Pit 65%								Own Mill
Willecho Mines Ltd.	Willecho	Manitou-wadge, Ont.	1964	Pb,Zn,Cu,Ag, Au	Massive	R&P	314,294	Tr.	74	0.44	0.26	3.43		Willroy Mill
Willroy Mines Ltd.	Willroy	Manitou-wadge, Ont.	1957	Pb,Zn,Cu,Ag	Massive	S.L.S.	167,824							Own Mill
Zenmac Metal Mines Ltd	Zenith	Schrieber, Ont.	1965	Zn	Lens	O.S.	44,065					17.12		Zenmac Mill

SURVEY OF WORLD LEAD AND ZINC PRODUCTION IN 1968

MILLS

Country and Company Name	Name/ Location of Mill	Year First Operated	Mines Milled	Rated Daily Capacity	Milling Method	Tonnage Milled	Concentrate Produced (1968)								Other Products
							Type	Tonnage	Analysis						
									Au	Ag	Cu	Pb	Zn	Other	
Canada (Cont'd)															
Orchan Mines Limited	Orchan/P.Q.	1964	Orchan New Hosco	1,724	Flotation	630,355	Zinc	59,496			0.48		52.30	Fe 10.4	
Pine Point Mines Ltd.	Pine Point/ N.W.T.	1966	One	5,443	Flotation	1,905,000	Lead	78,564				79.0	3.0	Fe 2.0 S 15.0	
							Zinc	201,852				1.4	60.0	Cd 0.1 Fe 3.0 S 32.0	
Quemont Mines Limited	Quemont/ P.Q.	1949	One	1,814	Flotation/ Chemical	389,469	Zinc	11,561	3.77	51	0.7		53.0		Au, Ag Bullion
							Pyrite	150,680			0.09		0.45	S 50.0	
Reeves MacDonald Mines Ltd.	Reeves MacDonald/ B.C.	1949	One	9,072	Flotation	280,597	Lead	4,654		187		47.82	7.23		
							Zinc	17,353		30		1.92	53.1	Cd 0.363	
Sullivan Mines Ltd.	Solbec/P.Q.	1962	Solbec Cupra	1,361	Flotation	442,512	Lead	3,426	5.21	640	3.72	51.71	3.43	Fe 13.8 S 25.2	
							Zinc	26,878	0.82	86	1.18	0.56	55.15	Cd 0.28 Fe 6.7 S 34.2	
United Keno Hill Mine	Elsa/Yukon	1947	One	454	Flotation	55,158	Lead	4,906		12,000		67.5	6.5		
							Zinc	4,527		429		1.2	55.2	Cd 0.7 Fe 6.5	
Western Mines Limited	Lynx/B.C.	1967	One	1,089	Flotation	365,148	Zinc	38,508	2.67	126	1.05	3.97	53.25	Cd 0.25 Fe 6.5	
Willroy Mines Limited	Willroy/ Ont.	1957	Willroy Willecho	1,542	Flotation	482,118	Lead	1,950		1,749	5.6	51.0	5.0		
							Zinc	22,154		55	0.40	0.20	53.5		
Zenmac Metal Mines	Zenmac/Ont.	1966	One	181	Flotation	44,065	Zinc	12,726			0.77		52.99	Cd 0.126	

SURVEY OF WORLD LEAD AND ZINC PRODUCTION IN 1968

MINES

Country and Company Name	Name of Mine	Location of Mine	Year First Operated	Principal Metals Mined	Type of Deposit	Mining Method	Ore Production (1968) Tonnage	Analysis Au	Ag	Cu	Pb	Zn	Other	Where Milled
United States of America														
Aho, George	Butterfly	Nevada	1968	Ag,Pb	Vein	S.S.	18							
Aluminum Co. of America	Hutson	Kentucky (Leased to Eagle - Picher - see Eagle - Picher)												
American Smelting and Refining Co.	Page	Idaho	before 1930	Pb,Zn	Vein	C&F/Sq.S	78,693		87		4.5	10.0		Own Mill - Idaho
American Zinc Co.	New Market	Tennessee	1963	Zn	Bedded Replacement	R&P	679,480				2.88			Own Mill - Tennessee
" "	Calhoun	Washington	1966	Zn	Lens	R&P	270,940				0.17	3.02		Own Mill - Washington
" "	Blackstone	Wisconsin	1955	Zn	Bedded Replacement		7,270				0.28	3.24		Own Mill - Wisconsin
" "	Champion	Wisconsin	1955	Zn	Bedded Replacement		121,650				0.03	3.93		Own Mill - Wisconsin
" "	Bearhole	Wisconsin	1968	Zn	Bedded Replacement		2,645				0.01	2.56		Own Mill - Wisconsin
" "	Thompson - Temperly	Wisconsin	1955	Zn	Bedded Replacement		76,090				0.03	3.36		Own Mill - Wisconsin
" "	Mascot No.2	Tennesse	1915	Zn	Bedded Replacement		482,665					2.45		Own Mill - Tennessee
" "	Young	Tennessee	1956	Zn	Bedded Replacement	R&P	946,075					2.98		Own Mill - Tennessee
" "	N. Friends Station	Tennessee	1952	Zn	Bedded Replacement	R&P	96,060					2.89		Own Mill - Tennessee
" "	Coy	Tennessee	1959	Zn	Bedded Replacement	R&P	137,710					4.50		Own Mill - Tennessee
" "	Immel	Tennessee	1968	Zn	Bedded Replacement	R&P	229,130					3.87		Own Mill - Tennessee
Antonioli, Peter	Mouiton - Broadwater	Montana	1968	Ag,Pb,Zn	Vein	S.S.	540		750	0.2	5.0	10.0		

SURVEY OF WORLD LEAD AND ZINC PRODUCTION IN 1968

MILLS

Country and Company Name	Name/ Location of Mill	Year First Operated	Mines Milled	Rated Daily Capacity	Milling Method	Tonnage Milled	Concentrate Produced (1968)								Other Products
							Type	Tonnage	Analysis						
									Au	Ag	Cu	Pb	Zn	Other	
United States of America															
American Smelting and Refining Co.	**Idaho**	**Before 1930**	**One**	**450**	**Flotation**	**78,695**	**Lead**	**5,220**		**892**		**62.4**	**14.2**		
							Zinc	**12,285**				**1.9**	**56.6**		
American Zinc Co.	**Tennessee**	**1962**	**One**	**3,265**	**Flotation**	**679,900**	**Zinc**	**29,850**					**63.2**	**Cd.31**	
" " "	**Washington**	**1966**	**One**	**1,090**	**Flotation**	**270,945**	**Lead**	**480**				**42.4**			
							Zinc	**13,140**					**57.8**	**Cd.1**	
" " "	**Wisconsin**	**1955**	**Four**	**725**	**Flotation**	**207,660**	**Lead**	**80**				**67.1**			
							Zinc	**11,140**					**57.1**	**Cd.14**	
" " "	**Tennessee**	**1913**	**Five**	**6,800**	**Flotation**	**1,891,640**	**Zinc**	**84,830**					**61.8**	**Cd.33**	**Stone**

SURVEY OF WORLD LEAD AND ZINC PRODUCTION IN 1968

MINES

Country and Company Name	Name of Mine	Location of Mine	Year First Operated	Principal Metals Mined	Type of Deposit	Mining Method	Ore Production (1968)							Where Milled
							Tonnage	Analysis						
								Au	Ag	Cu	Pb	Zn	Other	
U.S.A. (Cont'd)														
Arundel Mining Co.		Utah												
Bebb, Virgil	Douglas	Idaho	1967	Ag,Pb,Zn	Vein	O.S.	160		60		6.3	7.7		
Bunker Hill Co.	Bunker Hill	Idaho	1885	Ag,Pb,Zn	Vein	C&F	351,930		96		5.78	6.07		Own Mill - Idaho
" "	Crescent	Idaho	1897	Ag	Vein	C&F	25,940		1706					Own Mill - Idaho
" "	Star	Idaho	1903	Ag,Pb,Zn	Vein	C&F	172,310		75		4.9	8.8		Own Mill - Idaho
Byrd, John H.	Sam Gaty	Montana	1966	Au,Ag,Pb	Vein	S.L.S.	195	9	920	0.9	25.9			
" "	Franklin	Montana	1966	Au,Ag,Pb	Vein	S.L.S.	70	13	1130	0.6	28.6			
Callahan Mining Corp.	Penobscot	Maine	1880	Zn	Lens	Open Pit	101,600							Own Mill - Maine
Calvert City Chemical Co.		Kentucky		Fluorspar										Own Mill - Kentucky
Canyon Silver Mines	Canyon Silver	Idaho	1967	Ag,Pb,Zn	Vein	S.S.	2,100		586		22.6	1.6		
Christensen, Paul	Dorsey	Nevada		Ag,Cu	Vein	S.L.S.	35		2111	1.2	0.06			
Clipper Mining Co.	Clipper	Colorado	1889	Ag,Pb,Zn	Pipe	S.L.S.	Development Only							Own Mill - Colorado
Combs, Marvin W.	Liminite	Arizona	1968	Ag,Pb	Vein		34		1287		2.0			
Coronado Silver Corp.		Colorado					Development Only							
Crim, John D.	Henrietta	Colorado		Ag,Pb,Zn	Pipe	R&P	290		1066	0.74	14.0	6.0	Bi .21	
Cyprus Mines Corp.	Bruce	Arizona	1968	Zn	Vein	C&F								Own Mill - Arizona
Day Mines Inc.	Dayrock	Idaho	1923	Ag,Pb,Zn	Vein	Horiz. Cut	23,715							Own Mill - Idaho

MILLS

Country and Company Name	Name/ Location of Mill	Year First Operated	Mines Milled	Rated Daily Capacity	Milling Method	Tonnage Milled	Concentrate Produced (1968)								Other Products
							Type	Tonnage	Analysis						
									Au	Ag	Cu	Pb	Zn	Other	
United States of America (Cont'd)															
Bunker Hill Co.	Idaho	1886	Thirteen	2,175	Flotation	667,075	Lead Zinc	44,240 54,545		1234 137		63.0 2.0	7.9 52.4	Cd.23	Sand for Fill
Callahan Mining Corp.	Maine	1968	One	635	Flotation	101,600									
Calvert City Chemical Co.	Kentucky		Lead and Zinc Concentrates as by-products of Fluorspar mining												
Clipper Mining Co.	Colorado	1889													
Cyprus Mines Corp.	Arizona	1957	One	270	Flotation	17,770	Zinc	2,935					50.9	Cd.12	Cu. Conc..
Day Mines Inc.	Idaho	1941	One		Flotation	23,715	Mixed	2,530							

SURVEY OF WORLD LEAD AND ZINC PRODUCTION IN 1968

MINES

Country and Company Name	Name of Mine	Location of Mine	Year First Operated	Principal Metals Mined	Type of Deposit	Mining Method	Ore Production (1968) Tonnage	Analysis Au	Ag	Cu	Pb	Zn	Other	Where Milled
U.S.A. (Cont'd)														
Dresser Industries Inc./Cominco American Inc.	Magmont	Missouri	1968	Pb	Bedded	R&P	116,120							Own Mill - Missouri
Eagle-Picher Industries Inc.	Blackjack	Illinois	1854	Zn	Pitch & Flat	R&P								Own Mill - Illinois
" "	Birkett	Wisconsin	1926	Zn	Pitch & Flat	R&P								Own Mill - Illinois
" "	Bautsch	Illinois	1946	Zn	Pitch & Flat	R&P								Own Mill - Illinois
" "	Rehm-Bauer	Illinois	1966	Zn	Pitch & Flat	R&P								Own Mill - Illinois
" "	Shallsburg	Wisconsin	1949	Zn	Pitch & Flat	R&P								Own Mill - Wisconsin
" "	Hutson	Kentucky	1914	Zn	Vein/ Replacement	S.S. S.L.S.								Leased Mill - Kentucky
" "	Grace B	Oklahoma	1920	Zn	Bedded	R&P								Own Mill - Oklahoma
" "	Westside	Oklahoma	1920	Zn	Bedded	R&P								Own Mill - Oklahoma
Farrow Bros.	Diamond Jin	Nevada	1966	Au,Ag,Pb	Vein	R&P	360	2	718	0.2	23.0	3.5		
Ferganchich, James		Colorado					Development Only							
Gerlach, Keith H.		Nevada	1968	Pb		Open Pit	Development Only							
Hand, John	Hand	Montana	1942	Au,Ag,Pb	Vein	O.S.	2,050	4	111	0.1	15.0	2.3		
Hecla Mining Co.	Star - Morning	Idaho	1895	Ag,Pb,Zn	Vein	C&F	172,310		75		4.92	8.84		Own Mill - Idaho
" "	Silver Summit	Idaho	1947	Ag,Cu	Vein	C&F	19,900		583	0.54				Own Mill - Idaho
" "	Lucky Friday	Idaho	1941	Ag,Cu,Pb,Zn	Vein	C&F	87,020		538		10.0	0.9		Own Mill - Idaho

SURVEY OF WORLD LEAD AND ZINC PRODUCTION IN 1968

MILLS

Country and Company Name	Name/ Location of Mill	Year First Operated	Mines Milled	Rated Daily Capacity	Milling Method	Tonnage Milled	Concentrate Produced (1968)								Other Products
							Type	Tonnage	Analysis						
									Au	Ag	Cu	Pb	Zn	Other	
United States of America (Cont'd)															
Dresser Industries Inc /Cominco American Inc.	Missouri	1968	One	3,810	Flotation	116,120	Lead	22,680							
							Zinc	450							
Eagle-Picher Ind. Inc.	Illinois	1949	Four	1,360	Flotation	244,940	Lead	280				7.4			
							Zinc	14,400					57.8	Cd.15	Chat
" " " "	Wisconsin	1949	One	1,090	Flot./Grav.	346,545	Lead	825				77.75			
							Zinc	16,465					60.0	Cd.15	Chat
" " " "	Kentucky	1949	One	225	Flotation	53,525	Zinc	7,440					58.5	Cd.40	
" " " "	Oklahoma	1932	Sixteen	13,600	Flot./Grav.	348,360	Lead	4,175				70.4			
							Zinc	16,060					59.5	Cd.30	Chat
							Mixed	180				15.0	35.0		
Hecla Mining Co.	Idaho	1937	One	1,000	Flotation	172,305	Lead	10,240		762		63.9	12.1		
							Zinc	26,810		154		5.2	50.8		
" " "	Idaho	1926	One		Flotation	19,895	Mixed	670	2.4	18,288	17.42				
" " "	Idaho	1960	One	635	Flotation	87,020	Lead	11,900	1.6	3,821	1.01	71.45	4.52		
							Zinc	400	0.6	453	0.12	3.96	45.28	Cd.3	

SURVEY OF WORLD LEAD AND ZINC PRODUCTION IN 1968

MINES

Country and Company Name	Name of Mine	Location of Mine	Year First Operated	Principal Metals Mined	Type of Deposit	Mining Method	Ore Production (1968)							Where Milled
								Analysis						
							Tonnage	Au	Ag	Cu	Pb	Zn	Other	
U.S.A. (Cont'd)														
Hecla Mining Co. (cont'd)	Mayflower	Utah	1934	Ag,Cu,Pb,Zn	Vein	C&F	111,000							Own Mill - Utah
Holton, J.J.		Nevada		Au,Ag	Vein		Development Only							
Hopkins, John F.	Negros	Montana		Ag,Pb	Vein	O.S.	29	10	480	0.05	7.0	0.4		Own Mill - Montana
Idarado Mining Co.	Idarado	Colorado		Zn	Vein	S.S.	385,465							Own Mill - Colorado
Ivey Construction Co.	Graysville	Wisconsin	1956	Zn	Vein	R&P	17,330					3.0		Own Mill - Wisconsin
Kennecot Copper Corp.	Burgin	Utah	1966	Ag,Pb,Zn	Replacement	C&F/Sq.S	181,440							Custom - Utah
Kostelic, Louis		Colorado					Development Only							
Kraft Building Contr.	Treasure Key	Colorado	1968	Pb	Vein	S.S.								Own Mill - Colorado
Marshall, Douglas	Santiago	Colorado	1900	Au,Ag,Cu,Pb	Vein	C&F		32	1063	2.5	15			Own Mill - Colorado
McBride, G.V.R.	Montgomery	Montana	1968	Pb	Vein		Development Only							
McFarland & Hullinger	Iron King	Arizona		Ag,Cu,Pb,Zn	Vein	S.S.	92,610	3	70	0.16	1.63	4.4		Leased Mill - Arizona
Meissner, Donald O.	Good View	Nevada	1963	Ag,Pb,Sb	Lens	Drift	135		1206		10.6		Sb 11	
Minerva Oil Co.	Minerva No.1	Illinois	1944	Fluorspar,Zn	Bedded Replacement	R&P	209,272					2.1	CaF_2 26.4	Own Mill - Illinois
" "	Victory	Illinois	1930	Fluorspar	Bedded Replacement	R&P	2,880						CaF_2 44.1	Own Mill - Illinois
" "	Crystal	Illinois	1934	Fluorspar	Bedded Replacement	R&P	1,870						CaF_2 71.3	Own Mill - Illinois
" "	Fairbairn/ Jefferson	Illinois	1954	Fluorspar, Pb,Zn	Vein	S.S.	22,800				0.85	1.96	CaF_2 35.2	Own Mill - Illinois

MILLS

Country and Company Name	Name/ Location of Mill	Year First Operated	Mines Milled	Rated Daily Capacity	Milling Method	Tonnage Milled	Concentrate Produced (1968)								Other Products
							Type	Tonnage	Analysis						
									Au	Ag	Cu	Pb	Zn	Other	
United States of America (Cont'd)															
Hecla Mining Co. (Cont'd)	Utah	1961	One	410	Flotation	111,000	Lead	13,710	129	1,175	6.62	31.15	5.52		
							Zinc	4,395	8.6	135	0.93	0.77	59.38	Cd.46	
							Pyrite	440	73	456	1.05	1.68	18.46		
Hopkins, John F.	Montana	1942	One	45	Flotation	70	Lead	3	8.6	960	0.25	20.0	5.0		
Idarado Mining Co.	Colorado	1956	One	1,540	Flotation	385,465	Lead	12,540	17	1,543	4.05	71.0	2.2		Dore Bullion
							Zinc	24,540	1.2	95	1.03	0.8	58.9	Cd.25	
Ivey Construction Co.	Wisconsin	1965	One	270	Flotation	17,325	Lead	55				59.0			Agricultural Lime & Chat
							Zinc	705					58.0		
Kraft Building Contr.	Colorado	1968	Two	55	Flot./Grav.		Lead	20	45	685	1.0	20.0			
Marshall, Douglas	Colorado	1967	Dumps	45	Flot./Grav.	365	Pyrite	20	19	377	2.0	6.0			
McFarland & Hullinger	Arizona		One	545	Flotation	92,605	Lead	4,790	35	1,307	1.8	35.8			
							Zinc	6,035	2	66			53.3	Cd.12	
Minerva Oil Co.	Illinois	1944	One	360	Flotation	126,805	Zinc	5,920				64.2			
" " "	Illinois	1952	Three	225	Flotation	64,380	Lead	355				48.1			
							Zinc	1,545					57.6		

SURVEY OF WORLD LEAD AND ZINC PRODUCTION IN 1968

MINES

Country and Company Name	Name of Mine	Location of Mine	Year First Operated	Principal Metals Mined	Type of Deposit	Mining Method	Ore Production (1968) Tonnage	Analysis Au	Ag	Cu	Pb	Zn	Other	Where Milled
U.S.A. (Cont'd)														
Minerva Oil Co. (Cont'd)	Lafayette	Kentucky	1967	Fluorspar	Vein	Open Pit	16,135						CaF2 43.3	Own Mill - Illinois
Monte Cristo Mining Corp.	Jubilee	California	1963	Pb	Lens	S.L.S.	1,815	.7	624		51.5			Direct Smelting Ore
New Jersey Zinc Co.	Austinville	Virginia	1902	Zn	Replacement	R&P	598,025				0.7	4.0		Own Mill - Virginia
" "	Hanover	New Mexico	1903	Zn	Replacement	R&P	165,300				0.7	8.5		Own Mill - New Mexico
" "	Gilman	Colorado	1915	Zn	Manta/ Chimney	Sq.S/ Mitchell Slice Stoping	233,425		75		1.4	10.9		Own Mill - Colorado
" "	Sterling	New Jersey	1916	Zn	Vein	C&F/Sq.S	142,205					20.2	Fe 13.0 Mn 7.0	Own Mill - New Jersey
" "	Jefferson City	Tennessee	1956	Zn	Replacement	R&P	422,190					3.8		Own Mill - Tennessee
" "	Friedens-ville	Pennsylvania	1958	Zn	Bedded Replacement	R&P	570,750					6.4		Own Mill - Pennsylvania
" "	Flat Gap	Tennessee	1959	Zn	Replacement	R&P	461,910					3.2		Own Mill - Tennessee
" "	Elmo	Wisconsin	1967	Zn	Bedding Plane	R&P	194,505				0.3	4.6		Own Mill - Wisconsin
New Market Zinc Co.	New Market	Tennessee	1962	Zn	Replacement	R&P/S.S.								Own Mill - Tennessee
Nygren, Rudy	Ferdinand	Montana	1919	Pb,Zn	Vein	S.L.S.	13	.7	137	.06	12.5	10.0		
" "	Yellow Bird	Montana	1968	Ag,Pb,Zn	Vein	Open Pit	11	2.7	891		22.0	27.0		
Osceola Metals Corp.	Osceola	Colorado	1879	Pb,Zn	Vein/ Replacement	R&P/S.S.	12,975	1.4	24	0.3	3.0	4.5		
Ozark Lead Co.	Ozark Lead	Missouri	1968	Pb,Zn	Bedded Replacement	R&P								Own Mill - Missouri

MILLS

Country and Company Name	Name/ Location of Mill	Year First Operated	Mines Milled	Rated Daily Capacity	Milling Method	Tonnage Milled	Concentrate Produced (1968)								Other Products
							Type	Tonnage	Analysis						
									Au	Ag	Cu	Pb	Zn	Other	
United States of America (Cont'd)															
New Jersey Zinc Co.	Virginia	1913	Two	2,360	Flotation	598,025	Lead	4,315				76.0	0.4		Limestone
							Zinc	29,835				2.0	61.4		
" " " "	New Mexico	1926	Two	725	Flotation	165,300	Lead	1,905		857	1.4	55.0	8.0		
							Zinc	23,030				0.27	53.0		
" " " "	Colorado	1929	One	1,090	Flotation	233,425	Lead	3,435		1,543	2.5	55.0	5.0		
							Zinc	49,350			0.5	0.7	49.5		
" " " "	New Jersey	1962	One	1,090	No Concentrating - Crushing and Grinding Only										
" " " "	Tennessee	1956	One	1,995	Flotation	422,190	Zinc	24,985					63.5		Limestone
" " " "	Pennsylvania	1958	One	2,270	Flotation	570,750	Zinc	53,255					59.0		Limestone
" " " "	Tennessee	1959	One	1,995	Flotation	461,910	Zinc	17,025					60.0		
" " " "	Wisconsin	1967	Three	815	Flotation	194,505	Lead	330				69.0	0.1		
							Zinc	12,830				0.6	60.0		
New Market Zinc Co.	Tennessee	1962	One	3,265	Flotation	679,935	Zinc	32,295					63.3	Cd.25	
Ozark Lead Co.	Missouri	1968	One	5,545	Flotation										

SURVEY OF WORLD LEAD AND ZINC PRODUCTION IN 1968

MINES

Country and Company Name	Name of Mine	Location of Mine	Year First Operated	Principal Metals Mined	Type of Deposit	Mining Method	Ore Production (1968) Tonnage	Analysis Au	Ag	Cu	Pb	Zn	Other	Where Milled
U.S.A. (Cont'd)														
Ozark-Mahoning Co.	Shaft No.4	Illinois	1949	Fluorspar	Lens	R&P	106,095					3.05	CaF_2 35.1	Own Mill - Illinois
" "	Hill - Ledford	Illinois	1955	Fluorspar	Lens	R&P	60,110				0.37	1.59	CaF_2 29.66	Own Mill - Illinois
" "	Shaft No.10	Illinois	1959	Fluorspar	Lens	R&P	52,315					5.33	CaF_2 21.4	Own Mill - Illinois
" "	Burnett Complex	Illinois	1964	Fluorspar	Vein	S.S.	46,750				1.3	3.35	CaF_2 45.0	Own Mill - Illinois
" "	Taylor	Illinois	1965	Fluorspar	Lens	R&P	5,445				0.58	2.24	CaF_2 22.0	Own Mill - Illinois
Pend Oreille Mines & Met. Co.	Pend Oreille	Washington	1935	Pb,Zn	Replacement	R&P								Own Mill - Washington
Rico Argentine Mining Co.	Argentine	Colorado	1911	Pb,Zn	Replacement	O.S.								
St. Joseph Lead Co.	Edwards	New York		Zn	Vein	O.S.								Own Mill - New York
" "	Balmat	New York		Zn	Vein	O.S.								Own Mill - New York
" "	Federal	Missouri	Before 1900	Pb	Bedded Replacement	R&P								Own Mill - Missouri
" "	Indian Creek	Missouri	1954	Pb	Bedded Replacement	R&P								Own Mill - Missouri
" "	Viburnum	Missouri	1960	Pb	Bedded Replacement	R&P								Own Mill - Missouri
" "	Fletcher	Missouri	1967	Pb	Bedded Replacement	R&P								Own Mill - Missouri
Security Resources Corp	Old Russia	Colorado	1875	Ag	Lens	Dump	110	.4	178		1.0			
Silver Wreath Cons. Mines	Fairmont Group	Colorado	1952	Ag,Pb,Zn	Vein	O.S.	3,175	4.1	257	0.6	8.0	7.0	Cd 1.4	Own Mill- Colorado
Skyline Mining Co.	Tarn	Colorado	1968	Ag,Pb,Zn	Vein	S.S.	90		240		7.0	14.0		

MILLS

Country and Company Name	Name/ Location of Mill	Year First Operated	Mines Milled	Rated Daily Capacity	Milling Method	Tonnage Milled	Concentrate Produced (1968)								Other Products
							Type	Tonnage	Analysis						
									Au	Ag	Cu	Pb	Zn	Other	
United States of America (Cont'd)															
Ozark-Mahoning Co.	Illinois	1939	Seven	610	Heavy Media/ Flotation	185,740	Lead Zinc	1,030 11,270				73.43	61.25	Cd.77	Fluorspar 74990 tons
Pend Oreille Mines & Metals Co.	Washington	1951	One	2,180	Chemical/ Flotation	179,465	Lead Zinc	6,275 6,825				73.3	64.4		
Rico Argentine Mining Co.	Colorado	1939	One	130	Flotation		Lead	1,655	.7	1,121	0.09	77.3	2.6		
							Zinc	2,695		202		3.03	54.6	Cd.33	
St. Joseph Lead Co.	New York		One	545	Flotation		Lead	259,536	Total	St. Joe 1968 - Annual Report					
" " " "	New York		One	1,995	Flotation		Zinc	124,473	"	"	" "	"	"		
" " " "	Missouri	Before 1900	One	10,885	Flotation										
" " " "	Missouri	1954	One	2,275	Flotation										
" " " "	Missouri	1960	One	6,805	Flotation										
" " " "	Missouri	1967	One	4,535	Flotation										
Silver Wreath Corp. Mines	Colorado		Four	65	Flotation/ Jig	(Custom) ?	Mixed Jig		31 229	3,428 823	4.0 1.05	16.0 45.0	26.0		

SURVEY OF WORLD LEAD AND ZINC PRODUCTION IN 1968

MINES

Country and Company Name	Name of Mine	Location of Mine	Year First Operated	Principal Metals Mined	Type of Deposit	Mining Method	Ore Production (1968)							Where Milled
							Tonnage	Analysis						
								Au	Ag	Cu	Pb	Zn	Other	
U.S.A. (Cont'd)														
Smith, Geo. W.	Silver Eagle	Utah	1860	Ag,Pb,Zn	Vein	S.S./ S.L.S.	560	2.7	154	0.2	5.5	8.5		Direct Smelting Ore
Standard Metals Corp.	Sunnyside	Colorado		Pb,Zn	Vein	S.S.								Own Mill - Colorado
Strode, Emery D.	Funny Looking Rock	Nevada	1967	Ag	Vein	Drifting	50		342		4.0	2.5		Direct Smelting Ore
T. Geo. Inc.	Dobson	Oklahoma	1966	Pb,Zn	Vein	R&P	12,115							Custom - Oklahoma
Tennessee Copper Corp.	Eureka	Tennessee	1906	Cu,Zn	Vein	S.L.S.								Own Mill - Tennessee
" "	Boyd	Tennessee	1941	Cu,Zn	Vein	S.L.S.								Own Mill - Tennessee
" "	Calloway	Tennessee	1946	Cu,Zn	Vein	S.L.S.								Own Mill - Tennessee
" "	Cherobee	Tennessee	1962	Cu,Zn	Vein	S.L.S.								Own Mill - Tennessee
Tongaha Mining Co.	Piokee	Oklahoma	1936	Pb,Zn	Vein	R&P	24,235							Custom - Oklahoma
Uhalde, John H.	Aladdin	Nevada	1890	Ag,Cu,Pb	Replacement	S.S./ Open Pit	270	.7	181	1.3	35.0			Own Mill - Nevada
United Park City Mines Company	United Park City	Utah	1890	Pb	Vein	C&F	76,515	.5	132	0.1	6.3	9.3		
U.S. Steel Corp.	Zinc Mine	Tennessee	1930	Zn	Replacement	R&P								Own Mill - Tennessee
Wall, Lyman	New Chance	California	1956	Ag,Pb	Vein	Drifting								Own Mill - California
West Hill Exploration Inc.	Darwin	California	1967	Ag,Pb,Zn		S.L.S.	51,920		213		3.31	7.0		Own Mill - California

SURVEY OF WORLD LEAD AND ZINC PRODUCTION IN 1968

MILLS

Country and Company Name	Name/ Location of Mill	Year First Operated	Mines Milled	Rated Daily Capacity	Milling Method	Tonnage Milled	Concentrate Produced (1968)								Other Products
							Type	Tonnage	Analysis						
									Au	Ag	Cu	Pb	Zn	Other	
United States of America (Cont'd)															
Standard Metals Corp.	Colorado		One	635	Flotation	172,930	Lead Zinc	4,780 13,320	16 12	1,107 146	5.9 0.7	64.4 4.7	4.65 55.8	Cd.23	
(T. Geo. Inc. - Mine Ore Custom Milled)	Oklahoma						Lead Zinc	25 770				80.0	60.0		
Tennessee Copper Corp.	Tennessee	1922	Six	4,535	Flotation	1,473,635	Zinc Pyrite	15,825 769,715					51.21	S 40.4	Cu Conc.
(Tongaha Mining Co. Ore Custom Milled)	Oklahoma						Lead Zinc	230 785				80.0	60.0		
Uhalde, John H.	Nevada		Two	270	Gravity	2,775	Mixed	315	.7	185	1.3	36.8	4.7		
U.S. Steel Corp.	Tennessee		One		Flot/Grav/ Chemical										Ag Limestone
Wall, Lyman	California	1956	One Plus Dumps	45	Gravity	635	Lead	55		480		50.0			
West Hill Exploration Inc.	California	1967	One	455	Flotation	51,920	Lead Zinc	3,900 6,380	.7	2,823 317	1.35	49.37 3.07	7.84 51.7	Cd.28	

SURVEY OF WORLD LEAD AND ZINC PRODUCTION IN 1968

MINES

Country and Company Name	Name of Mine	Location of Mine	Year First Operated	Principal Metals Mined	Type of Deposit	Mining Method	Ore Production (1968)							Where Milled
							Tonnage	Analysis						
								Au	Ag	Cu	Pb	Zn	Other	
AMERICA SOUTH AND CENTRAL														
Bolivia														
Banco Minera de Bolivia	Various	Various		Pb,Zn	Various									
Corp. Minera de Bolivia	Animas	Chocaya	1917	Ag,Pb,Zn	Vein		153,433		530		3.61	3.64		Own Mill - Atocha
" "	San Jose	Oruro		Ag,Pb			148,486		137		1.21		Sn 1.05	Own Mill - Machacamarca
" "	Tatasi	Portugalete		Ag,Pb,Zn	Vein		28,191				5.81	5.61		Own Mill- Portugalete
Empresa Minera San Jose De Berque	La Espanola	Chagua	Unknown	Ag,Pb		Gallery Exploit-ation	600		300		70			Hand Sorted Concs.
" "	La Argentina	Mojo	Unknown	Ag,Pb,Zn		C&F S.L.S.	540		300		70	50		Hand Sorted Concs.
Brazil														
Companhia Mercantil E Industrial Inga	Ouro Podre	Vazante	1965	Zn	Bedded	B.C.	19,855			4.8	3.2	30.0		Own Mill - Rio
Mineracao Boquira S.A.	Boquira	Bahia	1955	Pb	Vein	S.L.S.	230,000				9.7			Own Mill - Bahia
Mineracao Lageado Ltda.	Rocha/ Besseti	Parana	1955	Ag,Pb	Vein	R&P	36,656		106		5.45			Plumbum S/A - Parana
Plumbum S.A.	Panelas de Brejauva	Parana	1938	Ag,Pb	Vein		53,744		66		4.56			Own Mill - Parana

SURVEY OF WORLD LEAD AND ZINC PRODUCTION IN 1968

MILLS

Country and Company Name	Name/ Location of Mill	Year First Operated	Mines Milled	Rated Daily Capacity	Milling Method	Tonnage Milled	Concentrate Produced (1968)								Other Products
							Type	Tonnage	Analysis						
									Au	Ag	Cu	Pb	Zn	Other	
AMERICA SOUTH AND CENTRAL															
Bolivia															
Banco Minera de Bolivia			Various				Lead	21,843				66.9			See Note No. 1
							Zinc	6,160					48.8		
Corp. Minera de Bolivia	Atocha	1923	Two	532	Flotation	153,433	Lead	12,722		5,190		39.81			
							Zinc	7,042		1,250			50.12	Cd.77	
" " "	Machacamarca			438	Flot/Grav. Heavy Media	148,486	Lead	2,420		4,740		45.65			
" " "	Portugalete		One	82	Flotation	28,191	Lead Zinc	2,495 808		3,630 790		50.55	43.28		
Brazil															
Companhia Mercantil E Industrial Inga	Rio	1965	One	20	Hydro-metall-urgical		Zinc								
Companhia Brazileira De Chambo	Bahia	1959	One	620	Flotation	217,630	Lead	30,220				57.3	5.97		
Plumbum S/A	Parana	1953	Four	300	Flot./Jig	94,228	Lead	8,021		812	0.96	48.4	2.5		

Note No. 1: Includes purchases of ores and concentrates by traders from Bando Minera during 1968.

SURVEY OF WORLD LEAD AND ZINC PRODUCTION IN 1968

MINES

Country and Company Name	Name of Mine	Location of Mine	Year First Operated	Principal Metals Mined	Type of Deposit	Mining Method	Ore Production (1968)								Where Milled
							Tonnage	Analysis							
								Au	Ag	Cu	Pb	Zn	Other		
Chile															
Empresa Minera De Aysen	Silva	Aysen		Ag,Pb,Zn	Vein	C&F	9,375		205		12.99	17.17			Own Mill - Aysen
Rasmuss, Juan E.	Raquel 1-5	Santiago	1966	Pb,Zn		C&F	6,500								Own Mill - Santiago
Colombia															
Frontino Gold Mines Ltd.	Cogote	Segovia	1905	Au,Ag,Pb,Zn	Bedded	R&P/ S.L.S.	23,074	18	31		6.6	5.78			Own Mill - Segovia
" "	Silencio	Segovia	1852	Au,Ag,Pb,Zn	Bedded	R&P/ S.L.S.	127,707	13	22		4.12	3.61			Own Mill - Segovia
Equador															
Compania Industrial Minera Asociada S.A.	Portovelo	El Oro	1951	Au,Ag,Cu,Zn	Vein	C&F									Own Mill - El Oro
Honduras															
New York & Honduras Rosario	El Mochito	Honduras	1948	Ag,Pb,Zn	Replacement	C&F	230,900	0.8	596		6.2	6.4			Own Mill - Honduras
Mexico															
Celestino Aguilar Munoz	La Quebralillo	Zacatecas		Ag,Pb	Vein	S.L.S.	360	1.2	1000		17.4				
Asarco Mexicana S.A.	Charcas	San Luis Potosi	1924	Ag,Cu,Pb,Zn	Veins, Beds	C&F/S.S.	289,879	0.2	129	0.44	1.2	5.7			Own Mill - San Luis Potosi

SURVEY OF WORLD LEAD AND ZINC PRODUCTION IN 1968

MILLS

Country and Company Name	Name/Location of Mill	Year First Operated	Mines Milled	Rated Daily Capacity	Milling Method	Tonnage Milled	Concentrate Produced (1968)								Other Products
							Type	Tonnage	Analysis						
									Au	Ag	Cu	Pb	Zn	Other	
Chile															
Empresa Minera De Aysen	Aysen		One	64	Flotation	9,375	Lead	1,548		800		62.68	10.91		
							Zinc	2,182		200		3.78	51.43	Cd.24	
Rasmuss, Juan E.	Santiago	1966	One	100	Flotation	6,500	Lead	185				46.0			
							Zinc	775					54.0		
Colombia															
Frontino Gold Mines Ltd.	Segovia	1891	Three	544	Flotation/ Jigs/Tables/ Cyanidation/ Heavy Media	150,772	Lead	818				55.01	3.12		Au,Ag
							Zinc	717				5.1	51.78	Cd 1.75	
Equador															
Compania Industrial Minera Asociada S.A.	El Oro	1951	Four	280	Flotation		Zinc	368		7	7.15		39.25	Cd.335	Cu Conc.
Honduras															
New York & Honduras Rosario	Honduras	1948	One	680	Flotation	230,395	Lead	20,087	5	4,640		59.3			
							Zinc	20,775		912		2.44	52.05		Dore Bullion
Mexico															
Asarco Mexicana,S.A.	San Luis Potosi	1925	One	1,000	Flotation	280,470	Lead	5,704	0.8	3,582	9.73	41.3	11.0		
							Zinc	23,012	0.2	180	0.93	1.2	57.6	Cd.7	
							Pyrite	13,830	1.3	165	0.45	0.9	3.4	Fe38.5	

SURVEY OF WORLD LEAD AND ZINC PRODUCTION IN 1968

MINES

Country and Company Name	Name of Mine	Location of Mine	Year First Operated	Principal Metals Mined	Type of Deposit	Mining Method	Ore Production (1968)								Where Milled
							Tonnage	Analysis							
								Au	Ag	Cu	Pb	Zn	Other		
Mexico (Cont'd)															
Asarco Mexicana S.A. (cont'd)	Parral	Chihuahua	1923	Ag,Cu,Pb,Zn	Vein	C&F/ S.S.	491,912	0.28	49	0.22	1.6	3.1			Own Mill - Chihauhau
" "	Plomosas	Chihuahua	1946	Pb,Zn	Bedded	R&P/S.S.	58,054		83		8.1	16.3			Own Mill - Chihauhau
" "	Santa Barbara	Chihuahua	1898	Ag,Cu,Pb,Zn	Vein	S.S.	501,100	0.7	165	0.87	3.0	5.5			Own Mill - Chihauhau
" "	Santa Eulalia	Chihuahua	1904	Ag,Cu,Pb,Zn	Beds/ Chimneys	R&P	99,033		124		5.5	6.0			Own Mill - Chihauhau
" "	San Martin	Zacatecas	1953	Ag,Cu,Zn	Veins/Beds	C&F/R&P/ S.S.	93,618		309	2.03	0.3	7.4			Own Mill - Zacatecas
" "	Taxco	Guerrero	1943	Ag,Pb,Zn	Vein	C&F/S.S.	306,000	0.44	160		3.0	7.3			Own Mill - Guerrero
Vicente Caballero Lujan	Margarita	Chihuahua		Ag,Pb	Vein	B.C.	98,802		14		37.9				See Note No. 2
Antonio Castaneda Amador	Dos De Marzo	Zacatecas	1969	Ag,Pb,Zn	Vein	Drifting	40		58		2.06	24.4			
Valente Chacon Baca	La Prieta	Chihuahua	1967	Ag,Pb,Zn		C&F/R&P									Own Mill - Chihuahua
Comision de Fomento Minera	None			Cyanide	Residues	from Cia	Real Del Monte								Own Mill - Hidalgo
Expresa Minera La Providencia S.A.															
Compania Fresnillo, S.A.	Grupo Proano	Zacatecas	before 1600	Ag,Cu,Pb,Zn	Veins/Beds	Under-hand Stoping/ C&F/R&P/ S.S.	361,536	0.35	161	0.11	1.91	2.95			Own Mill - Zacatecas

Note No. 2: 1969 Statistics

SURVEY OF WORLD LEAD AND ZINC PRODUCTION IN 1968

MILLS

Country and Company Name	Name/ Location of Mill	Year First Operated	Mines Milled	Rated Daily Capacity	Milling Method	Tonnage Milled	Concentrate Produced (1968)								Other Products
							Type	Tonnage	Analysis						
									Au	Ag	Cu	Pb	Zn	Other	
Mexico (Cont'd)															
Asarco Mexicana S.A. (Cont'd)	Chihuahua	1925	Eleven	1,700	Flotation	585,800	Lead	16,570	15	1,756	3.85	61.4	8.3		
							Zinc	29,380	1.1	191	0.77	1.6	57.5	Cd.45	
" " "	Chihuahua	1968	One	500	Flotation	53,700	Lead	6,016		126		50.5	11.6		
							Zinc	10,652		80		3.0	57.2	Cd.20	
" " "	Chihuahua	1903	Five	1,500	Flotation	501,100	Lead	22,583	13.5	2,472	5.7	56.7	7.0		
							Zinc	33,395	0.4	150	1.35	1.0	53.5	Cd.50	
" " "	Chihuahua	1941	Two	400	Flotation	105,100	Lead	5,795	1.1	1,553	1.32	61.8	6.3		
							Zinc	15,640	0.12	80	0.19	1.0	53.8	Cd.25	
" " "	Zacatecas	1954	One	300	Flotation	91,200	Zinc	10,222		157	0.76	0.3	55.8	Cd.40	
" " "	Guerrero	1943	Four	1,000	Flotation	306,000	Lead	12,247	4.4	2,587	1.51	66.0	4.5		
							Zinc	30,886	0.4	160	0.4	0.7	57.5	Cd.50	
Valente Chacon Bace	Chihuahua	1967	One	50	Flotation	24,000	Lead	178		1,556		70.0			
							Zinc	1,050		105			53.0	Cd.26	
Comision de Fomento Minera	Hidalgo	Unknown	Cyanide Residues	10,000	Flotation	1,760,000	Lead	800	2.0	4,000	3.0	40.0	10.0		
							Zinc	3,400	2.0	1,100	0.2	0.4	50.0	Cd.35	
							Mixed	15,720	2.0	698	0.5	3.0	14.0		
							Pyrite	720	2.0	380	0.3	0.1	4.0	Fe.32	
Empresa Minera La Providencia S.A.	Zacatecas	1958	One	100	Flotation		Lead	1,600		2,200	3.0	58.0	6.0		
							Zinc	1,100		160	0.9	2.0	51.0	Cd.65	
Compania Fresnillo S.A.	Zacatecas	1920	Thirty one	2,000	Flotation	471,537	Lead	21,937	4.88	2,370	2.18	42.09	4.68		
							Zinc	29,342	0.66	350	0.72	0.69	50.63	Cd.54	

SURVEY OF WORLD LEAD AND ZINC PRODUCTION IN 1968

MINES

Country and Company Name	Name of Mine	Location of Mine	Year First Operated	Principal Metals Mined	Type of Deposit	Mining Method	Ore Production (1968)								Where Milled
							Tonnage	Analysis							
								Au	Ag	Cu	Pb	Zn	Other		
Mexico (Cont'd)															
Compania Fresnillo, S.A (cont'd)	Unidad Niaca	Chihuahua	1950	Ag, Cu, Pb, Zn	Beds/ Chimneys	C&F/R&P S.S.	540,924	0.35	177	0.31	5.29	4.08			Own Mill - Chihuahua
" "	Unidad Zimapan	Hidalgo	1957	Ag, Cu, Pb, Zn	Chimneys	Under-hand Stoping	18,036	0.28	228	0.90	1.69	4.13			Own Mill - Zacatecas
Acinadora Monterrey S.A. Cia Minera Fundidora Y	Santa Elena	Coahuila	1888	Ag, Pb	Bedded	C&F/R&P									Beneficiadora San Antonio S.A.
" "	San Juan Bautisto	Nuevo Leon	1907	Ag, Pb	Vein	C&F/R&P									Beneficiadora San Antonio S.A.
Minera Guadalupe S.A.	El Burro	Guerrero	1964	Ag, Cu, Pb	Vein	C&F	16,000	1.0	480	3.0	2.0				Own Mill - Guerrero
Impulsora Minera De Anganguco S.A. de C.V.	Delores	Michoacan	?	Ag, Pb, Zn		C&F	98,444	0.37	406	0.2	1.3	3.8	Fe 10.0		Own Mill - Michoacan
Cia Minera "La Condesa" S.A.	Inglaterra	Chihuahua	1966	Ag, Pb	Beds/ Chimneys	C&F	3,195		400		10.0				
La Primera, S.A.	Santa Guillermo	Hidalgo		Ag, Pb, Zn	Irregular Pockets	S.L.S.	17,779		150		9.0	10.0			
Cia Minera La Union, S.A.	Anexas A La Unia	Chihuahua		Ag, Pb, Zn	Bedded	C&F/R&P	3,293		8		1.7	36.84			Asarco Mexicana and Zinc Nacional
Lomo De Toro, S.A.	Santa Guillermo	Hidalgo		Ag, Pb, Zn	Irregular Pockets	S.L.S.	7,677		200		10.0	11.0			
Cia Minera Los Angeles, S. de R.L.	Los Angeles	Coahuila	1956	Ag, Pb, Zn	Deposits/ Veins	R&P	22,682?		.7		15.0	38.0			
Ing. Eduardo A. Manderfield	El Rucio	Zacatecas	1955	Au, Ag, Pb, Zn	Chimneys	Under-hand Stoping	3,543	1.2	704	0.89	8.7	17.8			

MILLS

Country and Company Name	Name/ Location of Mill	Year First Operated	Mines Milled	Rated Daily Capacity	Milling Method	Tonnage Milled	Concentrate Produced (1968)								Other Products
							Type	Tonnage	Analysis						
									Au	Ag	Cu	Pb	Zn	Other	
Mexico (Cont'd)															
Compania Fresnillo S.A. (Cont'd)	Chihuahua	1950	One	2,000	Flotation	540,924	Lead	40,964	1.19	2,012	2.32	64.97			
							Zinc	31,794		88			54.03	Cd.35	Cu Conc.
Minera Guadalupe, S.A.	Guerrero	1964	One	50	Flotation	16,000	Lead	600	40	9,800	20.0	11.0			
Impulsora Minera De Angangueo, S.A. de C.V.	Michoacan		One	400	Flotation	98,444	Lead	3,534	3.2	7,440	1.7	29.3	8.2		
							Zinc	3,185	1.1	907	0.8	1.4	46.8	Cd.32	
							Pyrite	15,890	1.1	574	0.5	0.7	3.3	Fe34.0	

SURVEY OF WORLD LEAD AND ZINC PRODUCTION IN 1968

MINES

Country and Company Name	Name of Mine	Location of Mine	Year First Operated	Principal Metals Mined	Type of Deposit	Mining Method	Ore Production (1968)							Where Milled
							Tonnage	Analysis						
								Au	Ag	Cu	Pb	Zn	Other	
Mexico (Cont'd)														
Minera Metalurgica Mexicana S.A.	San Francisco Potosi	Coahuila	1954	Ag,Pb	Vein	C&F	34,057		984		7.7			
" "		Chihuahua	1965	Ag,Pb,Zn	Beds & Chimneys	R&P	185,062		207		7.37	8.25		Own Mill - Chihuahua
Cia Minera Ocampo, S.A.	Mineral Reformo	Coahuila	1896	Ag,Pb	Vein	C&F/R&P	700		170		19.0			
Preisser Y Martinez S. en N.C.	Balcones	Hidalgo	1947	Pb,Zn	Bedded	B.C./ R&P	17,240		236	0.28	4.7	13.5	Cd .086	
Cia Minera Sabinas S.A.	Sabinas	Zacatecas	1949	Ag,Cu,Pb,Zn	Vein	S.S.	18,500		162	0.3	6.0	4.5		
Minera San Francisco Del Oro, S.A. De C.V.	Frisco	Chihuahua	1926	Ag,Cu,Pb,Zn	Vein	S.S.	866,200	0.25	148	0.42	4.10	6.55	Cd.05 CaF2 13.28	Own Mill - Chihuahua
Melchor de los Santos	San Francisco del Puerto	Zacatecas	1954	Ag,Pb	Vein	S.S.	589	8.4	1079		33.35			
Cia Minera Suriana, S.A.	Peregrina	Morelos	1966	Ag,Pb,Zn	Vein	S.S.	37,137		650		2.5	1.8		Own Mill - Morelos
" "	San Francisco	Morelos	1966	Ag,Pb,Zn	Vein	S.S.								
Zimapan,S.A.	Unidad Zimapan	Hidalgo	1957	Ag,Cu,Pb,Zn	Chimneys	Under-hand Stoping	23,942	0.18	183	0.21	3.31	9.64		Cia Fresnillo, S.A. Zacatecas
" "	Unidad Amaltea	Jalisco	1967	Ag,Cu,Pb,Zn	Veins	C&F/S.S.	26,723	0.47	140	0.95	2.32	13.20		Own Mill - Jalisco

SURVEY OF WORLD LEAD AND ZINC PRODUCTION IN 1968

MILLS

Country and Company Name	Name/ Location of Mill	Year First Operated	Mines Milled	Rated Daily Capacity	Milling Method	Tonnage Milled	Concentrate Produced (1968)								Other Products
							Type	Tonnage	Analysis						
									Au	Ag	Cu	Pb	Zn	Other	
Mexico(Cont'd)															
Minerales Vacionales de Mexico, S.A.	Chihuahua	1965	One	1,800	Flotation	183,510	Lead	18,087		1,855		70.83	5.05		
							Zinc	23,556		46		0.35	48.54		
Beneficiadora San Antonio, S.A.	Hidalgo	1957	Two	200	Flotation	34,500	Lead	4,500		1,811		61.0	5.8		
							Zinc	6,200		62		0.9	54.0	Cd.50	
Minera San Francisco Del Oro, S.A. De C.V.	Chihuahua		Two	2,500	Flotation	866,200	Lead	46,752	2.01	2,198	4.78	67.28	2.70		
							Zinc	89,056	0.15	100	0.75	0.54	57.94	Cd.42	Fluorite
Cia Minera Suriana, S.A.	Morelos	1966	Two	105	Flotation	37,137	Mixed	1,061	2.0	13,000		40.0	20.0		
Zimapan, S.A.	Jalisco	1967	One	200	Flotation	26,723	Lead	1,135	2.27	1,426	8.0	37.29	17.12		
							Zinc	5,995	0.35	86	0.79	0.98	52.34	Cd.22	
							Cu/Pb/Zn	673	7.18	1,556	19.17	14.09	15.09		

SURVEY OF WORLD LEAD AND ZINC PRODUCTION IN 1968

MINES

Country and Company Name	Name of Mine	Location of Mine	Year First Operated	Principal Metals Mined	Type of Deposit	Mining Method	Ore Production (1968) Tonnage	Analysis Au	Ag	Cu	Pb	Zn	Other	Where Milled
Peru														
Cia Minera Aija, S.A.	Tarugos	Ancash		Ag,Pb,Zn	Vein	C&F	49,503		167		4.77	289		Own Mill - Ancash
Cia Minera Alianza, S.A.	Ticapampa	Ancash		Ag,Pb,Zn	Vein	C&F	21,260		405		4.65	5.82		Own Mill - Ancash
Cia Minera Arcata, S.A.	Arcata	Arequipa		Au,Ag			39,124	1.7	863		0.79	1.89		Own Mill - Arequipa
Cia Minera Atacocha, S.A.	Atacocha	Pasco	1936	Ag,Cu,Pb,Zn	Vein	C&F/Sq. S.	339,766	0.7	160	0.09	5.98	5.14		Own Mill - Pasco
Cia Minera El Brocal, S.A.	El Brocal	Pasco		Ag,Pb,Zn	Vein	C&F	114,608		254		5.37	8.75		Own Mill - Pasco
Cia De Minas Buenaventura, S.A.	Julcani	Huancavelica	1941	Ag,Cu,Pb	Vein	C&F	125,928	0.7	436	0.66	1.2			Own Mill - Huancavelica
" "	Recuperada	Huancavelica	1960	Ag,Cu,Pb,Zn	Vein	C&F	94,350		115	0.15	4.90	5.86		Own Mill - Huancavelica
Minas Canaria, S.A.	Catalina Huanca	Ayacucho	1968	Ag,Pb,Zn	Vein	C&F	2,233		315		50.0			
Castrovirreyna Metal Mines Co.	San Genaro	Huancavelica	1943	Ag,Pb,Zn	Vein	C&F	30,381	2.7	526		1.45	2.77		Own Mill - Huancavelica
" "	Astrohuaraca	Huancavelica	1965	Ag,Pb	Vein	C&F	20,799		477		3.52			Own Mill - Huancavelica
" "	El Palomo	Huancavelica	1966	Ag,Pb	Vein	C&F	7,193		422		0.3			Own Mill - Huancavelica
Corp. Minera Castrovirreyna, S.A.	Caudalosa	Huancavelica	1946	Ag,Cu,Pb,Zn	Vein	C&F	126,000		363	0.8	2.9	2.9		Own Mill - Huancavelica

SURVEY OF WORLD LEAD AND ZINC PRODUCTION IN 1968

MILLS

Country and Company Name	Name/ Location of Mill	Year First Operated	Mines Milled	Rated Daily Capacity	Milling Method	Tonnage Milled	Concentrate Produced (1968)								Other Products
							Type	Tonnage	Analysis						
									Au	Ag	Cu	Pb	Zn	Other	
Peru															
Cia Minera Aija, S.A.	Ancash	1966	Three	180	Flotation	47,477	Lead	3,437		1,930		52.43	10.48		
							Zinc	1,224		172		2.39	51.04		
Cia Minera Alianza	Ancash		Two		Flotation	19,331	Lead	1,610		4,501		52.73			
							Zinc	1,480		137		0.59	51.64		
Cia Minera Arcata, S.A.	Arequipa				Flotation	39,124	Au-Ag	2,592	24	11,352		10.61	16.07		
Cia Minera Atacocha,S.A	Pasco	1938	Two	1,200	Flotation	339,766	Lead	31,079	3.3	1,471	0.46	60.74	5.37		
							Zinc	25,354	1.2	148	0.27	2.14	55.71	Cd.30	
Cia Minera El Brocal, S.A.	Pasco		One		Flotation	114,608	Lead	7,773		2,092		49.70	8.80		
							Zinc	12,413		391		4.80	50.80		
Cia De Minas Buenaventura,S.A.	Huancavelica	1941	Three	455	Flotation	125,928	Lead	6,205	14.8	10,161	11.9	26.2		Bi 1-48	Cu Conc.
" " "	Huancavelica	1960	Five	272	Flotation	94,350	Lead	7,650		1,416	1.87	60.38	5.45		
							Zinc	9,766		138	0.46	1.32	56.64	Cd.30	
Castrovirreyna Metal Mines Co.	Huancavelica	1943	Four	200	Flotation	63,055	Lead	3,143	19.4	7,201	0.8	3.16			
							Zinc	350	6.1	851			55.20	Cd.25	
Corp. Minera Castrovirreyna,S.A.	Huancavelica		One	350	Flotation	126,600	Lead	8,800		4,525	9.77	34.09			
							Zinc	3,950		434			58.23		

SURVEY OF WORLD LEAD AND ZINC PRODUCTION IN 1968

MINES

Country and Company Name	Name of Mine	Location of Mine	Year First Operated	Principal Metals Mined	Type of Deposit	Mining Method	Ore Production (1968)							Where Milled
							Tonnage	Analysis						
								Au	Ag	Cu	Pb	Zn	Other	
Peru (Cont'd)														
Cia Minera De Caylloma S.A. Ltda.	San Cristobal	Arequipa	before 1890	Ag	Vein	C&F/ S.L.S.	96,035	0.56	201	0.21	0.55			Own Mill - Arequipa
Cerro De Pasco Corp.	Cerro De Pasco	Pasco	1905	Ag,Cu,Pb,Zn	Veins and/ or Bedded	Open Pit B.C./	246,536		47	4.34	1.14	5.21		Direct Smelting Cu Ore
						C&F/ S.S./ Sq.S			225	1.69	8.3	5.76		Direct Smelting Pb Ore
									72		2.89	7.97		Own Mill - Pasco
" "	Casapalca	Lima		Ag,Cu,Pb,Zn	" "	"	517,523		215	0.42	2.69	4.39		Own Mill - Lima
" "	Yauricocha	Lima		Ag,Cu,Pb,Zn	" "	"	418,496		154	1.65	2.13	4.89		Own Mill - Lima
" "	San Crist-obal (Mahr Tunnel)	Junin		Ag,Cu,Pb,Zn	" "	"	411,627		164	0.39	1.09	5.03	WO_3 .01	Own Mill - Junin
" "	Morococha	Junin		Ag,Cu,Pb,Zn	" "	"	478,878		124	1.43	0.87	2.21		Own Mill - Junin
Chavin Mines S.A.	Chavin	Huancaveli-ca		Ag,Pb,Zn	Vein	C&F	22,378		?		7.5	12.28		Own Mill - Huancavelica
Cia Minera Chungar,S.A.	Various Mines	Pasco	1948	Cu,Pb,Zn	Vein	O.S./ S.L.S.	90,395		74	0.68	1.18			Own Mill - Pasco
Cia Minera Chuvilca, S.A.	Chuvilca	La Libertad	1968	Ag,Pb,Zn	Vein/ Bedded	C&F	6,906	2.0	360		5.0	6.0		
Gran Bretana	Pasco			Zn			5,560					10.0		Own Mill - Pasco
Cia Minera Heraldos Negros, S.A.	Huascacan-cha	Junin	1957	Pb,Zn	Vein	C&F	12,000		86		5.0	15.0		

SURVEY OF WORLD LEAD AND ZINC PRODUCTION IN 1968

MILLS

Country and Company Name	Name/ Location of Mill	Year First Operated	Mines Milled	Rated Daily Capacity	Milling Method	Tonnage Milled	Concentrate Produced (1968)								Other Products
							Type	Tonnage	Analysis						
									Au	Ag	Cu	Pb	Zn	Other	
Peru (Cont'd)															
Cia Minera De Caylloma, S.A. Ltda.	Arequipa	1937	One	450	Flotation	96,735	Lead	2,183	19.8	7,827		1.12	5.1		See Note No. 3
Cerro De Pasco Corp.	Pasco	1940		5,000	Flotation	1,668,681	Lead	74,862		704	7.50	45.92			Cu Conc.
							Zinc	228,639		114		1.70	49.52		
" " " "	Lima	1935	One	1,500	Flotation	517,523	Lead	18,163		2,416	3.55	61.24	4.41		Cu Conc.
							Zinc	32,293		134	0.74	1.00	59.65		
" " " "	Lima	1966	One	1,250	Flotation	418,496	Lead	11,576		853	3.97	44.99	8.07		
							Zinc	24,153		249	1.16	1.29	52.63		
							Copper	41,930		572	9.35	5.06	9.3		
" " " "	Janin	1956	One	1,500	Flotation	411,627	Lead	6,223		3,455	5.35	52.83	5.77		Wo3 Conc.
							Zinc	31,015		292	0.56	0.68	57.13		
							Copper	7,153		4,706	13.01	10.97	14.67		
" " " "	Junin	1929	One	1,500	Flotation	478,878	Zinc	5,606		219	1.67	0.99	51.23		
							Copper	51,208		967	11.95	4.98	10.40		
							Pyrite	9,449		80	0.84	0.13	1.80		
Chavin Mines, S.A.	Huancavelica		One		Flotation	22,378	Lead	2,106		590		60.41			
							Zinc	3,913		215			54.37	Cd2.39	See Note No.4
Cia Minera Chungar,S.A.	Pasco	1948	Various	500	Flotation	90,395	Lead	1,557		2,600		54.45			
							Zinc	1,495					51.59		
Gran Bretana	Pasco		One			5,560	Zinc	922					56.0		See Note No.5

Note No. 3: 1968 Peruvian Government Statistics
Note No. 4: 1967 Statistics
Note No. 5: Operated by Banco Minera Del Peru which functions as an independent Governmental agency

SURVEY OF WORLD LEAD AND ZINC PRODUCTION IN 1968

MINES

Country and Company Name	Name of Mine	Location of Mine	Year First Operated	Principal Metals Mined	Type of Deposit	Mining Method	Ore Production (1968)							Where Milled
							Tonnage	Analysis						
								Au	Ag	Cu	Pb	Zn	Other	
Peru (Cont'd)														
Cia Minera Huampar, S.A.	Huampar	Lima		Ag, Cu, Pb, Zn	Vein		38,300		180	0.48	7.63	10.19		Own Mill - Lima
Compagnie Des Mines de Huaron	Huaron	Pasco		Ag, Cu, Pb, Zn	Vein	C&F	271,624		136		2.95	6.54		Own Mill - Pasco
Cia Minera Jecanca, S.A.	Jecanca	Ancash		Ag, Pb, Zn			19,703		159		3.55	7.40		Santo Toribio - Ancash
Cia Minera Korani, S.A.	Lola	Puno	1966	Ag, Pb	Bedded	C&F	1,400		1200		53.0			Hand Sorted
Fermin Malaga Santolalla e Hijos	Pasta Bueno	Ancash	1942	Ag, Cu, Pb, WO_3		C&F/R&P/ S.L.S.	72,062		93	0.92	1.27		WO_3 .6	Own Mill - Ancash
Minas de Millococha, S.A.	Cercapuquio	Junin		Ag, Cu, Pb, Zn	Vein	C&F	17,308		217	4.0	4.5	7.0		Own Mill - Junin
"	Millococha	Junin		Ag, Cu, Pb, Zn	Vein	C&F	2,437		200	2.9	4.7	1.8		Own Mill - Junin
Cia Minera Milpo, S.A.	Porvenir	Pasco		Ag, Pb, Zn	Metasco- matic Replacement	C&F	245,000		161		5.2	6.2		Own Mill - Pasco
Northern Peru Mining Co.	Quiruvilca	La Libertad	1967	Ag, Cu, Pb, Zn	Vein	C&F	68,743	1.9	18.7	3.03	2.11	4.76	Cd .029	Own Mill - La Libertad
Sindicato Minera Pacococha, S.A.	Purisima	Lima	1950	Ag, Cu, Pb, Zn	Vein	C&F	82,500		140	1.9	0.65	2.5		Own Mill - Lima
Cia, Minera Palca, S.A.	Recuperada	Puno	1954	Ag, Cu, Pb, Zn	Vein	C&F	23,814		2.0	0.23	4.98	7.50		Own Mill - Puno
Cia Minera El Pilar, S.A.	Estrella	Pasco		Ag, Pb, Zn	Vein	C&F	9,086		129		8.56	8.0		Own Mill - Pasco
Sociedad Minera Puquiococha, S.A.	Alejandria	Junin	1909	Cu	Vein	C&F	78,824		108	2.21	0.07	1.81		Own Mill - Junin

MILLS

Country and Company Name	Name/ Location of Mill	Year First Operated	Mines Milled	Rated Daily Capacity	Milling Method	Tonnage Milled	Concentrate Produced (1968)								Other Products
							Type	Tonnage	Analysis						
									Au	Ag	Cu	Pb	Zn	Other	
Peru (Cont'd)															
Cia Minera Huampar,S.A.	Lima		One		Flotation	38,300	Lead	4,043		1,362	3.45	65.31	8.20		See Note No.4
							Zinc	5,736		55	0.40	1.21	57.33		
Compagnie des Mines de Huaron	Pasco		One	1,500	Flotation	271,624	Lead	11,308		2,513		63.0			
							Zinc	27,671		180			53.2		
Fermin Malaga Santolalla e Hijos	Ancash	1942	Three	300	Flot./Grav.	64,136	Lead	543		1,998	8.6	21.75			See Note No.6
Minas de Millococha S.A	Junin		One		Flotation	17,308	Lead	580		1,862	5.5	60.0	7.0		Cu Conc.
							Zinc	893		186	1.3	2.0	48.0		See Note No.4
" " " "	Junin		One		Flotation	2,437	Lead	164		1,772	6.0	65.02	3.0		Cu Conc.
							Zinc	46		0.7	1.2	1.8	50.0		See Note No.4
Cia Minera Milpo, S.A.	Pasco	1952	Two	950	Flotation	245,000	Lead	19,800	3.6	1,874		64.0			
							Zinc	22,800		110			58.0		
Northern Peru Mining Co.	La Libertad	1967	One	275	Flotation	69,032	Lead	1,678	11.9	1,413	9.95	53.00	4.64		Cu Conc.
							Zinc	4,731	2.8	372	3.59	2.25	53.34	Cd.43	Cu Conc.
Sindicato Minera Pacococha, S.A.	Lima	1960	One	250	Flotation	83,000	Lead	590		1,760		6.70			Cu Conc.
							Zinc	2,900		300			48.00		
Cia Minera Palca, S.A.	Puno		One	150	Flotation	23,814	Lead	1,600		34	3.5	60.0			
							Zinc	2,947					60.86		See Note No.6
Cia Minera El Pilar	Pasco		One		Flotation	9,086	Lead	543		2,166		35.91			See Note No.4
							Zinc	569					34.09		
Sociedad Minera Puquiococha, S.A.	Junin	1939	One	300	Flotation	78,824	Zinc	2,501		140	1.08		57.12		
							Copper	571		1,650	18.11	10.14	11.20		

Note No. 4: 1967 Statistics
Note No. 6: Exported in 1968

SURVEY OF WORLD LEAD AND ZINC PRODUCTION IN 1968

MINES

Country and Company Name	Name of Mine	Location of Mine	Year First Operated	Principal Metals Mined	Type of Deposit	Mining Method	Ore Production (1968) Tonnage	Analysis Au	Ag	Cu	Pb	Zn	Other	Where Milled
Peru (Cont'd)														
Cia Minera Raura, S.A.	Raura	Huanaco	1961	Ag,Cu,Pb,Zn	Veins/ Mineralized Bodies	C&F	173,462		166	0.41	6.73	7.98		Own Mill - Huanaco
Sindicato Minera Rio Pallanga, S.A.	Alpamarca	Lima	1957	Ag,Pb,Zn	Replacement	C&F	132,230		101	0.13	1.83	2.47		Own Mill - Lima
" "	Carhuacayan	Junin	1965	Ag,Pb,Zn	Replacement	C&F/S.S.	115,278		128	0.10	3.0	4.5		Own Mill - Junin
Explotadora de Minas San Augustin, S.A.	San Augustin	Cajamarca		Ag,Cu,Pb,Zn	Vein	C&F	10,038		153	2.13	2.97	4.42		Own Mill - Cajamarca
Cia Minera San Ignacio de Morococha, S.A.	San Ignacio	Junin		Ag,Pb,Zn	Vein	C&F	67,466		497	0.51	3.53	3.90		Own Mill - Lima
Cia Minera San Juan de Lucanas, S.A.	San Juan de Lucanas													Own Mill - Ayacucho
Cia Minerales Santander Inc.	Santander	Lima		Ag,Pb,Zn		C&F	280,720		91	0.39	1.38	13.12		Own Mill - Lima
Cia Minera Santa Luisa, S.A.	Huanzala	Huanaco	1968	Ag,Cu,Pb,Zn	Vein	C&F/S.S.	77,577		93	1.27	6.42	11.93		Own Mill - Huanaco
Cia Minera Santa Rita, S.A.	Enano	Junin	1947	Ag,Cu,Pb,Zn		C&F	33,000		171	0.50	4.00	9.00		
Cia Minera Santo Toribio, S.A.	Santo Toribio	Ancash	1951	Ag,Pb,Zn	Vein	C&F	28,697		137		2.98	5.92		Own Mill - Ancash

MILLS

Country and Company Name	Name/ Location of Mill	Year First Operated	Mines Milled	Rated Daily Capacity	Milling Method	Tonnage Milled	Concentrate Produced (1968)								Other Products
							Type	Tonnage	Analysis						
									Au	Ag	Cu	Pb	Zn	Other	
Peru (Cont'd)															
Cia Minera Raura, S.A.	Huanaco	1961	Three	500	Flotation	173,462	Lead	13,012		1,231	0.56	68.86	5.82		
							Zinc	19,162		110	1.28	1.95	55.10		
							Mixed	3,922		1,027	3.28	41.14	23.34		
Sindicato Minera Rio Pallanga, S.A.	Lima	1957	Two	480	Flotation	132,052	Lead	4,398		2,845	3.30	55.00			
							Zinc	4,376					60.5		
" "	Junin	1965	One	380	Flotation	115,338	Lead	6,093		2,062	1.43	59.40			
							Zinc	7,909					53.00		
Explotadora de Minas San Augustin, S.A.	Cajamarca		One		Flotation	10,038	Lead	488		1,215	7.67	46.07			Cu Conc. See Note No.4
							Zinc	331		312			54.04		
Cia Minera San Ignacio de Morococha, S.A.	Lima		One		Flotation	67,466	Lead	5,079		5,665	4.35	44.33			See Note No.4
							Zinc	3,205		353			50.21		
Cia Minera San Juan de Lucanas, S.A.	Ayacucho		One	500	Flotation		Lead	1,003	129	11,656		6.14			See Note No.5
Cia Minerales Santander Inc.	Lima				Flotation	280,720	Lead	7,736		2,071	6.33	39.62	9.38		See Note No.3
							Zinc	62,983		70	0.66	0.55	49.88		
Cia Minera Santa Luisa, S.A.	Huanaco	1968	One	500	Flotation	77,577	Lead	5,521		583	2.0	53.12	17.65		
							Zinc	15,374		103	2.49	3.45	46.84		
Cia Minera Santo Tonbio, S.A.	Ancash	1951	Two	240	Flotation	73,212	Lead	3,560		2,072		53.40	9.03		
							Zinc	?		195		9.03	52.16		

Note No. 3: 1968 Peruvian Government Statistics
Note No. 4: 1967 Statistics
Note No. 5: Operated by Banco Del Peru

SURVEY OF WORLD LEAD AND ZINC PRODUCTION IN 1968

MINES

Country and Company Name	Name of Mine	Location of Mine	Year First Operated	Principal Metals Mined	Type of Deposit	Mining Method	Ore Production (1968)								Where Milled
							Tonnage	Analysis							
								Au	Ag	Cu	Pb	Zn	Other	
Peru (Cont'd)														
Cia Minera Sayapullo, S.A.	Sayapullo	Cajamarca		Ag,Cu,Pb,Zn	Vein	C&F	42,299		273	0.67	1.72	3.65		Own Mill - Cajamarca
Cia Minera Tascacocha, S.A.	Petain	Lima	1968	Ag,Cu,Pb,Zn	Vein	C&F	2,320		27494	2.2	3.0	3.5		
Empresa Explotadora de Vinchos Ltd.,S.A.	Various	Pasco		Pb	Vein	C&F	97,518		158		1.49			Own Mill - Pasco
Volcan Mines Co.	Carahuacra	Junin	1948	Ag,Pb,Zn	Veins/Beds	C&F	218,866		68		0.71	10.35		Own Mill - Junin
Sociedad Minera Yauli, S.A.	Yauli	Junin		Ag,Pb,Cu,Zn	Vein	C&F	126,963		235	0.46	3.65	6.27		Own Mill - Junin

MILLS

Country and Company Name	Name/ Location of Mill	Year First Operated	Mines Milled	Rated Daily Capacity	Milling Method	Tonnage Milled	Concentrate Produced (1968)								Other Products
							Type	Tonnage	Analysis						
									Au	Ag	Cu	Pb	Zn	Other	
Peru (Cont'd)															
Cia Minera Sayapullo, S.A.	Cajamarca		One		Flotation	42,249	Lead	892		3,938	8.95	53.47	3.90		
							Zinc	2,112		504	1.28	1.58	53.66		See Note No.4
							Copper	436		6,977	24.77	10.68	6.32		
Empresa Explotadora de Vinchos Ltda,S.A.	Pasco	1936	Various	320	Flotation	97,518	Lead	4,094		2,996		28.8			
Volcan Mines Co.	Junin	1957	One	1,100	Flotation	218,866	Lead	3,050	4.8	2,060	1.34	35.49			
							Zinc	35,661		111			57.99		
Sociedad Minera Yauli, S.A.	Junin		One		Flotation	126,963	Lead	7,093		2,045	2.17	55.29	8.50		
							Zinc	9,805		265	1.62	1.53	55.50		See Note No.4
							Copper	739		9,341	23.65	11.10	9.79		
Banco Minera Del Peru	Cajamarca (Hualgayoc)		Various	70	Flotation	14,467	Lead	1,488				61.85	1.88		Ag Conc.
							Zinc	2,507				6.56	56.64		
" " " "	Lima (San Mateo)		Various	200	Flotation	18,453	Lead	203		1,845	3.61	62.96	2.53		
							Zinc	60		197	0.70	1.85	49.95		
							Copper	312		496	22.12	2.69	9.86		
" " " "	Junin (Sacracancha)		Various	400	Flotation	50,502	Lead	2,848		1,688	5.04	56.84	9.88		
							Zinc	5,006		103		1.32	58.37		
							Copper	637		919	13.78	5.69	9.07		
							Silver	174		3,650		6.25	28.61		
" " " "	Huancavelica (La Virreyna		Various	125	Flotation	3,372	Lead	240			3.78	70.75	3.06		Cu Conc.
							Zinc	311				1.74	56.62		
" " " "	Huancavelica (Huachocolpa)		Various	400	Flotation	19,350	Lead	2,243		998		55.24	8.54		See Note No.5
							Zinc	1,889		115		1.93	54.42		

Note No. 4: 1967 Statistics

Note No. 5: Operated by Banco Del Peru

SURVEY OF WORLD LEAD AND ZINC PRODUCTION IN 1968

MINES

Country and Company Name	Name of Mine	Location of Mine	Year First Operated	Principal Metals Mined	Type of Deposit	Mining Method	Ore Production (1968)							Where Milled
							Tonnage	Analysis						
								Au	Ag	Cu	Pb	Zn	Other	
ASIA														
Burma														
People's Bawdwin Industry				Pb,Zn										Own Mill
India														
Hindustan Zinc Ltd.	Zawar	Rajasthan	1318-1813 1942	Pb,Zn,Ag, Cd	Vein	S.S./ S.L.S.	206,960				1.5	4.0		Zawar Mill
" "	Balaria	Rajasthan	1962	Pb,Zn	Lens	S.S.	143,393							Zawar Mill
Iran														
Bama Mining Co.	Shah Kuh	Shah Kuh-Esfahan	1953	Pb,Zn	Vein	C&F/R&P								Own Mill - Esfahan
Cherkate	Amaouran	N.W. Iran	1952	Pb,Zn	Lode	Open Pit								Own Mill - N.W. Iran
Mining & Metallurgical Co. of Iran	Nakhlak	N.W. of Anarak	1952	Pb	Vein	Gallery								Own Mill - N.W. of Anarak
Japan														
The Dowa Mining Co. Ltd.	Kosaka-Uchinotai	Kazuno-Gun	1962	Pb,Zn,Cu		U/H Hor. Slicing	467,000	0.75	80	2.40	1.30	3.90		Kosaka-Uchinotai Mill

SURVEY OF WORLD LEAD AND ZINC PRODUCTION IN 1968

MILLS

Country and Company Name	Name/ Location of Mill	Year First Operated	Mines Milled	Rated Daily Capacity	Milling Method	Tonnage Milled	Concentrate Produced (1968)								Other Products
							Type	Tonnage	Analysis						
									Au	Ag	Cu	Pb	Zn	Other	
ASIA															
Burma															
People's Bawdwin Industry							Lead	16,000 (Est.)				55.0 (Est.)			
							Zinc	7,000 (Est.)					55.0 (Est.)		
India															
Hindustan Zinc Ltd.	Zawar/ Rajasthan	1946	Zawar, Balaria	900	Flotation	191,629	Lead	3,566		67	0.03	72.6	5.62	Fe 1.4 Sb 0.033 S 15.2	Cd Conc.
							Zinc	12,839		54	0.05	0.95	55.5	Cd 0.33 Fe 4.5 Sb .0019 S 29.9	
Iran															
Bama Mining Co.	Esfahan Ab-El-Nil	1953	One	750	Handsorting/ Calcination		Mixed								
Cherkate	N.W. Iran	1952	One		Calcination										
Mining & Metallurgical Co. of Iran	N.W. of Anarak	1957	One	180	Flot/Grav	50,000	Lead	4,000		700		65			
Japan															
The Dowa Mining Co. Ltd	Kosaka-Uchinotai	1962	One	1,600	Flotation	467,000	Lead	8,400			2.50	56.50	11.00	S 19.0 Fe 3.5	Cd Conc.
							Zinc	35,000			1.00	3.00	52.00	S 33.5 Fe 7.0	
							Pyrite	132,500			0.25	0.10	0.30	S 50.0 Fe 43.3	

SURVEY OF WORLD LEAD AND ZINC PRODUCTION IN 1968

MINES

Country and Company Name	Name of Mine	Location of Mine	Year First Operated	Principal Metals Mined	Type of Deposit	Mining Method	Ore Production (1968) Tonnage	Analysis Au	Ag	Cu	Pb	Zn	Other	Where Milled
Japan (Cont'd)														
The Dowa Mining Co. Ltd. (Cont'd)	Hanaoka-Mathumine	Odate City	?	Pb,Zn,Cu,Ag		U/H Hor. Slicing	500,000	0.91	80	3.00	0.60	2.90		Hanaoka-Mathumine Mill
" "	Hanaoka-Doyashiki	Odate City	1915	Pb,Zn,Cu		Open Pit/X Cutting	265,000	0.35	23.0	1.19	0.30	1.30		Hanaoka-Doyashiki
Mitsubishi Metal Mining Co. Ltd.	Furutobe	Akita-ken	1963	Pb,Zn,Cu, Ag,Au	Lens, Massive	C&F								Furutobe Mill
" "	Hosokura	Miyagi-ken	1934	Pb,Zn,Cu, Ag,Au	Vein	C&F/S.S.								Hosokura Mill
Mitsui Mining and Smelting Co. Ltd.	Kamioka Mines (2)	Cifu Pref.	1887	Pb,Zn,Ag	Massive	Open Pit B.C./C&F S.S./ R&P/SLS X Cutting	1,555,760		26		0.59	4.75		Shikama (Mozumi) Mill
Oppu Mining Co. Ltd. (Subsidiary of Mitsubishi)	Yatani	Yamagata-ken	1956	Pb,Zn,Cu,Ag, Au	Vein	C&F,S.S.	109,833	0.6	49	0.12	2.18	4.84	S 11.6	Own Mill

SURVEY OF WORLD LEAD AND ZINC PRODUCTION IN 1968

MILLS

Country and Company Name	Name/ Location of Mill	Year First Operated	Mines Milled	Rated Daily Capacity	Milling Method	Tonnage Milled	Concentrate Produced (1968)								Other Products
							Type	Tonnage	Analysis						
									Au	Ag	Cu	Pb	Zn	Other	
Japan (Cont'd)															
The Dowa Mining Co.Ltd (Cont'd)	Hanaoka-Mathumine	1966	One	1,600	Flotation	500,000	Lead	3,200			3.50	54.00	6.00	S 23.0 Fe 10.0	Cd Conc.
							Zinc	14,000			2.00	1.50	55.00	S 33.0 Fe 5.0	
" " " " "	Hanaoka-Doyashiki	1943	One	880	Flotation	265,000	Lead	840			4.00	53.00	8.00	S 22.5 Fe 7.0	Cd Conc.
							Zinc	5,000			2.50	2.00	55.00	S 32.0 Fe 3.5	
Mitsubishi Metal Mining Co. Ltd.	Furutobe	1963	One	500	Flotation	116,957	Lead	847	6.3	638	3.07	50.60	8.66	S 24.5	
							Zinc	3,306	3.1	206	2.87	1.71	50.01	S 32.9 Fe 7.6 Cd 0.24	
" "	Hosokura	1934	One	2,800	Flotation/ Heavy Media	665,575	Pyrite	38,581	1.5	23	0.32	0.29	0.35	S 47.3	
							Lead	13,014	1.4	1,128	2.27	67.30	4.08	S 18.80	
							Zinc	45,856	0.2	73	0.33	0.81	57.15	S 32.3 Fe 6.0 Cd 0.29	
							Pyrite	83,866	0.5	46	0.06	0.17	0.44	S 47.0 Fe 41.9	
Mitsui Mining and Smelting Co. Ltd.	Shikama (Mozumi)	1887	Two	5,200	Flotation	1,555,760	Lead	12,864	1.38	2,163	0.29	60.5	5.8	S 14.1 Fe 2.3	318 M.T. Graphite Cu Conc.
							Zinc	116,668		49	0.13	0.36	58.4	S 31.5 Fe 5.6 Cd 0.33	
Oppu Mining Co. Ltd. (Subsidiary of Mitsubishi)	Yatani	1960	One	360	Flotation	109,833	Lead	3,474	9.9	526	1.32	61.48	7.80	S 20.26	
							Zinc	8,929	0.8	131	0.78	1.69	52.80	S 32.6 Cd 0.27	
							Pyrite	15,476	1.1	118	0.07	0.10	0.30	S 47.7	

SURVEY OF WORLD LEAD AND ZINC PRODUCTION IN 1968

MINES

Country and Company Name	Name of Mine	Location of Mine	Year First Operated	Principal Metals Mined	Type of Deposit	Mining Method	Ore Production (1968)							Where Milled
							Tonnage	Analysis						
								Au	Ag	Cu	Pb	Zn	Other	
Japan (Cont'd)														
Toho Zinc Co. Ltd.	Taishu	Nagasaki Pref.	1939	Pb,Zn,Cu, Ag	Vein	C&F								Taishu Mill
" "	Nan-Etsu	Niigata Pref.	1956	Pb,Zn,Cu, Ag	Vein	C&F								Nan-Etsu Mill
Korea, South														
Pung Jeun Sangsa Ltd.	Ul Jin	Kyung Buk	1961	Pb,Zn,Cu	Massive/ Replacement	S.S./ S.L.S.	60,000			0.27	2.91	7.50		Ul Jin Mill
" "	New Yemi	Kang Won	1944	Zn,Cu	Massive/ Replacement	S.L.S.	45,000			0.1		5.00	MoS_2 0.15	New Yemi Mill
Young Poong Mining Co. Ltd.	Yeoun wha	Keung Buk	1961	Pb,Zn	Massive	S.S./ S.L.S.	1,100,000		80		4.00	4.50		Own Mill
Philippines														
Benquet Exploration Inc.	Thanks-giving	Baguio	1957	Pb,Zn,Au	Vein	C&F/O.S.	20,847	34.6	145	0.78	0.24	13.30	Cd .01	Own Mill

MILLS

Country and Company Name	Name/ Location of Mill	Year First Operated	Mines Milled	Rated Daily Capacity	Milling Method	Tonnage Milled	Concentrate Produced (1968)								Other Products
							Type	Tonnage	Analysis						
									Au	Ag	Cu	Pb	Zn	Other	
Japan (Cont'd)															
Toho Zinc Co. Ltd.	Taishu	1943	One	1,000	Flotation/ Heavy Media	280,000 (800 MT/ day)	Lead	12,660		1,200	0.46	63.0	4.06	S 17.2 Fe 9.4 Bi 0.4	Cu Conc.
							Zinc	29,560		60	0.30	0.50	48.0	S 31.7 Fe 13.5 Cd 0.5	
							Pyrite	18,480		20				S 35.0	
" " " "	Nan-Etsu	1963	One	300	Flotation	87,500 (250 MT/ day)	Lead	1,960	2.0	1,400	0.5	67.0	4.50	S 17.0 Fe 9.3 Bi 0.15	Cu Conc.
							Zinc	5,950		70	0.7	0.9	46.0	S 33.0 Fe 16.2 Cd 0.4	
							Pyrite	3,770		10				S 36.0	
Korea, South															
Pung Jeun Sangsa Ltd.	Ul Jin	1965	One	300	Flotation	58,860	Lead	2,517				63.7			Cu Conc.
							Zinc	8,543					45.66		
" " " "	New Yemi	1961	One	150	Flotation	46,000	Zinc	4,275					50.0		Cu MoS_2 Conc.
Young Poong Mining Co. Ltd.	Yeoun Wha	1962	One	1,000	Flotation	40,000	Lead	15,000		800		67.0	3.20	S 1.0 Fe 2.0	
							Zinc	25,000				1.10	47.50	S 10.0 Fe 14.0	
Philippines															
Benguet Exploration Inc.	Thanks-giving	1967	One	63	Flotation/ Chemical	20,847	Zinc	4,345	11.6	118	1.66	1.08	52.45	Cd 0.27	Au Bullion
							Mixed	630	335.6	1,382	12.50	4.13	12.28		

SURVEY OF WORLD LEAD AND ZINC PRODUCTION IN 1968

MINES

Country and Company Name	Name of Mine	Location of Mine	Year First Operated	Principal Metals Mined	Type of Deposit	Mining Method	Ore Production (1968) Tonnage	Analysis Au	Analysis Ag	Analysis Cu	Analysis Pb	Analysis Zn	Analysis Other	Where Milled
Thailand														
Lead and Antimony Ltd. Partnership	Boh Ngam	Srissawat Kanchanaburi		Pb,Ag	Lens	Open Pit	10,000 (Est.)		34 - 68		10 - 15			Own Mill
Pring and Brothers	Nong Bhai	Nansawan Srissawat	1910?	Pb,Zn	Lens	Open Pit	30,000 (Est.)		10		10 - 15	(Pb&Zn)		Nansawan Mill
" "	Song Toh	Nansawan Srissawat		Pb,Zn	Lens	Open Pit	15,000 (Est.)		17		10 - 15 -	(Pb&Zn)		
EUROPE														
Austria														
Bleiberger Bergworks-Union	Blei-Zinkerz-bergtau Bleiberg-Kreuth	Carinthia	1333	Pb,Zn	Vein/ Bedded Replacement	Horiz. C&F								Own Mill - Carinthia
Finland														
Outokumpu Oy	Vihanti	Oulu	1954	Cu,Pb,Zn	Lens	S.S./ S.L. Caving								Own Mill - Oulu
" "	Pyhasalmi	Kuopio		Cu,Zn	Lens	Open Pit								Own Mill - Kuopio
" "	Metsamonttu	Turkupori	1952	Zn	Lens	S.S./ S.L.S.								Own Mill - Turkupori
" "	Korsnas	Vaasa	1961	Lead	Lens	S.L.S								Own Mill - Vaasa

MILLS

Country and Company Name	Name/ Location of Mill	Year First Operated	Mines Milled	Rated Daily Capacity	Milling Method	Tonnage Milled	Concentrate Produced (1968)								Other Products
							Type	Tonnage	Analysis						
									Au	Ag	Cu	Pb	Zn	Other	
Thailand															
Lead and Antimony Ltd. Partnership	Boh Ngam	1967	One	30	Flotation	10,000 (Est)	Lead	1,500 (Est)		1,000	5	70.0	0.1	S 13.6 Fe 0.6	
Pring and Brothers	Nansawan	1965	Two	100	Jig	25,000 - 30,000 (Est)	Mixed	3,000		100 - 150		25- 30	20- 25	S 17.0 Fe 1.15 Cd 0.2	
EUROPE															
Austria															
Bleiberger Bergworks - Union	Carinthia	1911	One	750	Flot/Jigs	187,163	Lead	7,700				76.82	3.12		
							Zinc	18,372				1.38	56.86	Cd.166 Ge.03	
Finland															
Outokumpu Oy	Oulu	1954	One	2,500	Flotation	706,326	Lead	2,261	1.9	579	0.6	53.06	4.61		Cu Conc.
							Zinc	66,768	0.2	.8	0.27	0.21	54.82		
							Pyrite	81,679	0.05	2.5	0.05		0.11		
" "	Kuopio	1961	One	2,500	Flotation	774,290	Zinc	48,839			0.37		54.77		Cu Conc.
							Pyrite	472,881			0.04		0.8		
" "	Turkupori	1949	One	300	Flotation	85,268	Lead	898	14	1,009		53.99			
							Zinc	1,829					49.79		
" "	Vaasa	1961	One	300	Flotation	101,294	Lead	5,060				56.13		RareEarth 3.31%	Cu Conc. Concs. La_2O_3

SURVEY OF WORLD LEAD AND ZINC PRODUCTION IN 1968

MINES

Country and Company Name	Name of Mine	Location of Mine	Year First Operated	Principal Metals Mined	Type of Deposit	Mining Method	Ore Production (1968) Tonnage	Analysis Au	Ag	Cu	Pb	Zn	Other	Where Milled
France														
Penarroya	La Plagne			Pb	Lode	C&F/R&P								Own Mill - La Plagne
"	Les Malines			Pb,Zn	Lode	R&P								Own Mill - Les Malines
"	Preyrebrune			Pb,Zn	Vein	C&F								Own Mill - Preyrebrune
"	Largentiere	Ardeche	1964	Pb	Bedded	R&P								Own Mill - Ardeche
Vieille Montagne,S.A.	Mines Du Midi	Pallieres	1911	Pb,Zn	Lens	C&F/R&P S.L.S.	82,024				1.87	5.25		Own Mill - Pallieres
Germany, West														
Altenberg	Luderich	Bensberg	1835	Pb,Zn,Ag	Vein	C&F								Own Mill - Bensberg
Preussag	Grund	Bad Grund	before 1400	Ag,Pb,Zn	Vein	S.L. Caving/ S.L.S.	300,000		94		4.6	4.7		Own Mill - Bad Grund
"	Rammels-berg	Goslar	968	Ag,Pb,Cu, Zn	Lens	C&F/R&P	280,000	0.5	100	0.95	6	14.5		Own Mills - Rammelsberg and Bollrich
Sachtleben	Meggen	Westfalen		Zn	Sedimentary	R&P/SLS	601,509				1.21	10.14		Own Mill - Westfalen

MILLS

Country and Company Name	Name/ Location of Mill	Year First Operated	Mines Milled	Rated Daily Capacity	Milling Method	Tonnage Milled	Concentrate Produced (1968)								Other Products
							Type	Tonnage	Analysis						
									Au	Ag	Cu	Pb	Zn	Other	
France															
Penarroya	La Plagne		One	500	Flotation	149,000 (Est)	Lead								
"	Les Malines		One	700	Flotation	213,500 (Est)	Lead								
							Zinc								
"	Preyrebrune		One	300	Flotation	90,200 (Est)	Lead								
							Zinc								
"	Ardeche		One	1,850	Flotation	507,000 (Est)	Lead								
							Zinc								
Vieille Montagne, S.A.	Pallieres	1911	Two	250	Flotation	83,944	Lead	1,853		200		74.26			
							Zinc	6,827					55.80		
Germany, West															
Altenberg	Bensberg	1896	One Plus Dumps	800	Flot/Heavy Media	191,760	Lead	3,495		350		68.51			
							Zinc	21,150					60.67		
Preussag	Bad Grund	1942	One	1,100	Flotation	300,000	Lead	17,000		1,450		72.0	2.7		
							Zinc	21,000		50		0.8	59.0	Cd.30	
" (Rammelsberg)	Goslar	1936	One	650	Flotation	150,000	Lead	19,000			1.8	37.0	17.0		Cu Conc.
							Zinc	54,000			1.0	5.0	43.0		
" (Bollrich)	Goslar	1952	One	550	Flotation	130,000	Lead	10,000			2.4	36.0	17.0		Cu Conc.
							Zinc	23,000			0.7	5.0	44.0		
Sachtleben	Westfalen	1963	One	1,900	Flot/Heavy Media	682,087	Lead	7,375				35.80	4.91		
							Zinc	102,617				1.43	53.81		
							Mixed	76,033				1.30	10.49	Fe40.6 S 31.1	
							Pyrite 1	23,659				0.43	0.93	Fe41.2 S 47.7	
							Pyrite 2	458,601				0.61	1.04	Fe34.9 S 40.2	

SURVEY OF WORLD LEAD AND ZINC PRODUCTION IN 1968

MINES

Country and Company Name	Name of Mine	Location of Mine	Year First Operated	Principal Metals Mined	Type of Deposit	Mining Method	Ore Production (1968)							Where Milled
							Tonnage	Analysis						
								Au	Ag	Cu	Pb	Zn	Other	
Germany, West (Cont'd)														
Stolberg (Maubach)	Bastenberg & Dornberg	Ramsbeck	1815	Pb,Zn	R&P	Vein	470,790				1.67	3.14		Own Mill - Ramsbeck
" "	Maubacher Bleiberg	Gey	1948	Pb,Zn	Bedded		822,960							Own Mill - Gey
Greece														
Laurium	Laurium	Laurium	550 B.C.	Pb,Zn	Lode	R&P	40,344							Own Mill - Laurium
Ireland														
Mogul of Ireland Ltd.	Mogul	Tipperary	1968	Pb,Zn	Lode	R&P	403,963				2.5	10		Own Mill - Tipperary
Irish Base Metals Ltd.	Tynagh	Galway	1965	Pb, Zn	Replacement	Open Pit	644,011							Own Mill - Galway
Italy														
Monteponi e Montevecchio	Monte-vecchio	Sardinia	1848	Ag,Cu,Pb,Zn	Vein	C&F/SLS	647,000							Own Mill - Sardinia
Pertusola	Argentiera	Belluno	1947	Pb,Zn	Replacement	Open Pit	71,100							Own Mill - Belluno
"	Salafossa	Belluno	1964	Pb,Zn	Lode	S.L.S.	593,100							Own Mill - Belluno

MILLS

Country and Company Name	Name/ Location of Mill	Year First Operated	Mines Milled	Rated Daily Capacity	Milling Method	Tonnage Milled	Concentrate Produced (1968)								Other Products
							Type	Tonnage	Analysis						
									Au	Ag	Cu	Pb	Zn	Other	
Germany, West (Cont'd)															
Stolberg (Maubach)	Ramsbeck	1927	One	2,000	Flot/Heavy Media	470,790	Lead	6,204		390		70.67			
							Zinc	11,165					55.77		
							Mixed	15,682		121		18.04	44.36		
" "	Gey	1957	One	2,300	Flotation	822,960	Lead	12,966		163	0.87	68.55			
Greece															
Laurium	Laurium		One	440	Flotation	40,344 (Est)	Pb,Zn								
Ireland															
Mogul of Ireland, Ltd.	Tipperary	1968	One	2,721	Flotation	405,963	Lead	11,202				28.95	2.62		
							Zinc	55,941				8.28	48.61	Cd.20	
Irish Base Metals, Ltd.	Galway	1965	One	1,814	Flotation	644,011	Lead	28,567		480	0.70	63.0	10.0		Barite
							Zinc	27,560		137		5.0	51.0	Cd.30	
							Mixed	52,562		274		29.0	25.0		
							Lead Oxide	54,780		206	3.0	43.0			
Italy															
Monteponi & Montevecchio	Sardinia	1938	Nine	3,000	Flotation	647,000	Lead	10,352		447	1.38	69.07			
							Zinc	38,330					60.64	Cd.49	
Pertusola	Belluno	1947	One	310	Flotation	71,100	Lead	580				59.78			
							Zinc	8,160					36.86		
"	Belluno	1964	One	2,200	Flot/Heavy Media	593,100	Lead	5,260				72.30			
							Zinc	44,110					56.30		

SURVEY OF WORLD LEAD AND ZINC PRODUCTION IN 1968

MINES

Country and Company Name	Name of Mine	Location of Mine	Year First Operated	Principal Metals Mined	Type of Deposit	Mining Method	Cre Production (1968)							Where Milled
							Tonnage	Analysis						
								Au	Ag	Cu	Pb	Zn	Other	
Norway														
Blei Kvassli	Blei Kvassli	Hemnes	1957	Pb,Zn	Lens	C&F	135,000							Own Mill - Korgen
Nord Norge A/S	Mofjellet	Mo 1 Rana	1928	Ag,Cu,Pb, Zn	Lens	R&P	88,000							Own Mill - Mo 1 Rana
Spain														
Real Cia Asturiana de Mines	Reocin	Santander	1855	Pb,Zn	Bedded	R&P	437,032				1.3	10.5		Own Mill - Santander
" "	Florida	Santander	1912	Pb,Zn	Bedded	R&P	60,106				0.6	5.0		Own Mill - Santander
" "	Arditurri	Cuipuzcoa	1928	Pb,Zn	Vein	Open Pit/ R&P	48,584				0.7	7.0	CaF_2 .30	Own Mill - Guipuzcoa
C.E.M.I.M.	Legorreta	Guipuzcoa	1960	Pb,Zn	Vein	U/H Stoping	10,031				6.5	20.0		Own Mill - Guipuzcoa
Espanola Del Zinc,S.A.	La Cierva	Murcia		Pb,Zn	Lens	R&P	60,000				1.5	2.5		Own Mill - Murcia
Minas De Cartes, S.A.	Goto Ponce	Murcia	1952	Pb,Zn	Bedded	R&P	96,900		100		0.81	2.54		Own Mill - Murcia

MILLS

Country and Company Name	Name/ Location of Mill	Year First Operated	Mines Milled	Rated Daily Capacity	Milling Method	Tonnage Milled	Concentrate Produced (1968)								Other Products
							Type	Tonnage	Analysis						
									Au	Ag	Cu	Pb	Zn	Other	
Norway															
Blei Kvassli	Korgen	1957	One	500	Flotation	135,000	Lead	6,500	2.0	800	4.0	50.0	7.0		
							Zinc	10,000	Tr	25	0.3	1.0	54.0	Cd.20	
							Pyrite	28,000	Tr	5	0.05	0.08	0.5	Fe47.0 S 50.0	
Nord Norge A/S	Mo i Rana	1928	One	400	Flotation	88,000	Lead	700	3.0	700	6.0	60.0	2.0		Cu Conc.
							Zinc	4,600	Tr	20	1.0	0.7	55.0	Cd.20	
							Pyrite	6,500	Tr	11	0.1	0.1	0.5	Fe46.0 S 49.0	
Killingdal A/S	Drontheim	1952	Two	350	Flotation		Zinc	1,500	0.1	25	0.8	0.1	48.0		
							Pyrite	35,000		12	0.15	0.1	0.4	Fe44.0 S 49.0	Cu Conc.
Spain															
Real Cia Asturiana de Minas	Santander	1927	One	1,800	Flotation	437,547	Lead	5,772				75.07	4.46		
							Zinc	70,128				0.6	56.92	Cd.08	
							Pyrite	44,586				0.27	1.24	Fe42.0 S 49.0	
" " "	Santander	1955	One	275	Flot/Heavy Media	60,106	Lead	467							
							Zinc	3,896							
" " "	Guipuzcoa	1928	One	175	Flot/Heavy Media	48,584	Lead	304				62.0			Acid Grade Fluorite
							Zinc	3,008					57.5		
C.E.M.I.M.	Guipuzcoa	1960	One	45	Flotation	10,031	Lead	1,023				59.0			
							Zinc	3,379					59.0		
Espanola Del Zinc S.A.	Murcia	1950	One Plus Dump	800	Flotation	85,910	Lead	1,118				62.6			
							Zinc	2,875					51.6		
Minas De Cartes S.A.	Murcia	1952	One	300	Flot/Heavy Media	96,900	Lead	995		627		53.89	7.38		Pyrite Conc.
							Zinc	3,248				1.80	48.45		

SURVEY OF WORLD LEAD AND ZINC PRODUCTION IN 1968

MINES

Country and Company Name	Name of Mine	Location of Mine	Year First Operated	Principal Metals Mined	Type of Deposit	Mining Method	Ore Production (1968) Tonnage	Analysis Au	Ag	Cu	Pb	Zn	Other	Where Milled
Spain (Cont'd)														
Penarroya	Los Silicatos	Murcia	1957	Pb,Zn	Lens	Open Pit								Own Mill - Murcia
Soc. Min. Picos de Europa	Aliva	Santander	1960	Pb,Zn	Lens	R&P	14,377				0.5	15.0		Own Mill - Santander
Sweden														
Boliden Aktiebolag	Langdal		1967	Cu,Pb,Zn										Own Mill - Boliden
" "	Langsele		1956	Cu,Zn										Own Mill "
" "	Kankberg		1966	Cu,Zn										Own Mill - "
" "	Renstrom		1952	Cu,Pb,Zn										Own Mill - "
" "	Kristineberg		1940	Cu,Zn										Own Mill -Kristineberg
" "	Kimheden		1968	Cu,Zn										Own Mill - "
" "	Rakkejaur		1966	Cu,Zn										Own Mill - "
" "	Rudtjebacken		1950	Cu,Zn										Own Mill - "
" "	Ravliden		1936	Cu,Pb,Zn										Own Mill - "
" "	Ravlidmyran		1950	Cu,Pb,Zn										Own Mill - "
" "	Laisvall		1943	Pb										Own Mill - Laisvall
" "	Garpenberg		1400	Cu,Pb,Zn										Own Mill - Garpenberg
" "	Kaveltorp		1640	Cu,Pb,Zn										Own Mill - "
" "	Ljusnarsberg		1700	Cu,Pb,Zn										Own Mill - "
" "	Saxberget		1880	Cu,Pb,Zn										Own Mill - Saxberget
" "	Svardsjo		1400	Cu,Pb,Zn										Own Mill - "
" "	Vassbo		1960	Pb										Own Mill - Vassbo
A.B. Statsgruvor	Stollberg	Morgard-shammer	1912	Ag,Pb,Zn	Vein & Lens	S.S.								Own Mill - Morgard-shammer
Stora Kopparberg	Falu Gruva	Falun	1950	Ag,Cu,Pb,Zn	Lens	C&F/R&P	150,000	0.4	50	0.5	1.2	3.1		Own Mill - Falun
Vieille Montagne	Nygruvan	Ammeberg	1857	Ag,Pb,Zn	Vein	C&F	241,303				1.47	9.14		Own Mill - Ammeberg

MILLS

Country and Company Name	Name/ Location of Mill	Year First Operated	Mines Milled	Rated Daily Capacity	Milling Method	Tonnage Milled	Concentrate Produced (1968)								Other Products
							Type	Tonnage	Analysis						
									Au	Ag	Cu	Pb	Zn	Other	
Spain (Cont'd)															
Penarroya	Murcia	1957	One	6,000	Flotation	1,640,000	Lead	25,900		760		72.0			
							Zinc	25,000					50.5		
Soc. Min. Picos de Europa	Santander	1960	One	40	Flotation	14,377	Lead	129				49.5			
							Zinc	2,980					53.5		
Sweden															
Boliden Aktiebolag		1953	Four	2,100	Flotation	683,000	Lead	4,500							Cu Conc.
							Zinc	31,500	Below is the average assay of all						
							Pyrite	193,000	concentrates from Boliden's mills						
" "		1940	Six	2,400	Flotation	780,000	Lead	700	.68	324		70.45			Cu Conc.
							Zinc	28,000					54.06		
							Pyrite	235,000						S51.17	Talc
" "		1943	One	3,600	Flotation	1,200,000	Lead	53,500							
" "		1953	Three	920	Flotation	659,000	Lead	29,700							Cu Conc.
							Zinc	31,300							
" "		1935	Three	440	Flotation										
" "		1960	One	600	Flotation										
AB Statsgruvor	Morgards-hammar	1912		600	Flot/ Magnetic Separation	190,000	Lead	6,200	1.0	900	0.4	70.0	3.0		Magnetite Conc. Fe64.0%
							Zinc	7,650		60	0.3	0.8	51.0	Cd.15	
Stora Kopparberg	Falun	1927	One	600	Flotation	150,000	Lead	2,200	1.5	500	1.0	45.0	5.0		
							Zinc	6,600	0.5	80	0.6	1.0	50.0		
							Pyrite	46,000			0.1	0.4	0.5	S46.0	
Vieille Montagne	Ammeberg	1857	One	800	Flotation	184,850	Lead	4,056		1,100		70.64			
							Zinc	35,037				55.47			

SURVEY OF WORLD LEAD AND ZINC PRODUCTION IN 1968

MINES

Country and Company Name	Name of Mine	Location of Mine	Year First Operated	Principal Metals Mined	Type of Deposit	Mining Method	Ore Production (1968)							Where Milled
							Tonnage	Analysis						
								Au	Ag	Cu	Pb	Zn	Other	
Turkey														
Etibank	Keban Simli Kursun Isktmesi	Elazig	1953	Pb,Zn	Vein	C&F	25,000							Own Mill - Elazig
OCEANIA														
Australia														
Broken Hill South Ltd.	South Mine	New South Wales	1885	Ag,Pb,Zn	Lens	C&F								Own Mill - New South Wales
" "		New South Wales					Reworking Old Dump Material							Own Mill - New South Wales
Cobar Mines Proprietary Ltd.	C.S.A. Mine	New South Wales	1965	Cu,Zn	Lens	C&F	N.A.							Own Mill - New South Wales
Conzinc Riotinto of Australia Ltd.	The Zinc Corp. Ltd.	New South Wales	1905	Ag,Pb,Zn	Lens	C&F/S.S.								Own Mill - New South Wales
" "	New Broken Hill Cons. Ltd.	New South Wales	1945	Ag,Pb,Zn	Lens	C&F								Own Mill - New South Wales
Electrolytic Zinc Co. of Australasia Ltd.	Rosebery	Tasmania	1920	Ag,Cu,Pb,Zn	Lens	C&F								Own Mill - Tasmania
Mount Isa Mines Ltd.	Mount Isa	Queensland	1931	Ag,Cu,Pb,Zn	Lens	C&F/SLS	1,689,354		174		7.6	6.0		Own Mill - Queensland
North Broken Hill Ltd.	North Mine	New South Wales	1885	Ag,Pb,Zn	Lode	C&F	479,877		231		13.02	10.81		Own Mill - New South Wales
United Uranium,N.L.	Evelyn	Northern Territory	1966	Ag,Pb,Zn	Vein	S.L.S.	26,360		310		6.4	8.1		Own Mill - Northern Territory

MILLS

Country and Company Name	Name/ Location of Mill	Year First Operated	Mines Milled	Rated Daily Capacity	Milling Method	Tonnage Milled	Concentrate Produced (1968)								Other Products
							Type	Tonnage	Analysis						
									Au	Ag	Cu	Pb	Zn	Other	
Turkey															
Etibank	Elazig	1953	One	80	Flotation	25,000	Lead	2,203	2.0	1,610	0.33	50.17	7.02		
							Zinc	1,333	1.4	443	0.35	10.66	35.57	Cd.03	
OCEANIA															
Australia															
Broken Hill South Ltd.	New South Wales	1927	Two	1,524	Flotation	206,764	Lead	31,084		1,240		70.2	5.0		
							Zinc	35,979					51.4		
" " " "	New South Wales	1966	Old Dumps	1,067	Flotation	245,068	Lead	10,578		1,393		39.7	7.0		
							Zinc	13,892					49.7		
Cobar Mines Proprietary Ltd.	New South Wales	1965	One	1,087	Flotation	212,306	Zinc	12,482			0.3	1.6	49.7		Cu Conc.
Conzinc Riotinto of Australia Ltd.	New South Wales	1939	Two	4,633	Flotation	782,503	Lead	111,385	.6	588	0.79	76.0	3.8		
							Zinc	126,911		31	0.12	1.2	51.6		Cd.20
	New South Wales	1952	Two	5,608	Flotation	941,991	Lead	95,372	.6	526	1.01	77.2	3.1		
							Zinc	236,520		18	0.14	0.94	52.8		Cd.19
Electrolytic Zinc Co. of Australasia Ltd.	Tasmania	1936	Three	874	Flotation	315,484	Lead	14,013	8.5	859	0.80	58.4	17.4	(EZ Co. statistics are for year ending June 30, 1969.)	
							Zinc	86,972	1.1	95	0.30	2.9	54.6		
							Ag Cu Pb Zn	12,973	56	2,673	10.40	37.1	11.4		
Mount Isa Mines, Ltd.	Queensland	1931	One	10,160	Flotation	1,655,858	Lead	261,226		1,017		43.0	6.7		
							Zinc	130,101		101		1.8	52.0		
North Broken Hill, Ltd.	New South Wales	1939	One	2,540	Flotation	486,215	Lead	83,991		1,269		73.3	0.86		
							Zinc	86,577		27		4.95	53.51		
United Uranium, N.L.	Northern Territory	1966	One	102	Flotation	26,423	Lead	1,959	2.2	3,169	2.5	58.9	1.9		
							Zinc	3,619		209		4.9	50.4	Cd.47	

SURVEY OF WORLD LEAD AND ZINC PRODUCTION IN 1968

ZINC PLANTS

Country and Company Name	Name/ Location of Plant	Year First Operated	Type of Plant	Type of Roast/Sinter Plant	H_2SO_4 (100%) Annual Capacity	Zinc Slag/ or Residue Treatment	Zinc Metal Production (1968)			By-Products
							Annual Capacity	Actual Production		
								<99.99% Zn	>99.99% Zn	
AFRICA										
Congo (Leopoldville)										
Societe Metallurgique Katangese (Metalkat)	Kolwezi, Katanga	1953	Electrolytic	Fluid Bed		Stocked	63,000	50,000	12,000	Cu, Cd
Zambia										
Zambia Broken Hill Dev. Co. Ltd.	Kabwe	1928 1962	Electrolytic I.S.P.	Flash Roaster Up Draft Sintering	21,500 -	Not Treated Not Treated	30,000 33,528	22,905 30,310	- -	Cd
AMERICA, NORTH										
Canada										
Canadian Electrolytic Zinc Ltd.	Valleyfield, P.Q.	1963	Electrolytic	Fluid Bed	132,000	Not Treated	130,500	44,540	56,430	Cd
Cominco Ltd.	Trail,B.C.	1916	Electrolytic	Suspension Roasting	313,000	Direct Smelting/ Slag Fuming	238,500	9,520	180,990	Cd, In
East Coast Smelting and Chemical Co. Ltd.	Belledune, N.B.	1966	I.S.P. plus Reflux Columns	Up Draft Sintering	199,000	Not Treated	63,500		22,880	Cd
Hudson Bay Mining and Smelting Co. Ltd.	Flin Flon, Man.	1930	Electrolytic	Wedge Modified to Split Draft		Slag Fuming	73,500	21,270	51,590	Cd
United States of America										
American Smelting and Refining Co.	Amarillo, Texas	1923	Horizontal Retort	Ropp/Dwight Lloyd - Down Draft		Direct Smelting	47,600	41,300		Cd Fume
" "	Corpus Christi, Texas	1941	Electrolytic	Flash Roaster	74,500	Direct Smelting	97,975		76,840	Cd

ZINC PLANTS

Country and Company Name	Name/ Location of Plant	Year First Operated	Type of Plant	Type of Roast/Sinter Plant	H_2SO_4 (100%) Annual Capacity	Zinc Slag/ or Residue Treatment	Zinc Metal Production (1968)			By-Products
							Annual Capacity	Actual Production		
								<99.99% Zn	>99.99% Zn	
U.S.A. (Cont'd)										
American Zinc Company	Dumas, Texas	1940	Horizontal Retort	Ropp/Dwight Lloyd - Down Draft		Treated Elsewhere	52,980	51,260		
" "	Monsanto, Illinois	1941	Electrolytic	Fluid Bed		Treated Elsewhere	76,200	19,050	46,270	
Anaconda Company	Great Falls/ Anaconda, Montana	1915	Electrolytic	Fluid Bed/Wedge		Treated Elsewhere	228,600	70,125	70,260	Cd, Cu, In, Pb
Bunker Hill Co.	Bunker Hill, Idaho	1928	Electrolytic	Flash Roaster	215,230	Direct Smelting	95,890		93,390	Cd
Eagle Picher Industries Inc.	Henryetta, Oklahoma	1916	Horizontal Retort/ Waelz	Fluid Bed		Leaching	36,285	25,850		
" "	Galena, Kansas	1954	Roasting Only	Dwight Lloyd - Up Draft	136,075	Leaching	90,720 Zn Nodules			Cd
Matthiessen & Hegeler Zinc Co.	LaSalle, Illinois	1858	Horizontal Retort/ Waelz	Dwight Lloyd - Down Draft/Wedge	69,855	Waelz	29,030			Au, Ag, Cd, Pb
" "	Meadowbrook, W. Virginia	1911	Vertical Retort	Fluid Bed	272,155	Not Treated	40,825	34,015		Se
National Zinc Co.	Bartlesville, Oklahoma	1907	Horizontal Retort	Fluid Bed/ Dwight Lloyd - Down Draft	72,850	Magnetic Separation/ Treated Elsewhere	56,955	43,375		Cd
New Jersey Zinc Co.	Palmerton, Pennsylvania	1899	Vertical Retort	Flash Roaster	147,870	Direct Smelting	107,050	45,360	61,505	Cd, In-Pb
" "	Depue, Illinois	1906	Vertical Retort	Fluid Column	362,875	Direct Smelting	63,505	25,215	26,856	In-Pb
St. Joseph Lead Co.	Monaca, Pennsylvania	1938	Electrolytic	Nich.-Here./Fluid Bed/Dwight Lloyd - Down Draft	281,455	Gravity	181,435	141,520	45,360	Cd, Hg

SURVEY OF WORLD LEAD AND ZINC PRODUCTION IN 1968

ZINC PLANTS

Country and Company Name	Name/ Location of Plant	Year First Operated	Type of Plant	Type of Roast/Sinter Plant	H_2SO_4 (100%) Annual Capacity	Zinc Slag/ or Residue Treatment	Zinc Metal Production (1968)			By-Products
							Annual Capacity	Actual Production		
								<99.99% Zn	>99.99% Zn	
AMERICA, SOUTH AND CENTRAL										
Brazil										
Companhia Mercantil E Industrial Inga	Itaguai, Rio	1965	Electrothermic			Hydro	7,200	Yes		Zn Dust
Mexico										
Asarco Mexicana, S.A.	Nueva Rosita, Coahuila	1925	Horizontal Retort	Skinner Flash Roaster	25,000	Direct Smelting	62,000	59,100		Bag House Dust
Zinc Nacional, S.A.	Monterrey, Nuevo Leon	1953	Waelz	Multiple Hearth		Not Treated	No Metal Production - Zn Oxide Only			
Zincamex, S.A.	Saltillo, Coahuila	1964	Horizontal Retort/ Overpelt	Fluid Bed	133,225	Waelz	30,000	9,914	15,244	Cd
Peru										
Cerro De Pasco Corp.	La Oroya, Junin	1940	Electrolytic	Fluid Bed	66,225	Oxidation/ Reduction Kiln	70,000	65,778		Cd
ASIA										
India										
Cominco Binani Zinc Ltd.	Binanipuram Kerala	1967	Electrolytic	Flash Roaster	35,000	Not Treated	20,000	10,324		Cd
Hindustan Zinc Ltd.	Debari, Udaipur	1968	Electrolytic	Waelz/Fluid Bed	30,000	Leaching	18,000	11,492		Cd

SURVEY OF WORLD LEAD AND ZINC PRODUCTION IN 1968

ZINC PLANTS

Country and Company Name	Name/ Location of Plant	Year First Operated	Type of Plant	Type of Roast/Sinter Plant	H_2SO_4 (100%) Annual Capacity	Zinc Slag/ or Residue Treatment	Zinc Metal Production (1968) Annual Capacity	Actual Production <99.99% Zn	Actual Production >99.99% Zn	By-Products
Japan										
The Dowa Mining Co. Ltd.	Kazuno-Gun	1953	Electrolytic	Fluid Bed	49,000	Flotation; floss treated in Cu smelting furnace	18,000		20,217	Cd
Mitsubishi Metal Mining Co. Ltd.	Hosokura, Miyagi-ken	1923	Electrolytic	Fluid Bed (Dorr)	36,000	Not Treated	21,000		20,738	Cd
" "	Barajima, Akita-shi	1953	Electrolytic	Fluid Bed (Dorr)	SO2 gas sent elsewhere	Sulphur-tising	72,400		72,286	Cd
Mitsui Mining and Smelting Co. Ltd.	Kamioka/ Gifu Pref.	1943	Electrolytic	Fluid Bed	120,000	Fuming	62,000		59,000	Cd
" "	Miike/Fukuoka Pref.	1913	Vertical Retort/ Electrolytic	Flash Roaster/Wedge/ Fluid Bed X 2/ Dwight Lloyd	117,000	Fuming	93,000	49,400	39,400	Cd
" "	Hikoshima/ Yamagouchi Pref.	1928	Horizontal Retort	Fluid Bed/ Dwight Lloyd	110,000	Fuming	26,000	25,100		Cd
Nippon Mining Co. Ltd.	Toyama-ken	1954	Electrothermic	Fluid Bed/Down Draft		Magnetic Separation	96,000	57,450	41,100	Cd
Nisso Metal Co. Ltd.	Fukushima Pref.	1916	Electrolytic	Fluid Bed/Down Draft	23,000	Fuming	31,200		29,438	Cd
Sumiko I.S.P. Co. Ltd.	Hyogo Pref.	1966	I.S.P.	Lurgi Up Draft	SO_2 gas sold	Not Treated	48,000	33,647	9,963	Cd
Toho Zinc Co. Ltd.	Annaka/Gumma Pref.	1937	Electrolytic	Fluid Bed (Dorr)	154,000	Distillation	204,000	40,730	110,125	ZnO2, Cd, In, Hg, Au, Se, Pt, Pa, Ag, Ga
" "	Onahama/ Fukushima Pref.	1963	(Roasting Only)	Fluid Bed	325,000					

SURVEY OF WORLD LEAD AND ZINC PRODUCTION IN 1968

ZINC PLANTS

Country and Company Name	Name/ Location of Plant	Year First Operated	Type of Plant	Type of Roast/Sinter Plant	H_2SO_4 (100%) Annual Capacity	Zinc Slag/ or Residue Treatment	Zinc Metal Production (1968)			By-Products
							Annual Capacity	Actual Production		
								<99.99% Zn	>99.99% Zn	
Korea, South										
Tong Shin Chemical Products Co. Ltd.	Seoul	1965	Electrolytic	Flash Roaster	20,000	Not Treated	3,000	2,159		Cu, Cd
EUROPE										
Austria										
Bleiberg (B.B.U.)	Gailitz	1955	Electrolytic/ Dor Furnace	Multiple Hearth	30,000	Volatization Leaching	155,000		15,300	Cd, Ge conc.
Belgium										
Overpelt Lommel	Overpelt	1893	Horizontal Retort	Fluid Bed	146,000		65,000	53,678	47,874	Cd,Pb,Cu Ag
" "	Lommel	1904	Horizontal Retort				45,000	34,732		
Prayon	Engis Prayon-Trooz	1947	Horizontal Retort	Down Draft sintering	95,000 14,000	Jig	44,800	44,741		
Vieille Montagne	Balen	1935	Electrolytic	Fluid Bed	302,000	Treated by Self	100,000		95,110	Cd, Ge,etc.
" "	Flone	1856	Horizontal Retort			Treated by Self	24,000 24,000 Zn Dust	19,075 17,455 Zn Dust		
France										
Penarroya	Noyelles-Godault	1962	I.S.P.	Dwight Lloyd	180,000	Treated by Self	100,000	24,662	23,761	Pb,Cd,Cu, Ag, Sb

SURVEY OF WORLD LEAD AND ZINC PRODUCTION IN 1968

ZINC PLANTS

Country and Company Name	Name/ Location of Plant	Year First Operated	Type of Plant	Type of Roast/Sinter Plant	H_2SO_4 (100%) Annual Capacity	Zinc Slag/ or Residue Treatment	Zinc Metal Production (1968)			By-Products
							Annual Capacity	Actual Production		
								<99.99% Zn	>99.99% Zn	
France (Cont'd)										
Asturienne	Auby	1870	Vertical Retort	Fluid Bed	100,000	Treated by Self	90,000	84,000	(23,500)	Cd,Pb,Sn
Vieille Montagne	Viviez	1922	Electrolytic	Fluid Bed	75,000	Direct Smelting	90,000		81,800	Cu,Cd
" "	Port de Bouc	1924	-	Flash Roaster	45,000					
" "	Creil	1915	Horizontal Retort			Treated by Self	7,200	6,755		Cd,Pb,Zn, Sn
Germany, West										
Berzelius	Duisburg	1907 (1965)	I.S.P./Waelz	Dwight Lloyd - Up Draft	120,000	Not Treated	80,000	50,560	18,629	Lead Bullion
Duisburger Kupferhutte	Duisburg	1958	Electrothermic	Chlor. Roasting		Treated by Self	20,000	16,216		Cu,Ag,Au, Co,Ni,Cd, Tl,In
Preussag	Nordenham	1906	Horizontal Retort/ Waelz	Fluid Bed	45,000 SO_3	Treated by Self Walzverf	40,000	12,300	25,000	Cd, Zn, alloys
"	Oker	1936	Vertical Retort	Dwight Lloyd	80,000 SO_3	Treated by Self	70,000	46,500	14,700	Hg
Ruhr-Zink	Datteln	1968	Electrolytic	Fluid Bed	221,000	Treated Elsewhere	135,000		18,361	Cd,Cu, Prec. Th Comp.
Italy										
Monteponi & Montevocchio	Porto Marghera	1936	Electrolytic	Fluid Bed	60,000	Volatization	32,000		30,000	Cd,Ge,Cu, Pb,In,
"	Monteponi	1967	Electrolytic	Waelz		Direct Smelting	30,000		12,000	Cd,Pb.

SURVEY OF WORLD LEAD AND ZINC PRODUCTION IN 1968

ZINC PLANTS

Country and Company Name	Name/ Location of Plant	Year First Operated	Type of Plant	Type of Roast/Sinter Plant	H_2SO_4 (100%) Annual Capacity	Zinc Slag/ or Residue Treatment	Zinc Metal Production (1968) Annual Capacity	Actual Production <99.99% Zn	Actual Production >99.99% Zn	By-Products
Italy (Cont'd)										
Pertusola	Crotone	1928	Electrolytic	Fluid Bed	80,000		70,000		50,087	Cd
AMMI	Ponte Nossa, Bergamo	1952	Electrolytic	Fluid Bed	30,000	Leaching/ Direct Fusion	34,000	23,940		Cd,Zn Dust, Alloys
Netherlands										
Kempensche Zinkmaatschappij	Budel	1892	Horizontal Retort	Fluid Bed Up Draft	80,000	Not Treated	50,000	42,100		Cd,Hg
Norway										
Det Norske Zinkkompani	Eitrheim	1929	Electrolytic	Fluid Bed	80,000+ 50,000	Leaching	75,000	29,713	30,308	Cd,Cu prec.
Spain										
Espanola del Zinc	Cartagena	1960	Electrolytic	Fluid Bed	40,000	Direct Smelting	30,000		21,830	Cd,Pb
Asturienne	Hinojedo Santander	1929	-	Flash Roaster	78,000					
"	San Juan de Nivea, Aviles	1963		Dwight Lloyd			40,000			
"	San Juan de Nivea, Aviles	1960	Electrolytic			Leaching	60,000	17,260	36,293	Cu,Cd

SURVEY OF WORLD LEAD AND ZINC PRODUCTION IN 1968

ZINC PLANTS

Country and Company Name	Name/ Location of Plant	Year First Operated	Type of Plant	Type of Roast/Sinter Plant	H_2SO_4 (100%) Annual Capacity	Zinc Slag/ or Residue Treatment	Zinc Metal Production (1968)			By-Products
							Annual Capacity	Actual Production		
								<99.99% Zn	>99.99% Zn	
United Kingdom										
Imperial Smelting Corporation Ltd.	Swansea	1960	I.S.P.	Up Draft Sinter	see Lead Smelter		50,000	49,400		Cd,Cu,Ag
" "	Avonmouth	1967	I.S.P.	Up Draft Sinter	see Lead Smelter		90,000	39,800	10,600	Cd,Cu,Ag
" "	Avonmouth (2)	1954	Vertical Retort	Up Draft Sinter	88,000		40,000	38,000		Cd
OCEANIA										
Australia										
Electrolytic Zinc Co. of Australasia Ltd.	Risdon, Tasmania	1916	Electrolytic	Fluid Bed	278,140	Leaching	157,486		152,406	Cd,Hg,Co Oxide, Cu Residue
Sulphide Corp. Pty. Ltd.	Cockle Creek, New South Wales	1961	I.S.P.	Up Draft	112,256	Not Treated	55,882	45,346	3,922	Cd

SURVEY OF WORLD LEAD AND ZINC PRODUCTION IN 1968

Country and Company Name	LEAD SMELTERS: Name/Location of Smelter	Year First Operated	Type of Roast/Sinter Plant	H_2SO_4 (100%) Annual Capacity	Type of Smelter	Lead Slag Treatment	Lead Bullion Production (1968): Annual Capacity	Lead Bullion Production (1968): Actual Production	LEAD REFINERIES: Name/Location of Refinery	Year First Operated	Type of Refining	Refined Lead Production (1968): Annual Capacity	Refined Lead Production (1968): Actual Production	By-Products
AFRICA														
Morocco														
Penarroya	Oed-El-Heimer	1946	Dwight Lloyd		Conventional	Treated by Self	32,000	30,171	Oed-El-Heimer	1946	Pyro	48,000	24,166	Na,Sb,Ag, Cu Matte
South West Africa														
Tsumeb Corp. Ltd.	Tsumeb	1963							Tsumeb	1963		82,000	55,697	Ag,Cd,As
Zambia														
Zambia Broken Hill Dev. Co. Ltd.	Kabwe	1962	Up Draft Sintering		I.S.P.	Not Treated	30,000	24,993	Kabwe	1946	Pyro	32,000	22,653	Ag
AMERICA, NORTH														
Canada														
Cominco Ltd.	Trail, B.C.	1899	Down Draft Sintering	118,000	Conventional	Zinc Fuming	204,000	178,450	Trail, B.C.	1902	Electro	190,500	172,400	Ag;Bi;Sn, Sb, as Pb Alloys
East Coast Smelting and Refining Co. Ltd.	Belledune, N.B.	1966	Up Draft Sintering		I.S.P.	Not Treated	32,700	14,630	Belledune, N.B.	1967	Pyro	32,650	10,850	Cu/Pb Dross; Pb/Ag Bullion

SURVEY OF WORLD LEAD AND ZINC PRODUCTION IN 1968

LEAD SMELTERS									LEAD REFINERIES					
Country and Company Name	Name/ Location of Smelter	Year First Operated	Type of Roast/ Sinter Plant	H_2SO_4 (100%) Annual Capacity	Type of Smelter	Lead Slag Treatment	Lead Bullion Production (1968)		Name/ Location of Refinery	Year First Operated	Type of Refining	Refined Lead Production (1968)		By-Products
							Annual Capacity	Actual Production				Annual Capacity	Actual Production	
United States of America														
American Smelting & Refining Company	East Helena Montana	1888	Dwight Lloyd - Up Draft		Conventional	Zinc Fuming Furnace	97,975	37,650						
" "	El Paso, Texas	1887	Dwight Lloyd - Down Draft		Conventional	Zinc Fuming Furnace	97,975	48,080						
" "	Glover, Missouri	1968	Dwight Lloyd - Up Draft		Conventional	Not Treated	81,650	4,080	Glover, Missouri	1968	Pyro	81,650	3,800	Au,Ag
" "	Selby, California	1885	Dwight Lloyd - Down Draft	10,885	Conventional	Zinc Fuming Furnace	65,315	28,575	Selby, California	1888	Pyro	65,315	29,480	Au,Ag,Bi, Sb,Sn
" "									Omaha, Nebraska	1870	Pyro	163,300	98,520	Au,Ag,Bi, Sb
Bunker Hill Co.	Bunker Hill Idaho	1917	Dwight Lloyd - Down Draft		Conventional	Zinc Fuming Furnace	113,035	111,220	Bunker Hill Idaho	1917	Pyro	111,220	111,220	Au,Ag,Cd, Cu,Sb
International Smelting & Refining Co.	Tooele, Utah	1912	Dwight Lloyd - Down Draft		Conventional	Zinc Fuming Furnace	59,875	33,080						
Missouri Lead Operating Company	Boss, Missouri	1968	Up Draft	47,175	Conventional	Diluent	90,720	19,050	Boss, Missouri	1968	Pyro	90,720	17,245	Ag,Cu
St. Joseph Lead Co.	Herculaneum Missouri	1891	Dwight Lloyd - Down Draft	99,335	Conventional	Not Treated	204,115	155,130	Herculaneum Missouri	1891	Pyro	200,115	155,130	Ag
U.S. Smelting, Refining & Mining Co.									East Chicago, Indiana		Electro	36,285	32,190	

SURVEY OF WORLD LEAD AND ZINC PRODUCTION IN 1968

Country and Company Name	LEAD SMELTERS: Name/ Location of Smelter	Year First Operated	Type of Roast/ Sinter Plant	H_2SO_4 (100%) Annual Capacity	Type of Smelter	Lead Slag Treatment	Lead Bullion Production (1968)		LEAD REFINERIES: Name/ Location of Refinery	Year First Operated	Type of Refining	Refined Lead Production (1968)		By-Products
							Annual Capacity	Actual Production				Annual Capacity	Actual Production	
AMERICA SOUTH AND CENTRAL														
Brazil														
Companhia Brazileira De Chumbo	Santo Amaro Bahia	1959			Conventional	Not Treated	15,000	14,040	(as refined lead)					
Plumbum S/A	Adriano-polis, Parana	1945	Dwight Lloyd - Down Draft		Conventional	Not Treated	8,500	5,400	(as refined lead)					
Mexico														
Asarco Mexicana S/A	Avalos, Chihuahua	1908	Dwight Lloyd - Down Draft		Conventional	Zinc Fuming Furnace	80,000	68,941	Monterrey, Nuevo Leon	1929	Pyro	150,000	80,000	Au,Ag,Sb, Se,Sn Res, Zn Res.
Cia Minera Los Angeles S. de R.L.	Ocampo, Coahuila	1967	Dwight Lloyd - Down Draft		Conventional	Not Treated	2,000	1,292						
Minera Metalurgica Mexicana, S.A.	Muzquiz, Coahuila	1962	Dwight Lloyd - Down Draft		Conventional		2,000	2,000						
Metalurgica Mexicana Penoles, S.A.	Torreon, Coahuila								Monterrey, Nuevo Leon			130,000	105,000 (Est.)	
Peru														
Cerro De Pasco Corp.	La Oroya, Junin	1930	Dwight Lloyd - Up Draft		Conventional	Not Treated	100,000	86,809	La Oroya, Junin		Electro	100,000	86,346	Au,Ag,Sb, Bi,In

SURVEY OF WORLD LEAD AND ZINC PRODUCTION IN 1968

LEAD SMELTERS									LEAD REFINERIES					
Country and Company Name	Name/ Location of Smelter	Year First Operated	Type of Roast/ Sinter Plant	H_2SO_4 (100%) Annual Capacity	Type of Smelter	Lead Slag Treatment	Lead Bullion Production (1968)		Name/ Location of Refinery	Year First Operated	Type of Refining	Refined Lead Production (1968)		By-Products
							Annual Capacity	Actual Production				Annual Capacity	Actual Production	
ASIA														
Burma														
People's Bawdin Industry	Namtu								Namtu				8,000 (Est.)	
India														
Hindustan Zinc Ltd.	Tundoo, Bihar	1945	Huntington Heberlein		Conventional	Not Treated	4,000	1,647	Tundoo, Bihar	1945	Pyro	4,000	1,647	Ag
Japan														
The Dowa Mining Co. Ltd.	Kazuno-gun Akita Pref	1953	Raw material Cottrel Dust Cu Converter	is from Furnace	Electric Furnace	Not Treated	3,000	1,850	Kazuno-gun Akita Pref.	1958	Electro	3,000	1,824	Bi
Mitsubishi Cominco Smelting Co. Ltd.	Naoshima Kagawa-ken	1966	Dwight Lloyd - Up Draft	SO2 gas sent elsewhere	Conventional	Not Treated	36,000	30,434	Naoshima Kagawa-ken	1966	Pyro	36,000	30,434	
Mitsubishi Metal Mining Co. Ltd.	Hosokura Miyagi-ken	1824	Dwight Lloyd - Down Draft		Conventional	Not Treated	19,200	19,105	Hosokura, Miyagi-ken	1937	Electro	19,200	19,105	Au,Ag,Bi
Mitsui Mining and Smelting Co. Ltd.	Kamioka, Gifu Pref.	1905	Dwight Lloyd		Conventional	Zinc Fuming Furnace	22,000	20,800	Kamioka, Gifu Pref.	1935	Electro (Betts)	20,400	20,100	Au,Ag,Bi Te
" "	Takehara, Hiroshima	1943			Conventional	Not Treated	12,000	11,000	Takehara, Hiroshima	1943	Electro (Betts)	10,500	10,200	Au,Ag,Sb, Sn
Nippon Mining Co. Ltd.	Saganoseki Oita-ken	1948	Up Draft		Conventional	Not Treated	29,000	27,500	Saganoseki, Oita-ken	1920	Electro (Betts)	28,800	26,650	Au,Ag,Bi, Sn,Sb_2O_3

SURVEY OF WORLD LEAD AND ZINC PRODUCTION IN 1968

Country and Company Name	LEAD SMELTERS: Name/ Location of Smelter	Year First Operated	Type of Roast/ Sinter Plant	H_2SO_4 (100%) Annual Capacity	Type of Smelter	Lead Slag Treatment	Lead Bullion Production (1968): Annual Capacity	Lead Bullion Production (1968): Actual Production	LEAD REFINERIES: Name/ Location of Refinery	Year First Operated	Type of Refining	Refined Lead Production (1968): Annual Capacity	Refined Lead Production (1968): Actual Production	By-Products
Japan (Cont'd)														
Nisso Metal Co. Ltd.	Bandai, Fukushima	1937			Soda Process	Not Treated	3,000	1,710	Bandai, Fukushima	1940	Electro	4,200	1,700	
Sumiko I.S.P. Co. Ltd.	Harima-cho, Hyogo	1966			I.S.P./ Lurgi Up Draft	Not Treated	24,000	18,425	Harima-cho, Hyogo	1966	Electro	20,400	18,570	Slime
Toho Zinc Co. Ltd.	Chigir-ishima, Hiroshima	1951	Hereshoff Up Draft	24,500	Conventional	Zinc Fuming Furnace	42,000	34,100	Chigir-ishima, Hiroshima	1955	Electro	39,600	35,500	Ag, Au, Bi, Sb, As, In, Cd, Sn, Te, Th, Cu, Zn
Korea, South														
Korea Mining and Smelting Corp.	Chang-Hang-up	1964	Straight Line D.L. Sinter		Conventional	Not Treated	6,500	4,500	Chang-Hang-up	1964	Pyro	4,000	3,500	Au, Ag, Bi Sb
EUROPE														
Austria														
Bleiberg (B.B.U.)	Arnoldstein	1882	none		Rotary Furnace	Blast/ Reverb	14,000	13,000	Gailitz	1882	Pyro	14,000	12,000	Sb
Belgium														
S.A. Metallurgie Hoboken	Hoboken	1902	Wedge/ Dwight Lloyd	144,000	Conventional	Brass Furnace	80,000	60,000	Hoboken	1888	Pyro	100,000	60,000	Sb, Sn, Ag, Au, Pt, Pd, Rn
Overpelt Lommel									Overpelt Lommel	1897	Pyro	6,000	962	

SURVEY OF WORLD LEAD AND ZINC PRODUCTION IN 1968

Country and Company Name	LEAD SMELTERS								LEAD REFINERIES					
	Name/ Location of Smelter	Year First Operated	Type of Roast/ Sinter Plant	H_2SO_4 (100%) Annual Capacity	Type of Smelter	Lead Slag Treatment	Lead Bullion Production (1968)		Name/ Location of Refinery	Year First Operated	Type of Refining	Refined Lead Production (1968)		By-Products
							Annual Capacity	Actual Production				Annual Capacity	Actual Production	
Belgium (Cont'd)														
Vieille Montagne	Balen	1910	Dwight Lloyd		Conventional	Direct Smelting	43,800	26,096	Balen	1931	Pyro/ Electro	51,000	25,138	Cd, Ag, Bi, As, Sb, Sn, Tb, Hg, Cu
Campine	Beersse						6,000					6,000 (Est)	9,200 (Est)	Sb
France														
Penarroya	Noyelles Godault	1936	Dwight Lloyd	46,000	Conventional	Treated by Self	110,000	87,440	Noyelles Godault	1936	Pyro	120,000	99,785	Ag, Cu-matte, Bi Sb-comp.
Germany, West														
Berzelius	Duisburg	1965	Up Draft - Dwight Lloyd		I.S.P.	Not Treated	36,000	32,600						
Braubach									Braubach	1896	Pyro	60,000	58,622	Au Bullion
Norddeutsche Affinerie									Hamburg	1912	Pyro/ Electro	40,000	25,014	Cu, Sb, Bi Ag, Au, Te, Sn
Preussag	Nordenham	1959	Down Draft	30,000	Conventional	Not Treated	75,000	75,000	Nordenham	1914	Pyro	75,000	73,000	Ag Bullion Cu Matte
"	Oker	1926	Dwight Lloyd	65,000	Conventional	Zinc Fuming Furnace	40,000	40,000	Oker	1958	Pyro	45,000	44,000	Ag Bullion Cd-Cu-Matte

SURVEY OF WORLD LEAD AND ZINC PRODUCTION IN 1968

Country and Company Name	LEAD SMELTERS: Name/ Location of Smelter	Year First Operated	Type of Roast/ Sinter Plant	H_2SO_4 (100%) Annual Capacity	Type of Smelter	Lead Slag Treatment	Lead Bullion Production (1968)		LEAD REFINERIES: Name/ Location of Refinery	Year First Operated	Type of Refining	Refined Lead Production (1968)		By-Products
							Annual Capacity	Actual Production				Annual Capacity	Actual Production	
Germany, West (Cont'd)														
Stolberger	Stolberg	1846	Down Draft	35,000	Conventional	Not Treated	50,000		Stolberg	1846	Pyro	75,000	72,000	Ag, Au, Cu, Sn, Bi, As, Ni
Greece														
Laurium	Laurium		Dwight Lloyd		Conventional	Treated by Self	15,000	9,275	Laurium		Pyro	15,000	8,465	Pb, Zn
Italy														
Monteponi & Montevecchio	San Gavino Monreale	1932	Dwight Lloyd		Conventional/ Lurgi	Soda Process	36,000	30,000	San Gavino Monreale	1957	Electro	36,000	27,000	Ag, Bi, Sb, Cu
Pertusola	La Spezia	1924	Dwight Lloyd		Conventional	Zinc Fuming	75,000	30,508	La Spezia	1924	Pyro	75,000	30,919	Ag, Sb
Tonolli	Paderno Dugnano						12,000					12,000		
Netherlands														
Billiton	Arnhem				Conventional		20,000		Arnhem			20,000	17,500	
Spain														
Asturienne	Cap Uchinos Gui Puzzoa	1859 (1965)	Dwight Lloyd - Up Draft		Conventional		7,500	5,409	Cap Uchinos Gui Puzzoa	1859	Pyro	18,000	6,132	
Penarroya	Cartagena, Murcia		Dwight Lloyd		Conventional	Reverb. Furnace	30,000	28,474	Cartagena, Murcia		Pyro	30,000	20,420	42 kg Ag
"	Pueblo Nuevo, Cordoba		Dwight Lloyd		Conventional	Reverb. Furnace	18,000	17,164	Pueblo Nuevo, Cordoba		Pyro	18,000	18,855	

SURVEY OF WORLD LEAD AND ZINC PRODUCTION IN 1968

Country and Company Name	LEAD SMELTERS								LEAD REFINERIES					
	Name/ Location of Smelter	Year First Operated	Type of Roast/ Sinter Plant	H_2SO_4 (100%) Annual Capacity	Type of Smelter	Lead Slag Treatment	Lead Bullion Production (1968)		Name/ Location of Refinery	Year First Operated	Type of Refining	Refined Lead Production (1968)		By-Products
							Annual Capacity	Actual Production				Annual Capacity	Actual Production	
Sweden														
Boliden	Skelleft-ehamn	1943	none	25,000	Electric Smelting	Zinc Fuming Furnace	55,000	48,000	Skelleft-ehamn	1943	Pyro	55,000	43,000	
United Kingdom														
Associated	Newcastle on Tyne; London; Chester								Associated				100,000	
Britannia									Northfleet	1931	Pyro	140,000	83,876 Ref. Lead 12,490 Alloys	Sb,Ag
British Lead Mills									Welwyn G.C.	1952	Pyro	14,000	11,000	Sn,Sb, Alloys
Capper Pass									North Ferriby				8,600 (Est)	
Enthoven	Rotherhithe	1770	none	none	Rotary Furnace	Not Treated	29,000	28,000	Rotherhithe	1770	Pyro	25,000	10,000 Ref.Lead 12,900 Alloys	Cu,Sn,Sb
Enthoven	Darley Dale	1941	none	none	Reverb/ Blast/ Rotary	Not Treated	30,000	28,000	Darley Dale	1941	Pyro	30,000	14,000 Ref. Lead 14,000 Ant. Lead	Cu,Sb

SURVEY OF WORLD LEAD AND ZINC PRODUCTION IN 1968

Country and Company Name	LEAD SMELTERS: Name/Location of Smelter	Year First Operated	Type of Roast/Sinter Plant	H_2SO_4 (100%) Annual Capacity	Type of Smelter	Lead Slag Treatment	Lead Bullion Production (1968): Annual Capacity	Lead Bullion Production (1968): Actual Production	LEAD REFINERIES: Name/Location of Refinery	Year First Operated	Type of Refining	Refined Lead Production (1968): Annual Capacity	Refined Lead Production (1968): Actual Production	By-Products
United Kingdom (Cont'd)														
Imperial Smelting Corp.	Swansea	1960	Up Draft Sinter	84,000	I.S.P.	Not Treated	25,000	19,500						
" "	Avonmouth	1967	Up Draft Sinter	260,000	I.S.P.	Not Treated	50,000	15,300						
OCEANIA														
Australia														
Mount Isa Mines Ltd.	Mount Isa, Queensland	1931	Simon Carves Up Draft		Conventional	Not Treated	142,246	103,849						
Sulphide Corp. Pty. Ltd.	Cockle Creek, N.S. Wales	1961	Up Draft	See Zn Plant Section	I.S.P.	Not Treated	22,861	19,114						
Broken Hill Assoc. Smelters Prop. Ltd.	Port Pirie, South Australia								Port Pirie, South Australia			233,700	200,000 (Est.)	

SECTION II

ZINC ROASTING PRACTICE

Chapter 3

SUSPENSION ZINC CONCENTRATE ROASTER AND ACID PLANT OF THE BUNKER HILL COMPANY
Kellogg, Idaho

Douglas Baker
Assistant to the Vice President - Operations

Gene M. Baker
Manager - Plant Engineering, The Bunker Hill Company

Robert L. Bird
Manager - Zinc Plant, The Bunker Hill Company

Abstract

Zinc concentrates assaying approximately 54% zinc and 30% sulfur are roasted in a suspension type roaster to yield a zinc oxide calcine assaying about 65% zinc and 0.40% sulfur. This calcine is the feed material to the sulfuric acid leaching section of an Electrolytic Zinc Plant. The SO_2 gases resulting from the elimination of sulfur from the concentrates are passed through a waste heat boiler for the generation of high pressure steam, cleaned by a baghouse, and delivered to the humidifying tower of a sulfuric acid plant system. The gases are then treated in a mist precipitator for final fume removal and then converted to sulfur trioxide in a three pass contact system using vanadium pentoxide catalyst for the manufacture of sulfuric acid. Waste heat steam is used to power the steam turbine which drives the acid plant blower.

Introduction

The Bunker Hill Company's Electrolytic Zinc Plant is located in Government Gulch at Silver King, Shoshone County, Idaho in the Coeur d'Alene Mining District about three miles from Kellogg. The plant began production on November 6, 1928 by casting its first 25 kilogram slab of 99.99+% zinc. Originally, the plant capacity was 45 metric tons per day, but over the years plant improvements and expansion programs have raised the figure several times until in 1968 it reached its present rate of 272 metric tons.

At the start of operations, roasting of concentrates was accomplished in Wedge multiple hearth type roasters and the number of these roasters grew from two to nine. The SO_2 gases were vented to atmosphere through an 80.8 meter high stack (following dust removal in a cottrell). In 1954, four suspension type roasters with a nominal capacity of 100 metric tons of zinc concentrates per day replaced eight of the multiple hearth roasters and the high strength SO_2 gas from these roasters was introduced to our first contact acid plant. In 1967, a 315 metric tons per day suspension roaster was put on stream along with our second contact acid plant. The suspension roaster was developed by Cominco Limited at Trail, B. C. and is licensed to The Bunker Hill Company by Cominco.

The calcine from the roasting operation is leached in dilute sulfuric acid; the leach residue is filtered, washed, and then sent to the Lead Smelter for further processing. The leach solution is treated with zinc dust to remove metal impurities and the purified solution is then fed to the electrolytic cells where the zinc is electroplated. The zinc metal is stripped from aluminum cathodes, melted, and cast into various sizes, shapes and alloys. This paper will discuss in greater detail only the process through concentrate roasting and sulfuric acid production.

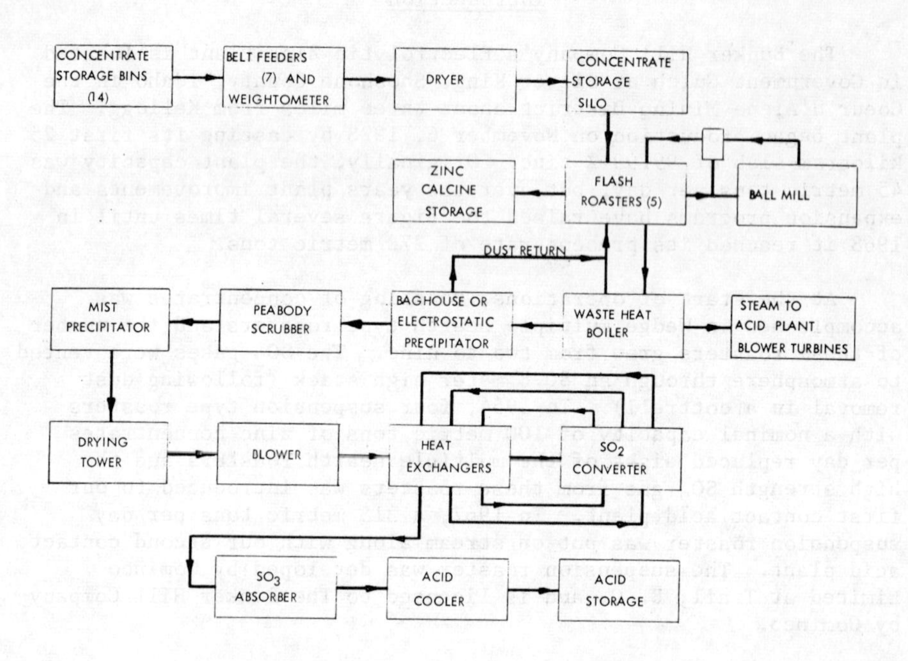

Fig. 1 - Flow Diagram of Concentrate Handling, Roasting, and Acid Plant.

Concentrate Handling

The Bunker Hill Company Electrolytic Zinc Plant is a Custom Smelter, treating concentrates from the Coeur d'Alene District of Idaho, the Metaline District of Washington, the Tintic District of Utah, and from foreign countries such as Canada, Mexico and Peru. These concentrates vary in the amount of contained zinc, sulfur, arsenic, antimony, and germanium. In order to minimize process adjustments which may be necessary because of individual impurities, the concentrates are blended to provide a uniform feed and pre-dried to a uniform moisture before being introduced into the roasting section of the plant.

Concentrates are received by rail or truck and emptied into one of fourteen primary storage bins, each of which has a nominal capacity of 900 metric tons. Each of the bins is reserved for a specific concentrate or a specific type of concentrate depending upon its principal impurity. These primary storage bins are flat bottomed and are open at the front into an area in which a large front end loader may be operated. In front of these bins are seven proportioning hoppers. Two of these hoppers feed a system which pretreats certain of the concentrates for removal of lime and magnesium. The remaining five hoppers proportion concentrates going to the dryer and subsequently to the roasters. Variable speed belt feeders proportion the concentrates from the proportioning hoppers onto a belt conveyor which passes over a weightometer and then empties into a vibrating chute which feeds the gas-fired rotary dryer. The dryer discharges onto an inclined belt conveyor which carries the dried concentrate to a 900 metric tons concrete storage silo. Two belt feeders discharge the concentrate from the silo onto belt conveyors which carry the material to the various suspension roasters.

Maximum flexibility is provided for blending of ore concentrates because of the number of different concentrates used for feed to the Bunker Hill Zinc Plant. The concentrates are also proportioned from the primary storage bins to the secondary hoppers which feed the dryer.

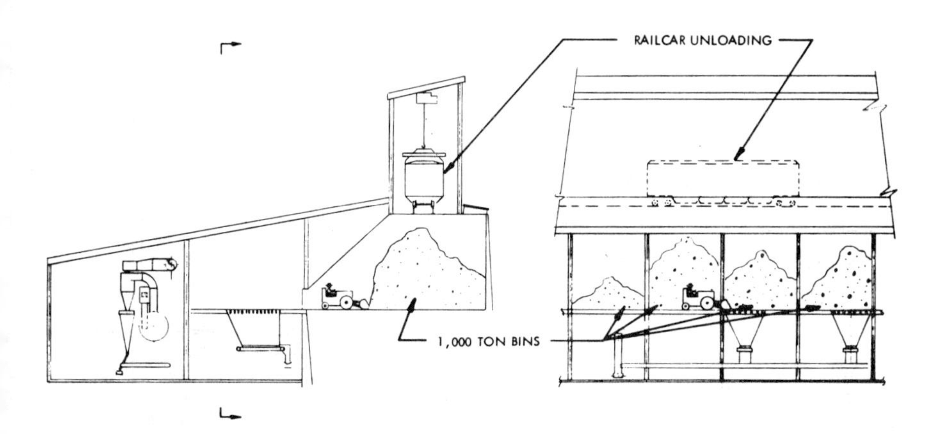

Fig. 2 - Cutaway View of Concentrate Bins and Proportioning Hopper.

Roasting

Roasting, in this instance, may be defined as the conversion of zinc sulfide into zinc oxide, which is soluble in dilute sulfuric acid. This may be expressed by the following equation:

$$2\ ZnS + 3O_2 = 2\ ZnO + 2SO_2$$

The reaction is exothermic, which sustains the reaction with no additional fuel requirement.

The roaster consists of a cylindrical steel shell lined with firebrick and covered with insulation. It has a large combustion chamber, four brick hearths, and a revolving center column which supports alloy steel arms carrying rabbles that rake material across the hearths. In the past, problems have been experienced with shell temperatures. It was found that the roasters, in general, were over-insulated and the shells became too hot, causing deterioration. A study of the problem indicated that temperature range must be maintained on the steel shell with just the right insulation thickness to prevent sulfation and corrosion which occur at the higher temperatures.

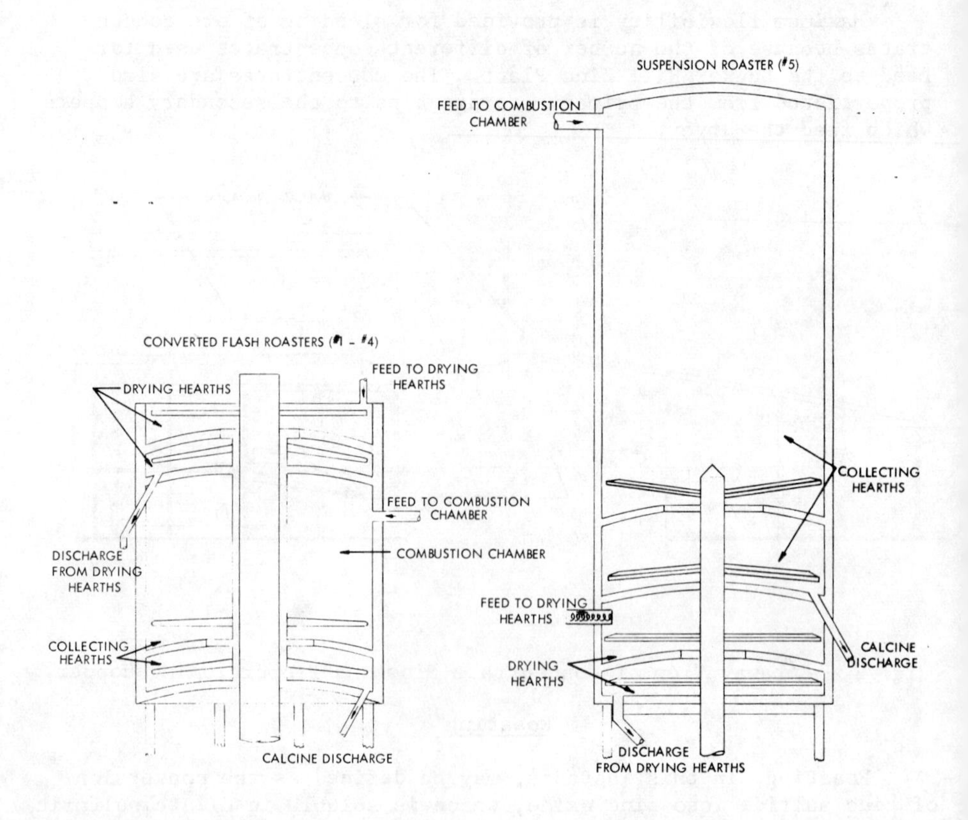

Fig. 3 - Comparison of Converted Multiple Hearth Roaster to Stub Column Suspension Roaster.

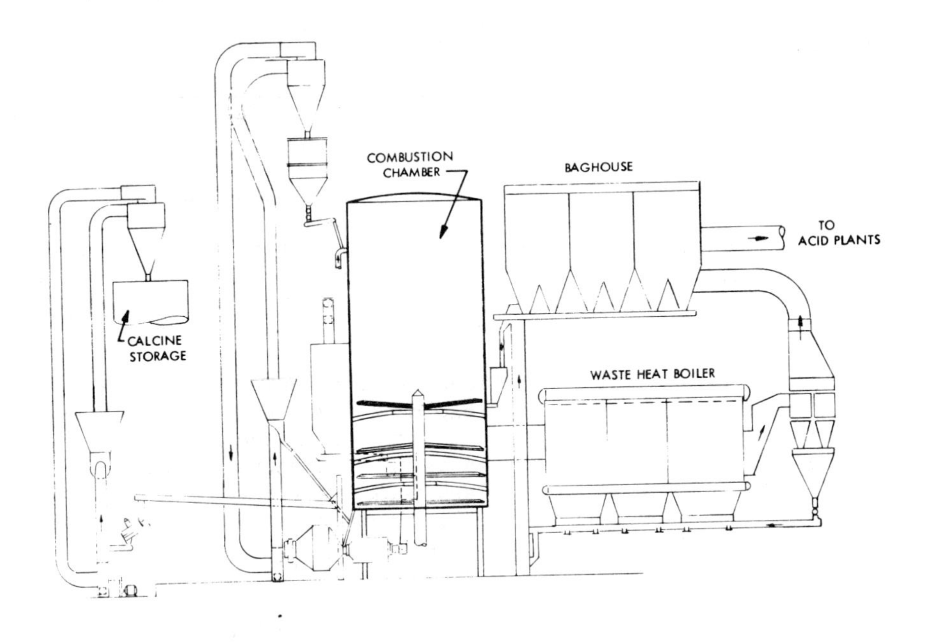

Fig. 4 - Suspension Roaster and Auxiliary Equipment.

The feed material to the roaster still contains 3-4% moisture. Therefore, two of the hearths are used for final drying of the concentrate prior to roasting. These hearths are heated with hot gases from the combustion chamber. The dried concentrate is then fed to a ball mill circuit with air classification to provide a satisfactory degree of fineness for the roasting reaction. The ground concentrate is then blown or air-injected into the combustion chamber of the roaster, along with the combustion air, where the roasting reaction occurs at a temperature of about 1273°K. The other two hearths are utilized to collect the roasted material (calcine) from the combustion chamber. These collecting hearths at the base of the combustion chamber provide the additional time needed for the elimination of the sulfide sulfur that is not oxidized in the suspension phase of the combustion chamber. The calcine is discharged to coolers and then proceeds to calcine storage. A typical analysis of zinc concentrate and calcine is listed.

Table I

Typical Zinc Concentrate Analysis	%	Typical Calcine Analysis	
Zinc	53.6	Total Zinc	63.0
Lead	2.4	Acid Soluble Zinc	58.2
Iron	5.5	Iron	6.4
Insolubles	3.4	Insoluble	2.7
Total Sulfur	30.7	Sulfides	.44

Seven roasters are operational at the Bunker Hill Zinc Plant. Two of these are original multiple hearth roasters, of which one is used to dechloridize zinc oxide dross from the melting furnace and the other is on a standby basis for concentrate roasting. Four of the roasters are old flash roasters (converted from the original multiple hearth roasters) with a capacity of 100 metric tons per day. The newest flash roaster is a 315 metric tons per day unit which was put into operation in 1967.

In recent months, the center column drive has been utilized for calcine hearth plowing to remove buildup, eliminating the need to fully cool the roasters for manual cleaning. This has resulted in a safer operation with less downtime, less labor required, and less possibility of losing brickwork. The method employed is to connect a chain or cable between two of the arms on that calcine hearth to give adequate support to the arms and, then, use the second arm (in rotational sequence) to plow the buildup. A sharpened rabble is used to plow the buildup and it is moved from one position on the arm to another position to plow all of the hearth. The alternative is to cool the roaster to the point where personnel can enter and manually remove the buildup, which has been the method in the past. This presents safety problems with the possibility of losing brickwork, in addition to requiring more downtime and labor.

Gas Cleaning

The hot gases, leaving the roaster, first pass through a waste heat boiler for heat recovery. Steam is generated from the waste heat boilers at 25200 newton/meter^2 for use in the acid plants to drive the turbines which power the large blowers which pull the gas from the roasters and push it through the acid plants. Generally, the steam produced must balance with the acid plant turbine requirements. Approximately one pound of steam is generated for each pound of concentrate roasted. The low pressure steam discharged from the turbines is utilized for plant processes. The waste heat boiler has a total of fourteen sootblowers, six of which are retractable and located in the superheater section, and eight of which are stationary and located in the main steam generating section of the boiler. About 3200-4500 kg/hr of steam are required for the sootblower operation for about fifteen minutes of each hour.

The gas stream passes from the waste heat boilers to either a high temperature baghouse or an electrostatic precipitator (cottrell). A portion of the calcine is carried in the gas stream beyond the roaster. The major part of this airborne calcine falls out and is collected in the waste heat boiler and most of the remaining calcine is collected by the baghouse or a precipitator. All of the collected calcine is returned to the roaster.

The high temperature baghouse (Western Precipitation Company) contains fiberglass bags with a surface area of 870 meter^2 (936 bags). A damper control is provided on the baghouse system, based on inlet temperature, that allows ambient air to bleed in with the inlet gas to maintain an inlet temperature of less than 575°K.

Even though the roaster off-gas is basically clean after passing through the two above steps, there are still some solids and fumes contained in the gas stream. Gas purification, then, actually begins with the roaster cleaning and recycling systems, but the purification for acid production begins in the wet Peabody scrubbers which follow the baghouse or precipitator. Here, the gas is cooled to approximately 305°K and humidified by the circulation of water. Most of the remaining solids, acid mist, and fumes are dissolved in the water.

The final gas purification step is the mist precipitators where the remaining particles of acid mist, metallic fume, and dust are removed by electrical precipitation. After the gas leaves the mist precipitators, it proceeds to a splitter box or mixing chamber where it can be sent to either or both acid plants.

Acid Plants

The Bunker Hill Zinc Plant has two sulfuric acid plants, one of which is a 270 metric tons per day Monsanto unit and the other is a 315 metric tons per day Chemico unit. The Monsanto unit was placed into operation in 1954 and the Chemico unit was started up in 1967. The acid plants prevent air pollution from the roaster off-gas as well as producing a valuable by-product.

The acid plant processes, excluding the gas purification step, consist of the following principal steps.

(1) Conversion of the SO_2 to SO_3 gas.
(2) Absorption of the SO_3 gas in H_2SO_4.

The purified gas flows first to the drying tower where 93% sulfuric acid is circulated to remove the moisture in the gas. Since this dilutes the drying acid, it is combined with the absorbing acid to control the strength of the acid to storage. The gas, then, passes through the gas blower which pushes the clean, dry gas through the balance of the acid plant. This blower has provided suction on the gas stream up to this point in the acid plant, and the steam from the waste heat boilers is used for driving this blower.

From this point, the clean, dry gas passes through a series of heat exchangers to attain the necessary inlet temperature for the SO_3 converter. Heat is evolved in the SO_2 to SO_3 conversion process and it is necessary to remove the gas from the converter for cooling twice, due to the fact that SO_3 reverts to SO_2 at elevated temperatures. The hot converter gas is the heating medium for the SO_3 converter feed stream. The SO_3 converter contains four layers of vanadium pentoxide catalyst and the conversion of SO_2 to SO_3 is normally 95-97%, depending on catalyst life and other factors.

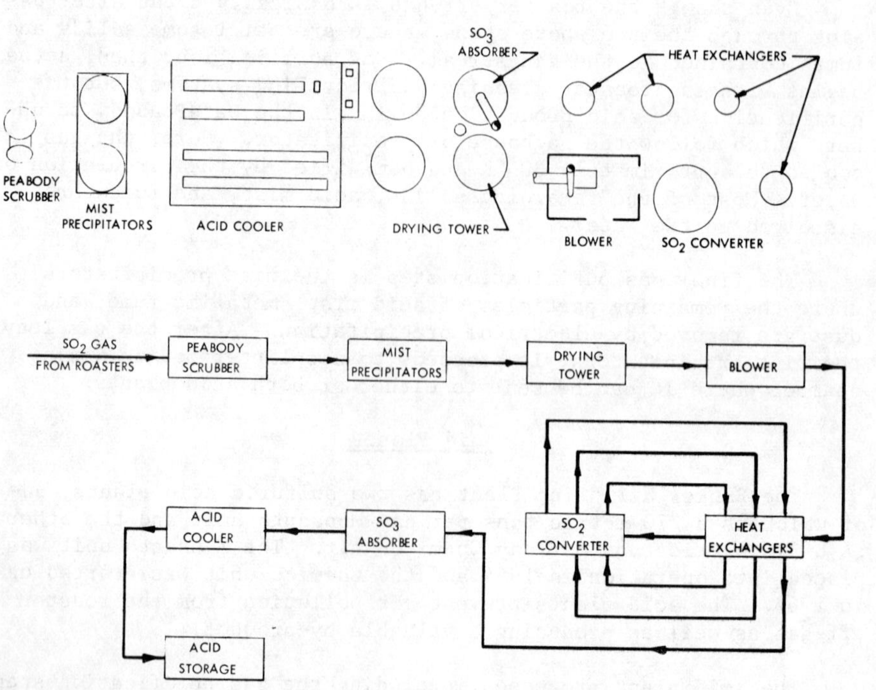

Fig. 5 - Flow Diagram of Gas Cleaning and Acid Plant.

From the SO_3 converter, the gas is cooled and then goes to an absorber where the SO_3 is absorbed in 99% acid that is flowing counter-current to the SO_3. As mentioned previously, controlled crossflows of the 99% acid from the absorbing circuit and the 93% acid from the drying circuit are maintained as well as water addition for control of acid strengths.

The acid to storage passes through coolers to control the acid temperature due to generation of heat from moisture pickup and SO_3 absorption.

Both units will operate on feed gas containing as little as 4.5% SO_2. Normal feed to the acid plants contains 6-7% SO_2. A gas-fired preheater is provided for startup.

Each heat exchanger in both acid plants is provided with a by-pass so the acid plant can continue to operate with an exchanger taken out of service. However, a short shutdown is necessary to blank out a heat exchanger for retubing or maintenance. Of course, taking an exchanger out of service reduces the acid plant operating efficiency, but it does allow the plant to continue operations. The preheater, supplied with the acid plant for startups, is also tied in with the by-pass system and can be utilized as a heat exchanger.

To facilitate catalyst handling and screening, a chain conveyor for handling five gallon pails is provided for moving the catalyst from the SO_3 converters to the screening equipment, and from the screen back to the SO_3 converter. The catalyst must be handled and screened gently to minimize breakage, and this system has proven to do an excellent job in this respect.

References

1. Eyre, R. E., "Suspension Roasting of Zinc Concentrate at Trail, British Columbia", Transactions of the CIM, vol. LXIV, pp. 325-330.

Chapter 4

FLUO-SOLIDS ROASTER AND ACID PLANT AT TREPČA LEAD & ZINC MINES & REFINERIES
Mitrovica, Yugoslavia

Gligorije Stanković
Consulting Engineer, Trepča Lead and Zinc
Mines and Refineries, Kosovska Mitrovica

Abstract

This paper describes the fluo-solids roaster and acid plants at the new 40,000-TPY Trepča electrolytic zinc plant. The electrolytic zinc plant units were constructed to the design of Singmaster and Breyer, New York and began operation in mid-1967.

The fluo-solids roaster plant, constructed according to the design of Dorr-Oliver, Paris, includes concentrate handling and storage facilities; two independent concentrate roasting circuits, each with a 110 to 155 TPD fluo-solids roaster; waste heat boilers; cyclones; electrostatic precipitators; calcine coolers; and calcine conveyors.

The acid plant uses the "Petersen System" contact process. The plant has one acid circuit with a capacity of 230 tons of monohydrate per day. Gases for the acid plant are obtained from roasting zinc concentrates. When the roaster plant is operating at maximum capacity, excess SO_2 is used in two other Petersen System circuits in the near vicinity.

Introduction

The Trepca mining area in the southeastern part of Yugoslavia was known in the Middle Ages. At that time the Trepča Mines were known not only for their mining importance, but also as a trading center in the Balkans. After many years of inactivity, mining production was resumed some forty years ago. Trepča became known for its refined lead production. In addition to lead, zinc and pyrite concentrates were produced and sold.

In the last several years Trepča has grown into a combine which includes 12 mines, some of which are still under construction. This growth has resulted from extensive exploration and purchase of additional mines in the vicinity. The present ore production of 1.2 million tons annually is expected to increase to over 3 million tons in the near future.

From mid-1964 to the end of 1966, a new 40,000 TPY electrolytic zinc plant was built. It began operation early in 1967. The plant was constructed in cooperation with Singmaster and Breyer of New York and was located near an existing sulphuric acid plant, which treats roasted mixtures of pyrrhotite and pyrite concentrates. Also located nearby is a superphosphate fertilizer plant. The electrolytic zinc plant is connected to this plant through pipelines for SO_2 gases, superheated steam, electric power, water supply, drainage, and accessibility roads.

The electrolytic zinc plant is a completely modern plant which includes, besides the zinc concentrate roasting plant, facilities for calcine leaching and purification, acid cooling and electrolysis, cadmium recovery, melting and casting, and pilot plant and subsidiary buildings.

The concentrate is supplied from our own mines, the expansion of which is projected in the near future.

This paper includes a detailed description of the first part of the plant:

- Fluo-Solids Roaster Plant
- Sulphuric Acid Plant

The fluo-solids system was selected for roasting zinc concentrates for these reasons. The product calcine was more suitable for leaching and subsequent electrolysis and the capital investment and operating costs were lower in comparison with other roaster types. The equipment was supplied by Dorr-Oliver, Paris, following semi-industrial tests at Milan, Italy and Westport, Connecticut (U.S.A.).

The contact process for the sulphuric acid production was selected for economic reasons and for enhanced possibilities for acid marketing. At the present most of our acid is sold. The design and equipment were supplied by Hugo Petersen, Wiesbaden, West Germany.

Fluo-Solids Roaster Plant

Plant Description

The roaster plant is divided into two independent circuits for roasting zinc concentrate. Each circuit includes a fluo-solids reactor, waste heat boiler, cyclones, and electrostatic precipitators. This arrangement insures continuous operation of the acid plant in case of temporary breakdown and supplies electrolysis units with a continuous supply of calcine. The gases from both circuits join together after passing through the electro-filter and enter the acid plant in a common pipeline. This same arrangement will be installed on the existing two circuits in the pyrite acid plant for maximum efficiency of that operation.

Flotation concentrates are fed to the reactor via a slurry feeding system. The moisture content of these concentrates may be over 9%.

To minimize the loss of concentrates during handling, a small capacity slurry storage facility has been built in the vicinity of the mine. Enclosed concrete paved yards are provided to store the concentrates when the supply is irregular. From here the concentrates can be handled by loaders as necessary.

The entire plant is in the open, except for the slurry preparation area and automatic controls which are located indoors. A diagram of the plant is shown in Figure 1.

1. Concentrate Handling and Storage - The concentrate is conveyed by dumpers and delivered to the 27 m^3 loading hopper (1) with an apron feeder at the bottom. From there it is carried by a 40 t/h belt conveyor with a scale (2) into a 2.4 m dia by 2.4 m high wood repulping tank with an agitator (3). Water is added to this tank to prepare an 80% solids slurry. The slurry then passes through a vibrating screen (4) which separates foreign material and flows by gravity to one of four 6 m dia by 4.8 m high concrete storage tanks containing agitators (5, 6). These agitators are the AFSA type to provide continuous mechanical and pneumatic agitation. The slurry from these tanks supplies both roasting circuits. The total storage capacity of these tanks is 1200 tons of concentrate on a dry basis. O.D.S. No. 3 pumps transfer the slurry from the tanks (7,8) or feed the reactor (9, 10).

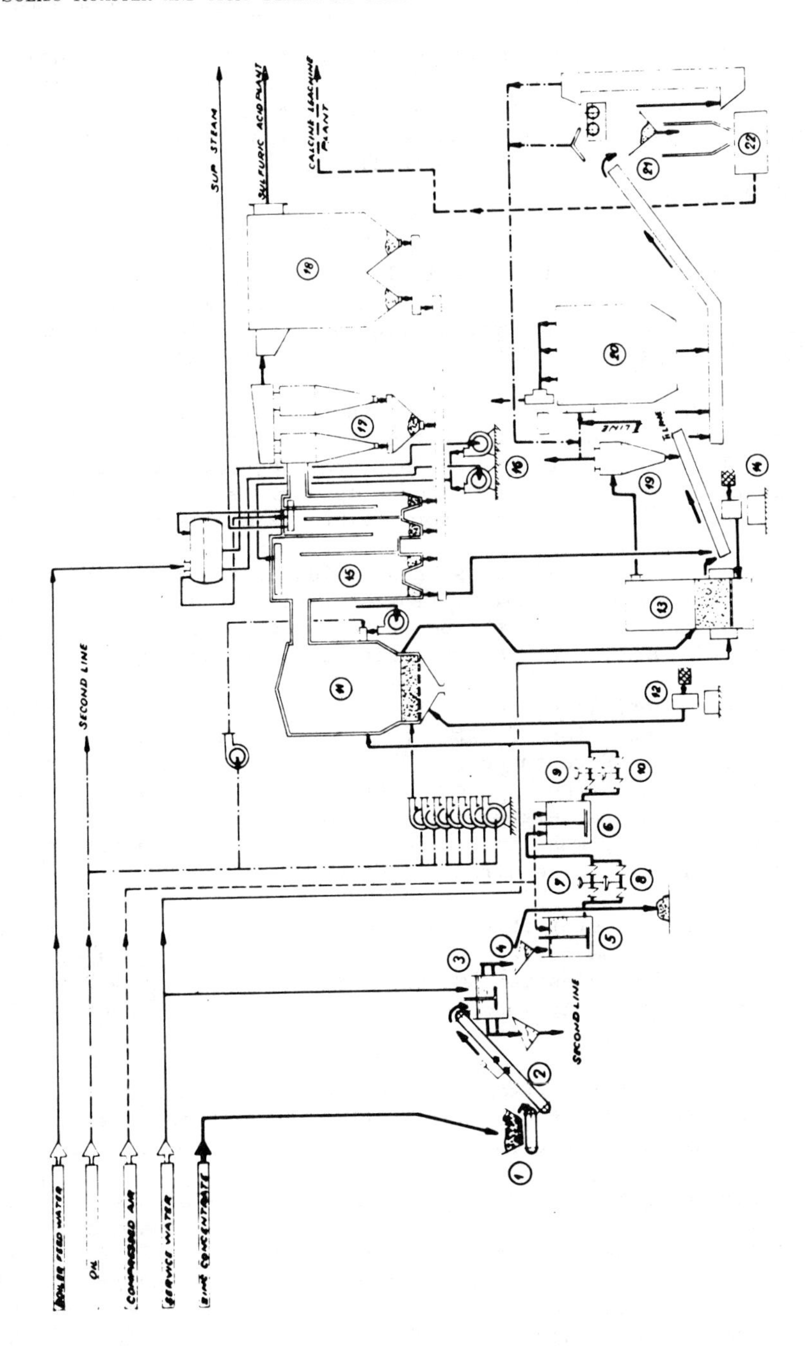

Fig. 1--Scheme of the roasting plant.

2. Roasting - The zinc concentrate is roasted in the fluo-solids reactor (11). This reactor consists of a reaction chamber and a wind box. These are separated by a distribution plate containing nozzles specially designed to ensure uniform air distribution in the fluidize bed and to prevent calcine from falling into the windbox during opera tion and shutdowns.

The reaction chamber is cylindrically shaped with a cone at the bo tom. It is constructed of steel plates with insulation and a refractory brick inner lining. The cone-shaped windbox is made of steel plate also. Fluidization air is provided by a HIBON blower with 20,000 m^3/h capacity at 3500 mm water pressure (12).

An oil burner is provided beside the reactor for drying and preheating the bed to 600°C at start-up. Eight oil injectors are insert directly into the bed to further heat the reactor from 600°C to the bed ignition temperature of 900°C. The slurried concentrate feed is introduced by a separate injector and atomized by compressed air.

The fluidized bed is a dense suspension of solids maintained in turbulent motion by the upward flow of gases. These gases effect the roasting action and cause the bed to act much like a liquid, with uniform particle size, chemical composition and temperature.

The excess heat liberated by the exothermic roasting reaction is absorbed by evaporation of water from the slurry and also by evaporation of water added to the bed. The desired roasting temperature of 900°C is thus maintained. When water is automatically added to the bed, there are no temperature variations either when the slurry composition changes or when the sulfur content of the concentrate varies. No additional heat is required for normal operation.

The reactor diameter at the nozzle level is 6.3 m and at the freeboard is 7.5 m. The reactor has an overall height of 9.5 m. The total number of nozzles is 780; the nozzle diameter is 4.7 mm. In operation the bed is 1.5 m deep; the reaction chamber pressure is 150 mm water gauge.

The velocity of the gases leaving the reactor effect a particle size separation. The fines are carried away with the gases, while the coarse material overflows the reactor at the top of the fluid bed.

3. Calcine Cooling - The coarse calcine moves across the bed, overflows from the reactor via a special fluoseal siphon device, and i cooled in the fluo-solids cooler (13). This cooler has forty-five 7.45 mm dia nozzles, is 1.2 m in dia and 3 m high, and is maintained at a temperature of 300°C. Air is blown into the cooler by a special HIBON blower with a capacity of 2000 m^3/h and a pressure of 2000 mm water gauge (14). A constant temperature in the cooler is maintained by automatic addition of cooling water.

The gases exit the cooler through a cyclone (19) where a major portion of the fines is separated. The gases are then filtered by a bag filter (20) which is common for both circuits before being released into the atmosphere. The bag filter also handles air from the crushing circuit and the calcine handling area. The main characteristics of this system follow:

Cyclone (19) is a gyraclone made by Tunzini, France:

capacity	2080 Nm^3/h
temperature	200°C
efficiency	95% for particles over 15 microns

Bag filter (20) is an Amerthem-type siliconized glass fibre cloth made by Tunzini, France:

capacity	6400 Nm^3/h
temperature	200°C
efficiency	97% for particles over 5 microns

The fan is made by Tunzini, France:

capacity	6400 Nm^3/h
temperature	200°C
differential pressure	435 mm water gauge at 200°C

4. Gas Cooling - The fluidizing gases leaving the upper part of the reactor entrain finer sized particles of the calcine and carry them to the LA MONT waste heat boiler (15) made by ALSTHOM, France. The gases are cooled from 950° to 350°C. The boiler operates with forced water circulation.

The waste heat boiler is constructed of steel, with interior insulation and refractory brick lining and external mineral fiber insulation.

The boiler is divided into four parts. The first part consists of an empty chamber with water-tube walls in which the hot gas and dust are cooled by radiation and by tube panels suspended from the top center of the boiler. Before entering the steam superheater, the temperature drops from 900°C to 600°C. The second and third parts have one superheater each. The fourth part consists of evaporators divided in two sections by a tube panel. Underneath each of these parts are discharge boxes for the calcine. The calcine enters these boxes through automatic flap valves and a chain shaking arrangement. The tube panels are transverse to the boiler; the gas flows parallel to the tubes. The tubes are shaken automatically by pneumatic hammers. The water is circulated through each boiler by two 77 t/h pumps (16) made by "BREGUET-KSB." One of these pumps is steam-driven and used as a reserve. A complete water treatment plant and pumps to feed the boiler through the steam tank are provided. Some operating data for the boilers follow:

capacity per boiler	4.45-4.7 t/h
outlet steam pressure	41 kg/cm^2
superheated steam temperature	450°C

5. Dust Collection System - The cooled gases leaving the boiler flow through two 1.4 m dia PRAT cyclones (17). The major part of the dust is collected here. The cyclone efficiency is 95% for particles over 10 microns.

The gas is finally purified in an electrostatic precipitator (18) made by VIM, Paris under license of SVENSKA. Each roasting circuit has one precipitator. The gas flows horizontally through two aligned chambers in each precipitator. These chambers contain two systems of both emissive and precipitator electrodes with their accompanying automatic shaking equipment. Two 60 kw, 200 mA selenium rectifying high-frequency transformers are on top of the precipitators. The gases flow through the precipitators at a rate of 0.465 m/sec at an inlet temperature of 300-350°C. Residence time in the precipitator is 15 sec. Precipitator efficiency is 98%.

Upon leaving the electrostatic precipitators, the gases mix and are conveyed by a common pipeline to the acid plant. A subsidiary gas pipeline has been erected for parallel process gas treatment to handle both lines of the pyrite acid plant at maximum discharge or in cases of breakdowns.

At the bottom of the cyclones and precipitators the calcine is discharged through rotary seal valves and flap valves.

6. Calcine Transport - The calcine from the electrostatic precipitators is collected by screw conveyors and conducted to the Buhler chain conveyor for indirect cooling with water. The calcine collected from the cyclones, the waste heat boiler and the fluo-solids roasters on each circuit also feeds to this chain conveyor. From the common chain conveyor the calcine is collected from both circuits and passed on to a vibrating screen (21) which operates in closed circuit with a hammer mill. The undersize from the 2 mm screen is conveyed for further treatment in the leach plant by two Fuller Kinyon pumps (22), one of which is a spare.

7. Control Panel - All control and regulation instrumentation required for proper operation of the process is arranged on the control panel located in the plant.

Plant Operating Data

Concentrate of the following composition is roasted:

Feed analysis:

Zn	49.0%	S	32.0%
Pb	0.85%	Ca	0.5%
Cu	0.35%	Mg	0.3%
Cd	0.24%	SiO_2..........	1%
Fe	13.0%	Al_2O_3.........	2%

Cumulative screen analysis:

+ 0.510 mm ...	1.1%	+ 0.100 mm ...	38.6%
+ 0.297 mm ...	4.7%	+ 0.074 mm ...	48.5%
+ 0.250 mm ...	15.4%	- 0.074 mm ...	51.5%
+ 0.149 mm ...	27.2%		

The plant has two roasting circuits, of the following capacity:

maximum 2 x 155 t/day dry concentrate
minimum 2 x 110 t/day dry concentrate

- Roasting temperature .... 900°C
- Excess air 30%
- SO_2 content from electrostatic precipitator.. abt. 10%
- Sulphur content in composite product (calcine):

  Sulphides 0.1%
  Sulphates 2.2%

- Sulphur efficiency of roasting and acid plant...abt. 91%
- Acid soluble zinc in calcine.................... 89%
- Calcine recovery from zinc concentrate.......... 84%
- Steam production 41.5 kg/cm^2 at 450°C........... 0.78 kg/kg dry concentrate
- Electric power consumption (with concentrate storage) .... 90 kWh/t dry concentrate

- Water consumption for slurry preparation and cooling.. 0.4 m^3/t dry concentrate

- Classification of calcine:
  - Overflow product 40%
  - Waste heat boiler.........15%
  - Cyclones...................40%
  - Electrostatic Precipitator....... 5%

- Plant operating time.................330 days/year

General Comments

Since the zinc concentrate is roasted to prepare it for treatment in the electrolytic zinc plant, the quality of the calcine with respect to solubility of zinc and controlled content of sulphate and sulphide sulphur, is of vital importance. This is particularly true because the concentrate is of marmatitic origin having a relatively high iron content. Satisfactory results are obtained due to proper construction of the reactor, accurate control of the roasting temperature by automatic water addition to the reactor and the calcine cooling system which yields an optimum content of sulphate sulphur for further treatment in the electrolytic plant.

Although an automatic shaking system for the boiler tubes is provided in the waste heat boiler via pneumatic hammers, these are very seldom used. Even during long, continuous operation there is no accumulation and sticking of dust to the boiler tubes. Accumulated dust could cause maintenance problems in the shaking system which would require additional air lancing or cause frequent breakdowns of the steam superheater.

This maintenance-free operation results from suitable construction of the waste heat boiler. The empty chamber and separation of dust in it avoids critical high temperatures of the gas and having calcine in direct contact with susceptible parts of the boiler tubing and thus promotes proper gas circulation along the boiler tubes.

There have been troubles, however, with dust stickiness in the connection between the reactor and the waste heat boiler (temperature 900°C). Since the whole system works under pressure, it is virtually impossible to clean it regularly. Therefore, these places are exposed to accumulations of deposits which later cause other troubles during discharge of the dust. Attachment of a fan in front of the electrostatic precipitator so that the whole system would work under pressure is being considered. Thus the whole unit would be more accessible for cleaning and during operation.

Since the number of mines supplying this plant with concentrate will be increased and eventual growth of the production capacity is anticipated, we are now scheduling construction of a bigger storage building with traveling crane transport.

Contact Sulphuric Acid Plant

Plant Description

In the Petersen System contact sulphuric acid plant, the SO_2 containing roaster gases are used to produce 98% sulphuric acid. The capacity of the acid plant is 230 t/d of monohydrate, but this capacity can be extended. The product sulphuric acid is purest quality, water-clear and sediment-free. The acid plant uses vanadium catalyst. The SO_2 is oxidized to SO_3 with the oxygen in the gas and is then converted to sulphuric acid by absorption of the SO_3 in 98.6% sulphuric acid. The catalytic conversion of SO_2 to SO_3 requires thorough cleaning and drying of the gas. The flow sheet of the plant is shown in Figure 2.

1. Cooling and Washing Section - After the SO_2-rich roaster gases are cleaned in the hot electrostatic precipitator, they enter the first washing tower (1). They enter the lower part of the tower at a temperature of 300-350°C and a concentration of 9-10% SO_2. Here they come into direct contact with weak sulphuric acid. The first washing tower is a lead tower with interior brick lining. The 5-10% sulphuric acid is sprayed in on top of the tower and falls down through the gas. The gases are cooled down to 75°C through evaporation of the water in the weak acid. The gases then leave the tower through the dome. The primary purpose of the first washing tower is to saturate the roaster gases with water vapor. Therefore, this tower is also called the humidifier. Besides the cooling effect, the separation of gas impurities will take place by spraying the acid into the gas. The impurities, which will be caught by the acid sprays, leave the tower with the circulating acid.

The dirty wash acid coming out of the first tower must be cooled and cleaned before it can be reused in the tower. To accomplish this, the acid from the first washing tower (1) is cleaned in three parallel settling tanks (18). The cleaned acid overflows these tanks and is led to the tube coolers (19) and flows from there to a circulating tank (20). From this tank the acid is circulated by a pump (21) to another tubular cooler (22) made of lead on top of the tower. The operation of the first washing tower is important to the efficiency of the gas cleaning section. The SO_2 gases must be well saturated with water vapor. Only in this way is it possible to get well-wetted dust particles. In the subsequent cooling operation, a supersaturated gas is obtained and by water condensation the small dust particles grow in size and can settle.

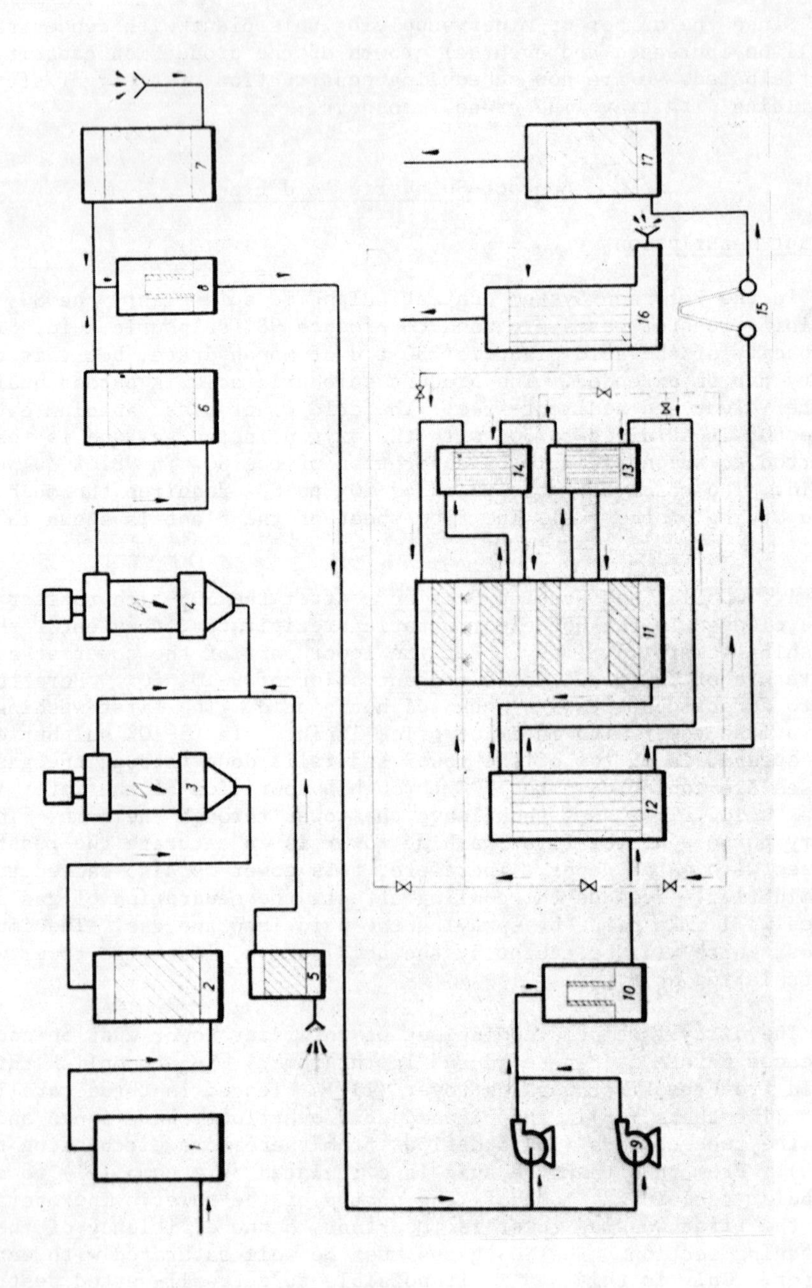

Fig. 2--Scheme of the acid plant.

The wetted and cooled gases leave the first washing tower through the dome and are conducted by a gas pipeline to the lower part of the second washing tower (2). This tower is also lined with lead and contains an interior brick lining. The tower itself is filled with a ceramic material which allows intimate contact of the gases with the circulating acid. Countercurrent to the rising gases, a weak, cool sulphuric acid is fed to the top of the tower and runs down over the surface of the ceramic filling material.

Contact poisons, which are still in the gas phase, are condensed and washed out of the gases by the circulating acid. Further on gaseous catalyst poisons are also washed out and absorbed by the circulating acid. By super-saturating the gas, water is condensed on the dust particles and increases their size. This water condensation is very important because it increases the size of the particles themselves and also has a wetting effect which encourages a better working and cleaning effect in the mist precipitator.

The weak sulphuric acid fed to the second washing tower leaves at the bottom and goes to the circulating tank (23). From here a pump (24) circulates the warmed acid to the acid cooler (25) and then back to the top of the tower. The acid leaves the tower at approximately 50°C. It is cooled to 40°C before returning to the tower.

The roaster gases contain a certain amount of sulphuric acid mist and SO_3 gas. All the sulphuric acid mist will be condensed in the washing operation. Thus the quantity of the recirculated acid increases slowly, so that some must be continuously removed from the circuit. The washing acid is pumped to the stripping tower (5), since the first washing tower acid contains quite a lot of SO_2. The stripping tower is also a lead tower with a special filling material which guarantees intimate contact of the acid with air. The air-SO_2 mixture is conducted into the main gas pipeline before the second stage of electrostatic wet purification. The degasified washing acid passes into a lead tank (26) from where it is taken by a pump (27) for further use. For optimum recovery of SO_2, proper regulation of the quantity of air is necessary. Proper regulation is accomplished by means of a butterfly valve in the degasifier suction pipe. The quantity of air permitted to pass through the degasifier is chosen so that the washing acid contains a minimum SO_2 content.

The electrical wet filtration removes all dust and mist particles from the gas. The particles are electrostatically charged and separated out on the precipitation electrodes. The impurities in the condensate pass through the drain socket in the bottom of the filter and to the pump tank of the first washing tower.

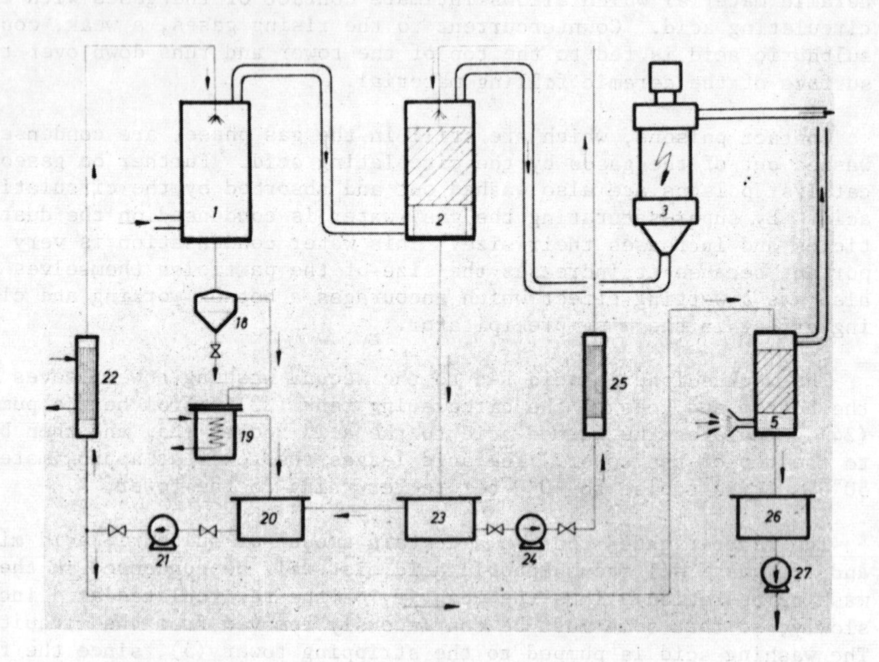

Fig. 3--Scheme of the washing plant.

Adequate removal of contact poisons such as arsenic and selenium from the gases requires that the gases be cooled in the second washing tower to a maximum temperature of 42°C to condense the gaseous impurities. At higher temperatures arsenic has a measurable vapor pressure and cannot be separated. Mist or dust can be removed by the electrical wet filter but gaseous ingredients cannot.

Thus the operation of the electrical wet filter is of prime importance for proper operation of the contact acid plant. Therefore, the separation must be observed through inspection glasses on the filters and in the pipeline between the second stage of electrostatic wet purification and the gas drying tower.

The wet filtration of the gases is accomplished in two steps by a pair of electrostatic filters (3) installed in series to the gas flow. Further on in both steps two filters are installed in parallel.

The filters are constructed of lead and supplied individually with 55-60,000 V direct current produced in four high tension selenium rectifiers. The advantage of using individual high tension units for each electro-filter is that each can be charged with its optimum voltage. The high tension transformer for each selenium rectifier is installed on top of the electro-filter. The regulating and switching devices for the low voltage are installed in separate switchboards near the control room.

2. Gas Drying Plant - The clean SO_2-rich gas is dried in a gas drying tower (6) with concentrated sulphuric acid. This tower is constructed of mild steel with an inner ceramic lining. It is filled with ceramic filler material. The gases enter the tower at the bottom and are dried by 96% sulphuric acid which flows down the tower through a cast iron plate with porcelain pipes.

The sulphuric acid is warmed by the absorption of water and must be cooled in cast iron coolers (28) before it can be pumped back to the tower. Figure 4 shows the acid circulation in the gas drying tower, the air drying tower, and the absorber.

Prior to catalysis, the 9 volume percent SO_2 gases must be diluted by secondary air. This air must be free of water vapor. To dry this air, a second tower identical to the above gas drying tower is provided. The gases and the air are dried until they contain 50 mg/m^3 water vapor. The drying is necessary to prevent condensation of sulphuric acid and subsequent corrosion of the equipment. The gas and air drying towers are fed by a common pump (29). The acid leaving the tower flows into a brick lined mild steel tank (30), from where it is recirculated to the towers. To get sufficient drying, certain operating conditions have to be observed. For instance, the gases must be optically clear and cooled to 40°C. If cooling is not sufficient, more water than necessary for forming sulphuric acid enters the plant. It would thus be impossible to regulate the concentration of the circulating acid

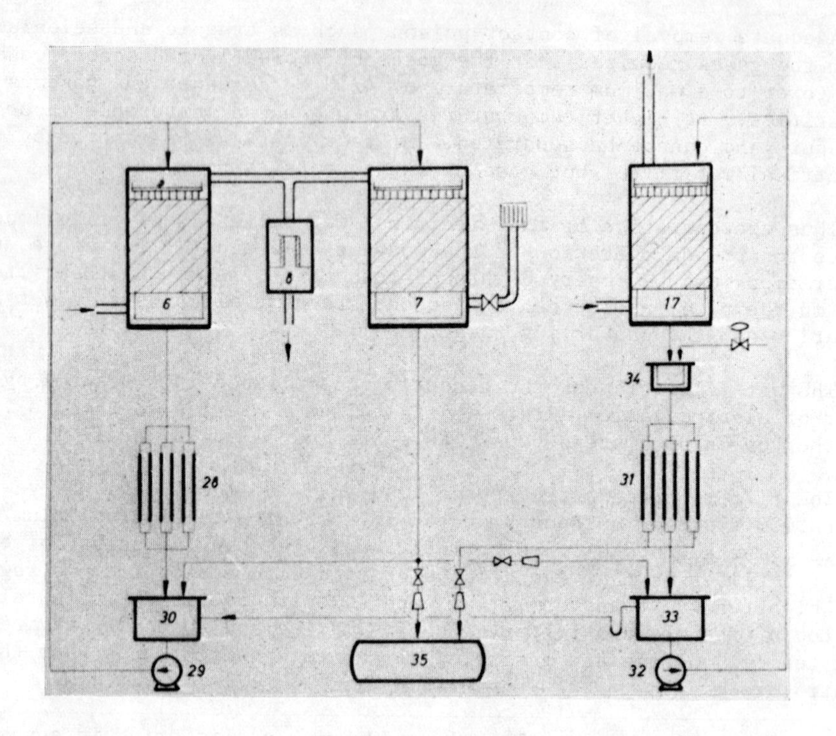

Fig. 4--Acid circulation of drying and absorption towers.

to the optimum value. Through continuous absorption of water the drying tower circulating acid is diluted and must, therefore, be strengthened by addition of strong 98.6% sulphuric acid from the absorber. A corresponding quantity of dilute acid flows back from the drying tower to the absorber.

After leaving the drying towers the gases and air are mixed and freed in a separator (8) from entrained acid droplets. From here the gases are pumped by the main gas blower (9) to the converter section. The second blower serves as a standby unit.

3. Converter System - The converter system consists of the converter (11) and three heat exchangers. The purified and dried gases first pass through a separator which contains a glass-wool filter (10) to prevent any dust particles or acid droplets from entering the converter system. Conversion of SO_2 to SO_3 takes place on a highly active vanadium catalyst distributed in four layers. The converter is constructed of boiler steel. The shell for the first two passes is brick lined to prevent burning of the steel. All other parts are aluminated. The catalyst is distributed on perforated cast iron plates, which have a layer of small ceramic filling rings to prevent drop-through of the catalyst.

Between the first and second catalyst layer, gas injection pipes for cold gas quenching are installed. The second and third as well as the third and fourth layers are separated by two gas-tight plates, which are protected and insulated with brick. The gases exiting the second and third catalyst layers leave the converter and are led to heat exchanger III (14) and II (13). Here they are cooled before entering the third and fourth catalyst layer. The heat contained in the gases leaving the last catalyst layer is transferred in the first heat exchanger (12) to fresh, cold SO_2 gas. This SO_2 gas is thus heated to approximately 280°C. Further heating takes place in the second and third heat exchangers by the partially converted gas which leaves the second and third converter pass. The heat exchangers, as well as the converter, are heat-insulated. The exothermic heat of the SO_2 oxidation reaction keeps the converter system at the necessary temperatures. The temperature for the first layer in practice is about 430°C. At this temperature the conversion of SO_2 to SO_3 begins on the catalyst surface.

To start the plant the converter and the heat exchangers must be heated to the initial temperature of the catalyst. This temperature is obtained through use of an oil-fired preheater (16). As soon as the catalytic reaction begins, this preheater is shut down.

The large heat capacity of the thoroughly insulated converter system allows shutdown periods of 36 hours and more without preheating the system. For a high conversion rate, however, certain temperatures of the catalyst must be maintained. It is absolutely necessary that the gases contain no catalyst poisons. These poisons will contaminate and eventually destroy the catalyst.

The oxidation of sulphur dioxide is a classic exothermic reaction It is reversible and heterogeneous, occurring on the catalyst. The thermodynamics of the reaction of SO_2 to SO_3 are shown in Figure 5. The theoretical conversion efficiency as a function of temperature is shown as the curved line on this figure. This theoretical conversion rate varies widely for various SO_2 and O_2 concentration and is also dependent on pressure. The dashed line on Figure 5 represents a gas mixture of 6.5% SO_2 and 12.0% O_2.

Entering the first converter pass the gases have a temperature of 430°C. With the conversion to SO_3 the gas temperature rises (line 1 on Figure 5). This temperature rise is typical for the adiabatic conversion of SO_2 in the first catalyst layer. The theoretical conversion rate will not, however, be attained. As soon as a temperature of 570-580°C and a conversion of 75% are reached, the conversion will be interrupted by quenching with cold SO_2 gases between the first and second catalyst layers. Thus the gas is cooled and due to the SO_2 concentration of the cooler gas, the conversion also goes down (line on Figure 5).

In the second catalyst layer the adiabatic catalytic reaction begi again (line 3). Before reaching the theoretical conversion equilibri the partially converted gases are again cooled in the third heat exchanger by fresh SO_2 gas (line 4), which is heated to the initial temperature of 430°C simultaneously.

In the third pass the catalytic reaction of SO_2 to SO_3 starts agai according to line 5. After cooling down in heat exchanger II the gas enter the fourth pass and conversion approaches 98%. The step curve shown in Figure 5 points out the necessity of cooling the gases befor the catalytic reaction can start again in the following pass. Withou any cooling the theoretical equilibrium will be attained rapidly, and the reaction will stop.

Temperature regulation is accomplished with heat exchanger gas by-passes and by cold gas quenching. The converter gases leave the syst at a temperature of 200 to 230°C and are conducted to the SO_3 absorption system. Further cooling in the SO_3 gas cooler (15) improves abs tion.

4. <u>Absorption Plant</u> - In the absorption plant sulphuric acid is formed from SO_3 and water. This process occurs in a tower similar to the drying tower. The SO_3 is absorbed in 98.6% sulphuric acid. This tower (17) is filled with a special filler material through which the descending absorption acid contacts the rising gases in the tower (see Figure 4).

The exothermic reaction between the absorbed SO_3 and the diluted water of the feed acid heats the acid. The acid must be cooled in the acid coolers (31) before it can be reused. The acid returns to the

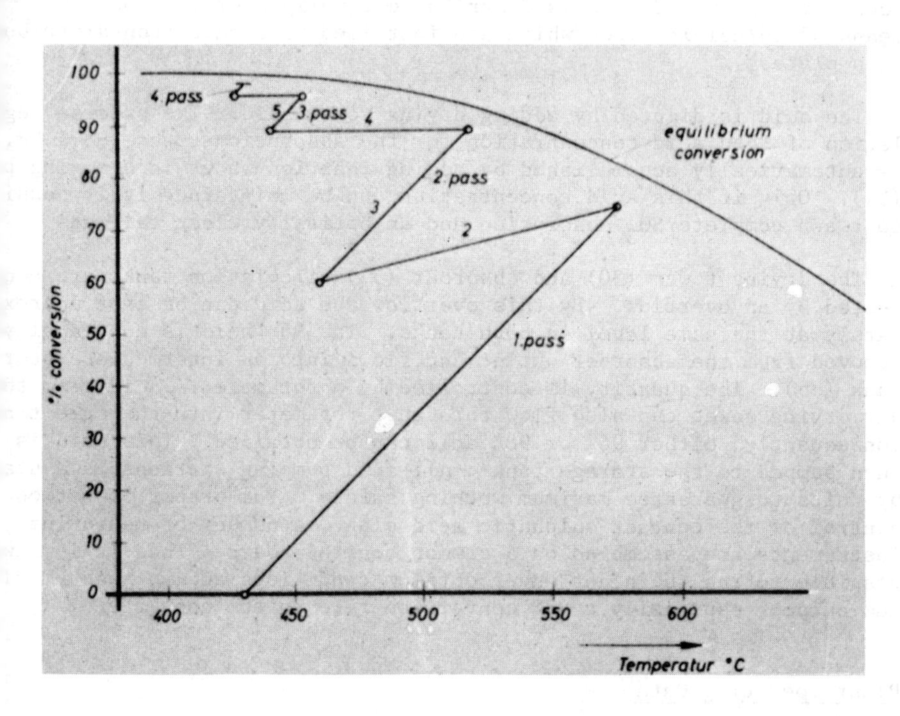

Fig. 5--Thermodynamics of the reaction of SO_2 to SO_3.

tower by a pump (32) and is distributed equally over the tower by means of porcelain pipes which are installed in a cast iron distribu tion plate.

The acid is diluted by adding drying tower acid. The precise reg lation of feed acid concentration for the absorption tower (98.5-98. is automatically accomplished by adding reaction water in a mixing p (34). Only if this acid concentration can be maintained is it possi to reach complete SO_3 absorption and an optically clear tail gas.

The drying tower (30) and absorber (33) circulation tanks are con nected by an overflow. By this overflow the acid can be kept approx mately at the same level in both tanks. The 98% acid is continually removed from the absorber outlet and flows into an intermediate stor tank (35). The quantity is controlled by a rotameter. Acid from th air drying tower can also flow through a rotameter into the same tan Consequently, either 96% or 98% acid can be obtained. This acid is then pumped to the storage tank. All acid pumping stations have sta by units to guarantee maximum working safety. For proper operation control of the contact sulphuric acid plant, a number of measuring instruments are assembled on a common control board. Thus it is alw possible to run the plant under optimum conditions and to reach maxi mum output, especially a 98% conversion rate in the converter.

Plant Operating Data

Plant capacity........................230 t/day H_2SO_4

Concentration.......................94-98% H_2SO_4

Acid Analysis:

Fe...........0.0015%
As...........0.0001%
SO_2..........0.001%

Conversion of SO_2 to SO_3.............98%

SO_3-Absorption in H_2SO_4..............99.9%

Consumption of electric energy.......37 kWh/t H_2SO_4

Consumption of cooling water.........45 m^3/t H_2SO_4

General Comment

The plant has been in operation from startup without any difficulties. Materials handling is easy; maintenance is very simple.

The scheduled production capacity of 230 t/day sulphuric acid can be exceeded especially during the winter period. At the maximum output of both fluo-solid roaster circuits (310 tons/day of zinc concentrate) approximately 270 t/day of sulphuric acid is produced. The excess SO_2 can be converted in the available capacities of the two nearby circuits of the pyrite contact sulphuric acid plant.

Acknowledgment

The author is grateful to Dorr-Oliver and H. Petersen for their cooperation in preparing this paper. Particular thanks are extended to H. Petersen for the detailed sulphuric acid plant data.

Chapter 5

FLUID BED ROASTING OF ZINC CONCENTRATE AND PRODUCTION OF SULPHURIC ACID AND PHOSPHATE FERTILIZER AT CANADIAN ELECTROLYTIC ZINC, LTD. Valleyfield, Quebec

K. H. Heino, Manager
R. T. McAndrew, Production Superintendent
N. E. Ghatas, Technical Superintendent

Canadian Electrolytic Zinc Limited

a n d

B. H. Morrison, Assistant Director of Metallurgical Operations
Noranda Mines Limited

Abstract

Two 200 T/da Lurgi Turbulent Layer fluid-bed roasters have been in operation at Canadian Electrolytic Zinc Limited since 1966. Zinc concentrate containing 52-54% Zn, 9-11% Fe,31-33% S is treated to produce calcine containing 60-62% Zn,10-12% Fe,.1-.3% S as sulphide and .8-1.2% S as sulphate. Each roaster train comprises a waste heat boiler, two cyclones in parallel and a two-field electrostatic precipitator. Distribution of calcine collected is 10-15 percent from bed overflow, 55-65 percent from boilers, 20-25 percent from cyclones and 2-6 percent from precipitators.

A Monsanto designed contact plant produces acid at a rated capacity of 365 T/da (100% H_2SO_4 basis) from roaster gases diluted to 7.0-7.5% SO_2. The process steps are gas cleaning and cooling by weak acid scrubbing, acid mist removal in electrostatic precipitators, gas drying in 93.5-96.5% H_2SO_4, conversion of sulphur dioxide to sulphur trioxide in a four-pass converter containing vanadium pentoxide catalyst, and absorption of the sulphur trioxide in 98.1-98.3% H_2SO_4. Product acid is 93.2% H_2SO_4. Conversion efficiency is 97-98 percent and overall sulphur recovery from concentrate is 87-90 percent.

The adjacent fertilizer plant has a capacity of 135 T/da of P_2O_5 The products are 54 percent phosphoric acid, run-of-pile triple super phosphate, and diammonium phosphate. The plant is of Ugine-Kuhlman design and consists of an air-cooled multiple tank reactor, a tilting pan filter, and a forced circultation vacuum evaporator. Triple supe phosphate is made on a continuous belt and partially cured in a rotar dryer. Diammonium phosphate is produced by ammoniating phosphoric acid in a single stage reactor. The slurry of ammonium phosphate is granulated in a blunger and dried.

INTRODUCTION

The original zinc reduction plant(1) built in 1963 with a design capacity of 180 T/da zinc did not have on-site roasting facilities. The entire roasting for this original plant was done by Allied Chemical Canada, Limited, located about five miles away.

In late 1966 the first North American installation of Lurgi turbulent layer roasters for treating zinc concentrate came on stream at the Valleyfield reduction plant of Canadian Electrolytic Zinc Limited (CEZ). The roasting plant was part of a general plant expansion which included construction of a Monsanto-designed sulphuric acid plant, a Ugine-Kuhlman designed phosphate fertilizer plant and expansion of the leaching and electrolysis division.

This new roaster installation of CEZ supplies 50-60% of the reduction plant's present capacity of 365 T/da of zinc metal with Allied Chemical roasting the balance.

CEZ is owned by five Canadian mining companies and managed on their behalf by Noranda Mines Limited. CEZ also has an interest in the adjacent fertilizer plant which is operated by St. Lawrence Fertilizers Ltd. (SLF). Valleyfield is 56 km south-east of Montreal on the St. Lawrence Seaway. This location provides convenient access to world markets, raw material and labour supply.

Flowsheet

The three unit processes of zinc concentrate fluid-bed roasting, sulphuric acid production and phosphate fertilizer production are depicted in Figure 1. Zinc concentrates are roasted to produce calcine suitable for recovery of zinc by leaching and electrowinning. Sulphuric acid is produced from the roaster gases. Three fertilizer products, phosphoric acid, triple superphosphate and diammonium phosphate are produced from sulphuric acid, phosphate rock and liquid ammonia. Excess sulphuric acid is shipped to other customers. Table I presents annual production figures since start-up.

ZINC CONCENTRATE ROASTING

Zinc concentrates are received in Valleyfield by rail from the Noranda Mines Limited Geco operation in northern Ontario and from both the Mattagami Lake Mines Limited and Orchan Mines Limited operations in north-western Quebec.

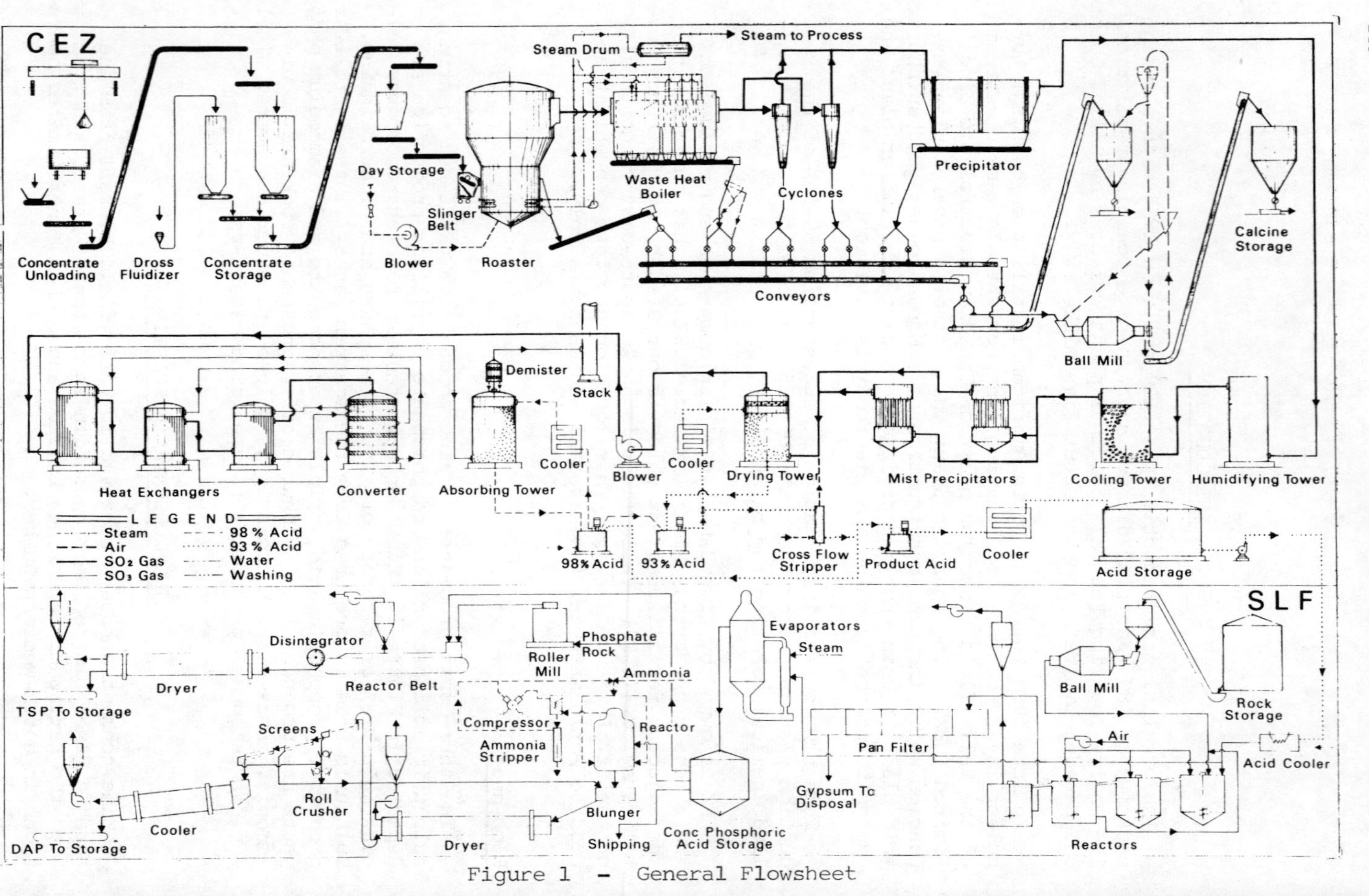

Figure 1 — General Flowsheet

Table I

Production Summary 1966-9

Material	1966	1967	1968	1969
Concentrate roasted - T	16,600	120,000	114,500	135,600
Calcine produced - T	14,200	105,300	99,200	116,900
Conversion concentrate to calcine - %	85.5	87.7	86.6	86.2
Sulphuric acid produced (100% basis) - T	14,700	110,000	102,200	120,000
Recovery sulphur in acid - %	87.9	90.2	88.3	87.7
54% Phosphoric acid produced - T	1,490	2,800	0	400
Triple super-phosphate produced T	2,060	24,600	21,500	25,600
Diammonium phosphate produced - T	210	19,700	30,600	23,000

CEZ treats mostly Geco and Mattagami concentrates, while Allied Chemical handles mostly Mattagami and Orchan concentrates. Table II summarizes tonnages and average analyses for concentrate receipts and calcine production during 1969.

Table II

1969 Receipt and Production Data

Receipts and Production	Tons	Analysis %					
		Zn	Cd	Cu	Fe	S/S	SO_4/S
CEZ receipts							
Geco	83,400	54.0	.36	.77	10.0	33.3	-
Mattagami	48,600	52.4	.12	.36	10.3	32.5	-
Orchan	2,200	52.4	.09	.40	10.2	32.7	-
Total CEZ	134,200	53.4	.27	.62	10.1	33.0	-
Allied receipts							
Geco	6,200	54.9	.36	.58	9.1	33.3	-
Mattagami	51,000	52.6	.11	.36	10.1	33.2	-
Orchan	67,200	52.1	.09	.38	10.8	33.5	-
Total Allied	124,400	52.5	.11	.38	10.4	33.4	-
CEZ production	116,800	61.4	.31	.74	11.6	.32	1.08
Allied production	106,300	59.4	.12	.45	11.8	.32	1.67
Total production	223,100	60.5	.22	.60	11.7	.32	1.36
Leach residue	70,000	21.4	.26	.97	37.1	.93	1.06

Note: Other constituents in concentrate receipts are typically: .7-1.5% SiO_2, .4-.6% MgO, .3-.4% CaO, .1-.2% Al_2O_3, .1-.3% Mn, .1-.2% Pb, .02-.03% Sb, .03-.04% As, .002-.003% Ni, .0003-.003% Co, .007-.01% F, .0005-.01% Cl, 1.2-2.0 oz/T Ag

The roaster plant operation includes concentrate unloading, storage and processing to produce zinc calcine and a gas suitable for sulphuric acid production. Concentrate is processed in two parallel roaster trains each comprising a feed bin, a Lurgi turbulent layer roaster, a forced circulation waste heat boiler, two dust cyclones and a Lurgi two-field electrostatic precipitator. The plant was originally rated for 400 T/da concentrate, but can handle up to 435 T/da of feed.

Concentrate Handling

Zinc concentrates are unloaded from 65 T flat-bottom railway cars by an overhead crane and subsequently either to a 610 mm conveyor delivering to four 250 T storage bins and then to two 80 T roaster feed-bins which are considered "live" storage, or to a 2,500 T concentrate storage bay in the unloading shed. The unloading operation requires two-man crews working two shifts per day, five days per week. The concentrate conveying system rated capacity is 180 T/hr and is operated from the central control room.

The concentrate moisture is typically 4-6 percent. In the winter months frozen concentrates are thawed in a 12-car storage shed for 12-48 hours prior to unloading. The thaw shed temperature is controlled at 55-60°C with steam heaters. Average steam consumption in mid-winter is equivalent to about 1,440,000 kcal/hr.

Zinc oxide dross containing 80-85% Zn and up to 1% Cl is returned to the roaster from the zinc melting operation at 9-14 T/da. This material is transported by truck to the concentrate storage area, blown into a 180 T storage bin and added to the concentrate being conveyed to the roaster feed bins.

Roasters

The Lurgi turbulent layer reactors are the heart of the roasting process. Figure 2 is a cross-section drawing showing roaster details. The bed grate area is 34 m^2 and contains 3,300 tuyeres of 6.35 mm i.d. mounted flush with the grate top.

Fluidization air for both roasters is furnished by three 187 kW Howden Parsons centrifugal blowers of which one is a standby spare. Usual air flow rates per roaster are 15,700-17,300 Nm^3/hr with up to 170 mm Hg discharge pressure and are automatically compensated for ambient temperature fluctuations. The air to concentrate weight ratio used at CEZ is about 1.43. However, there is an empirical absolute minimum of air volume required to maintain adequate bed fluidization and acceptable temperatures in the bed irrespective of the amount of feed. A small amount of bed material collects in the wind boxes and is removed twice per shift.

Roaster feed is drawn continuously from each feed bin on a variable speed feed belt which discharges to a weigh belt and then to a high speed "slinger" belt feeder. The belt feeder discharges to the bed centre through a side port about 1.7 m above the grate. Accurate feed control is maintained from the control room.

The bed and suspension temperatures are important factors in determining the calcine quality. In general, operating over 950°C will provide lower S/S with acceptable SO_4/S. The bed temperature is affected by the quality and quantity of the concentrates fed to the roaster and bed cooling.

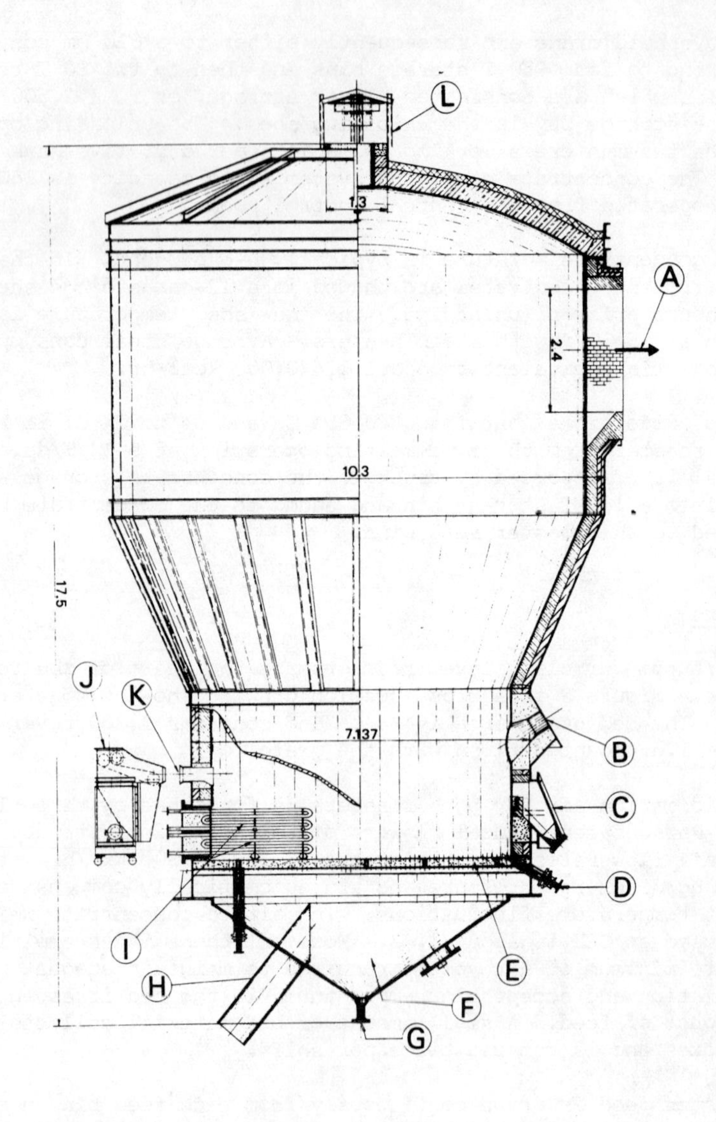

A - Gas Outlet
B - Oil Burner Nozzle
C - Bed Overflow Discharge
D - Underflow Discharge
E - Bed Grate
F - Wind Box
G - Wind Box Discharge
H - Air Inlet
I - Bed Coils
J - Slinger Belt
K - Charging Port
L - Safety Valve

0 0.5 1m
Scale

Figure 2 - Roaster Cross Section

The temperature of the suspension zone is maintained at about 970°C and in line with the bed temperature. This is achieved by spraying water over the concentrate on the feed belt. This is explained through the fact that the water acts as binding medium to the fine particles of the concentrates and tends to partially agglomerate them, thus confining them for a longer period in the bed, where the sulphur burns off rather than in the suspension zone. The amount of water required for suspension zone temperature control is also a function of the concentrate particle size. The limiting factor on the amounts of water sprayed or injected is predetermined by optimum operating temperatures.

While the amount of injection water to control the bed temperature may be adjusted according to the amount of concentrate fed, the cooling rate per bed coil is constant as it is tied in with the forced circulation system of the respective waste heat boiler and, thus, has a constant amount of water flowing through at all times because of the critical water velocities that have to be maintained in order to prevent coil failure. Depending on the forecast throughput of the roasters, the number of bed coils is determined as it involves major interruption to the operation to install or dismantle a bed coil. CEZ roasters operate normally with five cooling coils per roaster.

The equilibrium of the calcine discharging from the roasters is mainly determined by the rate of agglomeration in the bed. This agglomeration depends on the particle size, chemical analysis, moisture content of the feed and air flow through the bed.

When shutting down a roaster, air fluidization is continued for 15-20 minutes to completely oxidize residual sulphide after the feed is stopped and thereby ensure an unfritted bed for the next start-up. The roaster can be ignited directly with concentrate, if the bed temperature is above 700°C. Between 580 and 700°C the roaster should be started with elemental sulphur. Preheating with oil burners is required below 580°C.

The majority of the calcine is carried into the waste heat boilers with the roaster gases. Distribution of calcine collected is 10-15 percent from bed overflow, 55-65 percent from boilers, 20-25 percent from cyclones and 2-6 percent from precipitators. Although an underflow outlet was originally provided, the need for this has not been required and normal overflow control seems to be sufficient. The depth of the normal fluidized bed is about 1000 mm. The bed pressure differential is typically 935-1215 mm Hg.

Advantage was taken of a radioactive tracer test at the Orchan concentrator(2) to attempt to determine bed residence time and other relevant time factors in the roasters. Bed residence times were measured using about 60 T of radioactive zinc concentrate. At a concentrate feed rate of 10 T/hr the test results indicated an average residence time for the roaster bed overflow material of about five hours and an average bed residence time for the dust carry-over of about one hour(3). Complete renewal of the bed occurred in about 20 hours. Further tests are required to confirm these results.

Table III summarizes typical sulphur analyses and particle size data for roaster feed and the calcine fractions.

Table III

Roaster Products

	Analyses %		Screen size distribution %		
Material	S/S	SO4/S	+.15mm	+.075 mm	−.075 mm
Concentrate	32.5	–	11	37	63
Bed Overflow	.3	.2	28	78	22
W.H. boiler dust	.2	.8	3	23	77
Cyclone dust	.1	2.5	–	3	97
Precipitator dust	.1	5.5	1	2	98
Total calcine	.2	1.1	11	39	61

The calcine product should be low in sulphide sulphur to maximize metal leach extractions of zinc and cadmium and low in sulphate sulphur to minimize sulphate accumulation in the leaching and electrolyzing solutions. Incorporation of a water-cooled settling chamber as an inlet section of each waste heat boiler is a feature which contributes to producing calcine containing only .8-1.2% SO4/S.

Rapid separation of hot calcine from the roaster gases as quickly as possible is desirable, because the sulphate sulphur increases the further from the roaster the product is collected. CEZ was the first to use the water-cooled settling chamber concept which has gained wide acceptance in subsequent zinc concentrate roaster installation. Lower gas temperatures, finer particle size and longer contact times favour the sulphation reaction. Air infiltration anywhere in the roaster system is also a major contributing cause to sulphation. Provision to collect and recycle high sulphate precipitator dust through the roaster was made in the original plant but no significant decrease in overall sulphate was achieved and the practice was discontinued.

Attempts to control total sulphate in the plant system by the use of spent electrolyte for roaster temperature control were unsuccessful because this led to increased sulphate content in the calcine and a tendency for the bed to agglomorate excessively. Similarly, the use of weak acid from the acid plant humidifying tower for temperature control had to be discontinued because of excessive dust build-up in the boilers and gas cleaning systems.

Waste Heat Boilers

Each roaster has a separate waste heat recovery system rated at 13,500 kg/hr of steam production. The steam pressure is reduced from 39.1 atm to 8.8 atm for CEZ and SLF plant use. A waste heat boiler consists of a water-cooled settling chamber and four boiler tube bundles suspended in the gas stream after the settling chamber as shown in Figure 3. The settling chamber water cooled tubes are set in the refractory walls and roof. There are 120 tubes located on 45 mm centers.

Water at 250°C from the steam drum recirculates in parallel through each tube bundle, settling chamber cooling tube and roaster bed coil at 186,750 kg/hr. Make-up water is preheated in a de-aerator with process steam. Flow rates are fixed by orifice plates in each tube bundle. Well water is deionized in strong base type ion exchange units before being used for boiler feed water make-up.

A unique feature of forced circulation type boilers is that the steam drum is located externally from the boiler proper instead of being part of the total heating surface as in natural circulation boilers. Forced circulation boilers, although initially more expensive than natural circulation boilers, are more efficient because of better use of surface area and less water in the circuit, safer in case of tube leaks and can be integrated with bed coils for roaster temperature control. Gas temperatures decrease about 610-630°C through the boiler units. The steam to concentrate ratio averages 1.05-1.15.

Boilers must be kept clean of dust build-up to maintain maximum roasting rates and efficient waste heat recovery. Each tube bundle is equipped with a mechanized rapping device for removing loose dust particles. The rappers operate automatically on a sequential three-minute cycle. In addition, lancing of the boilers is done manually each shift with 6 atm air and requires 3-4 manhours per boiler.

In case of power failure, a diesel 210 kW generator automatically provides power for plant lighting and the waste heat boiler feedwater and circulating pumps.

Gas Cleaning System

Exhaust gases from each waste heat boiler divide between two parallel 8.2 m x 2.5 m diameter dust cyclones. Blockage of the cyclones was an initial problem which was corrected by removal of

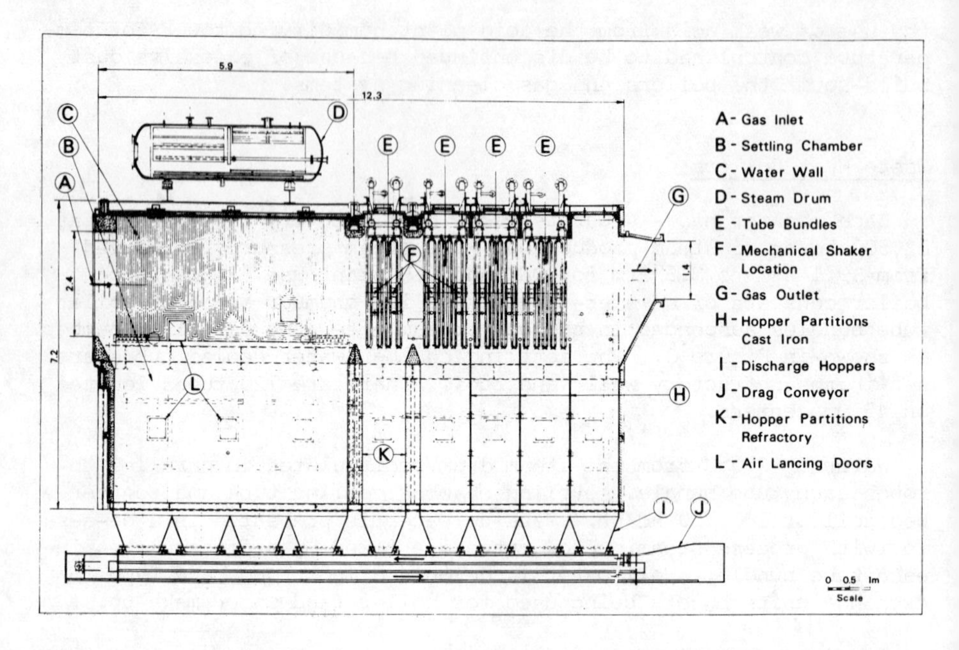

Figure 3 - Waste Heat Boiler Cross Section

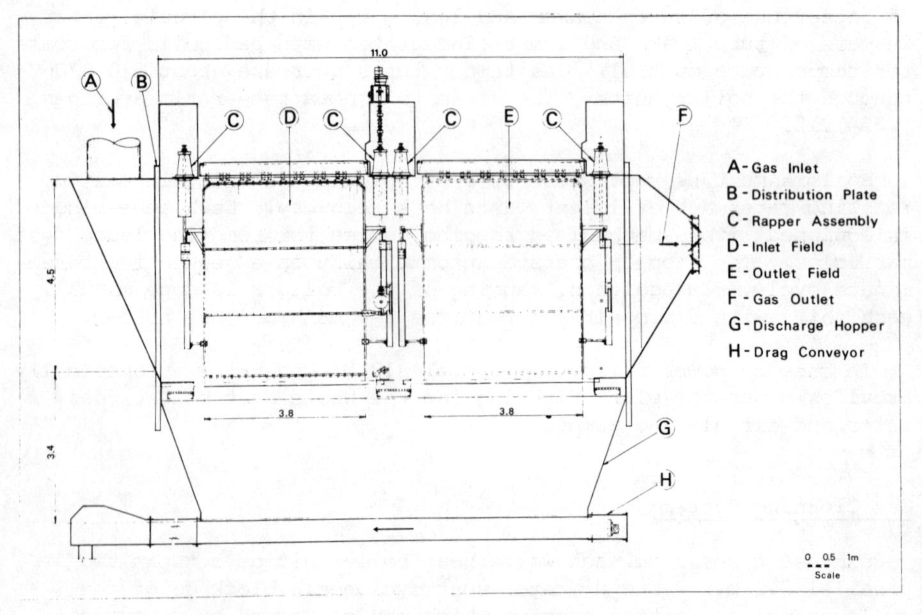

Figure 4 - Electrostatic Precipitator Cross Section

the vortex breakers. Some continuing problems in dust build-up in the ducts between cyclone outlets and cottrell inlets occur periodically and clean-out is required several times per year.

Gases from the two cyclones combine before entering a Lurgi two-field electrostatic precipitator shown in Figure 4. Each field section contains 16 frames of collecting plate electrodes and 15 frames of discharge wire electrodes. Each discharge frame supports 24 wires. The frames are vertically suspended alternately in the direction of gas flow. A perforated distribution plate at the inlet of each precipitator is installed in an effort to maintain uniform flow through the unit. Excessive dust build-up at the distribution plate has been a problem. Each set of frames has a separate automatic sequenced mechanical rapping system. Gases exit the precipitators at 320-340°C and contain about 500-1000 mg/Nm^3 of dust, although the units are designed for about 180 mg/Nm^3.

The most troublesome operating problem in the roaster plant is dust build-up in the electrostatic precipitators. Each precipitator must be cleaned every 8-12 weeks because nodular build-up on the discharge wire electrodes in the inlet sections causes short circuiting between wires and plates. During precipitator cleaning, gases from both roasters are directed through the second precipitator, but dust losses increase even at reduced roasting rates. The dust build-up on the wires is removed manually with fork-ended rods. Total cleaning time is 30-36 hours using six-man crews with only three men able to work in a precipitator at one time. Repeated cleanings have decreased the wire tension and thereby decreased the effectiveness of the rapping system. Air infiltration is a contributing cause of the build-up and scrupulous care must be taken to prevent leakage particularly around the precipitator inlet dampers.

Single phase 550 V power is fed to the precipitators through two Westinghouse ac-dc power units, each combining a 45 kVA step-up transformer with full-wave silicon diode rectifier rated for an average dc output of 700 mA at 45 kV. The inlet field sections of both precipitators are connected to one rectifier while both the outlet field sections are connected to the other rectifier. This is a definite disadvantage as each precipitator section should have separate power packs for maintaining maximum operation. Typical operating electrical outputs are 100 mA dc at 300-400 V ac and 10 A ac. Appropriate control circuits allow for either automatic or manual operation.

Since so much difficulty has been experienced with the dust build-up on the wires and the subsequent high dust losses it has been decided to make changes to the existing gas cleaning equipment. Separate power packs will be provided for each precipitator section so that maximum collecting efficiency can be maintained even though one section may be faulty. Design and materials of the rapping system are to be improved upon as these proved to be inadequate. The crossover duct, as shown in Figure 5, will be eliminated to prevent any air infiltration possibility. The cyclone efficiency will be increas from about 80-85 to 95 percent in order to reduce the dust loading to the precipitators. The entire discharge wires and frames will be replaced in the summer of 1970 because frequent cleaning has loosened t wires and thereby reduced the rapping effectiveness. Design does not permit individual replacement of wires. Minimizing the dust build-up the wires will decrease the required cleaning frequency and thereby maintain adequate wire tension for effective rapping.

If the above measures fail, it may become necessary to add more precipitator capacity with a third unit or more sections to the present units.

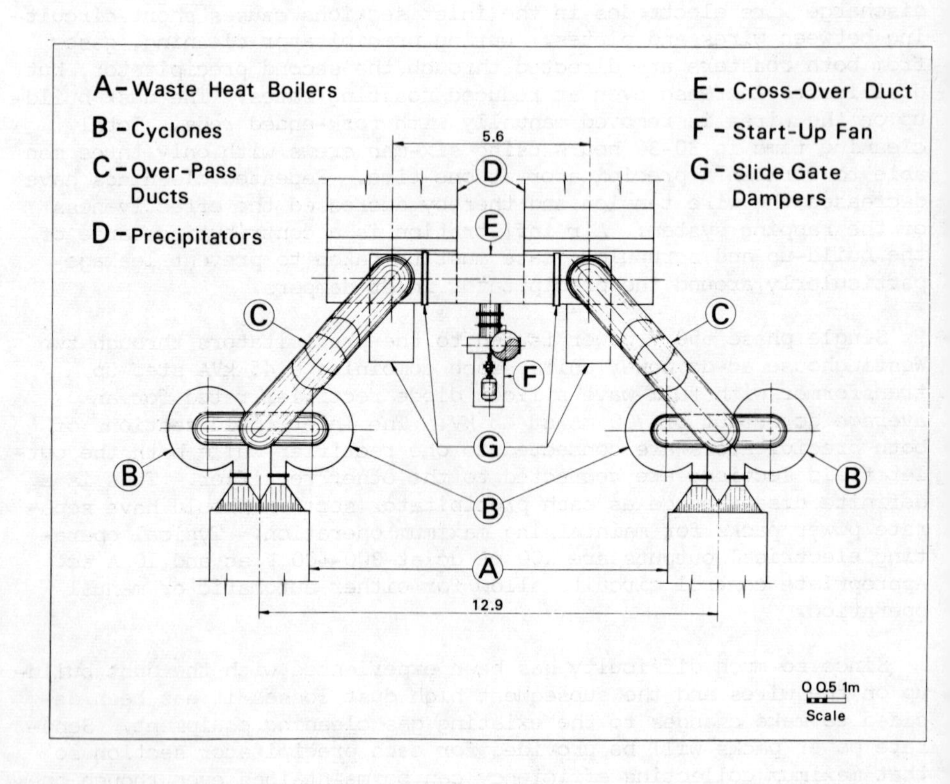

Figure 5 - Plan View of Roaster Gas Ducting Arrangement

Calcine Handling

Calcine collection and transfer in the roaster plant is by a series of 10 enclosed Buehler drag-type chain conveyors. Either of two main collecting conveyors transfers the various calcine products to a 1525 x 915 mm diameter ball mill. There are water cooling jackets on the bed overflow, boiler discharge and main collecting conveyors. Usual calcine temperature at the ball mill is about 200°C.

The ball mill discharge is conveyed to an 80 T surge bin before being pneumatically pumped 183 m to three of five 775 T storage silos at the leaching plant, using two Fuller-Kinyon dust pumps.

Excessive wear on the calcine pump screws has been a major maintenance problem. The ball mill was designed only to break relatively soft calcine agglomerations present mainly in the boiler calcine product and therefore does not have sufficient capacity to adequately grind the coarse bed over-flow material. To help alleviate pump wear and produce a finer calcine for leaching, the load on the existing ball mill will be reduced by installing an air classifier in closed circuit with the mill. Cyclone and precipitator dust will be collected in one of the main collecting conveyors and fed directly to the classifier with the ball mill discharge. Bed overflow material and the plus 1.5 mm fraction from the boiler discharge will go to the ball mill and all other products to the classifier. The system is scheduled for installation in 1970. A calcine product of 98 percent minus .15 mm and 90 percent minus .075 mm is expected.

General

An operator in a central control room monitors and regulates the complete roaster plant operation. Indicating, recording or control instruments are provided for temperature, pressures, flow rates, sulphur dioxide analysis, and precipitator electrical data. The acid plant operation is also monitored from the control room.

A superintendent, assisted by a general foreman, supervises both the roaster and acid plants as a single department. A foreman, two operators and two helpers comprise a normal shift crew. Concentrate unloading normally requires two men for ten shifts per week. Two department mechanics handle regular maintenance requirements. Major repairs and modifications require the Plant Engineering Department's assistance. Plant testing, instrumentation maintenance and laboratory services are provided by the Metallurgical Department.

Table IV summarizes the important roaster plant statistics for a typical operating month.

Table IV

Roaster Plant Operating Statistics - November 1969

	Unit	Quantity
Operating time	hr	1,421
	%	98.7
Concentrate receipts	T	13,248
Concentrate to roasters	T	13,596
Dross to roasters	T	303
Calcine production	T	11,969
Calcine S/S	%	.30
Calcine SO_4/S	%	.98
Moisture in concentrate receipts	%	4.1
Moisture in concentrate feed	%	5.1
Average water injection	m^3/hr	.9
Steam production	T	14,360
	T/hr	10.1
Steam to concentrate ratio	-	1.07
Average temperature:		
bed	°C	950
boiler inlet	°C	965
precipitator outlet	°C	330
ball mill outlet	°C	201
Average pressure:		
bed differential	mm Hg	166
roaster draft	mm Hg	.00
boiler differential	mm Hg	.34
cyclone differential	mm Hg	3.10
precipitator outlet draft	mm Hg	8.33
Power consumption	kWh	714,000
Operating labour	hr	3,676
Maintenance labour	hr	1,234

SULPHURIC ACID PRODUCTION

Sulphuric acid is produced from the roaster plant exhaust gases in a Monsanto-designed contact plant. The general principles and practice of producing sulphuric acid from sulphide concentrate roaster gases were presented by Monsanto at the 1967 AIME Annual Meeting(4). The CEZ operation is a typical example of the process. The original rated plant capacity was 365 T/da (100% H_2SO_4 basis) but the plant can produce at 10-15 percent overload.

Gas Purification

The roaster plant exit gas is typically 320-340°C and contains 10-11% SO_2, 5-6% O_2 and 9-11% H_2O. Gas flows from the two dust precipitators through a common duct to the humidifying tower where recirculated weak acid scrubs the gas to remove the dust particles, sulphur trioxide and other gaseous impurities. The temperature of the gases leaving the humidifying tower is 65-80°C. Weak acid is also pumped through Karbate tube and shell heat exchangers in parallel to a packed spray cooling tower where the gases from the humidifying tower are further cooled to 38-45°C.

Weak acid volume increases because of moisture condensation and is discarded regularly. Fresh water may also be added to the weak acid pump tank to control the acid and impurity concentrations. Typical weak acid analyses are 3-6% H_2SO_4, 2-8 g/dm^3 Cl, .3-.5 g/dm^3 F, and 15-40 g/dm^3 Zn. The weak acid discard is neutralized with limestone and pumped to the SLF gypsum residue pond. Figure 6 is the weak acid circulation flowsheet. The life of the antimonial lead spray nozzles in the humidifying tower is limited to 6-12 months by the abrasion of suspended solids in the weak acid. Carpenter 20 alloy test nozzles had shorter lifetimes because of excessive corrosion. The partially purified gases from the cooling tower pass through two parallel Koppers electrostatic precipitators to remove acid mist and remaining traces of dust and fume. Each precipitator chamber consists of a group of 122 vertical 254 mm i.d. lead tube collecting electrodes each concentric with an iron core lead wire discharge electrode. The mist laden gas enters at the bottom and the mist collects on the tubes and drains to a drip tank. The drip acid is pumped to the weak acid pump tank. Power for the precipitators is provided with two Westinghouse ac-dc power units each combining a 30 kVA step-up transformer with a full-wave silicon diode rectifier. Typical operating electrical outputs are 100 mA dc at 400-450 V ac and 30-35 A ac. The precipitators operate at over 99 percent efficiency and outlet mist loadings are less than 70 mg/Nm^3. Daily half hour washing periods remove dust and fume residue from the electrodes and the washings are diverted to a settling pond.

The gas is dried in a drying tower where moisture is removed to 40-50 mg/Nm^3 as the gas passes upwards through the tower countercurrent to the drying acid. Acid concentration is usually maintained at 95% H_2SO_4 but can vary between 93.5 and 96.5 percent. The acid temperature is maintained at a minimum of 35°C. The acid is circulated over the towers at 270 m^3/hr from a 60 m^3 pump tank.

Dilution air is added to the gas stream prior to the drying tower to adjust the sulphur dioxide concentration to an optimum 7.0-7.2 percent for subsequent oxidation. The Elliott blower is installed after the drying tower and has a rated capacity of 72,000 m^3/hr at 37.4 mm Hg inlet suction and 159 mm Hg outlet pressure. A 735 kW General Electric 2,300 V induction direct-connected motor drives the fan at 3,580 rpm.

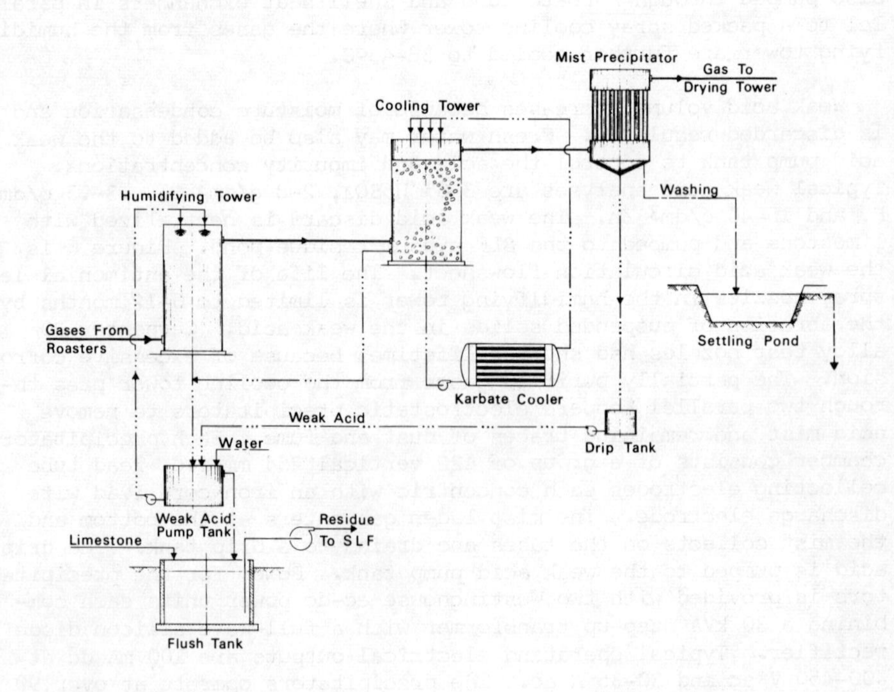

Figure 6 - Weak Acid Circulation

Conversion and Absorption

The clean dry gas from the drying tower passes to a four-stage converter containing vanadium pentoxide catalyst to accelerate the oxidation of sulphur dioxide to sulphur trioxide. The overall conversion efficiency averages 97.0-97.5 percent. The heat generated by the exothermic reaction in each stage or pass is used to preheat the sulphur dioxide gas passing to the converter through a series of three vertical tube and shell heat exchangers. The temperature rise is a measure of the conversion done in each converter stage. The relative amount of the overall reaction achieved in each successive pass is normally about 65, 25, 8 and 2 percent respectively.

Inlet gas temperatures to the first stage must be 415°C minimum to ensure initiation of the oxidation reaction. Outlet gas from the first pass is typically 580-600°C and is cooled in the "hot" heat exchanger to 440-450°C before entering the second converter stage. Temperatures over 600°C may damage the catalyst. Outlet gas from the second pass is typically 500-520°C and is cooled in the "intermediate" heat exchanger to 415-425°C before entering the third converter stage. Outlet gas from the third-pass is typically 435-450°C and is cooled in an atmospheric cooling duct to 415-420°C before entering the fourth stage. The temperature rise during the fourth pass rarely exceeds 5°C. Outlet gas from the fourth stage is cooled in the "cold" heat exchanger to 240-250°C before passing to the absorbing tower. The sulphur trioxide gases from the converter pass through the tube side of the three heat exchangers and are cooled on the shell side by sulphur dioxide gases from the drying tower. Each heat exchanger is provided with two by-pass ducts with control valves for controlling the converter bed temperatures.

A preheater is also provided to heat the converter catalyst to the 415°C minimum ignition temperature after an extended shutdown. The preheater consists of a brick oil-fired combustion chamber and a tube and shell heat exchanger. The hot combustion gases pass through the tubes which heat dry air from the acid plant main blower. Depending on the ambient temperature, shutdowns of less than 4-6 hours do not usually necessitate preheating.

Sulphur trioxide contained in the converter exit gases after cooling in the cold heat exchanger is absorbed by approximately 98 percent acid flowing counter-currently through the packed absorbing tower. The exhaust gases from the absorbing tower contain .15-.25% SO_2 and pass through a recently installed demister to the 64 m x 1.4 m i.d. mild steel stack.

A stack plume was a chronic problem prior to the demister installation mainly because of acid mist formation in the absorbing tower. The plume was minimized but not eliminated by controlling the absorbing acid at 98.2-98.3% H_2SO_4 and 85-90°C and by maximizing the acid circulation rate. These conditions produced an acid mist of 130-350 mg/Nm^3 with 10 percent minus 3 microns. The Plant Engineering Department designed and constructed a demister using York demister pads which reduced the acid mist to 30-50 mg/Nm^3 with 40 percent minus 3 microns and eliminated the plume. Figure 7 shows some of the demister details. Two .15 m x 2.4 m o.d. wire mesh demister pads of Carpenter 20 alloy are mounted in an acid resistant brick lined shell mounted on top of the absorbing tower. Care was taken to insulate all internal metallic components to avoid galvanic corrosion. A by-pass duct is provided so that any required maintenance can be carried out on the demister without incurring excessive down time.

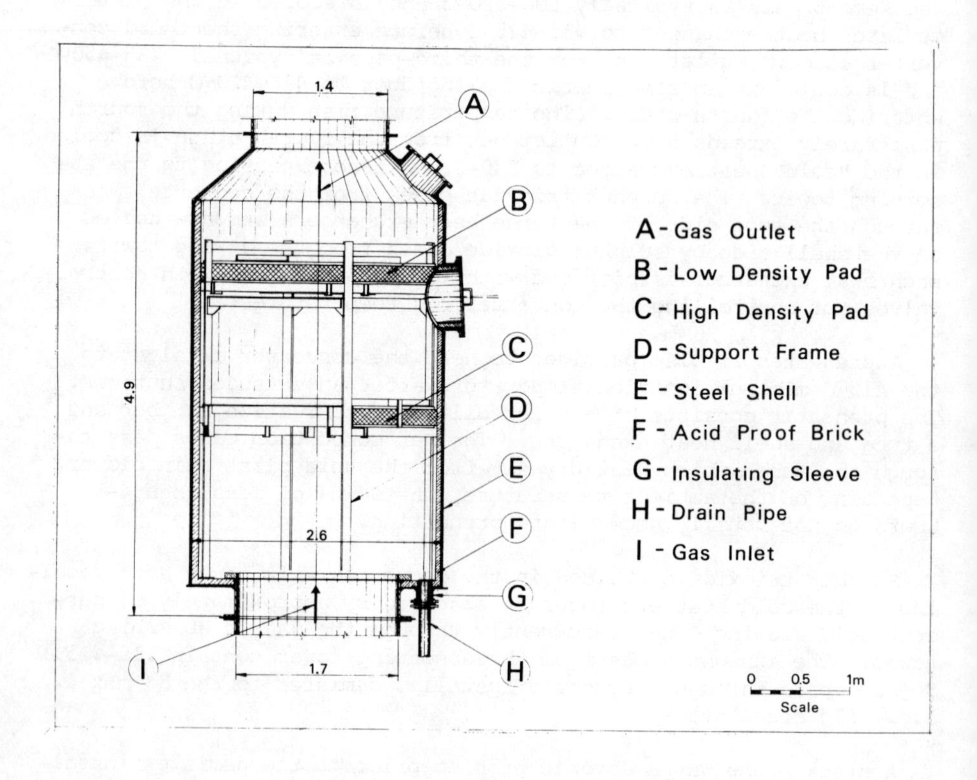

Figure 7 - Demister Cross Section

Acid Circulation and Storage

The concentration of absorbing acid is controlled by dilution with water and a cross-flow of 93 percent drying acid pumped from the drying acid pump tank. The concentration of drying acid is controlled by fortification with 98 percent absorbing acid pumped from the absorbing acid pump-tank. Drying acid is pumped continuously through a cross-flow stripping tower to the product acid pump-tank. Additional water may be added directly to the product acid pump-tank to maintain the product concentration at the desired 93.2 percent. Product acid is pumped to four 2,700 T storage tanks. All transfers from the three pump-tanks are continuous and automatically controlled at such flow rates as to maintain constant pre-set levels in the tanks. Product acid and recirculating acid to each of the absorbing and drying towers are pumped through separate cast iron pipe sections of a water-spray cooling tower for temperature control. Figure 8 is the concentrated acid flowsheet.

Dilution air required to control the sulphur dioxide concentration in the gas fed to the converter is added prior to the drying tower through the cross-flow stripping tower. Dissolved sulphur dioxide is thus removed from the product acid and the overall plant acid yield is increased. Product acid contains less than .008% SO_2.

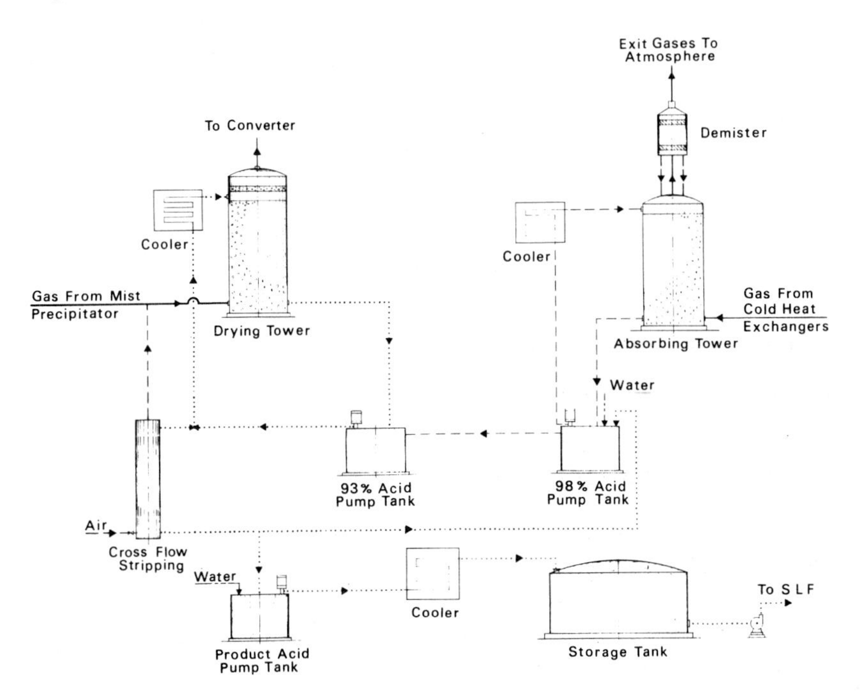

Figure 8 - Concentrated Acid Circulation

About 65 percent of the acid production is piped daily to SLF for fertilizer production. The remaining acid production is shipped to other customers by railcar or tank-truck. A 250 m line also allows direct loading of tanker vessels at the Port of Valleyfield.

General

Process tanks and towers are generally constructed of mild steel welded plate and lined with acid-resistant brick. A lead membrane is also used in the humidifying, cooling, drying and cross flow stripping towers, but not in the absorbing tower. All towers, except the humidifying tower, are packed with U.S. Stoneware Intalox saddles. The mild steel product storage tanks are not lined. In the weak acid section of the process fiberglass reinforced polyester (FRP) is used for the pump tank, gas duct work between the humidifying and drying towers, and for process piping over 50 mm diameter. Polyvinyl chloride (PVC) is used for smaller diameter piping. Impervious graphite (Karbate) is used for the weak acid heat exchangers and circulating pumps. The mist precipitators are fabricated of lead while the drain pumps are polypropylene. Concentrated acid circulates through cast iron piping. The hot gas heat exchangers and ducts are generally of mild steel but portions of the system have been metallized with a .25 mm coating of aluminum-silicon alloy. Fire brick lining is used in the first two converter passes and also for the preheater combustion chamber.

The vanadium catalyst beds become packed through prolonged use and must be periodically screened to prevent excessive pressure drop through the converter. Monthly pressure surveys are taken as a guide to the general condition of the plant and particularly for the converter passes. Such a survey is included in Table V. In this example, the pressure drop across the fourth pass is 2-3 times greater than for the other passes and a screening is therefore indicated at the next annual shutdown. The fourth pass has not been screened since the plant commenced operation. Experience indicates that screening is required annually for the first pass, every three years for the second and third passes and every four years for the fourth pass.

The acid plant operation is monitored with the roaster plant from the central control room by one operator from the combined four-man crew. A second operator makes control checks and adjustments in the field. He also handles water treatment for the waste heat boilers in the roaster plant. Instruments indicate and record temperatures, tank levels, acid concentrations, dilution water flow rates, sulphur dioxide concentrations, precipitator field strengths and cooling water pH. Pump tank transfers are automatically controlled to maintain pre-set tank levels.

Table V

Typical Gas Pressure and Temperature Survey - October 1969

(Production rate - 390 T/da, 100% H_2SO_4 basis)

	Pressure, mm Hg			Temperature °C		
	In	Out	Difference	In	Out	Difference
Humidifying tower	-12.0	-12.7	0.7	317	63	254
Cooling tower	-12.7	-19.1	6.4	63	39	24
Mist precipitators	-19.1	-21.5	2.4	39	38	1
Drying tower	-21.9	-26.4	4.5	-	-	-
Main blower	-27.1	115.0	142.1	-	-	-
Cold exchanger - shell side	115.0	114.6	0.4	-	-	-
Intermediate exchanger shell side	114.6	114.1	0.6	-	-	-
Hot exchanger - shell side	114.1	95.4	18.7	-	-	-
Converter first pass	95.4	85.1	10.3	443	590	147
Hot exchanger - tube side	85.1	75.7	9.3	-	-	-
Converter second pass	75.7	66.4	9.3	449	507	58
Intermediate exchanger tube side	66.4	59.8	4.7	-	-	-
Converter third pass	59.8	51.4	8.4	426	445	19
Converter fourth pass	39.3	15.9	23.4	423	427	4
Cold exchanger - tube side	15.9	7.5	8.4	-	239	-
Absorbing tower	6.5	3.4	3.2	221	-	-
Demister	3.4	0.4	3.0	-	-	-

Table VI summarizes the acid plant operating statistics for a typical month.

Table VI

Acid Plant Operating Statistics - November 1969

	Unit	Quantity
Operating time	hr	713
	%	99.1
Concentrate to roasters	T	13,596
Concentrate S	%	32.5
Acid production (100% H_2SO_4)	T	12,150
S conversion to H_2SO_4	%	87.8
Weak acid discarded (100% H_2SO_4)	T	14.7
Converter inlet SO_2	%	7.4
Exit gas SO_2	%	.2
SO_2 Conversion to SO_3	%	97.2
Power consumption - plant	kWh	132,000
Power consumption - blower	kWh	462,000
Operating labour	hr	1,080
Maintenance labour	hr	792

PHOSPHATE FERTILIZER PRODUCTION

When the roaster-acid plant installation at CEZ was being considered, one of the major concerns was the disposal of the by-product sulphuric acid. The local market could not absorb 126,000 tons of new acid and the value of sulphuric acid is such that it could not be shipped economically by rail more than about 800 km. Although low-cost water transport through the St. Lawrence Seaway is available for six months of the year, the construction of tanks for 60-70,000 tons of winter storage at the acid plant and at the plant of a potential buyer would be costly.

High-analysis phosphate fertilizers such as diammonium phosphate (18-46-6) and triple superphosphate (0-46-0) consume about 2.8 tons of sulphuric acid per ton of P_2O_5 converted to phosphoric acid. Thus substantial amounts of sulphuric acid can be consumed. However, the cost of the raw materials, phosphate rock and ammonia, represent in excess of 60 percent of the total manufacturing cost.

There appeared to exist a sufficient market for ammonium phosphate and phosphate fertilizer within an economic radius of Valleyfield to justify their production. However, the present sadly depressed prices for fertilizer products in North America make the venture much less attractive now than it seemed in 1965.

Although the plant is located adjacent to a dock on the Seaway, the delivery of rock by rail rather than vessel is less costly under current conditions as it avoids the large capital expenditure required to store 60,000 T of rock during the winter when the Seaway is closed and the financing costs of a large rock inventory.

Raw Materials

Phosphate Rock: At present, the plant is using calcined North Carolina rock as a source of phosphate. The specifications for this material are shown in Table VII. The bulk density is 1600-1760 kg/m^3. This rock differs from Florida rock in that it contains free lime and little organic matter as a result of its calcination; consequently, substantially more heat is evolved when the rock is attacked with sulphuric acid but no foam is produced in the reactors. The iron and alumina content is lower than most North American rocks of the same grade and this, with the absence of organic matter, allows the production of a good quality of 54% P_2O_5 acid.

In common with most calcined rock a small amount of hydrogen sulphide is evolved when it is reacted with sulphuric acid. This H_2S has not been a nuisance in the plant area but it is believed to have accelerated the corrosion of stainless steel equipment in the phosphoric acid production section.

Table VII (a)

Calcined Phosphate Rock Typical Screen Size Distribution

Microns	Percent
+1410	0.0
+ 420	4.0
+ 210	38.5
+ 142	67.8
+ 74	96.0
- 74	4.0

Table VII (b)

Calcined Phosphate Rock Typical Chemical Analysis

Component	Percent Dry Basis
Bone Phosphate of Lime (BPL)	72.3
Phosphate (P_2O_5)	33.16
Acid Insoluble	2.1
Calcium (CaO)	53.2
Iron (Fe_2O_3)	.8
Aluminum (Al_2O_3)	.4
Total Carbon as C	.6
Carbonate Carbon as C	.5
Organic Carbon as C	.1
Fluoride (F)	3.9
Magnesium (MgO)	.6
Chloride (Cl)	.02
Potassium (K_2O)	.1
Sodium (Na_2O)	1.0
Total Sulphur (S)	1.1
Sulphate Sulphur (S)	.7
Acid Evolved Sulphur (S)	.14
Hydrogen Sulfide (S)	.08
Bulk Moisture as shipped (H_2O)	.1

The rock is received in 10-car lots of covered hopper cars weighing 90 T each and unloaded by gravity through a track hopper and belt conveyor system to a 12,500 T capacity silo.

Ammonia: Ammonia is received as anhydrous liquid in 72 T cars and a small vapour compressor is used to transfer the liquid by displacement to a 200 T pressurized storage sphere.

Sulphuric Acid: Sulphuric acid is delivered by pipeline as 93 percent product from the sulphuric acid plant about 300 m away. Two, 330 T tanks are available at the fertilizer plant for the storage of acid.

Phosphoric Acid Production

The manufacture of phosphoric acid as shown in Figure 9 involves the digestion of ground phosphate rock with sulphuric acid. The principal reaction is represented by the following equation:

$$Ca_3(PO_4)_2+3H_2SO_4+2H_2O = 3CaSO_4.2H_2O+2H_3PO_4$$

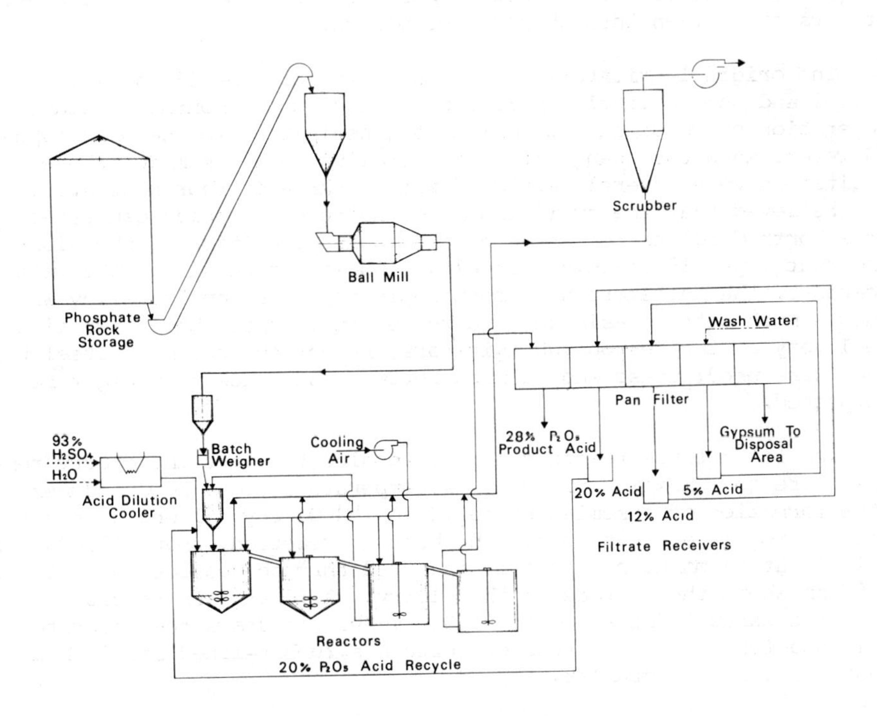

Figure 9 - Phosphoric Acid Production

Rock Grinding: To obtain maximum extraction of P_2O_5 and better control of the reaction, the rock is ground to a fineness of about 70 percent minus 74 microns by an air-swept, 3.05 m diameter by 2.14 m cylindrical length Hardinge ball mill driven by a 373 kW motor. The air is circulated through the mill and classifier by a 112 kW fan. Ground rock is elevated to a small storage bin ahead of the attack section by a bucket elevator.

Attack Section: The rock digestion equipment at SLF is a multiple tank system. That is, there are four tanks in series which hold the slurry in the digestion circuit about six hours, each tank has a capacity of 71 m^3. The first two reactors are equipped with dual 45° pitched turbines 1.66 m in diameter rotating at 68 rpm. The No. 3 reactor has a single 45° pitched turbine of the same diameter rotating at the same speed. In the No. 4 reactor which also serves as a slurry holding tank ahead of the filter, the reaction goes to completion allowing the dihydrate gypsum crystals ($CaSO_4 \cdot 2H_2O$) to stabilize. This tank is agitated by a large paddle mixer 4.3 m in diameter turning at 25 rpm. The agitators in the first three reactors are driven by 55 kW motors and absorb about 95 percent of the full load power. The agitator in the fourth reactor is driven by a 45 kW motor and absorbs only 55 percent of full load power. All the agitators are driven through fluid couplings.

The original agitators were constructed of Type 316 stainless steel and showed little corrosion after about 18 months of plant operation on Moroccan rock which was the initial source of phosphate. However, when the change to North Carolina rock was made, these agitators were severely attacked within three or four months. It is believed that the small amount of hydrogen sulphide generated by the North Carolina rock created a reducing condition in the slurry so that Type 316 stainless steel was no longer passive. The wetted parts of the agitators have been replaced by Jessop 700 alloy which has a much better resistance in these conditions. While awaiting delivery of the Jessop 700 agitators, rubber covered mild steel blades were used; these showed much better resistance than might be expected.

The first three reactors are air-cooled to limit the slurry temperature to a maximum of 79°C. A temperature above 80°C induces the formation of a semi-hydrate ($CaSO_4 \cdot \frac{1}{2}H_2O$) crystal which is difficult to filter. To remove the heat of reaction, about 15,000 m^3/hr of air at 56 mm Hg pressure is injected through nozzles located about 457 mm above the surface of the slurry. A fiberglass reinforced plastic exhaust fan rated at 27,000 m^3/hr withdraws the saturated air and fumes from the reactor through a rubber-lined steel, Model 535 Aeromix gas scrubber.

Ground phosphate rock and about 90 m^3/hr of slurry from the No. 3 reactor are premixed in a slurry mix pot, then flow to the No. 1

reactor. Sulphuric acid is diluted from 93 to 74 percent strength and cooled to 70°C in a Karbate falling film cooler. The acid is then mixed with 25 m^3/hr of 20 percent phosphoric acid recycled from the filter section and flows into No. 1 reactor.

To ensure maximum P_2O_5 recovery, the phosphate rock to sulphuric acid feed ratio must be closely controlled. An excess of free sulphuric acid causes an impervious layer of calcium sulphate to be formed on the surface of the phosphate rock particles, stopping the reaction. This effect becomes evident when the sulphuric acid concentration in the slurry exceeds 3.5 percent and unless it is corrected quickly, reaction ceases. Conversely, if the sulphuric acid content of the reaction slurry falls below 1 percent the formation of insoluble dicalcium phosphate in association with gypsum is promoted. Dicalcium phosphate ($CaHPO_4 \cdot 2H_2O$) is similar in crystal structure to dihydrate gypsum ($CaSO_4 \cdot 2H_2O$) and it is believed that groups of phosphoric acid ions replace some of the sulphate ions in the gypsum crystal lattice.

The slurry from No. 4 reactor containing about 28% P_2O_5 phosphoric acid and 40 percent gypsum solids is filtered on a Model 18 Bird-Prayon tilting pan filter having 38.7 m^2 of filtration area. After the separation of the 28% P_2O_5 product acid, the gypsum cake is given two washes with progressively weaker phosphoric acid and a final wash with hot water. The strongest wash filtrate, containing about 20% P_2O_5 is recycled to the digestion system. The 28 percent product acid is pumped to two storage tanks having a capacity of 284 m^3. The gypsum cake dumped from the filter is slurried with water and pumped to a 240,000 m^2 disposal pond.

Evaporation: To provide phosphoric acid of the appropriate strength for the production of phosphate fertilizers the plant has two forced circulation vacuum evaporators. The units can be operated in series or parallel to concentrate 135 T/da to P_2O_5 in 28 percent acid to 54 percent acid. Normally the units make 45% P_2O_5 acid for triple superphosphate and 39% P_2O_5 for the manufacture of diammonium phosphate.

The heat for evaporation is supplied by circulating the acid through a vertical heat exchanger heated by 0.7 atm steam on the shell side and containing 178 impervious graphite (Karbate) tubes, 5 m long. Evaporate is withdrawn and condensed by 100 m^3/hr of cold water and the non-condensable gas is removed by a two-stage ejector. The evaporator operates at a pressure of 100 mm Hg absolute with a solution temperature of 65°C. Concentrated acid is pumped to four rubber-lined steel storage tanks each capable of storing 170 m^3 of acid.

Triple Superphosphate Production

Triple superphosphate is made by the reaction of phosphoric acid and finely ground phosphate rock to yield water-soluble monocalcium phosphate. The principal reaction is represented by the equation:

$$Ca_3(PO_4)_2+4H_3PO_4+5H_2O = 3CaH_4(PO_4)_2.H_2O$$

Figure 10 is the flowsheet of the Kuhlman process employed at SLF. The same grade of rock as is used to make phosphoric acid is ground to 85-90 percent minus 74 micron in a 1.38 m diameter Raymond roller mill equipped with a Whizzer separator. The ground rock is delivered by a weighing feeder to a small, agitated mix pot where it is thoroughly mixed with a metered stream of 45% P_2O_5 phosphoric acid. The slurry then flows onto a rubber conveyor belt 1.2 m wide and 42.5 m long where it rapidly solidifies. At the end of the belt a rotating drum disintegrator breaks up the reaction mass before it passes to a rotary kiln dryer. The production belt is ventilated by a fiberglass reinforced plastic fan moving 10,000 m^3/hr through a Model 362 Aeromix scrubber.

The product is forced cured and dried in a co-current dryer 2.15 m in diameter by 24 m long equipped with a furnace burning No. 6 oil to give a heat release of about 1 x 10^6 kcal/hr. The dryer has the capacity to dry about 9 T/hr of product from 17 to 8 percent moisture. The dried product is transported 65 m to the storage building on a series of conveyors. Dryer gases are first cleaned in a cyclone separator then blown through a rubber-lined steel Model 400 Aeromix scrubber by a stainless steel fan having a capacity of 13,500 m^3/hr against a pressure drop of 15 mm Hg.

When the product is discharged from the dryer, the reaction to produce soluble monocalcium phosphate is 85-95 percent complete and proceeds to completion over a curing period of about 14 days in the storage building.

Diammonium Phosphate Production

Fertilizer grade "diammonium" phosphate (18-46-0) is a mixture of the compounds diammonium phosphate, mono ammonium phosphate plus impurities precipitated from the wet process phosphoric acid. The principal reaction is represented by the following equation:

$$H_3PO_4+2NH_3 = (NH_4)_2HPO_4$$

The vapour pressure of ammonia over a saturated, boiling solution of diammonium phosphate is such that ammonia vapour losses would be excessive unless special precautions are taken to recover this ammonia. Most plants in North America producing this product avoid the difficulty by partially ammoniating the phosphoric acid in a pre-neutralizer and running the slurry onto a dried bed of recycled product in a granulation drum or blunger and finish the ammoniation at this point. The excess ammonia is captured in a scrubber by a circulating solution of phosphoric acid.

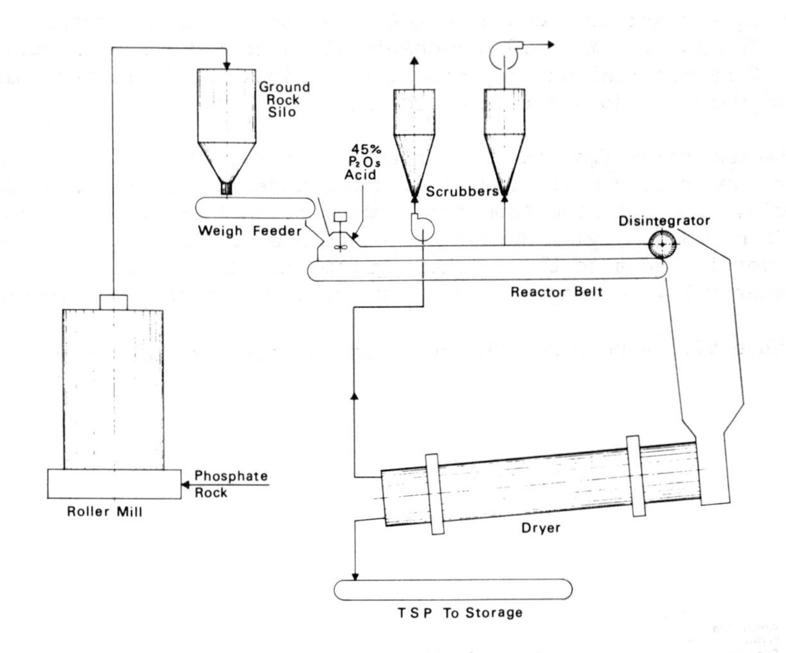

Figure 10 - Triple Superphosphate Production

The Kuhlman process used at SLF is shown in Figure 11. It is unique in that the phosphoric acid is ammoniated to diammonium phosphate in a single stage reactor. The problem of excess ammonia is overcome by passing the off-gas from the reactor through a heat-exchanger where the greater part of the steam is condensed and flows as condensate to a stripping tower and the ammonia recovered by steam stripping. The ammonia passing through the condenser is re-compressed by a small rotary compressor, combined with the ammonia from the stripper and re-injected into the reactor. New ammonia for the process is received as liquid from the storage sphere, converted to vapour in a small steel heat exchanger, combined with the recycle stream and injected into the reactor through eight spargers at a pressure of .5 atm. Phosphoric acid containing about 38% P_2O_5 flows into the reactor via a small tail gas absorber through which the inert gases are purged from the reactor.

The slurry of diammonium phosphate is bled from the reactor through a variable orifice directly to a twin-shaft blunger driven by a 55 kW motor. In the blunger the slurry coats a recycle steam of 80-90 T/hr of dried, granulated product.

The wet pellets drop directly into a co-current dryer 2.75 m in diameter by 24.5 m long heated by a furnace burning No. 6 oil to give a heat release of about 2 x 10^6 kcal/hr. The dried product is elevated by a continuous chain bucket elevator to three screens in series. The first 1 m x 2.5 m mechanically vibrated screen removes the plus 12 mm material and rejects it to a single roll crusher followed by two parallel double roll crushers.

The undersize from the lump screen is screened on a 1.25 m x 4.6 m Tyler Hummer screen at 1.00 mm with the undersize going directly to recycle. The oversize from the second screen is finally screened on a 1.25 m x 3.0 m Tyler Hummer screen with a 3.36 mm deck from which the oversize goes to the crusher system and the undersize to a 2.45 m diameter x 15.5 m long air cooled product cooler and then to storage.

Table VIII summarizes SLF operating statistics for a typical month

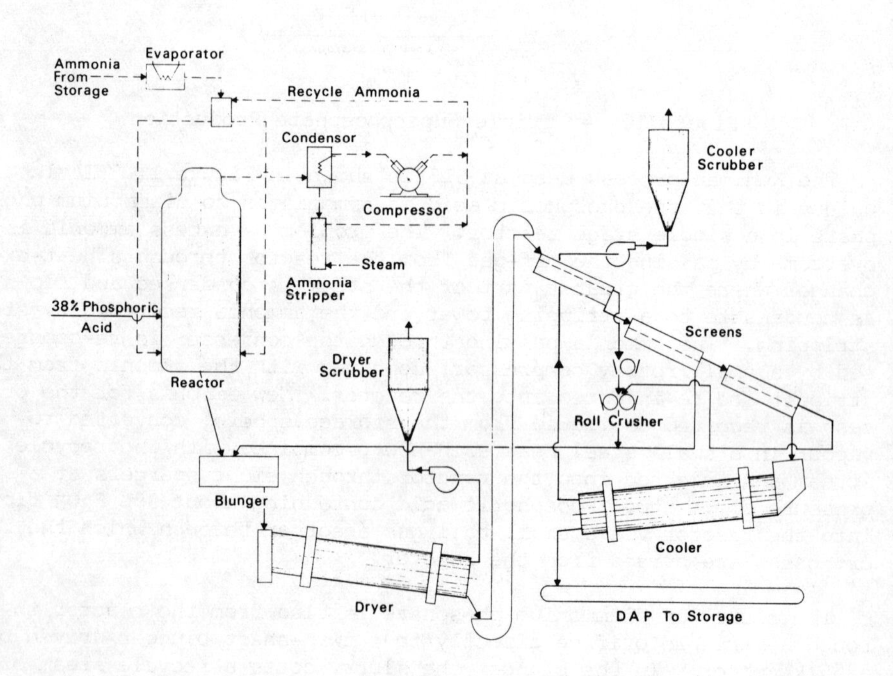

Figure 11 - Diammonium Phosphate Production

Table VIII

SLF Operating Statistics - February 1970

Phosphoric Acid Plant	Unit	Quantity
Operating Time	%	84
30% P_2O_5 Acid Production (P_2O_5)	T	2,760
Concentrated Acid Production (P_2O_5)	T	2,740
Overall gypsum efficiency	%	92.7
Total P_2O_5 losses in gypsum	T	224
Overall recovery acid plant	%	92.2
Phosphate rock consumed	T	9,020
Sulphuric acid (100%) consumed	T	7,630
Triple Superphosphate Plant		
Operating Time	%	70
TSP production	T	3,630
Insoluble P_2O_5	%	1.2
Available P_2O_5	%	46.1
Phosphate rock consumption	T	1,627
Phosphoric acid (P_2O_5) consumption	T	1,208
Fuel oil consumption	m^3	66.4
Diammonium Phosphate Plant		
Operating Time	%	80
DAP production	T	2,795
Chemical analysis : H_2O	%	.93
N	%	18.1
P_2O_5	%	47.3
Product size -3.36 mm	%	98.9
+1.41 mm	%	96.8
Ammonia consumption	T	654
Phosphoric acid (P_2O_5) consumption	T	1,470
Fuel oil consumption	m^3	57.8
General		
Total power consumption	kWh	865,000
Total steam consumption	T	6,630
Total operating labour	hr	6,364
Total maintenance labour	hr	2,700

REFERENCES

(1) Jephson, A.C., A.Y. Bethune and R.C. Kelahan, "Zinc Recovery at Canadian Electrolytic Zinc's New Valleyfield Plant", Journal of Metals, Vol. 18, No. 8, Aug. 1966, pp 947-956.

(2) Spira, P., "A Radioactive Tracer Test at the Orchan Concentrato 24 September 1969", Internal Report No. 188, Noranda Research Centre, February 1970.

(3) Spira, P., "A Radioactive Tracer Test in No. 1 Roaster at Canadian Electrolytic Zinc", Internal Report No. 187, Noranda Resea Centre, February 1970.

(4) Donovan, J.R. and P.J. Stuber, "Sulfuric Acid Production from O Roaster Gases", Journal of Metals, Vol. 19, No. 11, November 19 pp 45-50.

Canadian Electrolytic Zinc Ltd.
Valleyfield, Que., Canada
Chapter 5, page 144

S.A. Vieille-Montagne
Balen, Belgium
Chapter 6, page 178

Mitsubishi Metal Mining Co., Ltd.
Akita, Japan
Chapter 7, page 198

Ruhr-Zink GMBH
Datteln, Federal Republic of Germany
Chapter 9, page 247

American Zinc Co.
East St. Louis, Illinois, USA
Chapter 11, page 308

Cominco, Ltd.
Trail, B.C., Canada
Chapter 12, page 330

Nisso Smelting Co. Ltd.
Aizu, Japan
Chapter 15, page 409

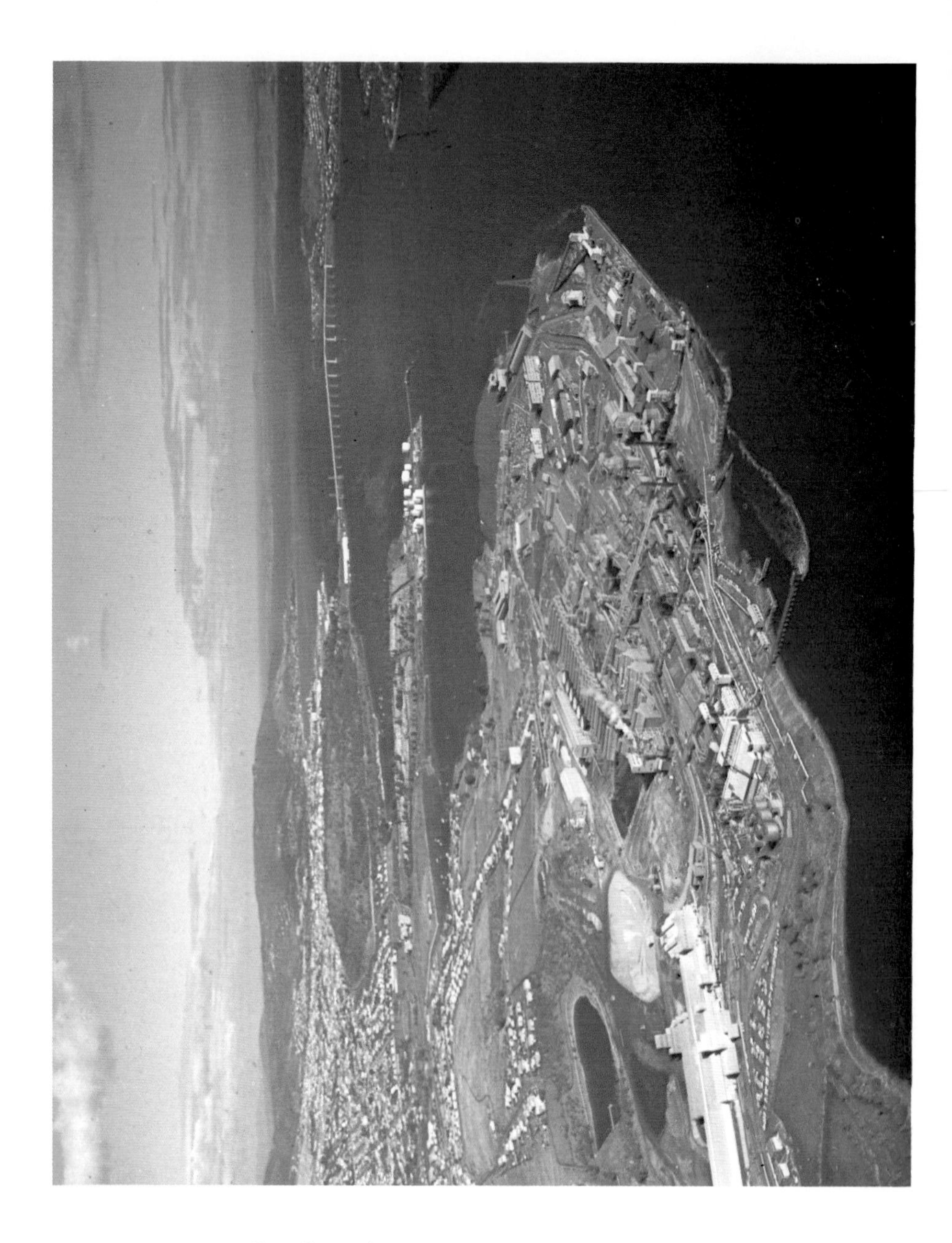

The Electrolytic Zinc Co. of Australasia, Ltd.
Risdon, Tas., Australia
Chapter 16, page 423

SECTION III

ELECTROLYTIC ZINC PRACTICE

Chapter 6

PRODUCTION OF ELECTROLYTIC ZINC AT THE BALEN PLANT OF S.A. VIEILLE-MONTAGNE

Balen, Belgium

Jean A. Andre, Manager of the Balen Plant

Roger J. Delvaux, Chief Metallurgist of the Balen Plant

Société des Mines et Fonderies de Zinc
de la Vieille-Montagne S.A.

Abstract

In 1969 "Société des Mines et Fonderies de Zinc de la Vieille-Montagne" produced 221,000 tons zinc ingots and 22,000 tons zinc dust, thus rating highest on the world's zinc producer list.

The Company's plant at Balen, Belgium, with an output of 135,000 tons electrolytic zinc is the most important one of this group; it is an integrated metallurgical zinc and lead unit with recovery of most by-products.

The present paper describes the zinc production facilities. The roasting section includes four fluid bed roasters (total concentrates charged: 740 tpd) and two sulfuric acid having a corresponding capacity.

Calcine is leached in a fully automated plant by a two-step continuous process. Leaching residues, mixed with lead furnace slag, are treated in a shaft furnace. The recovered zinc fume is leached separately. In the near future, the leaching residues are to be treated by a wet process, developed in the Company's own laboratories. Purification of solutions is accomplished in two steps: antimony and zinc dust are added in the first one, only zinc dust in the second one for removal of cadmium.

Electrolysis cells are partly of a conventional type. A new type of cell configuration was put onstream in October, 1969, planned output 60,000 tpy. Main features of the new cell rooms are the fully automatic pulling, stripping and replacing of the jumbo-size cathodes (immersed area 2.6 m^2).

Zinc cathodes are remelted in induction furnaces followed by in-line automatic casting and stacking machines.

INTRODUCTION

VIEILLE-MONTAGNE's name originated from an old mining concession at LA CALAMINE in the MORESNET district situated between LIEGE, Belgium, and AACHEN, Germany.

Industrial exploitation of zinc from smithsonite ($ZnCO_3$), achieved by J.J. DONY in the beginning of the eighteenth century, was taken over by F.D. MOSSELMAN, whose heirs founded in 1837 the Société des Mines et Fonderies de Zinc de la VIEILLE-MONTAGNE.

Vieille-Montagne was obviously international from the beginning: it owned mines and zinc smelters in the Liege area, rolling mills in France and England and another zinc smelter was in construction at Angleur (Liège), where the company was registered.

Vieille-Montagne's Balen plant was erected in 1889, on Campine's sandy grounds, at the crossing of the railroad Antwerp - Moenchen - Gladbach and a branch of the Campine canal joining Antwerp, port of ore discharge, and Liège, point of calcine delivery.

A simple roasting plant at first, Balen soon expanded with several units:

- 1898 : a lead chamber sulfuric acid plant, later replaced by contact plants;
- 1909 : a lead smelter, including a Dwight-Lloyd sintering machine, a smelting furnace and Harris and Betts refinery units;
- 1932 : a slag reduction furnace, where zinc from lead smelting slags (and later from leaching residues) was recovered as zinc oxide;
- 1932 : a power plant, originally fed with gas from the slag reduction furnace;
- 1932 : an electrolytic cadmium plant;
- 1935 : an electrolytic zinc plant;
- 1948 and 1959 : a semi-conductor plant producing germanium and silicon.

The plant's property extends over 500 hectares, 30 of which are covered by the production units.

500 ton barges come along the canal to the two discharge points of the plant.

The Antwerp-Liège highway is reached in less than 20 minutes.

Fig. 1 shows a complete plant flow-sheet.

Zinc and lead ores are the plant's main material sources. The processings of both ores are not independent but find a common

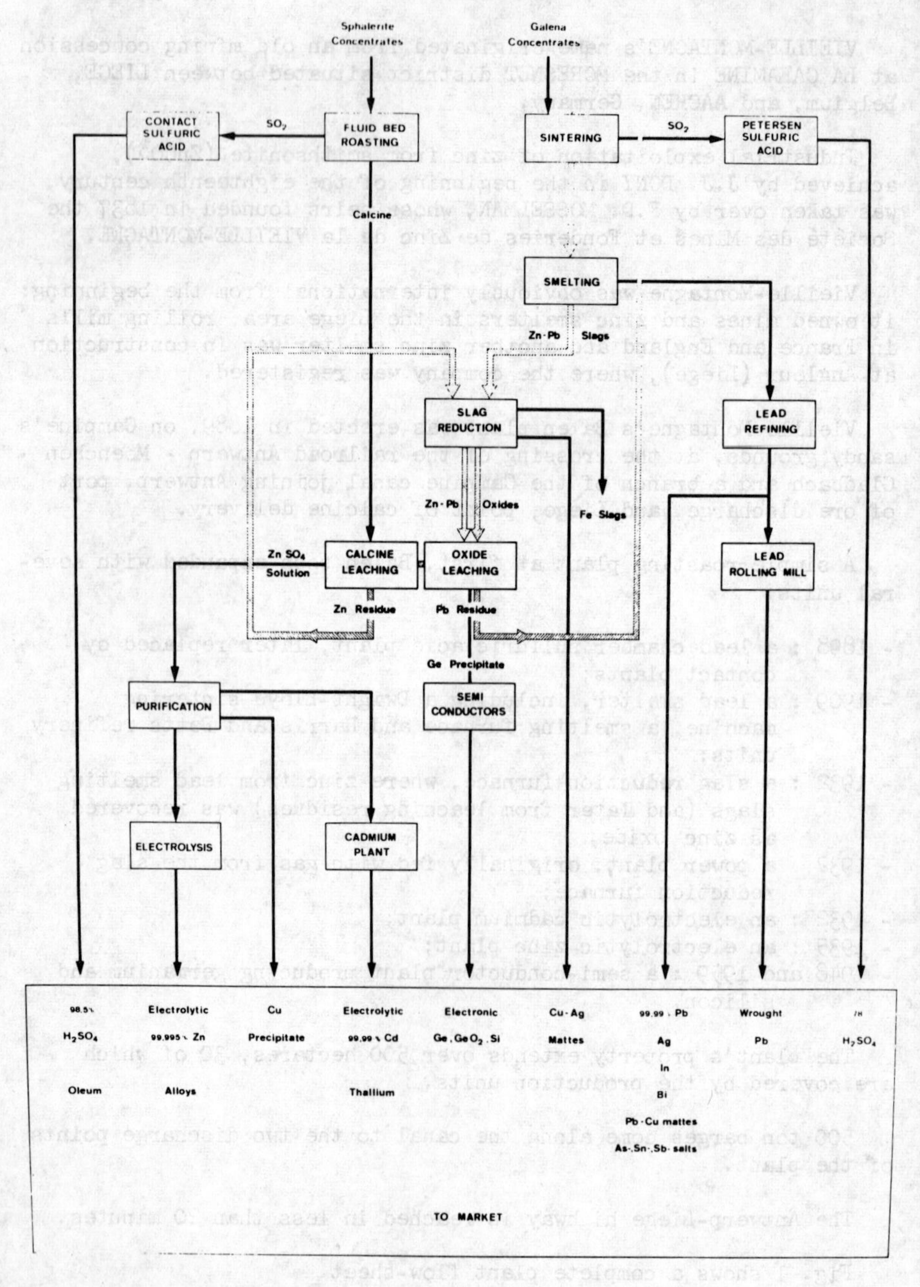

Fig. 1 Flow-sheet of the Balen Plant

link in the slag reduction furnace. Most elements present in the ores are circulated through the zinc or the lead circuit, can be concentrated if necessary and recovered at a suitable operating point. This interpenetration of two metallurgical processes is the main feature of the Balen plant.

Following items are to be discussed in the present paper:

1. the roasting plant
2. the contact sulfuric acid plant
3. the separate leaching processes of calcine and zinc oxide
4. the purification of the neutral solution
5. the electrolysis of zinc sulfate solution
6. the melting of zinc cathodes to marketable slabs
7. the hydrometallurgical processing of residues from the leaching systems.

1. THE ROASTING PLANT

Crude zinc sphalerite concentrates are discharged from the barges by a 100 t/h crane and piled up in the open on the plant's 80,000 ton storage area. Concentrates are then transferred to sixteen 120 ton storage bins located in the roasting plant.

Concentrates are automatically proportioned from the storage bins by rotating table to conveyor belts, and led to a screen eliminating the grains coarser than 30 mm. These are ground and returned to the feed.

It should be pointed out that no other feed handling is necessary, neither milling nor drying, although concentrate mixtures can contain up to 10% moisture.

Concentrates are projected into the furnace, on top of the fluid bed, by a high-speed belt feeder.

Roasting is performed in four separate units, each of which includes a fluid-bed roaster, a waste-heat boiler and a gas-purification unit.

Three roasters have a 130 tpd concentrates capacity; the fourth one, built in 1965, has a 350 tpd capacity. Surface areas of grates are respectively 16 m^2 for the smaller units and 50 m^2 for the larger one. In order to cut down the dust carry-over by effluent gases and to improve the oxidation of concentrates, gas velocity was reduced by the comparatively larger size of the furnace chamber above the bed.

The roasters were designed and built by the company.

Combustion air is blown without preheating under the dispersion grate, at a rate of 550-650 $Nm^3/m^2/h$, at 1,400-1,700 mm WG pressure.

The bed temperature is uniformly distributed by the fast heat exchanges due to fluidization and maintained at 850-1000°C by a water spray.

About 30% of the total product remains in the bed and finally overflows the discharge port in the wall of the reactor as finished calcine. The roaster is also provided with an underflow discharge, with automatic valve control, eliminating the coarser calcine conglomerates developed during the roasting process. Those conglomerates could interfere with a sound fluidization.

The remaining 70% of the product is carried out with the gas stream and is progessively precipitated, mostly as boiler dust, further as cyclone and Cottrell dust.

The vertical tube boiler is of the Lamont type with forced circulation. The gas stream is led horizontally around the pipes, that are periodically cleaned by the automatic traverse of a steel spear. Mechanical vibrations are generated by forcing the spear between the pipes, and the dust burden dislodged from the tube bank falls into steeply inclined hoppers and is evacuated by screw conveyors.

Superheated steam is produced at a 40 kg/cm^2 pressure by the first two boilers, at 65 kg/cm^2 by the later ones. Steam output reaches 1,080 kg/t calcine and is sent to the power plant.

Calcine and dust products are collected together in water-cooled screw or redler conveyors and delivered in five 600 ton steel silos. Calcine proceeds from there to the leaching steps of the zinc electrolysis, which will be dealt with later on.

Gases pass from the dry Cottrell to a cleaning and purification system including Venturi scrubbers or washing towers, indirect horizontal coolers, vertical gas coolers, a defluorizing tower and two stages of mist Cottrells. Gas purity is controlled continuously by an optical device and registered. The gas purification units are provided by LURGIBAU, Frankfurt/Main, Germany.

Three blowers and fans with variable speed are used in the unit: combustion air blower, Cottrell inlet fan, blower of sulfuric acid plant. The amounts of air or gases are interregulated in order to maintain a slight draft throughout the unit, from boiler inlet to mist precipitators. In the control room, a Panalarm device helps the operations monitor to check every possible deviation from the set-up values in feeding, pressures, temperatures, outputs, etc. The control panels are fitted with mimic flowcharts to monitor the four units operations.

The gas averages 10% SO_2 at the reactor outlet and 7% SO_2 after purification.

Production of 98.5% sulfuric acid equals 960 kg/t calcine. The total power consumed, from the receipt of concentrates to the delivery of calcines and the gas purification, remains under 50 kWh per ton of calcine. Operations take 0.5 man-hour per ton calcine.

Venturis and washing towers are provided with a closed scrubbing system. The recirculated acid is water cooled in liquid-liquid heat exchangers in order to cool the gases to the desired temperature. The scrubbing liquor contains sulfuric acid of varying strength and solids in rising concentrations. Small settlers are provided for the separating of solids, sent to the lead smelter. A small amount of the scrubbing liquor is periodically drained and sent to waste-disposal facilities for neutralization.

The mines owned by the company's group in Sweden and Germany can provide only a small part, approximately 20%, of the necessary concentrates. Additional supply is secured by concentrates of various origins. The fluid-bed roasting process as developed by the company made it possible to treat without trouble sphalerite containing copper up to 2% and lead up to 8%. Sulfide sulfur in the calcine remains below 0.25% and sulfate sulfur averages 2.00%.

2. THE CONTACT SULFURIC ACID PLANT

The gas from the roasting plant, containing about 7% of sulfur dioxide, is oxidized to sulfur trioxide in two vanadium pentoxide convertors producing 280 and 350 tpd of 98.5% sulfuric acid. The 350 ton unit is provided with an oleum tower.

Each unit consists of an air blower, a drying and an absorbing tower, a four-pass converter with internal heat exchangers, two external heat exchangers, an oil burner used for starting up and the usual acid coolers, storage tanks and acid pumps.

The cooled and supersaturated gases are dried by a 95% sulfuric acid counterflow in the drying tower. They are then heated to 420°C by indirect heat exchange with SO_3 gas leaving the converter. The dried and heated SO_2 gases are oxidized to SO_3 in the four-pass converter, with an oxidation rate of 98.5%. As the oxidation reaction is exothermic, the generated heat is removed after each stage and used to heat the incoming SO_2 gas flow. The partly converted SO_3 gas stream is thus cooled after each converting pass to an appropriate temperature, suitable with the kinetics of the following pass. In the absorbing tower, the finally converted SO_3 gases are absorbed by 95% sulfuric acid from the drying tower and 98.5% sulfuric acid is produced.

The units are provided with pyrometers measuring temperature before and after each heat evolving step of the process. Temperature is monitored by gas valves that by-pass the heat exchangers.

All values of temperatures, pressure drops, gas content, acid strength, rate of oxidation, are continuously registered in the control room. Power consumed is less than 50 kWh/t sulfuric acid. Operation is performed by 0.10 man-hour per ton sulfuric acid.

Industrial equipment is furnished by Kuhlmann and Krebs, France.

3. THE SEPARATE LEACHING PROCESSES OF CALCINE AND ZINC OXIDE

The first step in the production of zinc by the hydrometallurgical process is to dissolve the soluble zinc present in the source material. The commonly used solvent is dilute sulfuric acid, available as spent electrolyte. By the leaching process, zinc oxide is dissolved as impure zinc sulfate, while insoluble elements and unwanted impurities are obtained in a residue.

As the source material in the Balen plant is either calcine from sphalerite concentrate or zinc oxides from the slag reduction furnace, the composition of the residue varies consequently. Residues from calcine leaching have a high Zn content and low Pb and Ag contents and are therefore best processed in the slag reduction furnace. On the contrary, residues from oxide leaching are rich in Pb and Ag and poor in Zn, and are therefore sent to the lead smelter.

Balen was compelled to use two separate leaching systems, one for calcine, the other for zinc oxides. Both systems are of the continuous two-stage type.

A. Oxide Leaching System

In the first, the so called neutral leaching step, an excess of oxide is added to spent electrolyte. The reaction is carried out in a series of Pachuca tanks and ends at pH 5.2. Only part of the zinc present is dissolved, the attempt in this step being to remove from the zinc solution as many as possible of the unwanted impurities that may further interfere with the settling of solids and with the purification of the solution. The discharge from this step is sent to thickeners for separation of solids and solution. The solution overflowing the thickeners is sent to the neutral step of the calcine leaching process.

The solids settled out in the thickeners are leached in a second series of Pachuca tanks with spent electrolyte. The reaction in this second, acid, step ends at pH 3, the attempt being to dissolve more of the zinc oxide present. The discharge of the acid step is also sent to thickeners. The solution is treated to precipitate germanium and returned to the neutral leach. The solids are filtered and washed and, as final residues, find their way to the lead smelter for recovery of lead, silver, zinc, copper, cadmium, bismuth, antimony, indium, etc.

The equipment used in this leaching step was constructed by the company's personnel. It includes seven 14 m^3 Pachucas, four thickeners with a total settling surface area of 320 m^2, ten 80 m^2 Moore filters and four 22 m^2 vacuum rotary filters.

The unit has a rated capacity of 15,000 tpy of electrolytic zinc.

Compositions of neutral and acid solutions and of final residues are given in table 1.

Table 1. Oxide Leaching: Assays of Neutral Solution, Acid Solution, Final Residues

	Neutral solution	Acid solution	Final residue
pH	5.2	2.8 - 3	
Density	1380-1420	1375	
Zinc	155-160 g/l	145 g/l	8-12%
Cadmium	450-500 mg/l		0.05-0.15%
Copper	100 mg/l	200 mg/l	0.1-0.2%
Ferrous iron	10-30 mg/l		
Total iron			4-5%
Lead			30-40%
Silver			150-300 g/t
Total sulfur			9-11%
Silica	50 mg/l	200 mg/l	
Antimony	3-6 mg/l	9-18 mg/l	0.08-0.12%
Arsenic	1-3 mg/l		0.5-0.8%
Tin			1-1.5%
Indium			0.25-0.35%
Germanium	1 mg/l	30 mg/l	
Selenium	0.3 mg/l	0.5 mg/l	

B. Calcine Leaching System

This leaching is also carried out by a continuous, two-stage system. Compared to the oxide leaching, it presents several new improved features and actually includes three steps (see flowsheet fig. 2) :

-1) A wet, closed circuit grinding of calcine.

Calcine is added to an acid solution consisting of a mixture of 1) spent electrolyte, 2) manganese dioxide and ferrous sulfate liquors obtained by the cleaning of electrolysing cells and anodes, 3) leach solutions from the acid calcine leach, 4) neutral solutions from the neutral oxide leach, and 5) zinc solution from the leaching of purification cakes. Hydrocyclone classifiers separate the grains coarser than 75 microns, which are ground in ball mills and recycled. The classifier overflow, containing only fine calcine particles, is sent to the next step. About 25% of the zinc present in the calcine is dissolved in this first step.

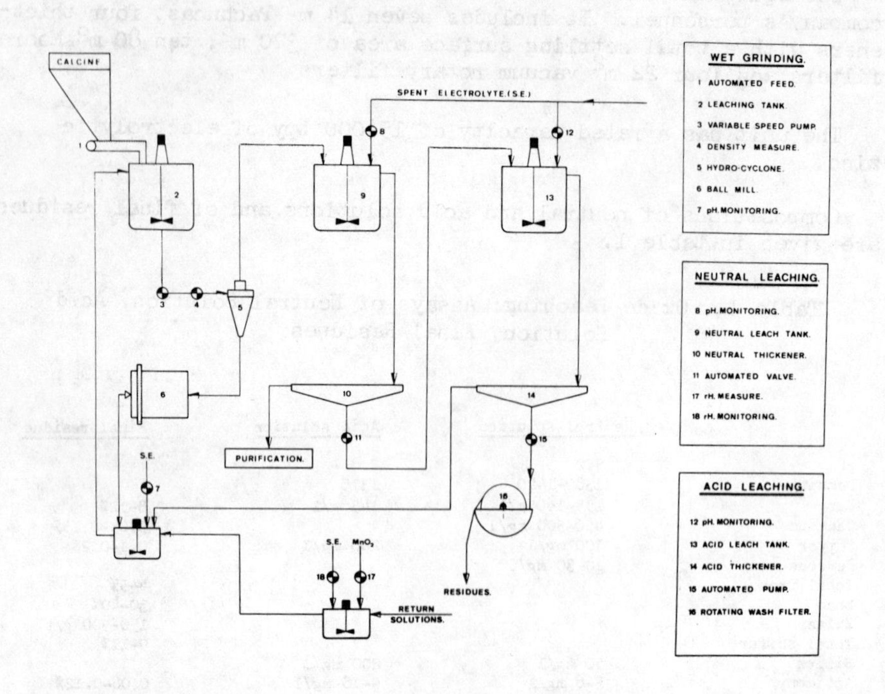

Fig. 2 Flow-sheet of Calcine Leaching System.

-2) The neutral leaching of classifiers overflow.

The reaction is carried out in a series of mechanically agitated tanks. Addition of spent electrolyte is monitored by pH meters. Iron oxidation is realized by air injection under the propellors. A good elimination of impurities is obtained by the iron hydroxide precipitation. In this step, for the same reasons in effect at the oxide neutral leaching, about 50% of the zinc present in the calcine is leached. The tanks discharge is sent to thickeners for separation of solids and solution. The solution overflowing the thickeners is sent to the purification unit, and the solids are going to the third step.

The adding of the neutral solutions from the neutral oxide leach brings a high chlorine and fluorine content in the solution to purify. Fluorine control in the electrolyte can only partially be achieved by precipitating a (AlF_2) complex. only for fluorine amount greater than 200 mg/l. A similar reaction cannot be found for lower fluorine contents. If the neutral leaching is continued for a couple of hours, at pH 5-5.2, aluminium hydroxide is precipitated, cutting down the aluminium amount in the solution from 50 to 25 mg/l without change in the fluorine content. Fluorine control by calcium fluoride precipitation cannot be performed on account of the solubility of this salt in magnesium sulfate. When amounts of 200 mg/l fluorine are to be dealt with, the leaching process should be specially adapted to dissolve and precipitate gradually the silica present in the calcine, in order to obtain a suitable decantation.

-3) The acid leaching of neutral leach solids.

The reaction is carried out in equipment identical to that of the former step and in a similar way. Acidity is higher, in order to dissolve as much as possible of the zinc oxide present in the neutral leach solids. About 14% of the zinc present in the calcine is dissolved in this last step, the total dissolution of the three steps being 89%. The solution obtained contains dissolved impurities and is recycled to the first step. The solids settled out in the thickeners are filtered and washed and the filtered residues are sent to the slag reduction furnace.

Table 2. Calcine Leaching: Assays of Neutral Solution, Acid Solution, Final Residue

Neutral solution			Neutral solution	Acid solution	Final residue
		pH	5.2	2.75	
Manganese	3.5 g/l	Density	1410	1400	
Germanium	0.4 mg/l	Zinc	160 g/l	150 g/l	18-22 %
Cobalt	10 mg/l	Cadmium	35% mg/l		0.15-0.20 %
Nickel	1.5 mg/l	Copper	500 mg/l	900 mg/l	0.5-0.8 %
Aluminium	25 mg/l	Ferrous iron	<5 mg/l	500 mg/l	
Selenium	0.075 mg/l	Total iron			20-30 %
Tellurium	0.002 mg/l	Lead			6-8 %
Chlorine	400 mg/l	Silver			150-250 g/t
Fluorine	200 mg/l	Total sulfur			approx. 6 %
		Silica	50 mg/l	100 mg/l	4-6 %
		Antimony	0.35 mg/l	2 mg/l	
		Arsenic	0.15 mg/l	10 mg/l	
		Tin			approx. 0.10 %
		Indium			0.04-0.06 %

The unit has a rated capacity of 160,000 tpy of electrolytic zinc. The equipment used include three Humboldt wet ball mills, ten 60 m^3 leaching tanks, eight 200 m^2 thickeners, four 50 m^2 Dorr-Oliver panel type filters.

Since all operations are automatic, they are performed by three operators, one from the control room and two in the processing units.

Assays of neutral and acid solutions and of final residues are given in table 2.

The total power consumed in both leaching systems amounts to 145 kWh per ton of electrolytic zinc. Further, 500 kg/t zinc of pressurized air is used in both systems.

Operations take 1.5 man-hour per ton electrolytic zinc.

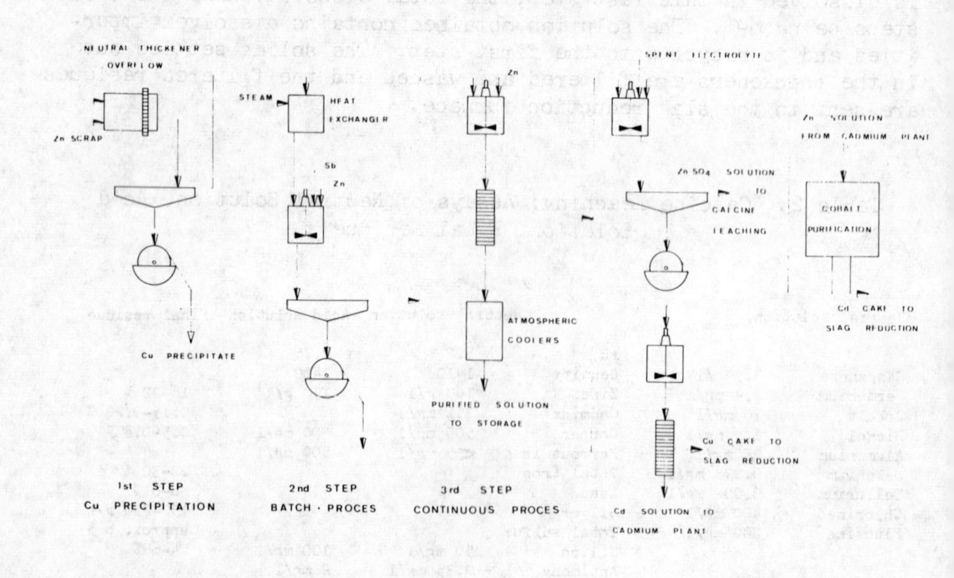

Fig. 3 Flow-sheet of Solution Purification and of Treatment of the Purification Cakes.

4. THE PURIFICATION OF THE NEUTRAL SOLUTION

The neutral solution of the calcine leaching process has to be purified, because it contains copper and cadmium as major impurities and also small amounts of arsenic, antimony, germanium, cobalt, nickel. The presence of the latter impurities in the zinc sulfate electrolyte would affect the hydrogen overvoltage and degrade the quality of the zinc deposit and the current efficiency.

Current practice in Balen is the three-stage purification of the neutral solution. The cakes from purification are treated for further recovery of zinc, cadmium and copper. (See flow-sheet fig.3)

Copper Precipitation

1) If the copper content exceeds 400 mg/l solution, zinc scrap is added. The copper precipitation is carried out continuously in drum reactors. The discharge is led to a thickener for the settling of the solids.

2) The second stage of purification is carried out as a batch process in mechanically agitated tanks. The solution is heated to about 75°C and approximately 10 mg/l of antimony dust and 6 g/l of zinc dust are added. Agitation is maintained until the cobalt content is lowered to 0.25 mg/l. The tank discharges are sent to thickeners.

Table 3 gives purification results.

Table 3. Purification Results

Assays in mg/l of the purified solution, end of second step.

Copper	less than 0.2	Tin	less than 0.02
Cadmium	5	Arsenic	less than 0.01
Ferrous iron	15	Antimony	approx. 0.01
Thallium	0.5-5	Germanium	less than 0.01
Rhenium	less than 0.005	Aluminium	10
Gallium	less than 0.005	Cobalt	0.25
Mercury	less than 0.2	Nickel	less than 0.01
Selenium	less than 0.002	Tellurium	less than 0.001

3) The third stage of purification is only a finishing step of the previous one, in order to eliminate cadmium from the solution. This purification is carried out as a continuous process, at 60°C, in a way similar to the second step. Only zinc dust is added and the cadmium content of the solution drops from 5 to less than 0.2 mg/l. The discharge is filtered in filter presses.

The second and third stages are performed at temperatures of 70 and 60°C, without any addition of spent electrolyte. Therefore the purification cakes are strongly hydrated and are at pH 5. The two cakes are leached at 60°C by means of spent electrolyte. This continuous operation is performed at pH 3, in order to dissolve zinc and cadmium without dissolving copper, arsenic, nickel. The cadmium liquor, with pH 4,5, is sent for precipitation to the cadmium plant, where 600 tpy of electrolytic cadmium are produced. The cadmium plant material sources are the precipitates from the electrolytic zinc plant and from the lead smelter.

After the removal of cadmium, the zinc sulfate solution is sent back for purification of cobalt and nickel by means of antimony and zinc dusts and recycled. The copper and cobalt cakes obtained during the processing of the purification cakes are sent to the slag reduction furnace for recovery of the remaining contents of copper, zinc and cadmium. Table 4 shows typical assays of the main solution and cakes obtained.

Table 4. Treatment of the Purification Cakes

Typical assays of solutions and residues

	$ZnSO_4$ solution to calcine leaching	Cd solution to Cd plant	Recycled $ZnSO_4$ solution	Cadmium cake	Copper cake
pH	5	4.5	5.2	-	-
Zinc	150 g/l	100 g/l	120 g/l	30 %	20 %
Cadmium	300 mg/l	30 g/l	< 5 mg/l	12 %	3 %
Copper	<1 mg/l	25 mg/l	< 1 mg/l	10 %	25 %
Arsenic	-	<1 mg/l	-	0.06 %	0.15 %
Antimony	-	-	-	0.20 %	0.50 %
Cobalt	5 mg/l	600 mg/l	50 mg/l	0.3 %	0.75 %
Nickel	<0.01 mg/l	20 mg/l	<0.01 mg/l	0.02 %	0.05 %
Lead				2.4 %	6 %
Silica					3.5 %
Alumina					1 %

Equipment used includes:
1) For the batch purification step: fourteen 25 m^3 tanks, two stainless steel 45 m^2 heat exchangers, two 16 m^2 thickeners;
2) For the continuous purification step: three 60 m^3 tanks, eight 30 m^2 filter presses.

The unit has a rated capacity of 130,000 tpy of electrolytic zinc. 125 g/t zinc of antimony dust and 70 kg/t zinc of zinc dust are consumed as reacting agents in the several stages. The total steam consumption amounts to 550 kg/t electrolytic zinc.

Operation is performed by 0.45 man-hour per ton zinc.

5. THE ELECTROLYSIS OF THE ZINC SULFATE SOLUTION

The Balen zinc plant consists of three cell houses, two of which are of the conventional hand-stripping type, the third one, put on-stream in October, 1969, having been redesigned for complete automation of all handling and stripping operations.

The oldest cell house includes 320 cells, arranged in parallel rows of 5 cells each. Electric power is supplied by six 3,500 amp mercury arc rectifiers. The later conventional cell house is divided into 4 electrolysing units of 80 cells each, arranged in similar rows of 10 cells each. Electric power is supplied by four 18,500 amp silicon rectifiers.

The automated cell house includes 168 cells, arranged in 6 parallel rows of 28 cells each. Electric current is furnished by a 20,000 amp silicon rectifier.

Common feature to the whole plant is the low current density, varying from 300 to 400 amp/m^2, whereby a deposition time of 48 hours can be practiced. Current efficiency averages 90%, with a voltage of 3.30-3.45 volt. The energy consumed for deposition varies from 3,100 to 3,250 kWh/t of zinc deposit.

The cathodes are rolled aluminium sheets of 99.5% purity, argon shielded arc welded to aluminium header bars. The thickness of the sheets is 7 mm. Polyethylene strips are used on the sides of the cathodes.

The anodes are of cast lead, 15 mm thick, and contain 0.90% silver. The anodes and anode header bars are cast together with a copper contact bar cast in the header. The anode surface is ridged, in order to help the building up of a protective coating of manganese bioxide.

Spacing is maintained at 90 mm centers.

Vacuum cleaning of the cells is performed every eight weeks to remove the manganese sludge and to clean and straighten the anodes.

Further description of equipment can best be done separately for the conventional and for the automated cell house types.

1- Conventional cells.

The lead-lined concrete cells are 4.550 m long, 0.870 m wide and 1.670 m deep, inside measurements. Lead cooling coils are used to cool the solution. Each cell is equipped with 46 anodes and 45 cathodes. Cathodes are fitted with rubber insulators in the lower portion, to serve as spacers.

Electrolyte is fed individually to each cell and overflows are not cumulative. By normal processing, electrolyte is depleted from 160 to 80 g/l of zinc. In a small group of cells further depletion is performed, from 80 to 50 g/l of zinc. In those depletion cells, electrolyte is only fed to the tops of the five cells cascades and overflows are cumulative.

The two conventional cell houses have a rated capacity of 100,000 tpy of electrolytic zinc. The amount of hand-stripped zinc averages 7 ton per man.

2- Automated cell house.

The concrete cells are lined with paraliner and their inside measurements are adapted to the larger electrodes: they are 4.550 m long, 1.230 m wide and 2.150 m deep.

The disposition of the cells was changed in order to avoid the bus-bars along them. Cathode and anode header contacts are shaped to fit in each other. Cooling coils were also avoided and the circulated solution is cooled by air in cooling towers. Fresh electrolyte is added continuously to the circulated solution that is fed individually to and overflows individually from each cell. Cells are temporarily equipped with 23 anodes and 22 cathodes, but are designed for 45 anodes and 44 cathodes, in order to meet with further expansion. Cathode submerged area is 2.60 m^2, this being twice the conventional area.

In order to improve the mechanical stripping, cathode spacer insulators were removed and replaced by conical plastic insulators, inserted into the anodes.

Stripping operations are monitored by means of a programmed electronic device. They include the removing of the cathodes from the cells, their transport to several stripping machines, their mechanical stripping and the removing of the deposit, the suitable conditioning of the cathodes, their transport to and correct positioning in the cells.

Automation increased the production of stripped zinc to 16 ton per man-shift, since operating is reduced to the mere supervision of cells and stripping machines. The new cell house has a capacity temporarily rated at 30,000 tpy of electrolytic zinc and will reach 60,000 tpy by full equipment of the cells with electrodes, production rate being 24 tons per man-shift.

The electric power equipment was furnished by ACEC-WESTINGHOUSE, Charleroi, Belgium; cathode travelling cranes by DEMAG, Germany; electrolyte cooling towers by HAMON-SOBELCO, Belgium. The stripping machines and the electronic monitoring equipment was designed and constructed by the plant personnel.

6. THE MELTING OF ZINC CATHODES AND CASTING OF MARKET SLABS

The cathodic zinc deposit is of S.H.G. quality, with 99.995% zinc content, the chief impurities being lead (20-25 g/t), iron (4-8 g/t), cadmium (2-4 g/t), copper (1-3 g/t) and silver (<1 g/t).

The final step in the zinc recovery process does not improve that purity. It is only performed to cast the metal into a shape readily accepted by the market.

The bulk of the electrolytic zinc production is sold as rectangular shaped slabs with an approximate weight of 25 kg. Furthermore, one ton jumbo slabs are cast in special moulds.

The melting of the cathodes is performed in four induction furnaces with rated capacities of, respectively, 5, 4, 11 and 15 tons per hour. The two smaller furnaces are used for the casting of jumbos, alloys or special quality zinc.

Zinc is ladled out by hand or pumped from the furnace by a centrifugal graphite pump. The larger units are provided with casting machines and stackers. All operations are automatic, with the exception of the skimming of the slab surface.

Three induction furnaces were furnished by S.I.C.E., Italy, the largest one by AJAX MAGNETHERMIC, England. The regulating transformers are from ACEC-WESTINGHOUSE, Belgium, and HAEFELY, Switzerland. The casting machines were manufactured by SHEPPARD and E & J ENGINEERING, both Great Britain. The first stacker was designed and constructed by the plant personnel; the second one was furnished by E & J ENGINEERING, Great Britain, based on the company's own designs.

Power consumption is 110 kWh/t of zinc cast. Dross production averages 2-2.5%. Automatic casting and stacking is performed by less than one man-hour per ton of zinc cast, including jumbo slabs and alloys.

7. THE HYDROMETALLURGICAL PROCESSING OF RESIDUES FROM THE LEACHING SYSTEM

As mentioned before, both a zinc sulfate solution and a final residue are produced when carrying out the leaching steps of the calcines. Those residues are sent to the slag reduction furnace for further zinc recovery. They contain valuable metals besides unwanted gangue minerals. Table 5 gives a typical analysis of this leach residue.

The constituents can be divided in two classes:

- the first one contains the elements occuring in insoluble compounds (SiO_2) or producing insoluble sulfates (Pb, Ca, Ag);
- the second one contains the elements whose sulfates are on the contrary easily soluble (Fe, Zn, Cu, Cd), but insoluble compounds of these elements were not dissolved at the temperature and acidity conditions normally used in calcine leaching.

Table 5. Calcine Leach Residues

Zinc	18-22 %	Arsenic	0.25 %
Copper	0.5-0.8 %	Calcium oxide	0.8-1.2 %
Cadmium	0.1-0.15 %	Silica	4-6 %
Iron	20-30 %	Alumina	1-1.5 %
Lead	6-8 %	Total sulfur appr.	6 %
Silver	150-250 g/t	Sulfate sulfur app.	5.5 %
Tin	approx. 0.1 %	Sulfide sulfur	0.5-1 %

The object of the hydro-metallurgical process is the selective recovery, as valuable products, of the constituents of the calcine leaching residue. It was developed by the plant's R and D departments and has been patented by Vieille-Montagne. It can briefly be described as follows:

-1) Leaching by sulfuric acid under conditions that will dissolve the second class elements, whereas lead, silver and tin remain insoluble in a slurry to be treated separately for their recovery;

-2) The solution obtained by leaching will contain zinc, copper and cadmium, but also iron, aluminium, arsenic and other impurities that will have to be precipitated again;

-3) Iron precipitation from the solution will have to be performed economically and efficiently, with elimination of the unwanted impurities.

Systematic experiments have shown that it is possible, starting from ferrous sulfate solutions, to precipitate iron as α-FeOOH, goethite, by oxidizing with finely dispersed air. As the iron present in the solution obtained by the acid leaching of the residue is 90% in ferric state, a prereduction will be necessary. For obvious economical reasons, zinc sulfide was chosen as reducing agent. In carrying out this reduction, a new residue is obtained, containing about 60% sulfur and 10-20% zinc, according to the type of concentrate used.

The patented process is based on the stated principles.

Equipment is now being erected in Balen, and towards the end of 1970 a first unit will be put onstream, able to process about one third of the produced leach residues. It will be extended in 1971 to the treatment of the total production of residues. Fig. 4 shows the basic flow-sheet.

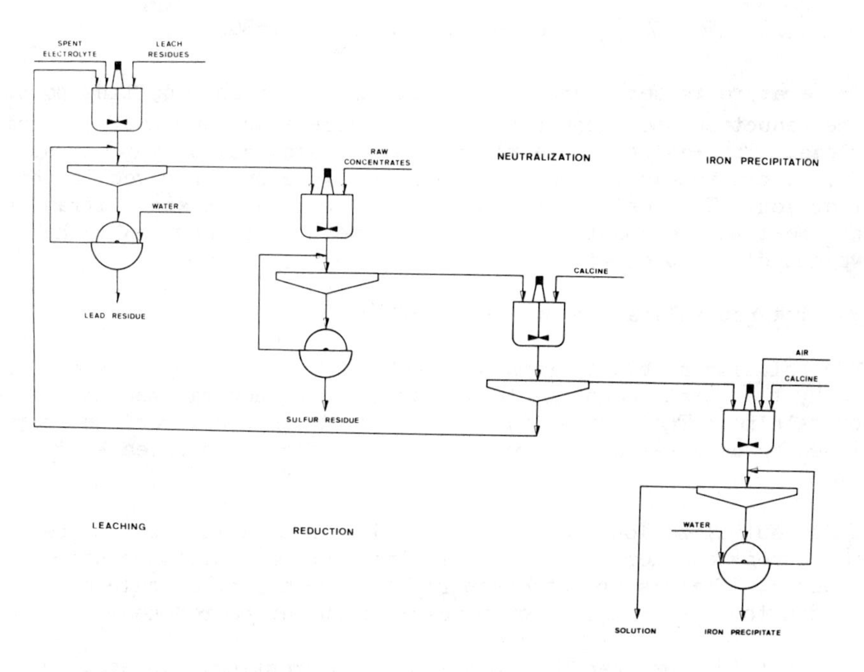

Fig. 4 Basic Flow-Sheet of the Hydrometallurgical Processing of Calcine Leach Residues.

The four operating steps are described hereafter:

1- The hot acid leaching of residues.

Residues are leached during 4-8 hours, at 90-95°C, by spent electrolyte. Acid strength at the end of reaction is between 20 and 40 g/l of sulfuric acid. A lead residue is obtained, containing lead, silver and tin, with a total weight of approximately one third of the treated material. It is separated by decantation and filtration, and washed before being sent to the lead smelter.

The thickener overflow contains zinc, copper, cadmium, iron, arsenic, germanium, cobalt and nickel, with dissolution rates above 90%. Soluble iron is 90% as ferric iron.

2- The reduction of ferric iron.

Raw zinc concentrates are added to the filtrate.

An excess of 10-30% of the theoretical amount of sulfide sulfur is needed to reduce iron according to the following reaction:

$$Fe(SO_4)_3 + MeS \rightarrow MeSO_4 + S\downarrow + 2FeSO_4$$

Temperature is kept between 90°C and the solution's boiling point. The reduction step should not require more than four hours to complete. The residue contains the precipitated sulfur and the sulfides, present in the concentrate, that were not involved in the reaction. The residue is separated by decantation and filtration and sent to the roasting plant. It's weight is about half the weight of the used zinc concentrates.

3- The neutralization of the overflow.

The solution's acidity remains 20-40 g/l sulfuric acid, as obtained by the first leaching step. It has to be neutralized to pH 2 by calcine. The neutralization step produces a new residue, separated by decantation and recycled to the first, acid leaching step.

This neutralization step can be avoided; neutralization can be performed together with the following iron precipitation step. However, if it is operated separately, the amount of calcine needed for the further iron precipitation can be reduced.

This cutting down can be economically interesting. Indeed, the calcine used in the iron precipitation step should be as pure as possible, with minimum silver and lead contents, since those elements are lost in the iron precipitate.

4- The oxidation and precipitation of iron.

This step is operated at 90-95°C, with finely dispersed air and calcine as a neutralizing agent. It already has been pointed out that the used calcine should meet specific requirements:

-minimum contents of lead and silver, since these elements will precipitate together with iron, their further recovery being thus impossible;

-high zinc dissolution rate: all residues coming from the used calcine are lost with the iron precipitate and further recovery of unleached zinc cannot be effected.

Iron precipitation can be achieved in less than one hour. Reaction is continued for 5-7 hours in order to dissolve most of the zinc of the neutralizing calcine.

The nature of the iron precipitate varies according to precipitation pH. By operating at high pH, a 50% iron precipitate can be obtained with good elimination of the unwanted impurities such as arsenic, antimony, indium, germanium and fluorine.

Chapter 7

AKITA ELECTROLYTIC ZINC PLANT AND RESIDUE TREATMENT OF MITSUBISHI METAL MINING COMPANY, LTD.

Akita, Japan

Eifu Moriyama, Assistant Manager - Metallurgy Department

Yuzo Yamamoto, Superintendent - Akita Plant

Abstract

In 1953, Akita Plant, having a capacity of 560 tons per month, was built at Akita city by Mitsubishi Metal Mining Co., Ltd. for the purpose of treatment of the Ikuno and Akenobe Mines's zinc concentrates. Akita city, in whose neighborhood the black ore has been discovered, is located about 500 Km north of Tokyo and faced with the Japan Sea. This plant has been continuously expanded to have the capacity of 7,500 tons per month by the end of 1969. Efforts have been made to mechanize installations and to achieve continuous process. One of the characteristics of Akita Plant is the recent establishment of the residue treatment process. Many processes had been investigated, and finally commercial sulphate roasting of the residue has been carried out since 1965.

At Akita Plant, special high grade electrolytic zinc, zinc alloy for die-casting (MAK brand), cadmium, cement copper and sulphur dioxide gas are produced. Sulphur dioxide gas is sent to the next door fertilizer plant to make acid. Table 1 shows production and the average assay of the electrolytic zinc and cadmium in 1969.

This plant is divided into four main sections, two subsections, and residue treatment sections:

Main sections are:
(M-1) roasting section,
(M-2) leaching and purification section,
(M-3) electrolysis section,
(M-4) melting and casting section,

Subsections are:
(S-1) cadmium section,
(S-2) flotation section,
Residue treatment sections are:
(R-1) sulphate roasting section,
(R-2) leaching and purification section,
(R-3) SO_4 controlling section

Table 1 Production and Assay of Zn and Cd Metal

Production (T/M)		Assay			
		Zn metal		Cd metal	
Concentrates	14,700	Zn	99.997 (%)	Cd	99.997 (%)
Zinc Production	7,500	Pb	0.0016	Pb	0.0014
Cd Production	26	Cd	0.0003	Zn	0.0004
MAK #2	2,200	Fe	0.0003	Fe	0.0001
		Cu	0.0002	Cu	0.0006
		Ag	0.0004	Ag	0.0005

Photo 1 Bird's-eye view of Akita Plant

The flowsheet of above-mentioned sections is given in Fig. 1.

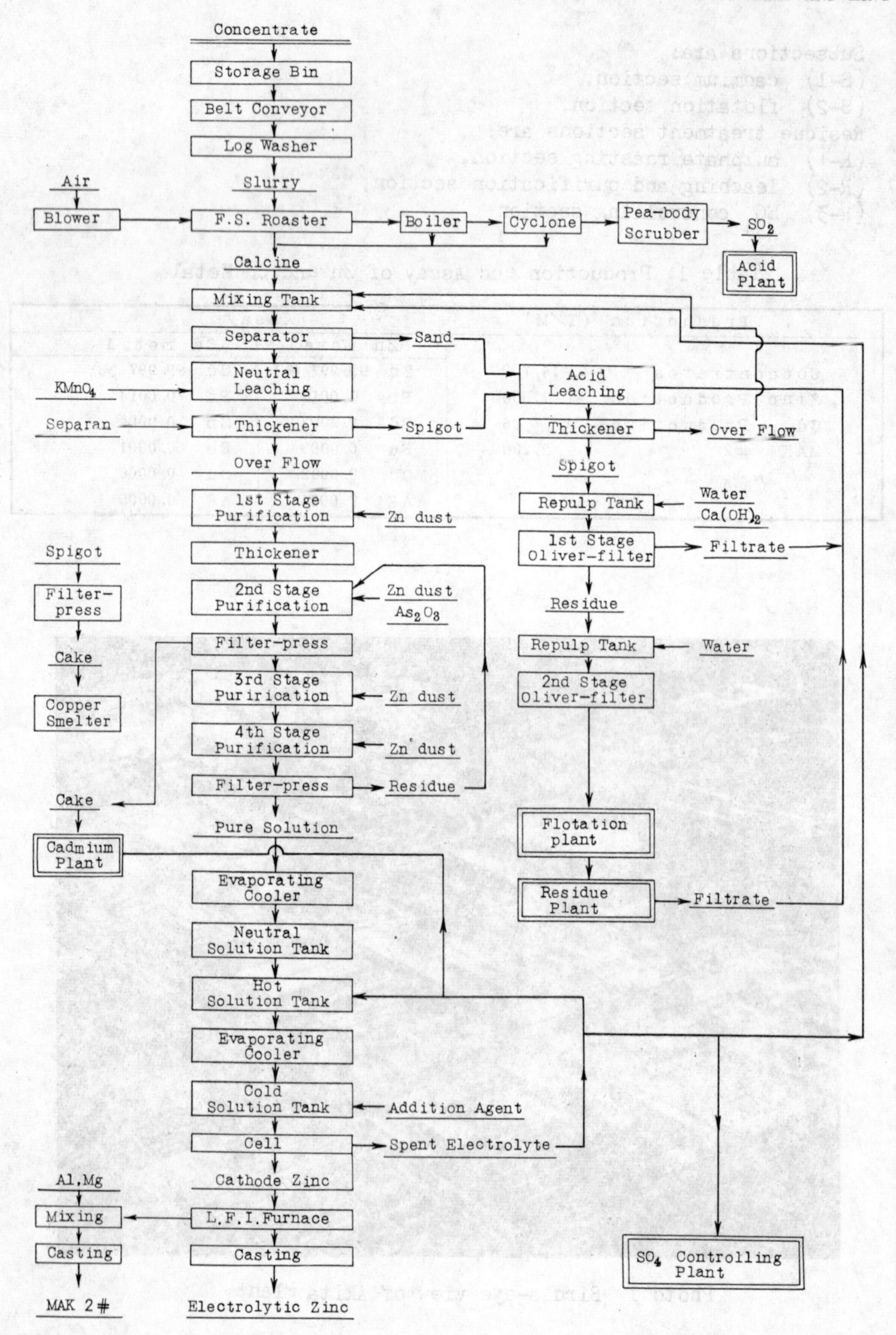

Fig. 1. Flow Sheet of Main Circuit

M-1 Roasting Section

1) Preparation of Raw Material

Various concentrates are treated at present, and it is important to control impurities in mixing. Seventy percent of concentrates is imported from foreign countries; for example Canada, Peru, Australia, etc., and landed on Akita port about 10 Km north from this plant. The rest of them is domestic. They are received by rail or truck. Impurities are checked and they are stored in twelve 1,200-ton bins classified on copper grade.

They are taken out from bins into mixing hopper by two 3-ton grab cranes, weighed by Merrick scale, and then discharged into a log-washer, a type of horizontal mixer, where concentrates are pulped with washed water of the residue to obtain a 75% solid slurry (slurry density 2.31 Kg per liter). Slurry is pumped by O.D.S. pump into agitation tanks for two fluo-solid roasters of Dorrco-type.

2) Roasting

There are two roasters for concentrates. One is 10.4 m in diameter, by 7.5 m high and the other is 4.3 m in diameter, 5.2 m high and the former treates 435 tons per day and the latter treats 70 tons per day. The bigger roaster has six special feed guns in order to have the uniform temperature of the bed. The combustion air is supplied by two series of 300 Kw turbo blowers and fluidization of the bed is maintained by passing combustion air through 1,288 stainless steel (AISI 309S) tuyeres having six 5 mmϕ holes. The feed guns are also made of stainless steel (AISI 316L). The roaster is constructed of 14 mm iron shell with 114 mm heat insulator bricks and 230 mm fire bricks.

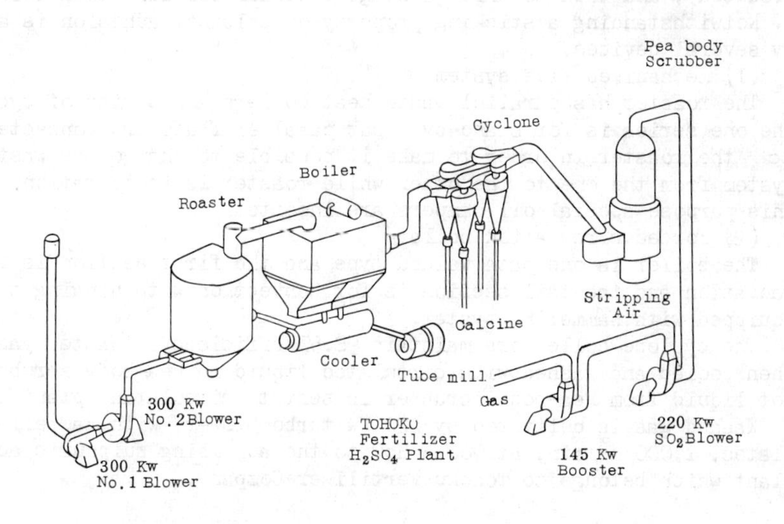

Fig. 2. Layout of Roasting Section

With normal concentrate of 52% zinc and 32% sulphur, the combustion air is calculated as follows:

$$435 \times 10^3 \text{ (Kg/D)} \times 1/1{,}440 \text{ (min/D)} \times 1.61 \text{ (Nm}^3\text{/Kg)} \times 110 \text{ (\%)}$$

theoretical air — excess air ratio

$$= 535 \text{ (Nm}^3\text{/min)}$$

The pressure in freeboard is controlled about -10 mm H_2O, by 220 Kw SO_2 blower. The roaster gas is diluted by the stripping air in Pea-body scrubber and sent to the acid plant, 670 Dry Nm^3/min by volume and SO_2 content is about 9.3%.

The temperature is maintained at 930°C by two automatic water sprays. The feed slurry is controlled by checking SO_2 content of the gas. As the fluidized bed is easy to coagulate, if the electric power is interrupted for more than twenty minutes, the electric power is supplied to the roasting plant by two different power circuits.

As a campaign of the roaster becomes long, the nozzles of tuyeres are blocked gradually and the pressure of wind box increases. The solids stuck around the nozzles is high in copper and lead, for examples, Zn 20%, Cu 20%, Pb 17%, T.S 6.5%, W.S 6.4%. These assays show that sulphating reactions have occurred to some extent. Therefore, in this plant, the roasters are repaired and tuyeres are cleaned periodically once in two years.

The roaster has two overflow outlets which are 1,100 mm above the tuyere level.

Calcine distributes 53.5% to overflow and 46.5% to carry-over. The roaster gas bearing fine calcine passes through a waste heat boiler for heat recovery (about 0.85 ton of steam per ton of concentrates is produced), and then to three 2-stage cyclones for dust collection.

Notwithstanding a sticking property of calcine, adhesion is avoided by several devices.

(1) Mechanized flue system

The roaster has parallel waste heat boilers and series of cyclones. The one series is for stand-by. But parallel flues are connected to the roaster in order to make it possible to change the waste gas system from the one to the other while roaster is in operation. For this purpose special oil dampers are inserted.

(2) Forced circulation boiler

The boiler is one path welded type and the first section is for radiation and the tail section is for convection with hanging tubes equipped with hammering system.

The cyclone collectors maintain 98.5% efficiency. Waste gas is then cooled and washed with circulated liquid in Pea-body scrubber. Hot liquid from Pea-body scrubber is sent to circulating plant.

Washed gas is delivered by 220 Kw turbo blower, with Hastelloy plates, 1,000 m^3/min, at 900 mm H_2O to the adjoining sulphuric acid plant which belongs to Tohoku Fertilizer Company.

Table 2 Forced Circulation Boiler

Heating surface	1,168 m^2
Maximum pressure	17 Kg/cm^2
Steam	14.7 T/Hr
Temperature of water supplied	105 ℃
Temperature of steam	203 ℃
Temperature of entrance gas	930 ℃
Temperature of exit gas	300±20 ℃

Overflow calcine is cooled to 150°C in water jacket type calcine cooler and screened through the low-head screen. Oversize of 40 mesh is pulverized in the 75 Kw tube mill and then sent into the stock bins by the chain conveyers together with undersize and the cyclone dust. There are five stock bins, each with capacity of 350 tons of calcine.

Table 3 shows assay of calcine. The leaching with spent acid depends on the solubility of calcine, i.e. on the formation of zinc ferrite ($ZnFe_2O_4$). The practical solubility is measured as follows. Acid soluble Zn/total Zn: Acid soluble Zn is the amount of soluble Zn from 1 gr. calcine with 10% H_2SO_4, 100 cc, at 20°C, for 20 minutes. Fig. 3 shows relation between iron content and insoluble zinc in calcine. This indicates that almost all iron forms zinc ferrite in fluosolid roaster.

An example of leach residue analysis is;

$ZnFe_2O_4$: 94.9%
$ZnSiO_3$: 1.8%
ZnO : 2.2%
$ZnSO_4$: 1.1%

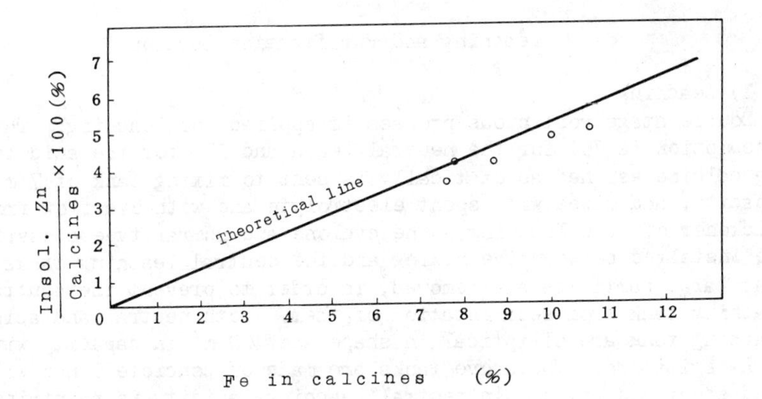

Fig. 3. Formation of Zn-ferrite

(3) Circulating Plant for Pea-body Scrubbers

Owing to the expansion of the plant by stages, we have four fluo-solid roasters and as mentioned before two roasters are used for oxidizing roasting of concentrates and the other two are for sulphating roasting of the leached residue.

Hot water or solution from four Pea-body scrubbers is treated in circulating plant. This plant has a 21 mø thickener, two vacuum evaporators in series and two Oliver filters.

The overflow of the thickener is cooled, from 70°C to 40°C, by the evaporator and then returned to the Pea-body scrubbers. As a result of circulation, Zn, Cd, Cu and SO_4 ions are accumulated in this solution. The solution is partly discharged and new water, about 500 l/min, is added to the system. The solution discharged is treated in SO_4 controlling section, and Zn, Cu, Cd are recovered.

Table 3 Operating Data of Roasting Section

Typical analysis								
Concentrate	Zn	Cu	Cd	Fe	S	Pb	Ag	
(%)	51.8	0.72	0.21	8.1	31.7	1.3	99(g/T)	
Calcine	T.Zn	A.Zn	Cu	Cd	Fe	T.S	W.S	S.S
(%)	59.7	54.8	0.81	0.23	9.2	2.4	2.1	0.3
Calcine Distribution (%)	overflow : 53.5			Carryover : 46.5				
Analysis	Zn	Cu	Fe	S				
Overflow (%)	61.6	0.77	9.18	1.22				
Carryover (%)	57.5	0.86	9.23	3.11				
Charging method	Slurry charge (25% H_2O)							
Excess air ratio	110 %							
Gas content (%)	SO_2 : 9.3	O_2 : 5.7						
Furnace temperature (°C)	bed 930							
Temperature control	automatic water spray							
Overflow height (m)	1.1							
Steam generation	0.85 T/ton-concentrate							

M-2 Leaching and Purification Section

1) Leaching

Double stage continuous process is applied for leaching. The acid consumption is 75% for the neutral leach and 25% for the acid leach. The calcine weighed automatically is sent to mixing tank of 7 m^3 capacity, and mixed with spent electrolyte and with overflow from the thickener of acid leaching. The cyclone and spiral type classifier are installed between the mixing and the neutral leaching tanks, so that large particles are removed, in order to prevent the neutral leaching tank from sedimentation of them. Both neutral and acid leaching tank are elliptical in shape and 400 m^3 in capacity with six 22 Kw agitators. The above tanks are made of concrete lined with lead sheet and brick. In neutral leaching, acidity is maintained at

PH 4.8 and Fe, Sb, Ge and As are precipitated by aid of oxidizing reagent. The finished solution is discharged by air-lift through a launder, about 3.6 m^3/min, to 21 mø neutral thickener.

Separan is added 5 - 10 mg/l to the solution and accelerates the separation of solid. Fig. 4 shows an example of solid distribution in thickener.

Spigot, density 1.4 Kg/l, is discharged (1.1 m^3/min) continously and pumped to the acid leaching tank.

The rotation of rake is 1/10 R.P.M.

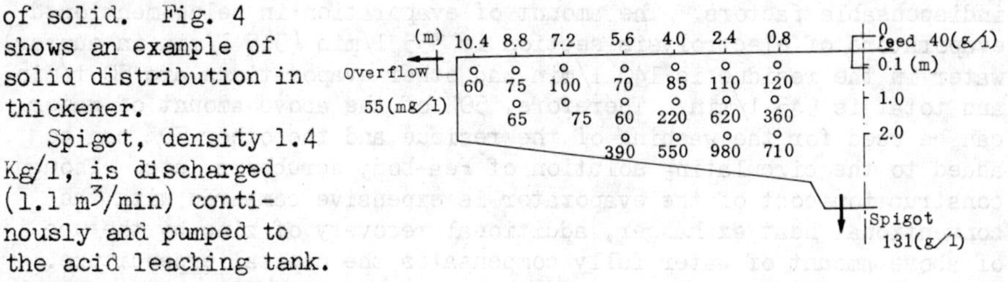

Fig. 4.
Solid distribution in the Neutral Thickener

In operation of the neutral leaching, special cares are necessary for agitators and rakes to prevent the accumulation of bottom solid and growth of basic salt crystals in both leaching tank and thickener.

Therefore, 400^3 m tanks has six agitators and ten air pipes (25 mm) and leached solution is discharged from the bottom of tank by air lift.

The load to the rake can be checked out at center drive bevel gear and alarm is given automatically. The device is by the horizontal level switch of mercury.

The thickener overflow, density 1.30 Kg/l, is sent to purification process for further treatment. The underflow is sent to the acid leaching tank. The solution of acid leaching is controlled at PH 1.8 and temperature is about 70°C.

The acid thickener overflow is sent to the mixing tank.

The spigot from the thickener, 100 l/min, density 1.8 Kg/l, is filtered and washed through two stage Oliver filters and the residue is further treated in flotation process for silver recovery and sulphate roasting process for additional recovery of zinc. First filtrate is returned to acid leach and second filtrate is used for the leaching of sulphate process.

There are six Oliver filters. Four filters are for the first stage and the rest for the second stage. Each filter is made of Oregon-pine wood, covered with nylon cloth (#161), 2.4 mø and 3.0 m long, surface area 33.5 m^2 and rotation is about 1/4 R.P.M.

The first stage filtration is difficult, and 1.5 - 2.0 times filter area of second stage is necessary. Glue and slaked lime is added in the first stage to get rapid filtration. The life of nylon cloth is about 1,000 hours.

Air pipes are connected to this plant from compressed, vacuum air supply shop where one 150 Kw ($43\ m^3$/min, 3.5 Kg/cm2) compresser, two 110 Kw ($32\ m^3$/min, 3.5 Kg/cm^2) compressers and three 37 Kw ($34\ m^3$/min) vacuum pumps are operating.

2) Water Balance

In hydro-metallurgical process, both balance of SO_4 and water are indispensable factors. The amount of evaporation in below-mentioned evaporators of electrolysis section is 355 l/min (515 l/min in summer), water in the residue is 140 l/min and other evaporations are 50 l/min, and total is 545 l/min. Therefore, 50% of the above amount of water can be used for the washing of the residue and the other 50% can be added to the circulating solution of Pea-body scrubbers, etc. Though construction cost of the evaporator is expensive compared with the conventional heat exchanger, additional recovery of zinc by the use of above amount of water fully compensates the capital expenditure.

Process water is pumped up from the river, which flows near the plant. Water is dechorinated in the double tower ion exchanger with a capacity of 900 m^3/d.

Photo 2 Leaching tanks and thickeners

Table 4 Operating Data of Leaching and Filtration

	Neutral Leach	Acid Leach
Equipment		
Leaching tank	elliptical×1	elliptical×1
dimension (m)	$86 m^2 \times 4.5 H$	$86 m^2 \times 4.5 H$
capacity (m^3)	400	400
material	concrete, lead and acid brick	concrete, lead and acid brick
Thickener	1	1
dimension (m)	21 Ø × 3.2 H	15 Ø × 2.5 H
capacity (m^3)	750	350
material	concrete, lead and acid brick	concrete, lead and acid brick
Oliver-filter	-	6
dimension (m)	-	2.4 Ø × 3.0 L
material	-	wood
Operating		
Temperature (℃)	70	70
PH	4.8 - 5.2	1.8
Time (min)	125	205
Calcine (T/D)	303	130
Spent electrolyte (m^3/D)	2,150	700
Residue (T/D)	-	121
Residue Assay (%)	Zn 20.4, Cu 1.21, Cd 0.20	Ag (g/T) 388, Au (g/T) 2,6

3) Purification

The continuous four stage purification is carried out with the addition of zinc dust and a small amount of arsenic trioxide.

In the first stage, about 70% of copper is precipitated by zinc dust. Neutral solution, overflow from the neutral thickener, is treated 2.5 m^3/min at 70°C and its composition is

Zn	110 - 115	g/l
Cu	0.2 - 1.2	"
Cd	0.25 - 0.40	"
Co	8 - 10	mg/l
Fe	10 - 15	"

If the content of copper in neutral solution is under 300 mg/l, this stage is not necessary. The first stage has two series of cylindrical tanks with cone 4.0 mø x 6.2 m, capacity 50 m^3. The purified solution is sent to 15 mø thickener for separation of precipitated copper. The spigot is discharged and filtered through the automatic filter-press which consists of twelve steel plates covered with rubber, 1.5 m x 1.5 m, filter area 43 m^2. The cake is sent to copper smelter. The solution from the first stage is further treated with zinc dust and arsenic trioxide for the removal of cobalt, remaining copper, cadmium and other impulities such as nickel and antimony.

The second stage has four tanks, two of which are each 5.0 mø x 4.0 mH cylindrical type with cone, capacity 50 m^3, and the other two are each 6.5mø x 4.0 mH cylindrical type with flat bottom, capacity 100 m^3. Usually three tanks are used in series and each tank is connected with launder. Fig. 5 shows test data of cobalt precipitation. The process takes from 1.5 to 2 hours. As observed in Fig. 5, if the retention time is long, cobalt is re-dissolved. An example of cobalt elimination at this stage is as follows:

Inlet solution	10	mg/l
1st tank	4	"
2nd "	2.5	"
3rd "	1.0	"
Filtrate	0.8	"

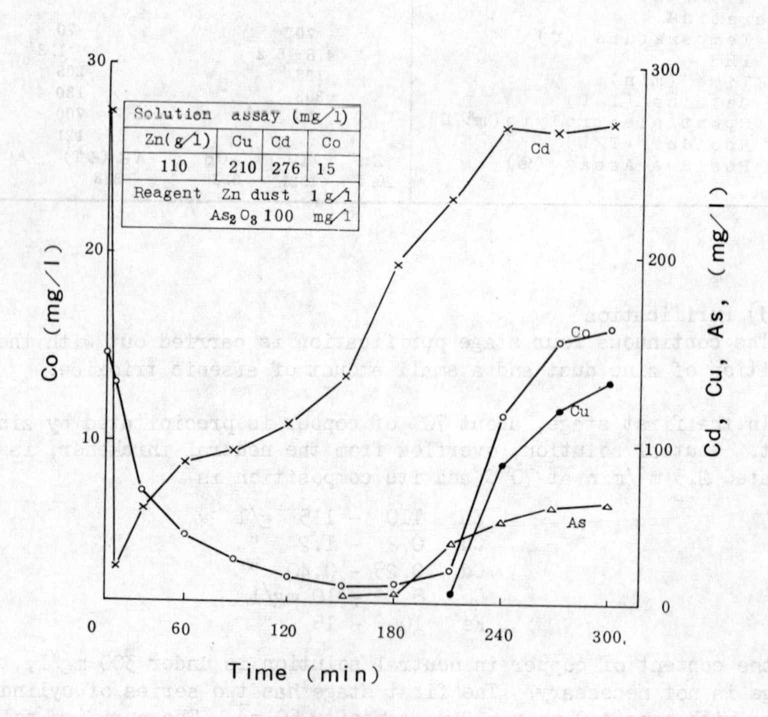

Fig. 5. The precipitating curves of Co, Cd, Cu, and As

Filtration of the solution is accomplished by wooden plate filter-press. Seven filter-presses are provided for second stage filtration, 0.9 m x 0.9 m, 37 plates. Filter-cloth is nylon (#202). The cake is treated as raw material at the cadmium section.

The third stage has one tank, 5.0 mϕ x 4.0 mH cylindrical type with cone, capacity 50 m^3, and the fourth stage has two tanks, 4.0 mϕ x 4.0 mH, cylindrical type with cone, capacity 30 m^3. Complete elimination of cadmium is carried out both at third and fourth stages. Zinc dust is used for each stage.

Solution from the third stage to fourth stage is not filtrated and final filtration after fourth stage is done with seven filter presses. The dimensions of which are the same as those of the second stage.

The filtrate is sent to the electrolysis section as the pure solution and the cake is returned to the second stage.

Table 5 Operating Data of Purification

Equipment	1st	2nd	3rd	4th
Tank				
dimension (m)	4.0 Ø×6.2H×2	6.5Ø×4.0H×2 5.0Ø×4.0H×1	5.0Ø×4.0H×1	4.0Ø×3.8H×2
capacity (m^3)	50	100, 50	50	30
Filter press	1	7	-	7
dimension (m)	1.5L×1.5H ×12plates	0.9L×0.9H ×37plates		0.9L×0.9H ×37plates
surface area (m^2)	43	43	-	43
Operating data				
temperature (℃)	70	75	70	65
time (min)	40	100	20	20
reagent	Zn dust	Zn dust, As_2O_3	Zn dust	Zn dust
Zn dust used (Kg/T-E.Zn)	3.7	22.7	4.5	4.5
AS_2O_3 used (Kg/T-E.Zn)	-	0.70	-	-

Assay of Purified Solution (mg/l)

	Zn (g/l)	Cu	Cd	Fe	Co	Cl
1st		470	330		8-10	
2nd		tr	70		0.8	
3rd		tr	7		0.8	
4th	112	tr	0.1	18	0.8	20

M-3 Electrolysis Section

1) Power

Power is purchased from Tohoku Electric Power Co., and delivered to this plant at 66,000 volts. The maximum demand is approximately 48,500 Kw, and about 6% (3,000 Kw) of this demand is supplied from own Mitsubishi Komatagawa Power Station. 40,000 Kw, 80% of the total power, is transformed down to the request voltage, rectified by the five rectifires and transmitted to the electrolysis plant. The remaining 8,500 Kw is used for plant motors, melting furnace and so forth. The electric station stand s independently.

Table 6 Rectifiers

Unit	I	II	III	IV	V
Transformer					
Capacity (KVA)	6,300	6,560	10,110	11,700	12,000
Si-Rectifier					
Capacity (KW)	5,500	5,400	8,645	10,200	10,184
Voltage (V)	550	540	680	680	675
Ampere (A)	10,000	10,000	13,000	15,000	15,200

2) Electrolysis

The electrolyte contains 115 g/l H_2SO_4 and 47 g/l Zn approximately, and current density is 490 Amp./m^2.

The current efficiency is about 89%. Deposition time is 48 Hrs. Half cathodes of a cell are lifted up at a time, washed in hot water, and hung on a stripping rack, by an electrical hoist provided to every row of cells. One stripping man stripps about 250 Al-cathodes with a hand tool. An automatic stripping machine has been used experimentally for fifth unit. The zinc sheets are dropped on a belt-conveyer, which connects to all stripping racks, and are conveyed to stacking machine. A pile of zinc sheets stacked up about 1 ton is conveyed to melting section by automatic roller-conveyer. And the stripped Al-cathodes are returned to the cell.

3) Cell

The cell room is divided into five electrical units. The first unit is the oldest constructed in 1953 and the fifth was constructed three years ago. Cells are made of P.V.C. with steel frames, and supported on acid-brick piers.

They are insulated from supports with block porcelain insulators to avoid current leakage. The steel frames are covered with fiber-glass reinforced polyester and the cell room basement is covered with asphalt for acid protection.

Owing to the expansion of the plant by stages, arrangement of the cells is a little complicated.

Two rows of cells consist of one block. Each rectifier unit has different number of blocks. Both first and second unit have 4 blocks and 1 block of stand-by for common use when one block of the above units is in cleaning stage. Therefore, 4 blocks are able to be alive and rectifier is always in full operation. Both third and fourth units have 6 blocks and 1 stand-by block. Fifth unit has 7 blocks with 1 stand-by.

Total number of cells is 926 and 832 of them are always in operation. Number of anodes and cathodes in a cell is different for individual unit. In the fifth unit each cell contains 24 anodes and 23 cathodes.

Cathode is made of 99.8% aluminum sheet, 680 W x 1,096 L x 5T (mm) and has rubber edge strips. The life is about 24 months. In the fifth unit, the total submerged area of cathodes in one cell is 31.2 m^2.

Photo 3: Akita Tank House

Anode is 1.3% Ag-Pb plate, 620 W x 1,086 L x 7 T (mm). The life of the anode is about 40 months.

Both anode and cathode bus bars are located on one side of the cell. Electrode spacing is 36.5 mm (anode center to cathode center).

The cells are cleaned and repaired every 40 days. Deposit of manganese dioxide with gypsum is removed from the cells by hand tools and vacuum system. At that time the anodes are transferred on the stripping rack, and the surface deposit is removed. The cleaned anodes are straightened by wooden hammer and then returned to the cells. The cathodes are strightened after washing in hot water and polished by brushing machine automatically.

New cast anodes are treated in extra cells for 40 days to avoid some dissolution of lead.

Furthermore, the formation of the sludge to the new anode is by far more than usual.

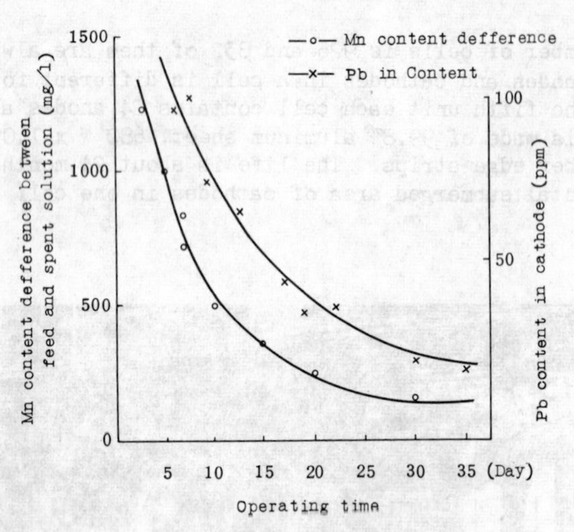

Fig. 6. New anode preparation in extra cell

Fig. 6 shows that reaction equilibrates in three weeks, and the new anode surface seems to be enough transformed. Pb content of the cathode in the cells is high for the period, then gradually drops down.

4) Electrolyte

The electrolyte is supplied continuously to each cell through the drop tubes, which are connected from the main feed pipe for every two rows. The drop tubes are 25 mm in diameter and made of soft P.V.C. with a cock for feed control.

The circulation and cooling of the electrolyte are independent in each unit. The hot electrolyte overflowed from each cell is collected by launders into the hot solution tank (made of brick and lead-lined concrete), having capacity of 50 m^3 and then pumped up to the vacuum evaporating cooler. The cold electrolyte from evaporator is fed to the 50 m^3 cold solution tank through launder, then pumped up to the head tank of each main-feed pipe, and supplied to the cells through the drop tubes. The temperature of the electrolyte is maintained, as nearly as possible, at 37°C.

The purified zinc sulphate solution from the purification process is stocked in 6 neutral solution tanks (total capacity 1,200 m^3) after being cooled by 4 evaporating coolers in summer. About 150 m^3 per hour of neutral solution is added continuously to the hot solution tan[k] from the neutral solution tanks.

Five evaporating coolers are installed for cooling electrolyte. They are similar to each other. Successively improved, the newest one for the fifth unit has two series of evaporating vessels made of lead-lined steel, and a set of cyclone made of P.V.C., water tube condenser made of stainless steel and barometric condenser is connecte[d] to each vessel. Fig. 7 shows the evaporating cooler. Nine cubic meter per minute of electrolyte at 37°C is cooled to about 34°C at the first vessel, the load of which is 1.79×10^6 Kcal/hr and then to 30°C at the second, the load is 1.86×10^6 Kcal/hr. The vapour, 6.3 T/hr, is condensed at the condensers. The total load of two water tube condensers is 1.9×10^6 Kcal/hr and that of two barometric condensers is 1.75×10^6 Kcal/hr. The vacuum is maintained by three 15 Kw vacuum pumps in winter, and two sets of three-stage steam ejecters of 6 Kg/cm^2 steam in other seasons.

Each evaporator has a set of stand-by vessel and cyclone for the purpose of cleaning-up in every three weeks for removing gypsum.

Adhesion of gypsum is troublesome problem to the system.

As addition agents, 100 g of glue and 50 g of beta-naphthol per ton of cathode are added continuously in the cold solution tanks. For the purpose of mist prevention, oil-free soya bean powder is effectively used. Above-mentioned operating figures are shown in Table 7.

Table 7 Operating Data of Electrolysis

Unit	1st	2nd	3rd	4th	5th
Current (A)	9,500	10,000	13,000	15,000	15,200
Current density (A/m^2)	490	490	490	490	490
Cell voltage (V) (include conductor loss)			3.55		
Current efficiency (%)			88-90		
D.C. Power consumption (KWH/T-cathode)			3,300		
Operating cell	144	144	180	182	182
Cell dimension (mm) (L)	1,362	1,355	1,655	1,780	1,780
(W)	736	736	736	736	736
(H)	1,367	1,380	1,380	1,380	1,380
Cell cleaning cycle (Day)			40		
Evaporating cooler		3	2	2	2
operating period (Day)			25		
evaporation (l/min)	40	40	80	90	105
water used (T/min)	5	5	8	8	26
temp. (℃)		2(winter) 15(summer)			7(winter) 20(summer)
solution treated (m^3/min)	5.5	5.5	9	9	9
Outlet temp.(℃)	33	33	32	31	30
Addition agent (g/T-E.Zn)					
Glue		100			
Beta-Naphthol		50			
Soya-Bean		45			

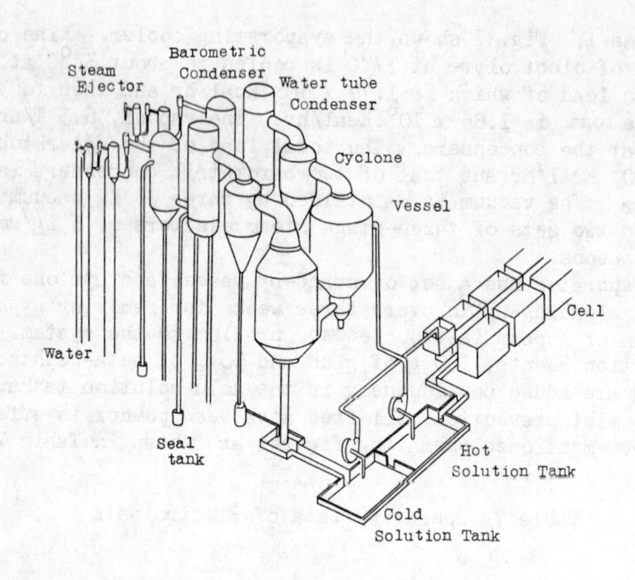

Fig. 7. Vacuum Evaporating Cooler

M-4 Melting and Casting Section

1) Special High Grade Zinc

Cathode zinc is melted in a 1,440 Kw electric low frequency induction furnace with a holding capacity of about 55 tons molten zinc.

The furnace consists of iron plate shell, indulating bricks (SK-32) and stamp mass (SiO_2 61.0%, Al_2O_3 21.5%). It has six inductors, 240 Kw at 500 V, cooled forcibly by air. Cathode sheets are conveyed from electrolytic cell room by belt conveyer and are piled up for one ton lot by automatic sheet stacker. Then piled sheets are sent up to the parallel charge chutes of the melter by roller conveyer. This roller conveyer conveys each pile in good order automatically. The charge chutes are operated by the signal of photo detectors. The temperature of molten zinc is maintained at 470°C. The furnace melts 10 - 11 tons of sheets per hour and power consumption is 100 KwH/ton - Zn. Two horizontal casting machines are arranged beside the furnace. Molten zinc is taken out from the furnace through launder into small holding bath. Metal flow is controlled by the float gauge of the bath automatically. From that bath constant volume of molten metal is taken out by a automatic cup periodically and poured into moving molds. A mechanical skimmer skims the scum. The zinc slab cooled by water spray drops on the pan conveyer and stacked by hydraulic stacker (2 x 30 slabs

Cd cathode sheets are melted in oil-heating furnace under a layer of caustic soda and cast to 1 Kg pencils and 5 Kg plates.

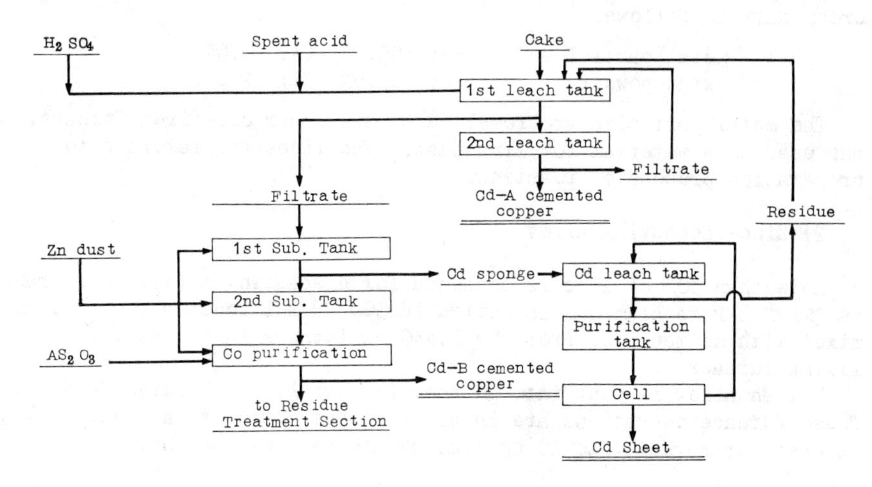

Fig. 8. Flow Sheet of Cadmium Section

Table 8 Operating Data of Cadmium Section

Cd-cake	Cu	Zn	Cd	
465 T/M	11.5	26.0	6.1 (%)	
Cd sponge	2.8	5.8	65.0 (%)	
Zn dust		2.0 T/T Cd-metal		
Electrolyte	Cd	Zn	Co	H_2SO_4
	45 g/l	75 g/l	800 mg/l	100 g/l
Cell voltage		2.6 V		
Power Consumption		1,610 KwH AC/T-Cathode		

S-2 Silver Flotation Section

Silver flotation process had been investigated, and the following process was planned in 1961.

Acid leaching residue → Silver flotation → Sulphate roasting → Residue → Iron factory

This combination process makes a great advantage. It is well known that zinc, copper, cadmium and indium are sulphatized by adequate sulphating admosphere but silver is not. The flotation test had been done for the recovery of silver from the acid leached residue. Finally, 75 - 80% of silver was recovered as Ag_2S and also a little gold, with ACC #404, as collector and M.I.B.C., as frother. In 1962 the silver flotation plant was established to the following flowsheet.

Ammonium chloride is used as a flux for the melting furnace. Metal recovery from cathode to slab is about 98%. An assay of the separated dross says as follows.

Metal particles	Zn: 95.0%	Cl: 0.6%
Oxide powder	Zn: 83.5%	Cl: 2.1%

The metal particles are remelted by the other oil-fired furnace, and used as a material for zinc dust. The fines are returned to preparation process of roasting.

2) Zinc-diecasting Alloy

More than 30% of zinc is consumed for diecasting alloy. Our brand is "MAK". Pure aluminum is melted in 300 Kw multiductor furnace, and mixed with molten zinc from the 1,440 Kw furnace in 240 Kw L.F.I. mixing furnace.

Molten alloy is sent into another 240 Kw. L.F.I. holding furnace. These furnace operations are in batch, about 8 tons at a time. Alloy is cast for market into 10 Kg slab by the casting machine.

S-1 Cadmium Section

The cadmium cake from second purification process is repulped and treated by 2 stage batch leaching with the spent electrolyte and a little H_2SO_4.

This stage has five leaching tanks. The first stage leaching is finally controlled at PH 3.0, 70°C. After filtration, the residue is sent to second stage leaching process with free acid 40 g/l. The second stage residue is sent to the copper smelter as cement copper and filtrate is returned to the first stage leaching. Cadmium sponge is precipitated from the first filtrate which contains 12 gr. cadmium per liter by zinc dust. Spent solution of the cadmium sponge making process contains 500 mg/l Co. Cobalt is precipitated by zinc dust and arsenic trioxide from 500 mg/l to 50 mg/l. The solution still has rather high cobalt, therefore, it is sent to the residue treatment section for special care.

Purification of the solution which is obtained from cadmium sponge is carried out by $KMnO_4$, $Ca(OH)_2$ and Zn dust. Purified cadmium solution contains 150 - 200 g/l Cd.

Thirty cells are prepared for electrolysis. The cell dimension is 1,400 L x 610 W x 1,080 H (mm). The electrolyte contains Cd 45 g/l, Zn 70 - 80 g/l and H_2SO_4 100 - 110 g/l. The current density is 60 A/m^2.

Cooling of electrolyte is carried out down to 25°C by two fleon coolers. The deposition time is 24 Hrs. Spacing between cathode and anode is 50 mm.

Cadmium plant has two rectifiers; one Si-rectifier, capacity 60V x 1,000 A, and the other Se-rectifier, capacity 40 V x 1,000 A.

This silver concentrate is sent to the copper smelter and the tailing is treated at the residue treatment plant. The final residue from the sulphate roasting process is not used for the material of the iron factory because of poor iron content and existence of arsenic. The silver flotation and the sulphate roasting have been operated satisfactorily.

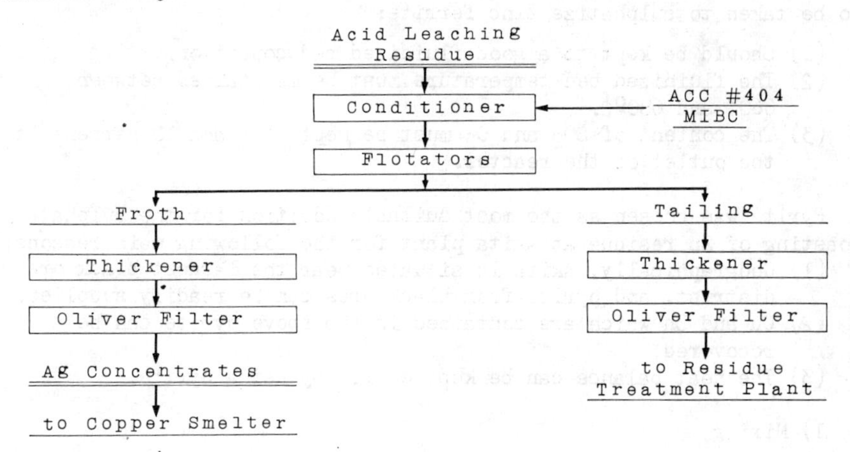

Fig. 9. Flow Sheet of Silver Flotation

Table 9 Operating Data of Silver Flotation

			Assay	Ag (g/T)	Au (g/T)
Density of pulp	(g/l)	1.25			
Concentrates	(%)	3.7	Concentrates	8,000	21
Tailing	(%)	96.3	Tailing	100	2

R-1 Sulphate Roasting

The development of the sulphate roasting of Zn residue using pyrite has been pursued actively at Akita since 1963, and entered into commercial operation in 1965. Although difficulties were encountered, the furnace trials showed that the process was essentially sound. The chemical reactions involved in the roasting of the mixture of zinc ferrite and pyrite at a temperature between 650 and 700°C are as follows:

(1) $4FeS_2 + 8\ ZnOFe_2O_3 + 15O_2 = 8ZnSO_4 + 10Fe_2O_3$
(2) $4FeS_2 + 11O_2 = 2Fe_2O_3 + 8SO_2$

(3) $2SO_2 + O_2 = 2SO_3$
(4) $ZnOFe_2O_3 + SO_3 = ZnSO_4 + Fe_2O_3$

Many experiments were tried for moving the equilibrium towards the right-hand side of the equation (1).

Consequently, it was realized that special conditions would have to be taken to sulphatize Zinc ferrite:

(1) Should be kept to a good fluidized bed condition.
(2) The fluidized bed temperature must be maintained between 660° and 680°C.
(3) The content of SO_2 and O_2 must be kept at 5 and 10 percent at the outlet of the reactor.

Pyrite was chosen as the most suitable addition for the sulphate roasting of Zn residue at Akita plant for the following main reasons;

(1) Geographically, Akita is situated near the largest black ore district, and pyrite from black ores can be readily supplied.
(2) Cu and Zn which are contained in the above pyrite can be recovered.
(3) The heat balance can be kept easily by using pyrite.

1) Mixing

The Zn residue, pulp density of 1.85 - 1.90 weighed by the electromagnetic flowmeter, is fed through a tank (30 m^3) into a log-washer. The pyrite transported from stock house by belt conveyer is weighed by Merrick-scale and then charged into the log-washer. The mixing ratio of Zn residue and pyrite is about 1 to 1. Slurry from the log-washer contains 25 - 26% water and is fed to the agitation tank.

The higher the ratio of Zn-residue to pyrite, the more profitable. But the original Zn-residue slurry contains about 37% water and consequently the mixed slurry has 25% water. For the purpose of keeping the furnace temperature 670°C, it is necessary to mix the pyrite up to 50%.

Sodium sulphate (Na_2SO_4) is added in 0.5% to the pyrite for activation of sulphate reaction.

2) Roasting

Two fluo-solid roasters of Dorrco-type are used for residue treatment, one is 4.3 m in diameter, capacity 70 tons per day, and the other is 7.3 m, capacity 180 tons. They can be used for zinc dead roasting, if necessary, with a little modification. Sulphate roasting is operated at 670°C and air ratio is 1.45 times (theoretical air is 1.19 Nm^3/Kg). When temperature is over 710°C, rate of sulphatizing is decreased rapidly.

For good sulphatizing, it is important to charge the slurry into fluidized bed by setting the feed guns at adequate level.

To achieve a good dispersion of the slurry into the bed, compressed air is introduced through the feed guns. If the ratio of pyrite is higher, heat balance can be maintained, but the material consisting of the fluidized bed decreases and consequently the rate of reaction decreases. The smaller roaster has 2 feed guns and the other roaster has five.

Over-flow is 2.5 m high. Feed guns are located 1.4 m high from the tuyere level and set into the bed 500 mm more from the wall. The bigger furnace is easier to operate than the smaller. This phenomenon is the same as the dead roasting. The start-up of the furnace is more difficult than that of the dead roasting, for the specific heat of the sulphatized Zn-residue bed is smaller. Compared with dead roasting, even if the electric power is interrupted, the bed does not coagulate.

R-2 Leaching and Purification

Combination of thickener and Oliver filter is applied in the leaching process, the same as in the main circuit. The characteristics of this process lies in the extraction of water soluble metals with the abundant quantity of weak solution available at the plant and in the preliminary separation of some metal ions which give injurious effects to electrolysis.

Two 50 m^3 tanks are used for leaching. In the first tank acidity is maintained 3-5 g/l H_2SO_4, and ferrous ion is oxidized by $KMnO_4$. In the second tank pH is controlled at 3.0-3.5 by $CaCO_3$.

Composition of the leached solution, for example, is Zn 60-80 g/l, Cu 3-5 g/l, Cd 0.4-0.7 g/l and Co 30-70 mg/l.

It is necessary to eliminate As, Sb, Ge etc. with Fe ions, and pH control is very important in order to avoid Cu precipitating into final residue.

Preliminary purification is carried out in two stages. The first stage is for Cu and the second stage is for Co. The filtrate is returned to the acid leaching tank of the main circuit. Final residue is filtered by Oliver filters. Filterability is twice easier than the residue of the main circuit. The residue is sent to the dump yard by tank car.

R-3 Controlling of SO_4

Calcium carbonate is used for the control of sulphate balance of the total plant. Especially Akita Plant has a new source of sulphate ion from the residue treatment section.

Three 70 m^3 reaction tanks and 10 automatic centrifuges (1.22 m bascket diameter) are provided for the purpose. The plant treats a part of spent electrolyte (300 m^3/d) from the electrolysis process and the enriched solution (150 m^3/d) from the circulating plant for the Pea-body scrubbers.

About 2,600 tons of gypsum is produced monthly and sold to cement factory. The assay is as follows.

H_2O 7.0%, Zn 0.4%, CaO 32%, SO_3 44%

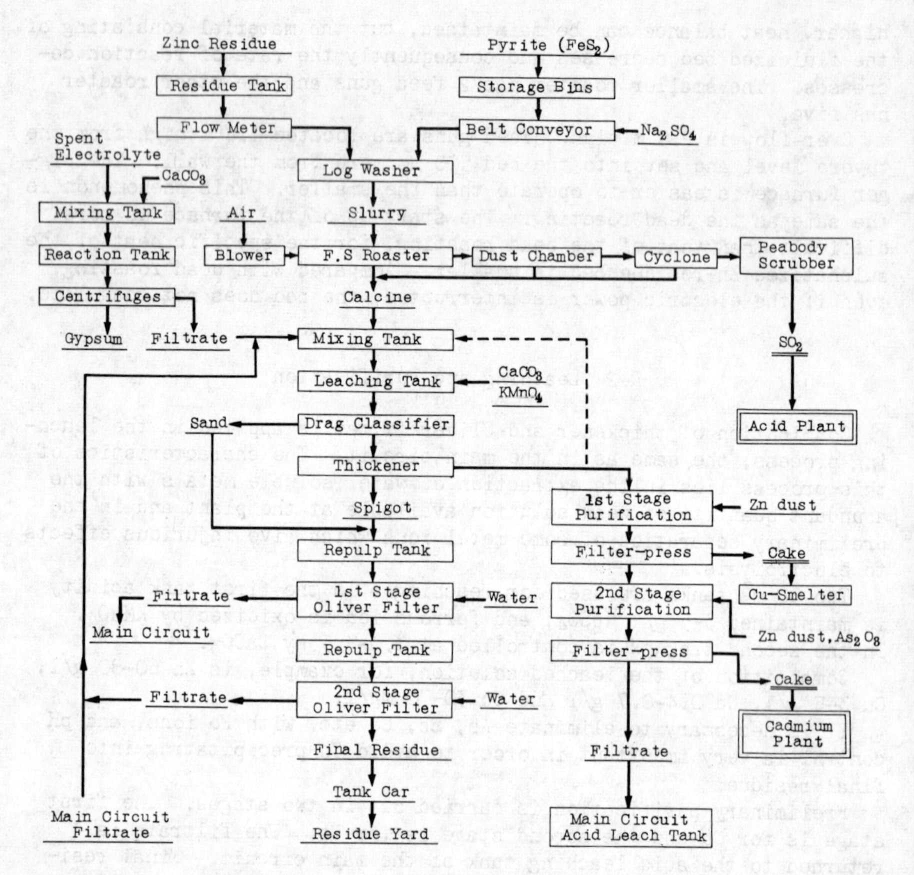

Fig. 10. Flow Sheet of Residue Treatment

Table 10 Operating Data of Residue Treatment

Zn-residue	(T/M)	3,550	
Pyrite		3,750	
Roaster		Dorrco Fluo-solid × 2	
dimension	(m)	4.3 Ø × 6.0 H	7.3 Ø × 6.1 H
capacity	(T/D)	70	180
Entrance air	(Nm^3/min)	85	215
Exit gas	(Nm^3/min)	121	275
SO_2 assay	(%)	4.7	5.2
temp.	(℃)	670	670

Assay	(%)	Zn	Cu	Cd	S	Fe
Zn-residue		19.7	1.21	0.19	-	31.5
Pyrite		0.35	0.38	-	46.36	41.5
Final residue		2.60	0.20	0.01	2.9	46.5

Conclusion

This plant has been expanded by stages from 560 T/M to 7,500 T/M in 16 years. Though nearly all of the old installations are still used with modification, much efforts have been made for the mechanization and for continuous operation every time new equipments were added.

The acid has been consumed in the subsiduary fertilizer plant. For the further expansion of Akita plant to 15,000 T/M, new constructions of titanium white plant and aluminum fluoride plant are under planning.

In order to get more economical power, a geothermal power plant in Akita district is under investigation.

Table 11
Labour, Power Consumption &, Yield in Akita Plant (1970)

Labour;	
Roasting	74
SO_4 Control	8
Leaching and Filtration	36
Purification	49
Electrolysis	114
Melting and Casting	23
Cadmium	18
Flotation	12
	(334)
Maintenance, Clerk, Staff and others	173
Total	507

Power Consumption;	
Dead Roasting	70 KwH/T-Zn ore
sulphate Roasting	120 KwH/T-treated ore
Refining	3,858 KwH/T-E.Zn
Electrolysis	3,457 KwH/T-Cathode
Melting	100 KwH/T-E.Zn
Motors and so forth	230 KwH/T-E.Zn
Cadmium	3,109 KwH/T-E.Cd
Total Power Consumption	4,296 KwH/T-E.Zn

Yield (%);					
Zn	Cu	Cd	SO_2	Au	Ag
93.6	82.4	84.1	86.7	21.9	75.2

References

1. Katsuji Nakanishi, "How Mitsubishi's New Akita Plant makes 99.997% Electrolytic Zinc," World Mining, Vol. 8, No. 11, October 1955, pp. 56 - 59.

2. Eifu Moriyama and Yuzo Yamamoto, "Zinc Smelting at Akita Plant," Journal of the Mining and Metallurgical Institute of Japan, Vol. 85, No. 976, August 1969, pp. 633 - 635.

3. Eifu Moriyama and Yuzo Yamamoto, "Zinc Residue Treatment by Sulphate Roasting," Journal of the Mining and Metallurgical Institute of Japan, Vol. 85, No. 976, August 1969, pp. 642 - 644.

4. Eifu Moriyama, Tokutaro Ito and Yuzo Yamamoto, Japanese Patent 537551

Chapter 8

ELECTROLYTIC ZINC PLANT AND RESIDUE RECOVERY
DET NORSKE ZINKKOMPANI A/S
Eitrheim, Odda, Norway

Georg Steintveit
Director of Research and Development

Abstract

Det Norske Zinkkompani A/S was established in 1924, on the initiative of the Compagnie Royale Asturienne des Mines. Experimental electrothermic zinc production was carried out on industrial scale for a two-year period, but the problems of electrothermic smelting were not solved. A license for the electrolytic zinc production process was then obtained from the Anaconda Copper Mining Co.

A plant for electrolytic zinc production was built, near the small fjord town of Odda in Hardanger, West Norway. The production was based on zinc ore from Spain, and cheap local hydro-electric power. The plant came into operation in 1929. Annual capacity, 36,000 tons.

In 1964 a long-term agreement was concluded with Boliden AB by which Det Norske Zinkkompani is secured the raw materials basis for an expansion of the annual capacity to 100,000 tons of zinc.

Since World War II, the company has been pursuing extensive research and development programs. As a result, various sections have been rebuilt: new unloading and storage facilities, a 250 ton per day Fluid Bed Roaster with contact plant, new continuous leaching system, integrating the Jarosite Residue Process, new solution purification section - upgrading the solution quality for a 600 Amp/m^2 current density Tank Room operation -, installation of induction furnaces for cathode melting with casting machines and automatic stacking of slabs.

Simultaneously, instrumentation, and methods of automatic control have been developed and introduced, providing conditions for optimal plant operations.

Introduction

Within the electrolytic zinc industry Det Norske Zinkkompani can be reckoned as a relatively old company. Due to constant development and modernization during the last 20 years, the company presents itself as a new plant with the most up-to-date production methods. A review of the historical development will be given in the following

The Company was established on the initiative of the Belgian Corpo ration of Compagnie Royale Asturienne des Mines in 1924. The same year development work on electrothermic zinc production started at Tyssedal, Hardanger, near the power station, A/S Tyssefaldene, where rights had been acquired for delivery of hydro-electric power. The production was based upon F. Tharaldsen's electrothermic process, which already had shown promising results in some preliminary industri al tests at Jössingfjord, Southern Norway.

However, experiments during the year 1924-26 could not be consider as satisfactory, and a license was then obtained from the Anaconda Copper Mining Company for the hydrometallurgical zinc process that had shown successful results in U.S.A. and Canada.

A plant was built at Eitrheim, a peninsula near Odda at the head of the Sörfjord, Hardanger, not far from the power station mentioned above. Production started in 1929, with a scheduled annual capacity of 36,000 metric tons of zinc slabs.

The production of zinc has subsequently increased, and supplementary production of byproducts has been taken up. The manufacture of cadmium was started in 1931, sulphuric acid in 1939, superphospha in 1949, and phosphoric acid with triplephosphate in 1957. In april 1970 an aluminium fluoride plant went on stream, replacing the manufacture of superphosphate, which was closed down in 1969.

Since World War II constant modernization of the plant has been going on. In 1970 the annual capacity is 75,000 tons of high grade zinc, 130 tons of electrolytic cadmium, 50,000 tons of 75 per cent Pettersen sulphuric acid, 75,000 tons of 98 per cent contact acid, 20,000 tons of phosphoric acid and 20,000 tons of aluminium fluoride Minor quantities of copper cement are also produced.
In 1968 a new leaching section was added, to permit separate leachin of zinc oxides. In the same year a Hot Acid Leaching and the Jarosi iron precipitation process, independently developed and patented in 1965, by Det Norske Zinkkompani and Electrolytic Zinc Company of Australasia, were integrated in the leaching plant.

Two new products, a lead tin residue from the oxide leaching, and a lead silver residue from the Hot Acid Leaching, have resulted.

Raw Materials

Originally the Eitrheim plant was based upon the treatment of zinc ore from the Reocin Mine in Spain, but the raw material situation changed completely during the years, and the plant operated until 1964 as a pure custom smelter with imports of a variety of ores from different parts of the world. In that year a long-term collaboration agreement was concluded between the company, Asturienne and Boliden AB of Sweden which secured for the company the basis of its raw materials supply, including about 30.000 tons per year of zinc oxides from Boliden's slag fuming plant, enabling a further expansion of the company's production capacity to 100.000 tons of zinc per year.

As part of this agreement Boliden AB became a 50 % shareholder of the company.

Unloading and Storage

Vessels of up to 20,000 tons can be received at the Company's 300 meter long quay, where unloading is performed with three cranes at an average rate of 3,000 tons per day.

The zinc ore is taken from the ship's hull by grabs, discharging to three weighing hoppers with automatic tare recording. The weighing hoppers are mounted on rails on a bridge along the quay. A reversable link-belt conveyor, forming the bottom of the hoppers, delivers the ores to a rubber belt conveyer leading to the storage silo about 100 meters from the quay.

The silo now consists of 20 bins with a capacity of 3,000 tons each, or a total of 60,000 tons storage capacity. Additional provisions have been made for storage in open air of up to 15,000 tons. Various grades of concentrates may thus be stored separately. Reclaiming of the concentrate from the bins and out-door storage is performed by a travelling crane equipped with grab and aided by pay-loaders, which deliver the ore to the Roasting Division.

Roasting and Treatment of Roaster Gases

Two Wedge furnaces and a Pettersen sulphuric acid plant were completed in 1929, but due to the difficult market situation for sulphuric acid in Norway, no roasting of zinc concentrate was performed until 1938. The entire supply of calcine had been delivered from roasting plants in Belgium, France and Spain.

That year roasting started at Eitrheim after the conversion of one of the Wedge-furnaces into the Cominco suspension roasting system. This was the first plant outside America to adopt the Flash-roasting technique. The rebuilding of the second furnace was finished in 1940. Each furnace can roast 90 tons concentrate per day.

In 1963 a new Fluid Bed Roaster was started, making the company completely independent of foreign roasting. The roaster was built by the company staff according to specifications from Société de la Vieille Montagne. With a roasting capacity of 250 tons concentrate per day, it was in 1963 the largest Fluid Bed furnace for zinc concentrate roasting in operation.

The basic data of the furnace are:

Height of combustion chamber	11.0 m
Maximum diameter of chamber	10.3 m
Diameter of roasting grill	7.0 m
Roasting area	38.0 m^2
Specific roasting capacity	6.4 tons/m^2/24h

The air pressure in the wind box is 1.6 m water column and is secured by two turbo ventilators, rotating at 3,800 rpm, power consumption 260 kW. One of the blowers serves as spare. Total air quantity is 18,000 m^3, distributed through 3,500 nozzles each of 6 mm diameter. The boiler is of Lamont type with forced circulation and equipped with mechanical cleaning devices. With an outlet gas temperature from the boiler of 250°C, the steam production is 1.1 ton per ton of concentrate, at a pressure of 3.9 MN/m^2 (40 kgf/cm^2).

The concentrate is taken by grab from the main silos and delivered by rubber belts to three 150 tons bins with link-belt bottom discharg The concentrate mixture from these bins, with moisture contents varying from 5 to 10 per cent, passes a 4" screen to remove lumps. The oversize is desintegrated and goes with the fines to a feed bin above the charging machinery, consisting of a disc feeder above two rubber belt slingers, throwing the concentrate into the furnace at a speed of 10 m per sec. Only one slinger is in operation at a time.

The fluidized bed is 1.6 m deep and is operated with no overflow. 5 to 10 per cent of calcine is drawn from the bottom of the bed to maintain the right pressure in the furnace.

Typical Analyses and Particle Sizes of Bed in per cent

Zn	54.3	+ 8 mesh	14.7	+ 100 mesh	15.6
Fe	9.8	+ 14 mesh	11.4	+ 150 mesh	8.4
S-SO_4	1.4	+ 28 mesh	6.2	+ 200 mesh	6.7
S-S	0.2	+ 65 mesh	33.5	- 200 mesh	3.5

The transport system for calcine from Cotrell, cyclones, boiler and underflow Fluid Bed Roaster to the elevators, lifting the calcine to storage, consists of 19 screw conceyors, 14 of which are of standard cross section with water-cooled shaft. The screws have no coolin jacket.

To minimize dust nuisance, the calcine is humidified to 7 per cent moisture before delivery to the Leaching Plant.

Typical Analyses and Particle Sizes of the Humidified Calcine in per cent

Zn	- 55.0	Cd	- 0.2	Co	- 0.003	+ 65 mesh	- 24.9
$Zn_{a.s.}$	- 93.0	Pb	- 1.5	Ni	- 0.001	+ 100 mesh	- 5.0
$Zn_{w.s.}$	- 0.5	SiO_2	- 2.0	Sb	- 0.070	+ 150 mesh	5.0
S-S	- 0.2	Al_2O_3	- 0.4	As	- 0.030	+ 200 mesh	- 10.9
$S\text{-}SO_4$	- 2.8	CaO	- 0.5	Ge	- 0.001	- 200 mesh	- 54.2
Fe	- 8.5	MgO	- 0.7	Cl	- 0.010		
$Fe^{++}_{a.s.}$	- 0.1	Mn_3O_4	- 0.2	F	- 0.002		
Cu	- 0.5	$BaSO_4$	- 0.4	Ag	- 80 g/t		

The gases from the Fluid Bed Roaster with 8 to 9 per cent SO_2 content are converted to 98 per cent sulphuric acid in a single contact Lurgi Acid Plant.
The conversion is 98 per cent. Daily capacity is 220 tons monohydrate.

The tail gases from the sulphuric plant are sent through 4 brick lined concrete absorption towers filled with limestone. The capacity of these towers is sufficient to absorb all SO_2 gas from the roaster, as they were originally erected to establish flexibility in the roasting operations, when the market situation for sulphuric acid was difficult.

For byproduct acid storage three 4,000 m^3 tanks serve for contact acid and one 4,000 m^3 neoprene lined storage tank for phosphoric acid, 46-48 per cent P_2O_5.

Another 250 tons fluid bed roasting unit with corresponding contact plant equipped with installations for mercury recovery is at present being planned to finally replace the flash furnaces and the old tower plant.

Leaching

The humidified calcine from the mixing station in the Roasting Plant is transported to the Leaching Plant by a 10-ton side-dump lorry and weighed there. The calcine is dumped into a hopper and discharged by a bottom link belt conveyor on to a rubber belt, running through an inclined steel pipe to the top of the Calcine silo in the Leaching building. Total lifting height 27 m.

This means of transportation replaced the original system of railway wagons and ship elevators in 1955.

The Anaconda Leaching Procedure, adopted in 1929, was being applie principally unchanged up to 1956. The original installations consist of 2 Pachuca tanks, 3 m Ø and 6 m height for Head Acid preparation, 11 similar Pachucas for Neutral Leach, and 6 for Acid Leach. Further there were auxiliary tanks for iron solution makeup, 3 Dorr Classifie for the Neutral Leach discharge, 5 neutral and 4 acid Dorr Thickeners each 500 m^3 capacity and 15 m Ø, for the settling operation. The tanks and thickeners were all made of Oregon fir, which had shown relatively satisfactory performance during years of operation.

However, after 25 years of service it became apparent, that complete renewal of the leaching equipment would gradually be necessary, and we found it accordingly logical to take our entire hydrometallurg cal zinc production up for consideration, in order to obtain optimal results.

The low-density low-acidity process has the advantage of being operated continuously. The drawbacks are the difficult leaching control when manually operated, particularly when treating varying raw materials, and the great volume of solution to be handled per unit of zinc extracted.

To obtain the benefits of minimum volume of solution and higher current densities during electrolyses, newer zinc plants have tended to choose a moderate form of the original Taiton process, based upon batch operation.

Extensive laboratory experiments carried out to study the dynamics of the process, however, did never indicate that the results would be from a continuous operation inferior to those obtained in a batch process, providing the right parameters actually could be determined and controlled.

It has been our experience that the Pachuca tank was not a particularly efficient type of reactor, in spite of its being widely used, and we decided to introduce normal agitation tanks for the leaching operation. Our preliminary plantscale tests indicated that the performance of the process improved radically, and the development of instrument control was much facilitated.

We were thus able to conclude that a new, continuous, highly automatically operated leaching system, might very well be established, with solution densities comparable to the modified Tainton process.

As provisional equipment, this system was gradually introduced as from 1956, until the permanent installations, including a control room, were completed in 1961, constituting the first step of the general modernization program for the entire leaching plant. In principle the process followed the established flowsheet: neutral leach, thickening, and acid leach of the neutral sludge. The leach residue, with 16 to 18 per cent zinc, was treated by sulphatizing roasting, first introduced in 1950.

In the hydrometallurgical zinc practice, which is a single leaching batch process, or a double leaching continuous process, in which a neutral leach is followed by an acid leach, or an acid leach is followed by a neutralization step, the acidities are kept sufficiently low to prevent the dissolution of the zinc ferrites, because of the difficult separation properties of ferric hydroxides.

The quantity of zinc dissolved according to common leaching practice has thus mainly been limited to the ZnO-content in the calcine only.

By the sulphatizing roasting the ferrites are broken up, and the separation of the iron and zinc is effected thermically at 650°C, at which temperature the ferric sulphates are decomposed. In a subsequent water leaching of the sulphatized residue the zinc sulphate is dissolved, while the iron oxides are left insoluble.

From an economical point of view, however, it was not interesting to increase the capacity of the sulphatizing roasting installation required for our expanded production. We therefore directed our efforts toward the possibilities of dissolving the ferrites completely in hot cell acid, and finding a procedure to precipitate the resulting great iron quantities brought into solution as compounds that might be separated from the zinc solution by standard separation practice.

The advantage of such a process would not only be high recoveries of zinc, copper and cadmium, but it might also be possible to separate an insoluble residue that would contain the lead and silver values present in the calcine in a rather concentrated form.

The Jarosite Process

From the original work by W.E. Mitchell, Anaconda Copper Mining Co., on treating zinc calcine and plant residue, ref.: U.S. Patent No. 1.834.960, 1930, it was known that iron to some extent could be precipitated as basic iron sulphate in a slightly acid solution. However, according to our experience, the precipitation of iron as ordinary basic sulphates was never complete, and was also difficult to control, resulting in a mixture of basic sulphates and hydroxides with difficult settling and filtration properties.

We discovered then that the presence of ammonium or alkali ions at certain acidities, temperatures and reaction times, favourably influenced the formation of very insoluble complex and crystalline basic iron compounds. Ref. Norwegian Patent No. 108.047, 1965, and the corresponding U.S. Patent No. 3.434.947.

From the chemical composition, from infra red and X-ray structure analyses we found, that these compounds were very similar to the carphosiderite and Jarosites found in nature.

The chemical reactions taking place during the precipitation of the basic iron sulphates are very complex, but may be summarized as follows:

(1): $3Fe_2(SO_4) + 6H_2O = 6Fe(OH)SO_4 + 3H_2SO_4$

(2): $4Fe(OH)SO_4 + 4H_2O = 2Fe_2(OH)_4SO_4 + 2H_2SO_4$

(3): $2Fe(OH)SO_4 + 2Fe_2(OH)_4SO_4 + 2NH_4OH = (NH_4)_2Fe_6(SO_4)_4(OH_{12}) + 5H_2$

(4): $2Fe(OH)SO_4 + 2Fe_2(OH)_4 \cdot SO_4 + Na_2SO_4 + 2H_2O = Na_2Fe_6(SO_4)_4(OH)_{12} + 6H_2SO_4$

(5): $2Fe(OH)SO_4 + 2Fe_2(OH)_4 \cdot SO_4 + 4H_2O = (H_3O)_2Fe_6(SO_4)_4(OH)_{12} + 5H_2$

(6): (1)+(2)+(3):
$3Fe_2(SO_4)_3 + 10H_2O + 2NH_4OH = (NH_4)_2Fe_6(SO_4)_4(OH)_{12} + 5H_2$
ammonium jarosite

(7): (1)+(2)+(4):
$3Fe_2(SO_4)_3 + 12H_2O + Na_2SO_4 = Na_2Fe_6(SO_4)_4(OH)_{12} + 6H_2SO_4$
carphosiderite

(8): (1)+(2)+(5):
$3Fe_2(SO_4)_3 + 14H_2O = (H_3O)_2Fe_6(SO_4)_4(OH)_{12} + 5H_2$
carphosiderite

The hydrolysis taking place according to (1) and (2) needs an initial period to get started, seems to be rather slow and may determine the speed of reaction required to get the iron precipitation completed.

From the chemical equations for the Jarosite formation it is emphasized that the sulphuric acid produced during the hydrolysis must be neutralized for the reactions to get completed. The best neutralization agent is pure ZnO, but any ZnO-containing material can be used. When soluble iron oxides are present together with the zinc oxides, the same iron oxides also take part in the precipitation of Jarosite as shown below.

(9): $ZnO + H_2SO_4 = ZnSO_4 + H_2O$

(10): $Fe_2O_3 + 3H_2SO_4 = Fe_2(SO_4)_3 + 3H_2O$

(11): (6)+5·(9):
$3Fe_2(SO_4)_3 + 5ZnO + 2NH_4OH + 5H_2O = (NH_4)_2Fe_6(SO_4)_4(OH)_{12} + ZnS$

(12): 3·(6)+5·(10):
$4Fe_2(SO_4)_3 + Fe_2O_3 + 6NH_4OH + 15H_2O = 3(NH_4)_2Fe_6(SO_4)_4(OH)_{12}$

The consumption of alkal ions necessary for the Jarosite formation can be calculated stoichiometrically according to the formulas. For NH_3 it is about 10 per cent of the precipitated iron quantity. The Jarosite compounds remove also SO_4-ion from the solution. The practical consumption is a little less than one part SO_4 for one part of iron.

In many cases fluid bed calcine with high content of S-SO_4 introduces excess SO_4 in the circuit. The Jarosite process will solve the difficult problem of keeping the sulphate inventory in balance.

It is desirable to use zinc oxide or roasted zinc ores low in iron as neutralization agents for the Jarosite precipitation, but in practical operation the main calcine raw material for the zinc production is often the only material available for the neutralization purpose.

At the acidities kept during the neutralization step, pH 1.5, only the acid soluble zinc and part of the iron oxides are dissolved, and the zinc ferrites are not broken up. Although not effecting the neutralization operation as such, this means less intensive leaching of the quantity of calcine used here, resulting in a reduction of the overall recoveries.

The Jarosite Acid Washing

To overcome this problem, we have introduced a special hot leaching of the jarosite precipitate. Ref. Norwegian Patent Application No. 3926-69. The acidities and temperatures during this Jarosite acid washing are similar to those in the Hot Acid Leaching, and are thus sufficient to dissolve zinc ferrites in the calcine residue, mixed with the Jarosites, while the acide insoluble Jarosites themselves are not attacked. The acid washed residue turns after this treatment pure yellow, the colour of the Jarosites.

The zinc recovery is increased by 1.5-2.5 per cent by the Acid Washing of Jarosite residue, and also for Cu, Cd considerable improvement in the recoveries can be taken into account.

Jarosite Precipitation in Leaching Plant Operation

The precipitation of crystalline Jarosite compounds is a clue to get higher degree of extraction of the valuable metals in the hydrometallurgy of zinc, since the dissolution of iron is no longer a limiting factor for the acidity strength applied in the leaching operation. How can now the Jarosite precipitation be applied in practical production?

Separate Residue Treatment

A straight-forward procedure is to precipitate iron as Jarosite from the zinc-iron sulphate solution obtained when leaching ordinary zinc plant residues in hot cell acid. This method is particularly valuable where a storage of old residues is available.

Zinc Sinter As Raw Material

Zinc sinter may in some very special cases be of interest partly as raw material for electrolytic zinc production. However, acid solubility of iron in a sintered zinc concentrate, a Robson Sinter, is about 90 per cent, which is not tolerable in normal hydrometallur cal zinc production. The application of the Jarosite precipitation the dissolved iron quantities, has been the answer to the iron recir lation problem.

Integration of the Jarosite Precipitation in the Leaching Process

The process flowsheet can be simplified and the plant operation optimized, if the Hot Acid Leaching and the Jarosite precipitation are integrated directly in the leaching operation.

We have in Figs. 1, 2, 3 and 4 given four examples of how this can be done.

In Fig. 1 we start with a neutral leach of the calcine. The resulting pulp is thickened and the sludge is leached in hot cell acid at conditions to dissolve the zinc ferrites. The remaining insolubl residue, containing the lead and silver present in the calcine, is separated from the acid iron-zinc solution. The iron is then precip tated as Jarosite, separated as a Jarosite residue, while the practi cally ironfree solution is returned to the Neutral Leach.

In Fig. 2 we start directly with Hot Acid Leaching of the calcine The pulp with the insoluble lead and silver residue is separated from the iron-zinc solution, which in the first hand undergoes Jarosite precipitation and then, as a second step, a final neutralization for complete removal of the iron to make the neutral soluti for the subsequent zinc dust purification.

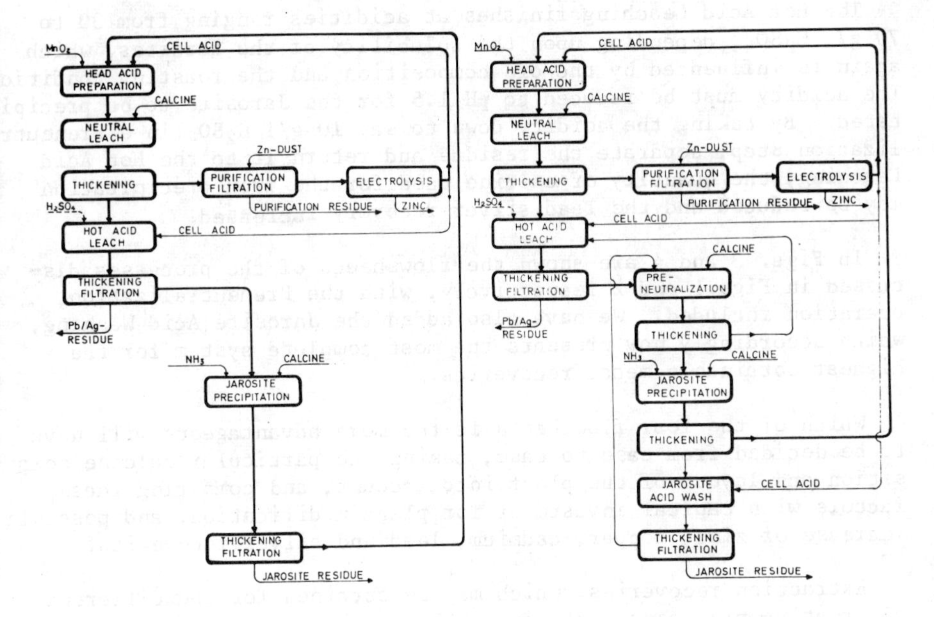

Fig. 1

Fig. 3

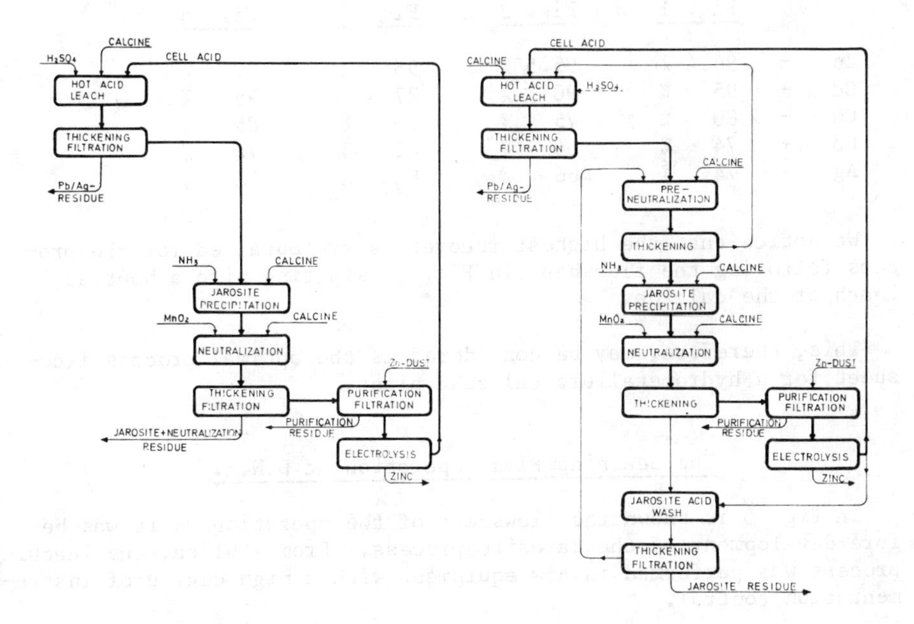

Fig. 2

Fig. 4

The Hot Acid Leaching finishes at acidities ranging from 30 to 70 g/l H_2SO_4, depending upon the solubility of the ferrites, which again is influenced by the ore composition and the roasting condition The acidity must be reduced to pH 1.5 for the Jarosite to be precipitated. By taking the acidity down to say 10 g/l H_2SO_4 in a Preneutralization Step, separate the residue and return it to the Hot Acid Leaching, the quantity of calcine used for the iron precipitation may be reduced and the lead silver recovery increased.

In Figs. 3 and 4 are shown the flowsheets of the processes discussed in Figs.1 and 2 respectively, with the Preneutralization operation included. We have also added the Jarosite Acid Washing, which accordingly now presents the most complete system for the highest obtainable metal recoveries.

Which of the four flowsheets is the more advantageous will have to be decided from case to case, taking the particular calcine composition and layout of the plant into account, and comparing these factors with capital investment for plant modification, and possible increase of zinc, copper, cadmium, lead and silver recoveries.

Extraction recoveries, which may be obtained for the different alternative processes, are given below. The figures are based upon calculation for calcines with 56-57 per cent Zn and 10-11 per cent Fe, and have been verified experimentally for several types of calcin

	Fig. 1	Fig. 2	Fig. 3	Fig. 4
Zn -	96.4 %	95.5 %	98 %	97 %
Cd -	95 %	90 %	97 %	95 %
Cu -	80 %	75 %	90 %	85 %
Pb -	74 %	66 %	82 %	78 %
Ag -	74 %	66 %	82 %	78 %

We notice that the highest recoveries are obtained for the process following the flowsheet in Fig. 3, starting with a Neutral Leach of the calcine.

This, therefore, may be considered as the optimal process flowsheet for a hydrometallurgical zinc plant.

The Leaching Plant Operation at D.N.Z.

In Fig. 5 is shown the flowsheet of the operation as it was before development of the Jarosite process. From 1961 on, the leaching process was performed in new equipment with a high degree of instrumentation control.

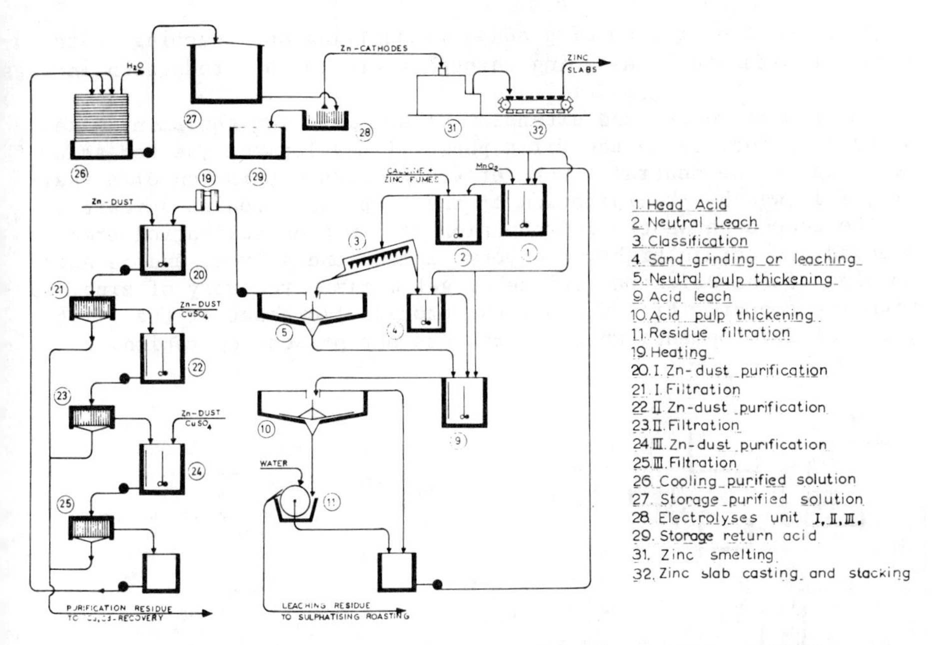

Fig. 5 - Flowsheet D.N.Z. from 1956 to 1968

The zinc dust purification was gradually changed into a two-step continuous operation. A new process for recovery of zinc, copper and cadmium without recycling the impurities cobalt and nickel, was also developed. As a result of higher solution purity we were able to raise the zinc content of neutral solution from the typical low density concentration 130 g/l to the medium density 180 g/l Zn. The corresponding cell acid is 190 to 200 g/l H_2SO_4.

In 1964, when we introduced the zinc oxide fumes from the new Boliden slag fuming plant as a 25 per cent mixture with the calcine, the level of impurities in the Neutral Thickener Overflow, particularly arsenic and antimony, increased, and we had to add a third zinc dust purification with copper sulphate activation to maintain the required purity of the zinc solution for the established Tank Room operation.

The fumes contain: 70% Zn, 0.005% Cd, 0.15% Cu, 1.0% Fe, 6% Pb, 1.0% Sn, 0.5% As, 0.5% Sb, 0.01% Ni.

After having developed the method of controlling the iron precipitation, realizing the possibilities for a simple and efficient residue treatment, we decided to incorporate the Hot Acid Leaching and the Jarosite process in our leaching system, in principle following the flowsheet shown in Fig. 3, rather than to establish a separate residue plant as an addition to our normal leaching procedure.

We faced the problem of gradual remodelling our leaching installation, simultaneously as going through a program of production increas

The rearrangement and extension of our leaching equipment were planned to include in the first phase of development the Hot Acid Leaching of the Neutral Thickener sludge with separation of a residue, followed by precipitation of the dissolved iron as Jarosite. In the second phase the introduction of a preneutralization step is planned, to obtain higher recovery of lead and silver, and an Acid Washing of the Jarosite residue to get maximum recovery of zinc, cadmium and copper. Fig. 6 shows the process flowsheet of the first phase of development, which represents our present operation.

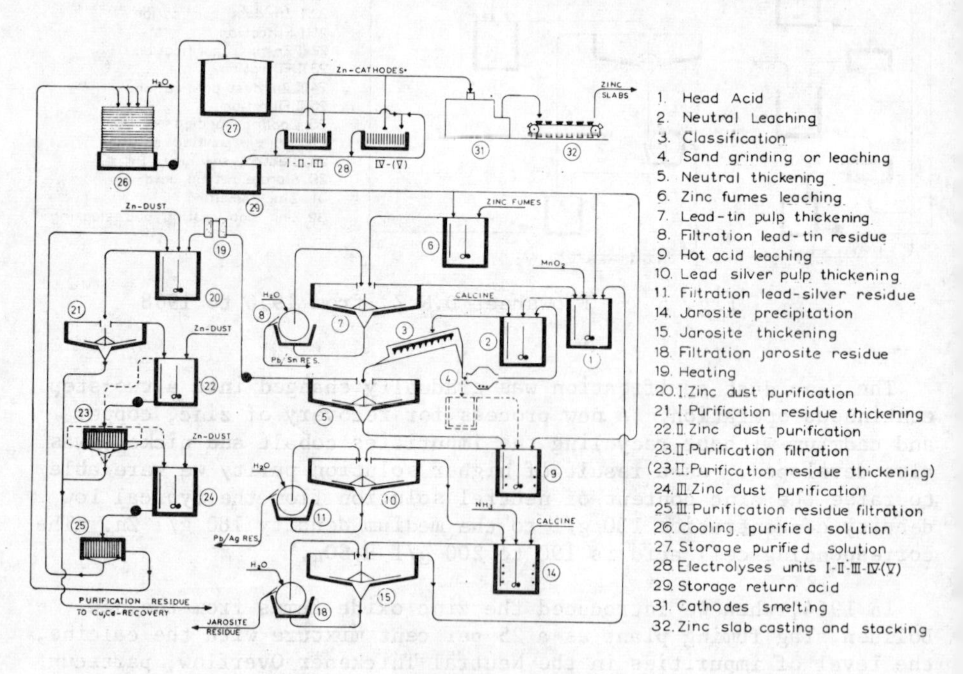

Fig. 6 - Flowsheet D.N.Z. from 1968 to 1971. Jarosite Process Integr.

In Fig. 7 is then shown the complete flowsheet of the zinc plant, where the process steps in the second phase of development also are added.

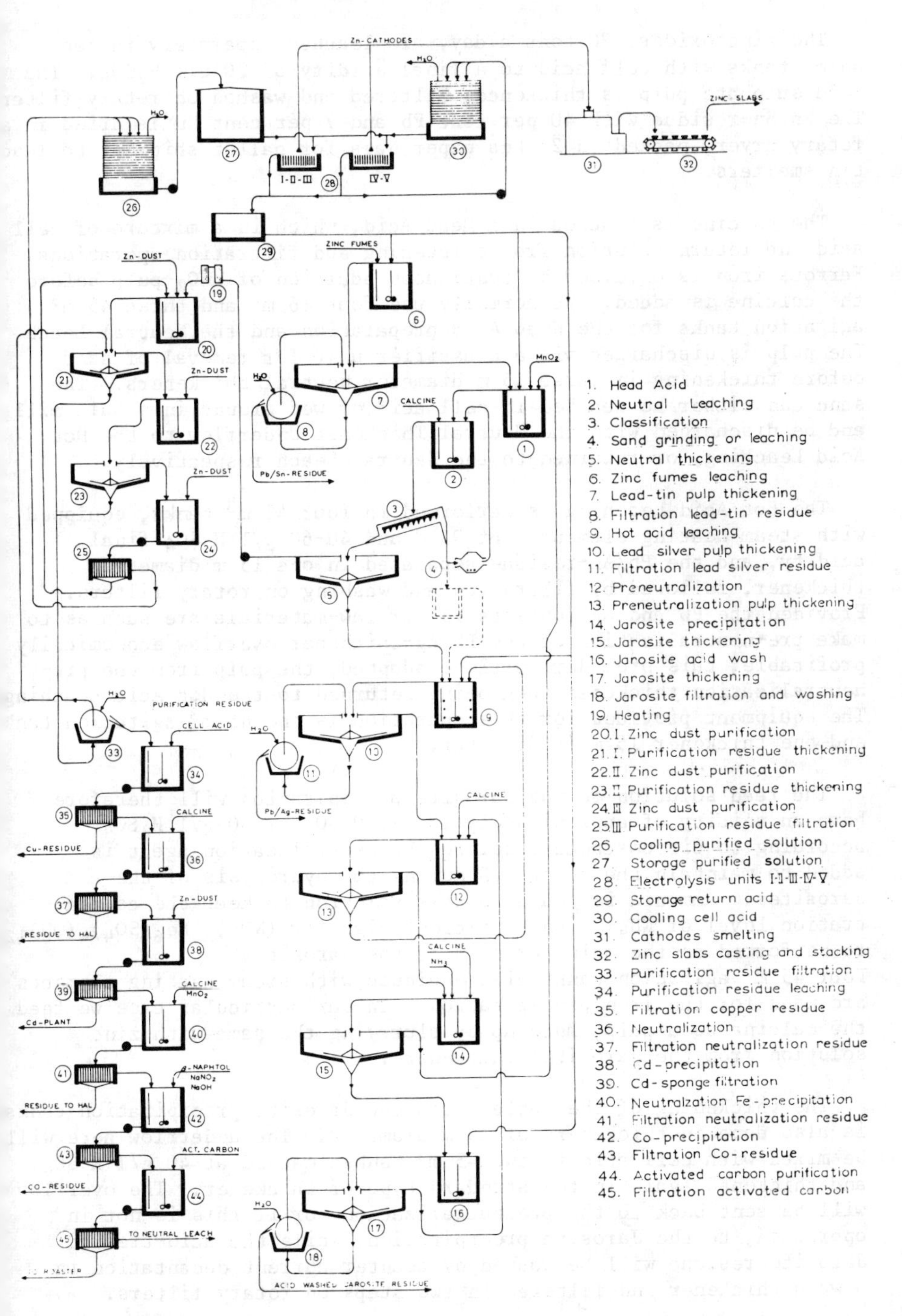
Zn-CATHODES
ZINC SLABS
H₂O
I-II-III
IV-V
ZINC FUMES
Zn-DUST
MnO₂
CALCINE
Pb/Sn-RESIDUE
PURIFICATION RESIDUE
CELL ACID
Pb/Ag-RESIDUE
Cu-RESIDUE
RESIDUE TO HAL
Cd-PLANT
β-NAPHTOL
NaNO₂
NaOH
ACT. CARBON
CO-RESIDUE
TO NEUTRAL LEACH
TO ROASTER
NH₃
ACID WASHED JAROSITE RESIDUE
1. Head Acid
2. Neutral Leaching
3. Classification
4. Sand grinding or leaching
5. Neutral thickening
6. Zinc fumes leaching
7. Lead-tin pulp thickening
8. Filtration lead-tin residue
9. Hot acid leaching
10. Lead silver pulp thickening
11. Filtration lead silver residue
12. Preneutralization
13. Preneutralization pulp thickening
14. Jarosite precipitation
15. Jarosite thickening
16. Jarosite acid wash
17. Jarosite thickening
18. Jarosite filtration and washing
19. Heating
20. I. Zinc dust purification
21. I. Purification residue thickening
22. II. Zinc dust purification
23. II. Purification residue thickening
24. III Zinc dust purification
25. III Purification residue filtration
26. Cooling purified solution
27. Storage purified solution
28. Electrolysis units I-II-III-IV-V
29. Storage return acid
30. Cooling cell acid
31. Cathodes smelting
32. Zinc slabs casting and stacking
33. Purification residue filtration
34. Purification residue leaching
35. Filtration copper residue
36. Neutralization
37. Filtration neutralization residue
38. Cd-precipitation
39. Cd-sponge filtration
40. Neutralzation Fe-precipitation
41. Filtration neutralization residue
42. Co-precipitation
43. Filtration Co-residue
44. Activated carbon purification
45. Filtration activated carbon

Fig.7 - Flowsheet D.N.Z. from 1971. Complete Jarosite Process Integrated.

The zinc oxides, 70 tons a day, are leached separately in two 45 m^3 tanks with cell acid to a final acidity of 20 g/l H_2SO_4. The lead sulphate pulp is thickened, filtered and washed on rotary filter The Pb/Sn-residue with 40 per cent Pb and 7 per cent Sn is dried in a rotary dryer, packed in 25 kgs paper bags for pallet shipment to lead tin smelters.

The calcine is leached in a Head Acid, which is a mixture of cell acid and return solution from thickening and filtration operations. Ferrous iron is oxidized by continuous addition of MnO_2-pulp before the calcine is added. We normally use four 16 m^3 and three 45 m^3 agitation tanks for the Head Acid preparation and the Neutral Leach. The pulp is discharged via a classifier unit for removal of sand before thickening in three 15 m diameter neutral thickeners. The sand can either be leached in cell acid or wet ground in a ball mill and be discharged with the Neutral Thickener Underflow to the Hot Acid Leaching, or returned to the Neutral Leach respectively.

The Hot Acid Leaching is performed in four 45 m^3 tanks, equipped with steam heating elements, at 95°C and 40-60 g/l H_2SO_4 final acidity, and the Pb/Ag-residue separated in one 15 m diameter thickener, followed by filtration and washing on rotary filters. Provided the Pb and Ag contents in our raw-materials are such as to make pre-neutralization of the Pb/Ag-thickener overflow economically profitable, this procedure will be adopted, the pulp from the pre-neutralization thickener then being returned to the Hot Acid Leaching The equipment provided for this operation is one 45 m^3 agitation tank and one thickener 15 m in diameter.

The feed solution to the Jarosite precipitation will therefore have an acidity of approximately 10 g/l H_2SO_4 or 40 g/l H_2SO_4 according to circumstances, before the neutralization agent is added to maintain the pH at 1.5 during the hydrolysis of the Jarosites. Ammonia is added to this solution to keep the concentration level of NH_4+ ion sufficient high for $(NH_4)_2 Fe_6(SO_4)_4(OH)_{12}$ to be formed as the main compound of the Jarosites.
Four 45 m^3 agitation tanks also equipped with steam heating elements are used for the iron precipitation. In our particular case we feed the calcine as a pulp, made up by slurrying the same with zinc solution from the Jarosites thickeners.

The thickening of the outlet from the Jarosite precipitation tanks is also done in thickeners of 15 m diameter. The underflow here will be mixed with cell acid in two 45 m^3 tanks leached at 40 g/l H_2SO_4, and thickened again in the standard type of thickener. The overflow will be sent back to the preneutralization, or if this is not in operation, to the Jarosite precipitation, while the acid-treated Jarosite residue will be washed by counter current decantation in a wash thickener and filtered in two steps on rotary filters.

Zinc Dust Purification

The Neutral Thickener overflow is heated to 70°C in heat exchangers and purified with zinc dust in three stages continuously. The first stage, carried out in five 45 m^3 agitation tanks in series, removes Cu, Co, Ni and the greater part of Cd, As and Sb.
The second and third stage, consisting of four 45 m^3 tanks each, remove the remaining traces of Cd, As and Sb. $CuSO_4$-solution is added to activate the zinc dust in these stages.

The zinc dust is charged to the first tank of each purification stage by means of a screw feeder with variable speed. The speed of the screw is automatically controlled by the quality index of the solution, determined by an automatic solution analyser at regular intervals for each purification stage.

The purification residue from the first stage is separated in a thickener, the residue from the second purification is at present separated in filter presses, but a thickener will later also be introduced for the second purification. We intend using thickeners with 10 m diameters for these operations.

The third purification stage is filtered in filter presses and the residue is returned to the first purification.

The purified solution is pumped via an atmospheric cooling tower to two 800 m^3 storage tanks located above the Tank Room.

The consumption of zinc dust is 50-60 kgs, and of copper sulphate 7 kgs per ton of slabs. Before the zinc fumes were introduced as raw material, no copper sulphate was used, and the consumption of zinc dust in two purification stages was 40 kgs per ton of slabs.

Typical Analyses D.N.Z. Leaching Section

Solutions, g/l	Zn	Cu	Cd	Fe	H_2SO_4	pH
Cell acid	50	-	-	-	190	-
Head Acid	140	-	-	0.8	50	-
Neutral Solution	180	0.5	0.3	0.005	-	5.0
Purified Solution	180	0.0001	0.00001	.010	-	5.0
Hot Acid Leaching	110	0.8	0.4	20	40	-
Zinc fume Leaching	162	-	-	-	20	-
Preneutralization	130	0.8	0.4	22	10	-
Jarosite precipitation	170	0.8	0.5	1.0	3-5	1.5
Jarosite acid washing	120	0.5	0.3	15	40	-

Solids, per cent	Zn	Cu	Cd	Fe	Pb	Sn	Ag
Neutral leach residue	27	0.5	0.1	24	4.5	-	0.02
Pg/Ag-residue, washed	4.0	0.3	0.05	15	14	-	0.07
Pb/Sn-residue, washed	4.0	0.05	0.005	1.0	40	7	-
Jarosite residue	6.0	0.4	0.05	30	1.4	-	-
Jarosite residue, acid washed	3.0	0.2	0.02	30	1.5	-	-

Purification Residue Recovery

In our zinc dust purification process we precipitate Cu, Cd, and the detrimental impurities Co, Ni, in the first purification stage at moderate temperatures, using antimony as activation agent.

Different in principle is the purification performed at high temperature, using arsenic to activate the zinc dust, where Cu, Co and Ni are removed in the first purification, and Cd in the second. This purification system has the advantage of producing a marketable copper residue directly.

The advantages of our system are lower working temperature and no risk of arsenic poisoning for the operating personnel. The drawback is the necessity of making a special treatment of the purification residue, separating Cu and Cd, and recovering the zinc content in the residue, without recycling Co and Ni to the leaching process. We ascribe the purity of our main solution to the thorough operation performed in the purification residue recovery plant. Fig. 7.

The purification residues from the first and second zinc dust purifications are leached in cell acid to a final acidity of 25 g/l H_2SO_4. Zinc and cadmium are dissolved, and a copper residue with 45-50 per cent Cu is recovered by filtration.

The acidity of the filtrate is reduced to 3 g/l H_2SO_4 in a neutralization stage, before cadmium is precipitated. The cadmium sponge, containing 60 per cent Cd, is dissolved, and the resulting solution purified and electrolyzed for cadmium production.

The cadmiumfree zinc solution is submitted to a careful purification before being recycled to the leaching circuit. In a first stage iron is oxidized with MnO_2, and precipitated at 95°C as a mixture of basic iron sulphate and ferric hydroxide. In filtrate 99 per cent of the cobalt and about 50 per cent of the nickel present are removed with b-naphtol and sodium nitrite. The excess of the organic reagent is absorbed by a final treatment with active carbon.

Electrolysis

The original Tank Room consists of three Units with each 144 lead-lined wooden cells, arranged in 12 cascades with 2 x 6 cells. Each cell contains 28 aluminium cathodes, 29 lead anodes, with 1 per cent silver, spacing 3½", and four lead cooling coils each with 1.2 m^2 surface. Rotary rectifiers delivered 12,500 Amps at 550 Volt per Unit, corresponding to a current density of 4 Amp/dm^2.

The wooden cells have been replaced by concrete ones, new busbars installed to take maximum loads up to 18-20,000 Amps, which is supplied from silicon rectifiers with automatic current regulation. This has increased the maximum current density to 6.0 Amp/dm^2.

In 1970 a new electrolysing Unit has been put into commission. In this Unit the size of cells, busbars, anodes and cathodes are similar to those of the rebuilt old Units for the reason of standardization, but the cells are all arranged on the same level. A silicon rectifier supplies 20,000 Amps to the Unit.

By a system of polypropylene launders the cell acid is recirculated and distributed to each cell individually in a quantity approximately 10 times the required volume of purified solution. The temperature, normally kept at 30-35°C, is controlled by four lead cooling coils in each cell, but provision is made to introduce later atmospheric cooling of the electrolyte.

Electric hoists are applied for transport of anodes and cathodes. The zinc cathodes are stripped manually each day, and one man takes care of 18 cells. In the new Unit the aluminium cathodes with the zinc deposit on, are lowered into a water bath for washing before stripping.

The cleaning of the cascades is done once every 6 weeks. The anodes are placed in special racks for 16 anodes, transported by trucks to a sloping rollerway, forming a part of the automatic cleaning station. The racks with anodes for one complete cascade are then rolled through a washing- and straightening machine, where each anode gets a thorough treatment by high-pressure water jets. The manganese sludge is removed from the cells by means of transferable rubber hoses, connected to central vacuum receivers, which deliver the pulp to a Thickener 10 m diameter. The overflow is led to the return acid reservoirs, and the underflow is pumped to the day storage tanks for MnO_2-sludge at the various consumer locations.

Instrumentation

The basic requirement of a continuous process is that there is no short circuit of solution in the reactors. The process may then, according to our experience, in principle well be manually operated, although the continuous operation lends itself particularly well to automatic control. We realized at an early stage of development tha the saving of man-power and optimization of the process might be obtained by the introduction of instrumentation. After having establi the desired process parameters, we found that the most difficult par of the development work was to perform the measurements with sufficient precision. The pulps and solutions in the zinc hydrometallurgy are no easy media in which to keep the measuring probes in reliable conditions. After 15 years of experience in automatic control of the leaching process we may conclude, however, that the problems have been overcome, and that the results are entirely up to our expectations. The measuring and control loops are now in operation with a minimum of maintenance.

The different control functions are:

Red/Ox - potential

The Red/Ox potential of the Head Acid is measured, the ratio of Fe^{++}/Fe^{+++} is determined and used to feed the MnO_2 pulp automaticall

pH - acidity

pH is measured in the Neutral Leach and controls the feed of calcine. The excess of calcine is kept at a minimum to precipitate the iron completely at the same time, keeping a maximum content of the copper in solution.

pH was previously also measured in the Acid Leach and controlled the addition of cell acid to this leaching step.

pH measurements direct the feed of calcine slurry to precipitate the Jarosite in the different precipitation tanks.

Conductivity

The conductivity is measured in the zinc oxide and the Hot Acid Leaching, where the addition of cell acid is automatically controlle to the predetermined quantity of oxides, or as the case may be, a variable volume of Neutral Thickener Sludge. Conductivity measurement will be used for addition of calcine at the preneutralization stage.

Conductivity control also directs the automatic feeding of the purified solution to the recirculated electrolyte in the new Tank Room, and a portable conductivity meter provides rapid and accurate g/l H_2SO_4-readings at manual control of the acidities in the 432 cells of the original Tank Room.

We have developed a special sampling instrumentation with automatic electrode cleaning for pH, and conductivity measurements in the leaching plant. These sampling instruments are now applied at all pH- and conductivity control stations, resulting in particularly long service life of the electrodes.

Volume

Variable volumes in storage and buffer tanks for impure solutions, purified zinc solution, and return cell acid are measured by special instruments with a probe that feels the surface level at regular intervals, but generally stays away from the solution to avoid any deposit formation. All instruments are connected to a digital voltmeter in the control room, where each separate volume as well as the sum of volumes can be read.

Solution quality

Based upon the principle of electrolysing and reelectrolysing the purified solution at standard conditions, we have developed a Solution Quality Analyser, that automatically samples the solution, prepares the same for measurement, electrolyses and reelectrolyses the solution at fixed intervals.

This quality analyser measures a Quality Index of the solution from each purification stage. Once the calibration has been made with reference to solution purity, the Index may be applied for the control of the zinc dust feeding.

We have also developed a laboratory model of this instrument which is a particularly valuable tool for checking the solution quality in general research work.

We use d/p cells for level control, timers for pulling the thickeners, temperature control of Hot Acid Leaching, Jarosite precipitation and purification, and magnetic flowmeters for controlling different acid and solution streams.

Computer control

We have started a study with the purpose of introducing digital computer control. The test work carried out in 1967 with a computer on-line in our process, indicated that such equipment may be a desirable investment within a few years. In the meantime we will devote our efforts to the instrument side, developing automatic chemical analysers, essential for closed-loop digital control.

Melting and Casting

Melting of the cathode zinc was when starting the plant done in two oil-burning reverberatory furnaces each holding 140 tons molten zinc.

In 1946 one of these was replaced by a 475 kW low frequency induction furnace with four single and one double transformer coils, with a capacity of 20 tons zinc. In 1951 a similar induction furnace was installed to replace the second oil-burning furnace. The melting capacity of each induction furnace is 4 tons slabs per hour at a consumption of 125 kWh per ton of slabs.

In 1958-59 each furnace was equipped with a Baggler Casting machine, having 72 moulds on the strand. The full benefit of the automatic casting equipment was not obtained until an automatic stacker was developed, working in synchronization with strand speed. The slabs, weighing 25 kgs, are of the interlocking type with 36 slabs per pallet.

A third 800 kW induction furnace, with four double transformer coils and 40 tons capacity of molten zinc, was then installed in 1967, also equipped with the combined automatic casting and stacking machines. The casting capacity is 7 tons per hour.

The three induction furnaces provide great flexibility in casting different zinc qualities. Normally Special High Grade is made in the two 475 kWh furnaces, while the 800 kW furnace is used for High Grade and alloys for continuous galvanizing, cast in special Jumbo moulds. The greater part of the zinc is shipped by sea.

Typical analyses of the zinc are:

		Cu %	Pb %	Cd %	Fe %
SHG,	Furnace I	.0003	.0015	.00002	.0003
SHG,	Furnace II	.0003	.0009	.00002	.0003
HG,	Furnace III	.0003	.0060	.00002	.0005

Dross Treatment

Dross is raked from the zinc bath into cast iron wagons and stored 24 hours. After cooling, the wagons, each with 450 kgs dross, are fed to the bin above an air-ventilated ball-mill, of which we have two units. The charging of dross, grinding and discharging of the zinc sand, is done automatically in cycles of 30 minutes. The sand is sent through a vibrating 1 mm screen, the oversize being remelted, while the fines are used for purificatio of zinc solution. The capacity of each ball-mill is 900 kgs dross per hour.

The Net Dross quantity amounts to 1.4 per cent of the cathodes.

Zinc Dust

Atomized zinc dust is produced in two identical units, each with a daily capacity of 11 tons.

Utilities

Steam

To provide sufficient steam for process and heating, a steam generating plant is part of the installations in addition to the Lamont boiler in the Roasting Plant.

Two Kestner boilers each with a capacity of 4 tons steam per hour, originate from the start of the zinc plant. Two high voltage electric boilers were installed later, capacities are 3,200 volts and 6,000 kW at 12,000 volts.

Steam is distributed at 0.6 MN/m^2 (6.1 kgf/cm^2). The peak steam load during the winter for process, leaching plant, phosphoric acid plant, and general heating is 24 tons per hour, 11 tons per hour of this is produced by the roasting operation.

Compressed Air

In the central compressor station there are:

Three low pressure compressors, capacity 95 m^3 per minute at 0.21 MN/m^2 (2.2 kgf/cm^2). Six high pressure compressors, at 0.62 MN/m^2 6.3 kgf/cm^2). Four with a capacity of 30 m^3, one with 45 m^3 and one with 9.5 m^3 per minute. One high pressure compressor producing oil-ree air at 0.62 MN/m^2, capacity 15 m^3 per minute.

Vacuum

In a central vacuum station three vacuum pumps, each of a capacity of 50 m^3 per minute and a fourth pump rated at 75 m^3 per minute, are installed.

Water

The fresh water supply flows from a mountain lake near the Folgefonn glacier 1050 m above sea level. With a total regulation of 24 m the capacity of the reservoir is approximately 2,600,000 m^3. Due to the altitude of the reservoir we can count on very little flow to the basin during the winter from November till May. By remote control from intake done at 132 m above sea level the valve at the reservoir can be adjusted according to need between 0 and 5000 m^3 per hour. Average runoff capacity from the reservoir for winter supply is approximately 700 m^3/h. The capacity of the pipeline 16" in diameter from the dam to the plant is about 2,300 m^3/h with an acceptable pressure drop. The total consumption of water during the summer season is approximately 1700 m^3/h. The variation in water temperature over the year is from slightly above freezing point to a maximum of 9°C. Average temperature is 3-4°C.

For winter supply we have three pumping stations at the fjord with a total of 10 pumps installed. Total capacity 3,000 m^3/h. At plant site 68 m above sea level we have two concrete reservoirs. One for fresh water 770 m^3 and one for sea water 550 m^3. (The pipelines are connected to these reservoirs in such a system that sea water under no circumstances will flow into the fresh water system.

Power

Power is purchased from A/S Tyssefaldene, in which company D.N.Z. have 40 per cent interest. The power is generated in two hydroelectric plants. The older one, utilizing the lower falls, has a total installation of 123,600 kVA generated at 12,500 volts, 25 CPS. At generator voltage power is transmitted to our plant by four transmission lines and ten sea cables across the fjord. System capacity of approximately 45 MVA.

The new generating plant at the upper falls has got an installation of two generators each rated 110 MVA. Over a transformer of the same power rating the generators can be connected to the 66,000 volts busbar system. Through transformers this system is connected to the Norwegian main grid at 275,000 volts. System frequency is 50 CPS.

Our plant is connected to this system by transmission line and by two sea cables across the fjord. A transformer rated 45 MVA, 66/12 kV, 50 CPS is installed in our power station.

Four rectifier transformers each rated 14,500 kVA may be supplied from 25 or 50 CPS 12,000 volts busbars. DC available up to 600 volts and 20,000 Amps. For plant operation power is distributed at 3,200 volts. Some motors are supplied with voltage at this level. The great majority of motors are supplied with 220 volts from 3,300/220 volts transformers placed in sub stations.

A distribution system at 12,000 volts, 50 CPS, is under development. For new plants motor supply is 380 volts with a possibility to load the grounded neutral.

From sub stations the power is distributed to centrally located motor control centers.

Chapter 9

THE ELECTROLYTIC ZINC PLANT OF RUHR-ZINK GMBH.
Datteln, West Germany

H. R. Wuthrich, Manager

A. von Ropenack, Superintendent

Abstract

The Metallgesellschaft AG decided in late 1965 to build an Electrolytic Zinc Plant at Datteln (W. Germany). Lurgi-Chemie was entrusted with the engineering and erection of the entire plant. Ground was broken in February 1967 and the operation was started on August 1st, 1968. The new Electrolytic Zinc Plant was designed to produce a minimum of 100,000 metric tons of special high grade zinc and 200,000 metric tons of sulphuric acid.

Concentrates from Meggen (W. Germany) and mainly Timmins (Canada) are roasted in two turbulent layer roasters. The sulfur dioxide containing gases are converted in a "Bayer double catalysis unit" to sulfuric acid. The calcine is leached batch wise, the leach residue separated from the pregnant solution by counter-current thickeners and drum filters. For maintaining the sulfate balance a modified jarosite leach is being used. After a two step purification the neutral solution is mixed with spent electrolyte and cooled in unpacked atmospheric cooling towers. Three electrical circuits are supplying the power to the tankhouse, each rated at 30,000 amperes. With a maximum current density of 750 amperes per square meter and a stripping cycle of 24 hours, an average current efficiency of 90 percent is obtained.

Cathodes are melted in one induction furnace and cast into shapes, or alloyed with aluminum and copper for die-cast metal.

The second purification residue is treated for cadmium recover in an electrolytic cadmium plant.

A total of 308 daily paid men and 59 employees are required to produce approximately 9,500 tons of zinc. Maintenance labour is not included in the foregoing.

Introduction

Metallgesellschaft AG has been active for many years in the production of nonferrous metals in Germany as well as in foreign countries. With the loss of its affiliates in foreign countries, after the world wars, a new approach had to be conceived. Modernization became imperative particularly in the field of lead and zinc plants which were located in the western part of Germany. The old report plant at Berzelius was replaced by an Imperial Smelting Furnace which successfully supplied lead and prime western zinc for the German market.

Simultaneously with starting up of the ISF operation, Metallgesellschaft decided to expand further the zinc production by building an electrolytic zinc plant. In postwar Germany this was to be the first venture to produce special high grade zinc in one step and was possible because Metallgesellschaft was successful in obtaining electrical power rates at an economical level.

The reasons for the choice of Datteln, a small town on the north-east border of the Ruhr district, were:

1. Favourable transportation, the plant is adjacent to the Rhein-Herne canal (inland waterway)
2. Consumers of sulphuric acid in the vicinity
3. Adequate labour supply
4. Reasonable power rates and a provision to deliver excess steam from waste heat boilers to power plant.

Metallgesellschaft is the owner of 140,000 square meters of land. Of this amount 45,000 square meters is covered by plant buildings and operating equipment.

The land is bound by the canal on one side, the federal railroad tracks on another and the main road leading through Datteln on the third side, forming a triangular shaped piece of property.

Fig. 1 - General view of the Datteln plant

Most foreign concentrates (shown by Table 1) are received by barges which are loaded at the sea ports of Rotterdam and Amsterdam. The barges are moved to Datteln along the Rhein River and Dortmund-Herne canal system. Domestic concentrates are shipped to the plant by Federal railroad. Most of the plant products are shipped to customers using the highway trucking system and by railroad. The layout of the plant facilities conforms to the receiving and shipping facilities.

Engineering

By March 1966 the metallurgical flow sheet and optimum capacity was established. Lurgi Gesellschaft für Chemie und Hüttenwesen mbH were instructed to design and construct the entire plant. In Feby. 1967 preparation of the ground site was started and on August 1st, 1968 the first concentrate was fed to the roaster (shown by Figure 2).

For the choice of equipment and the flowsheet the following factors were considered:

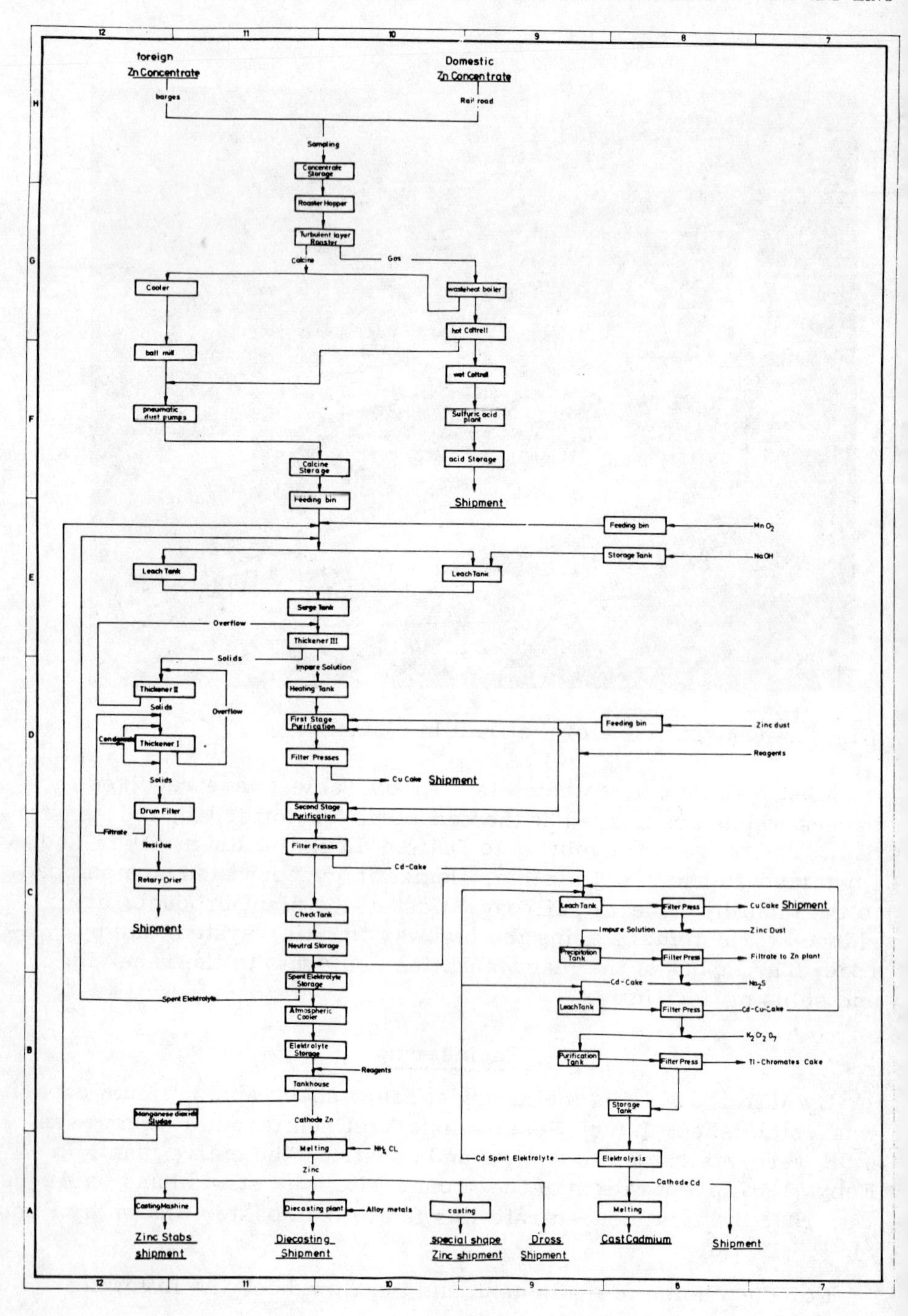
foreign
Zn Concentrate
barges
Domestic
Zn Concentrate
Rail road
Sampling
Concentrate Storage
Roaster Hopper
Turbulent layer Roaster
Calcine
Gas
Cooler
wasteheat boiler
hot Cottrell
ball mill
wet Cottrell
pneumatic dust pumps
Sulfuric acid plant
acid Storage
Calcine Storage
Shipment
Feeding bin
Feeding bin
Storage Tank
Leach Tank
Leach Tank
Surge Tank
Overflow
Thickener III
Solids
Impure Solution
Thickener II
Heating Tank
Solids
Overflow
First Stage Purification
Feeding bin
Zinc dust
Thickener I
Filter Presses
Reagents
Solids
Cu Cake Shipment
Drum Filter
Second Stage Purification
Filtrate
Residue
Filter Presses
Cd-Cake
Rotary Drier
Leach Tank
Filter Press
Cu Cake Shipment
Shipment
Check Tank
Impure Solution
Zinc Dust
Neutral Storage
Precipitation Tank
Filter Press
Filtrate to Zn plant
Spent Elektrolyte Storage
Cd-Cake
Spent Elektrolyte
Leach Tank
Filter Press
Cd-Cu-Cake
Atmospheric Cooler
Elektrolyte Storage
Purification Tank
Filter Press
Tl-Chromates Cake
Reagents
Tankhouse
Storage Tank
Manganese dioxide Sludge
Cathode Zn
Melting
Cd Spent Elektrolyte
Elektrolysis
Zinc
Cathode Cd
Casting Mashine
Diecasting plant
Alloy metals
casting
Melting
Zinc Stabs shipment
Diecasting Shipment
special shape Zinc shipment
Dross Shipment
Cast Cadmium
Shipment

Figure 2

TABLE 1a

Typical Analyses of different Concentrates, Calcine and Leach Residue

%	Zn	Fe	Pb	Cu	Cd	SiO2	Al2O3	S	Ag
TGS "high Ag"	51.6	9.5	0.24	0.36	0.22	2.4	0.1	32.7	0.019
TGS "low Ag"	52.9	8.8	0.11	0.46	0.25	2.2	0.2	31.6	0.008
Meggen	56.1	5.8	1.5	0.06	0.05	0.8	< 0.1	33.8	0.0005
Mt. Isa	51.5	7.3	2.1	0.14	0.21	2.7	0.5	30.6	0.014
Mattagami	52.0	10.5	0.16	0.38	0.11	1.6	< 0.1	32.1	0.007
Calcine	60.6	9.2	0.8	0.32	0.22	2.2		2.85	0.011
Leach Residue	19.5	29.2	2.3	0.43	0.18	6.8		5.10	0.035

TABLE 1b

Typical Contents of Impurities

%	CaO	MgO	Mn	Cl	F	Co	Ni	As
TGS "high Ag"	0.1	0.07	0.01	< 0.01	0.006	0.007	< 0.001	0.03
TGS "low Ag"	0.02	0.12	0.01	< 0.01	0.006	0.01	< 0.001	0.02
Meggen	0.03	0.05	0.10	< 0.01	0.004	< 0.001	0.005	0.02
Mt. Isa	0.6	0.3	0.04	< 0.01	0.01	0.004	< 0.001	0.01
Mattagami	0.2	0.3	0.3	< 0.01	0.006	0.004	< 0.001	0.02
				SO4/S	S/S	H2O/Zn		
Calcine			0.07	2.45	0.13			
Leach Residue			1.8	4.76	0.34	1.2		

Government permission would not be granted unless the emmission of gas and fume complied with the strict regulations and no discharg waste materials entering the biological sewage treatment plant wou interfere with its normal operation.

A flowsheet and equipment were chosen which would enable the operation to comply with the government pollution requirements and be able to treat a variety of raw materials. At that time a leach residue treatment process was not included in the flow sheet. The choice of a residue treating process was delayed in order to study the various processes being developed. Plans to include residue treatment were considered and space provided to add at a later date after the plant was in operation.

In order to obtain a maximum of flexibility it was decided to operate leach and purification as a batch process. For economical reasons a counter current thickener system for decantation of neutral leach solution and washing of leach residue was chosen. For the final dewatering of the leach residue vacuum drum filters were provided.

For electrolyte cooling unpacked water cooling towers were specified. The necessity to evaporate a maximum of water made this type of equipment desirable.

The total employment is shown by Table 7.

Concentrate Handling and Storage

The Meggen concentrate (shown by Table 1) which is being produced by a parentcompany in Germany, arrives at Datteln in train loads of 750 - 1,000 tons. After weighing and sampling, the botton dump cars are unloaded into an underground hopper. From there a belt conveyor system transports the concentrate at a rate of 200 tons per hour to the covered concentrate storage building.

All other raw materials, at present mostly from Canada, reach Datteln over the German inland waterway. Barges up to 1,375 tons holding capacity can pass the locks which are between the Rhein, the North Sea and Datteln. A harbor is provided to accomodate four barges simultaneously.

The concentrate is unloaded by crane into one of two automatic weighing hoppers which travel with the crane. The weighing system enables the operator to unload at maximum speed. Parallel to the dock a conveyor belt transports the concentrate from the weighing hoppers to the concentrate storage building.

The dock is also equipped for loading sulphuric acid into barges and loading or unloading other materials such as leach residues, metals and other bulk products. It must be mentioned that all the leach residue leaves Datteln by barges. The entire loading and unloading operation is handled by one operator.

The large concentrate storage building was designed to hold 65,000 tons of raw material. The large holding capacity was necessary to handle interrupted shipments from Canada, which are caused by the freezing of the St. Lawrence waterway during winter months.

From the belt conveyor system which is supported by the roof structure of the storage building, the concentrate is unloaded at the desired site by a belt tripper. The material can be stored up to a height of 15 meters. Should the concentrate arrive with a moisture of less than 6 percent a sprinkler system adds water to prevent dusting.

Each type of concentrate is stored separately, no partition walls are necessary. The moisture is such that an angle of repose of 60 degrees enables the piled concentrates to be reasonably divided.

An overhead bridge crane transfers concentrates from stock and discharges the material onto a belt conveyor. The belt is located along the side of the building and therefore movement of the crane is reduced to a minimum. In case of a crane failure, a portable inclined belt conveyor which can be fed by a front end loader is used and proved to be valuable for an uninterrupted roaster operation.

Roasting and Sulphuric Acid

The roasting plant is equipped with two Lurgi turbulent layer roasters each having a grate area of 55 square meters, with a load factor of 7 metric tons per square meter of grate area, the two roasters have a designed capacity of 770 metric tons of concentrate per operating day.

The concentrates (shown by Table 1) after beeing screened and the oversize denodulized in a hammermill, is conveyed by a belt system to the roaster feed bins, one each per roaster, having a holding capacity of approximately 100 metric tons each. A pan conveyor with a variable speed and depth regulator transports the concentrate at a predertermined constant rate to the roaster feeding system. The feeding system consists of a disc feeder to equalize the effect of the surges caused by the pan conveyor and a pair of slinger belts discharging directly into each roasting chamber. Usually the two slinger belts for each roaster are in service in order to assure an even tempera ture distribution throughout the bed.

The temperature in the roaster is controlled by the quantity of air blown through the grate plate, by the cooling coils in the roaster bed and if necessary by water injection. Cooling coils were not provided with the original roasting equipment but were added at a later date.

The cooling coils are connected to the waste heat boiler system.

The particular behaviour of the Canadian Timmins concentrates (shown by Table 1) require a very close temperature control in the roaster bed within a range of 20 degrees Centigrade, between 900 and 920, otherwise the bed has a tendency to form agglomerat and thereby lose uniform turbulence.

Bed fluidity is also influenced by the moisture content of the concentrates fed. The ideal moisture for Canadian Timmins concen trates is about 6 percent. At this moisture only a minor portion of feed enters the bed. About 90 percent or more will be carried by the air to the upper portion of the roasting chamber where combustion continues to take place. With 6 percent moisture the be temperature is approximately 910 degrees Centigrade and the outle temperature of the roaster will show 960 to 980 degrees Centigrade. concentrates, with higher than 6 percent moisture these temperatu differences will disappear or be reversed.

As most of the concentrates delivered have a moisture of 8 perc or more, additional cooling of the bed had to be provided. Each roas therefore was equipped with cooling coils, removing 4 million kilo gram calories per hour. At normal throughput rates of 350 tons pe day per roaster, moisture in the range of 9 percent can be tolerate

The method of cooling the bed with excess air was not successfu and increased the already excessive sulphate content of the calcine to still higher values. At a minimum air flow required for proper turbulence in the bed of 28,000 cubic meters per hour, the total sulphur was 2.5 percent of which 2.4 percent was sulphate. These results were obtained with a gas composition of 12 percent sulphur dioxide and 3.5 percent oxygen at the roaster outlet. Recirculation of calcine was also tried with good results for bed cooling but increa ed the sulphate sulphur content of the final calcine.

The roaster gases after leaving the furnace are cooled in a wast heat Lamont type boiler. As excess steam is sold to a power compa the steam produced was superheated to 400 degrees Centigrade at a pressure of 50 atmospheres to meet power plant specifications.

Thus the boiler is divided into evaporator and superheater sections. For each roaster an area of 441 square meters for evaporator coils, and 104 square meters for superheater coils are provided. Passing through the boiler the gases are cooled down to 350 degrees Centigrade. The boilers have a mechanical cleaning mechanism but due to the nature of the dust, hand blowing particularly of the first section of the boiler has to be done once every 24 hours. Low moisture in the concentrate and a minimum amount of water injected into the roaster gives a minimum of accretions and buildup in the waste heat boiler.

After the boiler the gases pass through cyclones and an intermediate fan. The gases discharging from the cyclones are divided and enter 3 hot cottrells operating in parallel to give maximum flexibility.

With the intermediate fan the draft in the roaster can be regulated and what is considered essential, the hot cottrells can be operated at a slight pressure of 10 millimeters of water. To this fact the trouble free operation of the hot cottrells can be attributed. No accretions or build up of dust on electrodes have been observed to date.

After the hot cottrells the gases have a dust load of 60 milligrams per cubic meter and a temperature of 330 degrees Centigrade. Six venturi scrubbers are used to cool and humidify the gas. The final cooling to 38 degrees Centigrade is done in six horizontal and six vertical lead heat exchangers. The remaining dust together with mist is removed in a two stage wet cottrell system.

The sulphur dioxide content of the gas is diluted to 8 percent with air. The gases are treated in a Lurgi-Bayer double catalysis acid plant with a conversion efficiency of 99.5 percent. This single unit has a rated capacity of 645 tons of 100 percent acid per day and the most outstanding feature is its flexibility. During the start up period it was operated for a period at 33 percent of its rated capacity without using the preheater. Since the plant has reached its full zinc production, the acid plant is working often at higher than designed throughput without a notable decrease of conversion efficiency.

The acid is stored in three storage tanks of 15,000 tons holding capacity each. From there it can be pumped to either railroad, highway or water loading points. As the bulk of the acid leaves Datteln by barge, the loading facilities are equipped to load at the rate of 200 tons per hour.

The calcine (shown by Tables 1 and 2) collected from each roaster, waste heat boilers and cyclones is cooled in an indirect rotary water cooled, heat exchanger, ground in a ball mill and transported by a redler conveyor to a small surge bin. The cottrell dust is added after the calcine is discharged from the ball mill. A star feeder regulates the flow of calcine from the surge bin to a Fuller-Kenyon pump. With an air pressure of 1.8 atmospheres this pump delivers the fine ground calcine at a rate of 28 tons per hour to either the storage bins or directly into the feed bins in the leachi section.

A small quantity of condensate from the venturi scrubbers and t gas coolers is withdrawn from the wash circuit, neutralized with soda ash and discarded into the sewage system. Usually this acidi water contains only 5 grams per liter acid, 3 - 5 grams per liter chlorine, 1 - 2 grams per liter fluorine and 20 milligrams zinc. A recovery system for zinc would not be economical as the total volur per day is approximately 10 cubic meters.

The cooling water for the roasters and acid plant is withdrawn from the adjacent canal. After passing a mechanical screen it is used without further treatment.

The cooling in the acid plant is done in a closed circuit and only about 200 cubic meters per hour make up is continuously added. The cooling water is circulated over forced draft atmospheric cooli towers.

Leaching Section

The leaching building measures 70 meters long by 45 meters wide. The lower section of the building up to a height of 4.3 meter is of concrete. Above this level the building is constructed of steel. The steel section of the building is covered and roofed with Roberts Galbestos. The ground floor is finished with concrete and suitably sloped to drain to a central sump. All spillage, etc., is recove red and returned to the solution circuit with pumping equipment. All other operating buildings have similar spillage recovery systems.

The leaching is conducted batchwise in five mechanically agitate tanks. These leaching tanks have a diameter of 7.60 meters and a height of 3.20 meters, giving an operating capacity of 130 cubic meters. The self supporting tanks are made of stainless steel No 4435 according to DIN standards. The thickness of the bottom plates are 6 millimeters, and the walls 5 millimeters. Particular for the jarosite leaching a thermal insulation of 80 millimeters thickness fibre glass mats are provided for the side walls. The

TABLE 2

Typical Screen Analysis of Calcine

< 0.07	mm	90 %
0.07 - 0.16	mm	5 %
0.16 - 0.5	mm	1.5 %
> 0.5	mm	1.0 %

TABLE 3

	Impure Solution	Neutral Solution	Spent Elektrolyte
Zn g/l	160	170	55 - 60
H2SO4 g/l	PH 4.5 - 5.0	PH 4.5	200
Mn g/l	2.4	2.5	2.0
Sp. Gr. g/l	1.400	1.420	1.270
Temp. ° C	75	70	40
Fe mg/l	16	25	30
Cu mg/l	327	< 0.2	< 0.2
Cd mg/l	275	0.28	< 0.1
Pb mg/l	9.8	0.5 - 1.0	0.5 - 1.0
Co mg/l	9 - 15	0.1 - 0.2	< 0.1
Ni mg/l	2 - 3	0.05 - 0.15	< 0.05
As mg/l	0.6	< 0.02	< 0.02
Cl mg/l	50 - 100	50 - 100	50 - 100
MgO g/l	N.A.	4.3	4.8
CaO g/l	N.A.	0.7	0.5
F mg/l	N.A.	2.0	2.0

tank tops are covered with plywood segments, supported by the agitator bridge. The lightning agitator is a propellor type, the blades have a diameter of 1.780 meters and rotate at approximately 45 revolution per minute and is driven by a 22 kilowatt motor. Four steam jets using 5 atmospheres pressure and 180 degrees Centigrade steam have rapid heating capacity. A polyester fibre glass stack with a diameter of 600 millimeters provides adequate ventilation.

Calcine is fed from two charge bins which are suspended on load cells. A predetermined quantity of calcine can be accurately fed by automatic controls. A screw conveyor system with variable speed feeds up to 100 tons per hour of calcine to each one of the leach tanks. The manganese dioxide used for oxidation of iron and sulphide sulphur is transported from a 50 tons holding bin using a similar conveying system to each of the leach tanks.

At present (January '70) two leaching procedures are in use. One system uses 55 percent of all calcine and is leached according to a standard practice, known as a semi reverse leach. The remaining 45 percent are leached using hot strong acid and the iron is precipitated as jarosite. This technique developed by Ruhr-Zink is based on the patents of Norzink, EZ Industries and Companie Royale Asturienne des Mines.

For the standard leach about 30 percent of the operating tank volume is filled with wash water and spent electrolyte (shown by Table 3), depending on the sulphide sulphur content of the calcine from 50 to 100 kilos of manganese dioxide (74 - 76 percent manganese dioxide) are added. With live steam the temperature of the solution is brought up to 50 degrees Centigrade. A predetermined quantity of calcine is fed to reduce the free acidity to maximum of 15 grams per liter. Subsequently spent electrolyte and calcine are added simutaneously until the leach tank is filled. The free acid should never exceed 15 grams per liter. The solution is allowed to react for one hour, whereby the acidity will decrease to approximately 5 grams per liter. With small quantities of calcine additions the pH of the slurry is brought to 3.5 - 4.0. The time required for one leach cycle including pumping time is 2.5 hours.

During the leaching period the temperature is maintained at 96 - 98 degrees Centigrade. This high temperature combined with the careful control of the acidity during the entire leach cycle is essential for a zinc extraction of 91 - 91.5 percent (based on zero water soluble zinc in the residue). Furthermore the sedimentation rate in the leach pulp clarification system is such that a minimum amount of solids are contained in the thickener overflow. Further filtration prior to purification is not required. The iron precipitated is present in the leach residue in the form of iron hydroxide and also in appreciable quantities as basic iron sulphate. The specific gravity of the leach solution is 1.5 kilograms per liter, corresponding to a zinc concentration of 180 grams per liter. This high zinc concentration is beneficial for the leach plant capacity. One batch leach dissolves 15 - 16 tons of zinc.

Like many other electrolytic zinc plants, during the start up period, Datteln was faced with an unbalanced sulphate condition. Sulphate increased in the electrolyte system in greater quantities than was removed by the leach residue. The known method of neutralizing excess electrolyte in the leach tanks with lime rock caused considerable troubles in the leach residue handling system. Through sales of zinc sulphate solutions to the Lithopone industry, the sulphate equilibrium was controlled.

In January 1967 some details of a process being developed at the Det Noske Zink Company's Odda plant became available. From this information Ruhr-Zink adopted a procedure which apart from increasing the leach extraction of zinc, cadmium and copper, also solved the sulphate problem.

The new leaching practice is conducted by charging a leach tank with electrolyte and calcine added simultaneously until the tank is two thirds full, resulting in an acidity of 15 grams per liter. The reaction is carried on for one hour. The free acid is then increased from 80 to 100 grams per liter by the addition of spent electrolyte. After an agitation time of 2.5 hours the acid concentration is reduced to about 30 grams per liter. With predetermined small quantities of calcine the acid is brought slowly to 10 - 20 grams per liter and the required sodium ions for the jarosite formation are added as a dilute sodium hydroxide solution to the leach tank. During the precipitation of the jarosite the free acidity is slowly reduced by further additions of small lots of calcine. Within 2 hours the iron in solution decreases to 1 gram per liter or less and with additional calcine for neutralization the reaction is terminated at a pH of 3.5 - 4.0. The temperature is maintained between 95 and 98 degrees Centigrade for the entire cycle. Zinc leach extraction is 94.5 percent and sedimentation rates are slightly inferior compared with a standard neutral leach.

This new leaching procedure solved effectively the unsatisfactory sulphate balance. However, in spite of the better zinc extraction, the economical benefit is relatively small. An additional step is planned for the immediate future. Before the jarosite is precipitated, the solids in the pulp will be separated in a thickener thereby recover-ing the bulk of the lead, tin and precious metals present in the calcine in a residue not contaminated with jarosite precipitate. This further improvement is not expected to increase the zinc recovery but the revenues from the sales of the acid insoluble residue will be more substantial.

The manganese concentrations in the plant solution are controlled, by occasionally conducting manganese leaches using manganese dioxide zinc concentrate and spent electrolyte at temperatures up to 95 degre Centigrade. About 65 cubic meters of spent electrolyte are agitated with 9 tons of manganese dioxide and the corresponding amount of concentrates. After a reaction time of 3 - 4 hours 95 percent of the manganese is dissolved. The reaction can be followed by the decrease the free acid. After having completed the desired reaction, the leach is continued by filling the free space in the tank with spent electrolyte and adding calcine to adjust the pH to 3.5 - 4.0.

Leach Residue Separation-Filtration

The hot leach pulp is pumped from the leach tanks through a surge tank and into the clarification thickener. The surge tank having the same dimensions and equipment as the leach tanks is needed to regulate the flow of leach pulp to the thickener. When the pulp reaches the thickener, a further neutralization has taken place, the pH is now 4.0 - 4.5. The clarification thickener has a diameter of 21.35 meters. By gravity the clear overflow (shown by Tables 3 and 4) is fed to the heating tanks of the purification section while the thickened underflow is washed by counter current flow through two additional thickeners each having a diameter of 15.25 meters. A total of 15 grams per cubic meter floculating agent Sedipur TF®, a product of the Badische Anilin und Sodafabrik, is used. The thickener tanks are made of wood, all submerged parts of the thicken mechanism are of stainless steel. A steel superstructure spans the top of the tank, supporting the mechanism. For reducing heat losses the surface of all thickeners are covered by floating styrofoam sheets.

The underflow of the second washing thickener is pumped to vacuum drum filters. A total of 3 units are installed, each having a filter area of 50 square meters. The filter rates are 150 - 200 kilograms per square meter per hour. Essentially all evaporation losses of the entire process are replaced by washing the residue on the drum filters with water. Condensate from the heating coils in the purification section and preheated city water are used for this purpose.

TABLE 4

	Thickener I	Thickener II	Thickener III	Drum Filter
OVERFLOW				
Solids g/l	< 0.1	< 0.1	< 0.1	2.2
Depth of Clear cm	150	150	150	
Zn g/l	40	70	160	26
Temp. ° C	45	50	75	45
Sp. Gr. g/l	1.090	1.200	1.370	1.070
UNDERFLOW				
Solids g/l	300	300	300	850 - 900
Zn g/l	-	-	-	-
Sp. Gr. g/l	1.450	1.550	1.650	1.850
Zn/H20 %	-	-	-	1.2
H20 %	-	-	-	45 - 50

Under normal conditions approximately 4 tons of water for each ton of zinc produced are required to compensate for evaporation losse including electrolyte cooling. Spray washing on the drum filters reduces the water soluble zinc in the leach residue to 1.2 percent or less. Filtrate and wash water from the drum filters are pumped into the second thickener from where they flow counter current to the unde flows from the first and clarification thickeners.

The vacuum drum filters are made of stainless steel. All piping is external, facilitating cleaning and maintenance. The polyproplyene filter cloth is treated on one side with silicones, facilitating the discharge of the cake. Filter cloth life so far averages 3 months.

The cake from the filters is transported by a belt conveyor to a repulping tank. By rigorous agitation, the plastic residue is repulped and transferred by a rubber lined centrifugal pump to the leach residu drier. The rotary drum drier has a length of 18 meters and a diamete of 2 meters. In the first part of the drum chains are used to prevent residue adhering to the walls.

The original drier was provided with internal braces to facilitate drying. Later these braces were removed because they interfered with the passage of residue through the drum. The shell is of mild steel having a wall thickness of 12 millimeters. An oil burner consum ing 500 kilograms of fuel oil per hour provides the necessary heat to evaporate 6 tons per hour of water. The exhaust gases are cleaned in high efficiency cyclones.

Purification

The clear overflow (shown by Table 3) from the clarification thickener is preheated in three storage tanks. These tanks as well as the purification tanks are constructed of special selected Oregon pine. The diameter of the tanks is 10 meters and the height 3.1 meters. The active available volume is 170 cubic meters. All tanks are covered with a plywood covers and ventilated through a 800 millimeters diameter stack. A positive draft is maintained by a dual set of air injectors. The agitation is supplied by a similar propeller type agitator as used in the leach tanks. The preheating tanks have ste coils made of stainless steel, in the purification coils of copper are satisfactory.

The preheated solution is purified in two stages. In the first operation copper, cobalt and nickel are removed. In the second stage cadmium and thallium are eliminated from the solution. These operations are again conducted batchwise. This method proved beneficial for Datteln, particularly as cobalt in the impure solution may vary between 5 and 25 milligrams per liter.

Air atomized zinc dust, copper sulphate and crude arsenic trioxide are used as reagents. In the first stage zinc dust with a grain fraction of 0.15 - 0.3 millimeter is used; for the cadmium removal stage finer zinc dust passing through a 0.15 millimeter screen is employed.

During the filling of the first stage purification tank 10 kilograms of arsenic trioxide and 200 kilograms of coarse zinc dust are added to the agitated solution. When the tank is filled another 100 kilograms of zinc dust and 25 - 75 kilograms of copper sulphate are fed. The pH is controlled at 4.0 by continuous additions of clarified spent electrolyte. After one hour's reaction time the first determination for cobalt and arsenic is made. Usually another addition of 100 kilograms of zinc dust is required to bring the cobalt to the desired concentration of less than 0.2 milligram per liter. At this stage the arsenic is entirely removed and after a safety addition of another 25 kilograms of zinc dust the solution is pumped to the filter presses. The entire first stage purification requires 2 hours. The temperature is maintained at 95 degrees Centigrade in order to prevent cadmium from coprecipitating.

A total of 5 filter presses are provided for the separation of the solids. One filter press is provided as a spare. Each press has an effective filter area of 43 square meters. The material of construction is bronze. Polypropylene felt-type filter cloth is used which is covered with kraft paper. Filtration proceeds at a rate of 700 to 900 liter per minute per press at a pressure of 5 atmospheres. Usually a filtration cycle requires 50 minutes using 4 presses in parallel.

For the second stage purification the temperature is lowered to 75 degrees Centigrade in order to precipitate the cadmium. In the tanks of this stage water cooling coils are installed for temperature reduction. This water is subsequently used for leach residue washing. When the desired temperature is reached the solution is acidified with spent electrolyte to a pH of 3.2 - 3.4 and a first addition of 100 kilograms zinc dust made. If high purity zinc dust is used, a small addition of copper sulphate acts as an activator. After half an hour another shot of 100 - 150 kilograms zinc dust is added. The first test for cadmium is made after one hour reaction time. When the solution is found to contain less than 0.2 milligram per liter cadmium a final safety addition of 50 kilograms of zinc dust is made and the solution pumped through filter presses into the check tanks. Filter presses for second stage have the same number and dimensions as for the first stage, they are however made of an aluminium-silicon alloy. In the check tank a final analytical determination is done for cobalt, arsenic and cadmium by the operato before pumping the solution (shown by Table 3) to the neutral storag tanks. The check tanks have the same dimensions as the purificatio tanks while the neutral storage can accommodate 1.100 cubic mete of solution. The second stage purification usually takes 1 1/2 hours

The purification residue produced during the first stage contains 35 - 40 percent copper, 1 percent cobalt, 5 percent arsenic. It is sold to a copper smelter. The residue from the second stage with 15 - 22 percent cadmium and 55 percent zinc is treated for cadmiu recovery.

Cadmium Recovery

The fresh second stage purification cake is first dissolved with spent plant electrolyte in a 50 cubic meters agitator tank. When essentially all cadmium has been dissolved, the solution is filtered and its cadmium content precipitated with the stochiometric quantit of zinc dust. The resulting cadmium sponge is washed, dried and dissolved in spent cadmium electrolyte. The neutral cadmium solut is subjected to a thallium and copper purification before electrolyzing. A total of 12 cells, identical to those used in the zinc tank house and operating at current densities up to 100 amperes per square meter, are fed with an electrolyte containing 60 - 80 grams per liter cadmium, 40 grams per liter zinc and 170 grams per liter acid. The cathodes are stripped every 16 hours, washed, dried and sold as such or melted under a cover of caustic soda and into shapes.

Electrolysis

The tank house is divided into three electrical units. Each electrical circuit consisting of 168 cells with a silicon rectofier unit rated at 30,000 amperes and 650 volts. The primary voltage from the utility company of 35,000 volts is directly connected to the transformers.

The concrete, lead lined cells measure 0.8 meter inside width, 3.338 meters length and 1.45 meters depth. They are placed side by side in rows of 14. Every 35 days one double row is taken out of service and cleaned in from 6 to 10 hours. Each cell accommoda 40 cathodes and 41 cast anodes of corroding grade lead alloyed with 0.75 percent Ag. The anodes measure 965 millimeters x 550 milli meters x 8 millimeters while the aluminium cathodes measure 1,122 millimeters x 600 millimeters x 5 millimeters. The anodes and cathodes rest on porcelain insulators. These special shaped insulators act as spacers as well as supports for the electrodes. On the bottom of the anode two porcelain buttons keep the cathode properly spaced.

Electrolyte circulation for each cell is continuous at a rate of 60 liters per minute. The effluent from the cells is collected in individual launders and flows by gravity through the main collecting launder to the spent electrolyte storage tanks. From these tanks the solution is pumped over an atmospheric cooling tower and flows by gravity into additional electrolyte storage tanks. The electrolyte is returned to the tank house through an open launder feeding the 36 rows of cells by the way of individual feed launders.

The electrolyte cooling system has a total of 4 wooden tanks, each having a holding capacity of 550 cubic meters. The wooden tanks are lined with 5 percent antimonial lead. The entire launder system is of glass fibre reinforced polyester. All pipes used in this section are of polyethylene.

The spent electrolyte (shown by Table 3) is cooled in a forced draft atmospheric cooling tower which does not contain packing. The tower is divided into 10 individual units which can be operated independently. The wooden structure is lined with polyethylene sheets and the bottom pan is lead lined. The air velocity through the units is 3 meters per second. Three rows of mist eliminators prevent any acid carry-over into the atmosphere. The gypsum precipitated in the tower is cleaned every 2 weeks, the sludge in the electrolyte storage tanks every 3 months.

The addition of neutral solution to the spent electrolyte is pumped continuously into one of the electrolyte storage tanks. Reagents required to minimize acid mist formation in the tank house and to depress lead in the cathodes are fed continuously into the main electrolyte launder. Spent electrolyte is withdrawn from the electrolyte storage tanks and pumped to the leach section as required.

The ampere load to the tank house is varied throughout the 24 hour period. During the off peak nighttime periods reduced power cost rates are available. Current densities at the cathode surface vary from 500 to 600 amperes per square meter for the daytime periods. Current densities are increased to 750 amperes per square meter or higher during off peak periods which also include week ends. Cell temperatures of the spent electrolyte fluctuate between 39 to 40 degrees Centigrade. However, in the summer of 1969 temperatures of 45 degrees Centigrade were experienced without any detrimental effects on the current efficiency or cathode purity. Normal results are shown by Table 5.

Deposition time is 24 hours, except for the rows being cleaned, in which the cathodes remain from 38 to 40 hours in the cells. The stripping of the zinc deposit is done manually. An overhead air hoist removes 20 cathodes at one time from one cell. The load is moved, using a monorail to a stripping rack to the main floor of the tank house. The zinc is pulled from the aluminium cathode by a hand tool and stacked in racks. Two fork lift trucks transport the stripped zinc to the cathode storage area after the weight is recorded on a printing type scale.

The stripping of the cathode zinc is completed in 8 hours or less. One stripper completes the removal of zinc from one row of 14 cells. The weight varies between 9 and 10 metric tons. A stripper is permitted to leave the plant as soon as his allotted cells are stripped. A premium is paid for increased current efficiencies based upon the monthly average of his allotted row. Premiums may increase the basic pay as much as 30 percent.

Melting and Casting

After storing the cathodes for 48 hours, they are melted in one 1800 kilowatt electric induction furnace. The melting rate is 18 tons per hour. Normal results of the melting and casting department are shown by Table 6. The inductors are cooled with air. The cooling blowers are located in a closed room in order to lower the noise level at the melting furnace and to supply clean air to the inductors. The exhaust air is kept at 50 degrees Centigrade to prevent moisture deposition on the inductor coils.

Dross is normally skimmed from the surface of the molten metal every 2 to 4 hours using ammonium chloride pellets as fluxing reagent. The hot dross is treated in a rotary liquating furnace. The recovered metal is used for zinc dust production and the oxidized dross is sold. The gases from the liquating drum are filtered in a bag house which is not satisfactory and a venturi scrubber will be substituted.

Only one quality of zinc is cast on a straight line, inclined casting machine, having 160 molds. An air driven centrifugal pump made of graphite delivers the molten zinc to the casting machine. A variable speed air drive for the pump and the velocity of the casting machine can be adjusted to produce a uniform 25 kilograms slab. These slabs are stacked by hand, cooled for 12 hours weighed and transferred to the metal storage building. For continuous galvanizing, specification metal is cast in 1 ton blocks. Die casting alloy, containing 4 percent

TABLE 5

Electrolysis Data October 1969

Cathode Zinc produced	9.704 tons
Loss time for cleaning the cells	12.3 h
Current efficiency	91.3 %
Average current Load per unit (168 cells)	23.457 A
Average Voltage at rectifier	576 V
Average Kilowatt hours per ton of cathode	3.239 kWh
Average current density	597 A/m^2
Average spent electrolyte temperature	39.4°C
Average electrolyte temperature	34.2°C
Gum arabic used per ton of cathode	0.031 kg
Sodium silicate used per ton of cathode	0.9 kg
Cresylic acid used per ton of cathode	0.021 kg
Strontium carbonate used per ton of cathode	5.74 kg

TABLE 6

Results of the Melting and Casting Department October 1969

Cathodes melted	10.060 tons
kW Hr. per ton of cathode melted	103
Zinc produced per ton of cathodes melted	0.98
Dross	250 tons
Required Zinc dust	514 tons
Ammoniumchloride used per ton of cathodes melted	1.05 kg
Slab Zinc special high-grade	7.374 tons
Zamak (die casting alloy)	2.074 tons

aluminium and 1 percent copper is produced in two 300 kilowatt induction furnaces, holding each 15 tons of metal. The molten zinc is pumped from the cathode melting furnace into the die cast unit with an asbestos cloth lined steel launder. Load cells on the die cast furnaces are used to determine the weight. A master alloy of 80 percent aluminium and 20 percent copper is melted in two oil fired retorts and poured directly into the die cast furnaces. After agitating for 10 minutes the finished alloy is cast on a straight line casting machine at a rate of 6 tons per hour.

Other special die casting alloys are produced in small quantities. They are prepared in melting kettles and cast by hand into a variety of different shapes.

Modifications

Since the start-up of Datteln plant the excess of sulphates was a serious problem. In the roaster itself an improvement is obtained if the sulphur dioxide content of the roaster gases can be further increased. At present the limiting factor is the sulphuric acid plant capacity. It is planned to add another unit of 265 tons per day capacity.

In the leaching section the jarosite process will also help to establish a sulphate equilibrium. Once this improvement is in operation, the possibility of transforming the batch process into a continuous process will be studied. No economical gains can be expected but the work load of the operators could be eased.

TABLE 7

The total employment is 414 persons and is divided up as follows.

	Labour	Staff	Total
Roasting & Sulphuric acid	37	6	43
Leaching & Purification	44	7	51
Cadmium Recovery	15	1	16
Tank House	95	4	99
Melting & Casting	82	7	89
General Services	35	10	45
Maintenance	42	8	50
Administration	-	21	21
	350	64	414

Chapter 10

THE PORTO MARGHERA ELECTROLYTIC ZINC PLANT OF MONTEPONI e MONTEVECCHIO
Porto Marghera, Italy

Dr. Ing. Turno De Michelis
Technical Manager of Monteponi e Montevecchio - Milan

Dr. Ing. Ferdinando Gnesotto
Works Manager of Porto Marghera (Venice)

Abstract

The Porto Marghera plant was erected in 1936 for the production of 10,000 tons of electrolytic zinc annually. Since then it has been continuously enlarged until annual production of the metal reached 40,000 tons in 1969. At the same time the processing cycle was modified bringing it up to date with modern techniques, and was completed by installations for the recovery of by-products in the minerals treated and subsequent processing of the base metal. 90% of the zinc produced is of 99.995% purity.

At present the plant comprises, first of all, the zinc blende desulphuration department which has a single modern fluid bed furnace capable of processing 220 - 250 tons of dry crude mineral daily; it is connected to the sulphuric acid plant with its three catalysis sections each capable of producing 60-70 tons of sulphuric acid monohydrate daily.

The roasted blende is conveyed pneumatically to plants for leaching of the zinc and purification of the resulting solution.

During recent years this department has been completely transformed from the discontinuous cycle, for which it was built, to the continuous cycle, paying great attention to the problem of equipment for controlling and regulating the process; a part of the instruments used have been studied and lined up by our own technicians.

The solution, which is purified to very high purity limits, is sent to the electrolysis plant which has 524 cells. This plant has also been extensively modified in recent years as regards the cycle of solutions and their cooling. Moreover, mechanical stripping has been introduced using automatic machinery designed and lined up by our technicians.

The zinc, as cathodes, is melted in methane and electric furnaces equipped with machinery for the casting and stacking of ingots also built by us. The final zinc leaching sludges are treated in a special plant for recovery of the metals they cont Zn, Pb, Cu, Cd, Ag, Ge, In and Ga are thus recovered. In particular, the total extraction yield of the mineral in the case of zinc thus reaches more than 95%. The recovered cadmium is transformed into the metal in the special electrolytic department. Also the Ge recovered may be transformed into dioxi of electronic purity or into intrisic multicrystalline metal in a special plant.

Finally, the plant is completed by installations for the processing of metallic zinc. One of the most important of these is the plant for the production of zinc alloys for die-casting, which is equipped with electric furnaces and machinery for casting ingots and can produce up to 24,000 - 28,000 tons annually. The extremely modern rolling plant can produce zinc and zinc alloy - particularly Zn+Cu+Ti - sheeting and strips. It is complete with machinery and equipment for the production of zinc wire, zinc balls, special anti-corrosive anodes, etc.

Introduction and history

The plant was built during 1935-1936 by the Società Italiana dello Zinco.
During the course of the years the company underwent many changes until it became the present Società Monteponi e Montevecchio, which accounts for the greater part of Sardinian mining activities in the same field at three plants - two for the production of electrolytic zinc (one at Monteponi in Sardinia and the other at Porto Marghera, and one for the production of soft lead, at San Gavino, in Sardinia).

The Porto Marghera plant is located on the shore of the Venetian lagoon, in the industrial area of Porto Marghera which was created immediately after the First World War and characterised by the fact that the plants are linked directly to the sea, each with their own wharf for loading and unloading of raw materials and products directly from ships to the palnt and vice versa. Thus the plants are fitted with specific equipment which reduces the cost of delivery and shipping of goods to a minimum (1).

Our plant was built in a 12 month period during 1935-1936 to process the zinc blende produced in the Montevecchio mines in Sardinia. Choosing the location for the plant so far removed from the mine might nowadays seem somewhat ill-advised, but it is fully justified when referred to the construction period.

At that time Sardinia had little electric power available while Porto Marghera was supplied in abundance from the hydroelectric generating plants of Cadore and Carnia (Eastern Alps). Moreover, in those times, it would have been impossible to exploit in Sardinia the sulphuric acid produced through desulphuration of the zinc blende, while it could be used directly at Porto Marghera by the already known and rapidly expanding chemical plants or else easily sent to other users in Northern Italy.
To these reasons, already decisive in themselves, should be added the fact that the Venice province then had the problem of excess labour and that the Government granted large tax and customs inducements to whoever built new plants at Porto Marghera.

Furthermore, even today when the above reasons have almost completely lost consistency, the position of the Porto Marghera plant may still be considered valid. Its direct link with the sea, the still existent functional autonomy of the industr port, the nearness to the industries of Northern Italy which are consumers of its products, and the possibility of receivir economic supplies of zinc minerals from mines in the Alps, are all positive elements which will certainly retain their value also in the future.

As previously stated, the plant has been in operation since 1936. It was planned by Ing. Giovanni Rolandi, at that time. Generale Manager of the company, who was assisted by Prof.Livi Cambi; both were wellknown technical experts in the zinc electrolysis field.
The plant was designed for a yearly production of 10,000 tons of zinc in ingots, and this figure was reached immediately.

Later extensions were made, especially after the war; the last of these, completed in 1969, has brought yearly productiv capacity to 40,000 - 45,000 tons of zinc in ingots.

These enlargements have been accompanied by continuous research to improve the processing system, by plant moderniza (especially as regards its mechanization) and by completion of the production cycle.
At Porto Marghera, special attention has always been paid to the problem of the purity of the zinc produced.

In fact, production of zinc alloys for die-casting had started as far back as 1939, giving rise to the need for zinc with a purity of over 99.995%. The problem was solved at that time by building a New Jersey-type refinery for distillation of the metal, which went on operating until 1950.

That year a special originally designed electrolysis section entered in operation which permitted direct productio of superpure electrolytic zinc starting from the zinc sulphat solution prepared for ordinary hydrolysis.

The system, patented by our company (2), functioned regularly and with excellent economic results until 1960 when the changeover to the addition of Sr sulphate to the cells, according to the ASARCO patent, permitted an even more economical solution to the problem. Nowadays, nearly all the zinc produced at Porto Marghera has a purity of over 99.995%.

Particularly outstanding results have been obtained in the extraction yields of zinc from ores and in the current yield on electrolysis; they will be mentioned later on.

As for completion of the production cycle, it has followed two directions.

The first led to as high a recovery as possible of the metals present in the original ores; it started in 1937 with the recovery of cadmium, followed immediately by that of copper and cobalt and, after the war, with introduction of treatment of the final leaching sludges, achieving recovery of Pb, Ag, Ge, In, and Ga.

By contrast, starting from zinc metal, the second route led to the production of more products.

As already stated, production of alloys for die-casting started in 1939. Today the works has a rationally designed plant capable of producing up to 100 tons daily of various alloys, starting from zinc in cathodes.

The first zinc rolling plant, of pack rolling type, was installed in 1940; this was replaced in 1952 by a modern plant for strip rolling.
In recent years a very up-to-date continuous casting and rolling plant has been designed and built at Porto Marghera and is now in the lining-up stage.

The range of rolled sections produced is as complete as possible; not only are rolled sections in ordinary zinc produced but also types for printing, electric batteries, musical organs, and rolled sections containing Cu and Ti which are specially suitable for roofing purposes.

The plant is complete with equipment for the production of wire, balls, normal zinc and special zinc anodes which withstand salt-water corrosion. Fig. 1 reports the general summarized flow-sheet of processing in the plant.

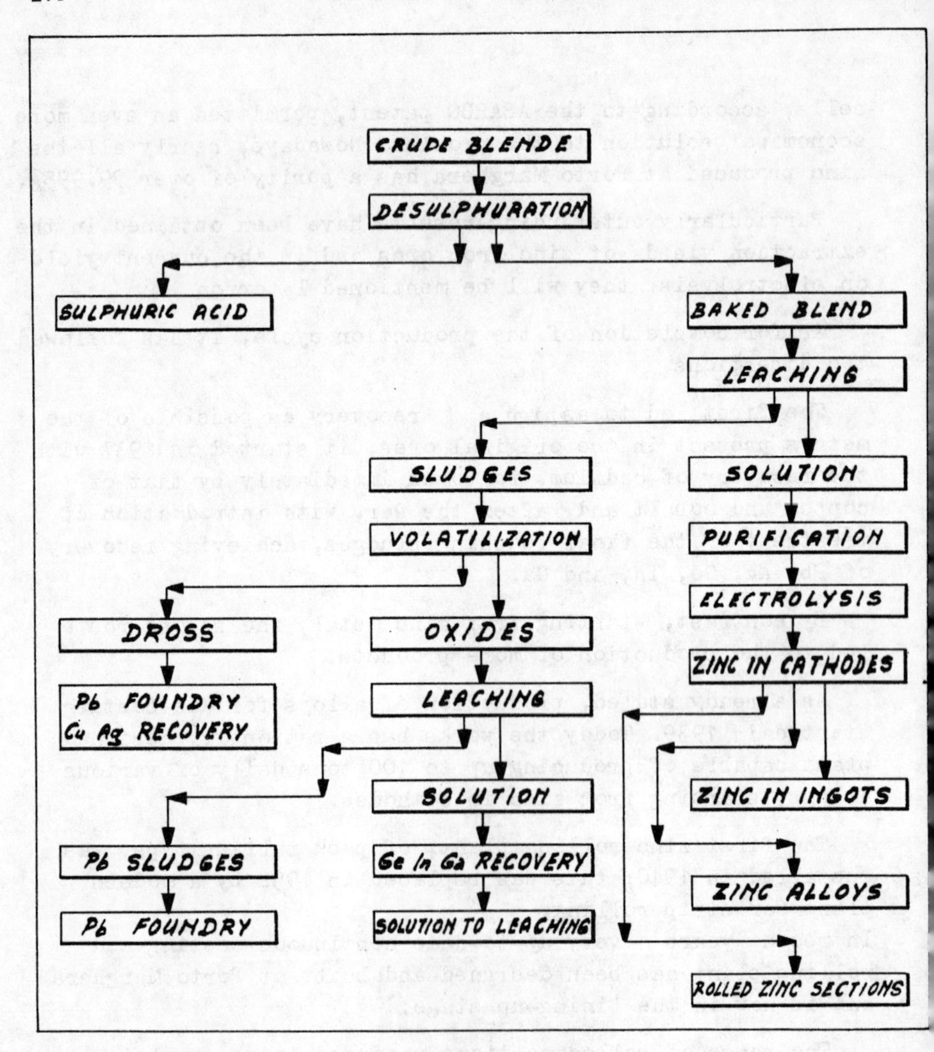

Fig. 1

Employees working in the plant comprise:

3 executives

68 white-collar workers

28 foremen

595 blue-collar workers

Desulphurization

Most of the mineral is shipped by sea and the cargo boats are unloaded by means of the port installation which has a capacity of 150 tons/hr.

The material is stored inside the plant in 4 silos which have a total capacity of about 10,000 tons. Conveyance is assured by two overhead travelling cranes with 6 ton hook and 2 ton bucket.

When the plant first started operating (1939) 2 Wedge-type furnaces built by Humboldt, with heat recovery by means of boilers, were in use. In 1953, a third furnace of the same type was added. The roasting capacity was 50 tons/day of dry zinc blende for each unit. The mixture consisted of:

Dry crude blende	70%
Electrostatic filter and boiler dusts	7%
Ground grit	12%
Leaching sand	4%
Moisture	7%

During 1947-48 one of the first two furnaces was transformed for flash-roasting, with a daily capacity of 120 tons, and filled with a steam boiler.

Since 1968 a Fluosolid furnace capable of processing 220 tons of dry blende daily has been in operation while the three Wedge furnaces have been shut down. The source and typical compisitions of the minerals used are as follows:

	Montevecchio	Monteponi	Rimisa
Zn	59.15 %	52.65 %	59.40 %
Total S.	32.10	32.65	32.55
Cd	0.45	0.26	0.34
Pb	1.60	1.50	0.27
Cu	0.22	0.06	0.16
Fe	3.00	4.00	3.35
Co	0.014	0.001	0.028
Ge	0.17	0.006	0.02
Sb	0.06	0.009	0.0035
Ca	0.3	0.4	0.132
Mg	0.03	0.13	0.05
Cl	0.015	0.07	0.001

F	0.01	0.002	0.0025
SiO2	1.90	2.00	3.43

Granulometric analysis of the two main types of zinc blende for roasting is as follows:

	Montevecchio	Monteponi
>0.147 mm	8.2 %	1.1 %
>0.104	14.2	2.2
>0.074	16.4	5.6
<0.074	61.2	91.1

The moisture content of the above blendes is around 6-9%.

The dusulphuration plant has been built by the Lurgi Company. The Fluosolids furnace is fed by means of cranes with buckets. The mineral is loaded into an 80 cu.m. hopper complete with vibrating screen variable speed conveyor belt, metering plate and belt loader.

The furnace has a grate area of 34 sq. metres, and is followed by a La Mont type boiler built by Sluldørs, with a total exchange surface of 376 sq. metres, 2 cyclones and an electrostatic filter. The later consists of two chambers with metal casing and grid electrodes (negative pole) and plates (positive pole) with axial flow of the gas. A centrifugal exhauster is placed at the end of the electrostatic filter.

The average temperature of the fluo-bed is 940°C. The gas outflowing from the electrostatic filter contains 8.5-9% SO_2, has a temperature of 370°C. and a dust content of 30-50 mg/cu.m. The air delivery is 18,000 Ncu.m./hr at a pressure of 1750 mm. of water. The vacuum at the tail exhauster reaches 170 mm of water.

Steam production is about 8 tons/hr, at a pressure of 40 atm. The roasted blende produced (190-200 tons/day) consists of two fractions:

- The first includes the overflow discharge and the first part of the boiler deposit
- The second includes the final part of the boiler deposit and the deposits in the cyclones and electrostatic filter.

These fractions differ essentially for their sulphur, fluorine and chlorine content, namely:

	1st fraction	2nd fraction
S sulphide	0.49%	0.19%
S sulphate	0.78	2.80
Cl	< 0.0005	0.002
F	≤ 0.001	≤ 0.001

The relative granulometric compositions and apparent densities also show a difference:

	1st fraction	2nd fraction
$>$ 0.174 mm	51.1%	0.1%
$>$ 0.104	2.2	-
$>$ 0.074	34.0	3.70
$<$ 0.074	12.7	96.2
apparent density	1.98 gr/cm^3	1.62 gr/cm^3

The weight ratio between the two fractions tends to be 1, but varies extensively according to several factors such as the hourly amount of air at the grate, type and hourly quantity of ore, moisture content; etc.

All the roasted blende produced is sieved on a 1 mm mesh screen. The large particles, about 5-6% of the total, are ground in a ball-mill and, after further sieving, added to the fine portion.

The sieved, ground portion for leaching has the following granulometry:

$>$ 0.174 mm	14%
$>$ 0.104	2
$>$ 0.074	40
$<$ 0.074	44

Gas and Sulphuric Acid cooling and washing

We have stated that the gases exit from the electrostatic filter at about 370°C., and with an average dust content of 40 mg/mc.

They travel a long route during which the temperature drops to 280°C. Subsequent cooling and washing operations include:

1) 3 "Venturi" AISI 316 stainless steel water injection type towers, with Teflon-lined head. Outgoing temperature about 80°C.

2) 2 parallel water condensers, built of lead

3) 3 washing towers, with Raschig rings and water in counter-current (6.20 metres high, 3.40 metres in diameter).

4) 3 wet type electrostatic filter units

5) 3 coke filters

The wash waters, which eliminated, contain, on the average:

Zn	0.07	g/l
Cl	0.3	
H2SO4	1.7	
SO2	3.5	

At the outlet of the coke filters the temperature of the gas is 35-38°C. The gas then flows through three parallel drying towers where the SO_2 concentration drops to 5.8-6.2% following the entry of filtered air, and then goes on to 3 contact towers, the same which were used for the first Wedge furnaces. The catalytic mass layers were modified before the Fluosolid furnace was placed in operation in order to potentiate the single units and make them suitable for the increased monohydrate production.

The conversion yield on catalysis is 97.5 - 97.8%. The SO_3 outflows at 150°C. and is conveyed to two absorption towers where the acid circulates at a temperature between 70°C. and 90°C.

The acid has a content of 98.5-98.8%; the concentration is adjusted and recorded by a Kent type automatic device.

Thermal control of the acid circulating in both the drying and absorption sections is performed by means of water-cooled acid-proof cast iron exchangers. Average daily production is 180 tons of monohydrate.

Possible dilution of the monohydrate to 92% or 75% is carried out separately, cooling by means of Karbate type graphite exchangers.

Leaching and purification

Figure 2 gives the flow-sheet for this department.

We wish to point out, first of all, that our plant has the specific feature of producing a zinc sulphate solution for electrolysis possessing very high and constant purity.

Leaching

The zinc blende, the average composition of which is given in table 1, is conveyed pneumatically from the desulphurating department and stored in a raised tank which directly feed, by means of mechanical conveyors, the 1st attack vats. Leaching takes places in two stages, both of which reach neutrality; they run discontinuously but have recently been changed to continuous operation, with consequent numerous advantages which may be summarized as follows:

a) increased productive capacity. Without increasing the existing number of vats, the leaching department, which could supply electrolysis for yearly zinc production of 30,000 tons, now succeeds in producing the solution necessary for 45,000 tons yearly.

b) introduction of continuous control and automatic regulation of the process.
Attempts made in the past to automate vat operations working discontinuously were, by contrast, failures.

c) improvement of the technological results. This depends on introduction of the above-mentioned controls and adjustments and has led to smoother running which, in turn, ensures constancy of results, lowered reagent consumptions, improved zinc extraction yields and, above all, improved ease of

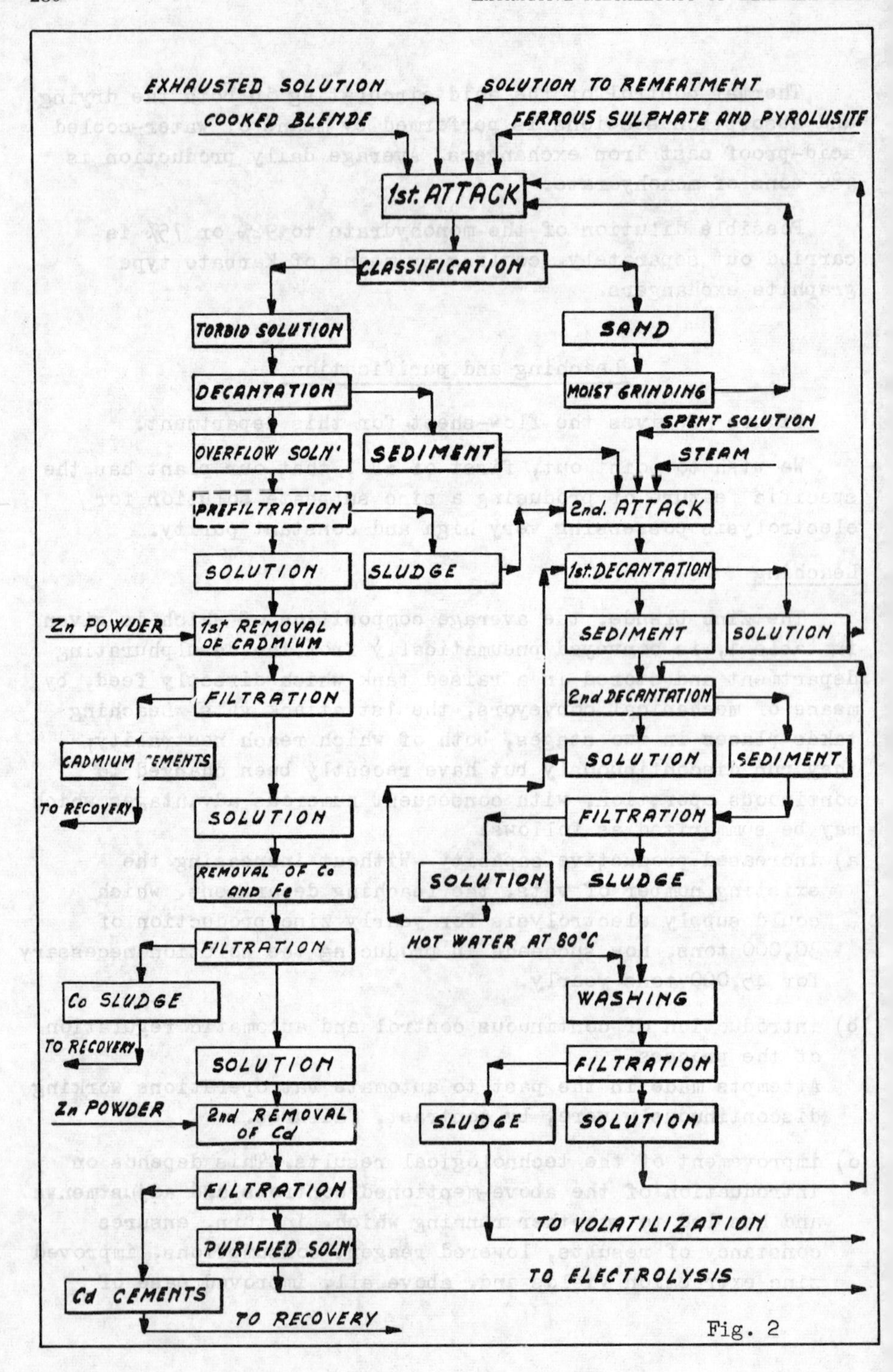
EXHAUSTED SOLUTION
COOKED BLENDE
SOLUTION TO REMEATMENT
FERROUS SULPHATE AND PYROLUSITE
1st. ATTACK
CLASSIFICATION
TORBID SOLUTION
SAND
DECANTATION
MOIST GRINDING
SPENT SOLUTION
OVERFLOW SOLN'
SEDIMENT
STEAM
PREFILTRATION
2nd. ATTACK
SOLUTION
SLUDGE
1st. DECANTATION
Zn POWDER
1st REMOVAL OF CADMIUM
SEDIMENT
SOLUTION
FILTRATION
2nd DECANTATION
CADMIUM CEMENTS
SOLUTION
SEDIMENT
TO RECOVERY
SOLUTION
FILTRATION
REMOVAL OF Co AND Fe
SOLUTION
SLUDGE
FILTRATION
HOT WATER AT 80°C
Co SLUDGE
WASHING
TO RECOVERY
SOLUTION
FILTRATION
Zn POWDER
2nd REMOVAL OF Cd
SLUDGE
SOLUTION
FILTRATION
TO VOLATILIZATION
PURIFIED SOLN'
TO ELECTROLYSIS
Cd CEMENTS
TO RECOVERY
Fig. 2

decantation and filtration of the thick liquid.

Six vats are used for the 1st attack, five in operation and one as a reserve.

The vats (like all those used in other operations) have a working capacity of 60 cu.m., a diameter of 4.8 metres, cylindrical height 3.4 metres and conical base. They are built of reinforced concrete and lined with a double layer of antacid sandstone tiles. This system has proved to be more than satisfactory and is confirmed by the fact that vats built in 1936 are still in use. Notwithstanding this, a vat with inner lining of AISI 316 stainless steel is being tested.

The five vats run in series and continuously. In the first are conveyed:

a) exhausted electrolysis solution
b) ferrous sulphate in solution
c) ground pyrolusite
d) desulphurated zinc blende, for about 96% of the total used
e) ground leaching sand
f) solutions for purification: these are all those solutions produced in subsequent stages likely to contain dissolved elements such as As, Sb, Ge, which should be eliminated.

The main solutions are those deriving from the 2nd attack, from the attack of the volatilization **oxides of the final leaching** sludges and from the cadmium production cycle.
A device for the continuous pH determination is placed in the vat and serves to check the acidity of the solution but its main purpose is to meter the addition of ferrous sulphate and pyrolusite.
The second vat contains a device for continuous pH determination which automatically regulates the addition of exhausted solution to the first vat, in order to maintain the pH of the second vat itself constantly at the required value (2.8).
The third and fourth vats complete the attack on the baked blende adjusting the pH of the solution to values above 4 at the end.
In the last vat a final small addition of baked blende is made, which brings the final pH of the solution to 4.8 - 4.9.
A pH-meter checks the final result, permitting to limit the last addition of baked blende to the very minimum.

With this system the attack capacity may reach 130 cu.m./hour.

The sludge from the last vat is discharged into three paddle classifiers which separate the leaching sand. This is moist-ground in a ball mill and then returned to the first vat of the 1st attack.

The sludge is sent to four decanters - 18 metres in diameter and of 800 cu.m. capacity, built of reinforced concrete lined with lead and with wooden shaft and arms.

Changeover of the 1st attack to the continuous system ensures such good and, above all, such regular and constant decantation that it is usually possible lo leave out prefiltrati of the overflow before sending it to purification.

Analysis of the neutral overflow solution is given in table 2.

The moist sediment in the decanters is extracted according to the programme, collected in tanks and sent to the 2nd attack.

This is performed continuously, using three vats linked in series, and is also regulated automatically by the pH measurement in the second vat. The moist sediment from the decanters and the spent electrolysis solution are sent to the first vat.

In the third vat the final neutralization is carried out by adding milk of lime.

All three vats are kept at temperatures exceeding 750°C., with direct inlet of steam at 3 atm.

The sludge is discharged into two decanters in series which also receive the wash solution in counter-current. The 1st decanter overflow is sent to the head of the 1st attack, while the moist sediment of the 2nd decanter is filtered through rotating filters.

The resulting sludge is washed with hot water in 10 cu. metre vats and then filtered (always through rotating filters).

The sludge thus obtained, the analysis of which is given in table 3, is sent to the volatilization department described further on.

At this point the extraction yield relative to the zinc content of the minerals reaches 91-92%.

Purification

Also in the case of purification operations on the neutral attack solution, we have changed-over in recent years from the discontinuous processing system to the continuous one (3), achieving the following marked advantages:

a) increased productive capacity, for the same reasons reported in connection with leaching
b) simplification of operations (as will be seen later)
c) sharp improvement in the results, as regards both the purification level and reagent consumption.

To explain things better, we shall briefly describe our purification cycle as it was before the change-over to the continuous cycle, recalling once again what we started in our premise to this chapter, namely that we have always considered it essential to obtain a very thorough purification of solutions for electrolysis. Purification was performed "in the cold" (that is, at the temperature reached by the solution during the attack) and carried out in four stages:

1) 1st cadmium removal with powdered zinc, produced by pulverization with compressed air
2) Cobalt removal with beta-naphthol
3) final iron removal with potassium permanganate

Using the discontinuous system it was necessary to perform over 100 operations daily, each of which had its own history, and it was inevitable that, notwithstanding the experience and care of the operators, the average results were not only worse than required but also far from what could actually be achieved.

Moreover, it was impossible to consider carrying out complete analytical control of all the operations without incurring a prohibitive expenditure.

By contrast, with continuous processing it was also possible to perform a continuous check of the methods in use and of analytical results of the various purification stages. We have dedicated and are still dedicating all our attention to this aspect of the problem and thus far our results have confirmed the validity of the trend we have chosen.

Purification now consists of the following stages:

1) 1st cadmium removal - Three vats of the same type as that described for leaching are used for this operation. The solution for purification is run into the first vat at a controlled and constant rate (which may reach 100 cu. metres/hour), together with the amount of powdered zinc required. This latter is added continuously by means of an adjustable metering device.
   The residual quantity of powdered zinc is added to the second vat by means of an identical metering device and, if necessar[y] a controlled amount of copper sulphate solution may also be added. The solution is withdrawn from the third vat by means of a filter pump and sent to filtration in 100 sq. metre filter presses.
2) Cobalt removal and final iron removal - These two purificatio[n] stages, at first performed separately, have been combined in a single operation. Five vats are used in this stage. The solution for purification is run into the first vat, at a controlled and constant rate, followed by the acid solution - to adjust the initial pH to the required value (abt. 2.8) - and nitroso-betanaphthol (prepared separately as a solution of the sodium salt). To the third vat, by means of a metering device similar to that used for the powdered zinc, we add activated carbon which absorbs any excess of reagent, to the fourth aqueous potassium permanganate, and to the last vat milk of lime for the final neutralization.
   The solution is pumped from this vat to fully automatic "Stella" pressure filters.
3) 2nd cadmium removal - Three vats are used for this stage and the method is the same one used for the 1st cadmium removal. However, in this case, copper sulphate is always added to the 2nd vat to assure a more thorough purification also of Ge and Sb.

Control equipment

Check of solution delivery. This is carried out very simply by measuring the head of the solutions before a weir placed in

the pipe feeding the solution into the vats. The measurement is given on a large indicator, clearly visible to the operator.
Analytical control of the results of cadmium removal - Our Metallurgical Research Centre has developed a device based on the polarographic method, which analyses samples taken after filtration, recording the Cd content of the solution.
At the first removal, when cadmium is present in the proportion of 2-3 mg/litre, the determination is made every 5 minutes, while at the second removal where the content is of the order of 0.3 mg/litre, the recording rhythm is every 20 minutes.

Each apparatus is fitted with an alarm which is set off when the value determined exceeds the fixed limiting value (4 mg/litre for the 1st cadmium removal and 0.4 mg/litre for the 2nd).
Check of the initial acidity on cobalt removal -
This is done with a pH-meter which automatically ajusts addition of the acid solution keeping the pH at the required value.
Analytical control of the results of cobalt removal - Our Metallurgical Research Centre is lining up a unit consisting of a continuous analyser and recorder for this purpose.
For the time being the check is made directly in the department using a rapid and sensitive colorimetric method lined up by our laboratory.
Control of the purity index of the solution - On the basis of an article by Russian scientists, we have lined up an apparatus at Porto Marghera (4) which, within a few minutes, gives with remarkable accuracy the measurement of the global purity of the solutions.

Its use, introduced into industrial practice six years ago, has given excellent results because it enable us to promptly intervene should irregularities emerge during purification, and also to carry out very useful investigations in the case of abnormalities.
Thanks to this apparatus we are now in a position to control the running of our cycle with greatly improved results compared with the past.

This device, which is also extremely simple to use, is installed not only in the chemical laboratory but also in the department.

Furthermore, we are studying its transformation into a continuous recording apparatus.

Results

Table 4 reports the composition of the final purified solution. By applying all the know-hows thus far described, we have been able to assure constancy in time of the results.

This is particularly important for the purity index which assures a good current yield on electrolysis and for the Cd content which ensures regular production of Zn with low Cd content, specifically indicated to meet the requirements of zinc alloy production.

Finally, table 5 reports the average consumption of reagents used in Kg. per ton of zinc in ingots production.

	with discontinuous system	with continuous system
Ferrous sulphate	68	60
Pyrolusite	23	17
Powdered zinc	36	29
Sodium nitrite	0.6	0.6
beta-naphthol	1.5	1.5
Permanganate	1.4	1.0

Table 1 - Average percentage composition of desulphurated zinc blende

Zn	62 - 64
S_{SO_4}	1.70 - 1.90
S_S	0.3
Stot	2.0 - 2.2
Pb	1.7
SiO2	1.9
Cd	0.40
Cu	0.20
Fe_2O_3	7.5
Co	0.012
Ni	0.004
Ge	0.0140
Sb	0.03
Cl	0.003
F	0.001
Mn	0.07

Table 2 - Average analysis of overflow solution in g /litre

Zn	145	Mg	6.5
Cd	0.55	Cl_{tot}	0.075
Mn	3.5	F	0.0025
Co	0.011	Ge	0.00007
Cu	0.09	Sb	0.0004
Fe	0.0010	As	0.00002
Ni	0.0020	solid	0.5 g/l

Table 3 - Washed sludge of 2nd attack

$Zn_{sulphate}$	3.5%	Pb	6.5%
Zn_{oxide}	5.5%	Ge	0.05%
$Zn_{sulphate}$	0.9%	In	0.04%
$Zn_{ferrite}$	5.5%	Ga	0.03%
Cd	0.35%		

Table 4 - Analysis of final purified solution in gr/litre

Zn	144	Fe	0.0002
Cd	0.0003	Ni	0.0002
Mn	3.5	Ge	0.000005
Co	0.0004	Sb	0.00002
Cu	0.0001	As	0.000003

P.I. 75 - 80

Electrolysis

The Porto Marghera electrolysis plant was erected in 1936 and designed to operate at a current density of 600 amp/sq. metre. The distance between electrodes of equal sign was then 75 mm; by reducing it to 70 mm it has been possible to increase the number of cathodes in the cell by 20%, thus reducing the normal current density.

The electrolysis cell room is divided into three sections which roughly correspond to successive enlargements of the department.

The first two, one comprising 216 cells and the other 128, are located in the same building, in line with one another, while the third, housing 180 cell, is in separate building. Each one receives the power supply from its own D.C. plant which in turn receives it A C. at 50,000 volts, reduces it to the required voltage, with a wide adjustement range, and transforms it into D.C. using a silicon rectifier.

All three plants are fitted with an automatic current regulator. The effective electrical efficiency, from A.C. at 50;000 V to D.C. exceeds 96%.

The cells are arranged in cascades of three cells each; only one group of 80 cells consists of 5-cell cascades, for space reasons.

They are in reinforced concrete lined with PVC sheets; a characteristic feature of the Porto Marghera cells, right from the start in 1936, is that they have a hopper base which makes it possible to discharge the anodic sludge from the bottom. This device not only makes removal of the anodic sludges easider but also permits cleaning of the cells about every 10 months. The anodes are made of rolled lead and contain 0.75% Ag. The size is 980 x 570 x 10 mm, and each anode has 60 holes, 25 mm in diameter, drilled in it. Resin spacers are placed in 5 of these holes. Due to the low Cl content of our solutions and to the working temperature of the cells, the life of the anodes exceeds 6 years. They are removed from the cell every three months and freed from the manganese-bearing sludges.

The cathodes measure 1020 x 600 x 4 mm, corresponding to a 1 sq. metre working surface. They are made of 99.5 Al, with rods also in Al, to the extremities of which welded, with a special process, two 4 cm copper plates.

For raising, two Al lifting lugs are welded to the rods. The cathodes are perfectly symmetrical as is also their position in the cells. The edges are covered with an insulating polythene strip; in one of the two sides, in the water-line area, the strip is replaced for 17 cm by an special design edge-cover, also in polythene, which we have studied in order to adapt the cathodes to the mechanical stripping. The life of the cathodes, since we have lined up the mechanical stripping, is 2 to 2½ years. This is also due, naturally, to the low F content of our solution. As regards the cell cooling problem, which we consider extremely important in view of our wish to produce all the zinc at high purity; we had to overcome two difficulties; industrial soft water is in short supply at Porto Marghera and what there is hot and not very clean. Moreover, during the summer the local climate is not at all suitable for cooling, because of the high temperatures reached (34°C. and even 36°C.) and the high humidity due to the predominance of scirocco type humid winds.

For this reason, we have used a mixed cooling system. It consists of blown air tower cooling of the purified neutral solution and of that feeding the cells, and is completed by the action of Pb coils, placed in the cells, through which industrial water is run, cooled in closed cycle in atmospheric towers.
Drawing 3 shows the cooling system used; the temperatures obtained in the summer are listed therein.

The cooling towers are of our own construction; the information obtained from Risdon experts in 1964 has been of great assistance in improving them.
They consist of an iron framework and a covering in PVC sheeting reinforced with pierced iron sheeting.

The tower for the neutral solution is empty to aid cleaning out the crystals of salts which deposit in it, while the others are filled with polypropylene resin rings (Ø 31.5 cm - height 12.5 cm) which are easy to remove and clean.

The blower is coupled to a 40 HP motor and supplies 170,000 cu.metres/hr of air at a pressure of 36 mm water.

The towers are cleaned from incrustations every 45-60 days, with the help of a special Woma high pressure pump; 5-6 days of work are required.

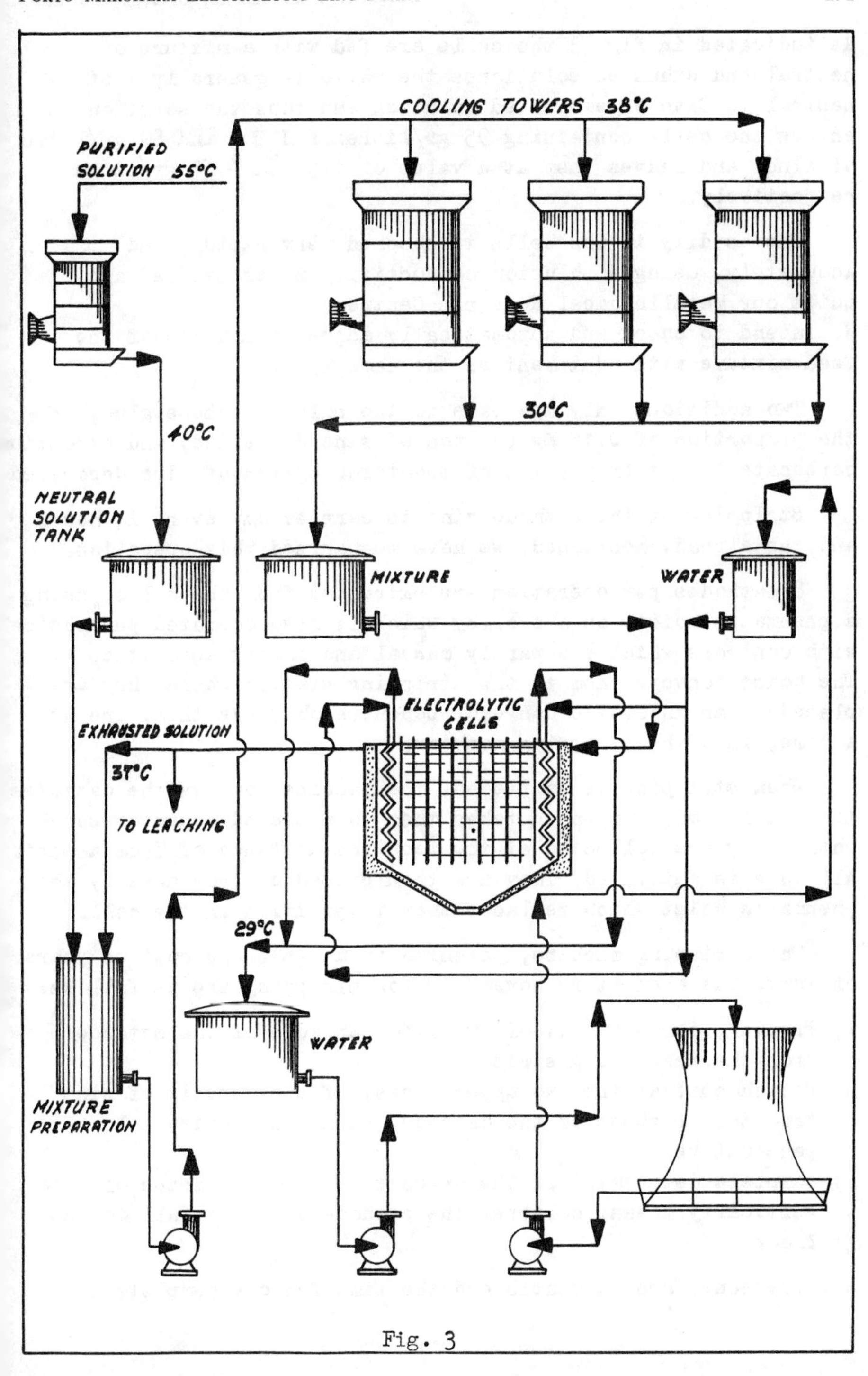
COOLING TOWERS 38°C
PURIFIED
SOLUTION 55°C
40°C
30°C
NEUTRAL
SOLUTION
TANK
MIXTURE
WATER
ELECTROLYTIC
CELLS
EXHAUSTED SOLUTION
37°C
TO LEACHING
29°C
WATER
MIXTURE
PREPARATION

Fig. 3

As indicated in fig. 3 the cells are fed with a mixture of neutral and exhusted solutions; the ratio is generally 1 of neutral to five of exhausted solution and thus the solution entres the cells containing 95 gr/litre of H_2SO_4 and 80 gr/litre of zinc; and leaves them at a value of 115 and 67 gr/litre respectively.

The acidity in the cells is checked very rapidly and accurately, using a solution conductivity meter studied and built our Metallurgical Research Centre.
We intend to check and automatically adjust formation of the feed mixture with equipment of the same type.

Two additions only are made to the solution: bone glue, in the proportion of 0.15 Kg per ton of zinc deposited, and strontiu carbonate in the proportion of two-three Kg/ton of zinc deposited

Stripping of the cathode zinc is carried out every 24 hours and, as already mentioned, we have mechanized this operation.

8 cathodes per operation are extracted from the cells, using a pneumatic hoist, on a trolley which is also operated pneumatica with controls which are partly manual and partly automatic.
The hoist conveys them to the stripping station where they are placed on an automatic conveyor bench which feeds them, one at a time, into the stripping machine.

When stripping is completed, the machine conveys the cathodes to a chain conveyor which takes them to a second conveyor bench where they are collected at the required distance of 7 cm a part. All this is automated. They are then picked up from here by the pneumatic hoist which replaces them in position in the cell.

The stripping machine, patented by us (5), has cost us years of work. The elementary movements for stripping are as follows:

1) Freeing, for a height of 10 cm, of an edge of the cathode from the insulating strip.
2) Detachment, at the two upper edges, of the deposit of zinc from the Al sheet of the cathode, using two horizontal penetrators.
3) complete detachment of the deposit of zinc, by means of two vertically moving colters. The cathode deposits fall to the floor.

All movements are automatic and the time for one complete

operation is about 10 second. The machine's efficiency with zinc deposits of our type is extremely high; waste is much less than 0.1%. Moreover, we have been able to observe that also in the presence of zinc which is hard to strip, the machine succeeds in working even when hand stripping becomes difficult and slow.

Each machine is tended by three men: one remains between the cells and sees to the extraction, conveyance to stripping and replacement of the cathodes in the cell; the second receives the cathodes and places them on the transporter bench, takes the already stripped cathodes from the second bench and returns them to the cells, while the third supervises the machine.

Here, briefly, are the final results we have obtained in zinc production.
Daily production - Daily production of zinc in cathodes may easily reach 150 tons.
Purity of the zinc produced - All the zinc produced has the purity required for zinc alloys. The analysis is as follows:

Pb	from 10 to 22	gm/ton
Cd	3	
Cu	3	
Ni	3	
Fe	1	
Zn	from 99.9978 to 99.9966%	

The two values given for Pb correspond to the results obtained in winter and in summer.
Electric efficiency - The average specific power consumption calculated in A.C. was 3.43 Kwh/Kg zinc in cathode, during 1969.
However, already in the last months of the year, due mainly to progress made with regard to the purity of the solution, consumption had fallen to about 3.3 Kwh/Kg.

This corresponds to a current yield of about 1120 gm of zinc per Kah and per cell, and thus to a current efficiency of about 92%.

Zinc Smelting

Cathode deposits of zinc, after stripping, are collected in suitable containers for transportation to the foundry.

The containers have been designed so that the zinc cathodes are kept in a vertical position during transportation, thus facilitating wash water drainage.

In view of the assured constant purity of the zinc produced, the cathodes can be used directly for the productions of alloy and of alloyed zinc for rolling; a large part of them are thus conveyed to these departments for smelting, as will be seen later.

At Porto Marghera, two types of furnaces are available, for the smelting of zinc into ingots for sale (6). The first is an electric low frequency induction furnace, the second is a reverbatory furnace heated with natural gas (methane).

The electric furnace, supplied by Siemens, has a bath capacity of about 27 tons of metal and a maximum electric rating of 400 Kw, with wide regulation possibilities. We have made some changes to it during recent years, in order to be able to extract the melted metal with a graphite rotary pump operated by a compressed air motor. The furnace is divided into smelting chamber and withdrawal chamber connected by a sifon. The zinc cathodes are loaded into the first, from the top, by means of a chute which allows them to become immersed vertically in the metallic bath. Maximum productive capacity is 75 tons/day of zinc cast in ingots, with a corresponding power consumption of 110 Kwh/ton.

This consumption rises to 120-125 Kwh/ton when the productive rhythm is slower.

Oxidation of the metal during smelting corresponds to 4.6% of the cast zinc.

Loss of metal is less than 0.3%.

The true thermal efficiency is 60% when operating at maximum capacity.

The reverbatory furnace, designed and built by us, has a basin capacity of 60 tons of melted metal.
At one end are the casting well and natural gas burners, at

the other the outlet for the fumes and the area where the zinc cathodes are loaded.

The loading system is the same used for the electric furnace. Here too the melted metal is withdrawn by means of a graphite pump. Maximum productive capacity is 100 tons/day of zinc cast in ingots corresponding to a natural gas consumption of 21.5 cu.m./ton. This consumption rises to over 30 cu.m./ton when the productive rhythm is slower.

If the furnace is well run and combustion well adjusted, oxidation of the metal during smelting may even be less than that for the electric furnace.
By contrast, loss of metal is greater, due to dragging over of dusts with the fumes: it may reach o.4%.

The true thermal efficiency is less than 30%.

The convenience of using one or other furnace naturally depends on the price paid per cu.m. of natural gas and per Kwh of electric power.
As stated, the melted metal is withdrawn from both furnaces by a pump which feeds the casting machine.

This machine, designed and built by us, includes a casting chain which holds 72 ingot molds, water-cooled, and a piling machine which stacks up the ingots to be transported by fork trucks.

Thus far our attempts to mechanize also the ingot skimming operation have been unsuccessful and this operation is therefore performed manually.

The total productive capacity is 6 tons/hour, but true production, also in function of the smelting capacity of the furnaces, is 34 tons/8 hours for the natural gas furnace and 25 tons/hours for the electric one.

Three operators are required: the first attends to loading of the cathodes, the second to the casting machine and skimming of the ingots, and the third to movement of the ingots produced. At the end of the shift, all three operators clean the furnace bath. The extracted oxides (tutty) are ground and sieved; the coarse, metallic part is returned to the smelting furnace, while the fine portion is added to the crude zinc blende which feeds the desulphuration furnace to eliminate the Cl deriving from treatment of the bath with ammonium chloride.

Purity of the zinc remains very high, as the use of the graphite pump for withdrawal of the metal has reduced Fe conta mination to a minimum.

The following is a type analysis:

Pb	from 11	to 23	gm/ton
Cd	3		"
Cu	3		"
Ni	3		"
Fe	from 15	to 20	"
Zn	from 99.9965	to 99.9950%	

Here are some indicative figures which summarize the progres of zinc production at Porto Marghera.

Electric power consumption. The specific consumption of electric power relative to all processing stages, starting from the roasted zinc blende and arriving at zinc in ingots that is, comprising leaching, purification of the solutions, electrolysis and smelting, in 1969 was 4 Kwh/Kg of zinc in ingots.

During recent months this figure has fallen to values under 3.9 Kwh/kg.

Labour. Drawing no. 4 shows its course during the last eight years. The values shown correspond to the number of hours necessary to produce 1 ton of zinc in ingots, starting from the roasted blende.

The marked improvement achieved during recent years is due to increase of the productive capacity which have risen from 23,000 to 40,000 tons/year, and also to that achieved in the cycle and by the introduction of mechanization of operations wherever possible.

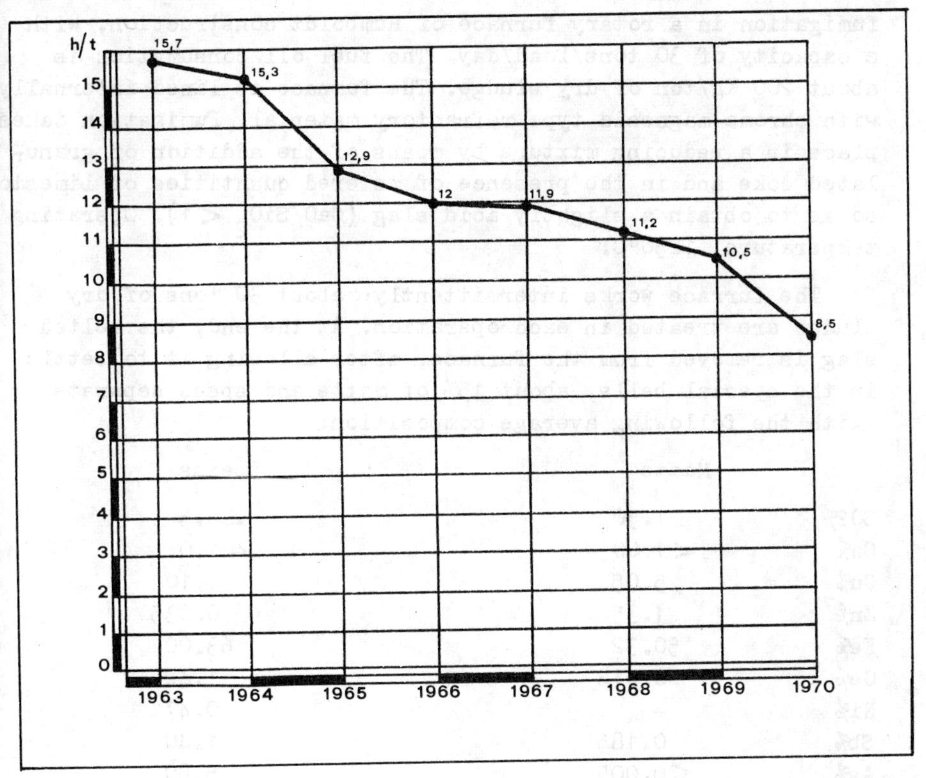

Fig. 4

Recoveries

The sludge left over after leaching of the roasted zinc blende contains:

Moisture	40%
Zn	18%
Cd	0.4%
Pb	6.0%
Ge	0.06%
In	0.04%
Ga	0.02%

It is dried until the moisture content is reduced to 3-4% in a rotary furnace heated with fuel oil. Consumption of the latter totals 100 Kg/ton of dry sludge. It then passes to fumigation in a rotary furnace of Humboldt construction, with a capacity of 30 tons/load/day. The fuel oil consumption is about 200 Kg/ton of dry sludge. The furnace is lined internally with chrome-magnesia type refractory material. Fumigation takes place in a reducing mixture by means of the addition of granulated coke and in the presence of metered quantities of limestone so as to obtain a slightly acid slag ($CaO/SiO_2 < 1$). Operating temperature, 1250°C.

The furnace works intermittently; about 30 tons of dry sludge are treated in each operation. At the end, the melted slag is removed from the furnace; after allowing it to settle in the special bells, about 15% of matte and speiss separate with the following average composition:

	Matte	Speiss
SO2%	1.50	<0.5
Ca%	<1.00	<1.0
Cu%	5.05	4.10
Zn%	1.35	0.035
Fe%	50.32	63.00
Ge%	0.012	1.42
Ni%	-	0.47
Sb%	0.185	1.40
As%	<0.005	5.80
Ag%	0.154	0.147
S. sulphurous%	18.75	7.85

This material is also sent to the San Gavino foundry for recovery of Cu and Ag.

The furnace is equipped with a boiler for steam production (4 tons/hour), with a heat exchange surface of about 230 sq. metres and bag filters to recover the fumes, whose production is about 10 tons daily.

The oxides produced undergo a first dechlorinating wash in the presence of sodium carbonate (pH 8) so as to reduce the chlorine content to the minimum and thus avoid loss of Cd and Zn.

After washing, the dry fumes have the following average composition:

Zn	56%

Cd	1%
Pb	15%
Ge	0.1%
Cl	0.008%

The attack is carried out in 10 cu. metre vats, with exhausted solution with the addition of potassium and ferrous sulphate. Gradual addition of the fumes neutralizes the acidity down to pH 5.5. The liquid is filtered and the solution which contains nearly all the Zn and Cd passes to the Meaching department.

The sludge which contains Pb, Ge, In and Ga is attacked with dilute sulphuric acid and calcium sulphite to reduce the ferric Fe. The thick liquid is filtered at pH1, the Pb separating as sulphate which is washed and sent to our own company's foundry at S. Gavino near Cagliari (Pb content about 40%). The residual solution is treated with tannic acid to separate the germanium.

After filtration of Ge tannate, the liquid is neutralized with caustic soda and a sludge precipitates containing 12% (dry weight) of In and 2.5% of Ga; it is sent to the Turin Metallurgical Research Centre for recovery of these metals. The germanium tannate is calcined at 600°C.; the resulting crude product contains 25% of Ge and forms the raw material for the production of pure dioxide for electronic use and of the metal germanium with a resistivity exceeding 50 ohm. cm.

Very pure germanium dioxide has the following impurity contents:

Si	1	ppm	Sn	0,05	ppm
Mg	0,4		Ga	0,05	
Al	1		In	0,1	
Pb	0,1		Ni	0,1	
Fe	0,6		Zn	0,2	
B	0,5		Cd	0,05	
As	0,05		Cu	0,05	
Sb	0,05		Ti	0,05	

Cadmium cycle

All the cadmium, whether coming from attack of the roasted blende or from that of the fumes, is extracted in the two phases of the electrolyte purification cycle under the form of "cements" which are enriched up to a content of about 60%.

After transfer to the special department, the above cements are dissolved by sulphuric attack and then filtered to eliminate a first copper sludge. The solution, containing 160 gr of Cd/litre undergoes a further double purification with potassium permanganate and sodium bichromate to remove harmful impurities (particularly Tl), and then further purification with activated carbon and powdered zinc.

The solution thus obtained is diluited to 140 gr/litre and submitted to electrolysis using aluminium cathodes and Pb-Ag anodes, current density 80 A/sq. metre.

The sheets of Cd, stripped every 48 hours, are smelted into ingots, spheres, rods, etc. Here in the average analysis:

Cd	99,99%
Pb	0,0011%
Cu	0,0007%
Ag	0,0007%
Tl	0,0005%
Zn	0,001%
Fe	0,0002%
Ni	0,0004%

The solution discharged from the cells contains:

Cd	60	g/l
Zn	30	
H2SO4	90	

The cadmium is reprecipitated with poor cements, zinc powder or Zama alloy. The spongy material so obtained is set aside to oxidize Cd with the air; the residual solution is treated with diacetyldioxime to eliminate the Ni and sent to the zinc cycle.

The copper sludges containing 60% Cu, are sold to third parties.

Cobalt

The precipitate obtained in the second purification phase (Co beta-naphtolate) which contains about 2% Co is now sold to third parties for the manufacture of inorganic dye-stuffs.

Time back, processing cycles were lined up for recovery of the cobalt in the form of oxides or salts, or as metallic cobalt.

Zinc Alloys

Table no. 6 groups together the zinc alloys at present produced at Porto Marghera.

Other types are under study.

All in all, production of alloys greatly exceeds 20,000 tons/year and is continuously increasing.

However, Zama 13 and 15 on their own account for over 95% of the total and thus, quite logically, greatest attention is given to their production.

The processing cycle used is very simple and has been fully mechanized to the point of bringing average specific consumption of labour to a value of 0.8 worker hours/ton of alloy produced.

The stages are as follows:

a) Smelting of zinc cathodes. Two electric induction furnaces, like that already described for zinc smetling, are available for this operation.
The smelted matter is withdrawn from these, when required, with the previosly described graphite pump and sent on to the successive stage.

b) Preparation of the alloy. This takes place in two electric furnaces of induction and crucible melting type, working capacity about 2 tons, tiltable, and each with a 100 kw rating. They operate together, in order to feed alternately and successively, the following portion of the plant. The alloying metals are added in the solid state, at the start of the operation, when the metallic bath is low.
The temperature is then raised to 650-680°C. and the copper and Al dissolve rapidly, also aided by the motion impressed

on the metallic bath by the electric current. At this point the missing zinc is added, using the graphite pump 10-15 minutes are allowed to elapse to homogenize the alloy and reach the required temperature, and then the Mg, also in the solid state, is added, the bath is carefully skimmed and the alloy thus produced is rapidly emptied into the next forehearth. At this point the furnace is ready for starting another run.

c) Forehearth. This is a tiltable crucible holding 2 tons of alloy, the function of which is merely that of automatically feeding the subsequent casting chain.

d) Automatic casting chain. This also has been designed and built by us. Its casting rate is one ingot every 15-20 seconds and it itself regulates the upturning of the previously mentioned forehearth which feeds it.

e) Piling machine - Receives the solidified ingots from the casting chain and prepares 1 ton stacks.

The whole plant is run by two workers and regularly produces 66 tons/day of alloy in pallets of mercantile shape ingots. Other tiltable electric induction furnaces are used for the production of other alloys; the ingots are cast manually.

Table 6 - Zinc Alloys produced at Porto Marghera

Use	Denomination	Alloying metals			
Thermal zinc plating	Zinal	Al			
Moulds	Kayem 1	Al	Mg	Cu	
	Kayem 2	Al	Mg	Cu	
Die-casting	Zama 13	Al	Mg		
Die-casting	Zama 15	Al	Mg	Cu	
Die-casting	ILZRO 14	Al	/	Cu	Ti
Drop casting	ILZRO 12	Al	Mg	Cu	
Cathode protection	C.R.M. 1	Hg			
Cathode protection	C.R.M. 3	Al			

Rolling Mills

In 1940 a Krupp pack rolling mill was installed, consisting of a cogging machine and two finishers with auxiliary machines for shearing and flattening, as well as a Schmitz reversible rolling mill for strips and strap metal. This plant followed the by then classical scheme for European zinc rolling mills and had reached the utmost degree of evolution with standardized and definitive work programmes.

It had the characteristic of producing sheet-metal with marked changes inthickness and gave large amounts of scrap. It was demolished in 1960 to make room for the new Electrolysis Department.

In 1952, in line with world technical progress, production of zinc sheeting obtained with strip processing was started, abandoning the concept of production of many small plates.

The plant was designed for the processing of foundry plates weighing 700-900 Kg, obtained in horizontal tiltable ingot moulds with flame cover to avoid surface shinkage. (7).
The smelting furnace, which runs on natural gas, has a capacity of 60 tons.

The strip rolling mill consists of 3 machines in line: one mechanically irreversible, functionally reversible Tric cogging machine with cast-iron cylinders diameter 750 x 1500 mm, a Quarto reversible intermediate machine with steel cylinders diameter 300 x 730 x 120 mm with reels, and a Duo finisher, which is also reversible, with cylinders diameter 630 x 1200 mm. This machine produces finished strips varying from 1 to 0.1 mm thick. The plant is completed by a flying shearing machine complete with flattener for cutting sheet-metal and a narrow strip or strap metal cutting line with the possibility of flattening and polishing for the latter.

While the first machine, complete with flywheel, is operated by a 500 HP A.C. motor, the other two are supplied by D.C. motors of 400 HP and 300 HP rating respectively connected, together with the motors for the reels, to two rotating converters.

The mechanical part of the plant has been built by Pomini Farrel and the electrical part by CGE.

Ordinary zinc alloy for rolling, to be used for coverings and linings, has the following composition:

Pb 0.015%, Cd 0.001%, Fe 0.01%; Ni and Cu, traces; Al, Sn, not detectable with the spectrograph.
Other alloys are processed for various purposes.
Their compositions are:
Pb 0.4%, Cd 0.15%, Fe 0.02%, Sn 0.003%, Cu 0.005% for zincograph
Pb 0.02%, Cd 0,02%, Fe 0.02%, for litography
Pb 0.8%, Cd 0.04%, Fe <0,005% for dry-batteries
Ti 0.13%, Cu 0.5% for roofs and gutters (building uses).

This last alloy, which has the property of low creep, has taken hold in Italy during recent years and extensive applicatio a part from roofing purposes, is expected.

The strip rolling mill has a capacity of 800-850 tons/month of rolled sections and was at the end of the nineteen-sixties the only one of such type operating in Italy and Europe.

Productivity as well as its flexibility are high due to the Quarto intermediate rolling mill which is partially used also as a finishing plant.

The yield by weight from the plates to the finished rolled section, is around 70%.

In 1958, studies were started at the Plant for a continuous zinc casting-rolling plant, as the neutral and consequent derivation of progress and rationalization of productive process

The course of these studies, performed using an experimental Duo machine with strips of increasing progressive width from 150 to 400 mm, was marked by many difficulties of technological nature, especially in connection with thermic control of the solidification gradients.

A method going back to experiments by Sir Henry Bessemer in 1846 was chosen; it consists of solidifying the liquid metal between internally cooled cylinders and in directly obtaining a solid strip already with a certain degree of rolling.

The product is free from gases and porosity and issues already thin, so that the ultimate thickness can be obtained with low electric power consumption. The plant, designed on the basis of experiments with the test machine, was ready at the end of the nineteen-sixties and it is now in the lining-up stage (8).

The plant consists of a 20 tons capacity induction smelting

furnace built by DEMAG. The electrolysis cathodes are loaded in it automatically.
It is followed by holding and degassing furnaces also of induction type, in which the temperature is kept within exact limits and at a pre-set level.

It is flanked by a pair of furnaces for continuous preparation of zinc alloys for rolling.

The metal is conveyed to an inclined machine, with hydraulic tightening, and four cylinders diameter 420 x 800 x 1500 mm. The cylinders of smaller diameter are intensely cooled and here is where the strip of 5-7mm thickness is formed.

Auxiliary machines for flattening, edging and dragging of the strip then follow and, always in line, a tandem of four cylinders diameter 275 x 730 x 1450 mm, which reduce the thickness of the finished strip to about 1 mm.

Below the tandem are a movable shearing machine and two 10 tons capacity reels.

The machines have been supplied by Pomini Farrel and the electrical system by ASGEN.
For thinner strips, the rolled section is finished in another reversible Quarto rolling mill.

The line is driven by D.C. motors, supplied by a rotary converter unit, and they are synchronized with each other.

The plant is fitted with numerous measuring and control instruments; it hourly capacity is 3 tons, productivity is high, the yield from smelted metal to rolled section is above 85%.

The rolled sections are checked methodically in a testing room, for metallography, mechanical and technological properties, and quality.

A study, planning and application centre for Zn-Ti-Cu alloy rolled sections has been in existence for several years now; the purpose of this centre is to promote widespread use of this product in the building and similar sectors.

References

1. "Across the Lagoon" - Journal of Metals - September 1965, page 923

2. Italian patent no. 633.857 in the name of "Montevecchio - Società Italiana del Piombo e dello Zinco", granted February 12, 1962. Filed July 6, 1960.
Title of patent: "Process for the electrolytic production of super-pure zinc".
Inventor: Prof. Giovanni Scacciati

3. "Passage from the intermittent to continuous system for the purification of zinc sulphate solutions to be used for electrolysis"
Authors:
P. Benvenuti, T. De Michelis, A. D'Este, F. Gnesotto.
"La metallurgia italiana" no. 5, Maggio 1968 (May 1968)
Memorandum presented at the "Non-ferrous metals meeting" held by the Italian Association of Metallurgy, Milan, October 8-11, 1968

4. Effects of impurities present in a zinc electrolyte on the current efficiency and relative automatic measuring equipment
Authors: A. D'Este, R. Guerriero
"Montevecchio", no. 3/4, 1965, pages 1-11

5. Italian patent filed with application no. 24.183 in the name of Monteponi e Montevecchio S.p.A." on November 10, 1969
Title of patent: "Machine for shipping metals obtained by electrolytic deposition from aluminium or similar cathodes
Inventors: G. Casagrande, T. De Michelis, A. Rossi, F. Gnesotto

6. "Zinc smelting furnaces"
Author: T. De Michelis
"Il Calore", no. 8 - 1965

7. "The production of zinc sheets"
Author: F. Gnesotto
"Montevecchio", no. 4, December 1953, pages 1-13

8. "Principles for a new continuous casting and rolling plant for large size zinc strips"
Author: F. Gnesotto
"La metallurgia Italiana" no. 6, June 1968 - pages 519-527
Memorandum presented at the "Non-ferrous metals meeting" held by the Italian Association of Metallurgy, Milan, October 8-11, 1967

Chapter 11

ELECTROLYTIC ZINC PLANT OF AMERICAN ZINC COMPANY

East St. Louis, Illinois

O. H. Banes
Manager

R. K. Carpenter
Assistant Manager

C. E. Paden
Superintendent of Metallurgy

ABSTRACT

The electrolytic zinc plant of the American Zinc Company located at Sauget, Illinois started operations in April 1941. The plant had a designed capacity of 45(T) per day. The original flow sheet was quite simple, incorporating the low density process. Through the years the capacity of the plant has been increased to the current design of 214(T) cathodes per day. This paper describes the current operation along with typical metallurgical data.

I. HISTORY

In 1929 the Evans-Wallower Zinc Company built an electrolytic zinc plant at Monsanto, Illinois (later renamed Sauget, Illinois) and operated it for about two years. This plant was idled until 1940 when the property was purchased by the American Zinc Company.

Aside from calcine storage bins and a motor generator set, the plant was completely dismantled and rebuilt. The new electrolytic plant was designed for a capacity of 45(T) a day and operated at a current density of 344 A/m^2. In 1943 the plant capacity was expanded to 91(T) per day in cooperation with the Defense Plant Corporation for the war effort. Shortly after the war American Zinc Company purchased the Defense Plant Corporation interests and proceeded to increase the plant capacity to 136(T) per day through operation at higher current densities. Since then the plant's capacity has been gradually increased to its current rated capacity of 214(T) of cathodes per day. Production at this capacity was first attained in October 1969 when the daily average cathode production was 220(T).

II. CONCENTRATE STORAGE

About 50 to 60% of the zinc concentrates received are shipped by water freight via the Mississippi River to Cahokia, Illinois, which is about three miles from the plant. Concentrates are transferred from barges to dump trucks which deliver the material to the plant storage facilities.

Most of these concentrates are from South America and Canada. Because of frozen or unpassable waterways in the north during the winter, most of the shipping is done in the summer months and a large stock is accumulated for winter operation at the plant.

To accommodate this program, a large outside concentrate storage pad capable of storing about 68,000(T) has been provided adjacent to the inside storage facilities. The balance of the required concentrates are recieved by rail throughout the entire year.

Incoming trucks and cars are weighed on plant scales and sampled when unloaded. Outside storage truck unloading is accomplished by dumping. The concentrate stack is built and shaped by a bulldozer. Inside storage rail car unloading is carried out by a crane which transfers the material from gondola cars to a system of feeders and conveyors which ultimately discharge into one of six concrete bays, each having a capacity of about 1,800(T) for a total of 10,886(T).

Blending and feeding concentrates to the roaster storage bins is handled with gasoline-powered Hough payloaders fitted with a

Aerial view of East St. Louis plant

Sulphuric Acid Plant and Raw Material Storage

two cubic yard bucket. The concentrate flows from a hopper to a pan feeder and finally discharges over a magnetic pulley for tramp iron removal. Discharge from the belt is passed over a 63.5mm trash screen before going to one of two 272(T) storage bins. These bins have a capacity for thirty hours of roaster operation, and concentrate charging is usually done on the day shift.

III. ROASTING PLANT

Concentrates are roasted in two Lurgi fluo-solid type roasters. These furnaces have a diameter of 6.36m at bed level and a design capacity of 218(T) of dry concentrates each per day. The combustion chamber above bed level increases in diameter to 9.5m. The furnace height from the base to the dome is approximately 12.5m. Cooling coils in the bed area have been varied from two to five.

When operated at design capacity the calcine produced assays about 0.1% sulphide sulphur and 2.25% sulphate sulphur. Operation at 112.5 percent design results in a product assaying 0.5% sulphide sulphur. Bed temperatures range from 930°C. to 970°C. and are usually held at 950°C. Temperature of the exit gases is about 950°C.

Concentrates from the surge bins are transferred by a variable speed belt onto a weigh belt which controls the tonnage fed to the roasters. This discharges into a table feeder which insures a smooth constant concentrate delivery onto a slinger which feeds the roaster. Roaster air is supplied by two of three 7.4m^3/s Buffalo Forge blowers, one of which is steam driven.

Roaster gases leave the combustion chamber at the top of the furnace and enter a Dominion Bridge & Iron waste heat boiler. This boiler is equipped with six tube bundles designed to produce 8,981kg per hour steam at 38.8(atm) with a concentrate feed rate of 9.1(T) to 10.9(T) (dry) per hour. City water is treated in one of two sets of water treating units consisting of a cation removal stage followed by an anion removal stage. The purified water goes to a storage tank which also received returning condensate. From this tank the water is pumped to a deaerator unit and then through the boiler feed water pumps to the steam drum. One of three boiler feed water pumps as well as two of five boiler recirculating pumps are steam driven. Steam driven pumps are normally used. The number three tube bundle in the boiler is the super heat bundle. The high pressure steam produced passes through a coil in the steam drum and then to either the turbine driving the main blower in the acid plant or to a pressure reducer which discharges 8.5(atm) steam which is tied into the plant process steam system. The 8.5(atm) steam is also used to drive the boiler water feed pumps.

Gases from the boiler enter a header which feeds four 1.2m Buell cyclones operating in parallel. Exit gases from the cyclone pass through a 1.1m Clarage induced draft fan which discharges into Buell electrostatic precipitators. Each roaster has two units in series equipped with independent power supplies. A unit consists of 400 wires, 3.05m long. Primary voltage and current are 250 volts and 30 amperes respectively. Secondary voltage and current are 35,000 volts and 15 milliamperes respectively. Collector plate rappers operate continuously, each plate being hit every fifteen minutes. Emitter wire vibrators operate two minutes and forty five seconds out of every six minutes. Design capacity is for $16m^3/s$ at 349°C. The cyclone efficiency is 70% and the precipitator efficiency is 99% for an overall efficiency of 99.7%.

Dust collected from the waste heat boiler and cyclones joins the roaster overflow and is cooled in a Stearns-Roger rotary cooler. This unit is basically a double shell drum operating in a water tank and reduces the calcine temperature from 660°C. to 90°C.

Dust from the electrostatic precipitator joins the cooled calcine and is conveyed to any one of eight 1,361(T) concrete block storage silos by means of screw conveyors and bucket elevators.

Gases leaving the precipitators are delivered to the acid plant by means of an insulated mild steel duct. Original equipment included S. S. expansion joints and duct but this failed in service and was replaced with insulated mild steel.

IV. ACID PLANT

The acid plant is a contact unit of Monsanto-Leonard design with an equivalent capacity of 363(T) per day of 100 percent sulphuric acid. Sulphur dioxide gas from the roasters enters the humidifying section of a Peabody scrubber. The humidifying tower is 3.8m in diameter and 7.6m high and is equipped with twelve sprays circulating $0.044m^3/s$ of water. Cooling at the top of the humidifying section consists of three plates handling a water flow of $0.085m^3/s$. The temperature is controlled by circulation through three Karbate heat exchangers. The weak acid passes through the graphite tubes of the three units operated in parallel, while cooling water is connected so the flow through the units is in series. Design of the Peabody scrubber calls for $28.8m^3/s$ at 300°C. inlet gas and $16.7m^3/s$ at 45°C. outlet gas. In operation the circulating cooling water is controlled by addition and discharge of enough water to hold the chloride concentration to a maximum of 125 ppm in the cooling section. Acid concentration is also held to one percent or less. Cooled gases from the Peabody scrubber enter two Western Precipitation mist precipitators operating in parallel. These units are of the tube and wire type and are entirely constructed of lead. Each unit has ninety six wires 5.6m long. Both units operate from the same power source, each unit pulling a primary load of 410 volts at 50 amperes.

The gases leaving the mist precipitators pass through the drying tower and then to a steam turbine driven main blower. The Roots-Connersville blower is powered by a 903(HP) Terry turbine. At full speed the turbine uses about 5,897kg per hour of 38.8(atm) steam and discharges steam into a Graham condenser at a vacuum of 20 inches of mercury. The blower moves 16.5m^3/s at 39(mm Hg) suction and pressure. The dry gas then enters the converter-heat exchanger system. Conversion of SO_2 to SO_3 takes place in the four pass V_2O_5 catalyst converter at an efficiency of 97 - 98 percent. Sulphur trioxide gases enter the absorber tower which is equipped with a Brinks mist eliminator. The plant produces both 98% and 93% acid.

TABLE I

TYPICAL ROASTER DATA AND ANALYSES

Wet concentrates roasted per year	163,293(T)
Percentage SO_2 in gases to acid plant	7.5%-8.0%
Temperature of fluid bed in roaster	950^oC
Temperature of over-bed zone in roaster	900-1000^oC

Constituent	Concentrate Percent	Calcine Percent
Total Zn	54.55	62.97
PB	.68	.79
Cu	.58	.67
Cd	.40	.47
Fe	5.64	6.51
Total S	30.65	
Sulphate S	---	2.25
Sulphide S	---	0.30
Insoluble	2.11	2.44
CaO	.99	1.14
MgO	.66	.77
Moisture	8.00	Nil
	Oz. per Ton	Oz. per Ton
Au	.003	.0035
Ag	5.885	6.7930

V. LEACHING SECTION

A. Leaching

Calcine is transferred from the storage silos at the roaster plant by means of a bucket elevator and screw conveyor system to storage bins at the leaching plant. Calcine storage capacity at the leaching plant consists of twelve bins with a total capacity of 1,451(T). Leaching is carried out on a continuous basis. Calcine is withdrawn from the storage bins by screw conveyors. Material is transferred over an Ohmart nuclear scale giving a continuous integrated weight. Feed rate is controlled by a variable speed feed screw which is fed from a small surge bin ahead of the scale. Weighed calcine discharges from a screw into a small cone which received cell acid simultaneously. Cell acid enters the cone on the tangent and the resulting slurry is conveyed by means of a short launder to a Dorr duplex rake classifier. A 1.6m x .56m Hardinge conical ball mill of stainless steel construction powered by a 61(HP) motor operates in closed circuit with the classifier. The classifier overflow (about 95 percent minus 100 mesh) is continuously pumped through a 0.38m dia. Krebs cyclone to the first of four leach tanks. The cyclone underflow returns to the rake classifier.

The leach tanks are steel, lined with rubber and acid-resisting brick. They are flat bottom and baffled; powered with a turbine type agitator and operate with a load of 46 - 51(HP). The working capacity is $91m^3$ each. Actually about 70 percent of the leaching is carried out in the slurry-grinding-classifying circuit ahead of the first leach tank. Cell acid is added continuously to the first leach tank to maintain a pH of about 2.5. Iron in the form of an acid ferric sulphate solution is added to the second tank, the iron addition is equivalent to about one gram per liter of cell acid. Iron solution is prepared by dissolving scrap iron turnings in cell acid and oxidizing the ferrous sulphate to ferric sulphate with MnO_2. The four leach tanks are in series with a resulting leach retention time of about four and one-half hours. The last tank in the string has a pH of about 5.4 and discharges through an open chamber Allen-Sherman-Hoff pump feeding a twelve inch Hyle-Patterson cyclone which discharges to a 24.4m primary thickener. A synthetic polymer flocculant is added under flow meter control to the thickener feed for coagulation and settling control. The cyclone underflow (plus 0.104(mm) portion) is returned to the rake classifier. Leaching extractions vary from 88 to 94 percent depending on feed composition.

B. Residue Filtering and Drying

Residue is handled through a three thickener C.C.D. circuit, in which the first thickener is 24.4m in diameter and the last two in the series are 15.2m in diameter. The underflow from the final thickener is pumped to a bank of four 3m dia. x 4.9m stainless steel Eimco filters using polypropylene filter cloth with a steam and air blow. The filter cake is repulped with a small quantity of water and pumped to a 3.5m dia. x 6.1m Eimco filter located adjacent to a residue dryer. Cake from this filter can be directed to truck loading screw conveyors or to the 2.4m dia. x 27.4m long, gas-fired Hardinge dryer. Dried leach residues are shipped by rail or by barge to pyrometallurgical recovery plants.

VI. SOLUTION PURIFICATION

Overflow from the 24.4m diameter primary thickener is pumped to a 15.2m diameter surge tank equipped with rakes for additional settled solids removal. A side decant line from this tank delivers a nominal .02 gpl solids solution for pumping to the first stage purification. Copper sulphate solution is added as needed to maintain about .3 gpl in the incoming feed.

A. First Stage Purification

The first stage purification consists of five 5.5m dia. x 4.7m high wood stave tanks equipped with S.S. turbine type agitators and S.S. steam coils. This purification was originally operated as a batch process, but is now being operated as a continuous process by means of a vacuum assisted 0.25m siphon between tanks. Flow through this stage is set by a flow meter which in turn automatically controls the rate of zinc dust and arsenic trioxide addition. Temperature is normally held at 95°C. Cobalt is normally lowered to .0002 gpl and arsenic to less than .0001 gpl.

The solution discharged from the first purification is filtered in four 0.8m bronze plate and frame presses with the filter cake being repulped and pumped to the leach residue filtration section. The filtrate at 95°C. must be cooled to about 65°C. prior to entering the second purification stage. This is accomplished in two parallel flash evaporators constructed of mild steel and using waste cooling water from the cell room flash evaporators.

B. Second Stage Purification

The second purification, where the bulk of the cadmium and residual traces of cobalt are removed, is carried out on a continuous basis in a series of five 3.9m dia. x 4.7m high wood stave tanks agitated by S.S. turbine type agitators. Zinc dust and copper sulphate are routinely added by continuous feeders. Antimony tartrate is added as required to remove traces of cobalt passing the first purification stage. Filtration is accomplished in four 0.9m bronze plate and frame presses, with the press cake directed to the cadmium recovery department and the filtrate flowing to the final purification stage.

C. Third Stage Purification

The final purification stage is a clean-up and polishing operation which enables the second purification to operate with a minimum zinc dust addition and a press cake of optimum cadmium content. This stage is also continuous and consists of three 4.0m dia. x 5.6m high wood stave tanks equipped with S.S. Turbine type agitators.

TABLE II

TYPICAL DATA FOR LEACHING SECTION

Tons calcine leached per day	454(T)
Tons MnO_2 ore used per day	9.1(T)
Volume spent electrolyte per hour	$102.2m^3$
Volume C.C.D. wash water per hour	$5.7m^3$
Maximum gpl free acid permitted	5
Leaching time, hours	4 to 5
Residue produced percent of calcine leached	27

Analyses	Calcine Percent	Residue Percent
Total Zn	62.97	20
Water-Soluble Zn	1.50	2
Fe	6.50	25

PRIMARY THICKENER OVERFLOW

Zn grams per liter	150.0
Cu grams per liter	0.3
Cd grams per liter	1.0
Fe mg. per liter	10.0
Co mg. per liter	30.0

PURIFICATION

Time Cu-Co-As-Sb removal, hr.	4 to 5
Time cadmium removal, hr.	3 to 4
Analysis of purified solution:	
Zn, grams per liter	175
Mn, grams per liter	3.0
Fe, mg. per liter	15
Cu, Cd, Co, As, Sb, mg. per liter or less	1

VII. CADMIUM RECOVERY

The filter cake from the second stage purification is charged into a primary leach tank along with water and sulfuric acid. The tank is prepared on day shift with a starting charge of about 30 percent acid. Filter cake is added throughout the twenty-four hour period. Following overnight agitation and additions the acid concentration has decreased to 1 or 2 percent. The accumulated slurry is transferred to a secondary leach tank where the acid is adjusted to 4 - 5 percent. The transferred slurry is again agitated overnight and the finished acid concentration is 2 - 2.5 percent. The pulp is filtered on a plate and frame press. The cake is pulped up with cell acid and returned to the leaching plant. The cadmium-rich filtrate is treated with a small amount of zinc dust and strontium carbonate to remove impurities. Again the pulp is filtered on a plate and frame press, the cake being pulped with cell acid and returned to the leaching plant. The purified filtrate is then treated with zinc dust, reducing the cadmium content from 50 - 60 grams per liter to about 0.5 - 1.0 grams per liter. This precipitation is carried out in the presence of 2 - 3 percent acid. The sponged cadmium is collected and washed in a box with a perforated false bottom. The zinc solution and wash water are returned to the leaching plant and the sponge is packed in drums for market.

VIII. ELECTROLYSIS

A. Cell Room

The electrolyte is circulated in closed circuit with accessory equipment to facilitate spent acid bleed to the leach, cooling, and the makeup of a mixed cell feed solution fortified in zinc and reagent additives. The cell mix solution is delivered to each cell at the rate of 2.3(m^3/hr). This causes the displacement of a like amount of warm spent solution to exit at the cell overflow lip. The overflow moves in parallel through a series of three cells in cascade fashion then to the spent acid system and accessory equipment to complete the loop.

The cell room has 372 cells, is divided into two units, one with 15 cascades of 12 cells each and the second unit with 16 cascades of 12 cells each. Each unit has its own electrical circuit with some flexibility in switching rectifier and motor-generator output to either or both circuits. A typical cell has 27 cathodes and 28 anodes; these electrodes rest on respective bus bars which carry the current in a series-parallel network. The maximum current is limited by the cable and rectifier equipment and is at present about 24,000 amperes. This allows a current density of 807A/m^2 at the cathodes.

Each cascade is made up of 12 cells arranged in two adjacent rows of six, broken into four sets of three cascading cells. This is the basic operating unit. A 0.5m aisle between each basic unit provides access for service and maintenance. An area 13.4m x 91.4m between the two electrolyzing units serves as a cathode stripping, stacking, and truck pickup point for the cathode product.

The cells are constructed of cast reinforced concrete with 38.7 kg/m^2 lead liners. Experimental construction of cells in other materials is on test but none of these have yet proven satisfactory.

The anodes are fabricated at the plant from punched rolled 99% Pb-1.0% Ag sheet and cast chemical lead covered copper header bars with a copper "hook" contact. The punched pattern in the anode sheet is 25(mm) diameter holes spaced on 76(mm) centers. The anodes are spaced on 76(mm) centers. Five porcelain button insulators are placed on the anode near each submerged corner and in the center of the sheet to aid cathode alignment and correct spacing.

The cathodes are fabricated by welding rolled aluminum sheet cut to size and extruded aluminum header bar cut to length. The header bar has welded aluminum hooks for lifting and a welded copper hook insert for the electrical contact. A cathode lifter raises nine cathodes per pull or 1/3 of a cell at a time for stripping. An arrangement of lifter, air hoist, and trolley is used to transfer cathode zinc from the cells to the stripping floor and return the starting sheets to the cells.

B. Solution Cooling

Hot cell overflow solution is conducted by enclosed launders to spent acid receiving tanks. Two 15.25(cm) pumps, constructed of Carpenter 20 S.S. and equipped with cathodic protection, each capable of 7.57m^3 per minute, deliver a regulated flow to the evaporator head tank. Spent acid in excess of this quantity required for recirculation through the cooling and feed system is delivered to spent acid storage for use at the leaching plant. The two evaporator head tanks each have two remote controlled outlet valves, one conducting controlled flow to a flash evaporator and the other conducting controlled flow to an atmospheric cooling tower.

The cooled solution is combined continuously in a cold sump which serves as the cell feed surge tank and a mixing container for the neutral zinc solution and all cell acid reagents. Neutral zinc sulphate is added at the rate of 1.36(m^3/min), strontium carbonate, sodium silicate, and gum arabic are also added at this point as needed. The cooled fortified solution is recirculated to the cells by one 20.3(cm) pump with a nominal capacity of 15.14 (m^3/min). All stainless steel equipment in the recirculation section is equipped with cathodic protection to control corrosion.

The recirculation system is troubled with gypsum accumulations. Parallel lines and pumps are provided so that the gypsum accumulations can be removed by high pressure water cleaning while the companion system is operating. Cleaning operations are variable depending on the size of the solution conductor. Cell feed orifices are "reamed" twice per shift, the cell feed header is cleaned by high pressure water after 48 hours of service and the pumps and manifolds are cleaned after 96 hours of service. The flash and atmospheric evaporators are cleaned on a two week cycle.

Gypsum together with manganese dioxide is troublesome in the cells also. Two cascades are regularly scheduled for cleaning each day, five days per week. The anodes are machine washed with high pressure water and returned to the cleaned cells.

Typical spent electrolyte analyses: H_2SO4, 200 gpl; Zn, 55 gpl; Mn, 3 gpl.

The following data are typical of daily operations:

Zinc cathodes produced, tons	214(T)
Average current, amp. per unit	22,000
Maximum voltage per circuit	670 - 750
Typical current efficiency percent	89
Maximum current density A/m^2	807

IX. MELTING AND CASTING

Cathodes are transferred in 1,361 kg stacks by gasoline powered trucks to a storage area or directly to a conveyor system in the casting plant. The cathodes are washed in hot water, fluxed in an aqueous solution of ammonium chloride, and dried in preparation for melting. The dried cathodes are discharged onto a vibrating conveyor which feeds a 1200 (KW) induction melting furnace. Metal overflows from the melting furnace into a 72 (KW) entrance furnace ahead of the 600 (KW) holding furnace, which has a capacity of 408(T) and a working range of 272(T). The holding furnace is pressurized to deliver metal through a 72 (KW) exit furnace to a launder which serves the various casting lines. The holding furnace is drossed once every 12 to 18 months. With good physical cathodes this system gives a primary melting recovery of 97.5 percent. After the dross has been treated and its metallic content separated from the oxide, an overall recovery of 98 percent has been attained with good dense cathode deposits. Molten metal from the launder can be directed to any one of the following:

(1) A straight line slab casting conveyor. This conveyor is served by a 72 (KW) pressurized induction furnace which pours four 25.4 kg slabs simultaneously. The slabs discharge onto a vibrating pan conveyor, which in turn discharges onto a steel plate conveyor that feeds a mechanized stacking machine. 907 kg stacks of slabs are produced on this machine, consisting of four pallet slabs and thirty-two regular slabs. The stacked slabs pass over a scale and then to a runout conveyor from which they are trucked to storage.

Cell Room

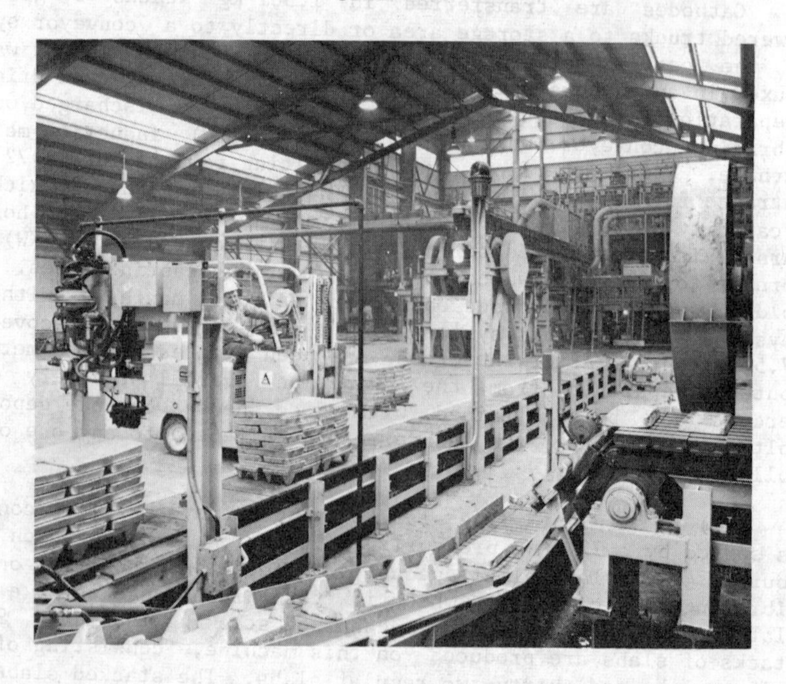

Production Line from Mechanized Casting Machine

(2) A block casting line which produces blocks weighing about 1,089 kg or 1,270 kg. The molds on this line pass through a water pan for cooling and the block is discharged from the mold by dumping as the endless mold chain inverts. The blocks pass over a scale and then to a runout conveyor from which they are trucked to storage.

(3) A 200 (KW) alloy induction furnace where numerous alloys containing small additions of lead, cadmium, aluminum, or antimony are produced. After the particular alloy has been made, it is cast on a straight line machine. Production from this line is hand stacked, then weighed and trucked to storage.

(4) A special shape casting area where various shapes of special high grade and alloy metal are cast.

(5) A molten metal delivery area where 1,814 kg of molten metal are transferred at a time in a "thermos bottle" to the specialty plant where special shapes and die casting alloys are produced.

The melting furnace is drossed once a shift. Because of the cathode pretreatment, the dross formed is dry and requires no "working up with sal". The dross is raked out of the furnace into a screw conveyor located below the drossing doors. The screw delivers the dross to a mobile hopper with a capacity of 10(T). Once a day the hopper is weighed and the material is delivered to the skimmings plant.

X. ALLOY AND SPECIAL SHAPES

The primary product of this department is No. 3 Diecasters alloy. It is cast in 9 kg bars and 1,225 kg blocks. Other alloys of zinc are also produced. Cathode zinc is washed and fluxed and melted in a 400 (KW) induction furnace. The proper amount of alloying metals such as copper and aluminum are added to the heel of a 200 (KW) alloying furnace, dissolved, then diluted with molten zinc from the cathode melting furnace to complete the batch of alloy. This is then transferred to a 35 (KW) pouring furnace which serves a straight line bar casting machine. Bars are hand stacked in 907 kg bundles containing two pallets and one hundred regular bars.

Other products produced in this department are 0.454 kg balls for the plating industry. Both pure zinc and a one percent aluminum alloy ball are made. Various shaped anode bars for plating are also cast.

XI. SKIMMINGS TREATMENT

Skimmings received from the cathode melting operation, along with any other skimmings produced from the zinc dust or alloy production, are treated in the skimmings plant. The material is fed to a Williams Patent Crusher swing hammer mill which reduces it to minus 21.3(mm). Crushed material is fed to a Williams Patent Crusher air swept ring-roll mill. The light oxide portion is ground in the mill, picked up by the air stream and collected by a cyclone-baghouse system. The metallic portion is rejected from the mill and passed over a 1.168(mm) aperture screen. The fine fraction is collected and used as zinc dust in the first stage purification step. The coarse fraction is delivered to the zinc dust plant for melting and blowing into zinc dust. The oxide produced from the operation is either sold or returned to the roasters.

XII. ZINC DUST PRODUCTION

Zinc dust is produced at the rate of about 13.6(T) per day in a small plant. Coarse metal from all sources including the skimmings plant, slabs or scrap is melted in a 72 (KW) induction furnace with a capacity of 1,361 kg. When the charged metal has melted, the furnace is tilted and the metal poured into a crucible fitted with a lava plug with a 5.9(mm) hole for metal delivery to an atomizing air stream. The blown dust is collected in a bin with sides tapering down to a screw which delivers the zinc dust to an elevator feeding a vibrating screen. A typical screen analysis is shown below.

Screen Size Aperture (mm)		Percent
	+0.833	0.4
-0.833	+0.208	20.2
-0.208	+0.147	20.4
-0.147	+0.074	31.0
	-0.074	28.0
Total		100.0

XIII. MANNING TABLE

The total employment of 564 is distributed as follows:

	Labor	Staff	Total
Roasting and Acid	39	6	45
Leading and Purification	51	9	60
Cadmium Recovery	5	-	5
Electrolyzing	91	4	95
Melting & Casting	63	8	71
General Services	97	45	142
Maintenance	119	20	139
Administration	-	7	7
	465	99	564

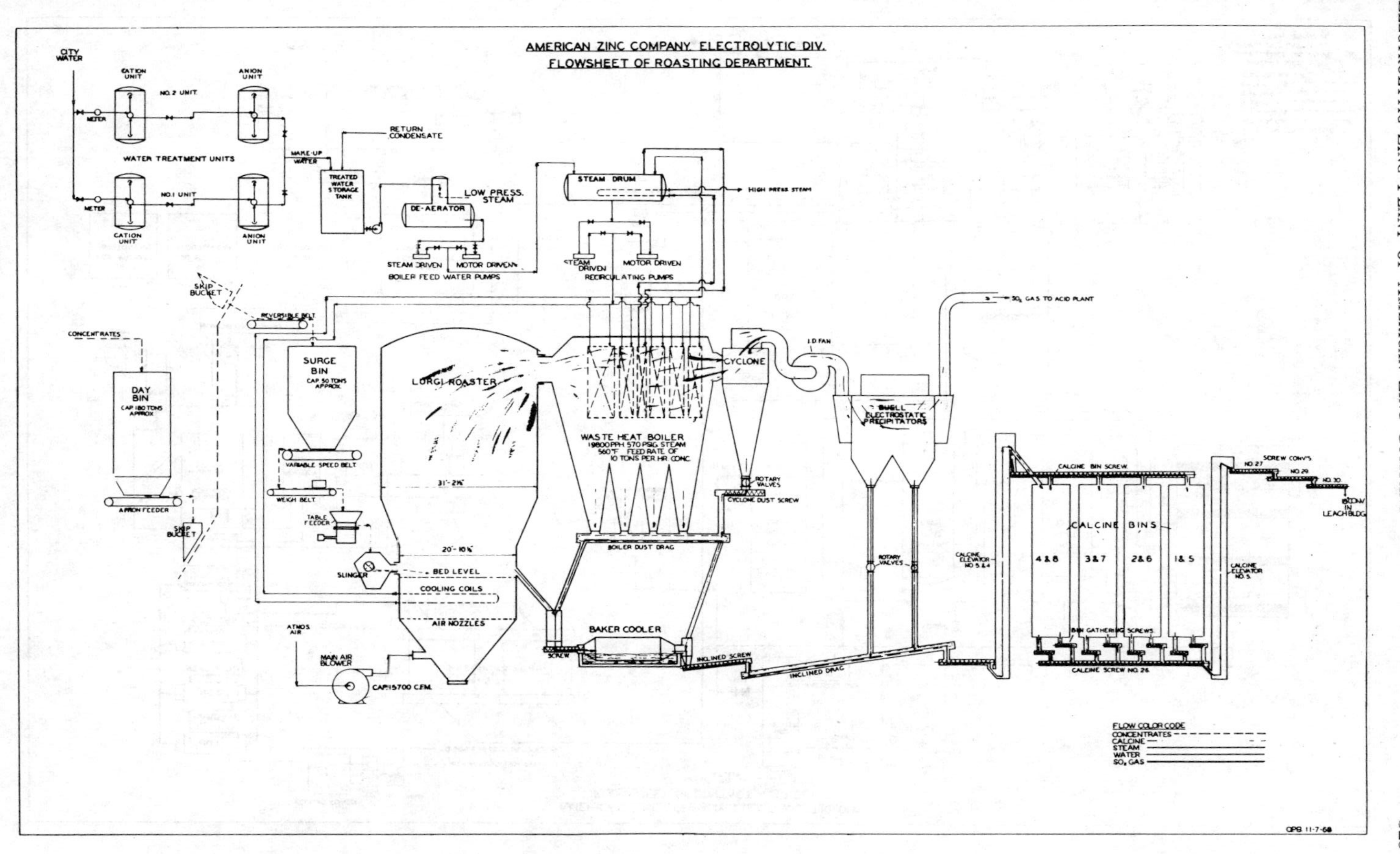
AMERICAN ZINC COMPANY ELECTROLYTIC DIV.
FLOWSHEET OF ROASTING DEPARTMENT.
CITY WATER
CATION UNIT
ANION UNIT
NO. 2 UNIT
NO. 1 UNIT
METER
WATER TREATMENT UNITS
MAKE-UP WATER
RETURN CONDENSATE
TREATED WATER STORAGE TANK
LOW PRESS. STEAM
DE-AERATOR
STEAM DRIVEN
MOTOR DRIVEN
BOILER FEED WATER PUMPS
STEAM DRUM
HIGH PRESS STEAM
RECIRCULATING PUMPS
SKIP BUCKET
REVERSIBLE BELT
CONCENTRATES
DAY BIN
CAP 180 TONS APPROX
APRON FEEDER
SURGE BIN
CAP 50 TONS APPROX
VARIABLE SPEED BELT
WEIGH BELT
TABLE FEEDER
SLINGER
LURGI ROASTER
31'-2⅜"
20'-10⅜"
BED LEVEL
COOLING COILS
AIR NOZZLES
ATMOS AIR
MAIN AIR BLOWER
CAP. 15700 C.F.M.
WASTE HEAT BOILER
19800 PPH 570 PSIG STEAM
560°F FEED RATE OF
10 TONS PER HR. CONC.
BOILER DUST DRAG
BAKER COOLER
SCREW
INCLINED SCREW
INCLINED DRAG
CYCLONE
ROTARY VALVES
CYCLONE DUST SCREW
I.D. FAN
SMALL ELECTROSTATIC PRECIPITATORS
SO₂ GAS TO ACID PLANT
CALCINE ELEVATOR NO. 3 & 4
CALCINE BIN SCREW
CALCINE BINS
4&8
3&7
2&6
1&5
BIN GATHERING SCREWS
CALCINE SCREW NO. 26
CALCINE ELEVATOR NO. 5
SCREW CONV'S
NO. 27
NO. 29
NO. 30
IN LEACH BLDG.
FLOW COLOR CODE
CONCENTRATES
CALCINE
STEAM
WATER
SO₂ GAS
OPB 11-7-68

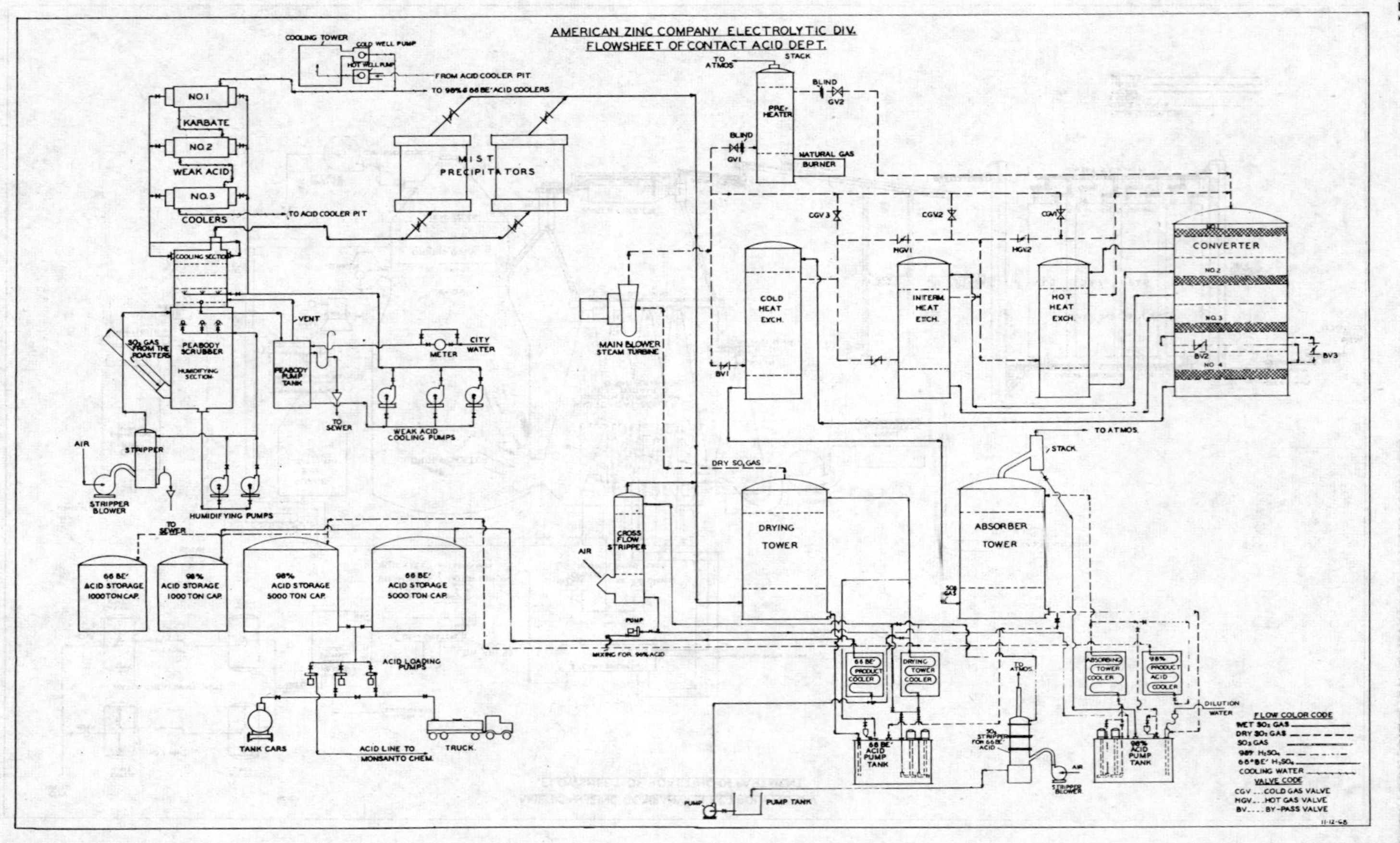
AMERICAN ZINC COMPANY ELECTROLYTIC DIV.
FLOWSHEET OF CONTACT ACID DEPT.
COOLING TOWER
COLD WELL PUMP
HOT WELL PUMP
FROM ACID COOLER PIT
TO 98% & 66 BE' ACID COOLERS
NO. 1
KARBATE
NO. 2
WEAK ACID
NO. 3
COOLERS
TO ACID COOLER PIT
MIST PRECIPITATORS
COOLING SECTION
SO₂ GAS FROM THE ROASTERS
PEABODY SCRUBBER
HUMIDIFYING SECTION
VENT
PEABODY PUMP TANK
METER
CITY WATER
TO SEWER
WEAK ACID COOLING PUMPS
AIR
STRIPPER
STRIPPER BLOWER
HUMIDIFYING PUMPS
TO SEWER
66 BE' ACID STORAGE 1000 TON CAP.
98% ACID STORAGE 1000 TON CAP.
98% ACID STORAGE 5000 TON CAP.
66 BE' ACID STORAGE 5000 TON CAP.
ACID LOADING PUMPS
TANK CARS
ACID LINE TO MONSANTO CHEM.
TRUCK
TO ATMOS.
STACK
PRE-HEATER
BLIND
GV2
BLIND
GV1
NATURAL GAS BURNER
MAIN BLOWER STEAM TURBINE
CGV 3
CGV2
CGV1
HGV1
HGV2
BV1
COLD HEAT EXCH.
INTERM. HEAT EXCH.
HOT HEAT EXCH.
CONVERTER
NO. 2
NO. 3
NO. 4
BV2
BV3
TO ATMOS.
STACK
DRY SO₂ GAS
CROSS FLOW STRIPPER
AIR
PUMP
MIXING FOR 98% ACID
DRYING TOWER
ABSORBER TOWER
SO₂ GAS
66 BE' PRODUCT COOLER
DRYING TOWER COOLER
66 BE' ACID PUMP TANK
TO ATMOS.
SO₂ STRIPPER FOR 66 BE' ACID
STRIPPER BLOWER
ABSORBING TOWER COOLER
98% PRODUCT ACID COOLER
98% ACID PUMP TANK
DILUTION WATER
PUMP
PUMP TANK
FLOW COLOR CODE
WET SO₂ GAS
DRY SO₂ GAS
SO₃ GAS
98% H₂SO₄
66° BE' H₂SO₄
COOLING WATER
VALVE CODE
CGV...COLD GAS VALVE
HGV...HOT GAS VALVE
BV...BY-PASS VALVE
11-12-48

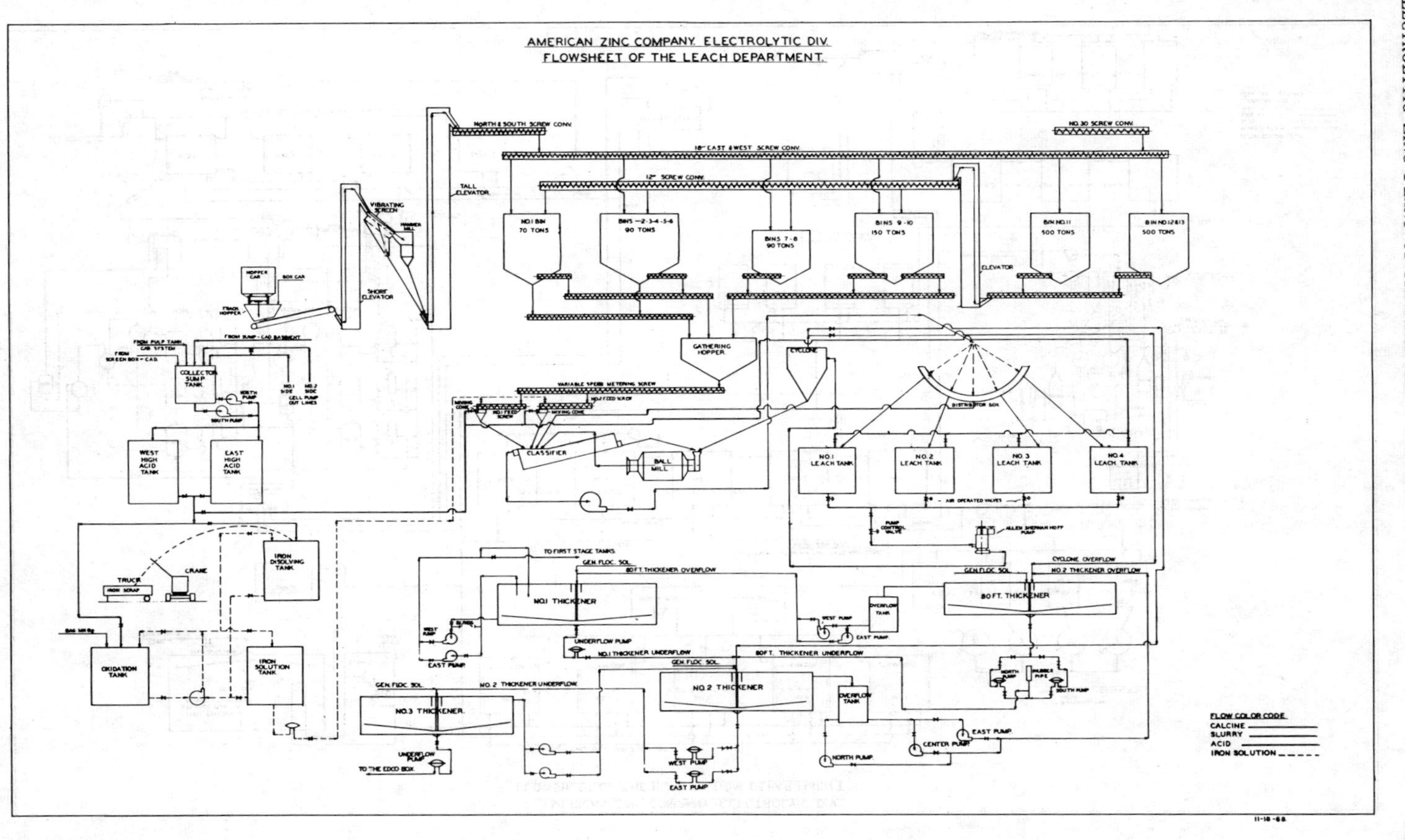
AMERICAN ZINC COMPANY. ELECTROLYTIC DIV.
FLOWSHEET OF THE LEACH DEPARTMENT.
NORTH & SOUTH SCREW CONV.
18" EAST & WEST SCREW CONV.
12" SCREW CONV.
NO. 30 SCREW CONV.
TALL ELEVATOR
VIBRATING SCREEN
HAMMER MILL
SHORT ELEVATOR
HOPPER CAR
BOX CAR
TRACK HOPPER
NO. 1 BIN 70 TONS
BINS 2-3-4-5-6 90 TONS
BINS 7-8 90 TONS
BINS 9-10 150 TONS
BIN NO. 11 500 TONS
BIN NO. 12 & 13 500 TONS
ELEVATOR
GATHERING HOPPER
VARIABLE SPEED METERING SCREW
CYCLONE
DISTRIBUTOR BOX
CLASSIFIER
BALL MILL
NO. 1 LEACH TANK
NO. 2 LEACH TANK
NO. 3 LEACH TANK
NO. 4 LEACH TANK
AIR OPERATED VALVES
PUMP CONTROL VALVE
FROM SUMP - CAD BASEMENT
COLLECTOR SUMP TANK
NORTH PUMP
SOUTH PUMP
WEST HIGH ACID TANK
EAST HIGH ACID TANK
IRON DISOLVING TANK
TRUCK
IRON SCRAP
CRANE
OXIDATION TANK
IRON SOLUTION TANK
TO FIRST STAGE TANKS
GEN. FLOC. SOL.
80 FT. THICKENER OVERFLOW
NO. 1 THICKENER
WEST PUMP
EAST PUMP
UNDERFLOW PUMP
NO. 1 THICKENER UNDERFLOW
80 FT. THICKENER UNDERFLOW
NO. 2 THICKENER
OVERFLOW TANK
NO. 2 THICKENER UNDERFLOW
NO. 3 THICKENER
TO THE EDCO BOX
CYCLONE OVERFLOW
NO. 2 THICKENER OVERFLOW
80 FT. THICKENER
CENTER PUMP
FLOW COLOR CODE
CALCINE
SLURRY
ACID
IRON SOLUTION
11-16-68

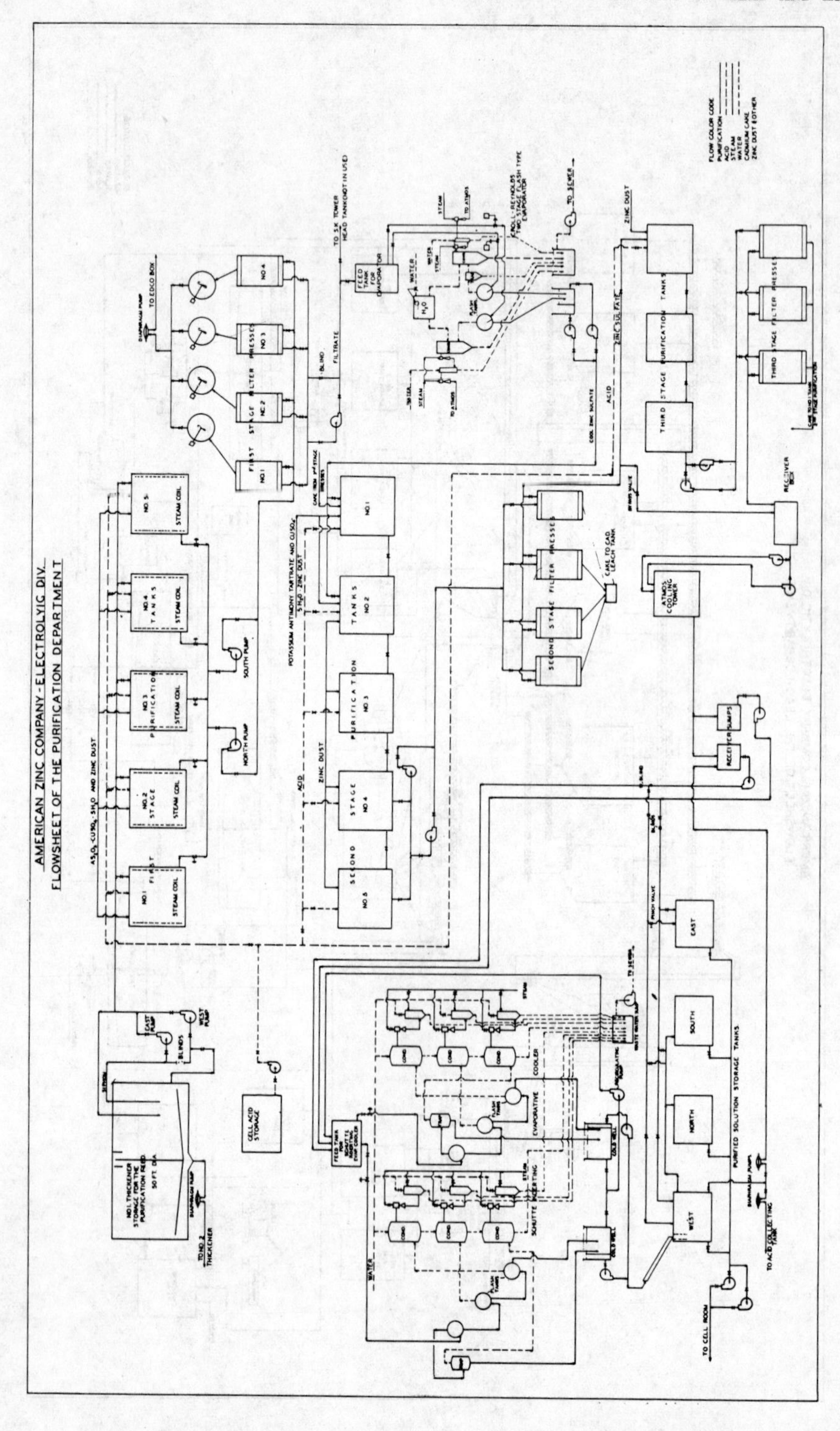
AMERICAN ZINC COMPANY - ELECTROLYIC DIV.
FLOWSHEET OF THE PURIFICATION DEPARTMENT
NO.1 THICKENER STORAGE FOR THE PURIFICATION FEED 50 FT. DIA.
TO NO. 2 THICKENER
BLINDS
EAST PUMP
WEST PUMP
FIRST STAGE PURIFICATION TANKS
STEAM COIL
NORTH PUMP
SOUTH PUMP
CELL ACID STORAGE
TO EDCO BOX
FIRST STAGE FILTER PRESSES
POTASSIUM ANTIMONY TARTRATE AND CUSO4
ACID
ZINC DUST
SECOND STAGE PURIFICATION TANKS
FILTRATE
TO S.K. TOWER HEAD TANK (NOT IN USE)
FEED TANK FOR EVAPORATOR
WATER
STEAM
TO ATMOS
CROLL - REYNOLDS TWO STAGE FLASH TYPE EVAPORATOR
TO SEWER
COND
FLASH TANKS
SCHUTTE KOERTING EVAPORATIVE COOLER
COLD WELL
SECOND STAGE FILTER PRESSES
CAKE TO CAD LEACH TANK
COOL ZINC SULFATE
ZINC SULFATE
THIRD STAGE PURIFICATION TANKS
ATMOS COOLING TOWER
PINCH VALVE
WEST
NORTH
SOUTH
EAST
PURIFIED SOLUTION STORAGE TANKS
TO CELL ROOM
TO ACID COLLECTING TANK
RECEIVER
SUMPS
RECEIVER BOX
THIRD STAGE FILTER PRESSES
FLOW COLOR CODE
PURIFICATION
ACID
STEAM
WATER
CADMIUM CAKE
ZINC DUST & OTHER

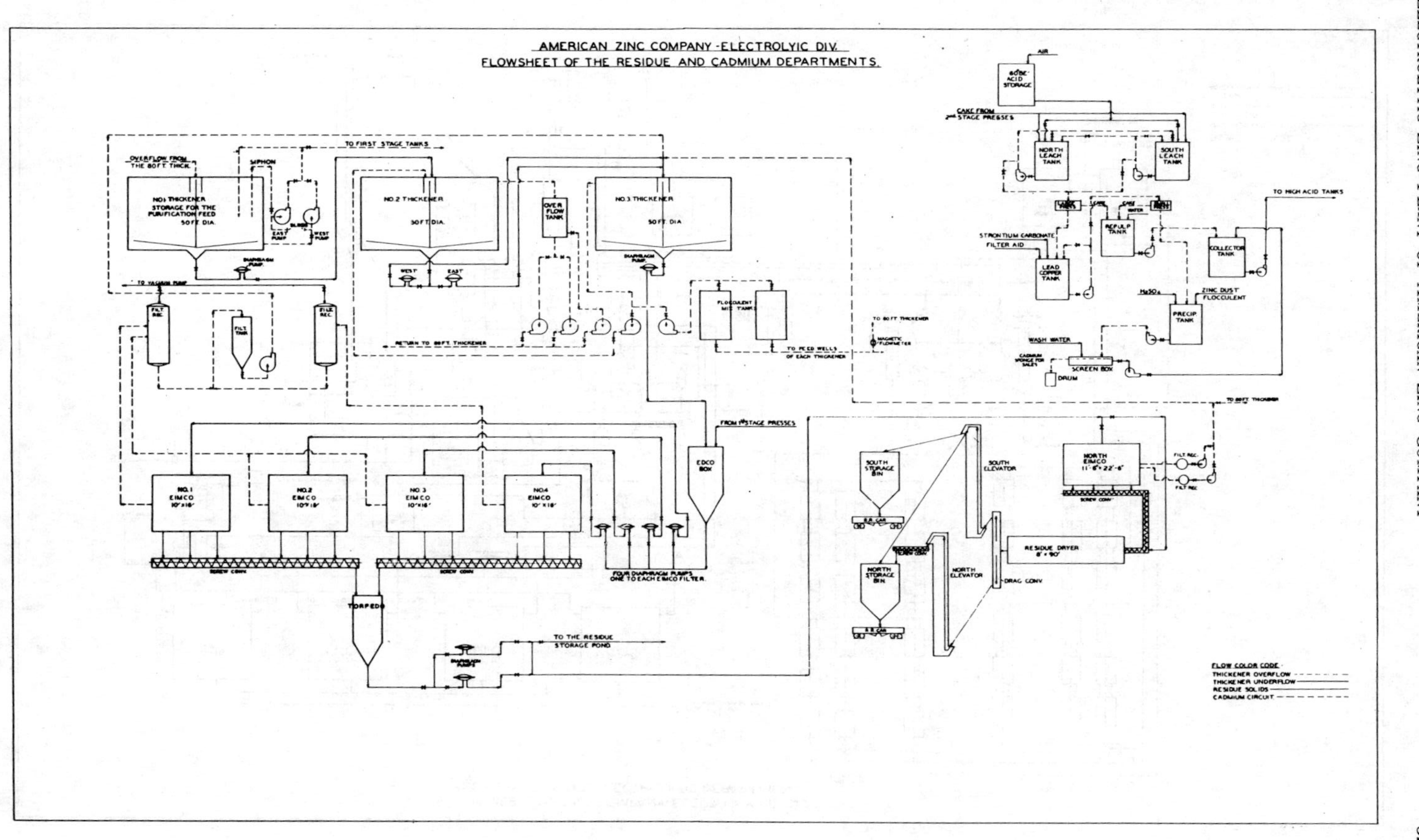
AMERICAN ZINC COMPANY - ELECTROLYIC DIV.
FLOWSHEET OF THE RESIDUE AND CADMIUM DEPARTMENTS.
TO FIRST STAGE TANKS
OVERFLOW FROM THE 80FT. THICK.
SIPHON
NO.1 THICKENER STORAGE FOR THE PURIFICATION FEED 50 FT. DIA.
EAST PUMP
WEST PUMP
DIAPHRAGM PUMP
TO VACUUM PUMP
FILT. REC.
FILT. TANK
NO.2 THICKENER 50 FT. DIA.
WEST
EAST
OVER FLOW TANK
NO.3 THICKENER 50 FT. DIA.
RETURN TO 80 FT. THICKENER
FLOCCULENT MIX TANKS
TO FEED WELLS OF EACH THICKENER
TO 80 FT. THICKENER
MAGNETIC FLOWMETER
NO.1 EIMCO 10'×16'
NO.2 EIMCO 10'×16'
NO.3 EIMCO 10'×16'
NO.4 EIMCO 10'×16'
SCREW CONV.
FOUR DIAPHRAGM PUMPS ONE TO EACH EIMCO FILTER.
EDCO BOX
FROM 1st STAGE PRESSES
TORPEDO
DIAPHRAGM PUMPS
TO THE RESIDUE STORAGE POND
AIR
60°Bé ACID STORAGE
CAKE FROM 2nd STAGE PRESSES
NORTH LEACH TANK
SOUTH LEACH TANK
STRONTIUM CARBONATE
FILTER AID
LEAD COPPER TANK
REPULP TANK
CAKE WATER
COLLECTOR TANK
TO HIGH ACID TANKS
H_2SO_4
ZINC DUST FLOCCULENT
PRECIP. TANK
WASH WATER
SCREEN BOX
DRUM
TO 80 FT. THICKENER
SOUTH STORAGE BIN
R.R. CAR
SOUTH ELEVATOR
NORTH STORAGE BIN
NORTH ELEVATOR
DRAG CONV.
RESIDUE DRYER 8' × 90'
NORTH EIMCO 11'-6" × 22'-6"
FILT. REC.
FLOW COLOR CODE
THICKENER OVERFLOW
THICKENER UNDERFLOW
RESIDUE SOLIDS
CADMIUM CIRCUIT

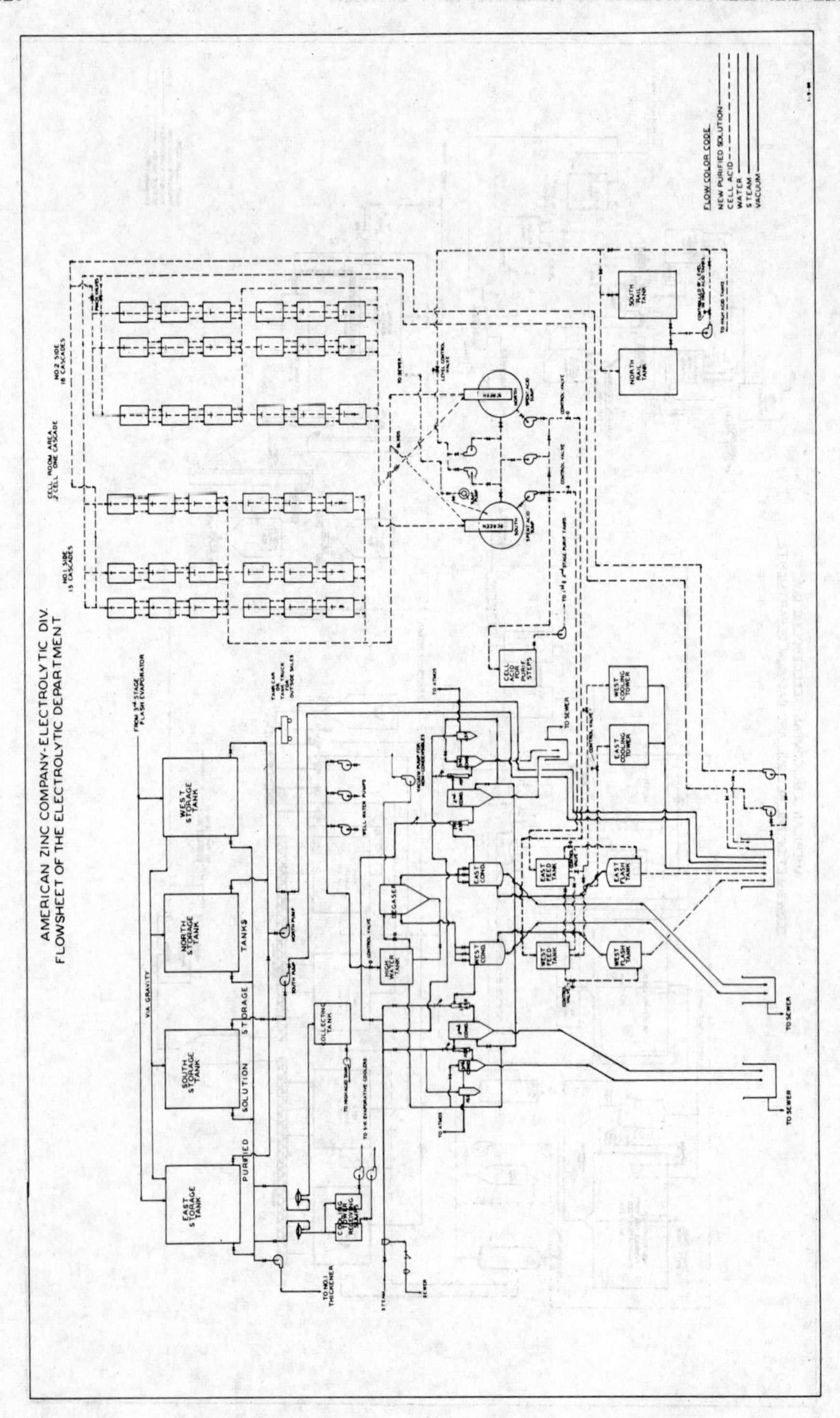
AMERICAN ZINC COMPANY-ELECTROLYTIC DIV.
FLOWSHEET OF THE ELECTROLYTIC DEPARTMENT
EAST STORAGE TANK
SOUTH STORAGE TANK
NORTH STORAGE TANK
WEST STORAGE TANK
PURIFIED SOLUTION STORAGE TANKS
VIA GRAVITY
COLLECTING TANK
HIGH WATER TANK
DEGASER
WEST COND.
EAST COND.
WEST FEED TANK
EAST FEED TANK
WEST FLASHING TANK
EAST FLASHING TANK
EAST COOLING TOWER
WEST COOLING TOWER
CELL ACID FOR PURIF. STEPS
NO.1 SIDE 15 CASCADES
NO.2 SIDE 18 CASCADES
NORTH RAIL TANK
SOUTH RAIL TANK
TO NO.1 THICKENER
TO SEWER
TO SEWER
FLOW COLOR CODE
NEW PURIFIED SOLUTION
CELL ACID
WATER
STEAM
VACUUM

SECTION IV

RESIDUE TREATMENT PRACTICE

Chapter 12

SLAG FUMING PROCESS AT THE COMINCO SMELTER

Trail, British Columbia

George A. Yurko
Plant Superintendent, Lead Furnaces,
Cominco Ltd., Trail, British Columbia, Canada

Abstract

The Cominco smelter, located at Trail, British Columbia, Canada, produces 180 000 metric tons of lead bullion annually in conventio blast furnaces. The resulting slag from these furnaces, 210 000 metric tons annually, containing 18 per cent zinc and 2.5 per cent lead, is treated directly in the slag fuming plant for the recover of these metals and other valuable metals present in smaller quantities.

Slag fuming is carried out on a 55 metric ton batch process in completely water-jacketed furnaces where the slag is blown with a mixture of powdered coal and air. The coal-to-air ratio is controlled to maintain strongly reducing conditions, thus, fuming the metals from the slag. The metal vapours are subsequently re-oxidi with air above the bath. The mixture of oxides is carried from th furnace by the gases through waste heat boilers and cooling flues to a baghouse where they are collected.

The slag fuming plant, under normal conditions, will treat 700 metric tons of slag daily. The throughput in the plant is depende on the fuming rate of zinc, which is a function of the composition of the slag, and on the economics, which dictate the extent to whi zinc is fumed from the slag. Zinc and lead collected daily as fum average 113 metric tons and 17 metric tons, respectively, correspo ing to recoveries of 89 per cent zinc and 98 per cent lead from th slag. The waste heat boilers produce 61 metric tons steam per hou which is distributed to other processing plants.

The slag fuming plant shown in the foreground in Figure 1 is located on the west bank of the Columbia River at Trail, British Columbia, Canada. The history of slag fuming at Trail[1] began in 1920 when a comprehensive program was initiated to develop an economical process for recovering zinc from lead furnace slag that was accumulating into large stockpiles. This situation existed at all lead smelters throughout the world. The slag fuming process as it is known today was developed with complete plant design by 1928. Construction of the plant was completed and in full operation by 1930[2].

Fig. 1 - Slag Fuming Plant at Cominco Ltd.
Trail, British Columbia

Fuming Plant

The fuming plant consists of two fuming furnaces and their accessories, two waste heat boilers, one for each furnace, followed by a common cooling flue connecting to a baghouse. The plant was designed to treat 750 metric tons of hot lead furnace slag on a two furnace operation. In the initial construction only one furnace was built to obtain some operating data, necessary to establish the optimum configuration within the furnace for efficient fuming. The general layout of the fuming plant is shown in the

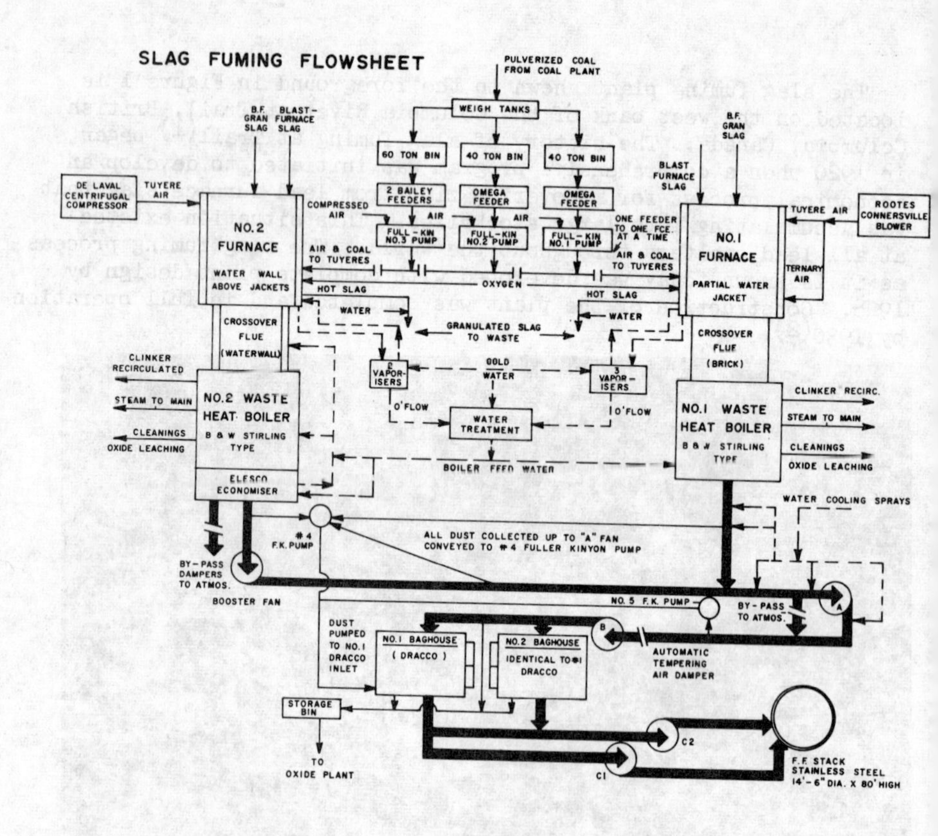

Fig. 2 - Flow Sheet of the Slag Fuming Plant at the Cominco Smelte

Fuming Furnaces

The two furnaces are of water-jacketed construction and similar in design. For No. 1 furnace, the first constructed, inside nominal dimensions are: 3m x 3m x 7.3m long. No. 2 furnace, constructed 17 years later, has the same dimensions for width and height but is 0.6m longer. The floor in each furnace consists of 0.61m wide cast iron sole jackets. These jackets have extra-heavy 25.4mm diameter pipes cast into them and are cooled with fresh water. The lower part of the side walls on each furnace is formed by mild steel tuyere jackets, 0.61m wide and 1.83m high. The inside face of these jackets slopes inward towards the centre line of the furnace, giving a water space of 101.6mm at the top and 317.5mm at the bottom. Welded to these faces and onto the end jacket faces on 76.2mm centres are bell-shaped studs. The studs are 12.7mm long and 20mm in diameter at the "bell". The grid work of studs and slope serves to retain a slag coating on the face of the jackets. The slope also aids slag circulation on blast penetration. The upper tier jackets have parallel faces and a 101.6mm water space. The water jackets on each furnace are connected to Nesmith type thermosyphon vaporizing systems controlled automatically at 95°C. Water circulation is from the vaporizers to the bottom inlets of the tier and tuyere jackets, flowing up these jackets and out back to the vaporizers.

The roofs of the furnaces differ in design. On No. 1 furnace the roof is of water jacket construction and is horizontal for the front half of its length, and then rises as part of the water jacket uptake connecting into the waste heat boiler inlet flue. The walls on this connecting flue, known locally as the "cross over", are of fire brick construction supported by water cooled beams. The floor of the cross-over flue is water jacketed and slopes down toward the furnace uptake flue. The walls of the furnace uptake flue are also of fire-brick construction. Experience gained with the operation of No. 1 furnace was incorporated in the roof design of No. 2 furnace. Above No. 2 furnace is a combustion chamber of water-tube membrane construction that carries straight to No. 2 waste heat boiler. This combustion chamber contributes significantly to the steam raising capacity of this boiler and also serves as a shock absorber for the sudden puffs of gases produced from miniature explosions occurring in the furnace. The construction of No. 2 furnace and boiler is shown in Figure 3.

No. 1 and No. 2 furnaces contain 68 and 74 tuyeres, respectively, which are located on each side, 178mm from the bottom of the furnaces. The tuyere design consists of a double inlet, one for handling pulverized coal supplied through a 19.1mm pipe and the other for blast air supplied through a 38.1mm pipe. The tuyeres are fitted with a ball valve for "rodding through" and insert type liners. The liners are of T1 - steel and last 3 - 4 months. These liners were once made of special high quality wear-resistant steel but the increase in life did not justify the increased cost. The inside diameter of the tuyeres is 38.1 mm.

Molten slag and potshell is charged through water cooled hoppers which project from the front of each furnace in the blast furnace crane aisle. Granulated blast furnace slag from stock is fed from bins, in front and above the furnaces, by gravity to either air ejectors on No. 1 furnace or a Stephens-Adamson Swiveloader. The granulated slag from these feeders is projected diagonally across the surface of the slag bath. The fumed slag is tapped through two 139.7mm tap holes located in the opposite end of the charge hopper and positioned 63.5mm below the tuyere line of the furnace. The tap holes are set in a water cooled cast-iron block. The fumed slag passes through a cast-steel rectangular receiver, split into three streams, each of which is struck by a 63.5mm jet of water at 481 629 N/m^2 pressure. Low pressure zinc plant waste water is introduced below the jets to sluice the slag down the launder. The total volume of water used for granulation is 0.34 m3/s or 2.6 tons water per ton of slag granulated. The tap holes are closed using clay dobies secured in position by water cooled keepers.

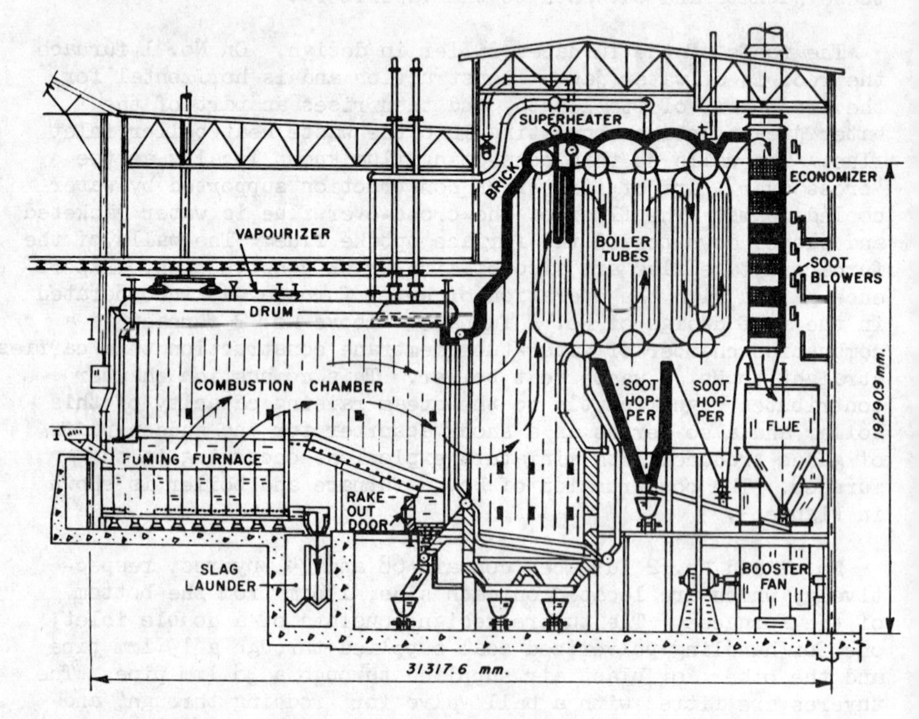

Fig. 3 - No. 2 Slag Fuming Furnace and Boiler

Coal and Air Supply

Coal as received at Cominco is minus 50.8mm size, and is dried and pulverized in a central preparation plant to 85 per cent minus 0.074mm size. The pulverized coal is delivered pneumatically to three cylindrical steel-hoppered bins located at the slag fuming plant. The coal from these bins is metered to size 5 Fuller-Kinyon pumps using gravimetric belt-type Omega feeders. About 0.35 m^3/s of air (primary air) at 481 629 N/m^2 pressure is passed through the Fuller-Kinyon pump injector to carry the coal to the tuyeres, through headers located on each side of the furnace. An auxiliary system using two Bailey feeders is available and can be used on either furnace.

Blast air (secondary air) for No. 1 furnace is supplied by a turbo-blower delivering 7 m^3/s of air at 90 000 N/m^2 and 3600 rpm. This blower is driven by a 912 HP, 700 rpm variable-speed motor. The volume to the tuyeres of No. 1 furnace from this blower will range from 5.9 to 6.2 m^3/s at 55 000 to 62 000 N/m^2. The remainder is used as tertiary air above the bath to insure satisfactory oxidation of the metallic vapours. No. 2 furnace is supplied by a centrifugal compressor capable of delivering 9 m^3/s of air at 105 000 N/m^2 and 3200 rpm. This unit is driven by a 1215 HP, 590 rpm constant speed motor. No. 2 furnace uses between 6.8 and 7.6 m^3/s at a tuyere pressure of 55 000 to 62 000 N/m^2. Again tertiary air is added above the bath in this furnace for oxidation of the metallic vapours.

Gas Cooling

The gases from both furnaces, laden with lead and zinc oxides, pass through separate boiler systems in which a total of 61 metric tons of steam per hour is produced. The gases enter the boiler at approximately 1300°C and leave No. 1 boiler at approximately 475°C and No. 2 boiler at 300°C. The gases leaving No. 1 boiler pass through a short flue known locally as the "breach" to merge with a common 22 m^2 cooling flue. This cooling flue is of mild steel construction and is hoppered to accommodate dust conveying systems. In the breach are located high pressure water sprays to cool the gases. The off gases from No. 1 boiler are cooled from 475°C to 315°C using these sprays. The gases leaving No. 2 boiler (290 - 300°C) are further cooled to 250 - 260°C by passing them through an Elesco economizer. After the economizer is a 150 HP variable speed booster fan, rated at 44.5 m^3/s of air at 240°C, which delivers these gases to the common cooling flue. A fan, which will be referred to as fan "A", rated at 85 m^3/s of air at 315°C and 750 N/m^2, directs the gases through the cooling flue containing water sprays to another fan, fan "B", at the baghouse inlet. There are fifty-four Myers spray heads located along the cooling flue, twenty-four of which are plumbed in banks of six. Each bank is controlled automatically to positions of "full on" or "full off" to maintain the temperature of the gases at 185°C. The spray heads are supplied with 2.2×10^6 N/m^2 water from a central high water pressure pumping system. Water consumption for cooling ranges from 9.5×10^{-4} - 15.5×10^{-4} m^3/s. An automatically energized damper ahead of the baghouse inlet fan completes the cooling by admitting sufficient ambient air to regulate the gas temperature entering the baghouse inlet flue at 140°C. Fan A, of paddle wheel design, is driven by a 200 HP variable speed motor through Texropes. The speed of Fan A is automatically controlled to maintain a negative pressure of 125 N/m^2 at the inlet to Fan B.

Waste Heat Boilers

Both boilers were supplied by Babcock and Wilcox Company and differ from one another in detail. Experience gained from 17 years operation of No. 1 boiler was used in the design of No. 2.

No. 1 boiler, a five drum B&W Stirling with pendant type super heaters, has a 1600m^2 heating surface with the capacity to genera 22 T./hr. steam at 1.3 x 10^6 N/m^2 and 260°C.

No. 2 boiler is a seven drum B&W Stirling with pendant superheater that with the economizer and water-walled combustion chamber has a total heating surface area of 3500 m^2. It has a steam generating capacity of 41 T./hr. at 1.3 x 10^6 N/m^2 and 260°C. The economizer contains 2000 meters of 50.8 mm tubing through which treated boiler feed water is pumped to preheat the water prior to entering the boiler. The economizer is cleaned by 24 air puff soot blowers operated automatically. Air is supplied at 1.4 x 10^6 N/m^2.

The source of boiler feed water is treated Columbia River wate from the furnace jacket cooling system. The overflow from the furnace vaporizers is collected then pumped through three pressur filters arranged in parallel. Any two filters will provide ample flow for two boiler operation. The filtered water is passed thro sodium Zeolite softeners where the hardness is reduced to trace levels. The softened water is then passed through a Deaerating heater where the water temperature is raised to 101°C and the oxygen and CO_2 are liberated. The treated water is collected in a 100m^3 storage tank from which it is pumped to the individual boilers using either two Babcock & Wilcox three-stage centrifugal pumps driven by 60 HP electric motors or one of two turbine drive two-stage Allis Chalmers centrifugal pumps.

Boiler water level is controlled by a Bailey two element contr with steam flow issuing the primary control signal and a boiler d level sensor providing secondary over ride.

Both boilers and inlet flues are equipped with numerous ports and doors for high pressure air lancing and removal of clinker and boiler cleanings.

Baghouse

The baghouse was supplied by Dracco and consists of two separa but identical installations housed in the same building. The inl flue is common to both. The baghouse contains a total of sixteen units, each consisting of ten cylindrical sections. There are eighteen bags, 3m long and 203mm in diameter, in each section making a total of two thousand eight hundred and eighty. The total cloth area is 5000m^2. The bags are shaken automatically on a preset cycle, using mechanical shakers supplied by the baghouse manufacturer. The load/unload cycle is determined by the dust load to the baghouse and the draft conditions at the furnaces. The bags currently used are made of synthetic fibre called Dacron and are found superior to the woolen used previously.

The baghouse inlet fan, fan "B", has a rated capacity of 140 m^3/s of 110°C gas at 500 N/m^2 of draft. It consists of two-paddle wheel impellers connected to a common shaft that is driven by Texropes with a variable speed motor. The speed of this fan is controlled automatically to maintain the baghouse inlet flue at neutral draft.

The cleaned gases are exhausted from the baghouse by two fans, C_1 and C_2, each rated at 71 m^3/s of 95°C gas at 1120 N/m^2 of draft. Both fans discharge into a stainless steel stack 4.4m in diameter and 24m high.

Dust Recovery

The heavy dusts settle out in the boilers and the cooling flues. These are conveyed by either closed screw conveyors or air slides to two centralized collection bins. From these bins the dusts are conveyed by Size 5 Fuller-Kinyon pumps to the baghouse inlet flue. The gas velocity in this flue is very low and the dusts settle into hoppers below. Attached to these hoppers are two 304.8mm closed screw conveyors that operate in parallel. The lighter baghouse dust shaken from each section drops into a steel hopper fabricated from light gauge boiler plate to facilitate "rapping". The sections are arranged in rows of ten and between each two rows is a common inlet flue that is also hoppered. Beneath each row of five sections and the common inlet flue are 228.6mm screw conveyors that collect the dusts that drop into the hoppers and discharge them into the larger main inlet flue collector screws described earlier. The dusts from these collector screws drop onto a 457.2mm wide rubber belt. This belt travels 110m to a 200 T. storage bin mounted 20m above and to one side of a standard gauge track. The dust from this bin is loaded into dust-tight 74.5m3 cars for delivery to the zinc oxide leaching plant for further processing.

Control Instruments

Control of the slag fuming process is maintained with instruments of the indicating and automatic type, mounted on a panel in a central air conditioned control room located on the tapping floor and between the two furnaces. A photograph of the control panel is shown in Figure 4. The control equipment is very similar for each furnace and waste heat boiler. The control equipment includes :

1. Continuous recorders on slag bath temperatures.
2. Pressure gauges and flow recorders on secondary blast air.
3. Temperature controllers on the furnace jacket cooling water, set to maintain a temperature of 95°C.
4. Multipoint draft gauges on boiler and furnace drafts.
5. Pressure gauges and temperature recorders of boiler feed water.
6. Water level recorder-controllers on waste heat boilers.
7. Recorders on steam flow, steam temperature and pressure and economizer temperature.
8. Temperature controller-recorder operating spray-water volume flow to cooling flue.
9. Draft recorder-controller on the flue between boiler outlets and the baghouse inlet.
10. Temperature controller-recorder operating the tempering air damper.
11. Draft recorder-controller on the baghouse inlet flue. The two draft controllers operate as a unit to regulate the draft conditions from the fuming furnaces up to and including the baghouse inlet flue.
12. An annunciator system to draw attention to important conditions that vary from preset limits.
13. An X-ray diffraction spectrograph for on the spot zinc analysis of slag to establish tap out times of each furna[ce] charge.

Fig. 4 - Slag Fuming Plant Control Panel

Operation

The capacity of the fuming plant to treat lead furnace slag is in excess of the current annual production from the blast furnaces; as a consequence, the operation of this plant is programmed to the availability of slag. The operation follows a one and a two fuming furnace schedule. The two fuming furnace operation is normally scheduled for the winter months when steam requirements are greatest. The operation of the fuming plant and the lead blast furnaces is so integrated that an extended stoppage in the latter, resulting in a shortage of liquid slag, will cause a stoppage also in the former. However, production from the blast furnaces can continue in the event of a stoppage in the fuming plant. Lead furnace slag may be granulated directly from the blast furnaces. If required, the slag fuming furnaces can be kept running for short periods of up to 48 hours by treating only cold slag either in the form of potshell or granulated slag. The slag fuming plant is also closely integrated with the zinc oxide leaching plant which processes the fume produced in the former. The zinc in the fume, known locally as white dust, is recovered by leaching with sulphuric acid and electrolysis of the purified solution. The lead returns to the smelter as lead sulphate in the leached residue.

The entire fuming operation is controlled from the central control room manned by a control operator, who relays information to process operators responsible for specific areas of the plant. The operating crew works a forty hour week on a seven-three schedule. The operating crew consists of:

3 supervisors
3 control operators
3 furnacemen (6 for two furnace operation)
3 furnaceman helpers (6 for two furnace operation)
3 boiler operators (6 for two furnace operation)
3 boiler lancers (6 for two furnace operation)
3 dust pump operators
3 baghouse operators
4 coal mill operators
1 dust car loader
1 baghouse repairman (2 for two furnace operation)

The shift supervisors, control operators and boiler operators are holders of steam certificates, to comply with the Boiler Act in effect for the province of British Columbia.

Lead blast furnace slag is collected in 9 T. cast-steel pots and transferred by a 20 T. crane to the fuming furnaces on the opposite side and at the one end of the crane aisle. The procedure of charging liquid slag to No. 2 fuming furnace is shown in Figure 5. The shell formed in these pots will range from 10 per cent to 25 per cent depending largely on the length of time the pots are held between charges. The shell is broken loose from the pots by bumping the pots against a 20 T. lead block located to one side of the crane aisle. The shell is either charg to the fuming furnaces or stockpiled. The stocked shell is eventu crushed and used as a diluent in the sinter charge. The fuming furnace charge is augmented with granulated slag when the supply of liquid slag is limited. Additions of granulated slag are usually made when operating the two fuming furnaces. The average charge weight to No. 1 furnace is 50 T. and to No. 2, a larger furnace, 59 T. The time required to complete a charge ranges from 15 min. for all hot slag to 30 min. for charges containing approximately 20 per cent cold slag. The fuming furnaces operate on approximately 210 min. cycles for charges containing 20 per cent cold slag and fumed to 2.5 per cent zinc. Allowing 30 min. for charging and 12 min. for tapping, leaves 168 minutes for "blowing".

Fig. 5 - Charging of No. 2 Slag Fuming Furnace

Air supply to the tuyeres is held constant at 6.1 m3/s for No. 1 furnace and 7.0 m^3/s for No. 2 furnace. The coal addition, however, is adjusted. The rate during the blow cycle is adjuste to maintain strongly reducing conditions and to hold the slag bath temperatures at 1200°C. At the end of each blow, the coal rate is reduced approximately 20 per cent, from about 4.1 T./hr. to 3.3 T./hr., to raise the bath temperature for the tap out. For the same air volume, more carbon is burned to CO_2 rather than CO, resulting in a greater quantity of heat being liberated in the slag bath. The slag becomes more fluid, thus flows more freely on tap out. The reduced coal rate is maintained during charging in order to bring the slag bath to operating temperature quickly. Oxygen, when available, is used to enrich the tuyere air to allow for more fuel to be burned. Therefore, at reduced coal rates, combustion of carbon to CO_2 is even greater and the bath is brought up to temperature quicker. Oxygen-enriched blast air normally contains 23 per cent oxygen.

The tap out time of each charge is determined by the control operator, by obtaining on the spot analyses of zinc in the bath during the blow cycle. A single element x-ray spectrograph is used for this purpose. A feature of the fuming process is that a plot of the log per cent Zn versus time is a straight line; therefore by obtaining two or more concentration levels of zinc on samples taken from the bath at specific times during fuming, an exact tap out time is determined for a prescribed zinc level in the tail slag. The method described is illustrated in Figure 6.

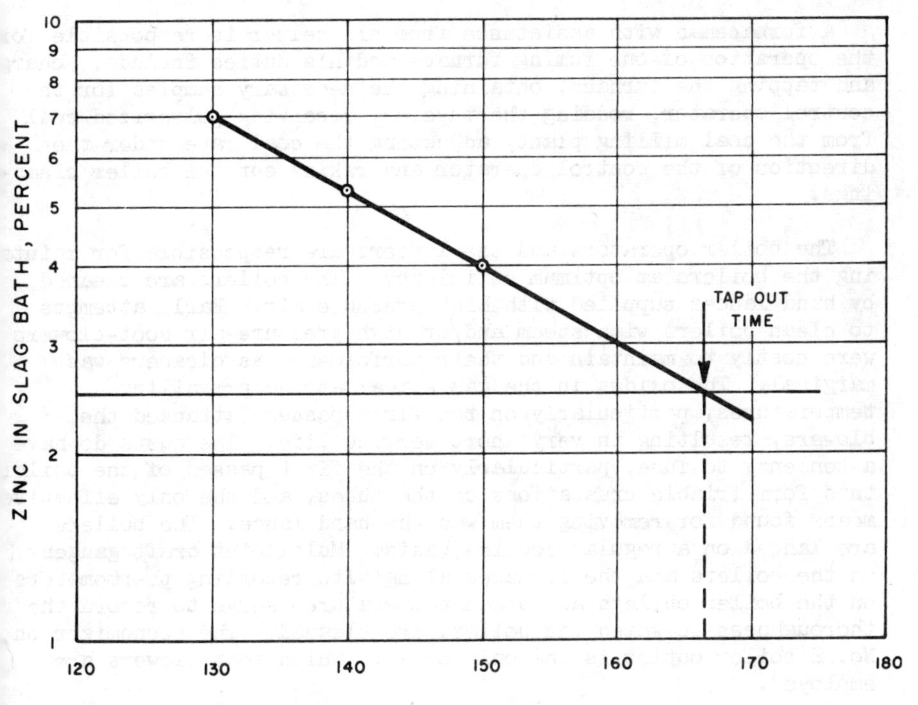

Fig. 6 - Determination of Tap Out Time of a Fuming Furnace Charge

The samples are obtained by rodding a tuyere with a cold steel bar The slag frozen to the bar is removed, pulverized and screened. The minus 0.149 mm portion is used for zinc analysis.

Slag is tapped below the tuyere level by opening the two tap holes in succession, and granulating it using high pressure water jets. This slag is considered barren and is not recovered.

Cleanings from the cross-over flues and the first pass of the boilers consist of a mixture of clinker and semi-fused oxide dust. The clinker is formed by the actual splash-over of slag caused from the violent turbulence within the furnace and by mechanical carry-over of slag entrained in the gas stream. The cleanings are raked over a grizzly to separate the clinker from the fine semi-fused dust. The clinker is recirculated to the sinter plant where it is crushed and blended into the sinter charge. The semi-fused oxide dusts are delivered to the zinc oxide plant for grinding and leaching.

A furnaceman with assistance from his helper is responsible for the operation of one fuming furnace and his duties include: charg and tapping the furnace, obtaining the necessary samples for the control operator, rodding the tuyeres, receiving pulverized coal from the coal milling plant, adjusting the coal rate under the direction of the control operator and raking out the boiler cleanings.

The boiler operators and the lancers are responsible for mainta ing the boilers at optimum efficiency. The boilers are cleaned by hand lances supplied with high pressure air. Early attempts to clean boilers with steam and/or high pressure air soot-blowers were costly to maintain and their performance as cleaners was marginal. The oxides in the gas stream at the prevailing temperatures, particularly on the first passes, attacked the blowers, resulting in very short service life. The dusts do have a tendency to fuse, particularly on the first passes of the boiler thus form friable crustations on the tubes, and the only effective means found for removing them was the hand lance. The boilers are lanced on a regular routine basis. Multipoint draft gauges on the boilers and the furnaces along with recording thermometers on the boiler outlets and steam temperatures serve to record the thoroughness to which the boilers are cleaned. The economizer on No. 2 boiler outlet is the only area in which soot blowers are employed.

All dust dropping out of the gas streams after the first pass of the boilers to the baghouse inlet fan is collected by covered screw conveyors and air slides, and conveyed to two centralized bin hoppers. The dust fall-out in the boilers, economizer and cooling flue amounts to an estimated 25 per cent of the total dust in the gas stream. A dust pump operator is assigned to each shift and his responsibility is to see that the dust dropping out is removed from the system. His duties include hand lancing the flues and ensuring that the dust dropping out does not bridge in the hoppers below these flues. The dust does have a tendency to pack and hang up in the hoppers. Bin flows are used to advantage on the bin hoppers to fluidize the dust and thus allow it to flow freely into the Fuller-Kinyon pumps. The inlet and outlet flues on the fans are blown down once per shift to avoid the occurrence of slides that could damage the impellers.

The baghouse operator, like the dust pump operator, is responsible to oversee that dust collected in the baghouse is removed via the 50 screw conveyors installed for this purpose. The hoppers below each section are rapped manually, using a rubber mallet, to avoid dust build up. The baghouse inlet flue is hand lanced daily to prevent the dust from accummulating on the walls and in the hoppers. The baghouse operator under the direction of the control operator makes the necessary adjustments to the shake cycle on each section, required to maintain adequate drafts in the fuming furnaces. The shake cycle for a two furnace operation is normally an 8 minute load followed by a 5 second unload, while for a one furnace operation the load period is 30 minutes followed by a 5 second unload. During the unload, or shake cycle, the outlet damper on the section closes automatically and the section is placed under a slight positive pressure with ambient air to enhance dust removal from the bags. Each section of the baghouse is inspected daily for dust leaks and damper malfunction. Any irregularities are noted on the operator's record sheet for the attention of the baghouse repair crew. The crew consists of two men on a two furnace schedule while one man with occasional assistance from the baghouse operator handles the repairs when the plant is on a one furnace operation. The crew, in addition to performing emergency repairs to individual bags to maintain dust loss at a minimum, change the bags in each section on a fixed rotation to provide for optimum gas volume throughput at all times. The average gas volume passing through the bags on a two furnace operation is 95 m^3/s at 115°C or 0.019 m^3/s per square meter of cloth area. The bags are made from filament Dacron and have a normal service life of 30 months. The normal emission of fume from the baghouse stack corresponds to an operating efficiency of 99.95 per cent for the baghouse.

Metallurgy

The chemistry of the slag fuming process may be described by the following three end equations:

$$2C + 3/2\ O_2 \longrightarrow CO + CO_2 \quad (1)$$

$$CO + ZnO \longrightarrow Zn + CO_2 \quad (2)$$

$$Zn + 1/2\ O_2 \longrightarrow ZnO \quad (3)$$

Pulverized coal with insufficient air for complete combustion is blown into the slag bath through the tuyeres. Equation 1 takes place within the bubbles dispersed throughout the bath. The fuel, primarily carbon, except for volatiles, serves a two-fold purpose: (a) chemical reducing agent and (b) heat source. Sufficient heat must be made available to maintain the slag bath at 1200°C. That is, a balance must be maintained between the exothermic combustion reaction (equation 1) and the endothermic zinc oxide reduction reaction (equation 2) plus the heat requirements associated with the introduction of blast air at ambient temperature and furnace losses. Equation 2 takes place in the immediate boundaries of the gas bubbles, releasing zinc vapour that rises with the gas. Above the bath the zinc vapour is re-oxidized, equation 3. This reaction is exothermic, thus a large quantity of heat is released. The net thermal effect of the above reactions is simply the complete combustion of the reducing agent. This thermal energy is, in turn, harnessed in the product of steam in the boilers.

It is generally accepted that near equilibrium conditions are approached in the slag fuming process, therefore the extent of the reaction in equation 2 is governed by the relation:

$$K = \frac{pCO_2 \cdot pZn}{pCO \cdot aZnO}$$

where p represents the partial pressure of the gaseous components a_{ZnO} is the activity of ZnO in the slag and K is the equilibrium constant of this reaction. From this relationship, the rate of zinc elimination from the bath is determined by: (a) the combust conditions as represented by pCO_2/pCO. A greater partial pressure of CO would be beneficial and may be achieved by oxygen enrichment[3] and preheating of the blast air [4]. (b) the partial pressure of Zn vapour. Larger gas volumes passing through the bath will tend to purge the bath free of zinc vapour, thus reducing the potential for the reverse reaction in equation 2 to occur. (c) the activity of ZnO in the slag. The activity of ZnO is essentially fixed by the composition of the slag and decreases rapidly with concentration, thus the rate of elimination of zinc from the slag decreases rapidly as the reaction proceeds toward completion. The elimination of zinc from a typical furnace charge (55 metric ton charge containing 20 per cent cold slag) is shown in Figure 7. The fuming rate curve takes a sharp drop as the level of zinc in the bath approaches 2.5 per cent. The economical cut-off value of zinc is determined by the prevailing price of zinc and the operating costs incurred in the recovery of zinc by this process.

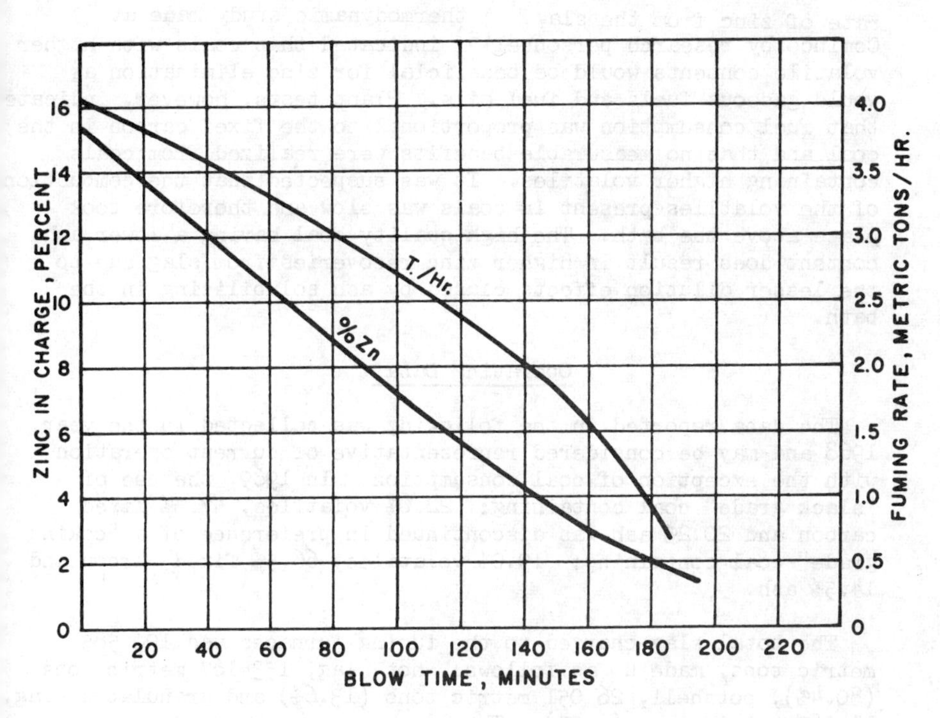

Fig. 7 - Elimination of Zinc from a
Typical Fuming Furnace Charge

The elimination rate of zinc from lead furnace slag produced at the Cominco smelter is better for slags containing low quantities of sulphur and higher levels of lime. From operating data it is surmised that lime increases the activity of ZnO in the slag; and sulphur, thought to be present as ZnS, tends to nullify the influence of lime by the reaction:

$$ZnS + CaO + C \longrightarrow Zn_{vapour} + CaS + CO$$

Lead and other minor elements present in the slag are readily volatilized as metals, oxides and sulphides. It is known that lead and most elements associated with lead and zinc have appreciable vapour pressures at 1200°C, the temperature of the slag. Trace elements such as silver, indium, cadmium and tin are recovered from slag produced at Cominco. Recoveries range from 80 - 95 per cent.

The fuel currently used in Cominco's slag fuming process is a high quality bituminous coal. A typical analysis is: 66.5 per cent fixed carbon, 19 per cent volatiles and 14.5 per cent ash. Studies on bituminous and sub-bituminous (higher volatile content) coals indicated no significant differences in the elimination rate of zinc from the slag. A thermodynamic study made at Cominco by research personnel[5] indicated that coals with higher volatile contents would be beneficial for zinc elimination as would gaseous fuels and fuel oils. Plant tests, however, indicate that fuel consumption was proportional to the fixed carbon in the coal and that no measurable benefits were realized from coals containing higher volatiles. It was suspected that the combustion of the volatiles present in coals was slow and therefore took place above the bath. The high quality coal having a lower ash content does result in higher zinc recoveries from slag due to the lesser dilution effects caused by ash solubilizing in the bath.

Operating Data

The data reported in the following was collected in the year 1968 and may be considered representative of current operation with the exception of coal consumption. In 1969, the use of "slack grade" coal containing: 22.0% volatiles, 57.5% fixed carbon and 20.2% ash was discontinued in preference of a "coking grade" coal containing: 19.0% volatiles, 66.5% fixed carbon and 14.5% ash.

The total slag charged to the fuming furnaces was 190 585 metric tons, made up as follows: hot slag, 153 167 metric tons (80.4%), potshell, 26 051 metric tons (13.6%) and granulated slag, 11 367 metric tons (6.0%). The average throughput for a two furnace operation was 700 metric tons per day.

Typical analyses of the lead furnace slag charged to the fuming furnaces and the furnace products recovered are given in Table 1.

Table 1. Typical Analyses of Fuming Furnace Charge and Recovered Products

Products	Analysis Percent							
	Cd	Pb	Zn	S	SiO_2	Fe	CaO	Al_2O_3
Lead Blast Furnace Slag	0.09	2.5	17.5	1.8	20.8	27.5	10.3	4.6
Fuming Furnace Dust	0.10	9.8	63.0	1.8	0.5	0.2	0.2	-
Boiler Cleanings (Clinker excluded)	0.09	10.5	59.6	0.7	1.8	2.5	-	-
Boiler Clinker	0.06	14.0	42.8	1.0	6.5	8.0	-	-

Coal consumption was 56 180 metric tons dry weight, or approximately 29 per cent of the charge treated. The ratio of coal used per ton of contained metal in fume was 1.71.

Metal production was 28 344 metric tons of zinc and 4004 metric tons of lead in fume, which corresponds to recoveries of 89 per cent of the zinc and 98 per cent of the lead from that present in the furnace charge. The lead and zinc contents averaged 0.05 and 2.5 per cent, respectively. The average daily fume production for a two fuming furnace operation was 170 metric tons, corresponding to 113 metric tons of zinc and 17 metric tons of lead.

Waste-heat steam production amounted to 364 713 metric tons, or 6.5 metric tons steam/metric ton dry coal. The average steam production for a two boiler operation was 61 metric tons steam per hour. Steam produced was fed into a main distribution line that serviced the numerous processing plants, shops and office facilities located in Trail.

The operating schedule for the year 1968 was: 6 months of a one furnace operation and 5.5 months of a two furnace operation with a two week complete shutdown for vacation. The fuming furnaces operated on the average of 95.7 per cent of the scheduled operating time. Semi-annual boiler inspection and granulating launder repairs, leaking furnace jacket replacements and quarterly tuyere liner replacements along with occurrences of shortages of hot slag were the normal major contributors to furnace shutdowns.

References

1. Murray, G.E. "The Recovery of Zinc and Lead from Blast Furnace Slag at Trail, B.C." Transactions of the Canadian Institute of Mining and Metallurgy, Vol. 36, 1933, pp. 75 - 103.

2. McNaughton, R.R. "Slag Treatment for the Recovery of Lead and Zinc at Trail, British Columbia" Transactions AIME Vol. 121, 1936, pp. 721 - 736.

3. McNaughton, R.R., T.H. Weldon, J.H. Hargrave, L.V. Whiton, "The Use of Oxygen Enriched Air in the Metallurgical Operations of Cominco at Trail, B.C.", Transactions AIME, Vol. 185, 1949, pp. 446 - 450; Journal of Metals, Vol. 1, August 1949, pp. 446 - 450.

4. "The BHAS Slag Fuming Plant", Australian Mining, 15 June 1968, pp. 16 - 19.

5. Bell, R.C., G.H. Turner, E. Peters, "A Thermodynamic Study - Fuming of Zinc from Lead Blast Furnace Slag", Transactions AIME, Vol. 203, 1955, pp. 472 - 477.

Chapter 13

TREATMENT OF THE LEACHING RESIDUES AT THE ELECTROLYTIC ZINC PLANT OF ESPANOLA DEL ZINC, S.A., CARTAGENA, SPAIN

Jose Luis del Valle Alonso
Director of Engineering

Antonio Fernandez de Palencia y Roc
Mining Division Engineer

Abelardo Rovira Pereira
Production Control

Joaquin Moreno Clavel
Process Control

Ricardo Guzman Jimenez
Professor, University of Murcia

Abstract

Although present electrolytic zinc manufacturing processes are aimed at the direct wet process recovery of the metal, and, with this end in view, several industrial scale patents have been applied for during the last few years, the object of this paper is to enhance the possible metallurgical interest in the conventional recovery of zinc and other metals from leaching residues.

Therefore, its main end is the description and discussion of the recovery process of zinc, lead and cadmium from leaching residues.

Fundamentally, the process consists of the following:

Flotation processing to recover the non-roasted blende still contained in the residues.

Pyrometallurgical processing of flotation tails in low-shaft furnaces (kilns) and open-flame rotating furnaces and the ensuing recovery of zinc, lead and cadmium as a mixture of their oxides through volatilization.

The authors gratefully acknowledge the contributions of Diego Juan Garcia, Laboratory Chemist, in the development of the process and preparation of this paper.

Photo No. 1 - Aerial view of plant - W-E Direction - Left: Rotating drying furnace - Right: Clinkering furnace - Lower right: Open-flame rotating furnace loading system.

Photo No. 2 - Aerial view of plant - E-W Direction - Center: Open flame rotating furnace - Lower right: Rotating drying furnace - Background: Low-shaft furnace.

Clinkering of this oxide mixture to separate zinc oxide from lead-cadmium oxides, as well as the elimination from the zinc oxide of tho obnoxious elements interfering with electrolysis and the communicatio of those physical characteristics which favor its use in the leaching plant.

Processing of the lead-cadmium oxide together with the cadmium pla residues in the open-flame rotary furnace with the end of recovering lead, silver, and cadmium as volatilization dust.

The metallurgical processing of neutral leach purification residue in this plant with cadmium upgrading and zinc and copper recovery are described.

An annex describes the analytical procedure adopted in the control of the process.

1. Introduction - The Espanola del Zinc, S.A. Cartagena, Spain plant was planned with a view to processing the blende obtained by the differential flotation of Cartagena Range ores.

1.1 Situation - Cartagena Range is the designation given to the mountainous region extending through the southwest of the Iberiar Peninsula at 37° North latitude and 2° East longitude, and stretc ing from Cartagena to Cape Palos bordering the Mediterranean coas

1.2 Geology and Metallogeny - The evident intensity of metamorphism in practically the whole sedimentary series has modifiec its primitive facies to a greater or lesser degree.

The formations correspond to the crystalline Permian, Trial, Miocene and Pleistocene strata. The rest of the stratigraphical series is based in the Permian, which is represented by metamorphic slates and crystalline limestones. It's an archaic facie horizon, disturbed by displacements and faults.

The most interesting metallogenic horizon from the mining poir of view of the Cartagena Range is the Trial which is made up of dolomitic limestones which have experienced an intense metamorphi

Interesting ore deposits have also been formed in the Miocene region, which covers small areas lying to the north of the coast highlands.

Stratigraphical studies reveal the existence of a sheaf of longitudinal fractures running SW-NE as well as others normal to these, which determine a wide diversity of metallogenic properties in the soils which configure the voussoirs resulting fror the combination of both sheafs.

A series of volcanic outcrops, running in a SW-NE direction, are related to both fractures.

These volcanic masses are localized in the intersections of both fractures, due to the fact that these points offer an easier path. Their ascension is superficial in character, extensive or intensive, and affects the whole of the stratigraphical series.

We believe that the metallogeny of the Cartagena Range is linked to this intermediate depth eruptive stage, which, therefore, is of a subvolcanic character.

This genesis has originated the following deposits:

a) Low-strike vein deposits
b) Substitution and impregnation deposits
c) Lattice deposits in volcanic dykes

All these deposits have been subjected to intense metamorphism.

1.3 Mining - The most generalized mining procedure employed has been the classical pillar-and-stall method both in horizontal and inclined mines. As far as possible it has been adjusted to metal-ore distribution in the deposit.

1.4 Differential Flotation - In the past, the mineralogical composition of the mine run dictated gravimetric concentration methods, because the galena-blende-pyrite components are partially interlinked.

More recently, however, flotation and, specifically, differential flotation, has been the most generally employed process, although bulk flotation is partially employed in a few plants.

One of the problems created by differential flotation was most efficient limit crushing. The mixed presentation of sulphides is important in the case of blende-pyrite-chalcopyrite and rather less in that of galena.

In blende flotation, sizes smaller than 250 mesh are necesary. This has the drawback that the proportion of fines obtained is rather high.

1.5 Blende Characteristics - These characteristics, which are a result of the metallogeny of the region and of the methods employed in its recovery, govern the whole zinc metal manufacturing process employed in the Espanola del Zinc plant

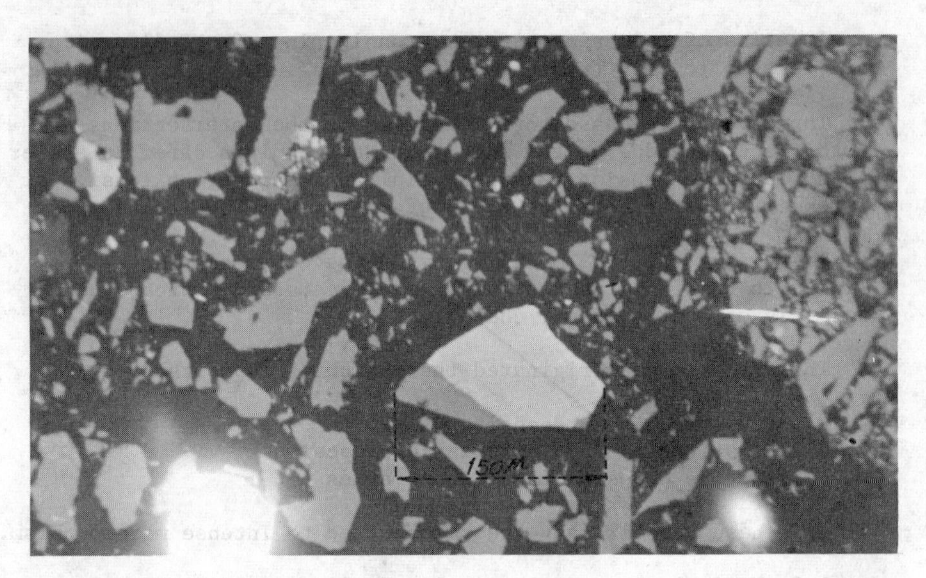

Photo No. 3 - Chalcopyrite - blende binary associations - A high proportion of fines is observed.

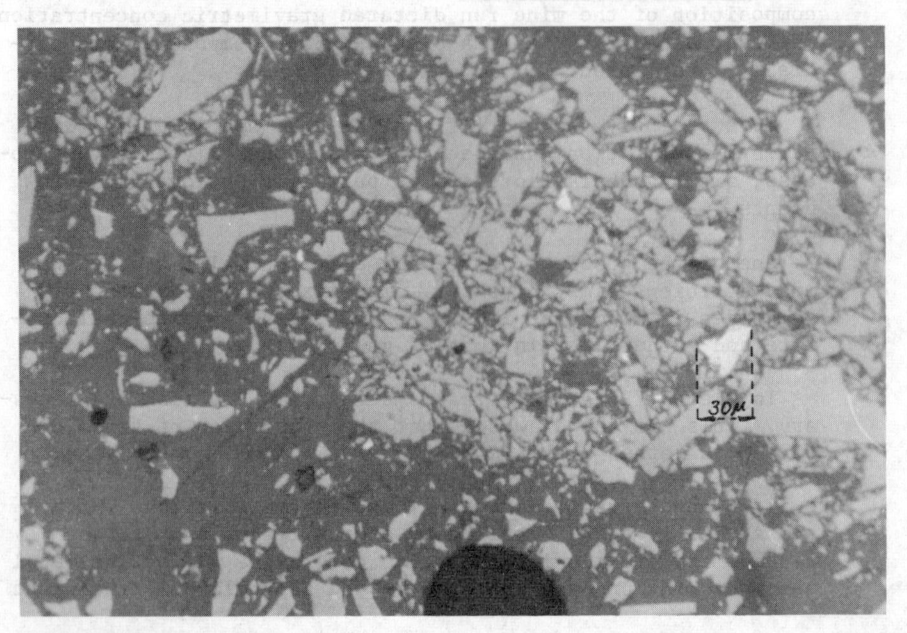

Photo No. 4 - Blende fines, with two liberated grains of cp and go. Purer concentrate.

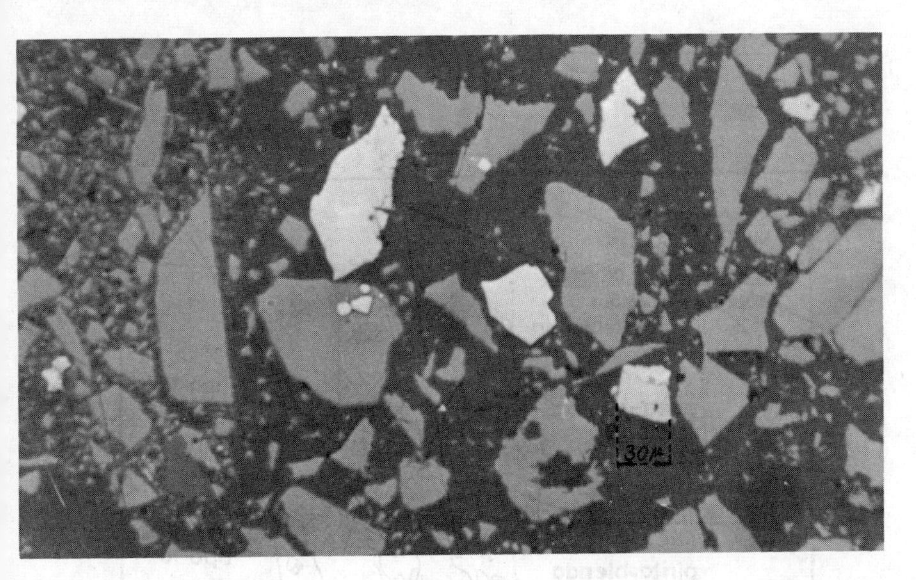

Photo No. 5 - Binary py-sl associations in high-fines proportion blende concentrates.

The varied composition of the average zinc concentrate type induced us to undertake a microphotographic study (Photos Nos. 3, 4 and 5) which revealed the presence of the following metal components:

Blende (sl) (Sphalerite and marmatite), pyrite (py), marcasite (mc), pyrotite (po), limonite (go), chalcopyrite (cp), chalcosine (cc) and galena (gn).

On the basis of the international mineral intergrowth tables, the following types, which are indicated in Graph 1, were identified:

a) 1a - type association......... very frequent
b) 1b - type association......... slightly frequent

The most generalized associations are of the galena-blende and pyrite-blende types, although chalcopyrite-blende, pyrite-chalcopyrite and galena-pyrite associations have also been identified.

On the basis of a statistical count of the best specimens studied, the following conclusions were reached:

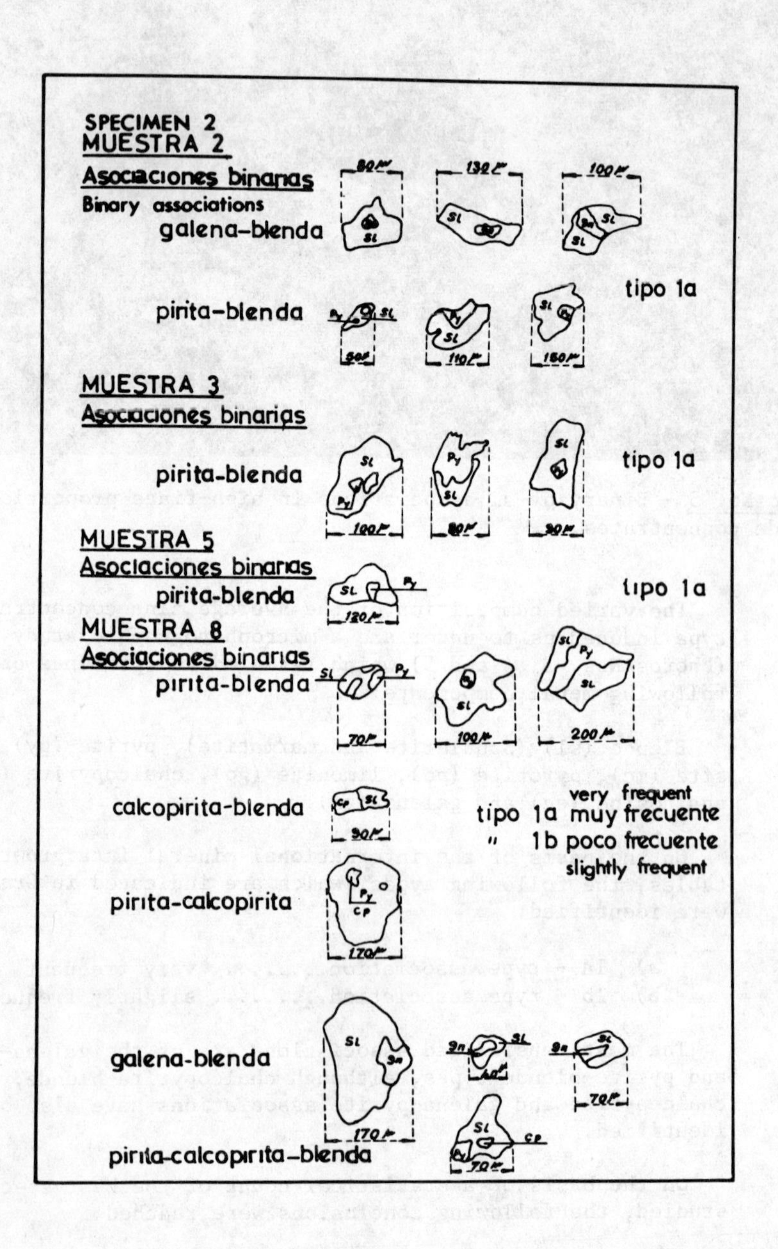

Graph No. 1 - Associations discovered in test specimen count.

a) They are blende concentrates with over 90% free blende, with the sole exception of specimen No. 3, which has an 80% blende content.

b) The milling degree required to achieve these liberations is extremely high and results in a high proportion of these fines in sizes less than 50 mu. In most cases the proportion of these fines is 75% and, in some instances, climbs as high as 84%. In no case is this proportion smaller than 55%.

The typical chemical analysis of Cartagena Range blendes processed in our plant follows:

	High	Low	Half
Zn	50,50	48,00	49,30 %
Fe	13,30	11,60	12,30 %
Pb	1,50	0,60	1,00 %
S	33,00	32,00	32,60 %
Cu	0,20	0,10 %	
Cd	0,20	0,10 %	
SiO_2	3,50	1,50 %	
CaO	1,00	0,50 %	
MgO	0,50	0,10 %	
Al_2O_3	0,05	0,10 %	
Cl	0,30	0,10 %	
Mn			0,0400 %
F			0,0300 %
In			0,0200 %
As			0,0200 %
Ag			0,0050 %
Ni			0,0012 %
Co			0,0040 %
Bi, Ga, Te, Ge, Hg			0,0005 %

Table I

The mineralogical components identified by chemical analysis and microphotography follow:

		High	Low
ZINC Blende	Sphalerite	53	60 %
	Marmatite	30	35 %
Pyrite, Marcasite and pyrrhotite		3	4 %
Silica and silicate		3	4 %
Galena		1	2 %
Chalcopyrite and chalcocite		0,1	0,3 %
Cadmium Blende		0,1	0,3 %

Table II

2. Roasting - Blendes obtained by flotation from Cartagena Range ores are stocked, still wet, in an open-air yard while awaiting transportation to the roasting plant.

In this plant the blende is subjected to an oxidizing-roasting operation in two different types of furnaces. These are of the conventional hearth type, with a 50 MT/day raw blende capacity, and of the fluid-bed type, which has a 120 MT/day raw blende capacity.

With the object of achieving maximum roasted zinc recovery, the characteristics of our blende determine how both processes are conducted. Best conditions are those which result in a minimum content of sulphate and sulphide-type sulphur while also minimizing the effec of those impurities which reduce the Anaconda zinc content of the roasted product.

The high proportion of fines in the concentrate, described in the preceding section, leads to the production of a large amount of fly-dust, particularly in the fluid-bed roaster.

The elements which result in a loss of soluble zinc are the following:

a) Maratitic iron in the concentrate which, on roasting, is transformed into ferrite. In oxidizing roasting, there is no possibility of coping with this loss of soluble zinc.

b) In its simultaneous oxidation with a zinc sulphide particle, pyritic- or pyrotitic-type iron may lead to ferrite formation.

c) Galena-type lead contained in blende may result in soluble zinc losses, due to the fact that, by melting, it agglomerates the grains of blende thus preventing their roasting.

d) If completely soluble in the spent electrolyte, pyrite-, marcasite-, or pyrrotite-type iron may lead to soluble zinc losses due to the difficulties they present in the separation of leaching solutions and residues. Therefore, only the iron necessary for the elimination of those impurities impairing electrolysis must be in soluble form.

These factors govern the development of the roasting process which, in our case, is the following:

2.1 Hearth Furnaces - The plant has two conventional nine-hearth furnaces operating in parallel. The exit gases pass through a cyclone dedusting system and, subsequently, through common piping to an electrofilter.

The process is conducted as follows:

Hourly feed	3840 kgs/mixture
Mixture	60% raw blende, 40% feedback
Average residence time	8 hours
Gas flow	5500 - 6000 m^3 N on entry
Operating temperature.	820 - 870°C

2.1.1 Composition of the roasted product obtained in the hearth furnaces - This product is delivered by the last furnace hearth free from grain agglomerates which are eliminated in a 0.5 mm jigging system. Material retained in the jig is ground and fed back to the furnace.

The composition of this product is given in Table III.

2.2 Fluid-bed Furnace - This furnace has a 4.8 m diameter hearth and a 1.10 m bed depth. It is equipped with a gas latent heat recovery system and a cyclone dedusting system. Gases from the furnace join those from the hearth roasters in the entrance to the electrofilters.

Some process parameters follow:

Hourly feed .... 5 MT/h raw blende
Average residence time .... 1 hr.
Gas flow .... 9500 - 10,000 m^3 entering furnac
Bed temperature........ 990 - 1000°C
Temperature of gases leaving furnace.. 900 - 1000°C
Bed pressure .... 1400 - 1500 m/m water column
MT/hr of steam produced .... 4.8 - 5.1
Pressure of steam produced .... 40 Kgs/cm^2

The bed is cooled with water at the rate of 0.6 - 1.0 m^3/hr.

2.2.1 Composition of the roasted product obtained in the flui bed furnace - The test sample is an average composed of the following parts:

34% Bed overflow
35% Boiler dust
27% Cyclone product
4% Electrofilter (of both hearth and fluid-bed furnaces) dust

Table III shows its analytical composition.

3. Leaching

3.1 Neutral Leaching - The products obtained in both roasting processes follow independent paths but come together in the preparation of leaching plant feeds.

If the roasted product proceeds from the hearth furnace, it is conveyed by a travelling band and stocked in two concrete 300 MT capacity bunkers.

	Multiple - Hearth Furnace	Fluid - Bed Furnace	Half
Zn	56,50 - 57,00	55,50 - 56,60	56,00 - 56,80
Fe	12,50 - 13,00	12,00 - 12,50	12,00 - 12,80
Pb	1,00 - 1,50	1,00 - 1,50	1,00 - 1,50
Cu	0,15	0,15	0,15
Cd	0,14	0,15	0,15
S-total	3,50 - 4,00	3,00 - 3,50	3,00 - 3,50
$S-SO_4^=$	1,50 - 2,00	2,50 - 3,00	1,50 - 2,50
$S-S^=$	1,50 - 2,00	0,40 - 0,60	1,00 - 1,50
SiO_2	1,50	1,50	1,50
CaO	0,50	0,50	0,50
MgO	0,50	0,50	0,50
Al_2O_3	0,10	0,10	0,10
Zn-Sulfate	1,00 - 1,50	3,50 - 4,00	1,50 - 2,00
Zn-Oxide	43,50 - 44,50	41,00 - 41,50	42,50 - 43,50
Zn {Carbonate / Silicate}	1,50 - 2,00	2,00 - 2,50	2,00 - 2,50
Zn-Ferrite	5,00 - 5,50.	6,00 - 6,50	5,50 - 6,00
Zn-Sulfide	3,50 - 4,00	0,80 - 1,00	2,00 - 2,50
Fe-Ferrite	9,00 - 9,50	10,00 - 11,00	9,50 - 10,50
As	0,0200	0,0200	0,0200
Ge	0,0010	0,0010	0,0010
Sn	0,0400	0,0400	0,0400
Co	0,0011	0,0011	0,0011
Ni	0,0015	0,0015	0,0015
Cl	0,1000	0,2500	0,2000
Ag	0,0055	0,0055	0,0055
In	0,00200	0,0200	0,0200
Te	0,0005	0,0005	0,0005

Table III

If, on the other hand, it proceeds from the fluid-bed roastin process, it is conveyed pneumatically by Fuller pumps to a 100 M capacity metal hopper.

This metal hopper, which can also be fed from the two concret bunkers, is situated at one end of the plant in such a way that it can feed a weighing hopper. This hopper travels on rails lai along the leaching section so that the roasted product may be fe to any one of the five leachers with which the plant is equipped

The average composition of the roasted product feeding the leaching plant is shown in Table III.

In a neutral leach the roasted product is attacked by a mixtu of 75 - 80% spent electrolyte and 20 - 25% leaching solution recovered in the plant (made up of leaching solution from the acid leach, wash and recovered waters and leaching solution recovered flotation). Manganese dioxide is added in order to oxidize ferr iron which may be present in the roasted product. The operation complete when pulp pH is 5.4 and the Fe and Al content of the fi tered leach is under 1 mg/l.

Processed feeds are discharged into a 435 m^3 capacity thicken circuit. There are four thickeners; two operate in parallel in blende circuit, another in the oxide circuit residue processing, and the fourth in the acid leaching circuit.

To improve decanting, the addition of SEPARAN NP-10, TYLOSE i required.

3.2 Acid Leaching - Muds decanted from the neutral thickener exit through double-valve-equipped cones. Two diaphragm pumps f them into two 50 m^3 tanks arranged in parallel and coated with a acid-resistant lining where they are leached.

The acid leaching of the neutral residues of our plants has been studied in pilot and industrial scales. The following conclusions have been reached:

a) The process must be carried out with spent electrolyte if this is unavailable, with water and the addition of concentrated sulphuric acid up to an acid content of 35 400 g/l.

b) During processing care must be taken that the pH is nev lower than 3, for, if it were to drop below this value, pulps which are difficult to neutralize and filter woul be obtained. This may be due to the fact that the equi brium solubility limit of ferric hydroxide lies between pH 2.5 and pH 3. This results in the formation of minu mieelles of $Fe(OH)_3 \cdot n\ H_2O$ hydrogels, in which, as long favorable conditions prevail, the gel size increases, while its structural lattices enclose considerable amounts of water. This phenomenon is accompanied by a similar transformation in the silicic acid hydrogel which is always present.

If the pH were to drop below 2.5, the Fe $(OH)_3$ solubility region would be reached, thus freeing the solids dispersed throughout the precipitate which forms the pulp. This, in turn, results in a fast sand sedimentation which is wholly undesirable due to the ensuing circuit complications which occur.

Once the acid leaching operation has come to an end, the pulp is discharged into the acid thickener, the overflow of which pours into a 60 m^3 tank. From this tank it is delivered to the leaching section, where it is employed in the preparation of the feeds.

Muds are removed from the acid thickener by means of a diaphragm pump and delivered to a 15 m^3 conditioner tank and, from this, into the drum filters.

3.3 Washing of Residues - The acid pulp is sent to two drum-filter batteries, one of which has three drum-filters and the other two, prepared to operate either in series or parallel.

The characteristics of these filters are:

Filtrating surface .... 24 m^2
Operating depression ...... 0.4 Kg/cm^2
Vacuum drum .... 2 m^3

Together with the wash waters, the filtrate is pumped to the acid thickener in order to reincorporate it into the circuit.

Filters are equipped with an atomization system, the object of which is the displacement washing of the cake in the filter.

The amount of water employed is governed by circuit availability and residue characteristics. The optimum value lies between 0.25 and 0.35 m^3 per MT of wet residue.

Residues obtained in the drum filters are dropped on conveyor belts, which deliver them to a depot where they are conditioned for the flotation process.

3.4 Analytical Composition of the Products Obtained - Shown in Table IV.

	Overflow Neutral Thickener	Overflow Acid Thickener	Residue
Zn	120 - 130 gr/l	100 - 110 gr/l	25,0 - 26,0 %
Fe	0,001 "	0,8 - 1,0 "	28,0 - 29,0 %
Pb	0,000.03 "	—	3,0 - 4,0 %
Cu	0,050 "	0,20 - 0,30 "	0,3 %
Cd	0,12 - 0,20"	0,15 - 0,20 "	0,15 %
S-total			6,0 - 6,5 %
S-So_n			3,5 - 4,0 %
S-S=			2,5 - 3,0
Co	0,012 - 0,015 gr/l	0,010 -0,012 "	—
Ni	0,0003 - 0,0006 "	0,0005 -0,0007"	—
Ge	0,00001 - 0,000015 "	0,00002 -0,000025 gr/l	—
As	0,00003 - 0,00005 "	0,002 - 0,003 "	—
Mn	0,5 - 0,7 gr/l	0,3 - 0,5 "	—
Na	4,5 - 5,5 "	4,5 - 5,5 "	—
K	0,5 - 0,7 "	0,5 - 0,7 "	—
Mg	5,0 - 6,0 "	6,0 - 7,0 "	—
Ca	0,1 - 0,3 "	0,6 - 0,8 "	—
H_2O			38 - 40 %
SiO_2			6,0- 6,5%
CaO			0,5- 1,0%
MgO			0,2- 0,5%
Al_2O_3			0,2- 0,3%
Zn-Sulfate			3,5- 4,5%
Zn-Oxide			0,2- 0,8%
Zn-silicate			0,5- 0,7%
Zn-ferrite			12,5-13,5%
Zn-sulfide			3,5-4,5%
Fe-ferrite			23,5-24,0%
Flow capacity	1.000 - 1.200 m3.	200 - 300 m3	90-120 Tm/secas.

Table IV

4. Flotation Processing of Residues - Drum-filter residues are sent to a preconditioning tank, from which they are pumped into two 7.5 m^3 unit conditioners arranged in series.

Tail pond recovery waters are delivered into a tank, from which they are either distributed to the preconditioner and conditioners or to the leaching plant. Make-up and recovered water is regulated to achieve a 33% pulp concentration on entry to the first cell.

The collecting agent, normally potassium ethylxanthate, is added in the first conditioner. The activator, generally copper sulphate, is added on discharge from the second conditioner. Due to the excellent flotability of blende under these conditions, attention must be drawn to the fact that additional minima are necessary.

The preconditioner - conditioners circuit is designed so that it can be fed either directly from the leaching plant or from the residue stock or low-grade blendes.

The flotation circuit has 10-12 0.65 m^3 capacity cells; two of these are employed in cleaning and the rest in roughing operations.

Tails are pumped to the tailing ponds, which are rectangular, concrete-lined tanks, to recover the supernatant waters which will be reemployed in the flotation or leaching circuit.

The process is carried out in the same way as the ordinary one, while striving to maintain entrance pulp concentration and to keep plant stream capacity in the required limit.

It must be said that process waters have a zinc (as sulphate) concentration of 30-35 gr/1, when operating in a slightly acid (pH 5.0-5.5) medium. Blende has an excellent flotability.

4.1 Products Obtained - Their analyses are shown in Table V.

	Zinc Concetrate	Tailings	Water
Zn	51,50 - 52,00	23,50 - 24,00	30 - 35 gr/l
Fe	7,50 - 8,50	30,00 - 30,50	
Pb	1,50 - 2,00	3,20 - 3,70	
Cu	1,00 - 1,30	0,15 - 0,20	
Cd	0,25 - 0,35	0,10 - 0,20	
S-total	26,50 - 27,00	4,70 - 5,40	
$S-So_n^=$	0,50 - 0,70	3,80 - 4,30	
S-S =	26,00 - 26,30	0,80 - 1,00	
SiO_2	1,10 - 1,30	5,00 - 7,00	
CaO	0,20 - 0,30	0,50 - 1,00	
MgO	0,10 - 0,20	0,30 - 0,70	
Al_2O_3	0,10 - 0,20	0,10 - 0,40	
H_2O	12,00 - 15,00	55,00 - 60,00	

Table V

4.2 Processing Conditions - They are shown in Table VI.

	RESIDUES	BLENDE AND RESIDUES	BLENDE
Initial Zn %	25 - 26	33 - 33,5	38 - 38,5
Mt dry blende/Mt dry residue	—	0,6- 0,7	—
Zn % in concentrate	51,5 - 52,5	49,0-50,0	50,5- 51,0
Zn % in tails	23,5 - 24,0	23,0-24,0	13,0- 14,0
% Zn recovered/total Zn	11 - 13	56 - 58	88 - 89
% Zn recovered/Zn sulphide	65 - 75	—	—
Kgr. dry blende/initial dry Mt.	55 - 65	375 - 390	660 - 670
M^3 make-up/initial Mt.	0,7 - 0,75	0,9 - 1,0	0,9 - 1,0
M^3 of recycled water/initial dry Mt	1,5 - 1,6	1,5 - 2,0	1,8 - 2,3
M^3 leaching water/initial dry Mt.	0,25 - 0,30	—	—
Gr/l Zn in recycled water	30 - 35	15 - 20	—
Initial dry Mt/hour	3,5 - 4,5	2,5 - 4,5	1,5 - 2,5
Cell volume, M^3	0,65	0,65	0,65
Roughing cells	10	10	10
Refining boilers	10,2	10,2	1

Table VI

4.3 Economic Conditions - They are shown in Table VII, per MT dry residue.

	RESIDUES	BLENDE AND RESIDUES	BLENDE
Labour, man-hours	0,5	0,6 - 0,7	0,9 - 1,1
Potassium ethylxanthate, in Kgs	0,2	0,28	—
Speld 3456, in Kgs.	—	—	0,4 - 0,45
33% Sodium bisulphite, in Kgs.	—	0,2	1,0
Copper sulphate, in Kgs.	0,4	0,7	0,7
Tall-oil in Kgs.	0,1	0,15	0,06
Power, in Kwh.	9,0 - 10,0	12,0 - 14,0	15,0 - 20,0
Miscellaneous, in $	0,065	0,065	0,065

Table VII

5. Pyrometallurgical Processing of Residues

5.1 Materials Treated in the Plant - According to their importance, these are:

a) Normal residues from flotation processing of leaching residues.
b) Copper-cadmium residues obtained in the purification of the neutral thickener overflow.
c) First filtration residues obtained in the phase separation of an acid leach, which is a source of cadmium-enriched products.

A series of plant intermediate products are also processed. These are:

d) Lead-cadmium oxides obtained in kiln processing of the zinc-lead-cadmium oxides mixture.
e) Copper clinker, obtained as a by-product in the cadmium volatilization of the copper-cadmium residue.

Typical analyses of the materials which are processed are shown in Table VIII.

	Zn	Fe	Pb	Cu	Cd	S-total	S-So4	Cl	Sio_2	Cao	MgO	Al_2O_3
Flotation Residues	24	30	3,5	0,2	0,15	5,5	4,0	0,06	6	0,8	0,6	0,3
Cu - Cd Residues	45	2	1,5	1,8	4,1	8	6,5	0,01				
1º filtration Residues	10	0,8	50	0,01	0,6	10	8,5	0,30				
Lead-cadmium Mixed oxide	14	0,4	55	0,03	5,5	7	6,5	0,50				
Copper-Klinquer	63	1,9	1,3	3,5	0,6	1,5	1,2	—				

Table VIII

5.2 Plant Description - Normal residues are dried countercurrently from 32 - 45% to 1 - 2% water content in a 2.92 MT/hr dry residue capacity drying furnace.

This is a 14 m long and 1.85 m useful diameter rotary furnace which rotates at 3.24 rpm and has a 2° 30' slope.

Photo No. 6 - A view of the drying furnace.

The static gas exit cone, through which the mud to be dried is also fed by means of a water-cooled pipe, is situated at the rear of the furnace.

A 3.3 m^3 hopper and a swivel plate provided with a discharge regulator deliver the material to the feed pipe. In turn, the hopper is fed from tanks in which the material is brought from the flotation tailing ponds.

The waste gases are led through four 0.71 m diameter, 4 m high cyclones into the aspirating end of a 20,000 m^3 W/h, 38 HP blower, which expels them through a 20 m high chimney.

The air is heated by fuel oil combustion in the 4.05 m high, 1.1 m useful diameter burner cone.

This fuel oil burner is the atomizer type and operates at a 10 Kg/cm^2 pressure and a 110 - 140°C temperature. Maximum consumption is 265 l/hour of fuel oil.

The fuel oil heating and pressure system serves the whole plant.

Dry mud is stored in four 32 m^3 capacity hoppers. The transportation circuit to the hopper includes the following: a 5 m long, 500 mm wide mobile scraper-collector to which the mud proceeds directly from the drier; two vertical bucket elevators, which discharge into an eccentric tank equipped with two sieves of 20 mm and 4 mm mesh sizes, respectively. The intermediate product (4-20 mm) is fed into a roller mill, which grinds the material down to 3 mm size.

The product under 4 mm is sent through a 8 m long redler, which feeds it to the hoppers. Dry mud is the feed of the open-flame rotary and blast furnaces.

The open-flame rotary furnace is a cylindrical shell, pressure and volatilization furnace with cone-frustrum-shaped ends, one of which is adapted to the burner cone and the other to the mobile waste gases cone. It has a 24 MT/day dry residue capacity.

Its dimensions are as follows:

Total length .... 7 m
Useful diameter .... 2,680 mm

This cylinder is limited by two cone-frustrum-shaped elements, fitted 0.75 m from its ends with minimum diameter of 1.5 m.

Photo No. 7 - A view of the open-flame rotary furnace.

Total volume is to 33.5 m^3 and useful bath volume is 4.4 m^3. It has two rotating speeds, 0.09 and 0.45 rpm, and is provided with two diametrically opposite, 0.35 m useful diameter tapping holes.

Feed can be effected through the tapping hole either when the furnace is shut down or through a door in the burner cone and a centrifuge shuttle when it is in operation.

The first type of feed is effected after tapping and the material is stacked in the central part of the furnace; the second system permits continuous feed along the total length of the furnace.

Feed vessels are brought in place by a 10 MT capacity overhead crane equipped with a 3 MT auxiliary tilting hook.

The furnace heating system burner cone moves along two directions which are normal to each other.

The heating system is a fuel oil burner operating at 10-25 Kg/cm^2 pressure and 110 - 140°C final temperature. Maximum fuel consumption is 424 liters per hour.

The waste-gases cone is mobile and employs the same system as the burner cone. It is the linking element between the non-stationary furnace and the static heat-recovery boiler structure.

Slag-matte is tapped through one of the two holes after a 22 hour period. It is then delivered to 1 m^3 capacity ladles with tilting hooks.

The waste gases from this furnace, which contains the volatilized metals, flow through the gas cone at 850 - 950°C into the radiation chamber. The chamber is an empty space the walls and ceiling of which are formed by a 55 m^2 heating area pipe sheaf system. There is a dust-collecting hopper in the underside of the furnace.

On leaving the radiation chamber at a temperature of 700 - 800°C, the gases flow into a double pipe steam boiler. Here gas flows in the downward direction externally and in the upward direction internally.

Heat exchange area is 450 m^2 and steam generation amounts to 2.9 MT per hour at a 40 Kg/cm^2 pressure.

The metal dusts deposited as a result of velocity, temperature and directional changes are collected through a hopper door provided in the lower side of the boiler.

In order to eliminate the dust deposited inside the pipes, the furnace is provided internally with rotary steel bands. The pipes are cleaned externally with air darts which are introduced through cleaning holes.

The gases leave the boiler at 320°C. After flowing through a 600 m^2 heat exchange area heat-exchanger in countercurrent with cold air, gas temperature descends to 100 - 110°C. Hot gases flow upward inside the pipes and the cold gases, impelled by a 16,800 m^3/hr and 250 mm water-column blower, flow downward on the outside of the pipes.

These heat exchangers are periodically hand cleaned, and the dusts are collected in hoppers similar to those described above.

280 m^2 filtering area filters, fitted with automatic cleaning equipment, are arranged in series with the heat exchanger. A worm gear in the lower part of the filter delivers dust into the hoppers, which, through a cellular wheel and a telescopic pipe, discharge into dust collecting tanks similar to those described above.

Gas flow in the circuit is governed by a 16,800 m^3/h, 250 mm water column and 52 HP gas exhaustor, situated behind the filter. It can operate with 100°C temperature gases.

The gases leaving the exhaustor escape to the atmosphere through a 20 m high chimney.

A thermoelement, which actuates a flapper governing the entry of false air required to keep the temperature below 100°C, regulates the gas temperatures in the entrance to the hose filter. This thermoelement is fitted to the gas pipe.

Blast furnace processing requires the preparation of the feed, which is made up of self-melting briquettes and coke.

Briquettes are prepared as follows:

Dry residue hoppers are prolonged by three 16 m^3 hoppers containing lime, sand and coal.

The hoppers of each row discharge (Fig. 1) through a repeating faceplate, provided with a discharge regulator, on to a reversible, horizontal, 500 mm wide and 5 m long conveyor. This conveyor discharges the dry residue and additives into a rotary mixer through a cellular wheel weir.

The homogenization of the residue, fluxing agents, reducing agents and pitch is effected in this mixer.

The homogenized mixture is first discharged into a bucket elevator feeding a 2 m^3 capacity hopper which regulates feed by means of a repeating faceplate and then delivered to the kneader where the mixture is kneaded at 80°C. This temperature is attained by the injection of steam.

The kneader is a 700 mm diameter and 1470 mm high cylindrical vessel internally lined with steel plates. It has a vertical ax rotating at 25 rpm and is equipped with eight shovels which fit tightly in the cylinder. Two steam nozzles introduce 6 Kg/cm^2 steam into the mixture.

The hot material is delivered from the kneader to the briquetting press by means of a continuous belt conveyor.

The briquetting press is the roller type. The briquette mold ovoid in shape, are fitted on the rollers. Peripheral velocity 0.25 m/s and capacity is 6-7 MT briquettes per hour. It is driv by a 30 HP engine.

The briquettes discharged from the press fall on to a flat ir grate, which operates as scalping screen and then pass on to a 2 mm mesh wire-heddle continuous band conveyor which transports th to the storage hoppers. The hoppers have a 25 MT capacity and d charge the briquettes through a wire screen into suspended trip cars.

The 60 x 55 x 40 mm briquettes are ovoid in shape and weigh 170-190 grs. They are fed through the blast furnace throat; eac layer of briquettes is followed by a layer of coke.

The blast furnace is the Hellwig type. It has a 70 MT/day briquette capacity, equivalent to a 45 MT/day mud capacity.

The furnace is prism shaped. It is 1.120 mm high and has a 3.500 x 780 mm rectangular base. There is no difference whatsoever between the shaft and the well, although, up to 120 mm height, the lower part of the shaft can operate as a well.

The throat is placed laterally. It takes up all the front of the furnace and discharges in the high part of the shaft by mean of two manually-actuated waterboxes.

The gas exit, which connects the shaft with the radiation chamber, is a rectangular upper base pyramid frustrum. Two oxidizing air intakes are provided in its smaller lateral faces at a 2,170 mm distance from the bottom of the well.

To the full height of the shaft, the whole furnace front is covered by five water jackets. The smaller faces are equipped with two water jackets each. Therefore, only the shaft bottom and back wall are of refractory material.

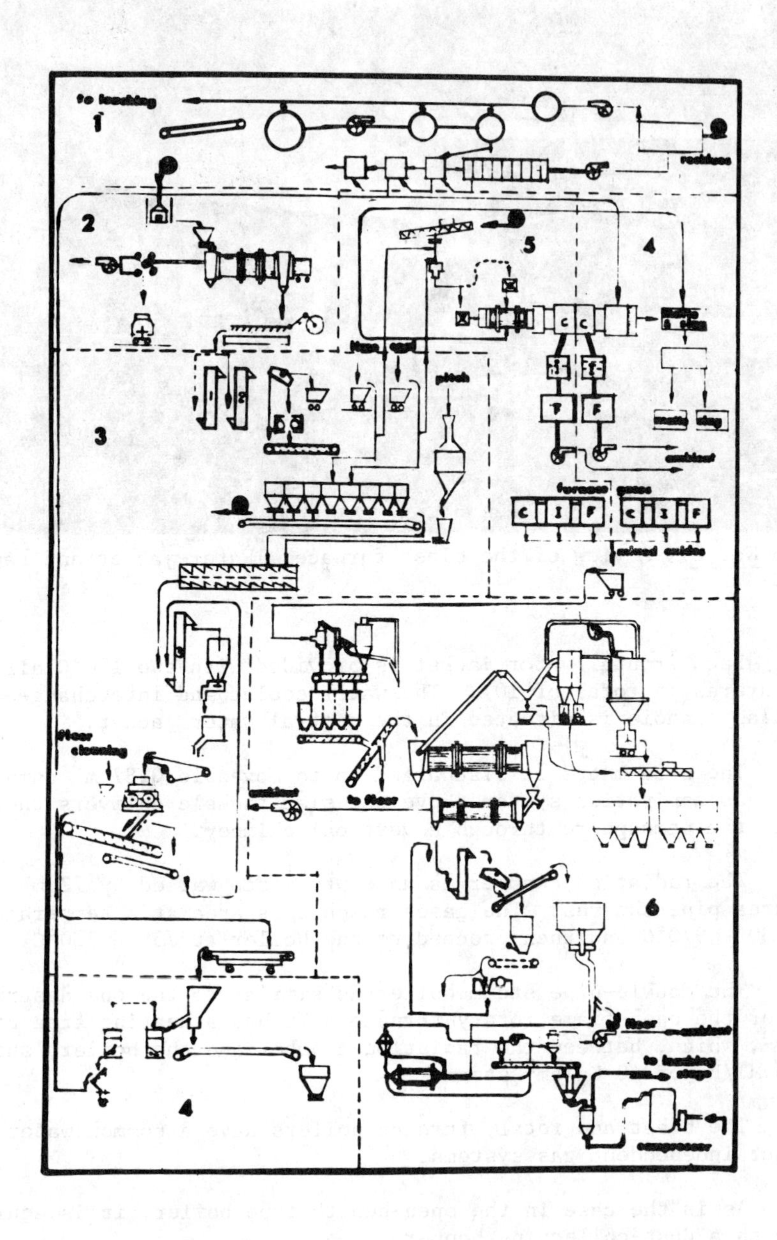

Graph No. 2 - Diagram of the residue processing plant.
1 - Flotation circuit. 2 - Drying circuit. 3 - Briquetting circuit.
4 - Shaft furnace circuit. 5 - Open-flame rotary furnace circuit.
6 - Clinker circuit. A - Tail pond residues. B - Dry residue.

Photo No. 8 - A view of the blast furnace. Water jacket and taphole zone.

Each frontal water jacket is provided with two 100°C air tuyeres (a total of 10). The water-cooled and interchangeable slag taphole is situated in the central water jacket.

The slag-matte is discharged on to moveable 0.87 m^3 dumpers. A gas aspiration system above the slag taphole delivers the gases to the atmosphere through a vertical chimney.

The radiation chamber is an empty space walled by 72 m^2 heatin area pipe sheaves. The gases reach this area at a temperature of 930 - 970°C and then proceed to the boiler at 750 - 780°C.

The double-pipe steam boiler is similar to the one described for the open-flame rotary furnace. It has a heating area of 600 m^2, which, between the radiation chamber and the boiler, supplies 5 MT/hr of 40 Kg/cm^2 steam.

The blast and rotary furnace boilers have a common water syste but independent gas systems.

As is the case in the open-hearth type boiler, it is equipped with a dust-collecting hopper.

The gases, which leave the boiler at a temperature of 320°C, are cooled to 100 - 110°C by passing through a cold-air counter-current heat exchanger. The system, constituted by three cells, has a 900 m^2 total heat-exchange area. The first cell receives the cooling airstream from a 500 mm water column, 9,000 m^3/hr blower. This air leaves the cell at 100°C and is injected through the tuyeres into the blast furnace. Airflow into the furnace is regulated manually before it reaches the air-distribution pipes.

The cooling air to cells 2 and 3 is delivered by a 16,800 m^3/hr and 250 mm water-column pressure blower. After cooling, the air escapes to the atmosphere.

The system employed in the slacking and collection of dusts is similar to the one described in the open-hearth case. It has a 336 m^2 filtering area.

An exhaustor situated behind the bag filter is responsible for gas flow in the entire circuit. It has a 40,000 m^3/hr capacity at a 250 mm water column pressure and can handle gases as hot as 100°C. It vents directly to the atmosphere.

The gas temperature regulation at the entrance to the filter system is achieved by a system similar to the one employed in the open-flame rotary furnace.

The metal oxides, which are known as mixed oxides, proceed from both furnaces and are stored in a 4-hopper system. Three of these hoppers have a 40 MT capacity (and are filled through a redler) and the fourth a 20 MT capacity.

Transportation of the mixed oxides to the storage hoppers is effected by pneumatic equipment.

The hoppers discharge on to a 7 m long horizontal chain conveyor, from which they are delivered to another 8 m long chain conveyor having a 60° inclination to horizontal. This hopper feeds the kiln through a 260 mm interior diameter, 20 mm thick and 2,170 mm long feed pipe.

The kiln is a rotary tubular furnace, 15 m long and 1,700 mm in useful diameter, inclined 2° to horizontal and rotating at a speed of 1-1.5 rpm. It has a 30 MT/day mixed oxides capacity in countercurrent operation and is provided with means to control the kiln atmosphere.

The metal-oxide laden gases leave the kiln at 700 - 850°C through an escape gas cone situated in the rear and are led to a cold air countercurrent heat exchanger to decrease the temperature to 100°C.

The heat exchanger consists of four cells totaling 300 m^2 of exchange area.

Photo No. 9 - A view of the kiln. Burner cone in the foreground.

The first two heat exchanger cells are cooled by the filtered escape gases. Once these have been reheated, they can either be introduced in the kiln to regulate its atmosphere or led off to the exterior.

The last two cells are cooled by atmospheric air provided by a 2,400 m^3/hr and 250 mm water column blower. These gases are then either employed as fuel in the furnace burner or led out to the atmosphere.

The dust collecting system is similar to that of other plants of the bay.

At a temperature of 100 - 150°C, the escape gases from the exchanger are led into a 64 m^2 filtering area bag filter, which i similar to the others existing in the plant.

Gas flow is accomplished by a 4,800 m^3/hr and 400 mm water column exhaustor. A part of these gases can be led to the heat exchanger while the rest is exhausted to the atmosphere.

Flydust from the kiln, also known as mixed lead and cadmium oxides, is collected in tanks and sent to six 50 MT capacity storage hoppers.

Heating is achieved under pressure with a manually regulated fuel-oil atomization burner. Maximum consumption is 265 l/hr.

This burner is mounted on a non-stationary burner cone, through which the solid clinkered material is discharged at temperatures ranging from 1,100 to 1,180°C.

The solids are then led to a cooling drum where their temperature is brought down to 200°C by a cold air countercurrent heat exchanger. The 1,300 mm inner diameter, 8,500 mm long drum rotates at a speed of 5 rpm with a 2.5% slope towards the discharge end.

There are seven pipes inside the drum. The solid circulates through six of these, which are distributed in a hexagonal pattern and have a 375 mm diameter. The seventh pipe, 385 mm in diameter, is situated in the cylinder axis. Air to the 7,200 m^3/hr and 200 mm water-column blower, which can operate with air temperatures of up to 250°C, is led through the open end of the front part of the cooler.

The cooling drum discharge is transferred to a bucket elevator which discharges in an eccentric tank equipped with a sieve to reject material of sizes larger than 15 mm. This material is collected in a 10 m^3 capacity hopper from which it is conveyed by a continuous belt to a 30 HP jaw crusher, which, in turn, discharges in the bucket elevator.

Sieve discharge sizes smaller than 15 mm are conveyed to two 60 MT capacity hoppers by a 500 mm wide and 10 m long continuous belt.

Fuel oil is heated in a 10 Kg/cm^2 steam heating plant and distributed to the furnace at the operating pressure by the corresponding pumps.

5.3 Normal Residue Processing in the Open-Flame Rotary Furnace - After a reducing process and a slagging fusion, the residues are submitted to volatilization. The reducing process may be reducing roasting, fusion roasting, or a combination of both.

Maximum extraction of volatile metals is aided by proper slag chemistry. These factors were considered: 1) Slags attack basic linings; 2) zinc is more soluble in ferrous than in calcium slags; 3) though lime and magnesia exert an influence on oxygen activity, they lower iron oxide activity and, consequently, diminish the amount of ferrites in slags; and 4) silica in excess of that required to form $(2R^{++})$ SiO_4-4 is completely dissociated in $(2R^{++})$ and SiO_4-4.

Since the reverberatory furnace has a magnesite lining with the object of employing it for other ends (specially in obtaining silver lead) and since the muds employed have an excess of iron and a small amount of sulfur, studies were undertaken to obtain

a calcium slag with minimum addition of silica which would contai
no zinc and have a reasonable melting point (around 1,200°C). We
were unable, however, to obtain a slag of a density very differen
from that of the matte. This is undoubtedly a disadvantage.

Since the zinc contained in the slag (26% SiO_2, 26% CaO, 22% FeO) was less than 1%, it was eventually established that, if the SiO_2: CaO = 1 ratio remained invariable, the slag composition cou be modified within the limits below. If zinc content remained be tween 0.3 and 1%, its melting point was in the neighborhood of 1,150°C.

- SiO_2 content between 22% and 30%
- CaO content between 22% and 30%
- FeO content between 20% and 29%
- Al_2O_3 content always less than 11%

The physical-chemical study of reduction reactions lead us to the conclusion that it was unnecessary to maintain the melting temperature through the whole process. Consequently, the process was divided into the two stages: volatilization without fusion o the feed, and fusion of the remaining solid into slag.

This physical-chemical study gave due consideration to the chemical combinations found in our muds as well as to Kubaschewsk Evan's thermodynamic data.

The study of the chemical combinations of our mud revealed tha 1) 60% of the copper was present as sulphide and 40% in ferrite form; 2) practically all the lead was in sulphate form; 3) cadmium was present as sulphide, sulphate and oxide in practically equal proportions; 4) all the iron present was in the form of it most oxidized compound; 5) zinc oxides accounted for more than 50% of this metal present, and according to the types of acid leach, washing and flotation, sulphide and sulphate zinc amounted to 20-30% of total zinc.

On the basis of sulphur balances, we found minimum desulphurization of the reactants. Consequently, oxidation roasting was either nonexistent or was evident in only a small proportion limited to very specific regions of the furnace. It was also established that the elimination of sulphur in the gaseous form was due either to sulphate decomposition or to the following reactions:

$$ZnS(s) + 3\ Fe_2O_3(s) = ZnO(s) + 6\ FeO + SO_2(g)$$

$$\Delta G° = 101{,}790 - 68.15T - 2.25T \log T \ (1170 - 1624°K).$$

This reaction takes place above 960°C.

$$ZnS(s) + 3ZnSO_4(s) = 4ZnO(s) + 4SO_2(g)$$

$$\Delta G° = 124{,}530 - 63.13T - 40.79T \log T + 22.44\times10^{-3}\ T^2 + 3.24\times10^5\ T^{-1} \ (298\text{-}693°K).$$

This reaction takes place inside the mass above 420°C.

Since $ZnSO_4$ is decomposed at 720°C into 3 Zn + 2 SO_3 and over 800°C into ZnO and SO_3(g)

$ZnS(s) + PbSO_4(s) = ZnO(s) + PbS(s) + SO_3(g)$

$\Delta G° = 85,190 + 29.77T - 35.40T \log T + 12.54x10^{-3}T^2 + 2.5x10^5 T^{-1}$ (1100-1170°K). This reaction takes place from 925°C on and is accelerated above 930°C due to partial volatilization of PbS and depression operation of the furnace.

$ZnS(s) + PbO(s) = ZnO(s) + PbS(s)$

$\Delta G° = -40,310 - 3.89T + 5.8T \log T$ (1150-1170°K). This reaction takes place from 930°C on with partial PbS volatilization.

$Cu_2S(s) + 2\ CuO(s) = 4\ Cu(s) + SO_2(g)$

$\Delta G° = 22,980 + 16.24T \log T - 85.23T$ (623-1300°K). This reaction takes place from 500°C on; copper metal displaces zinc, lead, iron and cadmium from their sulphides

$CdS(s) + CdSO_4(s) = 2\ Cd(g) + 2\ SO_2(g)$

$\Delta G° = 115,372 - 79.98T - 8.24T \log T + 7.16x10^{-3} T^2 + 1.42x10^5 T^{-1}$ (594-1043°K). This reaction takes place at 850°C for SO_2 concentration <5% in contact with the reactants.

$CdS(s) + 2\ CdO(s) = 3\ Cd(g) + SO_2(g)$

$\Delta G° = 89,708 - 63.16T + 0.19T \log T + 1.26x10^{-3} T^2 + 0.7x10^5 T^{-1}$ (594-1100°K). This reaction takes place at the same time as the previous one.

$PbS(s) + PbSO_4(s) = 2\ Pb(l) + 2SO_2(g)$

$\Delta G° = 169,330 - 45.38T + 32.25T \log T - 12.54x10^{-3} T^2 - 2.5x 10^5 T^{-1}$ (600-1140°K) which takes place from 1030°C on. However, above 930°C PbS is volatilized and at 1,090°C lead sulphate liquefies and liquid lead is obtained. The latter starts to vaporize at 1,130°C and the gases contain PbS(g) and Pb(g). Above 1,160°C the liquid lead sulphate begins to decompose, according to the equation:

$$PbSO_4(l) = PbO(s) + SO_3(g)$$

Therefore, if a temperature over 960°C is maintained in the open-flame rotary furnace in a non-reducing atmosphere, the mud metal components are present as zinc oxide, ferrous and ferric oxide, copper sulfide and lead sulfide, while part of the lead sulfide and most of the cadmium are volatilized.

If M is any metal whatsoever, the reactions which interest us are the following:

$$MO + C = M + CO(g) \qquad MO + CO(g) = M + CO_2(g)$$
$$C(s) + CO_2(g) = 2CO(g) \qquad MSO_4 + 4C = MS + 4CO(g)$$
$$MSO_4 + 4CO = MS + 4CO_2$$

The main reactions are:

a) $ZnO(s) + C(s) = Zn(g) + CO(g)$

$\Delta G° = 88,720 + 10.35T \log T - 103.33T$ (1170-2000°K)

b) $ZnO(s) + CO(g) = Zn(g) + CO_2(g)$
$\Delta G° = 47,920 + 10.35T \log^2 T - 61.63T$ (1170-2000°K)

c) $C(s) + CO_2(g) = 2\,CO(g)$
$\Delta G° = 40,800 - 41.7T$ (298-2000°K)

The study of these reactions reveals that b) is the slowest and that, consequently, from 820°C on it limits the velocity of the general reaction:

d) $(X + 2Y)\,ZnO(g) + (X + Y)\,C(s) = (X + 2Y)\,Zn(g) + X\,CO(g) + Y\,CO_2(g)$

As in any other metallurgical process, we have to establish the minimum temperature required for continuous operation, the influence that exit gas composition exerts on this temperature and, considering that we are dealing with a volatilization process, the minimum metal content that the gases must have for profitable operation.

The above considerations imply the determination of both zinc vapor pressure, in terms of temperature and pressure, and minimu CO and CO_2 contents that the continuity of the reaction requires according to b), assuming that the atmosphere in which the react takes place is adequate.

If p is the total pressure of exit gases in this medium,

$P_{Zn} = -K + \sqrt{K(P + K)}$ where K is established by the equation $\Delta G° = 4.574T \log K$.

These data afford us the opportunity to trace the zinc vapor pressure and dew point curves. Furthermore, as the air concentr tion in the gases must be in excess of 5% if zinc extraction is be economically profitable, the reduction temperature is subject to this limitation; for p = 1 atmosphere, temperature = 880°C.

If pressures prevailing in escape gases (as well as in the - reacting atmosphere) are low, the reducing temperatures obtained compel us to bear equation a) in mind, considering that it gover the process. In this case, zinc vapor pressure would be:

$$P_{Zn} = 1/4\,(P - 3K + \sqrt{P^2 + 10PK + 9K^2})$$

Although this equation has no lower limit due to the zinc con tent in gases, it does have in terms of its condensation when th metal's dew point is surpassed. This allows us to establish the minimum operating temperature necessary to obviate any zinc condensation and which, for P = 1 atm, is equal to 900°C.

The above confirms Maier's findings that the general zinc reduction reaction is fulfilled, with an adequate yield, between 835° and 1250°C.

On the other hand, the vapor pressure of lead oxide at 1027°C is equal to 0.01 atmosphere. When we operate in the 960 - 1050°C range all the above mentioned reactions are fulfilled thus promoting the volatilization of zinc and cadmium in metal form. The same is true of the following compounds: lead sulphide, lead oxide, germanium sulphide, metal chlorides, metal fluorides and metal arsenides.

Consequently, operating conditions are the following:

A 960 - 1050°C volatilization period with a 10,000 - 12,000 m^3/hr escape gas stream.

A 1,050 - 1,200°C melting period with a $<$10,000 m^3/hr escape gas stream.

The zinc, lead and cadmium extraction yields are, respectively, 95%, 98% and 99%. Attempts to separate slag from matte were unsuccessful.

The gas stream during the volatilization period permits atmospheric air to rise to the radiation chamber. This air, which oxidizes metal vapors, is introduced between the furnace and the radiation chamber, thus keeping the CO + H_2 escape gas content under 0.5% and the CO_2 content under 8% of total volume.

Mixed oxides obtained account for 36% to 40% of mud weight. Their average content is: 60-66% Zn; 7-10% Pb; 0.3-0.5% Cd; 1-2% S; 0.1-0.5% Cl; 0.7-1% Fe; 1.000-1.500 gr/MT In, and 15 gr/MT Tl.

Slag-matte obtained accounts for 54-56% of mud weight. Average content is: 2% Zn; 13-15% SiO_2; 13-15% CaO; 55-60% Fe; 3% Al_2O_3; 0.5% Cu; 10-13% S; 60-100 g/MT In; 10-20 gr/MT Tl.

Daily analyses of the slag corroborate the persistence of the previously indicated values. Hand selected matte has a zinc content under 3%, a copper content under 1.1% and a sulfur content under 24%.

The reducing agent employed is anthracite coal which is added in an amount equivalent to 17-22% of total mud. Slaked lime, which is the fluxing agent, is added in an amount equivalent to 11-13% of mud weight.

With this operating procedure, we have succeeded in extending the life of the magnesite lining to 18-25 months, although a thorough repair of the entrance cone is required. We believe that this deterioration of the cone is due to the sulphur and vanadium content of the fuel oil employed and to the imperfect combustion.

Table IX shows the specific consumptions in the volatilization of a ton of dry mud in the reverberatory furnace, including dryin expenses, on the basis of a 70 MT/day dry mud production, with a yield of 67-86% in drying operations.

5.4 Normal Residue Blast Furnace Processing - Blast furnace meta volatilization is governed by the same premises as reverberatory furnace operation, although, in our opinion, carbon is responsibl for ferric oxide reduction. However, in this case slag compositi is different to assure continuous tapping despite well temperatur differences. The slag zinc content ranges from 1.5 to 2.5%, whil the variations recorded by the other components are the following

SiO_2, 32% to 36%
CaO, 22% to 24%
FeO, 24% to 32%
Al_2O_3 < 10%

This furnace is fed with selfmelting briquettes and coke in sizes over 60 mm and in an amount equivalent to 20-32% of the mud contained in the briquettes; in other words, equivalent to 13-15% of the briquette weight. Briquettes and coke are added in alternate layers. Each briquette feed batch weighs from 1,800 to 2,000 Kg.

With temperatures of 1,160-1,200°C in the well and 900-970°C in the upper part of the radiation chamber, slag-matte tapping is continuous.

Coke combustion air is injected through the tuyeres. The 5,00 to 6,000 m^3/hr airstream is equivalent to 1,715-2,060 m^3N/MT of briquettes, at temperatures over 100°C and a 220-300 mm W.C. pres sure. The air required for the oxidation of metal gases is introduced through the two lateral furnace windows in the proportio required for operation with a 12,000-15,000 m^3N/h escape gas stream and with CO_2 and ($CO + H_2$) concentrations of < 12% (generally 7-10%) and < 1.5% respectively.

The following materials are employed in briquette preparation: 20-22% fine coke, which is employed as a reducing agent in < 0.5 mm sizes; 11-12% 80°C maximum melting point pitch; and 8-9% slaked lime in < 0.1 mm sizes. Percentages are estimated on a dry mud basis.

Mixed oxides obtained account for 30-35% of mud weight. Their grade is similar to that of reverberatory furnace mixed oxides.

The slag-matte obtained amounts to 60-62% of total mud weight. The average content is the following: < 3% Zn; 18-21% SiO_2; 10-12% CaO; 50-55% FeO; < 4% Al_2O_3; < 0.5% Cu; 10-12% S; 60-100 gr/MT In; and 10-20 gr/MT Tl.

Slag obtained is analyzed daily and shows that the above mentioned limiting values undergo no variations whatsoever. The analysis of hand selected matte reveals that it contains zinc, copper and sulfur in the following proportions: < 3.3%, < 1% and < 2.4%.

Specific consumptions in the volatilization of a ton of dry muds in a semi-blast furnace are shown in Table IX. Drying costs are included.

	OPEN FLAME ROTATORY FURNACE	BLAST FURNACE	KILN
Fuel consumption Kg/processed unit	245	50	93
Coal	193	—	18
Lump coke	—	216	—
Fine coke	—	205	—
Pitch	—	114	—
Lime	120	85	—
Sand	—	31	—
Powe in Kw/processed Unit	62	75	117
Men-hours/processed Unit	8,2	7,3	3,2
Lining substitution/processed Unit in $.	1,3	0,5	0,5
Other $ expenditures/processed Unit	5,0	3	1,6
Daily capacity) MT dry mud ( ) MT mixed oxides	24	45	—
Operating days/year	320	292	30 265
% Zinc Yield	95	82	91
% Lead Yield	98	90	65
% Cadmium yield	99	92	90

Table IX

5.5 Kiln Processing of Mixed Oxides - The object of mixed clinkerization is the elimination of the lead and cadmium metals from the mixed oxide in order to obtain a product (clinker) containing 69-71% Zn, 1-3.5% Pb, less than 0.06% cadmium and flydusts (lead-cadmium oxides) containing 55-60% lead, 4.5-5% cadmium, 15-20% zinc and 6.5-8.5% sulfur.

Mixed oxides are fed to the kiln after addition of anthracite, the proportion of which should never exceed 2%. The anthracite i the reducing agent. The kiln temperature is between 1,050-1,100° in the discharge hole and between 800°C and 850°C in the charge hole. The CO_2 + 1/2 (CO + H_2) content of the kiln atmosphere mus be between 12% and 15%.

Under these conditions, after reduction, the total cadmium contained in the mixed oxides as well as sulphide and oxide lead are volatilized.

The kiln is lined with corindon in the high temperature zone and with sicromal (refractory steel) in the discharge hole zone.

Specific consumptions required by the volatilization of a ton of mixed oxides in the kiln are shown in Table IX.

5.6 Cadmium-Copper Residue Processing

5.6.1 Kiln Processing - The precipitation residue must be air-dried for a 45 day period and subsequently ground so tha 90% is smaller than 2 mm. If its moisture content is greate than 7%, a preliminary drying in the drying furnace is mandatory.

Under these conditions, the residue is processed in the kiln in order to volatilize the cadmium metal, either by simple volatilization of the metal or after submitting the oxide to a reduction process. The addition of anthracite must not be in excess of 8% of cement weight.

Both cement metal cadmium and carbon reduced cadmium oxide generate flydusts (cadmium oxides) which have cadmium contents amounting to 11-21% of their weight. Zinc metal is also carried along by these fumes.

The solid product called copper clinker discharges from the kiln and contains all the feed copper. Its analysis follows: % Cu > 2.5, % Zn > 60, % Pb < 0.8, % Cd < 0.3.

Since the decomposition of zinc sulphate starts at 800°C, if kiln temperatures are higher, escape gases will contain sulphurous anhydride. However, since the zinc metal vapor reacts with SO_2 rather than with oxygen at temperatures unde 1,270°C, all the volatilized sulfur is collected in the dust unless we effect a differential condensation at 600°C with escape gases retention. This is exactly what we propose to do in 2/3 of the furnace.

It must be also borne in mind that, at 800°C, of all the metal oxides and metals contained in the charge, only the zinc and cadmium metals can be vaporized and only lead and zinc are present in the molten state. These metals can, therefore, behave as binding cements of clinkered oxides (copper clinker).

Furthermore, under 730°C the stable oxidized form of carbon is carbon dioxide, and at 550°C, the vapor tension of zinc metal is sufficient to attain a 1% concentration (by volume) in the escape gases. On the other hand, the cadmium metal concentration is to 8%.

In view of the above, precipitation cement processing is carried out with kiln temperatures of 800 - 950°C in the discharge zone and 550° - 600°C in the feed zone. At the same time, CO_2 concentration in the escape gases is held between 15 and 20% with the object of oxidizing zinc vapor in conformity with:

$$Zn(g) + CO_2(g) = ZnO(s) + CO(g)$$

equation. This reaction takes place at temperatures in excess of 550°C.

In order to attain this CO_2 content, the greater part of the escape gases are recycled to the kiln.

Precipitation cement is fed at a 1-1.1 MT/hr rate, equivalent to 24-26.4 MT/day. This rate is sustained during a 7-8 day period, which is equivalent to a production of 200 MT. If operation is extended beyond this period, a compact copper clinker ring is formed on the inside of the furnace in the neighborhood of the discharge zone (3-5 meters). This clinker consists of nut-sized solids which are bound together by molten lead and zinc metal. This clinker is eventually oxidized giving birth to this compact structure which, as it grows in size, progressively narrows the free section of the kiln, preventing its normal operation.

Cadmium oxides obtained in the condensation of the metal vapors in the escape gases are used as cadmium feed in the electrolytic plant which exists in our factory.

The following yields are obtained in this process:

Zinc: 87% of which 50% reports in copper clinker and 37% in cadmium oxides.

Higher yields are not obtained because this process is a part of a mixed oxides processes and a proportion of copper clinker is always retained in the kiln.

Lead: 95% in cadmium oxides, in which it is mostly prese as lead sulphate.

Cadmium: > 95% in cadmium oxides, in which it is mostly present as oxide.

5.6.2 Copper Clinker Processing in the Open-Flame Rotary Furnace - The copper clinker obtained by the above procedure contains zinc, iron, lead, nickel and cobalt oxides and zinc sulphate. Consequently, it could be processed directly in the leaching section. Although copper clinker is easily soluble, processing would increase the nickel and cobalt contents in the electrolyte to such an extent that the manufacturing process would be subordinate to the purification of these metals.

In view of this, copper clinker is processed in the reverberatory furnace to volatilize the zinc, cadmium and lead metals. These are later oxidized and recovered as oxides in the dusts.

The process consists of reduction followed by volatilization. This volatilization is followed by a slagging fusion leading to the recovery of copper matte with a copper conten of over 16% and of a low melting-point slag containing less than 2% zinc. This slag is incapable of attacking the furna magnesite lining.

The composition of the flydusts obtained is the same as that of the mixed oxides. They, therefore, receive the same designation.

Slagging must be carried out for these reasons: the type of reducing agent (anthracite) employed and the utilization of calamine residues, containing 15% zinc and 6% lead, obtained in the selective leaching phase separation of a roasted calamine.

Since zinc in zinc-sulphide is displaced by copper when the temperature is over 1,100°C and zinc oxide has a greater tendency to combine with free silica then to undergo reduction, the feed must contain no free silica at all. Consequently, copper clinker is mixed with lime so that CaO can react with the silica before the silica has a chance to rea with zinc oxide, thus preventing zinc carry-over to the sla

In view of this, the temperature of the process is held between 1,150°C and 1,180°C. 30% of the sulphur in the fee is volatilized.

After being ground to a size smaller than 1 mm, copper clinker is processed at the rate of 1 MT/hr. Calamine muds, anthracite and slaked lime are fed to the kiln once the volatilization period of the previous batch has ended and 30 minutes before melting sets in. Generally speaking, each melting period corresponds to the processing of 40 MT of copper clinker.

The following products are obtained: mixed oxides amounting to 83% of copper clinker weight; a matte containing 17-27% copper and less than 6% zinc; and a slag containing less than 2% zinc, 26-30% silica, 26-30% CaO and 10-14% FeO.

The zinc extraction is 95% of the metal present in the metal oxides. In turn, these contain 71-74% of total Zn, more than 5% of total lead and 2% of total cadmium.

In the case of matte, the copper extraction is 90%.

5.7 <u>Silver Lead Recovery from Lead-Cadmium Oxides and First Filtration Residues</u> - Lead oxides and first-filtration muds have a similar composition except for their cadmium contents. In both, lead is present in the sulphate, oxide and sulphide forms. In both, the lead sulphate content is greater than that of the oxide, while the content of the oxide is greater than that of the lead sulphide.

The procedure followed in silver lead recovery is the following:

I) Reduction and volatilization of cadmium metal, in which a flydust (cadmium dust) with a cadmium content over 12% and a zinc content under 35% is obtained.

II) Recovery of silver lead from the lead compounds present in the feed.

III) Silver lead casting.

IV) Reduction and volatilization of zinc metal and production of a slag containing less than 2% of lead and less than 25% of zinc.

V) Slag casting with melting ladle tapping in order to recover the molten lead retained by the slag.

The physical-chemical reactions which permit the use of this procedure and the establishment of process temperatures are the following:

$PbSO_4 + 2C = PbS + 2CO_2(g)$ which takes place at temperatures over 830
$ZnSO_4 = ZnO + SO_3(g)$ " " " " " 800
$PbO + 1/3ZnS = Pb(l) + 1/3ZnO + 1/3SO_2(g)$ " " " " " 840
$2PbO + C = 2Pb(l) + CO_2(g)$ " " " " " 600
$2CdO + C = 2Cd(g) + CO_2(g)$ " " " " " 600
$PbS + Na_2O = Na_2S + PbO$ " " " " under 900
$ZnS + Na_2O = Na_2S + ZnO$ " " " " " 900

Therefore, in the presence of carbon and sodium oxide, the reduction and volatilization of cadmium and the recovery of molte lead can be achieved at temperatures over 840°C.

Considering that above 920°C the vapor pressure of lead sulphide is sufficient for the volatilization to take place, this temperature should not be exceeded to prevent or, at least, to reduce this volatilization to a minimum.

Consequently, in the case of the three first operations, the kiln temperature should never exceed the 840 - 920°C range.

The operations resulting in the recovery of lead by roast-reaction are the following:

$PbS + PbSO_4 = 2Pb(l) + 2SO_2(g)$ which takes place from 1,030°C on
$PbS + 2PbO = 3Pb(l) + SO_2(g)$ " " " " 1,050°C on

As zinc oxide reduction takes place at temperatures over 935°C the operating kiln temperature should be kept between 1,050°C and 1,150°C.

During processing, therefore, the kiln temperature is set between 840°C and 920°C for a 3 hour period. Next, lead, which is the only molten material present in the furnace, is tapped. The operating temperature is then raised to 1,050 - 1,150°C and the slag is tapped and collected in melting kettles. This slag is left quiescent for one hour and the lead that settles is tapped through the bottom.

1 MT of lead oxides per hour or 0.6 MT of lead oxides with 0.4 MT of first filtration muds are processed.

The weight of anthracite reducing agent and sodium carbonate added are 15-17% and 6-8% of the lead oxide weight respectively.

This operating procedure results in lead extraction yields of 85-93% from the silver lead obtained, which, furthermore, contain 430-560 grams of silver per ton.

The cadmium extraction yield from cadmium dusts is 85-90% and that of zinc from these same dusts is 40-65%.

With this procedure tin, silver and lead are eliminated from the general electrolytic zinc manufacturing circuit. More than 60% of arsenic, antimony and indium are also eliminated.

6. Annex. Analytical Methods Employed - The following are the analytical methods employed:

Zinc is determined by ferrocyanometry by St. Urbach's method (1) or by polarography in an ammonium chloride-ammonia medium (2); lead, copper and cadmium are next analyzed at the same time. If the expected contents are less than 10%, atomic absorption analysis (3) is resorted to and, if necessary, the joint analysis of copper, cadmium, lead, iron, silica and calcium oxides, magnesium, aluminum, sodium and potassium is undertaken. In leaches zinc is analyzed complexiometrically with EDTA and eriochrome T black.

Both total sulfur and sulphate are analyzed, as sulphate, by gravimetric methods. The attack on the sulfur is carried out by the Lunge method (1) and on sulphate by carbonate leaching (1).

Combined forms of zinc in roasted products and residues are determined by the "Cerro de Pasco" method (4). We have slightly modified the last part of this method, resorting to atomic absorption in the determination of iron and zinc in the different stages. Oxide is the exception, for after extraction with Musspratt solution, this compound is easily determined by ferrocyanometric or polarographic techniques.

Acid soluble zinc is analyzed by the Anaconda method.

Arsenic control in solids is based on conventional distillation of the trichloride and eventual iodometric evaluation (1).

Germanium is determined by polarography in a buffered alkaline medium, once the metal as tetrachloride has been separated by distillation.

In the solids, silver, cobalt, nickel, indium and thallium are determined by atomic absorption, (6), (7) and (8).

In leaches, zinc, copper, nickel, iron, cobalt, lead, magnesium, calcium, sodium, potassium, thallium and chlorine (9) are determined by atomic absorption.

Arsenic and antimony contained in leaches are analyzed colourimetrically with silver diethyl-dithiocarbamate, once the separation of arsine and stibine has been accomplished. (10).

Magnesium, as permanganate, is analyzed colourimetrically, after persulphate oxidation (1).

Germanium is analyzed colourimetrically with phenyl-fluorine; this is the method employed in Crotone (11).

1. Analisis de metales - Metodos de control industrial - Comisión de Quimicos de la Sociedad de Mineros y Metalurgicos alemanes.
2. D. Juan Garcia - Revista de Metalurgia. Vol 2, No. 3, 283-285, 1966.
3. Idem - Inform. Quim. Anal. Vol. 23, No. 6, 169-184, 1969.
4. Cerro de Pasco Corp. - Research Department - Private Paper.
5. D. Juan Garcia - Revista de Metalurgia. Vol. 3, No. 2, 174-180, 1967.
6. Idem - Inform. Quim. Anal. Vol. 23, No. 5, 132-138, 1969.
7. Idem - Pendiente de publicar. Publication pending.
8. Idem - Idem
9. Idem - Idem
10. E. Merck A. G. - Spürenanalyse and Reactivos orgánicos para el Análisis inorgánico.
11. S.M.M. de Pertusola - Private Paper.

Chapter 14

PROCESSING OF ZINC- AND LEAD-BEARING RESIDUES IN THE HALF-SHAFT FURNACE PROCESS BY PREUSSAG AG METALL

Oker, West Germany

Herbert Dumont
Hüttenwerk Harz
Preussag AG Metall, Goslar

Erich A. Müller
Humboldt Division
Klöckner-Humboldt-Deutz AG, Cologne

Abstract

Since 1947 Preussag AG Metall has used a process for fuming zinc- and lead-containing dump slags and residues from vertical retorts in a half-shaft furnace at their Hüttenwerk Harz at Oker. Contrary to the classic shaft furnace, only one side of the half-shaft furnace is fitted with tuyeres. The opposite side is a bricked slope. The upper shaft section is piped. There zinc vapor and combustion gases are burned by sucked-in air. Gases and fume enter a boiler located on the rear length of the furnace via a piped fire bridge. The gases are then cooled in an air preheater prior to dedusting in a bag filter.

The furnace is charged with briquettes of metal-bearing materials, coal and pitch. The leaded zinc oxide fume is comparatively rich in both lead and zinc. The copper in the feed is recovered in low-copper matte. The slag can be discarded.

The Oker plant comprises 13 furnaces of 2.9 to 4.9 m length in the tuyere area.

Two other plants in Italy and Spain are processing zinc leach residues by this technique.

Fuming of zinc-lead-oxide ores as well as partially roasted sulfide-zinc-lead-copper bulk concentrates will be possible.

Problems

As long as the extraction of zinc is performed on a commercial sca procedures must be available for recovering zinc from residues and sl which are obtained in various metal extraction processes. The normal high zinc content of residues or slags obtained when extracting zinc lead and sometimes copper, especially from complex starting materials provides incentive to develop such processes. Starting materials and intermediate products which are either technically impractical or un-economical to concentrate by mineral dressing procedures or direct pr cessing to metal will also be considered.

When dealing with these problems, the behavior of the accompanying lead, copper, and precious metals cannot be overlooked. The chemical metallurgical behavior of these metals presents difficulties when sim taneous extraction, separation, or concentration is desired.

The Half-Shaft Furnace Process

With few exceptions, which depend on local conditions or limited applications, large-scale techniques for treating residues and slags can all be described by the same basic chemical reactions. These re-actions are reduction of zinc compounds contained in residues, prefer ably by carbon monoxide, and generation of carbon monoxide from carbo dioxide and added carbon.

Due to the temperature required, zinc escapes as a vapor from the solid and liquid material. Oxidation of the volatilized zinc leads t a satisfactory separation of the zinc from the non-volatile constitu-ents of the starting material. The concentration which can be theore cally attained corresponds to the stoichiometric zinc percentage in zinc oxide. Practically, however, this concentration is limited by other constituents such as lead which volatilizes and also by mechani cally carried-over charge constituents.

Apart from some soda processes, liquid phases are generally found in only those portions which are absorbed from the residue. This is why a copper matte cannot be obtained from such volatilization pro-cesses. This disadvantage caused us to modify and further develop various zinc volatilization processes so that the copper and preciou metals, which are often found in the feed materials, can be concen-trated in a matte. The blast furnaces for zinc volatilization at Ha zer Hüttenwerke are examples of this type of development. Since 190 zinc-bearing slags from lead smelters have been blown to recover zin oxide at the Oker Works. Some of these slags have come from century-old waste dumps. Since 1945, carbonaceous residues from the company vertical retort zinc smelter at Harlingerode have also been treated. The primary materials processed by the Harz Smelters are concentrate from Harz lead and zinc ore mining but for many years were exclusive the complex, difficult-to-upgrade ores from the Rammelsberg mine at Goslar.

In 1909 a blast furnace was introduced at Oker. This furnace, proposed by Pape, could not be regarded as a shaft furnace because it still contained a grate (Fig. 1). Its charging height of 60 cm, however, was larger than the existing grate blast furnaces. The furnace chamber was a brick shaft 1.4 m wide, 2 m long, and 1.45 m high. Below the shaft was a water-cooled grate 0.7 m wide and 1.10 m long. This grate contained three 50 mm wide free slots through which blast air was originally introduced. However, since 1912 the air has been injected at a pressure of 200 to 700 mm WG. The zinc-bearing feed materials were briquetted with 16% fine coke and then charged with 6% coarse coke to the furnace. Waste gases were burned in a 6 m long channel by sucked-in secondary air. The flue dust was then separated from the waste gases. The waste gases were cooled from 800-900°C down to 280-300°C in a waste-heat boiler. The molten dezinced residues dripped through the grate into crucibles, thus providing a continuous mode of operation. Due to the quick solidification of the molten product, however, a separation into matte and slag was impossible. The capacity of the furnaces was 10 tons of lead blast furnace slag briquettes per 24 hours. Zinc removal was satisfactory, and a high grade oxide was produced. This oxide had the properties required by the pigment industry.

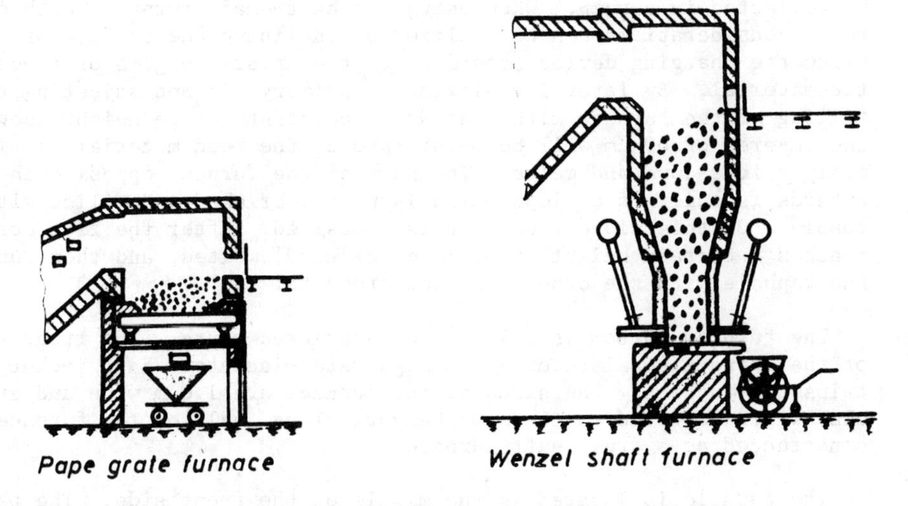

Fig. 1 Types of fuming furnaces formerly used at Oker

Since 1930 an improved blast furnace, proposed by Wenzel, has operated at Oker. This furnace can be classified as a real shaft furnace. The shaft was rectangular in cross section with these dimensions: 0.7 x 1.64 m in the tuyere area, and 1.1 x 2.2 m in the upper part of the shaft. The shaft itself was 1.6 m high. The water-jacketed crucible contained the tuyeres. Air blast pressure ranged from 400-600 mm WG. This furnace had a sump from which matte and slag were continuously tapped; separation of the matte and slag took place in the crucible. Due to the comparatively high charge column, the demand for secondary air was greater in this furnace thar in the Pape furnaces. Because of the high percentages of unburned charge components, the oxides were not suitable for use in the pigment industry. A blast furnace of this type processed 24 tons of lea blast furnace slag per hour contained in 36 tons of briquettes. Coar coke, amounting to 13-14% of the weight of slag to be dezinced, was necessary for proper furnace operation.

With the aims of producing a pigment grade oxide as well as recover ing copper and precious metals in matte, a furnace, proposed by H. & Hellwig, was developed in 1946. This furnace was a combination of bc of the previously described furnaces and had the advantages of both. This furnace has become known as the half-shaft furnace (Fig. 2).

The above aims demand a lower charge height and allow operation without a grate by blowing in primary air laterally so the melt can be collected in a sump. When using the half-shaft furnace, both of these considerations can be realized by inclining the surface of the briquette charging device according to the natural angles of repose c the material. By laterally blowing in primary air and adjusting the filling of the furnace with a slide, a constant charge height above the tuyeres of 60 cm will be maintained as the feed material continuously slides down and melts. The part of the furnace opposite the tuyeres is built as a slope which is partly bricked and filled with rubble. On this slope flue dust is deposited. After the flue dust reaches a certain height it will be dezinced, melted, and then run tc the taphole with the other dezinced products.

The furnace bottom is a 100 mm deep bricked chute. The front side of the furnace consists of 1.0 m high water-jackets. Each jacket cor tains two tuyeres. The sides of the furnace are 1.0 m wide and are also water-jacketed to the same height. Thus, half of the furnace is constructed as a true shaft furnace.

The taphole is located in the middle of the front side. The tapp arrangement is constructed as a siphon. The lower part of the mater inlet chute and the part of the wall between the chute and the water-jackets are also water cooled. The total internal height of the shaf above the tuyere area is 8-11 m. The gases containing carbon monoxi and zinc vapor are burned in the upper part of the shaft by secondar air which is sucked in through openings on the short sides of the shaft. The upper part of the shaft walls and the channel which

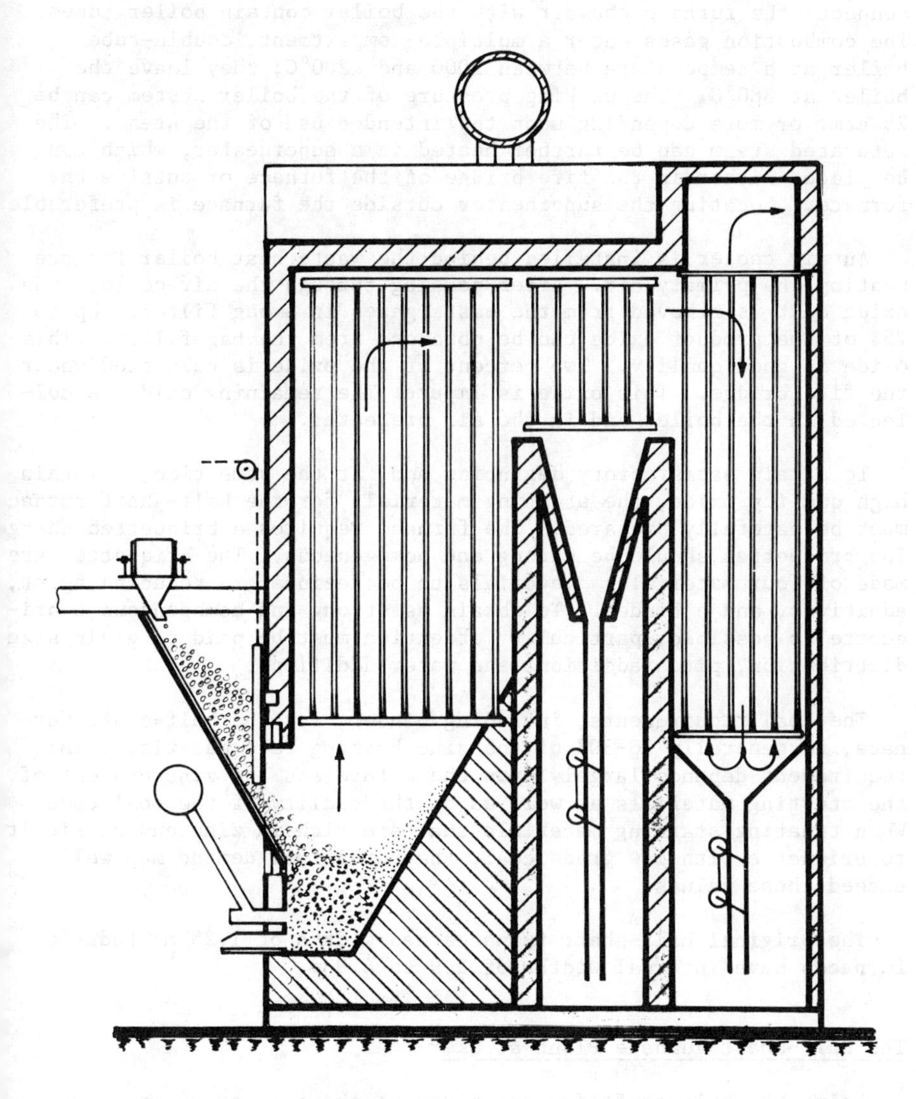

Fig.2 Half-shaft furnace

connects the furnace chamber with the boiler contain boiler tubes. The combustion gases enter a multiple-compartment, double-tube boiler at a temperature between 1000 and 1200°C; they leave the boiler at 380°C. The working pressure of the boiler system can be 25 atm. or more depending upon the intended use of the steam. The saturated steam can be further heated in a superheater, which can be placed either in the fire bridge of the furnace or outside the furnace. Locating the superheater outside the furnace is preferable

An air cooler is installed behind the waste heat boiler for preheating the primary air. After passing through the air cooler, the oxide dust is removed from the waste gases in a bag filter. Up to 75% of the product oxide can be obtained from the bag filter. This oxide is good quality. Two percent of the oxide is collected under the fire bridge. This oxide is impure. The remaining oxide is collected in the boiler and in the air preheater.

To attain satisfactory dezincing and, at the same time, maintain high quality oxide, the starting materials for the half-shaft furnace must be carefully prepared. The furnace requires a briquetted charge. The briquettes should be strong and homogeneous. The briquettes are made of four materials: materials to be dezinced, a reducing agent, additives, and a binder. To obtain as strong and homogeneous a briquette as possible, particular attention must be paid to grain size distribution, pitch additions and water additions.

The coal requirements, including binder, for the half-shaft furnace, is generally 20-30% of the zinc-bearing feed material. This requirement depends largely upon the nature and the zinc content of the starting materials as well as on the quality of the coal used. When treating starting materials that are rich in zinc and difficult to briquette with low grade coal, the total fuel demand may well exceed these values.

The original half-shaft furnaces had widths of 1.25 m; today's furnaces have internal widths of 2.9 to 4.9 m.

The Half-Shaft Furnace Plant at Oker

Using the half-shaft furnace plant at the zinc oxide works at Harz (the largest and oldest half-shaft furnace plant) as an example we wish to describe a plant which has proved suitable for processing zinc- and lead-containing slags and vertical retort residue. The physical natures of these starting materials differ considerably. They are characterized by notably different moisture contents, grain size, and hardness. When delivered, the slags have a maximum moistu content of about 7%; retort residues come in at approximately 34% moisture. The slags, mostly from dumps, have a lump size of about 100 mm, since only a small part of them were granulated. The portic of slags smaller than 4 mm is about 45%. Normally, retort residues also have a maximum size of about 100 mm although older dump stocks sometimes contain considerably larger agglomerates. Generally the portion of fines under 2 mm is about 23%.

Due to these differing physical characteristics, preparation procedures have been developed for each starting material (Fig. 3).

The raw materials arrive by truck or rail and are partly stocked in the open air. By using grab cranes a mixture of various types of slags and another mixture of retort residue, zinc concentrate, sand and coal are proportioned in railroad cars. These premixtures are stored in bunkers and then treated separately.

The mixture of retort residues is dried in two stages. In the first stage the residues are dried to a moisture content of approximately 17% in a uniflow rotary drier heated with heavy oil. The drier has an inside diameter of 2 m and an overall length of 10 m. The discharge material is crushed in a hammer mill to sizes less than 4 mm and then conveyed to the second drying stage. Second-stage drying is accomplished in an indirectly steam-heated, multiple-hearth furnace. The material, with a final moisture content of about 13%, is volumetrically apportioned into a screw feeder.

The slag mixture is precrushed in a jaw crusher to a size less than 30 mm and then ground in a flue-gas-heated Humboldt-type screening ball mill to a size less than 4 mm. The slag is simultaneously dried to a moisture content of 3 to 4%. The ground slag is then apportioned to the screw feeder together with the fines portion of the precrushed material.

The pitch is stored in a ground storage bin, precrushed in a hammer crusher, and conveyed into a hammer mill by means of a belt weightmeter, which discharges directly into the screw feeder.

Fig. 4 shows the grain size distribution of such a mixture.

Breeze from briquetting and briquette handling is recycled to the screw feeder also.

The mixture passes from a feed bin into a vertical kneader where it is homogenized and precompacted. In the kneader the mixture is heated to 90°C by passing in 250°C steam to soften the pitch. From the kneader the hot mixture passes to a roll press where cushion-shaped briquettes that weigh approximately 400 g and have the dimensions 100 x 50 x 40 mm are formed. The briquettes are then transported to a half-shaft furnace plant by a monorail overhead trolley conveyor. When the briquettes are fed to the furnace, their moisture content is about 5-8%.

To separate briquettes from the furnace charge, the inclined bottom of the furnace chute is constructed as a grizzly with a 10 mm slot width. The briquettes are collected in a bin pocket below the grizzly.

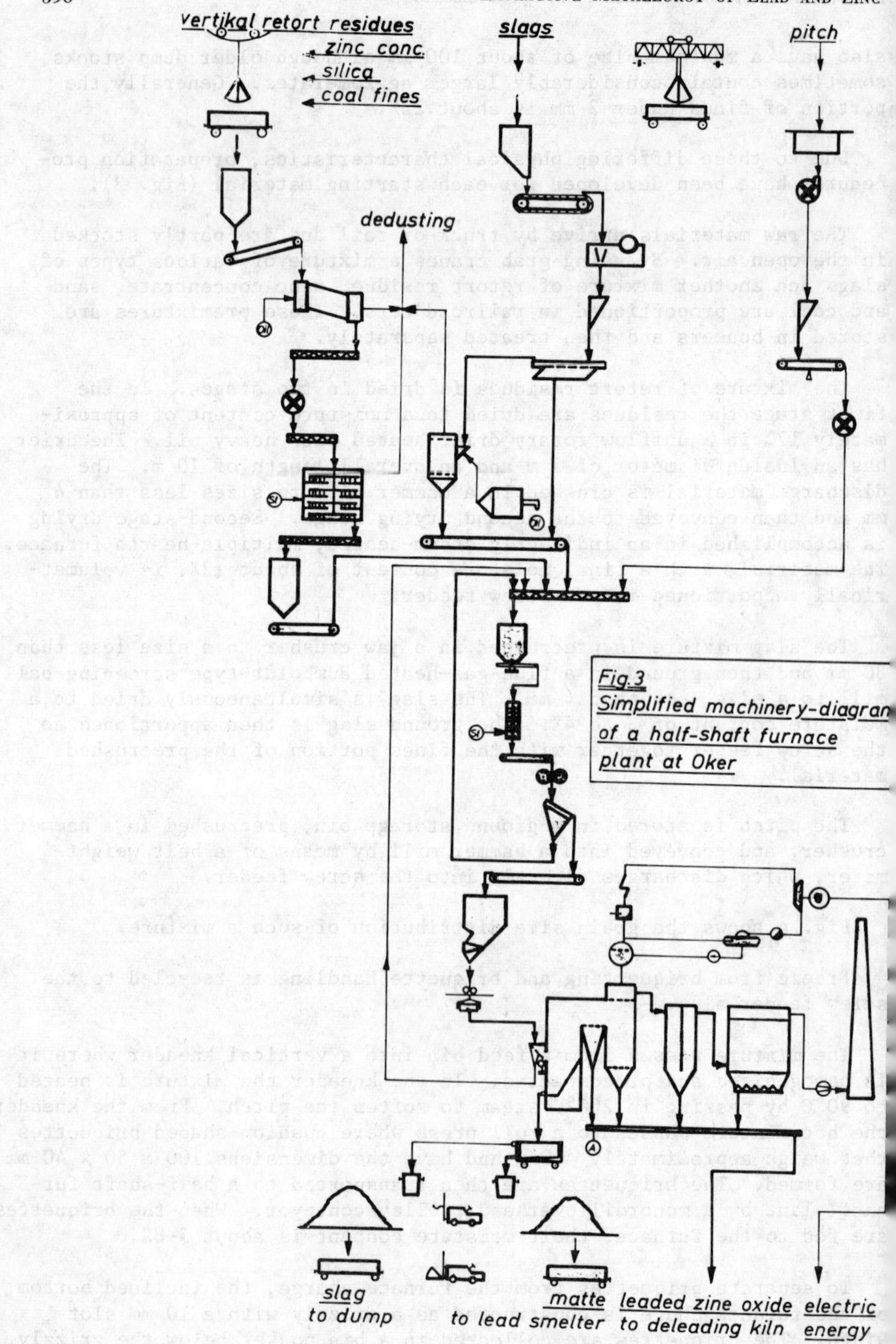

Fig.3
Simplified machinery-diagram of a half-shaft furnace plant at Oker

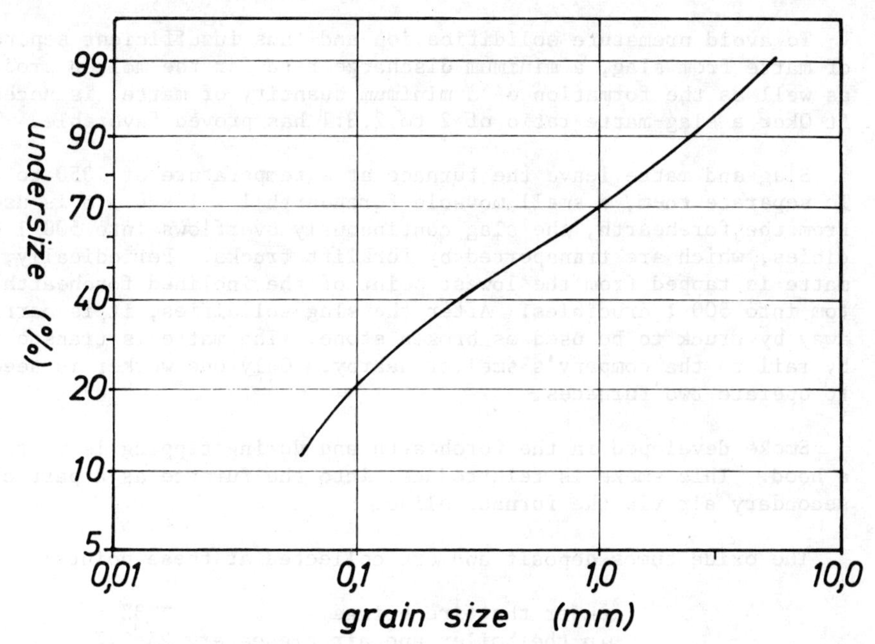

Fig.4 **Grain size distribution of feed mixture for briquetting at Oker**

The primary air pressure is 450 mm WG; the pressure before the tuyeres is between 300 and 450 mm WG. The tuyeres are conically widened toward the furnace cavity. Thus, the angle of the air inlets to the furnace is enlarged so that inactive zones between the tuyeres are reduced to a minimum.

The primary air enters the tuyeres at temperatures up to 60°C. The primary air demand is calculated from the net calorific value of the briquettes. For instance, a 2500 kcal/kg value requires an excess air factor of 1.5. This amounts to 4.5 Nm^3 of air/kg of briquettes.

From the furnace operation viewpoint, defining the most effective charge height is important. If the charge height is too low, the primary air is inefficiently utilized. The upper layers of the bed overheat. Burning is locally concentrated in the lower part of the shaft, while the upper part and the boiler are under a lower heat load. When the charge level is too high, the upper briquette layer is too cold and less active. This layer then tends to stick together with the melting flue ash which can then lead to deposits on the slope. The most favorable charge height, according to the nature of the material to be discharged, is between 55 and 75 cm. The optimum, however, is about 60 cm and can easily be set by means of the furnace slide.

To avoid premature solidification and thus insufficient separation of matte from slag, a minimum discharge rate for the molten products, as well as the formation of a minimum quantity of matte, is necessary. At Oker a slag-matte ratio of 2 to 2.8:1 has proved favorable.

Slag and matte leave the furnace at a temperature of 1050 to 1100° To separate them, a small movable forehearth 1 x 1 x 0.5 m is used. From the forehearth, the slag continuously overflows into 500 l crucibles, which are transported by forklift trucks. Periodically, the matte is tapped from the lowest point of the inclined forehearth bottom into 500 l crucibles. After the slag solidifies, it is carried away by truck to be used as broken stone. The matte is transported by rail to the company's smelter nearby. Only one worker is needed to operate two furnaces.

Smoke developed in the forehearth and during tapping is vented by a hood. This smoke is reintroduced into the furnace as a part of the secondary air via the furnace slide.

The oxide fumes deposit and are collected at these points:

under the fire bridge	3%
in the boiler and air preheater	25-27%
in the bag filter	70%

The oxide collected in the pocket under the fire bridge contains high amount of impurities due to the flue ash and can be recycled to briquetting.

By reversing the gas flow before it enters the inside tubes of the waste heat boiler, a comparatively large quantity of oxide precipitates in the boiler. The surfaces of the outer tubes are cleaned by steam blowing. The steam tuyeres are fitted into the back wall of the boiler.

Another portion of the oxides contained in the waste gas deposits in the waste gas tubular cooler/air preheater arrangement behind the boiler. These oxides are collected in pockets placed below the apparatus.

The waste gases leave the cooler at 150-170°C and are passed into a bag filter to recover the remaining oxide. The gases are cooled to 105°C (the highest permissible inlet temperature) by cooling in the tubes and drawing in air. "Dralon T 320" has proven satisfactory as a bag filter material. The cleaned gases are exhausted to the stack. The oxide is collected from the bag filters by a screw conveyor for pneumatic transport.

Operation Results of the Oker Half-Shaft Furnace Plant

Approximately 50% of the zinc-containing materials treated at the Oker half-shaft furnace plant are slags. Two typical analyses of these slags are given in Table 1.

More than 40% of the zinc-containing feed is retort residue which shows a comparatively high precious metal content. The contained carbon supplies a considerable part of the fuel demand. To maintain the proper sulfur balance, a certain amount of lead-containing zinc concentrate is added to the material before treatment. This addition is approximately 8% of the total zinc-bearing material.

The half-shaft furnaces are located in two separate plants which, as far as feed preparation is concerned, operate independently of each other. Up to some years ago, both plants operated temporarily on different mixtures of starting materials. These mixtures were distinguished by their lead-zinc ratio and by their percentage of zinc plus lead. The oxides obtained from these mixtures showed corresponding qualitative differences.

The slags produced at the Oker half-shaft furnace plant are characterized by their high silica and comparatively low iron content. Such compositions are necessary to produce a slag that is low in zinc. Since the slag contains only 2.2% zinc and 0.2% copper, it can be discarded. Table 2 shows a typical half-shaft furnace slag analysis. The analyses of the starting material components are listed in Table 1. When slags containing 2% copper and precious metals were blown, mattes with more than 6% copper, up to 480 g per ton silver, and 2.6 g per ton gold have been obtained. This matte is roasted in a fluidized bed furnace in the neighboring lead smelter and charged into the lead shaft furnace as an iron addition.

The oxide fume collected in the filter is high purity. Its zinc plus lead content is greater than 77%. The zinc-lead ratio in the oxides is determined by that of the feed mixture. A starting material with a high zinc-to-lead ratio yields a filter oxide which may contain less than 5% lead.

Due to their purity and high dispersing characteristics, these oxides were sold as suitable for use in the pigment industry. The Harz zinc oxides have become known on the European market under the brand of "Harzsiegel."

Today only oxides with fairly high lead contents are being produced in the half-shaft furnaces at Oker. The analyses given in Table 2 are for two filter oxides which differ considerably in quality. These oxides are obtained when processing the feed mixtures indicated in Table 1.

Table 1

Analyses of the most important zinc-bearing materials

	slag A	slag B	vertical retort residue	zinc bulk concentrate	briquette rich in lead	briquette poor in lead
Zn %	11,4	16,3	5,1	43,6	12,0	18,5
Pb %	3,9	2,1	5,5	5,0	4,3	1,4
Cu %	0,9	1,2	1,1	0,7	1,0	1,1
Au ppm	0,1	0,1	0,8	0,4		
Ag ppm	28	18	153	120		
Fe %	25,6	25,7	12	9,0		
S %	5,9	4,0	4,8	30,0		
SiO_2 %	18,9	20,0	9,3	2,2		
Al_2O_3 %	1,9	3,7	4,2	0,9		
CaO %	3,7	5,9	3,8	1,4		
BaO %	6,6	5,0	3,9	1,5		
C %			30			

Table 2

Products of a half-shaft furnace at Oker

	slag	matte	filter oxide rich in lead	filter oxide poor in lead
Zn %	2,2	1,8	55,9	72,6
Pb %	0,15	0,9	17,2	4,7
Cu %	0,2	4,1	0,07	0,02
Ag ppm	8	350		
Au ppm	0,1	1,7		
Fe %	21	58	0,17	0,06
S %	2,1	26	2,8	1,0
SiO_2 %	31,0		0,07	0,02
CaO %	8,5		0,06	0,01
BaO %	11,5			
Al_2O_3 %	5,6		0,08	0,1
C %			0,04	0,02

The leaded zinc oxides are sintered to remove the lead, volatile metals, and impurities. The deleaded zinc oxide densified during this process has the physical properties and chemical composition suitable for the production of zinc metal. This oxide is reduced to zinc at the Harlingerode Zinc Smelter. The lead-rich flue dust is melted to bullion. During the sintering process a secondary fume, rich in cadmium and other minor metals, as well as a slag rich in zinc are produced. The slag is recycled to the half-shaft furnace process.

In the half-shaft furnace at Oker, approximately 300,000 tons per year of moist briquettes are presently being processed. Only a small amount of the steam from the waste heat recovery system is necessary to provide Oker's internal demand. On the average, 5 to 6 kgs of steam is converted in a company-owned generator plant into electrical energy. The major portion of this power is delivered to the public electricity supply system.

To attain this capacity, 13 half-shaft furnaces with internal lengths of 2.9-4.9 m in the tuyere are are used. Each furnace treats 60-80 tons of briquettes per day, depending on the furnace length.

The furnaces operate about 90% of the time. The remaining 10% is downtime used for furnace cleaning and maintenance. At Oker, the total fuel demand is about 30% based on the carbon-free material to be processed. This demand can be completely satisfied by the carbon content of the retort residues. Since the lead-zinc ratio in the retort residue does not correspond to the relation desired in the lead-zinc oxide, the retort residue portion of the charge is decreased and coke fines or fine slack coal are substituted.

Coke fines of a commercially inferior quality will be used as reduction coal. These coke fines have an ash content of 17% and a net calorific value of 5900 kcal/kg. Instead of coke fines, fine slack coal can be used. This slack coal contains approximately 8% ash and has a net calorific value of 7600 kcal/kg. Only in certain exceptional cases is the addition of lump coal necessary.

The total electrical energy demand of the half-shaft furnace plant is up to 60 kwh/t of zinc-bearing material, irrespective of the auxiliary units.

A staff of 213 workers is employed in the half-shaft furnace plants. This does not include personnel in auxiliary workshops or in administrative areas.

The recovery of lead and zinc to oxide depends on the nature of the starting materials and their metal contents. The formation of a large quantity of slag naturally has an unfavorable effect on the recovery of zinc. With the starting material described in Table 1 as a mixture rich in lead, the recovery of zinc to oxide is about 90%, while that of lead is about 95%.

Using the same starting material, approximately 85% of the copper 80% of the silver, and up to 90% of the gold is recovered in the mat The losses of zinc and copper mainly occur in the slag while the maj loss of lead is to matte and the major loss of silver is to oxide.

Further Application of the Half-Shaft Furnace Process

Although the half-shaft furnace process was developed for the special conditions of the Harz Smelter, its use for processing other materials has been examined in large-scale tests at Oker during the past 20 years. Materials which have been tried are those which can neither be separated into richer lead-zinc concentrates and copper/ precious metal concentrates nor further upgraded. Such materials ar zinc leach residues with fairly high copper and precious metal conte calamines with precious metal and copper contents, and lead-zinc-cop bulk concentrates.

In general, these starting materials require a pretreatment. In the case of zinc leach filter cakes, this is drying; in the case of bulk concentrates, partial roasting; and for carbonate materials, ca cination. The mixture of zinc-bearing materials with necessary addi tions should not fall below 15% zinc plus lead. For economical and precious metal content considerations, the copper content of the zin bearing mixture should be greater than 1%.

Processing of Zinc Leach Residues

Zinc leach residues are presently processed in two plants buil by the Humboldt Division of Klöckner-Humboldt-Deutz AG, Cologne, West Germany.

The first plant was built in 1956 for Societa Mineraria e Meta lurgica di Pertusola (SMMP) zinc smelter at Crotone, Italy. The second plant was built in 1960 for the Española del Zinc (EDZ) zi smelter at Cartagena, Spain. Both plants are designed in nearly the same way. They use the same process and equipment.

To obtain good dezincing, briquettes must not have a final moi ture content over 8%. To produce these briquettes, the slurries with moisture contents of up to 40% must be dried to less than 5% For this purpose oil-heated rotary driers are used. Based on the weight of dry residues, 10-14% limestone, approximately 21% coke fines, and 10-12% pitch are added for briquetting. The briquette contain 17 or 23% zinc plus lead, due to different chemical com- positions of the two residues. The high zinc content of the Cartagena residues results from the marmatite processed there.

The copper, lead and cadmium contents are similar. A compari- son between the slag-forming constituents shows that, due to the high iron and the low SiO_2 and CaO content, the conditions at Cartagena are far more unfavorable than those in Crotone. This is why the iron content of the slag is higher and more matte is produced. The higher zinc content of the Cartagena slag can also be attributed to the higher iron content of the feed material.

The quality of the oxides produced at Cartagena and Crotone does not measure up to the quality of those produced at Oker. The total volatilized metal content is only 73-74%. Neither does the recovery, particularly zinc, reach the levels attained at Oker when processing zinc leach residues. The low furnace resistance of the briquettes is the most probable reason for these shortfalls. The extreme fineness and grain size distribution of the residues are probably responsible for the lower furnace resistance. We have found that adding granulated recycled slag to the briquette mixture has a favorable effect on operating results.

The half-shaft furnaces at both of these plants have a 3.5 m length in the tuyere area.

Table 3 summarizes the data from the two plants.

Processing of Calamine

Large-scale tests at Oker have shown that calamine can be processed in the half-shaft furnace. Although the material tested showed unfavorable chemical characteristics for treatment in this furnace (a low zinc content of 10.4% and unusually high silica content of 32.4%), slags with 2.2% zinc could be obtained after adding limestone and other zinc-bearing material. The 10.1% carbon dioxide content of the ore had no unfavorable effects. We have concluded that calamine ore is a suitable starting material for the half-shaft furnace provided that the zinc content of the mixed feed (ore plus fluxes) exceeds 13%.

Since, however, most calamine ores contain very little copper or precious metal, the half-shaft furnace cannot be regarded as a primary method of processing such materials. Ores, however, such as those occurring in the transition zones between oxidic to sulfidic zinc/lead-ore deposits which are not treatable by selective ore processing methods can be suitable for half-shaft furnace feed. These ores usually have low sulfur and carbonic acid contents in addition to low precious metal and copper contents. An ore which might be suitable for half-shaft furnace treatment should have an analysis approximating that given in Table 4.

Table 3

Data on half-shaft furnace plants for processing zinc leach residues

Residue analyses (%)	SMMP Crotone	EDZ Cartagena
Zn	16,1	27,0
Pb	5,5	5,0
Cd	0,17	0,2
Cu	0,34	0,5
Ag	0,021	0,006
Fe	13,5	26,5
S	8,7	11,0
SiO_2	11,3	3,5
CaO	5,8	1,5
Additions % referred to the dry residue		
CaO as limestone	7,2	5,8
coke fines	27,5	20,7
pitch	12,0	9,6
lump coke	14,7	12
Slag analysis (%)		
Zn	2,5 - 4,5	3 - 5
Pb	0,03	0,08
SiO_2	33,9	31,5
FeO	14,2	23,1
CaO	29,8	20,4
Matte analysis (%)		
Zn	approx. 5,2	approx. 6,4
Pb	0,7	0,5
Cu	1,6	1,4
Ag	0,093	
Fe	51,6	
S	28,3	
Filter oxide analysis (%)		
Zn	52,8	64,0
Pb	19,7	8,6
Cd	0,6	1,0
Ge	0,017	
Recovery (%)		
Zn in the oxide	85	88
Pb " " "	95	95
Ge " " "	88	
Cd " " "	92	
Cu in the matte	79	
Ag " " "	75	
Capacity t/24 h residue (dry)	45	36
t/24 h total charge	75	65

Table 4

Analysis (%) of an oxidic Zn-Pb-ore treatable in half-shaft furnaces

Zn	22	SiO_2	13
Pb	1	CaO	11
Cu	0,5	MgO	2
Ag	0,005	Al_2O_3	1
Fe	12	loss of ignition	20
S	3		

Processing of Zinc-Lead-Copper Sulfide Concentrates

Another interesting application of the half-shaft furnace process should be the treatment of lead-zinc-copper-bearing bulk concentrates containing comparatively high contents of these materials. Such concentrates can be fumed in shaft furnaces and in the half-shaft furnace as well, preferably after partial roasting to a leaded zinc oxide and matte as formerly practiced prior to the introduction of the selective flotation process. The normally higher iron contents of such concentrates require lime and silica additions to slag the iron so that high copper content mattes will be produced. We shall describe a modern half-shaft furnace plant designed to treat these bulk lead-zinc-copper sulfide concentrates. A diagram of the process is shown in Fig. 5.

Multiple hearth roasters, with accompanying waste heat boilers, would accomplish the partial roasting. Multiple hearth roasters should be selected because the simultaneously high lead and silica contents cause difficulties in other types of roasters. The roaster off-gases can be used for sulfuric acid production. After being crushed to a grain size below 4 mm, coke fines, fine slack coal, limestone and sand are bunkered like the roasted material and mixed with recycled briquette breeze and pitch. The mixture is continuously homogenzied in a steam-heated, double-shell centrifugal mixer by heating to 90°C and injecting steam to soften the pitch.

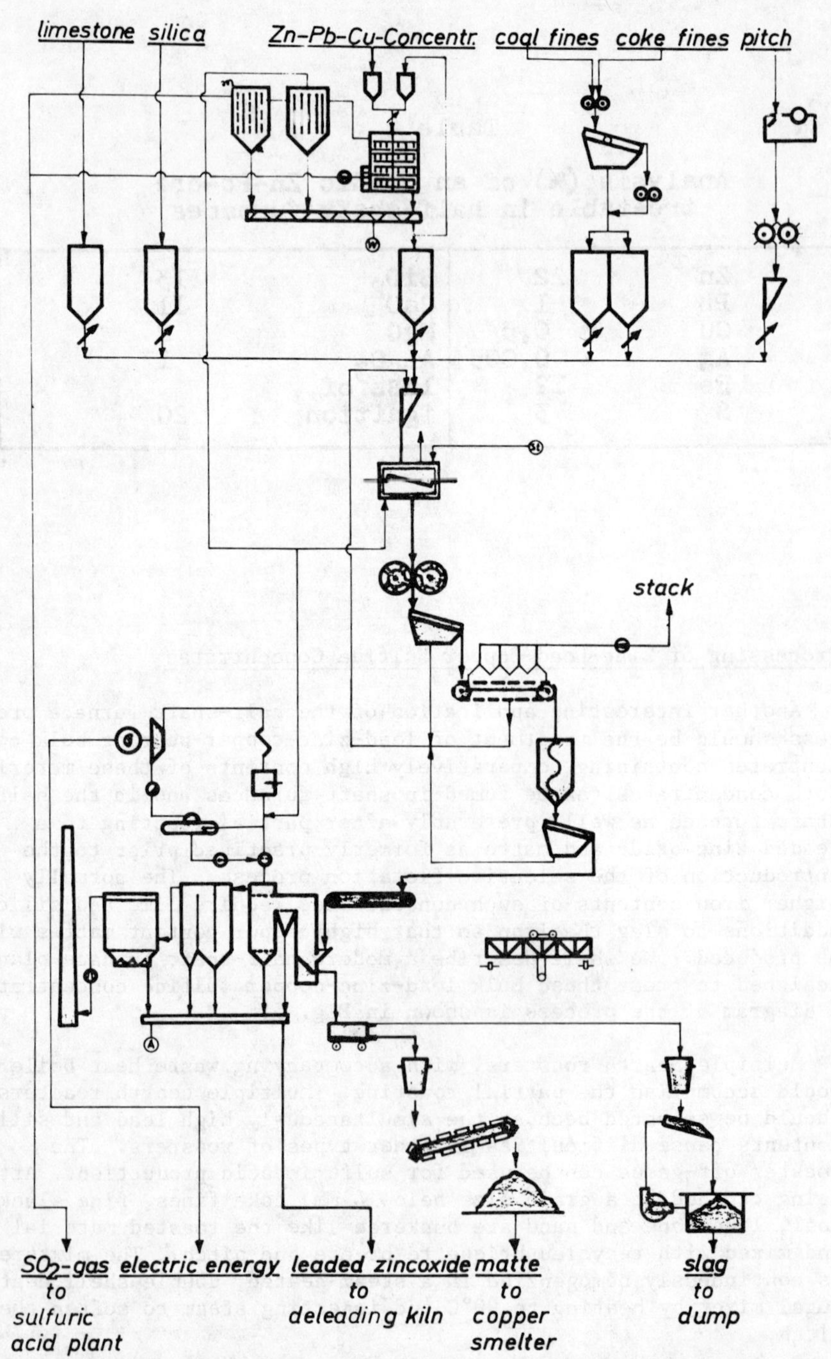

Fig.5 Simplified machinery-diagram of a modern half-shaft furnace plant project for processing Zn-Pb-Cu-bulk flotation concentrates

To increase their resistance and abrasion strength, the briquettes pass from the presses through a curved chute to a grizzly for screening out the briquette breeze. The briquettes then continue through a vibrating distribution chute on to a suction, draft-cooled wire belt. The briquettes are then belt-conveyed either directly to the reversible feed belts of the half-shaft furnace or into surge bins through spiral chutes for storage. The half-shaft furnaces would have a maximum internal length of 5.4 m in the tuyere area. The waste heat recovery system on the half-shaft furnace would produce only saturated steam at 25 atm. g. This steam, along with the steam from the waste heat boilers on the roasters, would be superheated to 460°C in a separate, natural gas-heated superheater. After supplying the internal demands, the superheated steam would be used for the generation of electricity.

Two-stage waste gas coolers serving as air preheaters would be placed after the waste heat boilers on the half-shaft furnace, as shown in Fig. 6. In the first stage the primary air for the half-shaft furnace is preheated to 240°C. From the second stage, part of the 180°C hot air is used as secondary air to the furnace. This air would be introduced over the total furnace length through float-regulating slides. At present, we are considering to what extent we can increase the preheating of the primary air. We feel that temperatures of 600°C can be realized by altering the present concept of waste heat utilization and by introducing a recuperator system. Each half-shaft furnace will have a bag filter system of its own. The waste gases are cooled down from 160° to 90°C by ambient air. After cooling, the waste gases will be cleaned. Up to now no decision has been made on whether to replace the proven bag filter units with electrostatic precipitators, particularly because of the possible higher lead content of the oxides produced when processing bulk concentrates.

The molten matte will be cast into pigs on a casting strand; the slag can be granulated. The product oxides might be deleaded and clinkered in a rotary kiln or introduced to the sinter plant of an Imperial Smelting furnace.

Prospects

Since the introduction of the first half-shaft furnace at Oker with a length of 1.25 m in the tuyere area, furnaces with increasing size have been used for rebuilding and expanding existing plants. Today several furnaces with a length of 4.9 m are operating at Oker. Although the extension of the equipment on the gas handling and waste heat recovery side could not always be fully realized and the results not fully utilized for the development of larger furnaces, they nevertheless encourage construction of furnaces with lengths of 5.4 m. The difficulties connected with the transition to larger furnaces, such as the occurrence of inactive zones between the tuyeres, could be eliminated

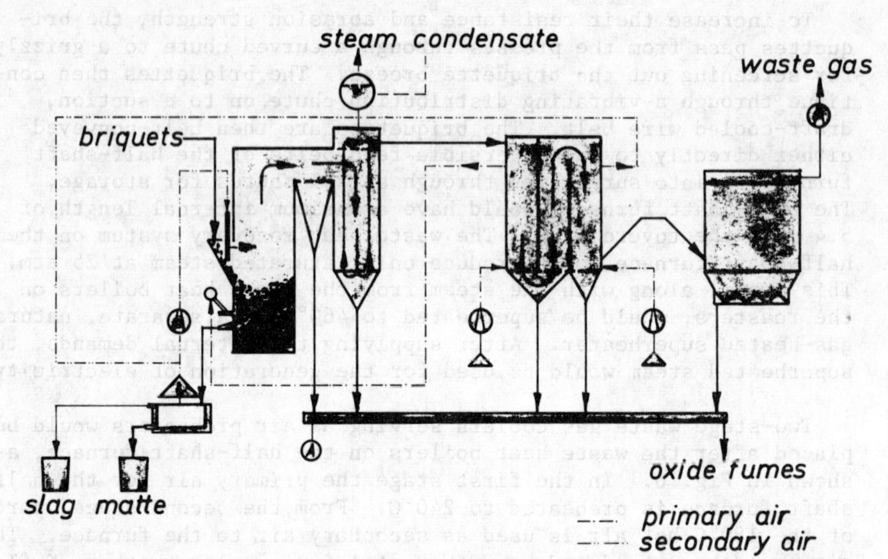

Fig.6 Half-shaft furnace with waste heat and fume recovering system

by measures described above. Recent tests using preheated blast air have emphasized these points.

The results of these tests indicate that a considerable increase in the specific combustion performance and a lower fuel consumption can be expected. We can assume that by oxygen enrichment of the blas air further improvements will be achieved.

References

1. Barth, O., Die Metallverfluchtigungsverfahren mit besonderer Berücksichtigung der Herstellung von Zinkoxid, Verlag von Wilhelm Knapp, Halle (Saale), 1935, pp. 82-95.

2. Tafel, V., Lehrbuch der Metallhüttenkunde, S. Hirzel Verlagsbuchhandlung, Leipzig, 1953, Vol. II, pp. 604-620.

3. Hellwig, H. & J., "Die Zinkoxid-Verblaseöfen der Unterharzer Berg und Hüttenwerke," Erzmetall Vol. II, 1949, pp. 263-268.

Chapter 15

WAELZ PROCESS FOR LEACH RESIDUES AT NISSO SMELTING COMPANY LTD.
Aizu, Japan

M. Kashiwada
Director, Nisso Smelting Company Ltd.

T. Kumagai
Technical Manager, Aizu Plant, Nisso
Smelting Company Ltd.

Abstract

The zinc leach residues are introduced into waelz kiln to fume volatile metals and before the end of 1967, the waelz-fume containing zinc, lead, cadmium and indium was directly recycled back to the leaching process for the production of electrolytic slab zinc. However, since 1968, we have been recovering with success those valuable metals contained in the fume separately instead of direct leaching.

According to the improved process, the waelz-fume, after being mixed with chloridizing agents, is fed into the rotary kiln to be roasted, wherein most of lead and cadmium content is collected as fume and most of zinc remains in the calcine. Zinc calcine thus obtained, containing 70 to 75 per cent zinc and less than 1.0 per cent lead is sent to zinc plant for further recovery and the fume containing 40 to 50 per cent lead and 3 to 6 per cent cadmium is further processed to recover lead, cadmium and indium.

The advantage of this process can be secured to the utmost when it is combined with the following subsequent treatments.

(a) Blast furnace smelting of non-magnetic waelz slag to recover copper, silver and gold as matte.
(b) Gallium recovering process from magnetic waelz slag.
(c) Soda process of lead bearing cake produced after removing cadmium and indium from the said fume.

Thus the extractions of zinc, lead and cadmium from leach residues account for 87 per cent, 72 per cent and 85 per cent respectively.

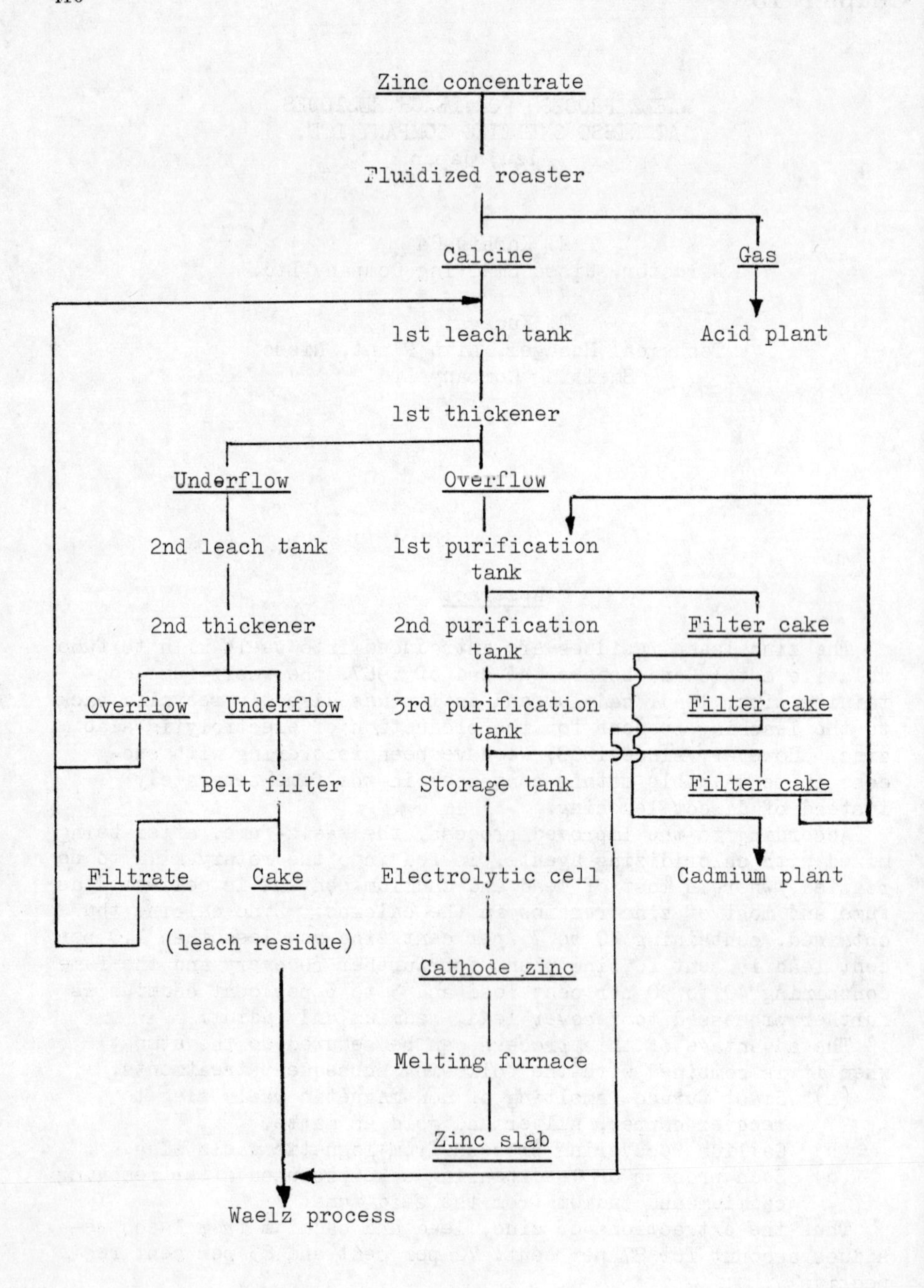

Fig. 1 - Flowsheet of the electrolytic zinc plant at Aizu.

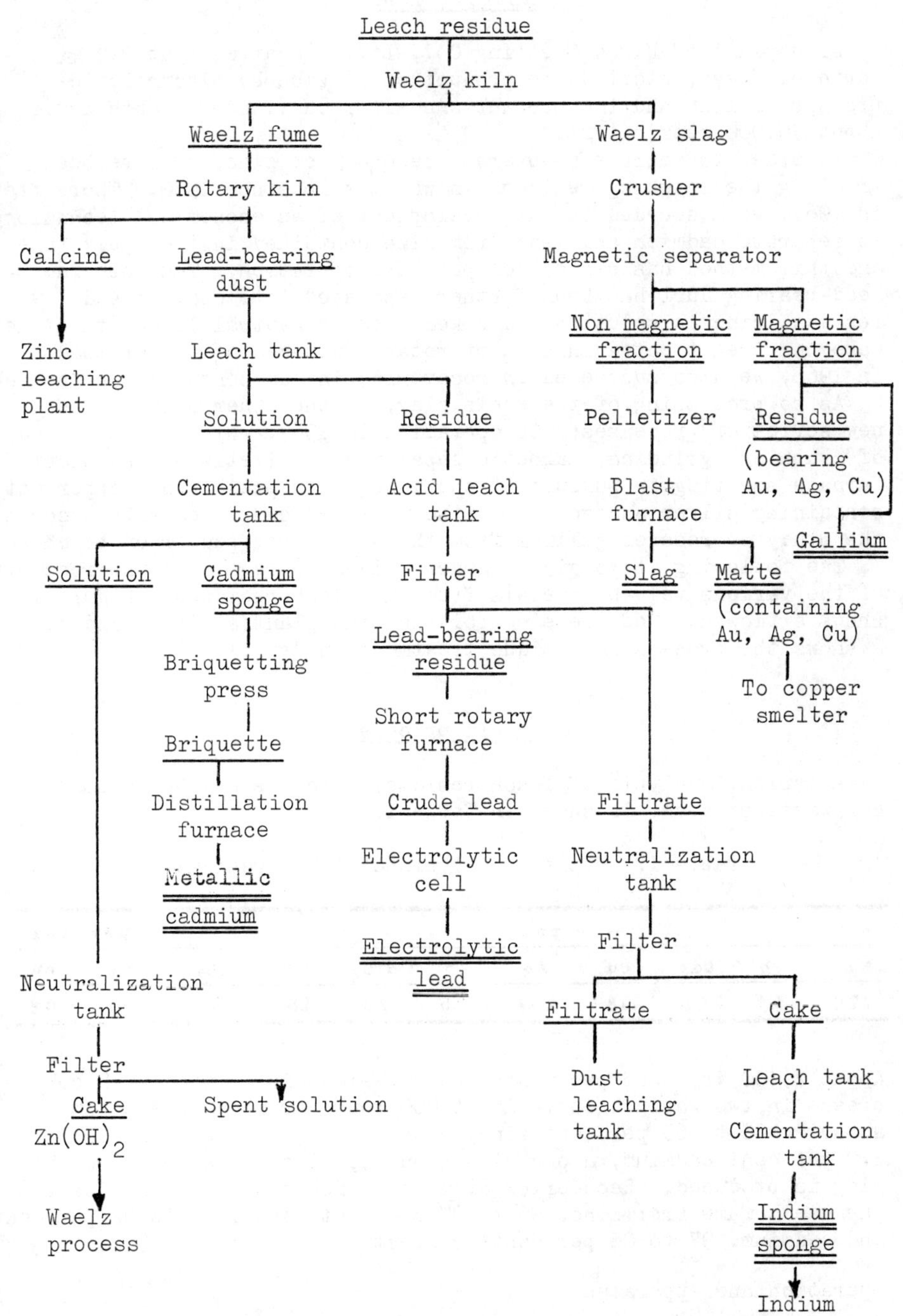

Fig. 2 - Flowsheet of the process of residue treatment.

Introduction

Aizu plant of Nisso Smelting Co., Ltd., located about 210 km north of Tokyo, started the production of zinc by electrolytic process in 1916 and the present annual production of slab zinc is about 30,000 metric tons.

In order to improve an overall recovery of zinc, we have been treating the leaching residues in waelz kiln since 1930. Thereafter, in 1967, we succeeded in the development of an economical technology to separate cadmium and lead from zinc contained in the waelz fume and this method has since been put into operation. Thus obtained lead-bearing dust has been further separated into cadmium and residual zinc in solution and caked lead by neutral leach, then the cake has been treated in a short rotary furnace to recover lead. In 1968, we also succeeded in recovering indium contained in the cak

As to processing of the waelz slag, on the other hand, we put a new series of processes into operation in 1967, which was composed of crushing, grinding, magnetic separation, pelletizing and blast furnace smelting in pursuit of obtaining iron powder and copper matt containing silver and gold. Furthermore, we completed with success the study to recover gallium from the above iron powder on bench sca

The following is to give a general idea in regard to the recovery of the various valuable metals from the leach residues. Figure 1 shows a flowsheet of the electrolytic zinc plant at Aizu, and Figure 2 shows the process of residue treatment in detail.

Waelz process

A typical analysis of leach residue, which is now being used in our waelz process, is shown in Table I.

Table I. Typical analysis of leach residue

pct									g per ton	
Zn	Pb	Cd	Cu	Fe	S	SiO_2	CaO	Al_2O_3	Ag	Au
22.0	3.4	0.28	0.8	28.7	5.5	2.8	1.8	3.5	320	0.8

About 2,400 dry tons per month leach residue is treated with coke breeze in two waelz kilns. About 800 tons per month waelz fume assaying 60 to 65 per cent zinc, 9 to 10 per cent lead, and 0.5 to 1.0 per cent cadmium, along with about 1,300 tons per month waelz slag is produced. Recoveries of metals from the leach residue to the waelz fume are: zinc, 96 to 97 per cent; lead, 90 to 92 per cent and cadmium, 97 to 98 per cent; respectively.

Operation and apparatus

The leach residue normally containing about 35 per cent moisture is dried in a rotary kiln (1.8 m in diameter by 18.3 m long) to reduce the moisture down to about 15 per cent. Optimum moisture is supposed to be about 15 per cent. Because if the moisture is far less than 15 per cent, it will cause to increase carry-over and if, on the contrary, the moisture should exceed a certain limit, it will turn into steam the moment when the wet residue is charged, and the charge particles will be blown up to be entrained into waste gas mechanically. In either case, no matter whether the moisture is excessive or short, it will lead to making the fume **inferior** in its quality.

100 parts of the dried residue and 30 parts of coke breeze (size; 3 to 10 mm) are fed into a rotary mixer. The charge-mix is introduced through water-jacketed spout with internal diameter of 200 mm into waelz kiln.

No.1 kiln has a diameter of 2.0 m by 30 m long and No.2 has 2.5 m by 38 m. They are inclined 3.0 per cent and 3.8 per cent respectively from horizontal. Both kilns are entirely lined with refractory bricks made of "Corhart-White", except the inside near the charging ends lined with "Chamotte" refractory bricks.

The capacity of each kiln is about 35 and 65 dry tons of charge per day respectively. Heat is supplied by oil burners for kilns. Volatilized metals such as zinc, lead, cadmium and others are carried over out of the kiln by the waste gas.

The waste gas normally has a temperature of 500 to 600°C and has static pressure up to 0.6 mm water at the charging end of the kiln. The composition of the waste gas ranges 19 to 21 per cent CO_2, up to 3 per cent O_2, up to 0.5 per cent CO and up to 0.8 per cent SO_2.

The non-volatile metals such as iron, copper, silver, and gold turn into slag to be discharged from the other end of the kiln. Table II shows the typical analysis of the slag.

Table II. Typical analysis of slag

pct										g per ton	
Zn	Pb	Cd	Cu	Fe	SiO_2	Al_2O_3	CaO	C	S	Ag	Au
1.32	0.64	0.003	1.34	49.3	21.8	6.9	3.7	10.2	4.7	527	1.5

In regard to the fume-collecting apparatus, in case of No.1 kiln system, the fume particles separated from the gas stream, are brought into cyclone and electrostatic precipitator successively. Two blowers are placed before and after the electrostatic precipitator. In case of No.2 kiln system, however, the fume-laden gas passes through dust chamber to two electrostatic precipitator installed in a row and two blowers are equipped after each electrostatic precipitator.

The duration of the operation depends considerably upon the growth of acceretion on the inside wall around the middle portion of the kiln.

Average analysis of the collected fume is shown in Table III, and the material balance in our waelz process is given in Table IV.

Table III. Average analysis of waelz-fume

Zn	Pb	Cd	Cu	Fe	SiO_2	C	Sb	As
61.9	9.8	0.81	0.06	3.1	2.3	0.8	0.003	0.05

Table IV. Material balance in waelz process

		proportion	Zn	Pb	Cd	Cu	Fe	Ag	Au
Input	Leach residue	100.0	100.0	100.0	100.0	100.0	98.8	100.0	100.0
	Coke breeze	29.0					1.2		
	Total						100.0		
Output	Fume	34.1	96.1	90.1	98.4	2.6	3.6	5.3	
	Slag	57.0	3.4	10.7	0.6	95.5	95.5	93.9	106.9
	Others		0.5	△0.8	1.0	1.9	0.9	0.8	△6.9
	Total		100.0	100.0	100.0	100.0	100.0	100.0	100.0

Reactions inside the kiln

Four different functions are performed inside the kiln. They are: (a) drying and preheating (b) reduction (c) volatilization and (d) slag formation. Taking No.2 kiln (2.5 m in diameter by 38 m long) as an example, they are (a) 0-8 m, (b) 8-22 m, (c) 22-33 m, and (d) 33-38 m respectively from the charging end.

In zone (a) of the kiln, the adherent water is evaporated and part of zinc sulfate is decomposed thermally and is reduced into sulfide and/or oxide.

In zone (b), the following reactions are supposed to take place.

$$ZnSO_4 + 2C = ZnS + 2CO_2$$
$$ZnSO_4 + 4C = ZnS + 4CO$$
$$ZnSO_4 + 4CO = ZnS + 4CO_2$$
$$ZnSO_4 + C = ZnO + SO_2 + CO$$
$$2ZnSO_4 + C = 2ZnO + 2SO_2 + CO_2$$
$$ZnSO_4 + CO = ZnO + SO_2 + CO_2$$

Through the reactions above, zinc sulfide and zinc oxide are formed and they are supposed to coexist.

Lead compound, contained in the residue mainly as sulfate, is reduced to either lead sulfide, metallic lead or lead oxide. However, as lead oxide under this atmosphere is theoretically less stable than lead sulfide and metal, most of lead in this zone easily turns into either sulfide or metal.

As to iron, ferric oxide is reduced to ferrosic oxide and further to **ferrous oxide.**

In zone (c), the temperature ranges from 1,000 to 1,300°C and such reduction of zinc ferrite by carbon as shown below begins.

$$3(ZnO \cdot Fe_2O_3) + C = 2Fe_3O_4 + 3ZnO + CO$$

Zinc oxide thus formed is reduced further to metallic zinc by carbon.

$$ZnO + C = Zn + CO$$

We assume that the volatilization of zinc sulfide and reduction of zinc sulfide by carbon would be negligibly slight in this zone. Under co-existence of CaO, MnO and FeO with carbon, such reduction of zinc sulfide to metallic zinc shown in the following equations may occur.

$$ZnS + CaO + C = Zn + CaS + CO$$
$$ZnS + FeO + C = Zn + FeS + CO$$
$$ZnS + MnO + C = Zn + MnS + CO$$
$$ZnS + Fe = Zn + FeS$$

As to lead, both lead sulfide and metallic lead are equally stable in this zone.

Treatment of waelz-slag

Waelz-slag passes through a series of such processes as crushing, grinding and magnetic separation. The non-magnetic fraction thus obtained is pelletized to be treated in a blast furnace.

3.5 tons per day matte containing 14 per cent copper is obtained from the furnace, into which about 50 tons of pellets and lump slag are charged. The copper recovery in the blast furnace accounts for about 74 per cent of the total content of the charge.

About 200 tons monthly of magnetic fraction contains 70 to 76 per cent metallic iron, 1.5 to 2.5 per cent copper, 500 to 700 gram silver per ton, 2.0 to 3.5 gram gold per ton, and some 0.01 per cent gallium. We have already succeeded in bench scale treatment to recover these valuable metals from the magnetic.

Operation and apparatus

The waelz-slag cools off on the belt while being conveyed to the grizzly, where fraction exceeding 20 mm is separated. The fraction under 20 mm is crushed by "impact breaker" down to 5 mm or below. The crushed slag is fed into 100 Hp-vibrating pebble mill manufactured by Allis-Chalmers Co. to be pulverized into powder with size of 50 per cent or more of which is minus 200 mesh. The powder is then charged into a vertical A.C. magnetic separator to recover most of the metallic iron.

The non-magnetic powder, after being processed further in disc-type pelletizer of 2.3 m diameter, is mixed with fraction of slag exceeding 20 mm to be charged into the blast furnace.

The present blast furnace is of conventional type, water jacketed, rectangular and is fitted with 8 tuyeres for admittance of the blast. It has a hearth area of 1.7 square meters. The total input of the blast furnace is approximately 70 tons per day. The blast volume ranges from 47 to 49 Nm^3 air per minute and the blast pressure 62 to 67 mmHg. The matte is tapped from the bottom of fore-hearth intermittently (9 to 12 times a day), and the slag is overflowed continuously and water-granulated for sale.

Table V shows representative analyses of the iron powder, copper matte and slag. The material balance of the blast furnace smelting is shown in Table VI.

Table V. Representative analyses of iron powder, copper matte and slag

	pct										g per ton	
	Zn	Pb	Cu	Fe	SiO_2	Al_2O_3	CaO	C	S	Ga	Ag	Au
Iron powder	1.6	1.3	1.6	81.7	2.7	0.6	0.6	1.7	3.6	0.01	554	3.2
Copper matte	1.0	1.2	13.7	51.0	0.4	—	0.3	—	23.5		5287	13.7
Slag	1.4	0.1	0.28	43.6	32.7	6.5	9.8	—	0.6		128	0.3

Table VI. Material balance in blast furnace

		proportion	Cu	Ag	Au	Fe
Input	Pellet	60.0	59.1	58.5	54.5	56.8
	Lump slag	40.0	40.9	41.5	45.5	42.5
	Coke	4.5				0.1
	Silica	15.0				0.6
	Limestone	6.5				
	Total		100.0	100.0	100.0	100.0
Output	Copper matte	6.8	71.2	71.0	70.8	7.5
	Slag	93.5	24.3	23.5	23.2	87.8
	Others	4.7	4.5	5.5	6.0	4.7
	Total		100.0	100.0	100.0	100.0

Treatment of iron powder

A certain portion of the iron powder is now being used as the precipitant in our lead smelting furnace, as discribed later. In order to make use of the rest, two different methods are now under development. They are:

(a) The iron powder, after being cast into anode, is refined electrolytically, and gallium is extracted from the anode slime.

(b) The iron powder is leached with sulfuric acid and filtered to obtain iron and gallium in filtrate and copper, silver and gold in residue. From the resulting solution, gallium is recovered, together with ferrous sulfate.

Treatment of waelz-fume

Until the end of 1967, the waelz-fume had been calcinated in a rotary kiln to remove chlorine and the calcine had been leached with sulfuric acid to extract zinc in solution. Lead content in fume, as a result, had remained in the leach-residue. This residue, containing around 30 per cent lead, had been smelted in 3-phases Héroult-type electric furnace to produce crude lead. Due to the following disadvantages of this process, since 1968 we have put a different process into operation which will be explained later.

(a) The calcined waelz-fume contains far more lead than the calcine from zinc concentrate does. Therefore, leaching and filtration of the calcined waelz-fume has to be carried out independently. This naturally requires extra labor and cost for the operation.

(b) The lead-bearing leach residue is not rich in lead enough to be treated economically in a electric furnace.

Since 1968, however, waelz-fume has been roasted in a rotary kiln by adding chloridizing reagents.

Lead and cadmium contained in waelz-fume convert to their chlorides and then volatilize, while most of zinc remains as oxide in calcine. About 45 to 50 tons per day of calcine and 6 to 7 tons of dust are produced from 55 tons of waelz-fume. The calcine assaying 70 to 75 per cent zinc and 0.5 to 1.0 per cent lead is returned to zinc plant for leaching.

Operation and apparatus

There are two rotary kilns equipped with such installations as charging devices and dust collecting apparatus including dust chambers and bag filters.

Dimensions of each kiln are 1.5 m in diameter by 12 m long and 1.8 m by 18 m, respectively. kilns are fired with oil at their discharging ends.

Waelz-fume, mixed with proper amount of chloridizing reagents and sulfur, is treated in kilns.

The lead and cadmium volatilized inside the kilns are collected while the exit gas stream passes through dust chambers and the bag filters.

On the other hand, the calcine discharged from both kilns is ground by 110 kilowatt- conical ball mill and conveyed pneumatically to the leaching plant, about 150 meters apart. Table VII shows typical analyses from the roasting plant of waelz-fume.

Table VII. Typical analyses from the roasting plant of waelz-fume

	Zn	Pb	Cd	Cl	F	In
Fume	61.9	9.0	0.81	2.18	0.128	0.089
Calcine	71.8	1.36	0.051	0.028	0.0035	0.037
Dust	8.67	44.4	4.34	12.5	0.265	0.307

The chloride-chlorine remained in the calcine is now maintained below 0.03 per cent, that is, 100 milligrams maximum per liter in leached solution under normal condition. Also, the partial pressure of oxygen inside the kiln is carefully controlled to assist oxidation of the iron contained in calcine.

Reactions inside the kiln

We assume that the lead and cadmium oxides might be chlorinated, according to the reactions expressed by:

$$PbO + 2NaCl + S + 3/2\ O_2 = PbCl_2 + Na_2SO_4$$
$$CdO + 2NaCl + S + 3/2\ O_2 = CdCl_2 + Na_2SO_4$$

Lead and cadmium oxides, contained in a large amount of zinc oxide, are so selectively chlorinated that zinc oxide is barely chlorinated during roasting. Even if zinc chloride should be formed during this process, it would be double decomposed as follows to leave lead and cadmium as chlorides.

$$PbO + ZnCl_2 = PbCl_2 + ZnO$$
$$CdO + ZnCl_2 = CdCl_2 + ZnO$$

Treatment of lead-bearing dust

Lead-bearing dust collected during chloridizing roasting contains besides lead and cadmium, a small amount of zinc and indium.

Lead-bearing dust is treated with weak acid in order to extract cadmium and zinc in solution. Lead and indium remain in residue. The sponge cadmium is precipitated from the solution by contact with zinc plates. Lead and indium are recovered from the residue.

The sponge is then briquetted in a briquetting press and is further refined by distillation to be metallic cadmium of 99.995 average per cent.

As the solution remaining after the precipitation of cadmium contains about 40 grams zinc per liter, slaked lime is added to the solution in order to recover the residual zinc as hydroxide which is recycled into waelz kiln.

Operation and apparatus

The lead-bearing dust is repulped with water and then pumped up to leaching tank, where about 90 per cent of cadmium and 85 per cent of zinc contained are extracted by adding sulfuric acid.

The residue produced here is processed for the further recovery of lead and indium, as to be described later.

The leach-solution is filtered by 160 mm Hg-rotary drum vacuum filter, and then the filtrate is introduced into the cementation tank fitted with zinc plates to precipitate cadmium as spnge. Sponge cadmium is briquetted under the pressure of 1 ton per square centimeter, fused with caustic soda, and then distilled.

The distillation is carried out at about 760°C at a rate of 25 kilogram distillate per hour in 20 KW-electric furnace, thereby the consumption of electric power is 2,300 KWH per ton cadmium produced. The purified cadmium contains 0.001 per cent lead, 0.0002 per cent copper and 0.002 per cent thallium.

Distillation-residue is tapped from the bottom of the furnace periodically per every 50 ton of the charge. The composition of the residue is copper 2 per cent, lead 68 per cent and the remainder being cadmium.

The distillation efficiency is about 99.7 per cent.

Treatment of lead-bearing residue

The residue obtained as a result of leaching lead-bearing dust contains most of lead as well as indium contained in the feed for waelz kiln. This residue is further treated with acid to dissolve indium out, and then, is, after being dried, submitted to smelting in a short rotary furnace to produce crude lead which is finally refined by Bett's process.

From this residue only, about 80 tons of lead ingots are now being produced monthly.

Operation and apparatus

A typical analysis of lead-bearing residue is given in Table VIII.

Lead-bearing residue is first dried in a rotary dryer to reduce moisture down to 10 per cent or less. Normally 100 parts of dried lead-bearing residue, 23 parts soda ash, 21 parts anthracite and 14 parts iron powder are blended. For economical reason, we use the iron powder as precipitant which is recovered in our plant.

Table VIII. Typical analysis of lead-bearing residue

pct							g per ton	
Pb	Zn	Fe	Cd	Cu	S	Cl	Ag	Au
59.1	0.327	2.50	0.175	0.22	7.37	6.72	210	—

The charge-mix is fed into the short rotary furnace, 2.1 meters in diameter and 2.3 meters long in inside dimensions. The furnace is lined with Chromium-magnesium refractory bricks and fired with oil.

We operate the furnace about 11 times a day. The capacity of the furnace is about 1 ton charge of lead-bearing residue per every batch. The melt at about 1100°C tapped from the furnace settles in fore-hearth to remove slag, then the crude lead runs into a kettle.

The typical analyses of crude lead, slag and dust are shown in Table IX. Table X shows the material balance in the rotary furnace smelting.

The operation data of electrolytic refining are:

current density, A/m^2	120
electrode spacing, mm	120
temperature of electrolyte, °C	25 to 35
circulation rate of electrolyte, l/min. ...	15 to 20

Ferroconcrete asphalt-lined electrolytic cells have inside dimensions of 2.48 long, 0.82 m wide and 0.92 m deep.

Typical analysis of the electrolytic lead and the anode slime are shown in Table XI.

Table IX. Typical analyses of crude lead, slag and dust

	pct											g per ton	
	pb	Zn	Cu	Fe	Cd	As	Bi	Sb	Sn	S	Cl	Ag	Au
Crude lead	98.5	—	0.1	—	—	0.20	0.47	0.20	0.45	—	—	500	0.73
Slag	3.2	0.5	0.6	—	—	—	—	—	—	13.0	1.5	40	—
Dust	43.3	0.57	—	3.0	1.24	—	—	—	—	—	—	—	—

Table X. Material balance
in the rotary furnace smelting

		proportion	Pb	Zn	Cd	Cu	Ag	Au
Input	Lead bearing residue	100.0	100.0	100.0	100.0	54.5	73.0	
	Iron powder	14	—	—	—	15.5	27.0	100.0
	Soda ash	23	—	--	—	—	—	
	Anthracite	21	—	—	—	—	—	—
	Total		100.0	100.0	100.0	100.0	100.0	100.0
Output	Crude lead	52.2	87	—	—	12.9	90	85
	Slag	55.0	3	75	2	81.7	7.6	12
	Dust	12.3	9	22	95	3.8	1.0	1.0
	Loss and others		1	3	3	1.6	1.4	2
	Total		100.0	100.0	100.0	100.0	100.0	100.0

Table XI. Typical analysis of lead ingot
and anode slime

	Pct								g per ton	
	Pb	Cu	Bi	Sb	As	Sn	Zn	Fe	Ag	Au
Lead	99.997	0.0003	0.001	0.0001	0.001	0.0001	0.0001	0.0001	2	—
Slime	15.0	4.5	22.0	8.5	8.5	3.5	—	—	24,800	36.2

Reactions inside the rotary furnace

In the lead-bearing residue, lead is present chiefly as oxychloride and sulfate. The reactions of these lead compounds inside the furnace are exemplified as follows.

$$2PbOCl + Na_2CO_3 + 4C = 2Pb + 2NaCl + 5CO$$
$$PbSO_4 + 4C = PbS + 4CO$$
$$PbS + Na_2CO_3 + 2C = Pb + Na_2S + 3CO$$
$$PbS + Fe = Pb + FeS$$

Recovery of indium

Lead-bearing dust is treated with acid to produce residue, which is leached and then filtered under acidic condition to obtain indium containing liquor. This liquor is neutralized with milk of lime to precipitate indium as hydroxide. This precipitate is treated with sulfuric acid to dissolve indium and then is filtered. The resultant solution, after being purified by adding zinc dust to precipitate arsenic and copper, is contacted with zinc plates in a cementation tank to precipitate indium as sponge. The sponge is briquetted in a briquetting press, fused with caustic soda, vacuum-distilled to separate cadmium as vapor and finally is refined by electrolysis.

Table XII shows material balance in the recovery process of indium.

Table XII. Material balance in the recovery process of indium

	products	pct			
		In	Cd	Zn	Pb
Primary residue	111T/M	0.250	0.520	1.60	55.0
Secondary residue	103T/M	0.065	0.175	0.327	59.1
Crude indium hydroxide	357OKg/M	6.00	0.500	4.920	—
Sponge indium	224Kg/M	85.0	7.80	—	—
Crude indium	177Kg/M	99.0	0.002	0.50	0.15
Metallic indium	170Kg/M	99.99	0.002	0.0005	0.003

*
Primary residue:
The residue obtained by leaching lead-bearing dust.

**
Secondary residue:
The residue obtained after removing indium from primary residue.

Conclusion

We take it as granted that the cleaner zinc concentrate we use, the better primary efficiency in zinc extraction we can achieve. However, it might be necessary at times for us to smelt miscellaneous ores less in zinc content with as good recovery rate as is the case with clean materials. Under these circumstances, we have succeeded in the establishment of a new series of technology to treat leach residue in order to attain as good over-all recovery as ever, no matter what grade of ores must be used. Viewed in the light of economics, in other words, we believe that the profit obtained as a result of residue treatment well exceeds the cost incurred. Besides, we are able to have a wider selection of zinc ores without deterioration in the total recovery. Taking the fact that the ores less in zinc content happen to contain more various valuable metals into consideration, it is reasonable for us to concentrate more efforts upon the recovery of these metals contained in the raw materials.

Chapter 16

THE TREATMENT OF ZINC PLANT RESIDUE AT THE RISDON WORKS OF THE ELECTROLYTIC ZINC COMPANY OF AUSTRALASIA LIMITED.

C.J. Haigh* and R.W. Pickering**

* Principal Research Officer, Electrolytic Zinc Company of Australasia Limited, Tasmania, Australia.

** Director of Research, Electrolytic Zinc Company of Australasia Limited, Tasmania, Australia.

ABSTRACT

Stockpiled and currently produced zinc plant residues containing zinc ferrite are to be treated at a rate of 350 tonne per day in a plant that is being constructed at the Risdon works of the Electrolytic Zinc Company of Australasia Limited (E.Z.). Start-up of the plant is scheduled for December, 1970.

The residue is to be treated by a hydrometallurgical process that was developed by E.Z. in Australia, by Det Norske Zinkkompani in Norway, and by Compagnie Royale Asturienne des Mines (Asturiana de Zinc) in Spain.

The process, as it is to be used at Risdon, is simple, consisting essentially of two stages:

1. A leaching stage at atmospheric pressure in which the zinc ferrite contained in zinc plant residue is dissolved in spent electrolyte, fortified with make up sulphuric acid, at a temperature in the range 70 to 95°C. Undissolved solids containing lead and precious metals are separated for sale to a lead smelter.

2. An iron precipitation stage at atmospheric pressure in which ferric iron is precipitated from a slightly acidic solution at 90 to 95°C as ammonium jarosite, a crystalline double sulphate which is relatively coarse, and is easily filtered and washed free of zinc-bearing solution. Calcine is used to neutralise the acid that

is liberated during precipitation of the iron.

Also included in the Risdon plant are a separate stage for oxidation of ferrous iron by injection of air, and a pre-neutralisation stage, using recycled oxidation stage pulp, to neutralise excess acidity from the leaching stage before the jarosite precipitation stage.

The residue treatment plant consists of conventional equipment such as covered agitated vessels, thickeners and filters. Operation will be continuous and product solution will join the main zinc plant circuit for further purifications and electrolysis.

Marketable zinc production will be increased by 70 tonne per operating day by the treatment of residue.

INTRODUCTION

For over fifty years the Electrolytic Zinc Company of Australasia Limited has operated an electrolytic zinc plant at Risdon, near Hobart, Tasmania, Australia. Zinc production is currently 485 tonne of cathode zinc per day. Since 1940 zinc plant residue produced at the Risdon plant has been stockpiled. Today the accumulated residue amounts to over 1,000,000 tonne. Prior to 1940 the residue was sold for its lead, silver and gold contents to Broken Hill Associated Smelters Proprietary Limited, Port Pirie.

Over the years alternative residue treatment procedures have been investigated at Risdon. Acid roasting of residue was examined in detail, and plans for a full scale treatment plant were drawn up. However, construction of the plant was deferred until the potentially more attractive pressure leaching process was fully investigated. As a result of these studies the jarosite process was developed. It is considered to be more profitable and simpler to operate than alternative hydrometallurgical or pyrometallurgical procedures.

While the Electrolytic Zinc Company of Australasia (E.Z.) was developing the jarosite process (1) for recovery of zinc and other metal values from ferritic zinc plant residues, similar processes were developed independently, by Det Norske Zinkkompani A/S (D.N.Z.) in Norway (2) and Compagnie Royale Asturienne des Mines (C.R.A.M.) in Spain (3). The three companies, C.R.A.M., D.N.Z. and E.Z. have agreed to act together to license users of the process throughout the world.

Stockpiled and currently produced residue is to be treated at a rate of 350 tonne/day in a plant that is under construction at the Risdon works of E.Z. Start up of the plant is scheduled for December,1970.

D.N.Z. have been operating a similar residue treatment plant at Odda, Norway since early in 1968.

Included in this paper are a general discussion of the jarosite process, a detailed description of the Risdon residue treatment plant, and a summary of the metallurgical performance expected from the plant.

THE JAROSITE PROCESS

During the roasting of zinc sulphide concentrates, portion of the zinc reacts with iron present in the concentrates to form zinc ferrite. Under the usual leaching conditions practised in electrolytic zinc plants very little of this ferrite is dissolved, and it reports in the zinc plant residue. As a consequence overall zinc recoveries from the leaching of calcines are usually in the range 87-93%, the limitation in recovery depending principally on the quantity of zinc ferrite formed in the roasting step.

It has been known for many years that the zinc ferrite content of zinc plant residues is readily soluble in solutions containing an excess of sulphuric acid at or near the boiling point. Ferric iron can be precipitated as the oxide or hydroxide from such solutions by the addition of a suitable neutralising agent such as calcine. Although the precipitated iron can be filtered effectively, there are losses of zinc due to entrainment of solution and due to incomplete utilisation of the zinc oxide content of the added calcine.

In the jarosite process ferric iron is precipitated from slightly acidic solutions as a crystalline double sulphate belonging to the jarosite group of compounds. The jarosites are a group of compounds which have the general formula $AFe_3(SO_4)_2(OH)_6$ where A can be Na, K, Rb, NH_4, Ag, Pb/2 or H_3O. The jarosites of particular interest in the residue treatment context are those of sodium, potassium or ammonium.

The precipitation of iron as a jarosite compound can be represented by the following typical equation

$$3Fe_2(SO_4)_3 + Na_2SO_4 + 12H_2O = 2NaFe_3(SO_4)_2(OH)_6 + 6H_2SO_4.$$

In practice the situation is more complicated as, under certain conditions, some hydroxonium jarosite may be formed and solid solutions of sodium, potassium or ammonium jarosite and hydroxonium jarosite are known to exist.

The particular advantages of precipitating iron as a jarosite compound are:

1. The precipitates are crystalline solids that can be readily thickened, filtered and washed free of zinc bearing solution.

2. The compounds contain only small amounts of sodium, potassium or ammonium and hence consumption of reagents is small. For example, the ammonium content of ammonium jarosite formed under conditions that are likely to exist in a residue treatment plant is usually less than 3%.

3. The amount of acid liberated during the precipitation of iron as a jarosite is much less than if the oxide or hydroxide is produced. Hence the neutralising agent requirements are minimised.

4. Because the jarosites are precipitated from slightly acid solutions efficient utilisation of the neutralising agents is obtained and losses of acid soluble zinc in the precipitate are negligible.

5. In zinc plants where a build up of sulphate tends to occur, precipitation of jarosites containing combined sulphate is a convenient method of sulphate control.

The extent of iron precipitation as a jarosite compound is increased by increases in temperature and in the concentration of sodium, potassium or ammonium ions and by a decrease in the free acid concentration. Thus, for example, the same degree of iron precipitation can be obtained at 180°C with a free acidity of 40 g/l, as at 95°C with a free acidity of 5 g/l (pH ca. 1.5).

Addition of Na^+, K^+ or NH_4^+ ions beyond the stoichiometric equivalent does not improve significantly the extent of precipitation Below the stoichiometric level, however, a change in the concentration of these ions has a marked effect. Potassium jarosite is the least soluble of the three jarosites of interest in the residue treatment context; but, as potassium salts are generally more expensive, economic considerations tend to favour the use of either sodium or ammonium compounds.

The choice of optimum operating conditions depends on many factors but a major one is the cost and availability of suitable neutralising agents. As electrolytic zinc plants normally have available on the site a suitable neutralising agent in the form of calcine, economic considerations tend to favour an operating temperature of less than 100°C. This avoids the need for relatively expensive autoclaves, pumps, etc. However, where suitable neutralising agents are costly, or where loss of the residue derived from the added calcine which is combined with and lost with the jarosite precipitate is particularly undesirable, the use of an autoclave may be justified.

APPLICATION OF THE JAROSITE PROCESS TO RISDON RESIDUE

Although in its simplest form the jarosite process consists of only two stages:

1. a leaching stage in which zinc ferrite is dissolved, and

2. an iron precipitation stage in which iron is precipitated as a jarosite compound,

in order to operate these stages efficiently, and to integrate the process with the existing Risdon zinc plant, it is necessary to include additional stages. Thus, the residue treatment plant being built at Risdon consists of 5 sections. These are:

1. a leaching section in which residue is leached in spent electrolyte fortified with added contact sulphuric acid,

2. a section in which undissolved solids from the leaching section are separated from the leach solution, and divided into a zinc sulphide rich fraction, which is returned to the Risdon roasters, and a lead sulphate rich fraction which is sold to lead smelters,

3. a pre-neutralisation section in which excess acid remaining after the leaching section is neutralised,

4. an iron hydrolysis section in which calcine and ammonia are added and ferric iron is hydrolysed and precipitated as ammonium jarosite, and

5. an oxidation section in which further calcine is added and ferrous iron formed in the preceding sections is oxidised and precipitated as hydrated ferric oxide. This precipitate (containing some excess calcine) is thickened and returned as the neutralising agent used in the pre-neutralisation section.

Spent electrolyte used in the residue treatment plant is taken from the supply to the main zinc plant; solution from the oxidation section is returned to the iron purification section of the main zinc plant circuit for further purification.

Figure 1 illustrates the way in which the residue treatment plant is to be integrated with the Risdon zinc plant.

The Risdon zinc plant has been described in detail in a series of papers (4-7). Although many changes and additions have been made to the plant, the leaching and purification procedures remain essentially unchanged.

A feature of the Risdon zinc plant, which distinguishes it from other electrolytic zinc plants, is that ferritic zinc plant residue is separated from the initial leach pulp at a pH of about 1.7, and iron present in the slightly acid solution is precipitated as hydrate ferric oxide in a separate iron purification section. In this sectic ferrous iron is oxidised by the injection of air, and ferric iron is precipitated, together with silica, at a pH of about 5.0 by the controlled addition of fine calcine. Impurities such as arsenic, antimony and germanium are largely adsorbed on the iron/silica precipitate and discarded in the filter cake.

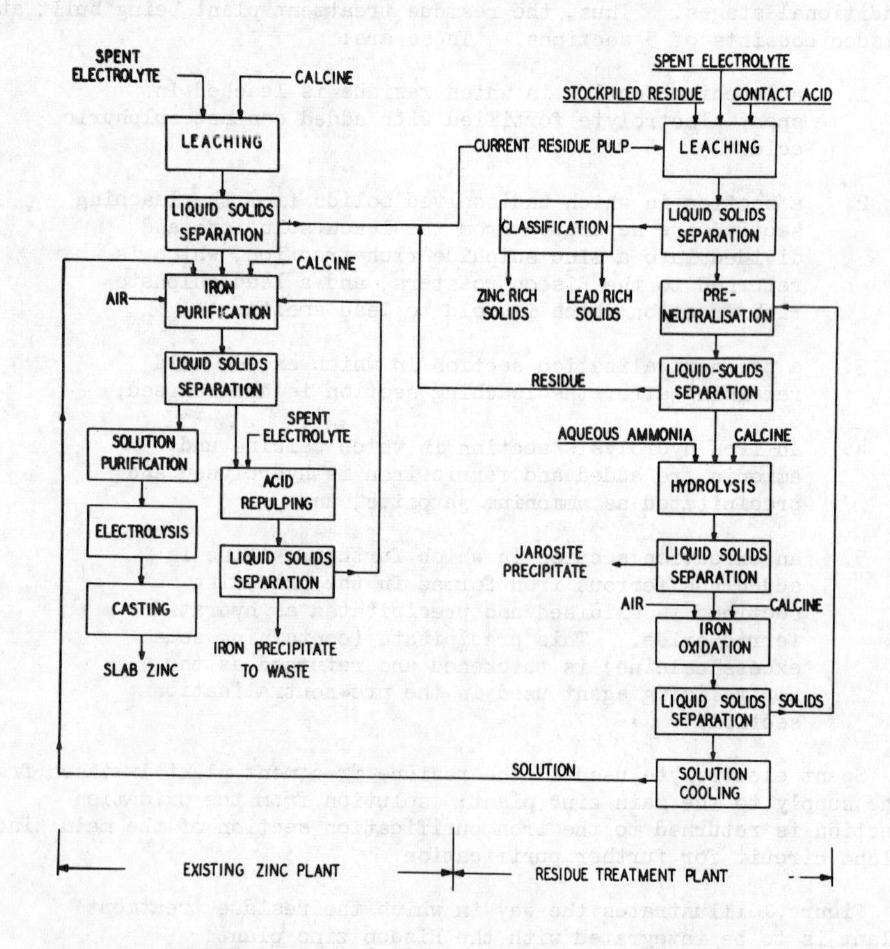

FIG. 1 RESIDUE TREATMENT PLANT FLOWSHEET SHOWING METHOD OF INTEGRATION WITH THE RISDON ZINC PLANT

Although partial removal of dissolved impurities, such as arsenic, antimony and germanium, is desirable in the hydrolysis section of the residue treatment plant, complete removal is not essential. The existing iron purification section of the Risdon zinc plant has the capacity to remove the additional quantities of impurities which will enter the circuit as a consequence of the treatment of residue.

If, however, the zinc plant was of the type where the leaching section of residue treatment could replace the acid leaching step of a neutral leach/acid leach combination, then efficient removal of impurities in the hydrolysis section would be more critical. However, an intensification of the zinc dust purification step in the zinc plant circuit, or a deliberate precipitation of some iron as hydrated ferric oxide could provide supplementary methods of impurity control.

PROPOSED RATE OF TREATMENT OF RESIDUE

The size of the residue treatment plant was selected so that it would be able to treat all current residue as soon as it is produced in the Risdon zinc plant and, in addition, to treat stockpiled residue at such a rate that the stockpile will be exhausted in about 20 years.

A treatment rate of 350 tonne per operating day (at 90% operating time) has been selected as best fulfilling the above requirements.

Current residue production from the Risdon zinc plant will be reduced from approximately 80,000 to 56,000 tonne per annum when a residue treatment plant treating 350 tonne per day commences operating. This is because portions of the calcine that would normally have been leached in the zinc plant will be diverted to the residue treatment plant. Approximately half of the residue derived from this calcine will be discarded with the jarosite precipitate and the remainder will be conserved and returned via the pre-neutralisation section to the leaching section of the residue treatment plant.

The quantities of residue to be treated in the residue plant are summarised in Table I.

TABLE I. Rate of Treatment of Residue in the Risdon Plant.

	tonne per annum	tonne per operating day (90% op. time)
Current residue	56,000	171
Stockpiled residue	48,000	146
Recycled current residue	11,000	33
TOTAL	115,000	350

Current residue production at Risdon is expected to increase progressively during the next 20 years and hence the treatment rate of stockpiled residue will decrease accordingly. It has been estimated that, by the time the stockpile of residue is exhausted, current residue production will have become sufficient to maintain approximately full capacity in the residue treatment plant.

COMPOSITION OF RESIDUE

The average composition of current residue and an estimate of the composition of residue stockpiled over the past 30 years are listed in Table II.

Up to 90% of the zinc in residue is present as zinc ferrite ($ZnO.Fe_2O_3$) the remainder being present mainly as zinc sulphide. The reduction in the sulphide sulphur content of current residuc compared to stockpiled residue is due to improvements in roasting practice and to the installation of hydrocyclones for the separation and return of imcompletely roasted sulphides.

TABLE II. The Composition of Current and Stockpiled Residue.

		Current residue	Stockpiled residue
Zinc	%	22.6	22.8
Lead	%	6.5	5.2
Iron	%	31.5	29.0
Cadmium	%	0.25	0.22
Copper	%	0.25	0.16
Cobalt	%	0.02	0.02
Manganese	%	2.35	2.35
Sulphide Sulphur	%	1.5	2.8
Silver	g/t	192	184
Gold	g/t	1.1	0.8

THE RESIDUE TREATMENT PLANT

GENERAL

The main vessels and equipment included in the residue treatment plant are shown diagrammatically in Figure 2.

The plant consists essentially of ten reaction vessels, and seven thickeners and their auxiliary vessels. In addition, use will be made of spare capacity in some existing thickeners, filters, dryers, etc., which will become available with start-up of the residue treatment plant.

The plant is to be operated continuously, and flow of process streams will mostly be by gravity. To accomplish this, there is a fall of approximately 15 cm between the liquor level in each reaction vessel or thickener and the next, thus creating a hydraulic gradient. In order to locate the plant in a compact site adjacent to the main zinc plant, it will be necessary to pump process liquors leaving the pre-neutralisation section thickener to a higher level to re-establish the hydraulic gradient through the remainder of the plant.

The ten main reaction vessels are of identical size and of conventional construction. They consist of a mild steel shell, lead lined, with an inner lining of 7.6 cm thick interlocked acid resistant bricks set in a furane based cement. The brick lining not only supports the lead against creep and from abrasion and attack by the acidic liquors, but also provides insulation against heat losses. No external insulation is provided.

The vessels have an internal diameter of 6.7 m and a working depth of 7.0 m giving a working volume of $250 m^3$. Wooden covers fitted with AISI 317 stainless steel vent pipes are used on all vessels. The covers are made from celery top pine, a Tasmanian timber resistant to hot acidic liquors. The vessels are interconnected by a launder system such that each vessel in a group can be taken out of service for maintenance without closing down the remainder of the plant. The launders and all pipe work in contact with the process liquors are fabricated in AISI 317 stainless steel. This material proved to be more resistant to corrosion in pilot plant trials than other grades of stainless steel and was therefore selected for the full scale plant.

Each vessel is fitted with a vertical standpipe 38 cm in diameter extending to within 2 m of the bottom of the vessels. Liquor leaving each vessel rises up the standpipe and overflows into a launder leading to the next vessel. By this system short-circuiting in the vessel is minimised, accumulation of heavier particles in the bottom of the tank is avoided, and the agitation required to keep the solids in suspension is minimised.

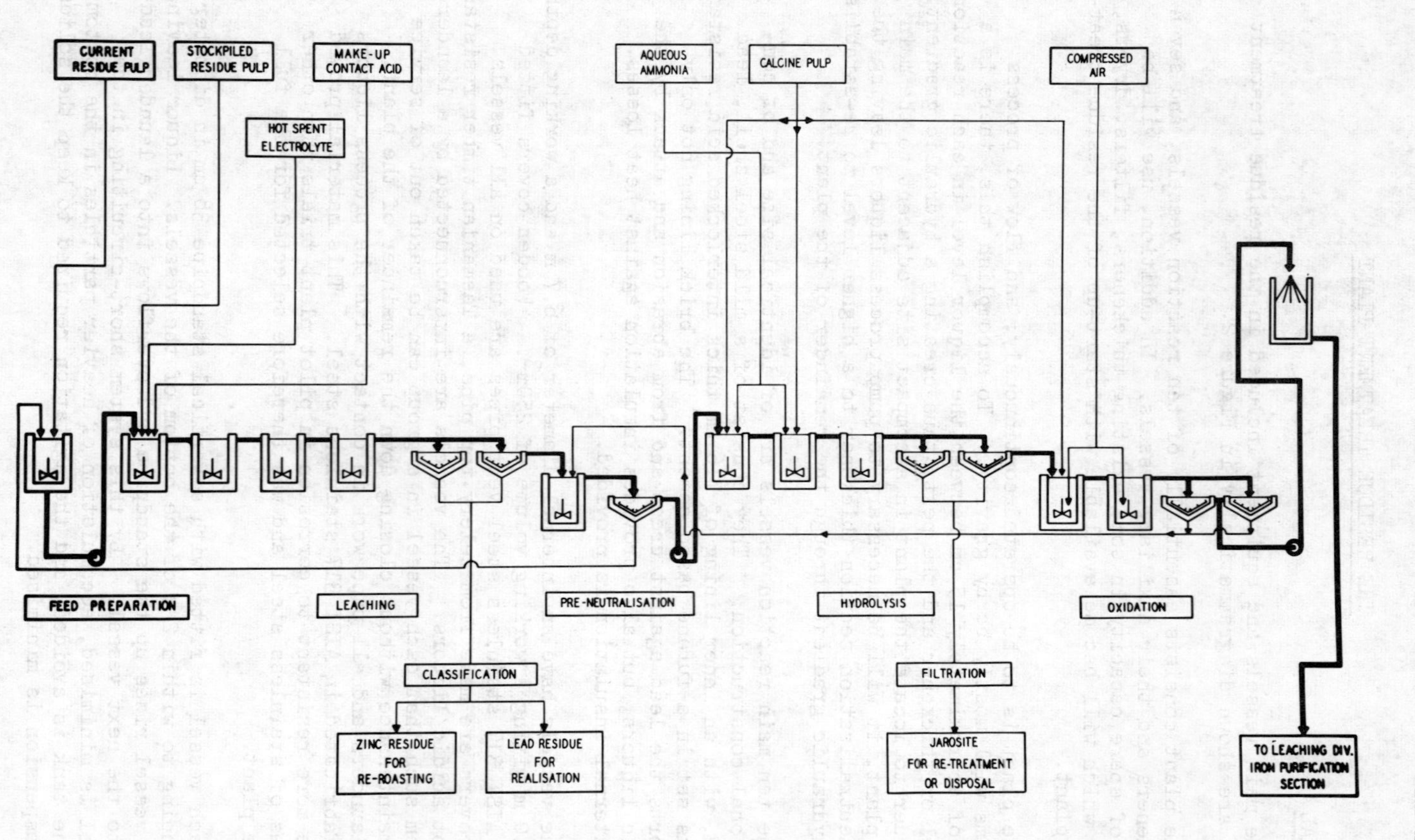

FIG. 2 RISDON RESIDUE TREATMENT PLANT FLOW SHEET

Agitation in the leaching and pre-neutralisation section vessels is by means of four-bladed down-thrusting axial-flow turbines 1.9 m in diameter, 0.6 m off the bottom of the vessels, rotating at 30 r.p.m. Power consumption is 6 kW per vessel transmitted through a centrally mounted rubber covered mild steel shaft. The impellers are fabricated in AISI 317 stainless steel. All vessels are baffled.

In the hydrolysis section vessels the impellers are 2.3 m in diameter, 0.8 m from the bottom and rotate at 30 r.p.m. The power consumption is approximately 18 kW per vessel. The greater power consumption in these vessels is needed to keep the comparatively coarse jarosite in suspension and to promote adequate crystal growth.

In the oxidation section vessels agitation is by curved six-bladed turbines 1.8 m in diameter, 0.9 m from the bottom of the vessels, rotating at 56 r.p.m. Power consumption is approximately 75 kW per vessel. Curved blades are used in these vessels to minimise shearing at the tips of the blades and to impart a high pumping efficiency.

All agitators, which have been supplied by Lightnin Mixers Australia Limited, are fitted with fluid couplings to prevent gear box failures in the event of the impellers "sanding in" following a plant shut down.

The seven thickeners are each 15 m in diameter with 2.7 m wood stave walls, lead lined, and with an inner lining of 23 cm thick acid brick set in furane cement. The thickeners are supported on conical reinforced concrete bases of slope 15°, with a 45° discharge cone. The discharge cone is mild steel, lead lined, with a lining of 2.5 cm thick acid resisting tiles. Rakes and all sub-solution gear are made of AISI 317 stainless steel fitted to rubber covered mild steel shafts.

Where two thickeners are operated in parallel, as in the leaching, hydrolysis and oxidation sections, the feed is divided by a venturi splitter (two venturi flumes in parallel) and enters the thickeners via centrally located stilling wells. The thickener overflows are collected in AISI 317 stainless steel, internal, peripheral launders, while thickener underflows are pumped or air lifted to pulp storage tanks.

FEED PREPARATION SECTION

(a) Current Residue

Current residue, in the form of thickener underflow from the main zinc plant, will be pumped from an existing storage vessel and metered into the first leaching vessel. The pulp contains 0.8 to 1.0 kg of solids per litre of pulp and has a specific gravity in the range 1.7 to 2.1. Most of the filter capacity which was previously used for filtration of current residue and which will become available when filtration of current residue ceases with start-up of the residu treatment plant, will be utilised in de-watering the lead residue produced in the residue treatment plant.

The mass flow of current residue solids entering the first leachin vessel will be controlled automatically by means of a swing launder actuated by a signal from a magnetic flow meter integrated with a pulp density meter.

(b) Stockpiled Residue

Stockpiled residue will be reclaimed from the stockpile, screened, and transported by existing conveyor belts to an elevated storage bin of 300 tonne capacity. This residue contains between 10 and 13% moisture, and it is in the form of free flowing agglomerates. A constant weight feeder will deliver this residue to a mixing tank where it will be repulped in spent electrolyte preheated to 75°C. The resulting pulp will overflow into a launder leading to the first leaching vessel.

The 18 m^3 repulp tank is fabricated in AISI 317 stainless steel. Agitation is by means of a four-bladed axial flow turbine 110 cm in diameter, 35 cm from the tank bottom, rotating at 58 r.p.m. Power consumption is approximately 6 kW.

(c) Spent Electrolyte

Spent electrolyte, containing approximately 95 g/l H_2SO_4 and 50 g/l Zn, will flow by gravity from existing storage tanks through shell and tube heat exchangers where it will be heated from approximately 35°C to 75°C. The wetted parts of the heat exchangers will be fabricated in a titanium alloy containing between 0.15 and 0.20% palladium. The temperature of the spent electrolyte will be controlled automatically by regulating the steam supply to the heat exchanger

Two identical heat exchangers are to be installed, and provision is to be made for regular cleaning of the tubes by mechanical means. A slow build-up of gypsum and manganese dioxide scale is anticipated. Because of the scale build-up, and a preference for its removal by mechanical means, titanium alloy was selected instead of graphite for the heat exchangers.

Flow of spent electrolyte will be continuously recorded and manually controlled to an approximately constant flow of 3,630 m^3 per day. About a quarter of the flow will be diverted through the tank where stockpiled residue is repulped, the remainder passing directly into the first leaching vessel.

(d) Sulphuric Acid

Additions of concentrated sulphuric acid at a rate of approximately 150 tonne per day will be made directly to the first leaching vessel. The acid will be supplied to a storage tank from the contact acid plant operating at Risdon. The flow of acid will be manually controlled from the storage tank and will be adjusted periodically to maintain an overall sulphate balance in the zinc plant circuit. The quantity of make-up acid required is determined primarily by the sulphate that is combined in the jarosite precipitate, and losses of sulphate in other plant discards. At Risdon, there will be an additional loss of sulphate due to discard of spent electrolyte, from which the zinc will have been stripped by electrolysis to maintain an optimum manganese concentration in the circuit. This will be necessary because of the extra manganese entering the circuit from the treatment of residue.

LEACHING SECTION

This section, which will be operated co-currently, consists of four leaching vessels in series followed by two thickeners in parallel. Nominal overall retention time in the leaching vessels is 7 hours. A leaching temperature in the range 85-95°C will be maintained by the use of spent electrolyte preheated to 75°C, augmented by the heat of reaction of zinc ferrite and sulphuric acid, and the heat of dilution of contact sulphuric acid. Provision has been made for live steam heating during start-up periods following plant shut downs.

Typical solution compositions and the percentage ferritic zinc and iron extractions expected in the four leaching vessels are listed in Table III. In Table IV are listed the approximate extractions of minor elements expected in the leaching section. These predictions are based on extensive laboratory and pilot plant investigations.

The extent of attack of zinc ferrite is increased by increases in temperature, time, and free acidity. Above a temperature of about 95°C, ferrous iron formation becomes significant due to reduction of ferric sulphate by zinc sulphide present in the residue. Because it is desirable to keep the oxidation stage small, thus minimising the quantity of pulp to be recycled, the formation of excessive ferrous iron will be avoided by maintaining the leaching temperature at less than 95°C.

Laboratory and pilot plant experiments have indicated that attack of zinc ferrite is sufficiently rapid at free acidities in excess of about 35 g/l, but that the rate falls off quickly below this level. The initial free acid concentration is determined by the volume of spent electrolyte and the quantity of added sulphuric acid. The quantity of concentrated acid which can be added is determined by the overall circuit sulphate balance. At Risdon the initial free acid concentration would be approximately 140 g H_2SO_4/litre, and the residue solids loading between 100 and 120 g per litre of spent electrolyte.

TABLE III. Solution Compositions and Ferritic Zinc and Iron Extractions.

	Solution Composition (g/l)			
	Zn	H_2SO_4	T/Fe	Fe^{2+}
Solution entering 1st leaching vessel	50-55	140-150	0	0
Solution leaving 4th leaching vessel	75-80	30-40	25-30	1-2

	Leaching Vessel Number			
	1	2	3	4
Concentration of H_2SO_4 in g/l	50	40	37	35
Percentage ferritic zinc extraction	82	94	98	99
Percentage total iron extraction	76	87	91	93

TABLE IV. Extraction of Minor Elements.

Element	Percentage Extraction	Element	Percentage Extraction
As	75	F	60
Al	45	Cl	60
Ca	90	Mn	90
Cd	50	Mg	65
Cu	80	Sb	30
Co	75	Ge	60
Bi	45	Si	30

The flows of current residue pulp, spent electrolyte and concentrated sulphuric acid will be maintained approximately constant, and the weight of stockpiled residue fed to the first leaching vessel will be altered to maintain the acidity in the fourth leaching vessel at about 35 g H_2SO_4/litre. Solution leaving the fourth leaching vessel will flow to two thickeners in parallel. Thickener overflow will pass to the pre-neutralisation section vessel and the thickener underflow will be air lifted to a pulp storage tank.

LEAD RESIDUE SECTION

The undissolved solids separated from the leach solution as thickener underflow pulp contain substantially all of the lead and precious metals originally present in the residue. In addition, these solids also contain a significant proportion of zinc sulphide which failed to oxidise during concentrate roasting and during the leaching of residue.

The thickener underflow will be diluted by return solution and the diluted pulp pumped through eight 15 cm diameter hydrocyclones. Hydrocyclone underflow, containing up to 80% of the zinc sulphide that was in the solids leaving the leaching section, will be thickened and the thickener underflow pulp filtered on an existing disc filter. The discharged filter cake will be blended with fresh concentrate and returned to the flash and fluid roasters for re-roasting. The weight of solids rich in zinc sulphide so produced will be approximately 40 tonne per day.

Hydrocyclone overflow containing the lead-rich solids will be thickened in an existing 15 m diameter thickener. Thickener overflow will be recycled and used to dilute the hydrocyclone feed pulp. Thickener underflow will be airlifted to a storage tank and the pulp neutralised by the addition of calcine pulp. The neutral lead rich pulp will be filtered on existing Moore filters. After washing, the lead-rich filter cake will be discharged and dried to 15% moisture in existing rotary driers. Finally, the lead-rich solids will be conveyed to an enclosed stockpile adjacent to the wharf, and periodically shipped to lead smelters. Approximately 90 tonne of lead-rich solids will be produced per day.

The compositions of undissolved solids separated from the leaching stage, and the compositions of zinc sulphide and lead-rich solids produced by hydrocyclone treatment, are listed in Table V.

The compositions listed are typical of results obtained in pilot plant tests of the process. In the full scale plant a range of compositions is expected depending upon operating conditions and variations in the composition of residue, especially stockpiled residue, being treated. Within limits, the composition of the lead-rich solids can be adjusted by altering the leaching conditions and the settings of the hydrocyclones so as to give a product that is particularly suitable for treatment in a lead smelter.

In this way all of the valuable metals originally present in the residue are either dissolved in the leaching section or report in the lead-rich or zinc sulphide rich solids. As the zinc sulphide rich solids are re-roasted and re-leached in the main zinc plant, good recoveries of contained metal values such as cadmium will be achieved. In the steady state the majority of the lead and silver will concentrate into the lead-rich fraction, and will be treated in a lead smelter.

TABLE V. Compositions of Undissolved Solids and of Zinc and Lead-Rich Solids.

Element	Undissolved solids % composition	Zinc-rich solids % composition	Lead-rich solids % composition
Zn	13.2	28.8	6.0
Pb	15.9	5.9	27.1
Fe	6.4	2.9	10.3
T/S	13.4	17.3	8.9
SO_4/S	7.0	1.9	5.3
S^o+S/S	6.0	15.4	3.6
SiO_2	12.0	-	-
Cd	0.19	0.58	0.08
Ag	608 g/t	968 g/t	463 g/t

PRE-NEUTRALISATION SECTION

Thickener overflow leaving the leaching section will contain a free acid concentration of about 35 g H_2SO_4/litre. To reduce the calcine consumption in the hydrolysis section it is desirable to lower the acid concentration of solution entering this section. This is achieved in the pre-neutralisation section by neutralising excess acid with thickener underflow pulp returned from the oxidation section. This pulp contains precipitated hydrated ferric oxide, unconsumed calcine and some residue.

Neutralisation of the acid is conducted in a single vessel identical in every respect to the leaching section vessels. Addition of thickener underflow pulp from the oxidation section will be made from a swing launder supplied with pulp from an intermediate storage tank. The swing launder is operated automatically by means of a pH controller, the electrodes of which are immersed in the pre-neutralisation section vessel.

The pH will be controlled to approximately 0.9, equivalent to free acid concentration of about 15 g/l. If the acidity is maintained at less than this value, premature hydrolysis and precipitation of ammonium jarosite is likely to occur, because of the small but significant concentration of ammonium ions in the recirculating plant liquors. If insufficient thickener underflow pulp from the oxidation section is available for pre-neutralisation, provision has been made to augment the supply with calcine.

Pulp from the pre-neutralisation section vessel is thickened in a single 15 m diameter thickener. Thickener underflow, containing the residue derived from the calcine added to the oxidation section vessels, is then returned to the current residue pulp storage tank.

Thickener overflow passes to an intermediate tank from which it is pumped continuously to the first hydrolysis vessel, thus re-establishing the hydraulic gradient required to maintain gravity flow through the remainder of the plant.

HYDROLYSIS SECTION

In this section the majority of the ferric iron in solution is precipitated as ammonium jarosite. Precipitation is achieved in three vessels in series, each identical in every respect to those in the leaching section except that the degree of agitation has been increased. The extra agitation is desirable to ensure rapid mixing of the reactants to promote crystal growth, and to maintain the comparatively coarse jarosite in suspension. Nominal overall retention time in the three vessels is 4.5 hours.

Aqueous ammonia (25% NH_3) will be added via flow recording controllers to the first two vessels. The total quantity of ammonia added will be determined by experience but it is expected to be between 0.5 and 0.75 times the stoichiometric requirement to precipitate all the ferric iron as ammonium jarosite. The proportion of ammonia added to the first vessel will also be determined by experience, but it is expected to be about two-thirds of the total.

Acid liberated during precipitation of ferric iron as ammonium jarosite will be neutralised by the addition of calcine repulped in neutral zinc sulphate solution. The calcine pulp will be added to the first two hydrolysis vessels by means of separate swing launders operated automatically by pH controllers, the electrodes of which will be immersed in the hydrolysis vessels.

The hydrolysis of iron can be readily controlled by the single stage addition of both calcine and ammonia. However, laboratory and pilot plant investigations have shown that, to obtain optimum conditions for precipitation of iron with a minimum usage of reagents, the two stage addition of both calcine and ammonia is beneficial. The two stage addition of ammonia is desirable to give a low residual concentration of ammonium ions in the hydrolysed solution (a necessary condition if premature hydrolysis in the pre-neutralisation section is to be avoided) while still maintaining an adequate rate of precipitation of iron.

The addition of calcine in stages is also desirable as it avoids the formation of hydrated ferric oxide which tends to precipitate if excess calcine is added to the first hydrolysis vessel. The exact proportion of calcine to be added to the first hydrolysis vessel will be determined by experience.

Aqueous ammonia was selected as the most suitable reagent because flow control is straight forward and only a simple storage installation is required. It is to be prepared in an ammonia plant operating within the Risdon works. Gaseous ammonia and water will be pumped continuously through a tubular absorber, the flow of ammonia, and hence the concentration of the aqueous product, will be controlled by the difference in temperature between water entering and product leaving the absorber. The ammonium hydroxide solution will be pumped to a mild steel storage tank located in the residue treatment plant. Flow from the tank into the hydrolysis vessels will be by gravity.

The use of anhydrous ammonia was rejected because of the more elaborate and costly storage facilities required at the residue treatment plant. The use of ammonium sulphate was also rejected because addition of the contained sulphate would involve the use of additional neutralising agents in the hydrolysis section without any compensating benefits.

Ammonia was selected instead of the alternative compounds of sodium or potassium because of its much lower cost at Risdon.

The pH in the hydrolysis vessels will be controlled in the range 1.3 to 1.7, corresponding approximately to free acidities in the range 3 to 8 g/l. The temperature of the hydrolysing solution will be maintained in the range 90 to 95°C by the injection of live steam.

Pulp from the last hydrolysis vessel will flow to two 15 m diameter thickeners in parallel. Provision has been made for addition of a suitable flocculant if required. Based on pilot plant results settling rates of 1 to 2 cm/min. are expected. Pilot plant work was done, however, with 95% minus 400 Tyler mesh classified flash roasted calcine as the neutralising agent. In the full scale residue treatment plant, fluid roasted calcine containing only 30% minus 325 Tyler mesh will be used, and faster settling rates are anticipated.

Thickener overflow will pass directly to the first oxidation section vessel. The composition of the solution at this point is expected to be as follows:- Zn 90-100 g/l, Fe^{3+} 0.5-1.5 g/l, Fe^{2+} 2-3 g/l, H_2SO_4 3-8 g/l, NH_4^+ 0.5 g/l.

Thickener underflow, containing precipitated ammonium jarosite and residue derived from the added calcine, will be filtered and washed on new Moore filters, and then transported to a stockpile. The solids will be stockpiled for a time while consideration is given to their further treatment or ultimate disposal.

The composition of the jarosite filter cake is expected to be as follows:-
Moisture 25%; Dry solids - T/Zn 3.5%, W/Zn 0.5%, Fe 32%, Pb 1.5%, SO_4 35%, NH_4 2.3%.
Approximately 450 tonne of wet filter cake will be produced per day.

Based on pilot plant results filtration rates in excess of 500 kg $m^{-2}hr^{-1}$ are anticipated, but this will depend in part on the type and degree of fineness of the calcine used for neutralising the acid liberated during hydrolysis.

Moore filters with a multifilament nap-finish terylene cloth were selected because of their proven ability effectively to wash the cake substantially free of entrained zinc. Because of the large tonnage of solids to be filtered per day efficient washing is of particular importance.

Because the solids produced in the hydrolysis section contain ferritic residue derived from the added calcine some re-treatment to recover metal values is indicated. As a result of preliminary hydrocyclone and flotation tests it is anticipated that methods based on the physical separation of the residue from the jarosite will be effective, but the results will depend largely on the particle size and size distribution of the precipitated jarosite. A detailed investigation of this aspect has been deferred until the plant has been operating for some time and producing a consistent product.

Laboratory and pilot plant investigations have shown that removal of toxic impurities during precipitation of jarosites is variable and dependent upon many factors such as:

(a) the pH of precipitation,

(b) the level of impurities in solution,

(c) the completeness of iron precipitation,

(d) the crystallinity and particle size of the precipitate.

Because any impurities remaining in the hydrolysed solution will be removed in the iron purification section of the main Risdon zinc plant, any variation in the removal of toxic impurities in the hydrolysis section will be of little consequence. However, once the plant has been operating for some time attempts will be made to optimise operating conditions in the hydrolysis section so as to obtain maximum removal of toxic impurities together with good thickening and filtration properties of the precipitate and minimum usage of ammonia and calcine.

OXIDATION SECTION

In the leaching section, portion of the zinc sulphide present in the residue reacts with ferric sulphate producing ferrous sulphate. The quantity of ferrous iron so formed increases with increases in temperature, in retention time, and in the zinc sulphide content of residue. Because the residue stockpiled at Risdon contains more zinc sulphide than does current residue from many zinc plants, ferrou iron formation in the residue treatment plant at Risdon will be significant.

The ferrous iron concentration of solution leaving the hydrolysis section is expected to be in the range 2 to 3 g/l. It would be possible to oxidise this ferrous iron in the iron purification sectic of the main zinc plant where ferrous iron is already oxidised at a pH of 4.5 to 5.0 by the injection of air. However, this section of the zinc plant is operating at near maximum capacity with regard to oxidation of ferrous iron and further expansion is difficult in that area.

Alternatively, the ferrous iron could be oxidised before or during the hydrolysis section by the addition of a suitable oxidant, such as manganese dioxide. However, when design of the residue treatment plant was commenced the manganese level in the Risdon circuit was approximately 15 g/l. In the leaching section at least 90% of the manganese in residue will be dissolved thus increasing the manganese concentration in the circuit. The principal effects of an increase in the manganese concentration are to increase the cell voltage, to decrease current efficiency, and to increase the viscosity of circuit solution. To avoid these disadvantages provision has been made for discard of some spent electrolyte at a rate to maintain the optimum manganese level. Under the circumstances, therefore, it was preferred not to oxidise ferrous iron by the addition of further manganese to the circuit.

It was decided to install a separate iron oxidation section after the hydrolysis section. In this section ferrous iron will be oxidised at a pH of about 5.0 by the injection of air. The ferric iron so formed is hydrolysed and precipitated as hydrated ferric oxide. Any residual ferric iron that was not precipitated in the hydrolysis section will also be precipitated here.

Oxidation will be conducted in two vessels of identical design to the leaching section vessels. Agitation is by curved six-bladed turbines rotating at 56 r.p.m. Power consumption will be approximately 75 kW per vessel. Air, at a rate of 42.5 m^3 per minute wil be introduced through an open ended sparger beneath each impeller.

Calcine pulp will be added to the first vessel by means of a swing launder operated automatically by a pH controller, the electrodes of which will be immersed in the oxidation vessel. The pH will be maintained in the range 4.5 to 5.2.

Overflow from the second oxidation vessel will pass to two 15 m diameter thickeners in parallel. Thickener overflow will be pumped to an unpacked spray tower where the solution temperature will be lowered from approximately 75°C to less than 50°C. The cooled solution will then flow by gravity to rejoin the main zinc plant circuit in the iron purification section.

Installation of the cooling tower is required for two reasons:

(a) it provides necessary evaporation to maintain an overall water balance, and

(b) without it, or an alternative form of cooling, the temperature of solution flowing through the copper/cadmium purification section of the main zinc plant would rise sufficiently to cause undesirable corrosion problems.

Thickener underflow, containing hydrated ferric oxide, unconsumed calcine, and residue derived from all the added calcine, will be air lifted to a storage tank. From this tank it will be metered under pH control into the preneutralisation section vessel.

In the preneutralisation section the unconsumed calcine and hydrated ferric oxide will react and residue will be thickened and returned to the current residue storage tank. Thus the ferric iron precipitated in the oxidation section will be redissolved and will eventually pass to the hydrolysis section. In effect, all iron dissolved in the leaching section, whether ferric or ferrous, will eventually be precipitated as ammonium jarosite in the hydrolysis section. This arrangement takes full advantage of the excellent filtering and washing characteristics of the jarosite precipitate.

FLOCCULANT SUPPLY

Provision has been made for the addition of a flocculant to all process streams entering thickeners. The rates of addition will be determined by experience once the plant begins operating. For convenience the flocculant, as a 1% solution in water, will be delivered from an existing storage tank supplying the main zinc plant circuit. In the residue plant the 1% solution will be diluted to 0.03% by addition of impure solution pumped from the cooling tower.

Flocculant consumption is expected to be approximately 45 kg per day.

CALCINE PULP SECTION

Based on previous experience at Risdon the most satisfactory form in which to add calcine, when used as a neutralising agent under pH control, is as a pulp in water. This method is used in the iron purification section of the main zinc plant circuit, However, in the residue treatment plant, because of the large amount of calcine required (300 tonne/day), the use of water as the pulp medium would impose a serious water balance problem. It was decided, therefore, to pulp the calcine in impure zinc sulphate solution, the most suitable source of which is thickener overflow from the oxidation section.

The calcine pulping plant consists essentially of a mixing tank, hydrocyclones, a tube mill and a storage tank. Fluid roasted calcine will be scraped continuously from a conveyor belt and agitated with neutral zinc sulphate solution at approximately 75°C in a 9 m^3 baffled tank fabricated in AISI 317 stainless steel. Agitation is by a 4 bladed axial-flow turbine 86 cm in diameter, 30 cm off the tank bottom, rotating at 85 r.p.m. Power consumption is 3.7kW.

Because of the tendency of calcine to agglomerate due to the cementing action of basic zinc salts which are rapidly precipitated at a pulp temperature of 75°C, calcine pulp will be pumped continuously through two 30 cm diameter hydrocyclones. Cyclone underflow containing the agglomerated particles will pass to a closed circuit tube mill. Cyclone overflow will pass via a swing launder to either a 160 m^3 storage tank or back to the mixing tank. Operation of the swing launder will be controlled by a level sensing probe fitted to the storage tank. The density of pulp delivered to the storage tank will be measured and automatically controlled by means of a valve on the solution line to the mixing tank. From the storage tank, calcine pulp will be pumped to a head box commanding the series of swing launders, each under pH control, supplying calcine to the appropriate process vessels.

Laboratory tests have shown that, provided the solids loading is maintained at less than about 500 g/l, such calcine pulps can be readily pumped and remain stable for long periods. The tests have also shown that such pulps are very satisfactory neutralising agents and superior in some respects to calcine/water pulps.

PRODUCTION DETAILS

(a) Operators:

Three operators per shift will be required to run the residue treatment plant.

(b) Zinc Balance:

Zinc extracted from calcine used in the residue treatment plant is excluded from this balance as the extraction obtained is identical to that achieved in the main zinc plant.

	Tonne per annum.
Zinc in residue leached:-	
Current residue : 67,000 t at 22.6% Zn	15,140
Stockpiled residue : 48,000 t at 22.8% Zn	10,940
	26,080
Zinc losses:-	
Lead residue : 30,500 t at 6% Zn	1,830
Jarosite precipitate (excluding residue from calcine used for neutralisation) 107,000 t at 0.5% Zn	535
Discarded spent electrolyte	360
Manganese mud, copper residue etc.	190
	2,915

Extra marketable zinc (by difference)

= 23,165 tonne per annum

= 70.7 tonne per operating day.

Recovery from residue leached

$$= \frac{23,165}{26,080} \times 100$$

= 88.8%.

Zinc in 13,000 tonne per annum of residue discarded with jarosite precipitate

= 2,940 tonne per annum

Overall recovery of zinc from residue leached and residue discarded

$$= \frac{23,165}{29,020} \times 100$$

$$= 80\%$$

(c) Extra Products:

In addition to recovering zinc, operation of the residue treatment plant will lead to increases in the production of the following products.

	Tonne per annum
Cadmium metal	220
Copper residue (containing 45.5% Cu)	230
Lead residue (containing approximately 22% Pb, 6% Zn, 700 g/t Ag)	30,500
Cobalt oxide (containing 70.7% Co)	18,300 kg per annum

(d) Reagents and Services:

The approximate quantities of the following reagents and services will be required to operate the residue treatment plant.

Contact acid	42,000 t/annum
Ammonia	2,200 t/annum
Steam	15,400 kg/hour
Compressed air	105 m^3/minute
Flocculant	18,000 kg/annum
Power	1,400 kW

CONCLUSION

For the treatment of zinc plant residues containing zinc ferrite, the recently developed jarosite process is considered to be superior to alternative treatment procedures. The process is essentially simple and only conventional equipment, operating at atmospheric pressure, is necessary. The reagent requirements are moderate, and supplies of the reagents are normally available or readily obtainable on the site of most electrolytic zinc plants. Zinc losses through entrainment are minimised because of the excellent filtering and washing properties of the jarosite precipitate. All metal values in the residue can be recovered in good yields. The process can be readily integrated with existing zinc plants and sulphate balance problems in the zinc plants are eliminated.

Construction of a residue treatment plant at Risdon to treat 350 tonne per day of residue by the jarosite process is on schedule. Start up is expected in December 1970. Based on current metal prices treatment of residue by the jarosite process is extremely profitable.

ACKNOWLEDGEMENTS

The authors wish to thank the Electrolytic Zinc Company of Australasia Limited for permission to publish this paper. They wish also to acknowledge that the development of the residue treatment process was due to the efforts of many members of the Company's staff.

REFERENCES

1. Australian Patent Number 401,724.

2. Norwegian Patent Number 108,047.

3. Spanish Patent Number 304,601.

4. Snow, W.C.
"Electrolytic Zinc at Risdon, Tasmania",
Transactions of the Metallurgical Society of A.I.M.E.,
Vol. 121, 1936, pp 483-526.

5. Ross, S.W.
"Electrolytic Zinc at Risdon, Tasmania. Major Changes Since 1936".
Transactions of the Metallurgical Society of A.I.M.E.,
Vol. 184, March 1949, pp 211-218.

6. Johnstone, D.W.
"The Production of Electrolytic Zinc at the Works of the Electrolytic Zinc Company of Australasia Ltd., Risdon, Tasmania".
Fifth Empire Mining and Metallurgical Congress, Vol. 4b, April, 1953, pp. 53-107.

7. Ashdown, N.C.
"Electrolytic Zinc Production at Risdon".
Eighth Commonwealth Mining and Metallurgical Congress - The Australian Mining,Metallurgical and Mineral Industry Vol. 3, 1965, pp. 95-105.

Asarco Mexicana, S.A.
Nueva Rosita, Coahuila, Mexico
Chapter 18, page 463

St. Joe Minerals Corp.
Monaca, Pennsylvania, USA
Chapter 20, page 549

Imperial Smelting Corp., Ltd.
Avonmouth, England
Chapter 21, page 581

Societe Miniere et Metallurgique de Penarroya
Noyelles-Godault, France
Chapter 22, page 619

Zambia Broken Hill Development Co.
Kabwe, Zambia
Chapter 23, page 649

Kiln Products Ltd.
Berg Aukas, South West Africa
Chapter 32, page 918

SECTION V

ZINC AND LEAD PYROMETALLURGY PRACTICE

Chapter 17

NODULIZING OF ZINC CALCINE AT EAGLE-PICHER INDUSTRIES Galena, Kansas

Morris A. Dodd
Manager, Metal Sales
Chemicals and Metals Division,
Eagle-Picher Industries, Inc.

Abstract

The nodulizing process described converts finely divided zinc calcine into a dense purified nodule. These zinc nodules are suitable for direct use in zinc reduction furnaces, especially the horizontal retort type, for the production of metal or American process zinc oxide furnaces for producing lead free zinc oxide.

The basic reactions are carried out in a rotary kiln fired with fuel oil or natural gas. The combustion gases travel countercurrent to the flow of the zinc bearing material. Volatile impurities are carried out of the kiln with the combustion gases and a small portion of the finely divided feed material. The gases are cooled and the larger solid particles are separated from the stream before the resultant fume is collected in a conventional cloth filter baghouse. The fume collected can be further processed by conventional wet processes for the recovery of metallic values such as lead and cadmium. In order to nodulize the calcine properly it is elevated to a point of incipient fusion. The agglomerated material falling from the kiln is cooled and then sized by passing through a screening and crushing system consisting of a jaw crusher and a roll crusher in closed circuit with a vibrating screen.

INTRODUCTION

The nodulizing process for the agglomeration of zinc ore was originally developed by the Athletic Mining Company at its plant in Fort Smith, Arkansas. The primary goal was to produce a dense, porous product from roasted flotation zinc concentrates which would be suitable for smelting by the horizontal retort process. In addition to preparing a product with desirable physical characteristics for smelting, it was also discovered that certain volatile impurities could be removed and the resultant zinc produced therefrom was of higher quality than had been possible with previous practice. In 1953 this process was licensed to Eagle-Picher Industries for use at their Roasting and Acid Plant then being constructed at Galena, Kansas. Eagle-Picher engineers, using metallurgical and engineering data provided by Athletic Mining Company, designed and constructed a nodulizing unit which was first placed in operation in the latter part of 1954. This first unit at Galena was successful in the production of a high purity nodule which was originally used for the production of zinc oxide at Eagle-Picher's plant in Hillsboro, Illinois. In 1956 a second unit exactly like the first was constructed in order that Eagle-Picher's zinc smelter at Henryetta, Oklahoma could be supplied with nodules as raw material for the production of slab zinc. Not only was the quality of metal improved by using nodules but handling losses inherent in the shipment of zinc calcine were largely eliminated.

Since the nodulizing process has been used to supply raw material for two different end products made by different processes, a campaign program was developed. Nodules produced for pigment usage were made from selected zinc concentrates and the impurity level of the nodules emphasized to a greater degree than the physical properties. Conversely, nodules intended for the production of metal by the horizontal retort process were produced with strict control as to the size, apparent density and porosity. As in many processes a certain amount of compromise between the optimum chemical and physical characteristics of the nodule is necessary in commercial practice.

Calcine for the nodulizing system at Galena is produced by a single large suspension roaster of the Cominco type. The roaster has a stub shaft with two drying hearths at the bottom. Flotation concentrates from Eagle-Picher concentrating mills (and sometimes purchased zinc concentrates) are pre-dried in a Hardinge rotary drier where any blending of ores is accomplished. Since the operation of a flash roaster requires a very fine feed, the completely dry ore from the drying hearths is ball milled and air classified before being blown into the top of the roaster. Calcines from the hearth, the waste heat boiler, cyclones and Cottrells are blended together, cooled and transported by screw and elevator to storage hoppers. Cleaned roaster gas is used to produce 94% sulfuric acid in a Monsanto designed contact acid plant.

PROCESS METALLURGY

Metallurgically speaking, the nodulizing process consists of simp heating zinc calcine at a controlled rate to the point of incipient fusion so that the heat and the rolling action within the kiln produ a generally spherical nodule which is dense but at the same time por During the heating period and at the point of maximum temperature in the kiln the volatile impurities of the zinc calcine are removed and swept out with the burner gases. Those common elements generally removed are sulfur, chlorine, lead and cadmium. Part of the sulfur in the calcine exists as zinc sulfate formed in the roaster. Such sulfate sulfur is removed by thermal decomposition since the maximum temperature of the nodules (about 1230°C) is well above the decomposition point of zinc sulfate. Sulfide sulfur is removed by simple oxidation to SO_2. Sulfur, as well as lead and cadmium, are also removed by the double decomposition reactions of lead and cadmium sulfides with their respective oxides to produce the metallic molecu and sulfur dioxide. These vaporized metals are immediately oxidized and swept from the kiln by the burner gases.

The major chemical reactions in the nodulizer are as follows:

$$2\ ZnSO_4 \longrightarrow 2\ ZnO + 2\ SO_2 + O_2$$
$$ZnS + O_2 \longrightarrow ZnO + SO_2$$
$$PbS + 2\ PbO \rightleftarrows 3\ Pb + SO_2$$
$$CdS + 2\ CdO \rightleftarrows 3\ Cd + SO_2$$

Since the operating temperature is well above the volatilization point of cadmium, a very high percentage of cadmium removal from the concentrates can be expected. Lead will also be removed from the nodules but the percentage of removal is generally less than that fo cadmium and much more care must be taken in the operation in order t effect appropriate lead removal.

Chlorine in the calcine will probably be present as zinc chloride which will simply be volatilized and removed with the sulfur dioxide and metallic oxides. Figure 1 on the next page shows the vapor pressures of the various compounds present in the kiln and indicates the relative ease with which cadmium and lead can be removed from the calcine.

Both lead and cadmium removal are dependent upon an adequate supp of sulfide sulfur in the feed material. In actual practice it has been found that about 3% sulfide sulfur will effect satisfactory removal of lead and cadmium from the normal ores. If for some reasc the feed material is particularly high in lead and cadmium or if it is desired to produce a particularly pure nodule, a somewhat higher sulfide sulfur feed to the nodulizer may be necessary. It might be pointed out that too much sulfide sulfur, however, is difficult to remove and may appear to some extent in the final nodule. At this point the sulfur is particularly deleterious since it will inhibit

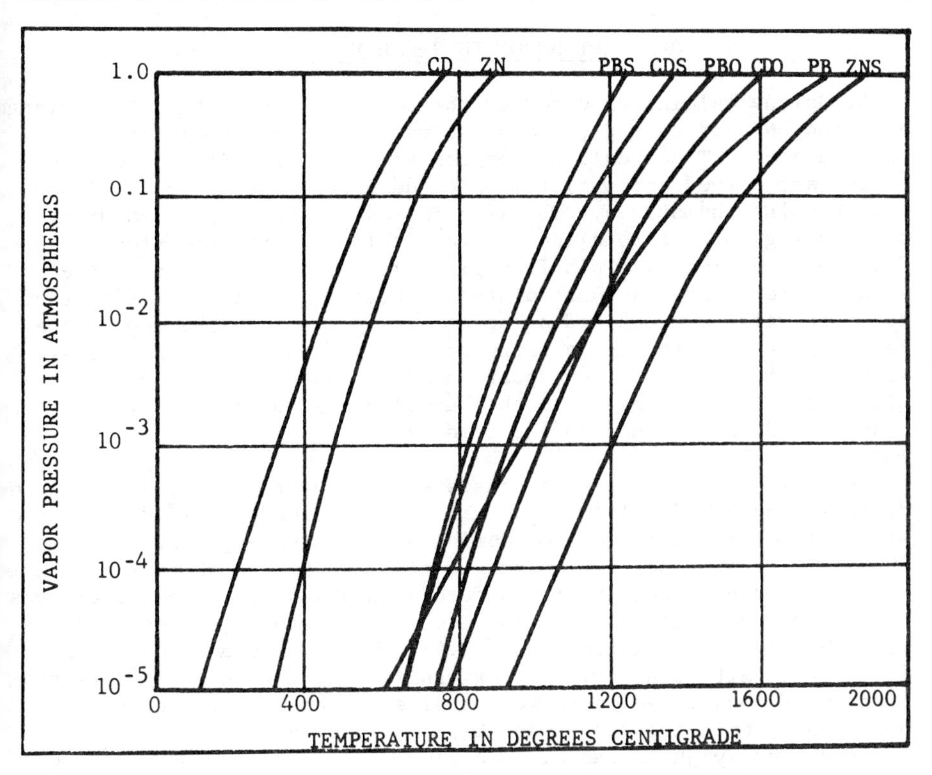

Figure 1. Vapor Pressures of Selected Compounds

the recovery of zinc in either the zinc oxide or the zinc metal furnace. Nodule density produced will vary from 1600 to 2320 kg/ cu.m. depending upon the type of concentrates being processed. If a sufficiently high grade zinc concentrate is used for roasting, the zinc content of an average nodule will be from 68% to 72% with a sulfur content of less than .5% and a lead content of .1% to .5%. The cadmium content of the nodules will generally range from .01% to .04% unless an ore of particularly high cadmium content is being treated. Over the years some high grade flotation concentrates have been treated which produced nodules having a zinc content of 75% with a lead content of less than .01% and a cadmium content of less than .005%. Conversely, nodules made from some high iron foreign concentrates have produced nodules as low as 62% in zinc content.

After the nodulized ore falls from the kiln it is cooled, crushed and screened in order to produce material of appropriate size for smelting. Generally speaking, the most satisfactory size for ordinary smelting operations has been considered to be 6.35 mm. The screening and sizing process will naturally produce some fines by abrasion, even though the ore has been completely agglomerated in the kiln itself. A small percentage of fines in the final product has not generally been considered deleterious to the eventual use of the nodules.

DESCRIPTION OF PHYSICAL PLANT

At Galena calcine produced by the roaster is stored in three large elevated hoppers having a nominal capacity of 500 metric tons of calcine each. These calcine hoppers are equipped with collecting screws and a feed screw system which delivers calcine to the nodulizing kilns themselves. The kiln is fed by the simple expedient of allowing calcine to slide down an inclined stainless steel pipe 20.4 cm in diameter. This feed pipe extends into the end of the kiln and terminates a short distance above the lining in order that the feed will be deposited as quietly as possible. The top of the feed pipe passes through a brick arch over a dust chamber at the feed end of the kiln. Some portion of the feed is swept out of the kiln almost immediately with the burner gases but settles in the chamber and is returned to the feed system.

The basic nodulizing unit consists of a rotary kiln 2.625 m inside diameter and 39.37 m long. The kiln shell is made of 15.875 mm mild steel plate except for a 1 m section at the discharge end which is 19.05 mm steel. The kilns have two tires with a 35.56 cm face running on single trunion rollers for a face with 40.46 cm. The drive mechanism is by means of a conventional electric motor and speed reducer driving a 16 tooth pinion and a 30.48 cm face main gear containing 148 teeth. Although auxiliary drives for use during power interruptions were considered, none was provided. Through the years the decision to omit this equipment has been proven to be economically and technically justifiable. The slope of the kiln is set at approximately 2.385° and the nominal rotational speed is 1.33 rpm. Originally the feed end of the kiln was fitted with a refractory dam made of special refractory blocks. This construction was somewhat unsatisfactory over the years and has more recently been replaced with a set of proprietary castings consisting of pie shaped alloy steel segments bolted directly to the kiln shell. The original installation of these castings is still in excellent condition after continuous operation for some eight years. The other kiln has also recently been so modified. At the discharge end of the kiln a set of high alloy "T" shaped castings are used to retain the lining. These castings have a life expectancy of several years before warpage makes further utilization impossible. The original castings were 38.1 mm thick but have been replaced by ones 19.05 mm thick which dissipate heat faster and warp less, thus prolonging useful life. The kiln is lined with 15.24 cm first quality firebrick using conventional kiln liners.

As the nodules fall from the kiln they pass through a heavy grizzly made of railroad rails with openings of about 15 cm. The grizzly serves to protect a vibrating conveyor which conveys the nodules to a high temperature elevator. The elevator delivers the product to an unlined cooling drum 1.968 m in diameter and 19.68 m long. At the end of the cooling drum there is a heavy duty jaw crusher to reduce the large pieces. After passing through the crusher, the nodules go over a vibrating screen, the oversize of which is in

General view of nodulizing kiln.

closed circuit with the heavy duty roll crusher. All the product is thereby reduced to a maximum size of 6.35 mm and emptied into the product elevator which delivers the nodules to two 500 metric ton finished storage hoppers. These storage hoppers are elevated in such a manner that nodules can be loaded into covered hopper cars through a simple loading pipe using gravity to accomplish loading. This system was devised because the nodules are being delivered to two separate plants for eventual use.

The kiln is fired with a dual fuel fan mix burner having a capaci of 4.9×10^8 J/s. The nominal firing rate is about 2.1×10^8 J/s using natural gas. The fan mix burner has a desirable heat pattern resulting in adequate temperature control throughout the length of the kiln. Also, an important part of the temperature control is the amount of induced draft applied to the kiln itself. After the burne gases and dust and fume pass through the kiln into the dust chamber at the end they go through a cyclone 3.937 m in diameter for the removal of large solid particles of calcine. From the cyclone the fume is conveyed through a steel trail to a standard automatic baghouse. The fume is collected continuously using glass fiber bags (because of high temperature). The fume falls from the bags into a large holding hopper beneath the bagroom cells from whence it is conveyed by means of a screw conveyor to a holding hopper. The clean air passing through the bags goes through an induced draft fan and is exhausted into the atmosphere.

The original gas cooling system consisted of 16 cooling loops 1 m in diameter and 13.125 m tall mounted on a continuous hopper from th settling chamber to the baghouse. These loops provided excessive cooling to the exit gas, bringing it below the dew point and causing severe corrosion to the cooling system and baghouse. Therefore, the loops were replaced with the present cyclone and trail which served to simplify operation and maintenance and make it possible to mainta gas temperature well above the dew point at the baghouse inlet.

The original vibrating conveyor handling the hot nodules has been replaced with a larger and stronger unit to more effectively combat the heat and abrasion of the product as it falls from the kiln. Mino modifications have also been made in the crushing and screening circ

The flow diagram on the succeeding page shows the flow of zinc calcine through the circuit and the path taken by the fume and gases exiting the kiln.

OPERATING TECHNIQUE

Feed rate to the kiln is controlled at the calcine feed hoppers by adjusting a feed control gate on each hopper. Since all three hoppers are connected by a double set of screws,it is possible to mix materials volumetrically from any combination of hoppers.

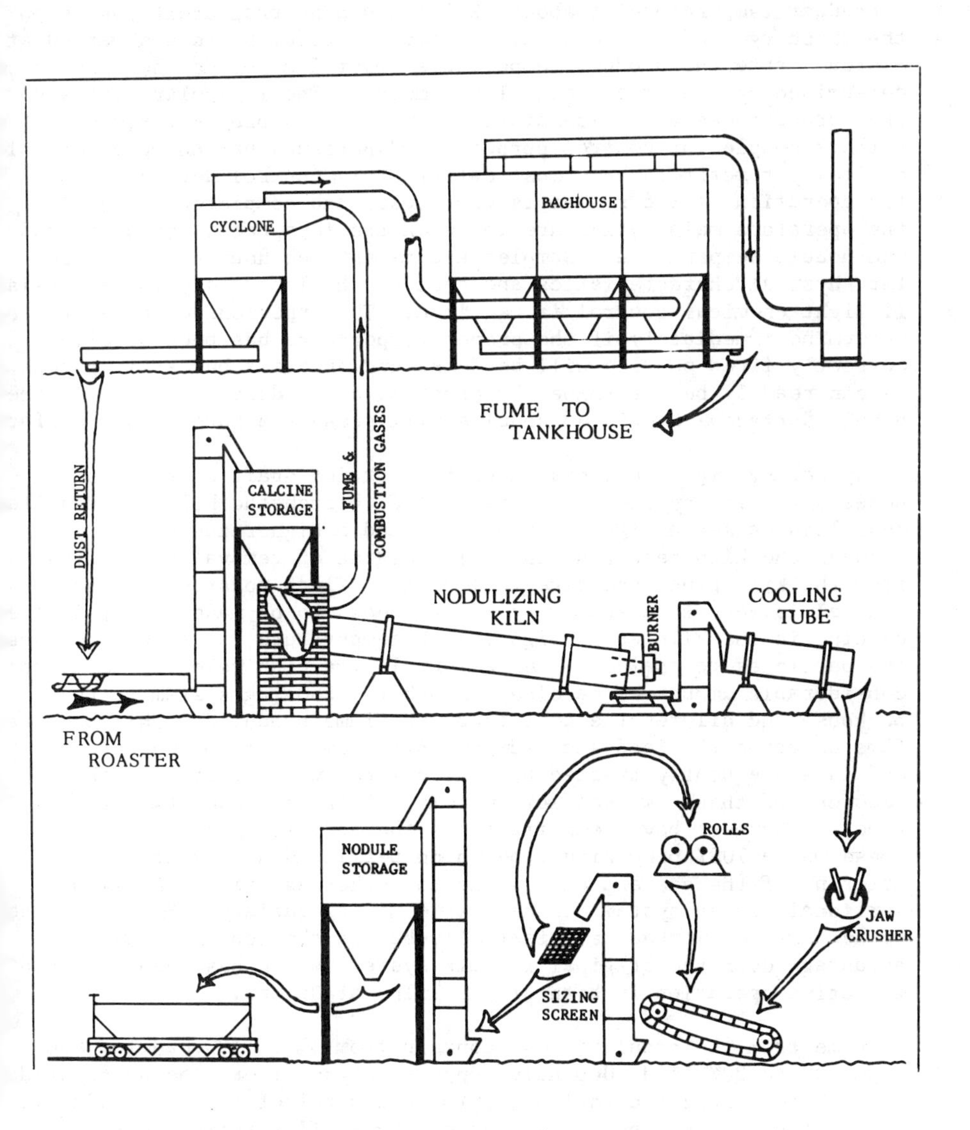

Figure 2. Process Flow Diagram

Retention time in the kiln is about one hour under normal operati conditions. The burner and draft (measured by a recording draft gau in the trail just beyond the dust chamber) are initially set to atta a product temperature of about 1200°C and a neutral draft condition the discharge end of the kiln. As soon as nodules are discharged at a steady rate, the product temperature about 5 m inside the kiln is determined by use of an optical pyrometer. The irregular size and the abrasiveness and temperature of the nodules prohibit the use of a thermocouple for control purposes. Experience has shown a portabl optical pyrometer to be a most satisfactory control device. Since the operation of the system is continuous and completely mechanized, the operators main duties are to check the feed rate, the draft and the nodule temperature. Samples are taken each hour and examined for physical characteristics and sent to the laboratory for analysis if tight chemical control is required. The experienced operator can determine immediately if the proper temperature has been attained. Correctly fired nodules will be dense and dustless but still porous as can readily be determined by dropping a few drops of water on the nodule surface. Overfired nodules will present a hard glassy surfac

Operating experience has shown that strict draft control is necessary. If any excess air is pulled through the kiln, the resulta heat loss causes a higher firing rate and a higher gas velocity through the kiln resulting in a high degree of removal of calcine from the kiln plus excessive fuel costs. Flash roasted calcine in general is very fine and every effort needs to be made to retain the calcine in the kiln until high enough temperature is reached to caus the particles to coalesce. As a correlary a high velocity delivers considerable amount of calcine through the cooling system to the baghouse and dilutes the quality of the fume produced. This baghous fume contains the lead and cadmium units removed from the calcine and is subsequently treated by conventional wet methods for the recovery of these two valuable metals. Over the years two other types of burners have been fitted on the nodulizing kilns. One of these was a 100% premixing type which permitted a very accurate metering of the gas and air, while the other was also a fully proportional burner system of the nozzle mixing variety. Both of these burner systems worked satisfactorily but in the long run gave no advantage over the original fan mix system, which has been returned to active operation in both of the kilns at Galena.

Fume from the nodulizer may contain from 5% to 15% cadmium and from 10% to 20% lead, depending upon the type of ores being treated. As has been indicated earlier, primary control of lead and cadmium elimination is made by adjustment of the sulfide sulfur content in the feed. Secondary control can be exercised by the operator by variation in the feed rate, kiln atmosphere and temperature gradien It is also possible to put a reducing agent such as coal in the fee and thereby effect some higher percentage of removal. This particu operation may be of interest if there is a desire to produce a part cularly low sulfur nodule and at the same time effect a good degree of cadmium and lead removal. It might be pointed out that in order to permit the double decomposition sulfide reaction to take place in the kiln, it is necessary to exclude practically all of the oxygen in the feed half of the kiln. Otherwise, sulfide sulfur in the feed is simply burned to SO_2 and escapes the kiln without taking place in any further metallurgical reactions. It might also be added that this burning of sulfur creates an exothermic reaction at the wrong place and may cause the feed material to overheat and stick to the kiln lining. This local overheating and sticking will produce rings in the kiln and may in fact stop the operation completely. High sulfide sulfurs in the feed or erratic and varying sulfide sulfur will also cause continued difficulty in the nodulizer operation. Varying sulfur contents makes it almost impossible for the kiln operator to maintain an even temperature through the kiln. This situation will affect the lead and cadmium removal and sulfur removal and the density of the final nodule produced. The presence of a sulfur fire in the kiln or odor of SO_2 at discharge end is a quick indication of excessive sulfur in the feed. For similar reasons the feed rate itself must be maintained at a constant rate once the firing and draft conditions have been established.

Some years ago, one kiln was fed with pelletized calcine for a period of about four months. This test work showed a slight increase in nodule density, improved feed rate control, less mechanical carry-over to the baghouse and some decrease in accretions in the kiln. However, these advantages were not deemed sufficient to compensate for the added cost of pelletizing and the project was discontinued. It is possible that with today's improved pelletizing techniques real economy might be had by using pelletized feed.

Another technique explored in the past was the possibility of automatic temperature control. For this purpose a control instrument was activated by thermocouples through the kiln shell and refractory lining. These couples were located at each end and center of the actual nodulizing zone and were connected through slip rings to the instrument. This procedure was also abandoned because accretions and breakage of thermocouple housing frequently rendered the system inoperative.

The shell at the discharge end of the kiln, being subjected to the highest temperature in the process, will eventually bell and make it impossible to hold the kiln liners in place. This belling process also warps the castings and makes their further use impossible. The kiln liners last indefinitely since the operating temperature of the kiln is somewhat below the softening point of first quality firebrick and there is little, if any, chemical attack. However, the product adheres to the brick lining and must frequently be removed by jack hammering. This cleaning of the kiln, plus some spalling action as the kiln temperature is brought up and down, results in eventual failure of the lining, especially in the last half of the kiln. Refractory replacement cost is not a large item but it will be necessary to replace several rings of liners during any one operating year. During long periods of operation of the kiln it is almost impossible to avoid the formation of rings at one time or another. These rings inhibit the flow of product through the kiln and must, of course, from time to time be removed. The original concept of the operation was to shoot the rings out using an industrial gun and a lead slug about 13 mm in diameter. However, this procedure was not always satisfactory so the practice was ceased and now the kiln is cooled and any rings or excessive adherence to the side of the kiln is removed by jack hammer. In effect, these rings are product and so they are passed on through the crushing and screening system into the final storage hopper.

Due to the extremely abrasive nature of the finished nodule the crushing and screening system are subject to rather rapid wear and constant replacement of wearing parts. The shell of the cooling drum itself has been completely worn through and has had to be replaced in its entirety. Repairs to the lining itself have been nominal as indicated above and maintenance of tires, trunions and drive mechanis consistent with good kiln practice in general. There is corrosion of the trail from the cyclone to the baghouse brought about by the SO_2 content of the gas and the water vapor produced by the gas burner This corrosion would probably be minimal were the kiln in continuous operation, however, the shutdowns for repairs to the screening and crushing system and for the removal of rings from the kiln permit cooling and condensation of the trail system with resultant corrosion due to the SO_2 content of the gases.

Manpower requirements for normal operation are one man per shift per nodulizing kiln plus one bagroom attendant during the day shift only. Another man not a member of the operating crew loads finished nodules into hopper cars on a five shift per week basis since storage capacity is ample to hold the weekend production. Extra help is provided the operating crew when it is necessary to clean the kiln and crush the accretions removed.

In Table I are given representative assays of the calcine fed to the nodulizing kiln and the zinc nodules and baghouse fume produced from such feed material. Except for the last set, the calcine was produced from a blend of zinc concentrates designed to produce a uniform product to be used in the production of metallic zinc. The last example is typical of a low cadmium ore used to produce nodules for zinc oxide manufacture.

As indicated above, variations in sulfide sulfur content and/or temperature can produce undesirable results. In Table II are shown typical results which may result from these factors.

The first two sets in Table II show that a very high sulfur conten in the calcine will result in excellent lead elimination but the excessive sulfur in the nodules cannot be tolerated by the smelter.

Table I. Representative Assays of Regular Production

	Zn	Pb	Cd	Sulfide Sulfur	Sulfur in SO_4
Calcine	69.2%	1.57%	.58%	2.92%	.37%
Nodules	71.0	.28	.037	.55	.05
Fume	45.1	20.1	12.32	.60	4.29
Calcine	70.0	.68	.40	3.7	.1
Nodules	71.3	.11	.032	.50	.08
Fume	33.1	25.4	14.4	.60	6.8
Calcine	69.1	1.18	.61	2.0	.6
Nodules	71.4	.15	.013	.55	.07
Fume	41.6	22.0	13.5	1.7	5.1
Calcine	68.1	.45	.13	3.21	.27
Nodules	70.9	.017	.002	.47	.06
Fume	43.8	14.2	4.92	.83	5.2

Table II. Representative Assays of Undesirable Operation

	Zn	Pb	Cd	Sulfide Sulfur	Sulfur in SO_4
Calcine	68.6%	.53%	.34%	4.98%	.33%
Nodules	71.1	.029	.010	2.26	.07
Fume	55.9	10.1	5.5	.30	3.8
Calcine	66.2	1.33	.46	7.3	.60
Nodules	70.8	.02	Tr	3.18	.02
Fume	52.2	12.3	5.9	.10	3.4
Calcine	68.6	1.20	.66	2.47	.52
Nodules	71.8	.019	Tr	1.3	.03
Fume	55.5	13.0	7.1	.92	3.24
Calcine	68.5	1.03	.49	4.22	.45
Nodules	70.6	.035	.005	2.34	.03
Fume	46.2	18.6	7.7	.50	3.5
Calcine	68.9	.86	.31	4.0	.3
Nodules	72.0	.036	.005	.33	.02
Fume	58.6	7.1	3.5	.26	3.57
Calcine	69.2	.73	.37	3.27	.33
Nodules	71.9	.013	Tr	.21	.02
Fume	62.9	8.8	4.7	.60	2.14

Examples three and four also indicate undesirable results brought about by improper temperature and draft control in the nodulizing kiln itself. Again elimination is good but excessive sulfur remains in the final product.

The last two examples show results from operations in which coal has been added to the calcine feed. In these cases elimination of lead and cadmium is excellent and the nodules produced are quite satisfactory. However, the fume has been diluted by an excess amoun of zinc (reduced by the carbon) and is thus a much less desirable product for further treatment.

SUMMARY

Nodulizing of zinc calcine has proven to be the most efficient method of agglomerating the superfine flash roasted material. Production per unit over several years has averaged 150 ± 5 tons per day. This capacity has exceeded roaster production enough to permit thorough cleaning of the kilns when required and replacement of worn equipment when needed. A majority of the unscheduled interruptions in operation have been occasioned by failure of the hot shaker conve or some component of the crushing and sizing equipment.

Treatment of new types of ores has from time to time required adjustment in firing techniques. It is literally true that each zinc concentrate is slightly different from another and any variatio in the refractory quality will necessitate a slightly altered nodulizing treatment. However, these difficulties have not prevented economic and metallurgical success of the nodulizing kilns. The use of the zinc nodules at consuming plants has improved the quality of the end products and in some cases increased capacities and recovery

Acknowledgements: The author gratefully acknowledges the invaluable assistance of the Galena, Kansas plant staff and the Research Depart ment, Joplin, Missouri, in the preparation of this manuscript.

Chapter 18

HORIZONTAL RETORT AND ACID PLANT
ASARCO MEXICANA, S. A. NUEVA ROSITA PLANT
Nueva Rosita, Coahuila, Mexico

M. K. Foster
Assistant Manager - Zinc and Acid Section

Abstract

Ten horizontal retort zinc blocks of a modified Hegeler design are in operation at Nueva Rosita, Coahuila, Mexico, and produce approximately 170 t of spelter daily, or 62 000 t/year. A block consists of two furnaces of 448 retorts each, making 8960 retorts as the plant complement. Each furnace block is fired with natural gas and air maintaining the combustion mixture in the furnace always slightly reducing. No attempt to recover energy through waste heat boilers is made.

The spelter moves to market by rail and truck either in palletized bundles weighing approximately 1060 kg, as loose slabs weighing 26.5 kg each, or as 1088 kg ingots. At present 46% of the metal is exported and 54% is consumed domestically in Mexico. The present day trend toward equalized or alloyed spelter, as well as special shaped castings results in sales of 35% of the entire plant's production.

Sulfuric acid is also produced by the Contact Process using vanadium pentoxide as the catalyst. The plant is basically a Monsanto contact system, producing approximately 68 t of 100% sulfuric acid daily. Both 98.5% sulfuric acid and 20% oleum are available.

All of the acid made is consumed in Mexico. Shipments are made in 26,900 dm^3 tank cars.

Introduction

Asarco Mexicana's zinc and acid plants together with its mining and coking of bituminous coal operations are located on a semiarid plain some 40 kilometers east of the Sierra Madre Oriental Mountains of northern Mexico. Establishment of a zinc smelter at this locale was to utilize the by-product gas of the coke ovens to smelt zinc concentrates produced by selective floation at Asarco's Mexican Mining properties. Limited in size by the quantity of gas, the plant started with two 800 retort blocks. All tiles, retorts, condensers, and furnace charges were made by Asarco's Amarillo, Texas smelter, and imported during construction of the roasting, sintering, and pottery departments. The first slab of zinc was produced in July 1925.

The "Flow Sheet" (Plate 1) will be followed, deviating at times, to better clarify the complexity of the operations. Some processes such as the Pottery and Concentrating Mill have been omitted but will be discussed. Parenthesized numbers and letters used in the text are those shown on the Flow Sheet. All tonnages, lengths, volumes, etc., are in metric SI equivalents.

Zinc Plant Operations

Ore Receiving and Sampling.

Zinc sulfide concentrates (1) arrive at the rate of ± 10 600 t monthly, shipment being made in boxcars, racks, and flat bottom gondolas. Upon arrival at the plant cars are weighed on a Fairbanks Morris, Model 11603-SU7-B, 16m platform railroad scale, having a 100 000 kg load capacity. Boxcars and racks carry approx 54 t of zinc concentrates and gondolas about 60 t.

Most of the concentrate is unloaded from boxcars and racks by front end shovels (torque convertor HA-Type G Houghs) and the gondolas by a 7 t traveling, overhead, P. & H. Crane. From time to time "Slicked over" shipments are received. This type of concentrate has either been loaded as a slurry at the shipment station or has been rained on while en route. Extremely wet concentrates tend to "set up" due railroad vibration and are unloaded by hand, using pick and shovel, or by mechanical shovel.

Ore shipments prior to unloading are sampled. An air operated auger sampler 38 mm dia. drills nine holes, by pattern, in each end of the car, receiving the sample in an especially designed pan with a hole in the center through which the drill operates. Every fifth car is pipe sampled in much the same manner, as a check against the drill sample. The pipe is 50.8 mm i.d. in the body and reduces, conically, to a sharpend 38.1 mm nose. This pipe is 1.32 m long with a reinforced head and pad to protect

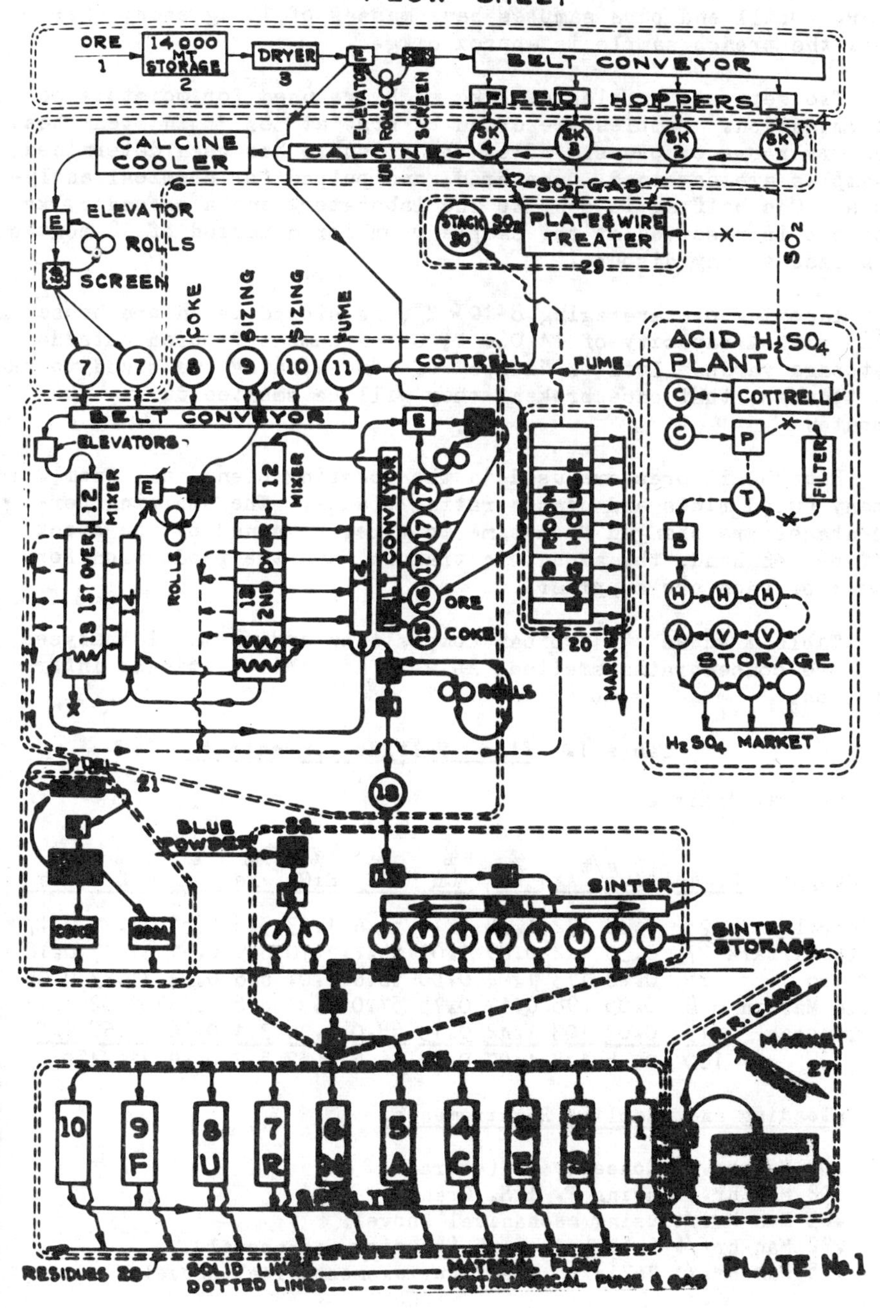
ASARCO MEXICANA, S.A.
ZINC AND ACID PLANT
FLOW SHEET
ORE
1
14000 MT STORAGE
2
DRYER
3
ELEVATOR
ROLLS
SCREEN
BELT CONVEYOR
FEED HOPPERS
4
SK 4
SK 3
SK 2
SK 1
CALCINE COOLER
6
CALCINE
5
SO2 GAS
STACK 30
PLATES WIRE TREATER
29
SO2
ELEVATOR
ROLLS
SCREEN
COKE
SIZING
SIZING
FUME
COTTRELL
FUME
ACID H2SO4 PLANT
COTTRELL
FILTER
STORAGE
H2SO4 MARKET
BELT CONVEYOR
ELEVATORS
MIXER
12
13 1ST OVER
ROLLS
13 2ND OVER
BELT CONVEYOR
ORE
COKE
BAG HOUSE
20
MARKET
ROLLS
21
BLUE POWDER
SINTER
SINTER STORAGE
R.R. CARS
MARKET
27
RESIDUES 28
SOLID LINES — MATERIAL FLOW
DOTTED LINES — METALLURGICAL FUME & GAS
PLATE No. 1

it from sledge hammer blows. Twice monthly each shipper is sampled at random "trench wise", a 305 mm wide by 1 m long trench being cut through the concentrate at each end and center of the car. Drill and pipe samples have masses of 15 kg each; whereas, the trench sample is approx 6 kg.

Two separate samples of 2 kg each are used for moisture determination. Samples are dried 24 hrs. at 383 °K in steam heated dry rooms or ovens. After the moisture has been determined, samples are combined, quartered, and pulped for chemical analyses. One half kg is sent to the laboratory and a secondary kg sample is reserved at the sample room for a period of 12 months in case of any dispute.

Incoming ore averaging 8-10% H_2O is stored in an ore house (2) with a capacity of 14 000 t, or on cement floored outside storage yards. Lots or "dumps" of concentrates are sized to such a tonnage, that once broken, they will be smelted during the month.

Five basic ores are used in the roasting blend, all from Company owned mines and concentrating plants. The smelting percentages are changed from time to time, governed by the stock of ore on hand, the amount in transit, and the production forecast of each ore supplier.

Table 1 shows the typical composition and chemical analyses of the concentrates smelted, as well as other pertinent information.

Table 1. Zinc Sulfide Concentrate

Chemical Analyses.

Shipper.	% Blend	Au g/t	Ag g/t	% Pb	% Cu	% Zn	% SiO_2	% Fe	% Cd	% S	% As
Parral	25	0.78	172	1.38	1.12	56.6	1.43	5.5	0.51	31.27	0.17
Sta.Barbara	27	0.30	142	0.89	1.07	55.2	1.70	6.9	0.61	31.17	0.18
Taxco	25	0.28	173	1.04	0.50	56.6	1.01	6.6	0.54	31.29	0.05
San Martin	8	0.05	98	0.17	0.75	57.0	2.31	4.8	0.43	30.52	1.17
Plomosas	15	0.03	103	1.42	0.13	58.0	1.76	3.1	0.20	31.62	0.00
	100	0.35	148	1.07	0.77	56.5	1.52	5.7	0.49	31.24	0.20

Unloading and Sampling Requirements.

.09 Man hr./t Concentrate (overall)
.02 Man hr./t using P. & H. Crane.
.03 Man hr./t using mechanical shovel.
.22 Man hr./t "slicked over" (by pick and shovel).
.15 Man hr./t "slicked over" (using mechanical shovel).

Drying.

A mixture of the concentrates with an average of 9.0% H_2O is dried in a Ruggles - Coles XH - 14 drier (3) made by the Hardinge Company. This is a direct heat rotary drier using combustion gases from coke oven gas (20.9 MJ/m^3) as the drying medium. The gases induced by an exhauster fan, travel through the drier in the same direction as do the concentrates (Parallel flow). The higher temperature gases are therefore in direct contact with the unheated, undried concentrate as it enters the drier. Thus, the initial heat transfer rate is very high, resulting in a large moisture removal per unit of drier volume.

The drier cylinder is 2.29 m dia. by 15.24 m long, and rides on tires supported by bearing wheels resting at 0.06418 radians or a drop of 20 mm in every 320 mm. Wheels and holders accept the thrust load caused from the inclination of the shell. The drier is driven through a pinion and girth gear, powered by a 37.3 kW, 440 V, 60 Hz motor, and turns at 4-1/2 RPM. The dried ore discharges into a screw feeding an elevator, is sized to pass a 6.4 mm screen, finally being conveyed by a 610 mm belt to storage in the roasting division. The drier fan (355 m^3/min. - STP) exhausts into a cyclone and lastly to the stack. Cyclone dust is returned to the elevator boot.

The drier works two eight hour shifts (16 hr./day) with a three man crew, drying the concentrate to 3% H_2O at a rate of 22.8 t/hr. or 365 t/day. The ore enters the drier at $\pm$ 289°K, and the ambient temperature is approx 303°K.

Table 2. Screen Analysis of Concentrates.

On Screen.	Preceeding Dryer.	After Drying.
6	0.26%	0.64%
8	0.20	0.52
10	0.16	0.54
14	0.04	0.34
16	0.08	0.06
20	0.10	0.10
35	0.40	0.54
48	0.66	0.56
60	0.70	0.70
80	2.60	2.80
100	4.00	5.00
115	4.40	5.20
150	4.40	5.40
200	11.20	10.60
Below 200	70.80	67.00

0.131 Man hr./t concentrate dried.

Roasting the Concentrate

Roasters

Four multiple hearth Skinner design roasters are in operation. The original castings, etc., were made by the Colorado Iron Works.

These roasters have been modified considerably over the years, so a description of the present day status will be given, with modifications being discussed wherever practical.

The roasters (Flow Sheet #4) are build of top quality fire brick with a 6.1 m i.d., a 343 mm wall, and an overall heighth of 12.2 m. Each roaster has twelve hearths, six in-drop, and six out-drop hearths. They are sprung from skewbacks held in place by a double back-band of 13 mm x 305 mm boiler plate restrengthened by a 25.4 mm x 254 mm band. The hearths are laid up with standard straight, No. 1 arch, and No. 1-X wedge brick. The walls use No. 1 keys and standard straight brick. Originally the walls were insulated with 114.3 mm Sil-O-Cel brick inside a 10 mm steel shell, and the roaster dome was used as a drying hearth. The shells have been stripped off, insulation removed, roaster off-takes relocated through the domes, and the domes abandoned as drying hearths.

The life expectancy of a hearth is hard to estimate; however, there are two of the four roasters with all twelve of their original hearths intact after 39 years of service. With proper care and barring accidental damage, the life of a hearth should be 40 to 50 years. Two roasters have been completely rebuilt, one in 1954, the other in 1956.

Each hearth uses two air cooled rabble arms extending from a ceramic tile covered, cast iron, center column. These arms are hollow, yet divided by a vertical fin in such a manner that the cooling air moves from the center column through one side of the arm and returns on the opposite side of the arm to the center column, traveling downward from the first hearth, finally exhausting to atmosphere below the twelfth hearth. The arms are located in line to one another hearthwise, yet on the next hearth are set at right angles to those of the preceeding and succeeding hearths. From these arms, on ledges running the length of the arm, hang yokes with replaceable rabble teeth set to move the ore at 0.5236 radians (30°) in the direction desired. The cooling air for the arms is force fed with atmospheric air at 26.7 kN/m^2 by fans located at the ground level.

Originally the arms, yokes, and rabble teeth were all of cast iron, with the arms having an average life of about six months depending on the location in which they were operating.

The hotter hearth arms naturally having a shorter life. The trend in recent years has been away from cast iron arms toward that of malleable iron for the cooler hearths, and heat - corrosion resisting steel with approximately the following composition: Chromium 28%, Nickel 3% (max.) Carbon 1%, balance iron for the hotter hearths.

The exact life of the steel arm is uncertain, yet excepting breakage from "plowing" (removal of hearth accretions by mechanical means), physical damage due to accidental yoke failure, etc., should be indefinite. It is the practice to weld steel arms when breakage does occur, and there are now in operation, welded arms with more than eight years of service.

The rabble teeth are made in such a manner that they may be removed and replaced without removing the yoke from the arm. Teeth give from three to six months service in the hotter hearths, and from six to nine months service in the cooler. Broken yokes are also repaired by welding, and rabbles which have become too short for usage are lengthened by welding on blanks. The yokes and rabbles are high Chromium steel (27%), Carbon (2.25%), and the balance iron.

The center column, protective tile, arms, yokes and rabbles, calcine build-up, etc., rests on a No. 29438 SKF spherical roller bearing which supports this entire mass of slightly over 91 t.

The roasters are driven by 11.2 kW motors, through 152 mm x 12 m transmission belt drives, No. 14 Dodge friction clutches and R.D.Nuttall (DVR-10) 9.17/1 ratio speed reducers (made by Westinghouse). Between the speed reducers and the drive pinions are shear pin couplings to prevent damage to the roasters in case of yoke or arm failures. The roasters turn at 1.4 RPM.

Roasting the Concentrate

Zinc sulphide concentrates must be converted by roasting into zinc oxide thus expelling the sulphur dioxide gas. The reaction is: $2\ ZnS + 3O_2 = 2\ ZnO + 2SO_2$
In practice this reaction never goes to completion, since some ZnS remains unoxidized and considerable ZnO is converted into $ZnSO_4$ (water soluable sulfur). The reaction is exothermic releasing approx 5.02 MJ/kg of ore oxidized. Theoretically this energy is sufficient to have autogenous roasting; however, it has been found beneficial in the sintering operation, which will be discussed later, to have considerable water soluable sulphate ($ZnSO_4$) present; consequently, the roast is made with excess atmospheric air and extraneous heat.

Green concentrates dried to ± 3.0% H_2O are stored in four 90 t feed hoppers, one for each roaster, finally being fed to the roasters via apron feeders and gas tight screw conveyors onto the first hearths of the roasters. (The top hearth is number one and the lower hearth is number twelve). The feeder is interlocked to the roaster drive in such a manner, that when the roaster stops the feeder also stops.

The ore is rabbled inward toward the center column on all odd numbered hearths, dropping by gravity through a circular opening near the center column and onto the hearth beneath. The concentrate particle then is moved outward toward the roaster wall, and falls onto the next hearth through 18 evenly spaced openings or "drop-holes". Approx 24 hours are required for an ore particle to pass from the concentrate feeder, through the roasting media to the calcine exit.

Calcines from all roasters enter a launder conveyor (5) first passing over a 38 mm grizzly to remove any oversized accretions resulting from the plowing cycle. This "push conveyor" (built by the plant) consists of 188 flights of hinged, movable blades, which ride freely back over the ore body, lock into place, and then push the calcine forward. Since all four roasters deliver their product to the same launder, by the time the conveyor discharges, the calcines are well blended and partially cooled. The conveyor is powered by a 22.4 kW, 440 V, 60 Hz motor coupled to 41.16/1 ratio Pacific Western D-58 speed reducer. The reciprocating action of the conveyor flights is created by means of a crankshaft and makes 22 "back and forth" alternations per minute. All hearth and arm accretions are broken by a Fiedler jaw crusher, sized through a 10 mm screen and delivered to the push conveyor at its discharge point.

Calcines drop onto an inclined No. 1273-STR Jeffrey pan conveyor with 124 pans 510 mm x 420 mm x 90 mm. The conveyor travels in a housing made from 6.4 mm boiler plate, at the rate of 50 m/min, delivering the "pre-roast" at 508°K to a rotary tube cooler (6) made by the Traylor Engineering and Manufacturing Company.

Eight boiler plate tubes 510 mm dia, 10.7 m long fit into crown sheets bolted to bells on each end of the cooler. Inside of the tubes are screw flights welded solidly to the tube walls. The cooler turns counterclockwise at 3.5 RPM immersing its tubes in a basin of water maintained at a constant level, with make up water being supplied from over head sprays of black pipe with 6.4 mm holes drilled 150 mm apart the length of the pipe. Excess water is pumped to the Acid Plant spray pond. A 11.2 kW motor coupled to a Pacific 42.8:1 ratio Pacific speed reducer, drives the unit through a pinion and girth gear.

The cooler discharges the calcine at 318°K into the boot of a 360 mm belt and bucket elevator in a closed circuit with a Hummer, 5 mesh screen, using a 1.22 m x 1.83 m Ty-Loy wire cloth section, and a smooth faced double roll Jeffrey crusher. A 7.46 kW motor through a jack shaft and a 203 mm wide transmission belt driving both rolls. The calcine is stored in two 400 t tanks (7) prior to sintering.

Roaster No. 1 supplies SO_2 gas for the Acid Plant and since its operation is quite different to the other three, it will be discussed in the Acid Plant section; however, the other three roasters operate as follows:

As the concentrate falls from hearth to hearth, the sulfur content drops accordingly. Temperatures are closely watched and recorded by a 40 point Leeds and Northrup instrument using Chromel-Alumel pairs. Table 3 gives total sulfur, sulfate sulfur, and the ratio of SO_4/total S, as well as gas temperatures of the various hearths. Note how water soluable sulfur increases as the ore body is roasted. This information covers the three roasters not in gassing service.

Table 3. Hearth Temperature and Sulfur Content.

Hearth Number.	Temperature. °K	% Total sulfur	% sulfate Sulfur	SO_4/total S
Feed	-	31.77	0.19	0.61
1	-	22.00	0.36	1.63
2	-	17.30	0.32	1.85
3	1103	16.90	0.52	3.07
4	-	16.20	0.47	2.91
5	1113	12.50	0.56	4.48
6	-	8.58	0.74	8.62
7	1123	6.38	0.98	15.36
8	-	4.63	1.00	21.60
9	1073	3.45	1.25	36.23
10	-	3.08	1.67	54.22
11	888	2.27	1.90	83.70
12	888	2.71	2.34	86.34

Temperatures are controlled by the burning of coke oven gas averaging 20.92 MJ/m^3 with approx 11 180 m^3 of gas being consumed per roaster day.

The gas is burned as required through door ports using standard 19 mm black pipe for the burners. Burner locations are on the lower six hearths.

Unheated atmospheric air is the oxidizing agent. Originally air used for cooling the arms, being preheated, was admitted through ports located 1.571 radians from each other on each of the lower four hearths. This practice has been discontinued. Oxidizing air is now admitted to the roaster through small ports cut through the walls at twelve equally spaced points around the periphery of the roaster, and are covered with sliding doors for air control. These ports also serve for visual inspection of hearth conditions. The roasters are under stack (30) draft.

Table 4. General Roasting Information

Power consumption/t calcine	46.8 MJ
Man hours labor/t calcine	1.87
Mass of 1 m^3 dry concentrate	1760 kg
Mass of 1 m^3 roasted calcine	1803 kg
Mass of 1 m^3 gas entrained calcine	1746 kg
Mass of 1 m^3 Cottrell fume	1746 kg
Center column without tile/roaster	59.0 t
Center column tile/roaster	8.7 t
Air cooled arms/roaster	8.3 t
Arm hole plugs/roaster	1.1 t
Yokes and rabbles/roaster	5.7 t

Dust Recovery and Roaster Gas Treatment.

Roaster outlet gases from Skinners No. 2, 3 and 4 at 1073°K, 3.0% SO_2, a dust burden of 480 mg/m^3, sulfuric acid content of 183 mg/m^3, along with spent combustion gases , and a volume averaging ± 510 m^3 STP leave through the dome of each of these three roasters via two 1.7 m dia. vertical off-takes. The gases from any of these roasters may be sent to the Acid Plant gas multiplex in case of failure of the No. 1 roaster. This gas shifting is accomplished by raising and lowering of 150 mm thick dampers made of Lumnite cement using calcined flint and silicon carbide as the grog (1 damper each off take).

Entering 1.7 m "down comers" the gases are directed into a 4.9 m x 3 m steel domed brick flue 42 m long and located at ground level. As the dust laden gases enter the larger collecting flue, gas borne particles of partially roasted calcine settle out into 30 hoppers located beneath the flue. These dusts are conveyed by screw conveyor and chain elevator to storage bins near the Acid Plant gassing roaster for further roasting. (see Acid Plant Section

After leaving the collecting flue and settling sections of the Cottrell proper, (29) the gases and fume enter a plate and wire electrostatic precipitator of ASARCO design loaded with 32 500 V of electricity rectified by "star disc" brush and shoe rectifiers located in the main Cottrell plant. The trend is away from this type of rectification and in the near future will be replaced with Silicon Diode Rectifiers made by General Electric Company.

Three sections or cells compose a treater 'line', and there are six parallel lines in this precipitator. Each cell has a gross electrical field of 3.65 m x 2.3 m x 2.6 m or 21.5 m^3 after deducting the volume occupied by the sheets, wires, etc. This gives a total field of 387 m^3 resulting in a residence time of 5 seconds (time in the electrical field), to precipitate the fume.

There are 306 corrugated plates (2.78 m x 700 mm) and 570 wires per cell. The bar iron holding the plates is bolted to I - beams supported on springs. Plate guides of angle iron are located at the bottom but not fastened to the plates allowing for expansion and contraction due to changes in gas temperatures. Theframes holding the wires rest on springs supported by insulators at its four corners. At the bottom the wires are guided by holes drilled through a pipe. Cast iron masses (4.5 kg) made in the form of a horseshoe keep the wires taut. If a wire breaks, the horseshoe weight is caught on a secondary pipe, thus preventing damage to the fume collecting screws.

All cells are manually rapped hourly for two to three minutes to remove the precipitated fume. The knocking is done by four Chicago Pneumatic (CP-426) compressed air hammers pounding the "cold" frame, and one Chicago Pneumatic (CP-427) hammer knocking the "hot" frame. The difference in the two hammers is that the CP-427 (hot hammer) retracts upward when the air is turned off. This is essential to prevent grounding of the hot wire frame.

The average potential against each cell is 70 milliamperes at 32 500 V (D.C.) measured by an electrostatic General Electric voltmeter (Catalog No. 5102938). A total of 15 rectifiers are used for all 18 cells. The first cells of each line have 3 rectifiers; whereas, the second and third cells operate with six.

Leaving the energized sectionsthe gases pass through a common settling flue under a draft of 213 N/m^2 thence to the 138 m stack, exhausting the cleaned gases to atmosphere.

The stack (30) is made of red brick lined with 76 mm x 102 mm x 229 mm vitrified brick and corbel tile. The inside diameter at the base is 14.5 m and 7.6 m topside; whereas the stack wall is 1.55 m thick at the base, and 0.4 m at the top. Gases from both the roasting and sintering processes are handled by this stack.

Dusts, both gas borne calcines and precipitated fumes, are

conveyed in the same type of screw conveyors, being 230 mm dia. flights in closed housings. Care is taken when emptying the hoppers so as to always leave a positive dust seal preventing infiltration of atmosphere air. The screws are powered by D. O. James Planetary gear reducers, the motive power varying from 3.73 kW to 11.2 kW electric motors depending on the length of the conveyor. As afore mentioned the calcine dust is stored in the Roasting section for use in the Acid Plant roaster; whereas, the precipitated fume is conveyed to the sinter plant (11) for storage and will be discussed under "Sintering".

Table 5. Flue Dust - Fume - Cottrelling.

	g/t		%	%	%	%	%
	Au	Ag	Pb	Cu	Zn	Cd	S
Roaster Flue Dust	0.40	132	0.54	0.85	60.3	0.49	17.7
Zinc Cottrell Fume	0.33	171	0.93	0.78	56.5	0.56	12.4
Acid Cottrell Fume	0.67	444	2.73	0.62	39.4	2.39	15.1

Man hrs./t Concentrate (Both Cottrells) including Dust and Fume handling 0.20

38.2 MJ/t Concentrate (Both Cottrells) including Dust and Flue Dust Fall - 14.4% of Green Concentrate

Cottrell Fume Fall (Both Cottrells) 13.0% of Green Concentrate

Cottrell Efficiency 98.5% - 99.0%

Sintering the Calcine

To densify the calcine, eliminate residual sulfur, lead, and cadmium, double sintering is practiced on two Dwight and Lloyd down draft machines (13) operating in series, the gases from both machines being cleaned in a standard nine section baghouse (20). Two types of finished sinters are produced, regular sinter, and low lead sinter commonly called 'green ore' sinter.

Description of Equipment

Tanks 7, 8, 9, 10 and 11 (Flow Sheet) are used for storing the feed constituents for first pass sinter. Two tanks (7) each with a volume of 220 m^3 will hold 400 t calcine (800 t total). The other tanks have a volume of 38 m^3.

Crushed and sized Rosita nut coke (6 mm) is stored in tank 8, sized (19 mm) 'under-cut' sinter is stored in tanks 9 and 10; whereas, tank 11 holds precipitated fume from the Cottrell treaters. Beneath these tanks are belt feeders 610 mm wide, which are driven from a line shaft motivated by the controls of the sintering machine, so that changes in the machine speed affects a like change in the feeders. Adjustable gates at the tank exit vary the quantity of the feed. The components are delivered to a variable speed 760 mm belt conveyor, thence to the boot of a 43 bucket, 360 mm belt elevator delivering the charge to a 1.83 m dia., 3.66 m long Stehli mixer (12), turning at 6 RPM on trunnion rolls. This is a rotating drum pug mill type mixer with a 127 mm square paddle shaft holding 48 paddles whose two blades are 203 mm long and 175 mm wide. Water is injected by a 38 mm pipe spray under a constant head from a float controlled surge tank. The mixer discharges into a 'swing-spout' feeder, finally laying the mix onto the traveling grates of the first pass sintering machine.

The Dwight & Lloyd sinter machines (13) (both identical) are 18.3 m long, with pallets 1.52 m wide by 610 mm long with 180 mm high side boards, equipped with four Timkin roller bearing wheels riding on narrow gage rails. There are 85 cast steel pallets per machine using 31 cast iron grate bars per pallet. The grate bars are made in such a manner that they can be replaced without removing the pallet from the rails. Grate bars are cast locally.

The first pass machine with a bed depth of 380 mm travels over four 4.57 m x 1.37 m wind boxes at 460 mm/min., and the second pass machine uses a 254 mm bed depth traveling at 588 mm/min. over the same size windboxes. Charge and sintered materials, drawn through the grates into the windboxes, are discharged onto Jeffrey pan conveyors (14) via gas proof star feeders operated mechanically through a pawl and ratchet arrangement motivated by the wheels of the pan conveyors.

One fan induces draft for the first pass machine. It is a Dwight & Lloyd High Pressure Sintering Fan, type F, with a 2130 mm x 510 mm impeller made by the Sintering Machine Corporation, and is direct coupled to a 223.8 kW 720 RPM Synchronous G.E., 6600 V motor. The second pass machine is equipped with two 1840 mm No. 15 type MD 60% width A.B.C. fans coupled to 186.5 kW, 1175 RPM, 6600 V, 60 Hz, Elliot Motors. One induces draft on the first two windboxes, the other on the last two. These fans are preceeded by polyclones which collect the majority of the entrained fine particles, (not fume). The polyclones are pairs of 1.83 m dia. units purchased from the Western Mist Precipitation Company. Collected dusts are returned with the first over sinter as feed for the second pass machine.

The charge is removed from the sintered bed by Bruderlin cutters which are essentially huge screws 890 mm dia. exterior rising from a 510 mm pipe with an interior screw. They turn at 32 RPM. The outer screw flights are made of 10 mm boiler plate, and are arranged in such a fashion to move the sinter toward the center of the cutter, i.e., away from the pallet sideboards. At the center of the screw is a 165 mm scoop or opening delivering the sinter to the interior screw, which conveys it to the product collecting system. One cutter is used on the first pass machine and two cutters are used on the second pass machine. All cutters are driven by 18.65 kW 440 V, 60 Hz, General Electric motors through 15:1 ratio Cleveland speed reducers. The sinter under the cutters ("under cut") is conveyed via Jeffrey pan conveyors (14) for sizing and storage.

The machines are driven by Falk gear reducers 137:1 ratio using 11.2 kW variable speed motors 400 - 1600 RPM, 230 V D.C. made by Westinghouse, the forward movement of the machines being either increased or decreased by a rheostat unit, similar to an electric street car controller.

Details of Operation

Rosita sintering is a two step process. The final sinter is a double sintered product commonly called 'Second over Sinter', and is a dense, very uniform, and friable material. The first pass sinter is known as 'First over Sinter'. The regular sinter process is briefly, as follows: Calcines with 3.5/5.0% sulfur content are mixed with coke, Cottrell fume, and return material (under cut). The mix is laid down upon the traveling grates of the No. 1 machine, sintered, and the entire bed (both cutter and under cut), after sizing, is sent to the No. 2 machine. Sized 'first over' sinter is mixed with coke and fed to the No. 2 machine. This sinter bed is cut off in two steps, the top cutter material is sent to the final sizing circuit as finished sinter, the second cutter product either accompanying the top cutter sinter or being returned to feed tanks according to the manner that lead and cadmium are being eliminated.

Under cut from the No. 2 machine is sized in a closed circuit to pass a 27 mm screen and Traylor rolls, (1110 mm dia. x 410 mm face), then stored in the 'first over' feed tanks as fines, the "return material" component.

Regular Sinter

Feed compositions (both machines) are closely controlled, being checked hourly, as follows: A unit length of canvas (± 1 m long) is laid on the feed collector belt, allowed to pass under the feeder, lifted off and the material weighed. The feeder gates are adjusted as indicated to deliver the percentages required. Control samples are also taken hourly, and are made into eight hour composite shift samples for chemical analyses.

The various feed components are delivered to the Stehli mixer and are mixed dry for two thirds of the mixer length and then water added by pipe spray. Moisture of the first pass feed will average ± 13% and the second over feed ± 12%. The materials remain in the mixers about 55 s both first and second pass feeds.

The first pass sinter after double ignition and with an average wind box draft of 3.53 kN/m^2 shrinks approx 15% during the sintering process; whereas, the second over sinter contracts by 13%. The two ignition muffles are lined with fire clay tile are located 152 mm above the bed and approx 1 m apart. The gas burners are manifolds made from 51 mm pipe with seven 6.4 mm pipes extending through the muffle sides. Natural gas (38.5 MJ/m^3) at 103.4 kN/m^2 pressure is used. The entire bed (sinter and undercut) is removed from the first over machine, delivered by screw conveyor and chute to the pan conveyor of machine No. 2 which moves countercurrent to the machine, discharges onto a 762 mm belt conveyor, delivered to the sizing circuit (12.7 mm), and stored as feed for the second pass machine.

First pass sinter and coke compose the feed for the second pass machine. Hourly samples for feed composition and chemical analyses are taken as described in the first pass sinter discussion.

The plant is very flexible since either machine may be used to produce first pass sinter, second pass sinter, or both, using a 'shuttle' belt conveyor to send feeds to either mixer.

Final sinter is sized through a 1.2 m x 2.4 m Aerovibe screen (7.5 mm opening) in a closed circuit with a 600 mm x 750 mm Jeffrey double roll crusher using corrugated manganese steel segments, then stored in a holding tank (18) for final delivery to the Mix Department. Table 6 gives information concerning "regular" sinter production.

Table 6. Feed Composition and Analyses.

Component	% Pb	% Cd	% Zn	% Total S	% SO_4	% 1st. Over Feed	% 2nd. Over Feed
Calcine	0.54	0.63	62.0	4.74	1.75	61.06	
Returned Sinter	1.96	1.71	61.4	0.19	0.08	22.74	
Cottrell Fume	1.67	0.87	55.3	13.80	2.76	13.32	
Coke						2.88	3.11
1st.Over Sinter	0.71	0.31	65.3	0.48	0.17		96.89
2nd.Over Sinter	0.24	0.02	66.2	0.01	0.01		
Moisture (H_2O)						13.00	12.00

Low Lead Sinter

Low lead (green ore) sinter is made "batch wise", twice weekly on a one shift basis, which is sufficient to keep two 448 retort furnaces in continuous operation.

The operation is the same as for regular sinter except when the % Pb in the heads of the first pass machine is excessive. If this occurs, then the undercut from the first pass machine is removed, stored on the yard, and returned little by little to the first pass mix of a regular sinter run.

The same type of mixture is used for first pass "green ore" sinter, as for regular, varying only slightly in the feed composition, (compare Tables 6 & 7). The machine is run slightly slower, its rate of travel being about 350 mm/min.

Second over sinter mix is composed of first over low lead sinter, coke, and 0.75/1.5% green concentrates to create a sulphurizing atmosphere for lead elimination. Too much concentrate seems to tighten the bed resulting in poor ventilation of the sintering mass.

Sizing of finished low lead sinter is exactly the same as regular sinter yet storage is in a separate tank not shown on the flow sheet. Table 7 contains compositions and analyses of low lead sinter, followed by information pertinent to sintering in general.

Table 7. Low Lead Sinter.

Component.	1st. Pass Feed.	2nd. Pass Feed.
Calcine	62.7 %	-
Returned Sinter	20.8 %	-
Cottrell Fume	12.0 %	-
Coke	4.5 %	5.40 %
1st. Over Sinter	-	93.60 %
Green Ore	-	1.00 %
Moisture	13.0 %	12.00 %
	100.0 %	100.00 %

Chemical Analyses - Feed and Sinter.

Component.	% Pb	% Cd	% Zn	% V.M.	% F.C.	% Ash
Calcine	0.54	0.630	62.0	-	-	-
Regular Sinter	0.55	0.090	65.4	-	-	-
Cottrell Dust	1.67	0.870	55.3	-	-	-
Coke	-	-	-	3.3	78.5	18.2
1st.Over Sinter	0.40	0.170	65.2	-	-	-
2nd.Over Feed	0.37	0.150	61.1	-	-	-
2nd.Over Sinter	0.06	0.002	65.5	(Final Sinter)		

Lead & Cadmium Elimination

Regular Sinter	% Pb	% Elim.	% Cd	% Elim.
Feed - First Pass	1.12		0.858	
Sinter - First Pass	0.67	40.2	0.231	60.0
Feed - Second Pass	0.67		0.231	
Sinter - Second Pass	0.221	66.8	0.005	97.6
	Overall	79.5		99.5
Low Lead Sinter				
Feed - First Pass	1.18		0.791	
Sinter - First Pass	0.72	39.0	0.101	87.3
Feed - Second Pass	0.72		0.101	
Sinter - Second Pass	0.075	89.5	0.007	93.0
	Overall	93.7		99.2

Additional Data

Machine #1.	Vol. m^3/min.	% SO_2	Temp °K	Dust Burden kg/24 hrs.
Wind box #2	420	0.07	344	170
Wind box #3	529	0.22	498	623
Wind box #4	526	0.10	553	785

Wind box volumes, dust burdens and temperatures are approximately the same for both types of sinter.

Component.	Density kg/m^3	Component.	Density kg/m^3
Calcine	1803	Regular 2nd. Sinter	1925
Regular Fines	1940	Low Lead Fines	1950
Cottrell Fume	1746	Low Lead 1st. Sinter	1915
Regular 1st. Sinter	1920	Low Lead 2nd. Sinter	1920

Grate Bars	% Replacement	Life Months	Tons Sinter per Grate Bar
Machine #1	2.4	41.1	137.0
Machine #2	17.8	5.6	18.3

Man hr./t finished sinter 1.14

Bag - House Fume Collection

The exhaust gases, fume, and entrained fine sinter particles, which have escaped the polyclones, pass through a 91 m long brick flue with a 16.3 m^2 cross sectional area into a 9 room baghouse (20). Fine sinter particles settle out in the flue and are pediodically picked up and fed back into the sinter circuit. Each room has 120 Microtain or Crysel S filter bags of 460 mm dia., 9.1 m long, thus each room has $\pm$ 1500 m^2 of filtering material or 13 500 m^2 compliment for nine sections.

The filter bags were originally purchased from the Albany

Felt Company, Albany New York; however, are now supplied by Albany Nordiska de México, S. A., México, D. F. The following specifications are given to the manufacturer.

Seam: French or flat type.

Weight: Not less than 0.435 kg/m^2.

Warp and Filling: Not less than 9 warp yarns/10 mm and not less than 10 filling yarns/10 mm.

Breaking Strength: Warp not less than 31.3 kg/10 mm, and the Woof not less than 27.7 kg/10 mm.

Air Permeability: Under a differential pressure of 127.4 N/m^2 the permeability shall be 5.12 m^3/m^2 ± 10%.

Operation

The baghouse fan is a No. 12-3/4 Sirocco turning at 360 RPM powered by a 149.2 kW General Electric 720 RPM 440 V, 60 Hz, synchronous motor through a 14 - Vee belt, section D drive. The fan handles 4245 m^3/min. STP and was made by The American Blower Corporation.

From a common distribution flue, the fume laden gases, at 583.4 N/m^2 enter the rooms thru 1.225 m target dampers located beneath the thimble floor of each section, filtering upward, and exhausting into a common exit flue under 124.5 N/m^2 stack draft.

The bags have a 305 mm stitched cuff that fits over the thimble, and are held in place by two extra heavy 'screen door' springs. The upper end of the sacks are secured to a closed bell using ordinary bailing wire to bind them in place. The bags are located on 610 mm centers, from one to the other, in six lines of 20 bags each per room. They hang from hooks extending from the bell, fastening into a long shaker bar at the top side of the section.

As the pores of the filter bags close up due to trapped fume, the pressure in the distribution flue increases accordingly, and upon reaching 981 N/m^2 pressure, an automatic shaking device takes over and the following cycle occurs:

(1) The two target dampers of one room, operated by air cylinders, close thus idling the section.
(2) A thirteen second settling period is allowed.
(3) A 32 second shake period occurs. The 20 bag lines moving back and forth at 132 reciprocations per minute, each line moving contrary to its neighbors. This movement is made by

5.6 kW, 1160 RPM, 440 V, 60 Hz, Westinghouse electric motors driving 18.8:1, Falk speed reducers.
(4) A secondary 10 second settling period occurs.
(5) The dampers open and fume laden gases re-enter the section.

If the pressure in the entrance flue has not dropped to 686 N/m^2 or less, then the next section enters a shake cycle and the process continues until the pressure is reduced. Any or all sections may be removed from the automatic control, shaken manually using the same shaking mechanism, or locked out of operation. The relays controlling the automatic system are Model G. E. J-22-9 General Magnetic switches.

An electric "Smoke-eye" made by The Bristol Company is located across the exit flue and trips an alarm in the control room in case of bag failure or if too much dust is escaping the filter system. Peepholes through the walls at the front ends of the sections, directed toward an incandescent lamp at the rears enable the operators to ascertain the trouble and correct it.

Baghouse efficiency is determined by withdrawing exit flue gas at the same velocity as that of the flue. This is done by pizometer rings, fan, Askania controlled damper, and a small filter bag. The dust collected is weighed twice weekly, and efficiency is calculated, based on the dust tonnage recovered by the baghouse. The Baghouse is 99.5% - 99.9% efficient.

Density of the dust as collected is 153.6 kg/m^3, yet will smolder when ignited increasing its density 10 times or to 1553.6 kg/m^3. Dust burning is done in the baghouse cellars on "down days" and is removed to storage by a Hough H.A. Payloader. The mechanical shovel operator is equipped with a full face respirator receiving filtered air from tanks carried on the machine.

Shipment is made in boxcars, and production is between 200 and 220 t per month. Table 8 gives analyses, and other pertinent information.

Table 8. Bag House and Fume Data

	gm/t		%	%	%	%	%	%
	Au	Ag	Pb	Cu	Zn	Cd	S	AS_2O_3
Fume Analyses	6.11		21.9	0.06	13.0	24.72	4.52	15.0

Fume collected 7.6 / 7.75 t/operating day
Fume collested / Bag day 7.0 kg
Volume filtered 4245 m^3/min. STP or 70.75 m^3/s STP
Average pressure in Bags - 87.27 N/m^2
Gas temperature 358°K max., 353° min., 356°K Ave.
Bag life (thru Nov. 1969) 1973 days or 64,9 months
Density crude fume 153.6 kg/m^3
Density burned fume 1553.6 kg/m^3
Man hrs./t concentrate 0.30 or 14.3/t burned fume

Coke and Coal Crushing

Coal and coke used by the Plant comes from Company mines and coke ovens located only a few hundred yards away. Fuel enters the plant in gondolas and dischargesdirectly thru a grizzly into a track hopper, is elevated to feeders, thence to one of two 1.83 m dia. by 3.65 m long rod mills (21) made by the Harding Company. The mills are lined with plates of AM-13 steel bedded in lead. One mill is a stand-by for the other in case or repair or motor failure.

The grinding media consist of 60 Cr - M_n steel rods 76 mm dia. x 3.35 m long with a mass of 125 kg each, or about 7.5 t per mill. The mills turn at 20 RPM being driven through girth gears and pinions directly connected to 8.24:1 Falk speed reducers and 93.25 kW 1180 RPM, 440 V, 60 Hz, totally enclosed G. E. motors.

The mill in service operates in a closed circuit with a belt and bucket elevator, a 1.22 m x 1.83 m Allis Chalmer screen with a 6 mm opening, the oversize is returned directly to the mill by chute. The sized materials are stored in concrete tanks being delivered by a 600 mm belt conveyor.

Three types of reduction fuel are milled - nut coke, coke breeze, and bituminous coking coal. Nut coke, the harder of the three, can be milled at the rate of 16 - 18 t/hr. and the rod consumption is one ton of steel per 1500 t of coke. The milling operation is done in the furnace charge preparation plant.

Table 9. Reduction Fuel.

	% V. M.	% F. C.	% Ash.
Nut Coke	4.5	77.3	18.2
Coke Breeze	3.3	78.5	18.2
Coking Coal	23.3	62.5	14.2

	Coke	Breeze	Coal
Density - kg/m^3	67.7	75.3	73.6

1000 kg steel rod prepares 1500 t fuel.

500 t prepared fuel is kept on yard storage.

0.45 Man hrs./t fuel sized.

Furnace Charge Preparation.

Sinter, blue powder, condenser concentrates, drosses from the equalizing furnaces, salt (NaCl), fluorspar, and reduction fuel make up the "uniform" furnace charge.

Sinter from holding tanks (18) is drawn into a bottom discharge R. R. gondola (19) moved by a geared car puller using a 14.92 kW Westinghouse 870 RPM, 440 V, 60 Hz, motor, weighed over a Type E, Fairbanks-Morris, 80 000 kg track scale, dumped over a grizzly into a track hopper conveyed by an inclined belt to the boot of elevator (E). The sinter is distributed by conveyor belt to the mix-room tanks and stored according to its type. There are eight 322 m^3 tanks for sinter storage. A swing spout arrangement allows the sinter to discharge directly onto the belt, or be diverted onto a 1.22 x 1.52 m, 5 mesh Tyloy Hummer screen. The screen discharges onto the belt, the fines are sent by chute to a tank, and used for mixing stuffing and loaming materials.

Blue powder is moved by truck from the furnaces to the blue powder plant, dumped on a vibrating screen (22) with 38 mm opening elevated by a belt elevator to a 25.4 mm opening screen, the oversize chute delivered to a set of disintegrating rolls in a closed circuit with the screen.

Condenser concentrates are brought in cement floored yard gondolas from the Concentrating Mill and unloaded by hand into open bins; whereas, salt and fluorspar are received in boxcars, and unloaded by hand into covered wooden storage rooms.

Sinter is drawn from the tanks into a 0.953 m^3 tram car running on a 610 mm gage track, weighed on a 5 t Fairbanks-Morse (W) beam scale, and adjusted to the mass required by hand shovel. The sinter is discharged thru a 63.5 mm grizzly into a "batch-hopper" (23) beneath the track. The tram car is completely filled and leveled twice each shift to determine the sinter density.

Blue powder, coal, and coke are weighed in a like manner, and added to the same "batch-hopper" (23); whereas, the condenser concentrates, salt, fluorspar and drosses are added to the hopper by hand, using a container of known volume. The dry batch is transferred to the charging chute of a 2.4 m^3 Ransome 84-S standard cement mixer (24) turning at 22 RPM being driven by a 37.3 kW Westinghouse dust proof motor. There are two of these mixers, one of which is a stand-by unit.

A 15 s dry mix is allowed, then water is added bringing the moisture up to $\pm$ 7.5%. An additional 120 s wet mix is allowed before discharging into the boot of a belt and bucket elevator with a wooden housing because of the salt in the mix. Approx 3-1/2 / 4, 1130 kg batches of prepared charge are loaded into wooden sided cars and trammed to holding sheds (25) located on each side of nine blocks. The charge cars run on a 1020 mm gage

R. R. track. Charge for block ten is delivered by dump truck discharged into a feed hopper beneath which runs 600 mm belt conveyor, 2.4 m long traveling 24.4 m/min. feeding the boot of a bucket elevator, and sent to storage in two covered 42.5 m^3 tanks located at the head end of the block. The conveyor is powered by a 746 kW, 440 V, 60 Hz, Falk integral type motor reducer, the elevator by a 5.6 kW, 440 V, 60 Hz, Nema B motor moving a Falk Allmotor reducer. All of this equipment was furnished by Jeffrey.

Condenser "stuffing" and loam are also prepared in the mix plant. A small amount of finely divided clay from the Pottery dust collector is added to the loam mix as well as a bit of 'furnace tops'. Fine mesh sinter, coke, etc., are used; the percentages of each, and screen size are shown on Table 10. These materials are delivered to the furnaces by dump trucks into open cement bins.

Table 10. Furnace Charge Preparation.

Charge	%	Loam	%	Stuffing	%
Sinter	57.38	Sinter	72.0	Sinter	80.0
Blue Powder	22.11	Breeze	21.0	Breeze	20.0
Condenser Conc.	1.43	Clay	3.0		100.0
Dross	0.25	Tops	4.0		
Coke	15.31		100.0		
Coal	2.56				
Salt	0.86				
Fluorspar	0.10				
	100.00				

Wet Charges.	Wet Loam.	Wet Stuffing.
7-7½% H_2O	8-10% H_2O	4-5% H_2O

Screen Analyses.

Screen Mesh.	Mix Charge.	Condenser Stuffing.	Loam
On 4	76	-	-
6	79	3	7
10	199	152	108
20	228	376	330
35	170	251	211
65	109	112	248
65	139	106	196
mkg	1000	1000	1000

Chemical Analyses.

	gram/t Au	Ag	% Pb	% Cu	% Zn	% Fe	% Cd	% F.C.
Regular Charge	0.32	79	0.40	0.70	53.5	5.74	0.52	16.5
Low Pb Charge	0.17	36	0.11	0.63	51.3	6.11	0.003	17.0
Regular Blue Powder	0.17	58	0.78	0.48	68.4	3.48	0.028	8.4
Low Lead Blue Powder	0.12	41	0.43	0.48	69.0	3.63	0.012	8.0
Condenser Conc	0.0	11	0.42	0.06	83.1	0.39	0.027	0
Dross	0.0	Tr	0.19	0.05	79.9	0.26	0.036	0

Furnacing.

Basically the reaction taking place in the retort is:

$$2ZnO + 2CO = Zn_2 + 2CO_2$$

$$CO_2 + C = 2CO$$

Carbon monoxide is burned at the condenser nose, the salt (NaCl) in the mix producing a yellow color helping the firemen advance or retard the furnace accordingly. Zinc chloride forms and distills over early in the cycle, the rate being highest as the cycle begins, and in doing so dissolves the zinc oxide film formed on the freshly condensed zinc globules thus permitting them to coalesce into a bath of liquid zinc. Fluorspar is used in the mix to aid in cleaning ZnO accretions from the condensers.

At the beginning of distillation the temperature is raised rapidly to the point at which CO_2 produced in the primary reaction is reduced to CO. If more than two percent CO_2 enters the condenser then the larger part of the zinc vapor will be either lost as fume or condensed as blue powder. The small amount of bituminous coal used in the mixture aids in heating the condenser and retort mouth prior to the distillation of the zinc vapor.

Furnace Description.

The Plant consists of 20 furnaces or 10 blocks (25), each furnace having 448 retorts in one single laboratory 48 m long by 2 m high, fired with natural gas 38.53 MJ/m^3 and air, each furnace exhausting its spent gases to atmosphere through a stub stack. (Two stacks per block). Approx 28, 320 m^3 of gas are consumed per 48 hr. cycle or 811 m^3/ton concentrate.

Four horizontal rows of retorts, 238 mm i.d. x 1.525 m deep, set at 420 mm centers both vertically and horizontally, compose a furnace. The fire clay cylinders are supported at the butt end on riser shelf tile, and at the mouth end on "front plates" (100 mm x 100 mm x 720 mm). The furnaces are held together by cast iron buck-stays and tie rods against skew-back tile, the arch tile butting a back wall made of 300 mm x 300 mm x 300 mm fire clay refractory blocks. (see Fig. 1). The arches are not brick, but special tile, manufactured by the Pottery Department of the Plant. They are made in the form of an arch brick 305 mm thick and 420 mm long.

Beneath the lower row of retorts is a bed of 6 mm calcined refractory flint approximately 200 mm deep, commonly called "furnace bottoms", and is used to prevent any slag, from leaking retorts, that falls to the bottom from welding into a tough mass. From time to time the slag is removed and the upper portion of the flint renewed. The 200 mm flint mass is 18 tons per furnace.

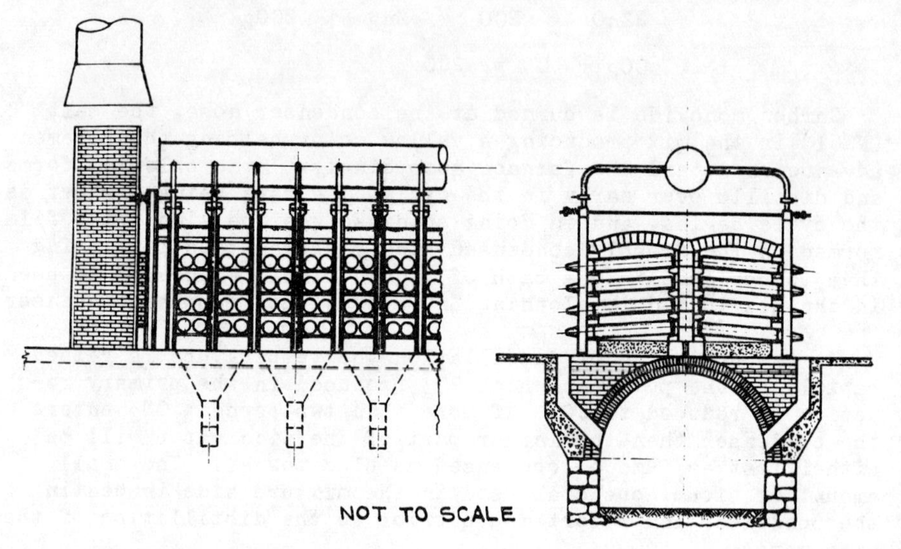

Fig. 1 - Horizontal retort furnaces.

The furnace face is sealed ("mudded up"), using a semistiff refractory clay to close the furnace front, leaving only the retort mouths open. Prepared charge is placed in the empty retorts, condensers set and positioned snuggly against the retort mouth then 'loamed in', sealing them to the retort mouth, and the condenser noses are 'stuffed'. (Table 10)

Gas and air are supplied at every half section (8 retorts) through air ducts and gas burners located between the buckstays. (Fig. 1). The burners are made from 40 mm black pipe with three 6 mm pipes welded to it. The small pipes extend through the air ducts and burner tile, just entering into the furnace laboratory. Natural gas enters the plant at 2.07 MN/m^2 pressure, is reduced to 172.8 kN/m^2 into a 150 mm header from which 305 mm feeder pipe take-offs for each block exit. Pressure is farther reduced to 20.68 kN/m^2 by individual reducers for each block. Gas entering the furnace proper is controlled by water gages located at the head end of the blocks using 155 mm Lunkenheimer gate valves to limit the gas flow. These valves are regulated manually, from ground level, using an endless chain to operate a sprocket wheel equipped with a chain guide.

Combustion air is supplied by a 3685 m^3/min. vertical discharge No. 1902 - A, class 20 M. ARMEE - Chicago, mechanical draft fan, with dual manual inter-comunicated vane inlet controls. It is powered by a 223.8 kW, 900 RPM, 440 V, 60 Hz, Westinghouse syncronous motor and 12 Vee-Section E-belts, turning at approx 900 RPM. Its blast at 62.05 kN/m^2 is delivered into a 1.75 m/dia. x 436 m long manifold at its mid point, i.e., between blocks 5 and 6. Individual block off-takes are 850 mm dia. air lines running over the center wall of each block. Between the main manifold and the block are sliding vanes in damper boxes adjusted by endless chains and sprocket wheels. Air intake is also adjusted using water gages as guides. Air drops from the furnace mains are made of light gage galvanized sheet, 105 mm dia. delivering air at each set of buckstays thru damper boxes with manually adjustable sheavers. There are two other fans, similar but smaller, used only as stand-by units both driven by electric motors, and another powered by a diesel engine in case of electrical failure.

Overhead, and running the entire length of the furnace face, circling at each end to the outside walls of the block house, are mono-rails from which draw-shields and man heat shields (when hand cleaned) hang from trolleys. Clean-out mechanization was completed in late 1969, prior to that, residues were removed by hand. Mechanical charging has been the practice for a number of years.

Clean-out and Charge Machines.

Three 25 kg/m railroad rails are laid, flush with the furnace floor, the length of the furnace and extend outside the building at the stack end of the block. The front rail is 1.21 m from the furnace face, the middle rail is 930 mm from the front rail, and the outer rail 1.5 m from the front rail. The "Clean-out Machines" operate from the wide gage, and the "Charging Machines" from the narrow gage rails. Power for the machines is delivered by a 440 V, 60 Hz, electric "Feed-Rail" made by the Feedrail Corporation. There is one feed-rail per furnace (total of 20) and this means of supplying power has been very satisfactory.

There are eleven "clean-out" machines, ten of which operate daily, with one as a stand-by. Fundamentally the machine consists of eight water cooled cast steel (ASTM-216-63 T - GRADE WCA) augers, 216 mm dia. by 190 mm long. When facing the augers the left set of four operates clockwise, and the right set counterclockwise. The two vertical files of screws are located horizontally on 645 mm centers; consequently, there is an open vertical file of four retorts between the retorts being cleaned. The two files of clean out augers can be moved independently or made to operate together through a clutch arrangement.

Hydraulic lifters position the augers as they advance toward the retort mouth and set them down in the retort about 100 mm inside the retort. They automatically lift at the same point when exiting thus protecting the retort lip.

A special fire proof hydraulic fluid, made by Texaco Incorporated, under the Code name 2185 RCX Hydraulic Fluid FR, is used as a safety measure.

Prior to entering the retort, the augers are started turning at 120 RPM, and water is circulated through them from a 768 dm^3 water tank carried on the machine. The rate is 378 dm^3/min. using a Jacuzzi-Universal water pump powered by a 1.49 kW, 440 V, 60 Hz, motor. The machine transports its own water supply since Rosita has a water shortage. Hot water and steam are returned to the tank, the steam is exhausted to atmosphere through the furnace ventilators. Additional water is added about three times during the clean out period. Water level gages determine the time for refilling. The machine is moved up or down the furnace face by an electrical traction motor and gear system. The units are changed daily from block to block using a low level dolly pulled by a tractor.

Twenty charging machines are in service. They are commonly known as "Slingers"; however, the more proper description should be 'moving belt projectors'. Basically they consist of two grooved 910 mm dia. pulleys with a 240 mm face and a groove 100 mm wide and 83 mm deep, into which the charge falls, through chutes, from an overhead hopper. There it is trapped by an endless rubber faced belt 185 mm wide, 8 mm thick, and 6.1 m long, traveling at 704 m/min., projecting the charge into the retort at a high rate of speed, and packing it from butt to mouth fairly evenly. The upper pulley belt charges the top retort, the lower belt charges next to the bottom retort; then through a lever adjustment, made by the operator, the belt position is changed and the second and lower retorts are charged. The charge is not 'spiessed'.

The charge hopper is filled by a 15 bucket, 305 mm belt elevator receiving its feed from a 305 mm wide belt conveyor running under the charge car. The car is coupled to and pulled by the charging machine, using a hand operated geared chain block combination for motivation. Elevator and conveyor belts are both driven by a gear motor, (746 W) through a pinion and gear arrangement. Table 11 gives additional information about the Clean-out and Charging Machines.

Table 11. Clean-out and Charging Machines.

Clean Out Machines.

All motors except for the water pump, are 440 V, 60 Hz, 1180 RPM, Reliance equipment.
Each machine uses one 1.49 kW traction motor, one 3.73 kW auger advance and regress motor with fluid drive, one 746 W hydraulic oil pump motor, one 1.49 kW water pump motor, and two 2.24 kW auger motors (right and left).
Augers at 120 RPM advance and regress at 14 m/min.
Dodge No. 80 - 25.4 mm pitch, rivited chain is used throughout.
Complete machine with water load weighs 8 148 kg.

Charging Machines.

Charge belt motors are 440 V, 60 Hz, 1165 RPM, 5.6 kW made by Westinghouse.
Elevator and Conveyor belt gear motors are 746 W, 440 V, 60 Hz, 1800 RPM U. S. Motors with a 14.4:1 Ratio, or 125 RPM output.
Charge Belt Pulleys are driven by three "B" section Vee Belts. (6 belts - 3 each pulley).
Charge Belt speed - 704 m/min.
Elevator Belt Speed 49 m/min.
Conveyor Belt Speed 38 m/min.
Machine weight - 2500 kg.

The Clean-out and Re-charge Process

Three and one half to five hours are required to remove the spent residue, charge the cleaned retorts, clean, set and loam the condensers, replace condemned retorts with new ones then charge them, and set, then loam their condensers. The following operations are performed in the order as listed.

1.- The furnace is drawn for the fifth and last time.

2.- The break down and removal of the condensers.

3.- Removal if necessary of zinc oxide accretions and loam from the mouth of the retort.

4.- Removal of the "Sample" - zinc rich crust within the first 210 mm of the retort mouth.

5.- Removal of the lean residue and slag from the retort.

6.- Charging the cleaned retorts with new mixed charge.

7.- The setting, loaming, and stuffing of the condensers.

8.- Replacement of condemned retorts, charging same, setting their condensers, loaming and stuffing them.

Clean-out Operation.

At 4:00 A. M. the furnaces are drawn for the fifth time during the 48 hour cycle. Two metal drawers per furnace tap the condensers, one drawing the top two rows, the other the lower two rows. By 4:30 A. M. they have removed the spelter from the first 5-6 sections, at which time the clean-out machine starts to work. Three men loosen the condensers, remove them, and stack them near the side doors of the furnace building.

The "Sample" (zinc rich accretions) is removed, by the machine, from a depth of some 210 mm within the retort mouth dropping it on sheet metal floor pans covering the residue chutes. During the sampling of the first four sections, condensers are removed from the second four sections, so the machine continues on down the furnace face and samples these. While the second four section sampling operation is underway the floor pans of the first four are removed, and drug to the "blue powder" pile.

Blue powder is the by-product of the furnace, and includes all high zinc bearing materials such as the sample, ladle skimmings, loam, zinc oxide accreations, etc, and perhaps 25 to 35 percent of all the spelter produced by the furnace will come from the blue powder.

This furnace by-product will average about 11,500 kg for each 28,800 kg of sinter charged or approx 40 % of the furnace pay load. Zinc will vary but usually is in the 68.5 - 69.0 % Zn range. (see Table 10, pg 10).

After eight sections have been sampled, the machine moves back to the first section and cleans the retorts dropping the spent residues into the cellar chutes. Augers turning at 112 RPM enter the first vertical row of retorts and travel inward to about 1/2 the lenghth of the retort then exit, dropping residue into the cellar. The next pass drives the augers to the retort butt, the right hand side of the retort as well as the bottom is cleaned, since the counterclockwise rotation (looking at the auger) causes the unit to try to climb the side. Another pass is made to the butt, the rotation stopped, and the augers drug out. Alternate, turning and dragging passes are made until 6 1/2 in total have been completed, then the machine moves to the second vertical row, and repeats. The first two sets of passes are made with one vertical file of augers operating, yet when the third row is entered, both sets operate, the trailing set entering the first row of retorts cleaning the left hand side and bottom; consequently, each retort receives 13 passes. As soon as possible any residue lodged on the lower front plate is scraped into the residue pit, and the floor pan replaced. The machine continues on down the furnace face alternately "cutting the sample" and cleaning the retorts until it finishes the furnace. This requires about 3 1/2 - 4 hours depending upon the residue.

Condemned retorts are marked by placing a piece of broken condenser in the mouth and are not charged.

Charging Operation.

After the first four sections have been cleaned and the floor pans replaced, the charge machine en tandem with the prepared charge car moves into position and charges the first row first and third retorts then second and fourth. Moving forward it charges the second and fourth, then the first and third, etc., thus saving undue motion. Spilled charge is cleaned up by broom and hand shoveled into a small hopper located over the tail pulley of the charge car conveyor belt. When the charge car is empty, it is uncoupled, pushed outside the block onto holding rails, and replaced with a loaded car. Normally two sections are open between the clean-out machine and the charger; however, at times three to four are open due to charge car changes, mechanical troubles, etc.

The machines charge the retorts firmly with a "pay load" of 0.993 kg/dm^3, and even though they are heavily packed, no speissing of the charge is practiced.

As soon as possible, the cleaned condensers are replaced, luted to the retort and stuffed. A hole is made in the topmost part of the condenser nose stuffing to allow escapement of water vapor and gases. The condensers are stuffed prior to luting so as not to disturb the loam while it is drying.

Retort Replacement.

Leaking retorts are replaced at the end of the charge cycle. The clay front or face is broken with a bar and the clay seal pulled outward with a hook. The retort is removed using huge pincers and cradle bars, taken outside the block house, later to be broken and removed by truck. Assays show that 0.1 - 0.2 % of the new zinc charged is contained in the discarded retorts.

At the head end of each block house are small kilns (42 retorts capacity) for pre-heating the silica flour retorts. The retorts in the kilns are raised from 313°K to 1573°K during 46 hours, at the rate of 298°K to 303°K temperature increments hourly, using coke oven gas or natural gas if necessary. At least 1450 to 1500°K must be obtained to stabilize the quartzite, converting silica flour to cristobalite. Retorts stand vertically in the kiln and when ready for removal are laid over on their sides using a 3.6 m pole made of 38 mm black pipe with a semi-hook on one end. The hook is used to drag the retort (mouth first) into the doorway where a three man crew, one with a 2.5 m "tail pole" having a 165 mm disk welded to the 44 mm black pipe 750 mm from the end. The "tail pole" is inserted into the retort and then the clay cylinder pulled forward until only the butt rests within the kiln. The other two men with a cradle bar receive the rear end of the retort about 300 mm from the butt, and the three men take the retort to its position, place it on a roller made of boiler plate and a short length of 12.7 mm pipe, push it part way into the furnace then go back for another retort. A 3.8 meter pole is inserted into the retort, and the clay cylinder pressed forward until its butt rests on the shelf tile of the backwall. It is positioned and the clay front of the furnace is "stamped in" with new clay. During retort changin the air and gas is cut back so no pressure is in the furnace laboratory.

When all leaking retorts have been replaced, the charge machine returns, fills them, condensers are set, loamed, and stuffed, then firing begins.

Clean-out and Charge Shift Crew.

Workmen on the charge shift are paid for a day's labor, but leave when the furnace has been properly cleaned, recharged and faulty retorts replaced. Table 12 shows the daily job assignments for one furnace, but does not include the total labor force, such as slab stackers, maintenance men, electricians, mechanics, etc. The assistant machine operators, connie boys, metal drawers, stampers, and loam cutters remove the floor pans to the blue powder pile as well as replacing them.

Table 12. The Charge Shift Crew

2	Metal Drawers
1	Clean out Machine Operator & Sampler
3	Assistant Clean out Machine Operators
2	Charging Machine Operators
1	Clean up (Spillage) Man
1	Bumper
3	Connie Boys
1	Loam Cutter
3	Stampers
1	Extra man
1/2	Straw Boss and Fireman (Covers 2 Furnaces)
1/10	Furnace Boss (Covers 10 Furnaces)

Firing the Charge.

Since the clean out and recharge cycle requires 4 - 4 1/2 hrs. for this maneuver, only 44 hours are left for the firing cycle.

This cycle is started off slowly allowing steam and hydrocarbons to be driven off and the front of the charge as well as the condenser to rise to operating temperature before the distillation of zinc begins. If the furnace is started off too fast crusts form at the retort mouth hurting furnace operation, yet when formed have no satisfactory remedy. On the other hand, if a furnace is started too slow it can still be remedied by firing. As soon as the retort front and condensers have reached operating conditions, the temperature is raised rapidly so that the CO_2 formed by the primary reaction is quickly reduced to CO. In case the furnace is coming along too fast, producing scrap, and burning zinc, further firing is suspended until the furnace settles down. Firing is advanced as the charge seems to require it, through the judgement of the firemen and the shift boss, and not by instrumentation.

After the loam has fully set speissing of the condenser is held to an absolute minimum, being "spot speissed" where necessary to relieve back pressure. The furnace is speissed 2 1/2 sections ahead of the metal drawer, yet this would not be done except for the safety factor involved. Zinc charged into the retort must end up in one of six furnace products - slab zinc, blue powder, condenser absorption and accretions, residue, retort absorption, and ventilator loss. The latter two are not economically feasible to recover, so the less the ventilator loss, the better the operation.

It is absolutely essential that the temperature at retort mouth, easy filtering of gas through the stuffing, etc., hold the condenser temperature above 753°K so that the condensed zinc vapors remain as a molten mass and do not freeze into a slug (frog) within the condenser. The condenser is heated through the heat of vaporization released by the condensation of zinc vapors, but more so by the hot gases exiting through the stuffing at the condenser nose. Fig. 2 shows temperature rise vs. time. This is not a composite nor an average plot but rather a graph of an operating cycle.

Metal Drawing and Casting.

The furnaces are tapped five times during the 48 hour cycle the fifth and last draw coming just before removal of the residue. The other four draws are spaced so as not to overload the condenser with zinc. Normally, the first draw starts at 5:15 PM, the second at 1:15 AM, the third at 9:15 AM, the fourth at 6:00 PM, and the fifth at 4:00 AM. Three and one half to four hours are required for each of the first four draws.

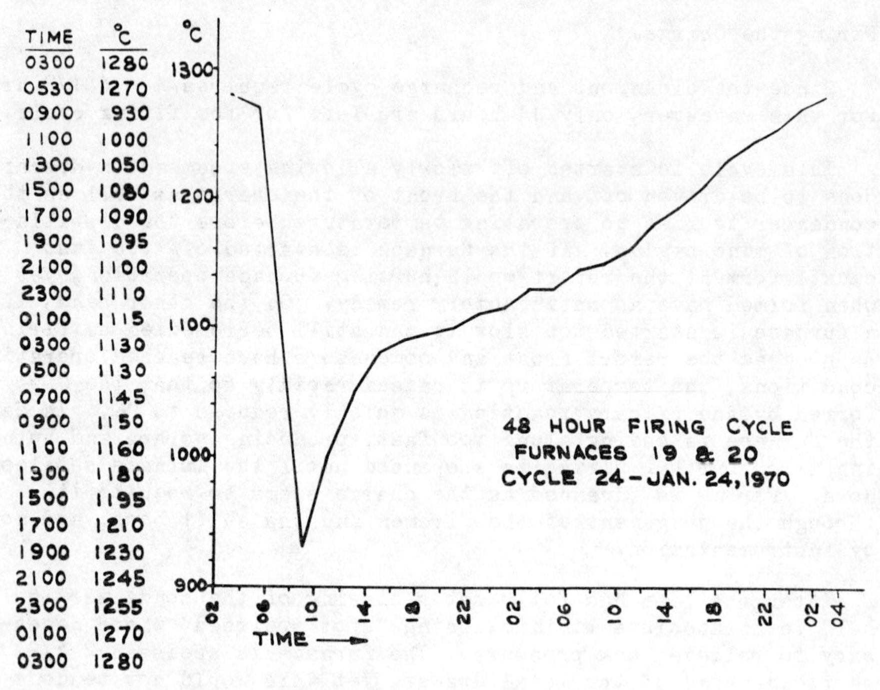

TIME	°C
0300	1280
0530	1270
0900	930
1100	1000
1300	1050
1500	1080
1700	1090
1900	1095
2100	1100
2300	1110
0100	1115
0300	1130
0500	1130
0700	1145
0900	1150
1100	1160
1300	1180
1500	1195
1700	1210
1900	1230
2100	1245
2300	1255
0100	1270
0300	1280

Fig. 2. - 48 Hour firing cycle.

Prior to tapping the furnace, the draw ladle is lined with a 12.5 mm layer of clay and moved into position, hanging from a Yale chain block secured to the draw shield frame. Approximately 30 minutes are needed to dry the clay. The ladle is made from 6.4 mm boiler plate and has a 100 mm wide lip. Around the upper periphery a 6.4 mm dia. bar is welded and serves as a root for the grout. The ladle can be tipped forward to discharge the spelter, and has a locking device holding it level until casting starts. The draw shield made of 3.2 mm plate, consists of two hollow rectangles (right and left), 600 mm wide, 1.85 m high, and each 100 mm thick thus acting as small chimney taking cold air from the floor then discharging it up the ventilators. They are set 760 mm horizontally apart, and from each a single 64 mm thick rectangular plate angles in toward the condenser nose leaving a 310 mm slot for the ladle spout to enter. The shield is moved on a monorail by a spur geared Yale trolley.

The ladle spout is placed below the second row of condensers (top rows) and the stuffing broken with a "scraper bar", which is a 12.7 mm cold rolled bar with a 62.5 mm dia. cast iron disc riveted on the end. Molten zinc flows by gravity into the ladle, the scraper being used remove that which does not issue. Stuffing, zinc dust, zinc oxide, zinc, and some residue falls into the ladle during this operation. The metal drawer moves to the second file, etc., until his ladle is about half full. The ladle is then lowered to the bottom two retort rows, then the blue powder and residue floating on the surface is removed with a perforated shovel and tossed into a wheelbarrow (also perforated) and deposited on the blue powder pile. Scrap zinc, from the floor pans (condenser leakage) is placed in the ladle, then the lower two rows are drawn, along with enough hot charge from the retort mouth to melt this scrap. Precaution is exercised in this maneuver since excess residue introduces iron and copper into the spelter. As soon as possible, the condensers are re-stuffed behind the metal drawer, to prevent excess loss of zinc.

Parallel to the outside walls of the block house cast iron mold stands are located. The molds are mounted in clusters of five or eight, and are arranged to dump the frozen slabs toward the wall. Two stands of five molds each are in front of sections five and sixteen and two stands of eight in front of section twenty. Each standard slab mold weighs about 38 kg and the pedestal molds are distributed in the clusters to supply four such slabs for every 36 regular slabs.

The full ladle of $\pm$ 212 kg of spelter is moved to the mold stands via trolley and monorail then cast into eight 26.5 kg slabs. A small dipper of spelter is extracted from each ladle and slowly poured, from shoulder level, into a bucket of cold water, forming a composite sample of the draw. Since most slabs are sold as originally cast, froth occurring from the pouring is carefully skimmed off and returned to the ladle. The metal drawer then repeats the above operation, in the meantime the eight frozen slabs previously cast are dumped.

Slabs of zinc are stacked "Rosita" brand name up 36 slabs on top of four pedestal bars upon small carts, running on rails outside the building. One slab from every fourth ladle is stacked brand name down to be drill sampled for lot formation.

Every morning the first and second draws of one cycle, together with the third, fourth and fifth draws of the previous cycle are picked up by fork lift trucks, placed on Eaton-Yale & Towne K 67-8 Wheel Steer Trailers and pulled by tractor to the metal yard where they are double weighed over "Print Weight" Toledo scales. The spelter is held on the yard without lotting until laboratory analyses are available.

Four such scales are used, two one week, the other two the next week. Prime Western lot formation, sampling, and metal analysis will be discussed along with refining and equalizing (26)

Plant Recovery and Furnace Efficiency.

Approximately two to four percent of the new zinc received in the concentrate is lost in unloading, roasting, sintering, bag house dust recovery, ventilator loss, residues, etc., yet the Plant recovery averages 88 to 90 %, with a furnace efficiency near 91 %. Quite naturally the high recovery results from the metallurgical skill of the supervisors, but interest and dedication of the workmen contributes even more, in such things as firing, metal drawing, condenser positioning, plant clean up, etc. Table 13 covers general furnace operational data of Cycle 24 - January 24, 1970.

Table 13. Furnace Data - Cy 24 - 1970

Number of Retorts	448/ furnace
Volume of Retorts	30 384 dm^3/furnace
Average "Pay-Load"	0.993 kg/dm^3
Zinc charged (10 furnaces)	190 017 kg
Zinc produced (10 furnaces)	172 331 kg
Furnace recovery	90.7 %
Total slabs produced	6508 - Ave. 26.48 kg/slab

Draw	Slabs	kg	% total	kg/cond.
1 st Draw	1601 slabs	42 390 kg	24.60 % total	9.5 kg/cond.
2 nd Draw	1678 slabs	44 443 kg	25.79 % total	10.0 kg/cond.
3 rd Draw	1527 slabs	40 442 kg	23.46 % total	9.0 kg/cond.
4 th Draw	1047 slabs	27 722 kg	16.09 % total	6.2 kg/cond.
5 th Draw	655 slabs	17 334 kg	10.06 % total	3.9 kg/cond.

20.3 Man hrs./t spelter.

Residue Handling.

The residue fall averages 22/24 % of the green concentrate smelted. Both finely divided (non-magnetic) residue, and oversized high iron slag are produced, however the latter is only 4.6 % of the total residue fall.

Residues are drug out of the cellars by means of scrapers with manganese steel cutting edges, resembling somewhat a 'fresno' scraper. The unit is powered through a 19 mm steel wire rope (cable) with a fiber core and a class CF- 211 Sullivan Electric Hauler using a 37.3 kW, 440 V, 60 Hz Westinghouse totally enclosed motor. The scraper skids back and forth on 19.9 kg/m R.R. rail running the length of the block, discharging over a 57.2 mm grizzly to remove the oversize slag, the fine residue dropping into a 1.37 m wide, 787 mm deep and 262 m long drag flight launder. Another Sullivan Electric Hauler (same as above, equipped with a 28.58 mm fiber cored steel wire rope drags the launder residues to a conveyor and elevator loading it into gondolas or racks for shipment. The cellar residue winch is movable on rails from block to block parallel to the trench launder which lies between it and the furnaces. The oversize (high iron) is loaded by Hough Payloaders into low sided gondolas. "Sows" (high iron slugs) previously removed from the retort belly no longer occur, since they are broken up by the augers of the clean out machines.

No attempt to 'up-grade' the residue is made, neither by magnetic separation nor by jigging, since the market, so to speak is captive with all of the product being shipped to Asarco lead smelters which naturally want the fixed carbon contained in the non-magnetic residue as well as the copper, gold, and silver contents of the slag. Table 14 lists assays, etc.

Table 14. Furnace Residues.

Approx 2330 t non-magnetic residue per month.
Approx 110 t high iron slag per month.
0.33 Man hr./t of residue

Chemical Analyses.

	gm/t		%	%	%	%	%	%	%	%
	Au	Ag	Pb	Cu	Zn	SiO_2	Fe	Mn	CaO	FC
Fine Residue	0.95	295	0.12	3.16	4.5	21.94	34.4	0.6	2.8	17.0
Slag Residue	1.58	343	0.50	3.72	0.5		32.3			1.5

Refining, Equalizing, Alloying, & Lotting Spelter

Slightly over 10 % of the furnace production is off grade to Prime Western specifications of 0.05 % Fe , 1.60 % Pb , and 0.50 % Cd. Practically all the fifth draw spelter is out of limits either in Fe or Pb quantities yet can be made saleable by liquation, redistillation or electrolitic refining processes. The Plant uses the liquation method to up grade this spelter. Liquation is basically a remelt of the zinc with close control of temperatures of the molten bath, taking advantage of the differences in solubilities and specific gravities of iron and lead, with respect to the liquid mass.

Refining of Off Grade Spelter

The furnace (26) used is a simple reverberatory design 6.1 m long, 2.4 m wide and 2.4 m high, constructed in a 1.2 m deep 6.4 mm boiler plate pan. An inverted arch of top quality fire brick is laid up on a bed of Lumnite cement and calcined flint grog. Care is taken to have brick to brick contact to avoid seepage of liquid zinc thru the fire brick joints. Side walls rise above the arch to the pan height and resting on the arch, yet jammed beneath a 182 mm angle welded to the upper portion of the pan, keeps the arch secure (prevents floating out of the arch). Side walls rise 1.2 m above the pan to skew back tiles from which the upper arch is sprung and is secured by buckstays and tie rods. Just under the skew back tile, 12.7 mm black pipe burners (6 per side) enter the furnace through burner tile at an angle so that the flames impinge on the arch thereby heating the spelter by radiation. Coke oven gas is used. (20.92 MJ/m^3).

The furnace is charged, little by little, with slabs through ports located in the side walls until some 70 t of molten zinc raise the bath level to the pan wall height. Surface oxides are skimmed off and the temperature lowered to ± 698° K, held at this temperature for 16 to 24 hours to allow the lead and iron zinc layer to settle (precipitate) from the bath. A small amount of NH_4Cl added to the skimmings frees entrapped zinc from the oxides. A vertical slot either in the side wall or end wall, preferable near the stack, mudded up while filling, is now opened and the molten zinc drawn off into clay lined, 270 kg ladles. After a ladle is drawn, 10 to 11 slabs are fed to the furnace to melt during the casting operation.

Temperature control is very important since iron is soluable in zinc (698° K) at 0.02 %, rising rapidly to 3.8 % at 973° K, and mutual solubility of lead and zinc rises from 1.4 % at 723° K to 15 % at 973° K. Approx 40 - 45 t per 24 hour day can be refined. When the percentage of iron and lead in the lower level of the bath increases to a point that the upper bath level approaches Prime Western limits, the temperature is raised to ± 1020° K, and the furnace then drained. Most of the zinc can be drawn off in the liquid state and cast into slabs. The iron - zinc compound is removed, granulated by hand using coke and an iron rake to divide the mass into small enough particles for recharging along with the furnace mix. Formerly the lead mass was drawn and cast as impure pig lead with about 2 % zinc, but now this also is granulated and mixed into the furnace charge. For quality of metal produced, see Table 15.

Equalizing and Alloying.

Four equalizing furnaces (built like the refining furnace) are in operation - two 50 t units, one 35 t, and one of 25 t capacity. Equalized and alloyed spelter demand has increased greatly over the past few years and now comprises 32 % of the Plant's production of metal. The larger part of this type of zinc is used by line or continuous strip galvanizers who specify lead, iron, and cadmium limits together with aluminum additions.

Dry cell battery companies require very low copper, tin, and iron impurities in the spelter mainly for shelf life of this product, so first and second draw spelter must be separated and equalized.

Metal is selected to meet the specifications of an order and formed into "Feed Groups" of 15-20 t, then drill sampled for assay. Usually the group will contain four different draws of metal and is fed to the equalizing furnace, slab by slab, alternating from stack to stack. A three man crew produces approx 10-12 t in an eight hour shift, charging, casting, and stacking the finished metal.

In practice the feed group is moved by lift truck to the charge ports of a furnace full of molten zinc at 723° K. The tap is broken and 250 kg equalized zinc is drawn into the ladle. As soon as the tap is replaced, 9-10 slabs of the feed group are charged by the metal stacker. The metal drawer with helper, takes a drop sample, casts and skims the zinc, returns to the furnace and the same maneuver is repeated.

Equalized and alloyed zincs are cast in "CONTIMEX" molds, a composite word meaning continuous galvanizing grade made in México. The molds are tailored to deliver a 25.0 kg slab both pedestal bar and regular slab. From every two ladles of metal one plate is reserved as a sample bar later to be drilled and analysed for lot formation. Drop samples are analysed only for operational control. Pedestal ingots of zinc are also cast, mainly in three sizes 227 kg, 1000 kg and 1088 kg. A clay lined aluminum trough attached to the furnace tap conveys the zinc, by gravity, to the large mold, composed of 2 % Ni, 1/2 % Cr cast iron. The mold is 610 mm high, 724 mm wide, and 102 mm long with a mass of 805 kg. Two cast steel (0.35 % C) hooks, 114 mm wide and 32 mm thick, rest on the lip of the mold (one at each end) and extend 178 mm into the mold. A gage bar hung on the lip of the mold indicates when to stop the metal flow. Ingots are skimmed in a like manner to slab zinc. After making the pour the furnace is recharged with slabs to bring it back to normal. A 45 min. freeze period is allowed before lifting the ingot from the mold. Usually a lift truck performs this operation but a chain hoist sometimes is used.

Aluminum ingots (99.8 % Al) are used for alloying. The metal is melted in stub retorts (235 mm dia. x 622 mm high) made in the Pottery Dept., from 60 % J-2280 Kentucky - Tennessee Clay Company's plastic clay and 40 % SiC. The heating medium for melting the Al is coke oven gas. "Starbide" crucibles have also been used. Molten Al is added to the 250 kg ladle of zinc using a small dipper cut to deliver the quantity needed to produce the alloy. The liquid metals are well mixed using an agitator resembling an oversized potato masher made from a 254 mm dia. disc of perforated plate (13 mm holes) welded to a meter long 13 mm dia. steel rod. At the start of each shift the quantity of metal delivered by the dippers is weighed.

Cadmium (99.9 %) rods are cut into slugs of predetermined length to produce the percentage of cadmium desired, and added in the solid state to the molten zinc, then mixed as described above.

Equalized and alloyed slabs are formed into 44 plate stacks of 40 regular slabs over four pedestal bars. The stacks are letter, and color coded designating the grade of spelter as well as its alloying agent. The upper two left hand slabs are color coded with identifying letters and stack numbers, using black for non-additive metal, blue for Al alloys, yellow for Cd alloys etc. The slabs are marked while hot using "Markal Crayons".

Metal stacks with a mass of 1100 kg are double weighed, then drill sampled and formed into metal lots.

Formation of Metal Lots.

Prime Western zinc lots are formed from third and fourth draw spelters along with rejected first and second draw zinc (originally held for equalizing) into 920 slab lots of 23 forty bar stacks having a mass of 24.0 plus tons. Sample bars are drilled, the drillings analyzed, and the metal lot formed.

Spelter produced during the stamper draw (5th draw) is formed into 'off-grade' lots of 920 slabs and drill sampled. Most of the 'off grade' is refined, still 100-150 t monthly are shipped to lead refineries for the desilvering of lead bullion. Occasional sales to electrolytic zinc plants are made. Zinc dust made from this spelter is used for purification of the neutral solution.

Refined spelter "off grade" zinc is formed into lots in the same manner as above. The slabs are cast in "Rosita" molds (26.5 kg) formed into 920 bar lots composed of 23 stacks of 40 plates each. The lot is coded as "PW 5" indicating refined zinc made from 5th draw spelter.

Equalized and alloyed Contimex spelters are lotted into 23 stacks of 44 slabs each with a total mass of 25.3 plus tons. Lot formation bars (sample slabs) are drilled and analyzed not only for the above noted impurities but also for the alloying elements.

Sampling the Formed Lot

Prime Western slabs separated as sample bars when the retorts were drawn are drilled with three holes diagonally across the slab using a 40.6 mm drill. Water is used to keep the drill cool. Drillings are placed in an aluminum pan and dried in an electric oven. When dry the 2.3 kg sample is well mixed by rolling, and divided into four 0.580 kg samples. One is sent to the Laboratory, one to the Mexican Federal Inspector, and the other two stored in the sampling department for three months.

Contimex slabs are sampled in the same manner, but a larger sample (3.060 kg) is taken. Distribution of the samples is the same. Drop samples taken during the casting of large ingots govern.

Bundling and Shipping.

All exported spelter is bundled either in 36, 40, or 44 slab stacks bound together with two transverse 31.75 mm x 0.88 mm galvanized steel straps passing around the stack at approximately the mid point of the top bars, with a third longitudinal strap lengthwise around the stack to keep the end slabs in place. Total mass of strap and clamps per 40 slab bundle averages 1.245 kg.

All exported spelter to be loaded on a ship is paintmarked using various colors and designs (dots, dashes, crosses, etc.) enabling the stevedores to keep the order intact.

Most zinc sold in México is not bundled, and is loaded loose. Strapped bundles are shipped as a "floating load" or is "in line" loaded. To float load a car, the quantity of bundles (usually 42) is divided and loaded 21 bundles in each end of the car 0.75 m from the end wall. These 21 bundles are arranged in three files of seven bundles each. In front and behind these 3 files, a 25.4 mm x 254 mm x 2.74 m board is placed, then bound together with three 31.75 mm straps, the bands running over the center of each of the files. This then binds 25 t together, so load shifting en-route is held to a minimum.

Double doored or an extra wide door boxcar must be used for "in line" loading. Two files of bundles are butted against both end walls of the car, the bundles jammed against one another - both sides. The files are advanced to the doorway far enough so that a fork truck can place bundles at right angles closing the gap as close as possible, then blocking the last of the opening with wedges. 50.8 mm x 101.6 mm lumber is nailed to the floor against the pedestal bars to prevent side movement. Ingots are loaded "in line" or in gondolas.

Table 15. Assay Range of Spelters.

Type of Spelter	%Fe	%Pb	%Cd	%Cu	%Sn	%Sb	%Al
Regular P. W.	0.033	0.60	0.035	0.0065	0.0006	0.0005	0.0006
Off Grade	0.182	1.07	0.007	0.0112	0.0032	0.0006	0.0010
Refined - PW5	0.020	1.03	0.007	0.0115	0.0035	0.0006	0.0009
Contimex No. 2	0.018	0.15	0.011	0.0046	0.0009	0.0010	0.0006
Contimex No. 3	0.016	0.08	0.018	0.0030	0.0005	0.0005	0.0006
Dry Cell alloy	0.015	0.20	0.050	0.0004	0.0003	0.0005	0.0006
Line Galv. Alloy	0.020	0.18	0.020	0.0046	0.0009	0.0010	0.30-35

Pottery and Concentrating Mill

Retort Manufacture

Silica flour retorts have been used since conversion to the 48 hour firing cycle in 1959 - 60. The retorts must endure temperatures up to 1550° K with out sagging (plastic flow), resist corrosion by ore slags, as well as penetration of zinc vapors, must be economical, and have a reasonable lifetime (70 - 85 days). Since no satisfactory clay (P.C.E.+1873° K) has been found in México to date so, refractory materials are imported resulting in a higher cost.

Retorts are made of 25 % calcined flint (3.5 mm), 40 % plastic clay (1.8 mm), 10 % light wad clay (1.8 mm) and 25 % silica flour (- 140 mesh). The refractories are weighed in 450 kg (dry) batches, belt conveyor fed to a 1.53 m dia. Clearfield, double muller pan mill, dry mixed 5 min., water added to 12 %, then wet mixed 5 min., totaling 10 min. mix time. The batch is then pug milled, extruded in a 400 mm ballot, cut into pieces 100 mm thick and stored in concrete rotting rooms (18 t) for a period of six days.

Due to the action of colloidal materials and uniform distribution of moisture, the mixture becomes more plastic while tempering, and it is then remixed in a de-airing Bonnet pug mill under vacuum. The wet 390 mm dia. ballot extruded by this unit is cut to 510 mm length with a wet mass of 139 kg. It is conveyed via trolley, monorail, and 1/2 t Yale electrical hoist to a Wettengel Clay Cylinder Retort Press, formed into a retort under 20.68 MN/m^2 and extruded (10.34 MN/m^2) thru a matrix bushing by a ram and anular piston. The matrix bushing (308 mm) determines the o. d. of the retort whereas the ram bushing (246.1 mm) governs the interior dia. The retort is extruded butt end up, cradled in a special pan, brought to rest, butt end down by a two man team, trimmed to size, mouth end finished, then carted to drying rooms. The drying rooms accommodate 1100 to 1500 retorts and when filled are dried 18 days at ambient temperature then gradually heated by steam coils beneath a slatted floor raising the room temperature to 345° K over a secondary 18 day period.

Dry retorts are taken to the pre-heat kilns of the furnaces (p.491) and raised to +1573° K during a 48 hour period. This temperature and time duration will stabilize the semi-silica mix and convert the silica flour to cristobalite. Retorts will shrink from the wet pressed size of 1.676 m long x 308 mm dia. (outside dimensions) to 1.600 m x 298 mm fired condition. Correctly made, dried, fired, and handled retorts under normal furnacing conditions will have a lifetime of 80 plus days.

Condenser Manufacture.

Condensers have a far shorter lifetime than do the retorts since they are subjected to thermal shock, physical breakage, etc., yet very little corrosion damage. Because the lifetime is short (6.3 - 7.5 days) the cost of components and labor must be held to a minimum. The Plant is fortunate in having a supply of naturally calcined mine waste available to use as grog for only the expense of gathering, washing and sizing. If this material was not so readily available, discarded retorts would be cleaned of slags, crushed, washed, sized and used as grog.

Mine waste grog (30 % Al_2O_3) is crushed to pass a 5.4 mm screen, washed in a Dorr - Rake classifier at the Concentrating Mill, and delivered to the Pottery for condenser manufacture. Clays are crushed and sized through a 1.8 mm screen, then stored in tanks from which a 50 % - 3 mesh grog, 41 % - 8 mesh Gilliam Clay, and 9 % - 8 mesh J-2280 clay mixture is drawn onto a small conveyor belt feeding a Simmons pug mill (knives only) and water added (16 %), extruded in a 178 mm dia. cylinder cut into 13 kg sections and fed by hand into the mold cans of a "Garrison - Whipple" condenser machine. This machine consists of a revolving conical plunger and rotating 'can table', forming the condensers at the rate of 1722 units in seven hours working a six man crew. 75 % kerosene - 25 % castor oil mixture is used as a lubricant to prevent the mud from adhering to the mold.

The day's production is set on slatted, wooden floors beneath which steam coils are located. After several minutes the condenser mouth is crimped by placing in a pan and rotating back and forth utilizing the condenser mass to make the crimp due to the pan design. The next day the production is transferred to dry rooms holding 3500 - 4000 condensers. After a four day dry period (343° K) the condensers are loaded into 3500 - 4000 capacity condenser kilns, stacked 4 high, raised to 1523° K over a 54 hour period, then cooled (66-90 hours) removed, and transferred to the furnace blocks. Kiln breakage will average

1-1/2/3 %. Coke oven gas (20.92 MJ/m^3) is used for firing.

Tile

Two different types of tile mixes are used, namely "A" mud composed of 54 % Harbison-Walker calcined flint and 46 % Light Wad Clay, and "B" mud using 50 % mine waste grog with 50 % Christ Clay. The cost of B mud is roughly 75 % of that of A, and is used to make furnace front plates, kiln floor tile, etc. All other tiles are made from the better grade mud.

Grogs are sized to 3.48 mm and clays to 1.80 mm. Mixes are weighed in 400 kg batches, dry mixed in a 2.44 m dia. Clearfield pan mill for 5 min., water added (13 %) and mixing continued an additional 5 min. The batch is transferred to a Wettengel pug mill (knives and augers) extruded as a 390 mm cylinder, cut into 100 mm thick discs, stored in a rotting room, and used as needed.

Wooden molds are used to form the desired shape allowing 12.7 mm per 304.8 mm for contraction. The mud is thrown into the mold little by little, then pounded into all corners and mold configurations using a large wooden mallet. The molds are liberally painted with a 50 % kerosene - 50 % castor oil mixture to prevent the clay mass from sticking to the mold. The formed block is air dried over concrete floors for 10/20 days, then transferred to a slatted, wooden floored drying room with steam serpentines below the floor level, and drying continues for seven days more. Dried shapes are loaded into a 6.1 m dia. down draft bee-hive kiln and fired to 1573° K over an 84 hr. period, using 20.92 MJ/m coke oven gas. Cooling also requires a 3.5 day period.

At times furnace front plates are extruded using the de-airing Bonnet pug mill with a shape formation nozzle and working with a stiffer mud (± 12 % H_2O).

Table 16. Refractories.

	H.W.Flint	Christy	Gilliam	Light W.	2280	Silica Flour
% SiO_2	47.7	58.25	50.00	66.90	70.48	99.9
% Al_2O_3	47.5	27.24	35.76	21.68	18.15	0.012
% Fe_2O_3	1.1	1.80	1.59	1.24	2.14	0.018
% TiO_2	2.5	1.20	1.25	1.23	1.22	0.007
% CaO	0.2	0.46	0.38	0.29	0.41	
% MgO	0.2	0.15	0.12	0.14	0.05	
PCE Cone	33/34	30	31	30/31	27/28	1983°K
Density kg/m^3	1377	1395	1395	1139	1457	830

Man hr./retort = 0.46

Man hr./100 Condensers = 8.65

Concentrating Mill.

This mill is mainly a crushing, washing, and up-grading (concentrating) unit, treating 550 - 600 t of rejected condensers, and ± 400 t of calcined mine wastes monthly on a one shift six day week basis.

Rejected condensers will contain 1.5 % - 2.0 % of the new zinc charged, and after crushed, washed, and jigged will yield a product of ± 84 % Zn, recovering approx 87 % of the zinc in the condensers.

Condensers are broken into 150 - 200 mm pieces at the furnaces to remove as much ZnO as possible adding to the blue powder production. The broken condensers (20 - 25 % Zn) are trucked daily to the mill and are concentrated during the latter half of each month. The chips are fed over a 35 mm grizzly, the undersize falling on a 457 mm inclined belt conveyor equipped with a magnetic head pulley to remove any 'tramp' iron. This material goes to a tank at the washing plant. Oversize goes to a secondary inclined belt conveyor and is delivered to a feed tank for crushing. Zinc frogs, iron, etc. are removed by hand from the conveyor. The crusher, a balanced Kue-Ken with 560 x 635 mm manganese steel jaws, and powered by a 18.65 kW, 1170 RPM, 440 V, 60 Hz motor (6 Vee sec. D belts.) This unit was made by the Straub Mfg. Co.

The crusher is set to deliver 38 mm chips to a belt conveyor also equipped with a magnetic pulley (iron removal) transferring the sized material into the same feed tank as that from the grizzly conveyor. This tank feeds an Allis Chalmers 1.5 x 3.04 m ripple flow screen (12.7 mm opening) in a closed circuit with a set of 610 mm dia. Allis Chalmers rolls powered by a 37.3 kW, 440 V, 60 Hz, Allis Chalmers motor. Sized still again thru a double roll Allis Chalmers mill with 1.11 m - 406 mm wide rolls each being driven by a 37.3 kW, 440 V, 60 Hz, Allis Chalmers motor. Crushed material (3.25 mm max), is fed onto a multiplex of five 4.27 m x 1.05 m Deister "Plate-O" Self Oiling Headmotion tables or jigs. They are covered with linoleum, and have wooden riffles 6.25 mm high by 9.5 mm wide, set 32 mm apart (41 per table). The table stroke is approx 19 mm with 280 oscillations per minute. The jigs are motivated by 1.5 kW, 440 V, 60 Hz, Howell Electric motors, and will up-grade their feed from 25 % Zn to approx 85 %, leaving only 2.5 % Zn in the tailings.

Water for working the tables is recirculated, that from the heads and middlings of the tables being sent to a Dorr Thickener by three 76 mm centrifugal pumps powered by 5.6 kW, 1730 RPM, 440 V, 60 Hz, Westinghouse motors. Water and tailings from the tables is picked up by a Modle C, 76 mm Wilfley pump using a 14.9 kW, 1160 RPM, 440 V, 60 Hz, Westinghouse motor, and sent to a 914 mm wide by 5.2 m long Dorr classifier. Rakes of the unit are 381 mm long and 89 mm high, set 634 apart in two lines operating inside the trough which has a slope of 0.2054 radians. The rakes reciprocate 19 times per minute, and are powered by a 1.49 kW, 1735 RPM, 440 V, 60 Hz, Westinghouse motor. Dewatered tailings drop onto a concrete yard, later to be trucked away to a tailings dump. Water from the back of the classifier is sent to the thickener. Rakes at the bottom of the thickener make 1 RPM in 5 min 30 s, the slimes being purged continuously to a sump. Overflow from the Dorr Thickener is collected in concrete reservoirs and returned to the system adding fresh make up water as needed.

Manufacture of Sulfuric Acid.

Sulfuric acid (100 %) is produced at ± 2500 t/yr from one roaster's metallurgical fume, yet this tonnage could be increased if the market so demanded by using all gases produced by the four roasters. Zinc, iron, and lead sulfides upon roasting yeild SO_2, the principal reactions being:

$$2\ ZnS + 3O_2 = 2\ ZnO + 2\ SO_2$$

$$7\ FeS_2 + 6O_2 = Fe_7S_8 + 6\ SO_2$$

$$Fe_7S_8 + O_2 = 7FeS + SO_2$$

$$3\ FeS_2 + 5O_2 = Fe_3O_4 + 3SO_2$$

$$2\ PbS + 3O_2 = 2\ PbO + 2SO_2$$

The roaster is operated under a smothered roast (insufficient air) to maintain a high percentage of SO_2 in the convertor gases, yet this insufficiency of air for total oxidation tends to oxidize the iron sulfides, preferable to the zinc sulfides, so the residual sulfur in the calcine is mainly that of zinc, The limited air and high temperature operation of the roaster produces magnitites (Fe_3O_4) as well as zinc ferrites ($ZnO.Fe_2O_3$) both troublesome in sintering and furnacing.

Hearth temperatures are considerably higher than those of the other three roasters and at times reach 1203° K. The roaster is a bit 'over-fed' with raw concentrates and treats all partially roasted calcines (flue dusts) collected from the four roasters, the latter being introduced at the seventh hearth level. This is done to deliver as much sulfur as possible to the Acid Plant, yet still produce a furnaceable calcine.

Gases exit the roaster above 1200° K, with approx 5.5 % SO_2, and enter a 1.07 m dia. serpentine gas cooling flue consisting of three 19.5 m pipes with dust hoppers at ground level. The abrupt change of direction in the gas flow drops out a considerable amount of entrained dust particles. From the hopper the gas enters a cyclone, into a Labbe tube cooler, and finally to settling chambers at the head end of a plate and wire electrostatic precipitator.

An American Blower fan (EL), Vee - belt driven at 850 RPM by a Size 15, Type S. C. fluid drive unit (A.B.C.) is powered by 37.3 kW, 440 V, 60 Hz, G. E. motor. Approx 255 m_3/min. (STP) of roaster gases are delivered to the three line (two hot sections/line) treater. This unit is essentially the same (with the same operation procedure) as the larger Cottrell (see Roaster gas treatment, p. 472), and is loaded with 38 000 V of rectified electricity. Originally the walls were of red brick, but have been replaced with 7.9 mm steel plate insulated by asbestos batts covered with asphalt mastic. Gases enter the treater at ± 553° K leaving above the dewpoint of H_2SO_4 or ± 503° K.

Target dampers operated by air cylinders control entrance and exit of gases into the 'hot' cells. The entire treater may be by-passed to the larger Roaster Cottrell if desired. The unit is operated under 248.8 N/m^2.

An American Blower fan, type E size 800, at 450 RPM sends the gas to cooling and scrubbing towers. The fan uses a seven Vee belt drive and a 44.8 kW, 440 V, 60 Hz, G. E. motor. The cooling tower (C) is a 3.4 m dia. x 5.8 m high lead lined steel plate cylinder with standard shapes of carbon brick set with Quibley acid proof cement covering the lead. Packing consists of carbon brick courses set on edge (310 brick/course) with 95 mm space between each row, and laid up dry. The water distribution trough (lead lined) is 610 mm wide 610 mm high and 9.25 m long with 32 nozzles on 31.75 mm pipe dropped 838 mm inside the tower. Spray nozzles are of antimonial lead, and flood the tower with 1.6 m^3 H_2O/min.

Gas is discharged at the top of the tower and enters the base of a 3.4 m dia. 9.1 m high lead lined boiler plate scrubber (C), with 'Duro' acid proof brick set in 'Vitrex' acid proof cement covering the lead. Duro brick is also used for the piers, checker work, etc. The tower has 1.5 m layer of 76 x 76 mm cross partition ring packing covered with a 1 m layer of 'Intalox' (25.4 mm) ceramic saddles. The water distribution trough and spray is a twin of the cooling tower. Fresh water 298/305° K enters the tower at 1.6 m^3/min., the effluent being sent to the cooling tower as its wash water. Flow is governed by a 76 mm 'Stabilflo' control valve with a cast iron body trimmed with 18-8 stainless steel and uses 'Teflon' gaskets. Gas leaves the tower (topside) thru a 760 mm dia. lead flue to a mist Cottrell at 303° K.

A Western mist precipitator (P) made of reinforced lead sheet and 254 mm dia. lead tubes drops the entrained mists (not absorbed moisture) from the gas. The unit composed of 118 lead pipes 3.7 m long housing star section, 14 ga, lead covered, iron wires, weighted at the bottom with 10.5 kg lead slugs to keep the wire taut and relatively stable against the gas flow. The wires are charged with 75 000 V of rectified electricity supplied by a Silicon Diode rectifier. The precipitator is not overloaded and can easily treat up to 300 m^3/min. of moisture laden gas.

Gases leave the treater at ± 303° K thru a 762 mm dia. lead flue, and can be sent either to a coke filter, or by-pass the filter and go directly to a drying tower (T). The Plant at present, is operating without the filter. The coke box is made of 6.3 mm sheet lead (steel reinforced) 6 m wide, 4.6 m long, and 1.85 m high, filled with sized 'rose coke' (38 mm / 30 mesh). A perforated lead grill at the exit prevents fine coke from being carried over into the drying tower. The inlet manifold consists of a 762 mm dia. lead pipe with twenty, 203 mm dia. outlets equally spaced. The outlet manifold is the same as the inlet except that it is located at the top of the filter box instead of at the bottom. The coke filter is used as safety measure in case of a failure in the mist precipitator.

Gases enter the bottom side of the 3.8 m dia., 9 m high Duro brick lined drying tower, at neutral pressure from a 762 mm lead flue, flowing upward countercurrent to 97 % H_2SO_4 being circulated over the tower packing. Packing consists of 76 x 76 mm cross partition rings topped off with a 1 m layer of 38 mm 'Intalox' saddles and another cap of 327 mm, 25.4 mm saddles. A Meehanite acid distribution pan with 48 outlet pipes orificed to 10.3 mm openings distributes the acid over the packing. Approx 1.33 m^3/min. H_2SO_4 is circulated over the tower packing, thru the cooling coils, interchange acid tanks, etc., to maintain 97 % strength drying acid.

Leaving the drying tower thru an acid mist 'catcher' in a 762 mm dia. steel plate flue the gas, now dried to 2/3 mg H_2O/dm^3, enters a positive displacement gas pump (B) made by Roots - Connersville. The pump is 356 x 915 mm type R C G H, belt driven by 10 Vee belts. Turning at 467 RPM powered by an 82.8 kW, 440 V, 60 Hz, Westinghouse motor, it delivers the gas to the convertor room at 36.9 kN/m^2. There is a stand-by pump of the same specifications and a smaller unit for start up operations after a long shut down when the convertor heats have been lost.

Three heat exchangers (H) in series (all identical) raise the temperature of the 5 % plus SO_2 gas from 313° K to 703° K at the entrance of the first converter (V). The heat exchangers are 1.83 m dia., 5.1 m high with 955 boiler tubes (38 mm dia.), the shell is of 9.5 mm boiler plate, heavily insulated with asbestos batting. Converted gases (SO_3) are inside the tubes, cold gas (SO_2) outside.

The two stage converter system consist of a 3.05 m dia. 2.43 m high, first converter with two trays of Vanadium Pentoxide (V_2O_5), each tray holding 2400 dm^3 of pellets. The second converter is also 3.05 m dia. but 3.9 m high and consists of three 2400 dm^3 trays of V_2O_5 pellets. Gases from the pumps enter the 3rd heat exchanger, then the second and finally the first, thence to the first converter. Approx 80 % conversion (SO_2 - SO_3) is accomplished in the first converter. Exit gases enter flues of the first heat exchanger at 793° K drop to approx 700° K prior to entering the second converter where additional conversion takes place so that the overall SO_2/SO_3 conversion is is 98.0/99.0 % efficient. SO_3 laden gases at 813° K exchange heats in the second, then the third exchanger so that it enters the final absorber at 383° K.

Absorber (A) is a 9.5 mm steel plate shell 3.35 m dia. lined with 'Duro' acid proof brick, leaving a 3.17 m dia. clear area. The 9.85 m high tower is packed with partition rings and Berl saddles. One course of 143 x 143 mm partition rings are set. On top of these, 72 mm partition rings are dumped at random to a height of 4.9 m. Packing is topped off with two caps of Berl saddles one layer of 25.4 mm saddles 1.37 m thick, the other is of 12.7 mm saddles 457 mm in depth. A 60 outlet distribution pan 2.54 m dia. and 305 mm deep made of Meehanite cast iron floods the packing with approx 1.7 m^3/min. of 98.5 % H_2SO_4. SO_3 is absorbed increasing the strength to 99.5 % at the tower exit where it enters a 'make-up' tank is diluted by weaker acid returning from the drying tower and if needed water. 17.5 mm dia. orifices in the mouths of the distribution pan tubes control the flow over the packing by keeping a 200/205 mm head of acid in the pan.

The make up tank is 4.2 m dia. x 2.36 m high made of 9.5 mm boiler plate lined with acid proof brick. Acid exiting the tower is ± 383° K but when diluted to 98 % will rise to approx 413° K. A size 5, MS, Form E Lewis external pump driven at 1720 RPM by a 1.87 kW, Louis-Allis, 440 V, 60 Hz, motor, sends the diluted acid to a cooling serpentine of 152 mm dia. centrifugally cast iron pipe approx 366 m long with 14 Sprayco nozzles each spraying 303° K water at the rate of 450 dm^3/min., cooling the acid to ± 308° K. The Lewis centrifugal pumps use Illium impellers (Ni, Cr, & Cu alloy) and are available from Chas S. Lewis & Co. Inc.

Oleum up to 109 % is also made in a batch process by a small absorbing tower preceeding the final absorber.

After cooling, the acid is sent to storage, to the drying tower, or returned over the absorbing tower. Three 187.5 m^3 covered storage tanks made of 9.5 mm steel plate are in service each capable of storing 480 t acid.

Instrumentation.

A Leeds & Northrup Micromax automatic SO_2 gas analyzer with a repeater instrument in the Roasting Department enable the operators to keep close control of the SO_2 percentage in the convertor room. The Micromax uses a strip chart, whereas the repeater is an indicator.

A 40 point Leeds & Northrup 'Speed-O-Max' indicating instrument with self neutralizing toggle switches allows the operator to instantly check essential temperatures such as SO_2, H_2O, and acid any place within the Acid Plant train. Iron - Constantan pyrometer couples are used exclusively throughout the plant.

A 'Speed-O-Max' Model G Leeds & Northrup 8 point strip chart recorder is used for converter temperature control. Any deviation from normal is quickly corrected thru valve adjustments.

A Leeds & Northrup 'Speed-O-Max' type G, conductivity cell instrument is used for control of absorber acid strength. A very narrow range of 98.4 % to 99.4 % H_2SO_4 is maintained with a preference of 98.7 %. As before stated weaker acid or water is used for diluting; however, the rate of dilution must correspond to the concentration rate in the absorber.

A Fischer & Porter Flowrator instrument size .05 - 10 controls the water used for dilution, and a Moore high frequency response (HFR) valve positioner controls the weak acid addition to maintain the wanted absorber, storage acid, and dry tower concentrations.

The entire plant is electrically interlocked so that any failure up stream trips and shuts down the operating units down stream.

Marketing.

Sulfuric acid, both 98.5 % and oleum, are shipped in 50 t steel plate tank cars. In cold weather, an antifreeze of HNO_3 is used in the fuming acids (oleums) usually about 4 %. Samples are taken after final loading of the acids.

General.

Rosita's Plants - Zinc, Acid, Coal, and Coke maintain and operate their own electrical power system consisting of two 4000, one 3000, one 2000, one 1000 and one 750 kW, 3 phase, 60 Hz turbo generators all made by Allis Chalmers. A water filtration and purification plant treating 16 742 m^3 daily. Two 100 t and and one 50 t Baldwin Diesel Electric yard locomotives. A 180 km natural gas line with 13 cathodic protection units as well as its service roads.

Since December 1968 a Sperry Rand Univac Data Processing System Model 9300 has controlled materials, accounting, salaries, etcetera, and additional programming is still in progress. In fact man hours per unit produced and power consumed, reported in this paper, was furnished by the Computer.

References.

1. C. H. Mathewson, "The Science and Technology of the Metal, Its Alloys and Compounds" - Reinhold Publishing Corporation - 1959.

2. Werner W. Duecker and James R. West, "The Manufacture of Sulfuric Acid" - Reinhold Publishing Corporation - 1959.

Chapter 19

THE VERTICAL RETORT ZINC SMELTER

AT NEW JERSEY ZINC COMPANY
Depue, Illinois

L. D. Fetterolf, Technical Assistant to Director,
Research and Development-Palmerton

W. R. Bechdolt, Manager of the Depue Plant

V. Stilo, Assistant Manager of the Depue Plant

J. A. Motto, Patents Department-Palmerton

Abstract

The New Jersey Zinc Company operates at Depue, Illinois, an integrated zinc smelting plant using the vertical retort reduction process. The overall operation comprises green concentrate roasting, sintering, vertical retort smelting and metal refining. In the roasting operation, the fine concentrate is pelletized, the dried pellets fluidized and autogenously roasted with air in a "fluid column" with minimal formation of dust requiring recirculation. The roasted pellets and any associated roaster dust are agglomerated in a rotating drum and laid down, in combination with coal for fuel, on a Dwight-Lloyd sintering machine which converts to a semi-fused mass - a physical state more suitable for vertical retort smelting. The smelting plant of 27 vertical retorts rated at 8 T zinc each per day on average requires the following major processing steps - mix preparation and briquetting, briquet coking, vertical retort reduction, vapor condensation and slab casting of metal. A portion of zinc production is converted to 99.99+ percent purity by boiling and fractional distillation in columns consisting of externally heated, superimposed trays of high-conductivity refractory.

Plate I

Aerial View of Depue Plant with Vertical
Retort Plant in Foreground - Left

Introduction

The New Jersey Zinc Company has operated a zinc smelter at Depue, Illinois, since 1905, the location being 90 miles southwest of Chica in proximity to a concentrated zinc metal market. The geographic si uation with respect to raw materials is a favorable compromise in vi of the scattered sources of the diverse raw materials required.

Prior to 1929, zinc smelting was accomplished by the then conventional horizontal retort process involving use of thousands of small retorts operating as individual units. In 1929, high capacity verti cal retorts were placed in operation and smelting capacity has since been expanded on this basis.

A major expansion was completed in 1967 with construction of all facilities required for an integrated zinc smelting plant - namely, zinc concentrate roasting, sintering, zinc smelting, metal refining and casting.

PART A - FLUID COLUMN ROASTING

The zinc concentrates available today are predominately zinc sulfide which mineral form requires roasting to zinc oxide for amenabil ity to reduction with carbon. With a few possible exceptions, there are three somewhat similar roasting methods currently in use - all based on oxidation during suspension in a medium of air. The choice for Depue was the Fluid Column roasting process developed by The New Jersey Zinc Company and licensed to Sherbrooke Metallurgical Company in Port Maitland, Canada. This method differs from others in that the green concentrate is pelletized (through 4 and on 28 mesh - Tyle Standard) preliminary to roasting. There is little degradation of pellets during fluid action with the result that carryover of gas-entrained dust from the roasting chamber is minimized as compared with in excess of 50 percent dust carryover during flash roasting. Furthermore, the coarse calcine may be crushed to a size suitable for smelting mix with avoidance of sintering whereas the very fine calcine of other roasting methods must be sintered to provide suitable sizing. In addition, pellet roasting offers the possibility of operation with over 90 percent elimination of lead and cadmium. This provides smelter feed for direct production of zinc at lead and cadmium levels which meets some market requirements without refining If elimination roasting is not practiced, roasted pellets constitute ideal feed for sintering machine elimination of lead and cadmium at greatly increased sintering machine capacity.

Raw Materials and Handling

The materials involved are primarily green concentrates, recirculated materials in the forms of green pellet fines and roaster dust bentonite binder, sulfuric acid for reaction to produce zinc sulfate

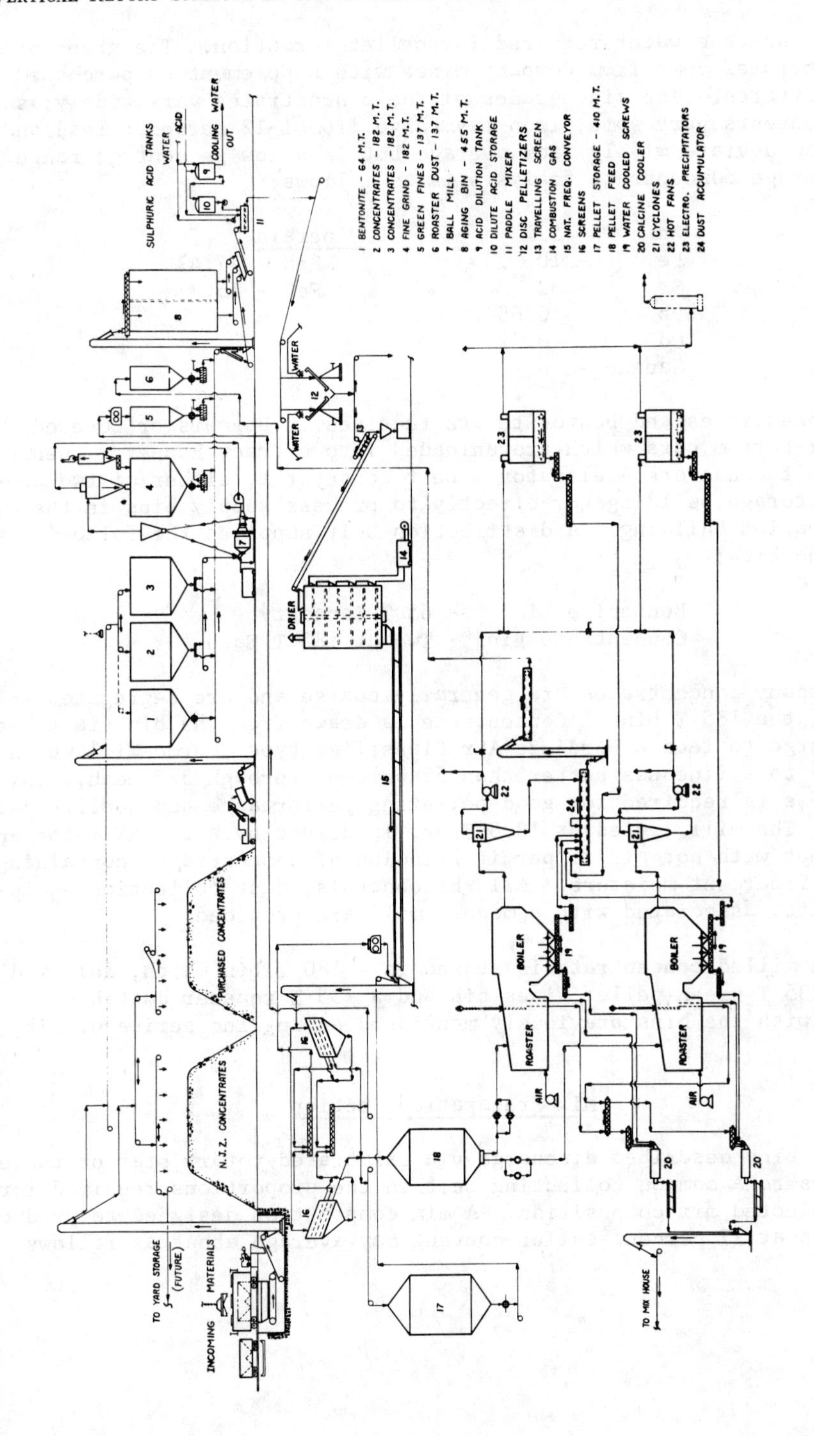
SULPHURIC ACID TANKS
WATER
ACID
COOLING WATER OUT
DRIER
WATER
WATER
BOILER
ROASTER
AIR
BOILER
ROASTER
AIR
PURCHASED CONCENTRATES
N.J.Z. CONCENTRATES
TO YARD STORAGE (FUTURE)
INCOMING MATERIALS
TO MIX HOUSE
1 BENTONITE - 64 M.T.
2 CONCENTRATES - 182 M.T.
3 CONCENTRATES - 182 M.T.
4 FINE GRIND - 182 M.T.
5 GREEN FINES - 137 M.T.
6 ROASTER DUST - 137 M.T.
7 BALL MILL
8 AGING BIN - 455 M.T.
9 ACID DILUTION TANK
10 DILUTE ACID STORAGE
11 PADDLE MIXER
12 DISC PELLETIZERS
13 TRAVELLING SCREEN
14 COMBUSTION GAS
15 NAT. FREQ. CONVEYOR
16 SCREENS
17 PELLET STORAGE - 410 M.T.
18 PELLET FEED
19 WATER COOLED SCREWS
20 CALCINE COOLER
21 CYCLONES
22 HOT FANS
23 ELECTRO. PRECIPITATORS
24 DUST ACCUMULATOR

Figure 1

Flow Sheet of Fluid Column Roaster Plant

binder and the water required for pellet formation. The green ore concentrates come from Company mines with supplement by purchased concentrates. The zinc grades of the concentrates vary widely; sulfur contents vary some; iron may range from 1-12 percent; lead and cadmium deviate widely from average but in a low percentage range. An average concentrate analysis is as follows:

		Minerals
Zn	- 52%	ZnS - 77.4%
Fe	- 10	FeS - 15.7
S	- 32	
Pb	- 0.65	
Cd	- 0.22	
Gangue	- 6	

Concentrates and bentonite are received in boxcars or covered hopper-bottom cars which are unloaded into a track hopper - thence via belt conveyors - elevator - belt conveyor to either of two covered storage buildings or directly to process supply bins in the mix preparation building. A distribution belt supplies the following in-line bins:

Bentonite Bin - 65 T Capacity
Concentrate Bins - Two at 185 T Each

Company concentrates are generally coarse and are segregated in one of the 185 T bins. Concentrate is drawn from the bin via table discharge to feed a Hardinge Air Classifier type Thermo-Mill which grinds to a fineness better than 65 percent through 325 mesh. This fineness is required for good pelleting performance and quality pellets. The mill, rated at 18.5 T/hr, is driven by a 260 KW motor and is swept with hot air to permit grinding of concentrates containing up to 5 percent moisture. All the controls, dust collection equipment etc. associated with a modern mill are provided.

The milled concentrate is stored in a 180 T bin which, followed by a 135 T green pellet fines bin and a 135 T roaster dust bin, forms with the bins previously mentioned an in-line series of six bins.

Mix Preparation Section

The bins described discharge via calibrated rotary star or table feeders to a common collecting belt in the proportions required for the selected mix composition. A mix composition designed to produce pellets at 27 percent sulfur content may average about as follows:

	Weight, %	T/hr	T/da*
Green Zinc Concentrate	64.5	20.5	410
Dry Green Pellet Fines	14	4.5	90
Roaster Dust	11	3.7	74
Bentonite	1	0.21	4.2
Sulfuric Acid (as H_2SO_4)	1.5	0.32	6.4
Water (added later)	8	3	60

*Based on 20-hour operating day.

The recirculated green pellet fines comprise the crushed oversize and the through 28 mesh fines resulting from screening dry green pellets for proper roaster feed sizing. The recirculated roaster dust represents the boiler, cyclone and precipitator dusts recovered from dust-bearing gas leaving the roaster. Bentonite, although subject to some addition limitations, is an excellent binder providing great assistance to pelleting and to pellet strength. The function of sulfuric acid is to realize the bonding properties of zinc sulfate formed by acid reaction with zinc oxide in recirculated calcine dust.

The collecting belt carrying the proportioned mix components feeds a pug mill into which the sulfuric acid and water are metered to bring the moisture content to 7-8 percent. Thorough mixing is accomplished with good binder distribution accompanied by mix conditioning resulting in improved pelletizing.

Pelleting Operation

The pug mill discharge is conveyed by belt to two Dravo pelletizer discs which may be fed singly or in parallel at controlled rates ranging from 13-18 T/hr per disc. The 3.65 m diameter discs are operated at 7.5 rpm with a pitch of 47°. The mix on arrival at the disc is deficient in moisture for pelleting and fine water sprays are played on the rolling bed in amount required to maintain an optimum pelleting condition which corresponds to about 9 percent H_2O. The objective is maximum production of through 4 and on 28 mesh pellets of good strength as required for best roaster operation (fluidization, sulfur elimination and minimum dusting).

Rather close attention to pelletizer operation is required and to this end the pelletizers are located near the central plant control room so that operators may monitor and perform remote control manipulations. The discs discharge continuously to a belt feeding a traveling screen for removal of large lumps, and thence via belt conveyor to the dryer.

Pellet Dryer and Screens

The Wyssmont Dryer, 8 m high by 6.7 m diameter, consists of a series of 32 superimposed trays mounted on a vertical shaft assembly which rotates at about 1 rpm. The wet pellets fed to the top tray of the dryer at a maximum rate of 32 T/hr, are distributed on that tray and progress downwardly from tray to tray by action of stationary levelers and scrapers. Drying is accomplished by hot combustion gas and air from an external source which is distributed through sid ports top to bottom and is circulated within the dryer by shaft-mounted turbofans running at 100 rpm. The top-zone dryer temperatur is maintained at 650°K by automatic regulation of the natural gas burned externally as described. Lower level dryer temperatures are held by circulating gas controls responding to temperature.

Retention time in the dryer is about 30 minutes which is ample to dry from 9 percent moisture to the prescribed maximum of 0.5 percent Exit gas is practically dust free and is vented to atmosphere.

The dried pellets discharged from the bottom tray are received by a natural frequency vibrating conveyor which feeds a bucket elevator delivering to either one or both of two Derrick, low amplitude, high frequency vibrating screens arranged to separate into four fractions

1. Plus 1.25 cm - crushed in a hammermill and returned to the green fines bin in the mix preparation building.

2. Minus 1.25 cm and plus 4 mesh - passed through a roll crusher and returned to screens for recovery of on-size agglomerates.

3. Minus 4 and plus 28 mesh product - delivered via conveyor to a 410 T pellet storage bin or to a 275 T pellet feed bin supplying the roaster. The recovery of this product fraction is about 85 percent of the pelletized mix.

4. Minus 28 mesh - represents pellet breakage and attrition fines - returned to the green fines bin in the mix preparation building.

The pellet product (item 3) in the pellet storage bin is recirculate to the screens before transfer to the roaster feed bin to insure dus free feed.

Fluid Column Roaster

There are two fluid column roasters in the plant - each 11 m long 4.3 m high as shown in the cross-section drawing, Figure 2. The hearth zone is 68.5 cm wide extending the full length of the roaster At the height of 112 cm, the sidewalls flare at an angle of 50° to a width of 3.65 m, which width is maintained to the top of the roaster

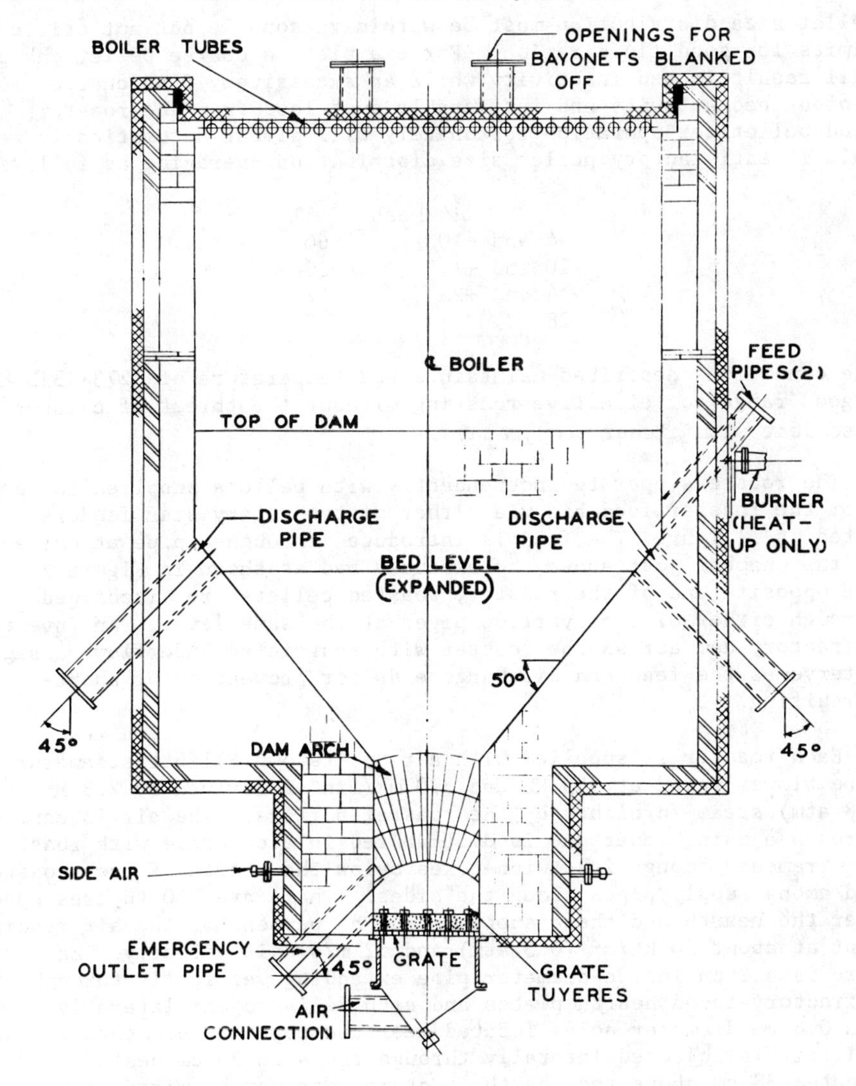

Figure 2

Cross Section of Fluid Column Roaster

A roaster operates with a charge of pellets about 1.2 m deep as a static bed which expands to about 2.15 m depth when properly fluidized by the air supplied for fluidization and the oxidation reaction. The maximum design air volume is 290 m^3/min representing 25 percent over theory requirement for oxidation of the sulfide minerals. With good fluidization, the pellets are uniformly distributed in gas suspension and temperature uniformity prevails throughout.

Pellet size distribution must be within reasonable but not critical limits for good fluidization. For example - a coarse pellet charge will result in bed inactivity while an excessively fine charge cause violent bed activity and intolerable dust loss from the roaster. Good pelletizer operation fortunately will almost automatically result in satisfactory pellet size distribution averaging as follows:

+4 Mesh	- 1%
-4 and +10	- 60
-10 and +14	- 20
-14 and +28	- 12
-28	- 7

The conditions described maintain a bed temperature of 1273-1323°K, a good range for effective roasting without the threat of clinkering attendent with higher temperature.

The roasters operate independently with pellets supplied to each from the roaster feed bin via either of two rotary star feeders, rated at 11 T/hr. The feed is introduced through a pipe at one end of the chamber just above the expanded bed as shown in Figure 2. At the opposite end of the roaster, roasted pellets are discharged through either of two overflow pipes at the same level. An inverted refractory dam across the roaster with restricted underflow passage intervenes the feed and discharge ends for prevention of short-circuiting.

Each roaster is supplied with air by its own Elliott steam turbine blower rated at 355 KW and 370 m^3/min and driven by 2.8 MN/m^2 (28 atm) steam furnished by the roaster boilers. The air is carried through a main header and is distributed in accordance with roaster requirements among eight wind-boxes below the hearth of each roaster and among supply pipes along the sides. There are 360 tuyeres space over the hearth and these supply about 85 percent of the air requirement at about 30 kN/m^2 (0.3 atm) and 52 m/s exit velocity. Each tuyere is a 2 cm inside diameter pipe extending vertically through the refractory-faced hearth plates and each delivers air laterally from six 0.8 cm diameter holes located near the top. Supplementary side-wall air is injected laterally through tubes on 30 cm centers and located 38 cm above the hearth. Natural gas may be mixed with side air for combustion to provide heat for start-up, to sustain temperature at low roasting rate or to compensate for sulfur deficiency in feed.

The expanded volume of pellets in a roaster is about 28 m^3 and the average retention time calculates to over 2 hours. Pellets of 28 mesh size obviously roast to low S content in a much shorter time Pellets of 4 mesh do not roast to comparable sulfur content even at full retention time. In addition to the pellet size factor - (1) some concentrates roast to low S content more readily than other (2) fine concentrate size is favorable to roasting rate and (3) high bentonite binder content has an adverse effect due to lowered pellet permeability.

The concentrate blends fed to the roaster generally produce calcines having analyses within the following limits:

Zn	-	58-59%
Fe	-	10-12
Pb	-	0.5-0.8
Cd	-	0.2-0.3
Total S	-	1.35-2.1
Fault S	-	0.6-1.5
Sulfide S	-	0.4-1.25

The difference between total sulfur and fault sulfur (that which should in theory be eliminated by oxidation or decomposition) is assignable to non-decomposable sulfates of calcium and magnesium. The zinc sulfate content of calcine is low but shows up in more important amounts in dust and fume collected later from the roaster gas stream. The elimination of lead and cadmium during conventional roasting is small and, in view of a 17 percent weight shrinkage on roasting, the lead and cadmium analyses of calcine slightly exceed those of the composite green concentrates. The lead and cadmium eliminated are recovered as described later.

It is sometimes advantageous to produce low lead and cadmium calcine but the Depue plant has not yet operated with this objective. Elimination roasting was demonstrated on a 50 T Fluid Column roaster at Palmerton, Pennsylvania, during development of the process and has been practiced commercially by Sherbrooke Metallurgical Company with excellent results.

Calcine discharges continuously from the roaster at about 1273°K through the overflow pipe at a rate in conformity with the charge rate. After passing gas seals, the calcine is discharged to a rotary drum cooler immersed in water bath which cools the calcine to 373-423°K. From the cooler, the calcine is moved progressively by vibrating conveyor, bucket elevator and belt to the mix house. At this point, the pellets may be crushed to finer sizing for direct use in smelter mix or may be sintered for lead and cadmium elimination.

Waste Heat Boilers and Roaster Dust Collection

The 290 m^3/min of air (25 percent in excess of theory) required for a 10.5 T/hr roaster feed rate produces 270 m^3 of roaster gas at 1273-1323°K with a composition approximately 11.6 percent SO_2, 4.4 percent O_2 and 84 percent N_2. Cooling of the gas and collection of entrained dust, amounting to 10-15 percent of feed, are accomplished in a series of units as follows - waste heat boiler, cyclone, intervening hot fan and electrostatic precipitator.

Each roaster has a waste heat boiler, especially designed by Babcock & Wilcox, built integral with the roaster and equipped with 400 m^2 of heating surface including boiler tubes forming the roaster roof and extending its full length. Up to 11,400 kg of saturated steam per hour are produced at 2.8 MN/m^2 (28 atm), the steam being used mainly for the turbine-driven fluidizing air blowers. Each boiler has six soot blowers and 11 lance doors for lancing. The unit and its associated facilities are equipped with the devices required for automatic operation.

Gas leaves the boiler at 620°K having deposited about one third of its dust load in dust collect hoppers which discharge continuousl through Western Precipitator Company motorized, double-flap valves. The dust collect, having lead and cadmium contents slightly higher than calcine product, represents carryover material ranging from fine pellets to coarse dust.

The gas passes through close coupling to two 1.2 m diameter Buell cyclones in parallel which effectively precipitate dust at a pressure drop of <700 N/m^2 (5 mm Hg) for the gas volume handled. The dust collect is discharged from the boiler dust hoppers in amount constituting two thirds of the total dust exiting the roaster. Its sizing is largely through 80 mesh with 20 percent through 400 mesh. Sulfate sulfur, lead and cadmium are 2-5 times higher than in calcine product.

Next in circuit is a Robinson hot fan (700 m^3/min rating - 59 KW) with 8.5 mm Hg suction at the inlet to maintain 1 mm Hg suction at roaster exit. The fan requires periodic sandblasting to remove accretions.

Gas is moved by the fan to a Wheelabrator (Lurgi) Electrostatic Precipitator with an inlet temperature of about 570°K, an exit temperature of 550°K and practically no pressure drop through the unit. With a rating of 570 m^3/min, the precipitator efficiency is high and residual solids in the gas are largely removed. They amount to abou 3 percent of the total solids leaving the roaster in the gas stream. The material is fume-like in nature being essentially <35 microns with 35 percent <5 micron size. Zinc sulfate, lead and cadmium will run 5-10 times that of calcine product - the first named being very high due to sulfation of the zinc oxide fume during slow cooling. The two last named are high because of selective transport as fume from the roaster. Under elimination roasting conditions (higher temperature and very low excess air), the amount of precipitator collect and its lead and cadmium contents are greatly increased.

Although the gas leaving the roaster has an SO_2 content of 11.5-12 percent, the analysis drops to about 10 percent leaving the precipitator. This is due to dilution by air inleakage at dust discharge valves on all units. The situation is being improved but does not, in fact, pose a problem in acid production other than the possible limited volume capacity of treatment units in the gas system beyond the precipitator.

The precipitator fume is discharged through gas valves to screw conveyors feeding a drag conveyor similarly servicing dust discharge from boilers and cyclones. Dust collects (bag filters) from various points in the plant are also routed to the common drag conveyor, thence to bucket elevator and again a drag conveyor returning the combined dusts to the roaster dust bin in the mix preparation building for recirculation in pellet feed mix.

Roaster and Boiler Heat Balances

Heat balances applying to roaster operation at capacity rating (10.5 T/hr feed at 27 percent sulfur and 25 percent excess air) are as follows:

Roaster (one unit)

Heat In (oxidation reactions)	9,650,000 kg cal/hr
Heat Out	
Gases at 1323°K	6,100,000 kg cal/hr
Solids at 1323°K	1,300,000 "
Radiation Loss at 5%	480,000 "
To Boiler Tubes in Roaster Roof	1,770,000 "
	9,650,000 kg cal/hr

Boiler: 1323-620°K

Recovery from Gas and Dust	4,520,000 kg cal/hr
Recovery Via Roaster Roof Tube	1,770,000 "
	6,290,000 kg cal/hr
Equivalent Steam Production	6,000 kg/hr

PART B - SINTERING

Although the pelleted roast from the Fluid Column roasters, after reduction to proper sizing, is an entirely satisfactory feed for the vertical retorts, the practice at Depue includes sintering for lead and cadmium elimination. Figure 3 depicts the flow of materials.

Roasted pellets, return sinter and sometimes roaster dust are mixed with 6 percent anthracite dust coal in a modified pug mill 1.1 m wide x 0.8 m deep x 4.3 m long. This mix is elevated to a pelletizing drum 2 m O.D. x 3.6 m long. The pelleted mix discharges to a chute and by means of a swinging spout is fed uniformly across

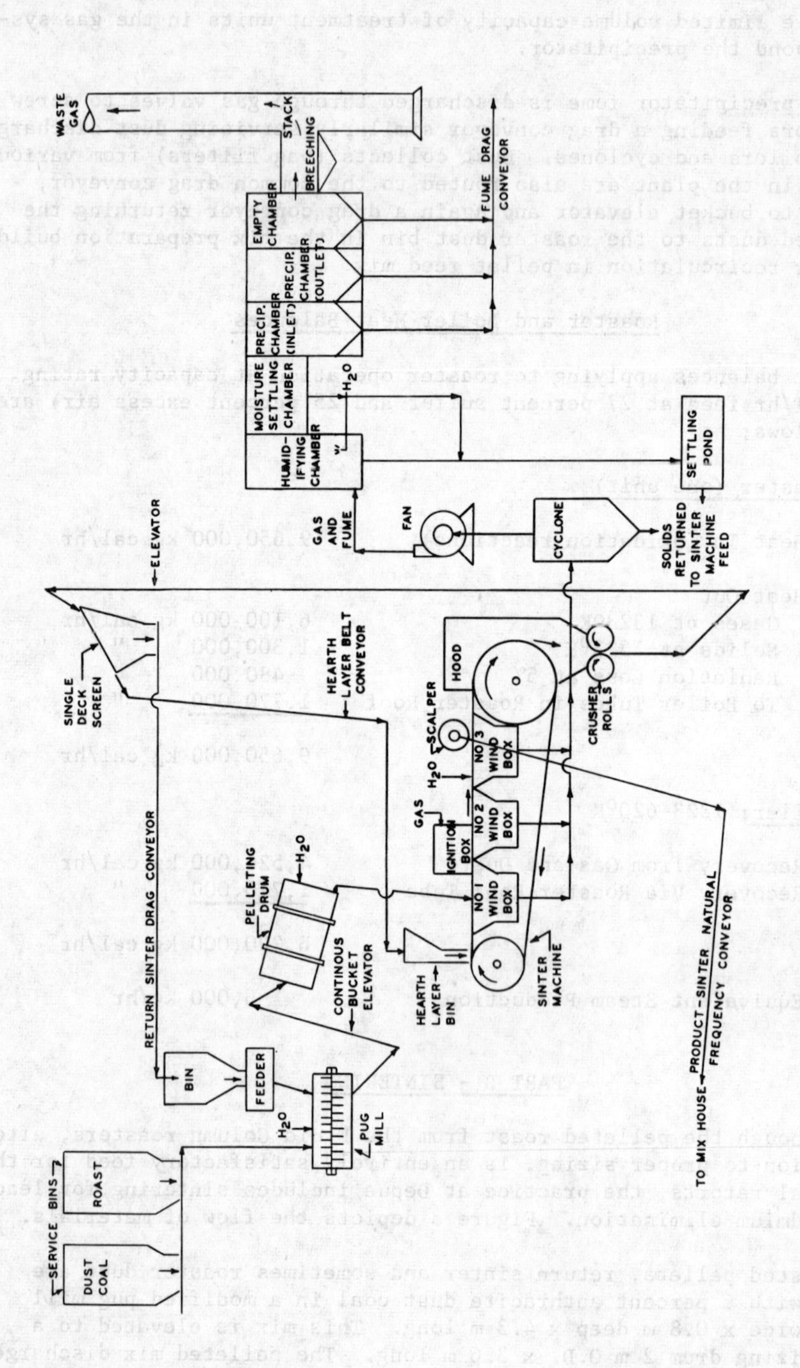

Figure 3

Flow Sheet of Depue Sinter Plant

the grates of the 1.0 m wide x 10 m long, downdraft Dwight-Lloyd sintering machine. As it enters the natural gas fired ignition box, the bed is 15 cm high; the lower 4 cm is hearth layer comprising return sinter larger than 1.5 cm. Just before the discharge end of the machine, the top 9 cm of the bed is shaved off by a rotating scalper. This top layer from which about 80 percent of the cadmium and 40 percent of the lead have been eliminated, constitutes the sintered product containing approximately 60 percent zinc, 0.35 percent lead and 0.05 percent cadmium. Fluid Column roasted pellets have proved to be an excellent sinter feed in that the current sintering capacity of 11 T/hr is more than twice that previously obtained with flash roast.

The lower portion of the bed not removed by the scalper, is discharged off the end of the machine to a set of crushing rolls and then fed to a single deck vibrating screen. The oversize (+1.5 cm) is returned directly as hearth layer while the undersize is recycled to the modified pug mill for incorporation into the feed.

Suction on the three wind-boxes is 10-25 mm Hg water with an air flow of 700 m^3/min. Dust and fume are removed from the waste gases before discharge to the stack by a cyclone and Cottrell electrostatic precipitator. The fume collected in the Cottrell contains about 20 percent each, zinc, lead and cadmium.

PART C - VERTICAL RETORT SMELTING

A vertical retort plant comprising eight retorts was placed in operation in July 1929. This followed closely the construction and operation of a similar plant in Palmerton, Pennsylvania, which was the outcome of intensive development work over several previous years. The horizontal retort plants, then operating in Depue and Palmerton, were becoming antiquated with decreasing profitability. It was necessary, therefore, to develop a continuous, mechanized process employing large smelting units of high production capacity with attending good economics.

The Depue plant has been expanded from time to time and 27 retorts are now in operation. Plate I is an aerial view of the composite plant with the vertical retort plant showing in the foreground extreme left.

General Description of Vertical Retort Process

The advantages of the vertical retort process derive from the mechanical handling of materials into and from a large, continuously operated retort producing zinc and reaction products of uniform composition at constant rates with high thermal efficiency and recovery. A fundamental requirement of the process is that the smelting charge be supplied to the retort in a form conducive to the rapid and efficient transmission and utilization of heat developed by combustion of gas in firing chambers adjacent the high-conductivity, refractory sidewalls of the retort. The required form of the charge is a large, loaf shape produced by roll-briquetting a specially prepared mix. The mix ingredients are so selected, sized and proportioned as to meet the requirement of maintenance of briquet integrity throughout the reduction process.

See Vertical Retort Flow Sheet - Figure 4.

The mix ingredients meeting prescribed specifications are prepared by an intensive conditioning treatment for development of the mix plasticity required for roll-briquetting. The green briquets from the press have strength permitting gravity flow via grizzly onto the moving grate of a coking furnace. The coking furnace is autogenously operated, the combustion of volatile from the bituminous coal in the mix supplying the heat requirement. This coal in the briquet converts to coke forming a continuous phase of coke structure which bonds the mass to produce a tough, indurated briquet capable of withstanding subsequent transport and handling.

Hot coke briquet charges are elevated to the retort charge floor in weighed hoist buckets which are emptied on a time schedule into the top extension of the retort to occupy the space provided by the continuous withdrawal of reduced briquets from the bottom.

During downward passage through the vertical retort with retention time correlated with the reduction reaction, the reduction heat is supplied by its transmission through the high-conductivity sidewalls from the combustion chambers external the sidewalls. The zinc vapor and reaction gases produced flow upwardly through the retort and the dezinced briquets are extracted at the bottom. The vapor and gases escape via a duct leading from an upper extension of the retort and are drawn into a zinc vapor condenser from which the liquid zinc is withdrawn for casting or refining. The permanent gases escaping the condenser are cooled and cleaned and piped to the retort firing chambers for supplementary fuel.

Mix Materials

Mix Composition

Mix composition is important inasmuch as analyses, proportions and sizings are variables to which briquet quality and subsequent processing behavior are critically related. A universal mix cannot be specified but a typical composition is about as follows:

Roasted Zinc Concentrate (generally sinter)	60%
Bituminous Coal	25
Anthracite Fines	5
Plastic Refractory Clay	10
Sulfite Liquor	1

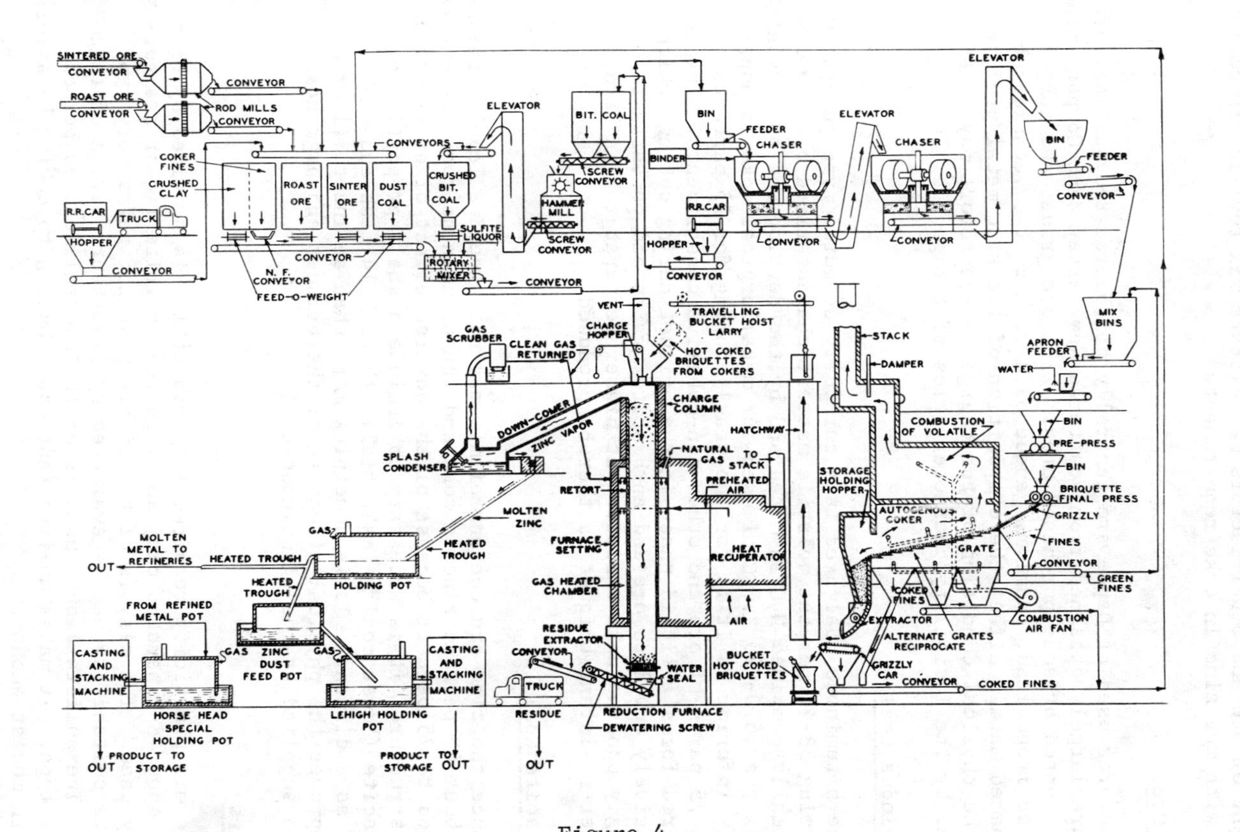

Figure 4

Vertical Retort Plant Flow Sheet

The zinc in the coked briquets from the above mix should fall in the range of 40-43 percent. Changes in zinc grade of ore, iron oxide content of ore and other factors may dictate mix revision in conformity with the zinc in coke requirement.

Zinc Ores

The ores used at Depue are generally of the roasted sulfide type and are largely obtained from scattered New Jersey Zinc Company mines supplemented by some purchased ores. Zinc ore grades and components such as iron, lead, cadmium, gangue oxides, etc. vary considerably. The named metals affect the composition of the zinc metal produced and the physical condition of the charge in the retort may be affected by the fusibility characteristics of the gangue.

Bituminous Coal

The bituminous coal used is a carefully selected type generally analyzing 38-42 percent volatile matter, characterized by very low chemically combined H_2O as mined and by the development of very high fluidity at 670-725°K. Coal used for metallurgical coke is hopelessly inferior as it is far too weakly coking for 25 parts to bond about 75 parts of ore and other non-cohesive constituents. The coal required forms a liquid phase in the briquet during coking, which effectively envelops ore and anthracite grains and converts to strongly bonding coke structure at higher temperature. A hard, shatter-resistant briquet is thereby produced.

Anthracite Coal

Since the zinc ore content of mix may not exceed a level furnishing about 43 percent zinc in coke and the bituminous coal content is limited to 25 percent because of the adverse effect of an excess on coke structure, it is necessary to include a small proportion of anthracite ("dust coal" - essentially through 14 mesh and on 200 mesh) as a diluent. It is something more than an inert filler as it improves the physical structure of the briquet and augments the carbon supplied by the bituminous coal.

Binders

The mix plasticity required for briquetting is provided by binders. About 8-9 percent clay and 1 percent sulfite liquor are currently used. The clay is of the highly plastic, refractory type and its suitability may be evaluated by laboratory firing of test bars. The sulfite liquor used is of the neutralized, 50 percent solids type. It makes an important contribution to coking behavior even in modest amount.

Materials Sizing

The major mix constituents, zinc ore and bituminous coal, have optimum sizing at a small percentage plus 14 mesh and about 30 percent through 200 mesh. This sizing represents a compromise as finer sizing produces much harder residue briquet structure but aggravates any tendency toward coking defects such as cracking, spalling and surface shelling - particularly in clay binder briquets - because of density of structure.

The bituminous coal is ground to size specification in two Pennsylvania Crusher Company hammer mills. The zinc ore in roasted pellet or sintered pellet form is reduced to size in two rod mills.

Raw Materials Handling

The mix materials as described are stocked in conventional, round, concrete stave silos - two for sinters, one for anthracite coal and a double compartment bin for crushed clay and coke fines. Each bin delivers by feeder to a weigh belt and in turn to a collector belt which continuously delivers the proportioned materials to a rotary drum mixer. Three bins provide for segregated storage of different bituminous coals which, after crushing, are delivered to one of two crushed coal bins. Crushed coal is fed independently via weigh feeders to the mixer. Sulfite liquor binder is metered into the mixer.

Mix Preparation

The rotary mixer discharge travels by belt conveyor into the first of a series of chasers or Chilean Mills. Four chasers are available; these are operated in series of two or three to avoid short-circuiting. The chaser is a massive unit 3.7 m in diameter in which two 10 T rolls are driven over an 8-10 cm bed of mix of about 2 T. Plows set on cross-arms are so adjusted as to return mix into the path of the rolls and to regulate the discharge through a central opening.

Water is added to the first chaser to plasticize the mix and to the second and third if required. The chaser power requirement is a good index of plasticity. Optimum plasticity is indicated by maximum power - usually 275 to 300 A at 440 V. The optimum briquetability of mix with clay binder is obtained with 6-7 percent water.

The highest possible chasing rate consistent with mix briquetability and green briquet quality is sought. Clay binder mix is favorable to chasing rate and a rate of 8+ T per chaser per hour may be maintained.

Plate II

View of Chasing Section of Mix House

Briquetting

The chased mix is belt conveyed to a holding bin with a bottom discharge opening superimposed over a roll-briquetting press into which mix feeds by gravity. The rolls are 61 cm in diameter, and run intermittently at about 10 rpm and produce 6 T of 6.4 cm x 2.4 cm pillow-block briquets per hour. The function of the press is to furnish continuous, uniform and densified feed to a final press with avoidance of pocket starvation.

The preliminary press discharges into a small hopper over the final "loaf" briquet press and feeds thereinto by gravity as the press assimilates the feed. The loaf briquet measures 6.3 x 10 x 7.6 cm thick (rounded surfaces) and weighs about 0.5 kg. The mass of the briquet is near ideal for the reduction conditions in the vertical retort as is the shape considering the shape limitations of roll-briquetting.

The loaf press rolls are 61 cm in diameter with two or three pockets staggered across the faces of the rolls. The press is driven by an 11 KW motor coupled by Reeves Vari-Drive to the press to produce up to 127 T of green briquets per day.

The briquets from the final press drop a minimum distance to an inclined grizzly down which they slide, with dropout of fines, to the inlet of the close-coupled coking furnace.

Briquet Coking

Coking treatment of briquets is required to convert the relatively weak green briquet to one having the strength to withstand the rough treatment incident to transport to and introduction into the vertical retort. In addition to insuring coke briquet quality measured by maintenance of briquet form during retort passage, the bituminous coal pays additional dividend in providing volatile for combustion to support a thermally self-sustaining coking operation. Furthermore, the low temperature coke developed is uniquely reactive in the reduction chemistry of the vertical retort.

The coking furnace is essentially a large refractory combustion chamber housing a series of downwardly inclined, alloy step-grates. Alternate grates have a slow reciprocating movement which imparts a forwarding impulse to the bed of briquets from feed to discharge ends. Green briquets are fed continuously from the press grizzly with the briquetting rate and grate speed so correlated as to provide a thin, uniformly distributed bed of briquets on the coker grate.

Upon arrival in the coker, the entrant briquet bed heats up, distillation of volatile from coal proceeds and autogenous operation is maintained by combustion with air supplied both above and through

Plate III

Loaf Briquetting Press and Densified Feed Above

the briquet bed from below. Temperatures are so controlled that briquets are largely volatile-free upon discharge but are under zinc reduction temperature. The grates discharge into a holding hopper of about 3 T capacity wherein the soaking heat may expel residual volatile.

Coked briquets are drawn from the holding chamber on a time schedule by roll-discharge mechanism onto a traveling grizzly and thence into coke buckets holding 1.35 T. Any fines formed in coking pass the grizzly thus providing an essentially whole briquet product. The weighed coke buckets are hoisted to the retort charging floor and are available to each individual retort as the burden demand requires.

Reduction Retorts

Construction and Firing

The smelting retort is a tall refractory structure consisting of two thin, parallel sidewalls, two massive endwalls, an upper refractory extension superimposed on the four walls and a lower extension of metal construction. The parallel sidewalls are 11.5 cm in thickness spaced 30.5 cm apart inside and, together with the endwalls, enclose the muffle space of 30.5 cm x 1.85 m or 2.44 m cross section through which the briquet charge descends by gravity. The ends of the sidewalls are recessed into vertical slots in the endwalls so that the four monolithic walls may move independently to accommodate the expansion and strains induced in walls of 10 m and 11.3 m height. The production capacity of a retort obviously depends upon the flow of heat through the walls, consequently use of the most highly conductive refractory - namely, silicon carbide. The refractory brick is a standard shape (usually 6.35 x 11.5 x 23 cm, tongue-and-groove type) bonded by high temperature, silicon carbide mortar.

A retort is heated by combustion of natural gas in a firing chamber external each sidewall. The gas is injected downwardly through five ports in the roof of the firing chamber. Air for combustion is admitted in controllable volumes through air ports at 9 or 10 levels. Quite uniform temperatures prevail from top to bottom of the chamber using the progressive combustion firing technique with near-perfect combustion attained at the bottom. Natural gas is supplemented, to the extent of about 30 percent of the total heat requirement, by carbon monoxide reaction gas from retort reduction. This gas enters the firing chambers through distribution ports just below the roof of the combustion chamber.

The temperature maintained in the firing chamber is at a selected level between 1550° and 1600°K as dictated by retort condition, production demand, etc. Combustion gases exit through flues at the bottom of the firing chamber and are moved by stack suction through three-pass recuperators of the concurrent type. With combustion gas at about 1570°K, the recuperators preheat air for retort firing to about 825°K with discharge flue gas at about 1120°K.

Plate IV

Withdrawal of Coked Briquets into Coke Bucket

Plate V

Top View of Retort and Firing Chambers at Roof Line

Retort Operation and Reduction

A weighed portion of hot coke briquets is charged into the upper extension (volume about 45 percent of that of the heated retort) through a charge cap at the top about once an hour and occupies the space created by continuous discharge of residue briquets at the bottom. The unheated extension is known as the charge column and performs several functions: the occupant briquets abstract heat from the hot gas ascending from the retort, some refluxing and selective condensation of lead take place, the reaction $C + CO_2 \rightarrow 2CO$ is permitted to occur in a zone too low in temperature for $ZnO + CO \rightarrow Zn + CO_2$ and entrained zinc oxide fume and charge dust which are detrimental to zinc vapor condensation are quite effectively filtered from the gas.

As the briquet charge enters the heated retort with external walls at 1573°K, the briquets adjacent to the walls heat rapidly and the production of zinc vapor begins via the reaction given above. Although zinc oxide reduction may begin at a relatively low temperature a practicable rate probably requires a temperature of 1273°K. The substantial thermal head results in rather rapid reduction of briquets adjacent to the walls and probable final attainment of an average briquet temperature near 1523°K as reduction comes to near-completion at the bottom of the retort.

The briquets in the mid-zone of the charge 15 cm remote from the walls are naturally penalized in availability of heat and it is this circumstance which fundamentally requires that the charge be briquetted and that the briquets pass through the retort without appreciable breakage or formation of fines. The interstices provided by briquets insures the penetration of radiant heat as well as free passage of hot gas for heating by convection. It is well known that briquet degradation in the retort imposes an unacceptable zinc production penalty because of the impediment to heat transfer as well as the difficulties caused by charge hang-up, by obstruction of gas flow and other factors. In addition to the above, the dense structure of a sound briquet favors heat transfer by conduction from surface to interior - a distinct advantage in comparison with fine, loose charge. To further emphasize briquet quality, it is noted that the coke structure must persist through the dezinced briquet stage corresponding to a residue briquet of only 40 percent of its original coke mass.

The residue briquets emerging from the retort should be reduced to 2½-3 percent zinc representing 97 percent elimination. The residue from Depue-type mix will contain 30-35 percent carbon and practically all the iron, copper, silver and gold in the feed. A large percentage of the lead in feed will also be present with high lead in feed but the proportion decreases as lead in feed decreases.

Plate VI

Hot Coke Briquet Charge Entering Vertical Retort

The residue leaving the heated retort enters a lower extension of fabricated metal. Its rate of withdrawal is regulated by a roll extractor, the rate being synchronized with the retention time in the retort required for 97 percent zinc elimination. The residue briquets drawn by the extractor fall into a bath of water in closed system for quenching and are continuously removed by an inclined screw.

About 0.25 m^3/min air is admitted into the bottom extension of the retort which after short ascent produces corresponding volumes of nitrogen and carbon monoxide. The purpose of the extraneous gas is to prevent back-diffusion of zinc vapor which would otherwise condense out on cold residue.

Condensation of Zinc Vapor and Recovery of Liquid Zinc, Blue Powder and Reaction Gas

The gaseous reaction products formed in the retort rise into the charge column at a rate of about 4.25 m^3/min (2.44 x 10.7 m retort) and with the approximate composition - 40 percent zinc vapor, 45 percent carbon monoxide, 8 percent hydrogen and 7 percent nitrogen plus some carbon dioxide in small but important amount. The hydrogen and nitrogen have origin in air, steam and residual volatile in coke. The gases exit near the top of the charge column into a downwardly sloping, refractory conduit which terminates in a zinc vapor condenser.

The problems inherent in the condensation of zinc vapor stem from the equilibrium conditions in the system of gaseous reaction products which favor reoxidation of zinc vapor by carbon dioxide with decreasing temperature. If the back-reaction, $Zn + CO_2 \rightarrow ZnO + 2CO$, is not suppressed during cooling for condensation, there is produced a copious quantity of metallic and partially oxidized zinc powder which subtracts correspondingly from liquid zinc production.

The splash condenser as used at Depue largely overcomes condensation problems as compared with earlier condensers which produced about 12 percent blue powder. Blue powder is decreased to 3-5 percent (sometimes less) by reason of (a) cooling vapor rapidly to avoid reoxidation, (b) regulating condenser temperature to prevent freezing of zinc mist, (c) increasing the surface of liquid zinc in contact with vapor and (d) assimilating a large proportion of blue powder formed into a bath of liquid zinc by intensive scrubbing with that liquid medium.

The retort gases pass through the conduit quickly without much cooling, thus reducing blue powder formation, before entry into the condenser. The condenser is an elongated refractory chamber holding a bath of zinc maintained at fixed level by continuous overflow and at about 773°K by cooling coils which submerge or emerge by thermostatic response. A motor-driven, inclined shaft passes through the remote end of the condenser and terminates in a 35 cm diameter

Plate VII

Removal of Water-Quenched Residue Via Inclined Screw to Transport Belt

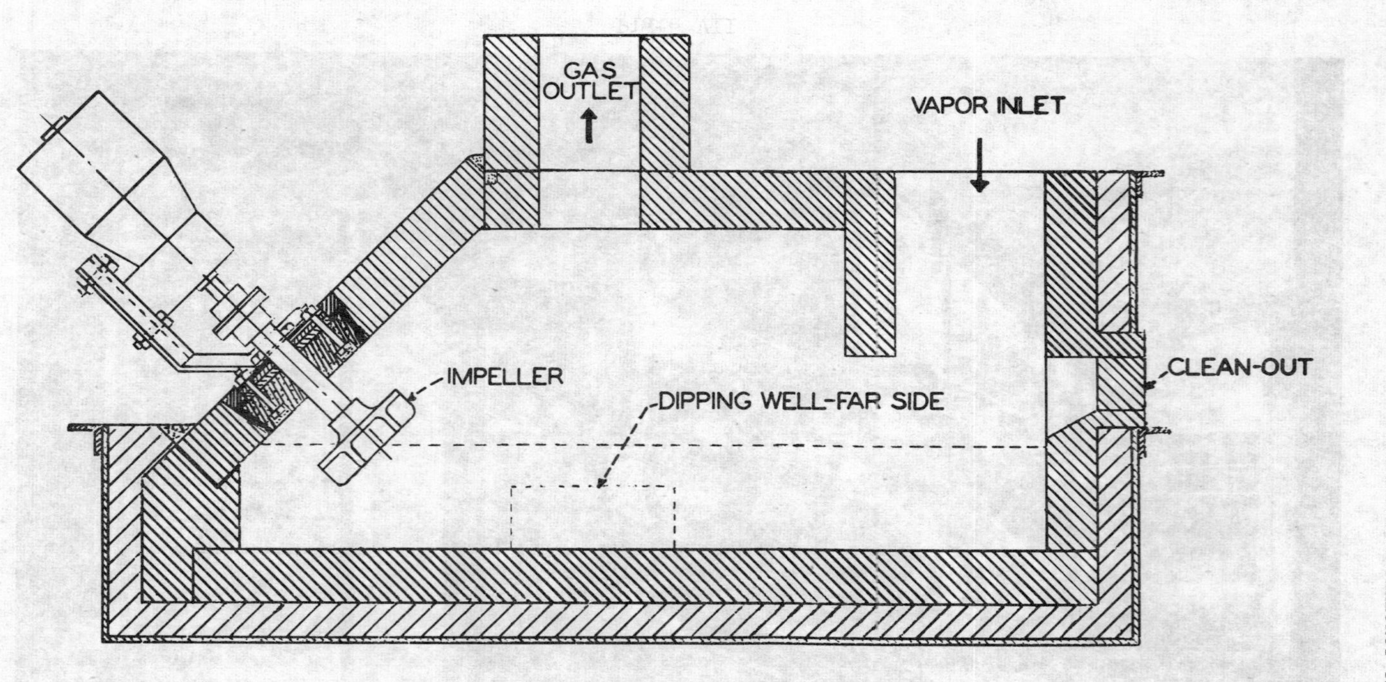

Figure 5

Lengthwise Cross Section of Splash Condenser

Plate VIII
Condensers on a Battery of Retorts

impeller dipping into the zinc bath. Rotation of the impeller at 400 rpm produces a shower of liquid zinc in such profusion that the cross section of the chamber is effectively curtained by the liquid spray. The entrant zinc vapor and accompanying permanent gases must traverse the shower with such intimacy of contact that immediate cooling and condensation are effected with the condensate joining the bath.

A small amount of blue powder, not assimilated by the bath, floats thereon and is periodically skimmed off. A somewhat larger amount accompanies the stack exit gases - perhaps 3 to 4 percent including the zinc vapor not condensible at 773°K.

Gases are moved through the condenser by suction developed by a water eductor in a scrubber-tower system which scrubs out the entrained blue powder and cleans the gas for use as supplementary fuel of 11.1 MJ/m^3 (2650 $kcal/m^3$) content. The separated blue powder collects in a trough and is periodically removed, partially dried and used as sealant over the charge caps on the retorts. Upon opening the charge caps for briquet charging, the blue powder enters the retorts and is rather promptly flashed off as zinc vapor.

Metal Handling and Casting

The molten zinc continuously overflows from the condensers into a launder; one launder services 13 retorts, while another collects from 14 retorts. Each launder delivers to a 15 T holding pot. Each holding pot is connected to a heated trough by which metal is transferred to the refining building. Each of the four lead column supply pots is fed from this trough. Constant level in the troughing system and in the supply pots is maintained by a dam in the trough beyond the lead column feed points. About half of the troughed meta overflows the dam and down a chute to a 160 T, gas-fired, reverberatory holding furnace on the ground level. This metal, designated as VFZ, has an as-produced composition averaging 0.3 percent lead, 0.10 percent cadmium and 0.01 percent iron with smaller contents of minor impurities. The lead and cadmium contents vary depending on the ore being processed.

A similar 160 T, gas-fired, reverberatory holding furnace is provided for the refined zinc. Flexibility is provided in the handling of molten zinc so that composition may be adjusted. For example, re fined and VFZ metal may be blended in an auxiliary holding pot to give intermediate compositions. Lead, aluminum or other metals may be blended with VFZ metal to produce compositions required for hot-dip galvanizing and other special requirement uses.

Each of the 160 T holding pots feeds, via vertical lift rotary pump, a Shepherd casting machine and Shepherd stacker. The integrated machines cast slabs and stack in standard shipping units. Each unit is rated at 16.5 T/hr but is operated at 13.5 T. The casting machine is equipped with 132 molds forming 25 kg slabs with the molds arranged in such sequence that four leg-slabs are first cast to provide the base course laid by the stacking machine. The 40 molds following cast flat slabs which the stacker arranges in 10 rows of four each on the leg-slabs in such orientation as to give stability to the stacked unit. Upon completion of the 11-row stack, the 1100 kg unit is removed by forklift and the cycle is repeated.

Metallurgical Data and Performance

Raw, Wet Mix	575 T/da
Coke (about 40% Zn)	490 T/da
Dry Residue	195 T/da
Zinc Production	182 T/da
Kg Zinc per m^2 Heated Retort Area per Day	160+
Zinc Recovery on Retort Input	95%
Overall Zinc Recovery	92-93%
Average Retort Operating Time	95%
Natural Gas	374.5 m^3/T Zinc
*Thermal Efficiency of Vertical Retort	45%

*An efficiency figure of 45 percent has been calculated for Depue retorts based solely on the theoretical thermal requirements of the ZnO reduction reaction at 1373°K (together with the heat necessary to raise the preheated charge to this temperature) in relation to the actual natural gas consumption rate of 375 m^3 per ton of zinc. This efficiency figure is low because the Depue heat requirement is penalized by the high iron oxide content of the ore and the relatively poor efficiency of the concurrent recuperators used for air preheat. Giving due credit to the process, the corresponding efficiency of Palmerton retorts which receive ore of lower iron content and which operate with countercurrent recuperation may be as high as 70-75 percent.

Plant Equipment and Specifications

The tabulation following gives some details as to plant equipment, specifications, capacities etc. since the foregoing text has been rather limited to coverage of general plant and process.

Raw Materials Storage Bins

Bin	Contents	Capacity	Discharge
1A	Clay	140 m^3	Feed-O-Weight/Belt Conveyor
1B	Coke Fines	140 m^3	Vibrating Trough/Belt Conveyor
2	Zinc Ore	280 m^3	Feed-O-Weight/Belt Conveyor
3	Zinc Ore	280 m^3	Feed-O-Weight/Belt Conveyor
4	Anthracite Coal	280 m^3	Feed-O-Weight/Belt Conveyor

Bituminous Coal Bins

Bin	Contents	Capacity	Discharge
205) 205A)	Uncrushed Coal for #1 Mill	46 m^3) 46 m^3)	45 cm Pan Conveyor
206	Uncrushed Coal for #2 Mill	153 m^3	107 cm Apron-Feeder, Variable Speed
204) 204A)	Milled Coal	56 m^3) 56 m^3)	50 cm Feed-O-Weight and Redler Conveyor

Hammer Mills for Bituminous Coal

#1 Pennsylvania Crusher - 75 HP - 4.5 T/hr
#2 Pennsylvania Crusher - 125 HP - 8.2 T/hr

At ratings given, both crush to nominal -14 mesh and 30 percent -200 mesh. Dust Collection: Model 70-A American Dustube Collector.

Rod Mills for Sinter/Ore Grinding

Marcy Mills (2) - 93 KW - 3.7 m Long x 1.5 m Diameter - 11 T/hr

Rotary Blender for Preliminary Mixing

Rotary Drum - 1.5 m Diameter x 11 m - 19 KW

Chasers for Mix Conditioning

Vulcan Iron Works - four in operation with various parallel - series paths possible - 150 KW - 4 m pan diameter - each has two 10 T mullers at 1.6 m diameter x 1 m wide - 21 rpm - rate of 8+ T per chaser per hour. Transfer of chased mix to briquet pressed by belt conveyor.

Preliminary Briquet Presses

New Jersey Zinc Company Design - six in operation - 7.5 KW - gear reducer and chain drive - 5 to 13 rpm - intermittent operation as required - rolls of special alloy mix - 51 cm diameter - 4 pockets wide in line across face of roll - briquet size 5 x 5 x 3.2 cm.

Final Loaf Briquet Presses

New Jersey Zinc Company Design - six in operation - 11 KW - Reeves drive with reducer - 1.8 to 4.5 rpm - continuous operation at speed conforming to coker requirement - rolls of cast manganese steel - 61 cm diameter - two pockets wide and staggered - briquet size 10.5 x 7.25 x 5.1 cm thick - briquet weight about 0.6 kg and production about 118 T/da.

Coking Furnaces

Fuller Company (step-grate clinker cooler) - six available - 3.7 KW with varia-speed drive - inside dimensions 2.45 m x 6.7 m - 21 grates - each eight bolted sections to form 40 cm x 244 cm grate - some special alloy - alternate fixed and reciprocating grates. Coked briquet holding well - 3 m high x 2.4 m to 1.9 m wide x 1.3 m to 0.7 m deep - 6.7 m^3 volume holding 7 T coke - 17 minute drawing cycle. Production: 90-110 T/da. Individual briquet weight: 0.45-0.5 kg.

Vertical Retorts

Nos.	Battery	Size	Levels	Heated Area	Nominal Production Rating*
1- 8	A	30.5 cm x 185 cm x 10 m	9	37.5 m^2	6.0 T/da
9-16	B	30.5 x 244 x 10	9	49	7.8
17-19	B	30.5 x 244 x 11.1	10	54.5	8.75
20-21	B	30.5 x 244 x 10	9	49	7.8
22-27	A	30.5 x 244 x 10	9	49	7.8

Total for 27 Retorts at 100% Operating Time - 200 T/da

*Assumes Normal Iron in Sinter

Condensers

Refractory Construction - 190 cm long x 58 cm wide inside and 40 cm deep bath holding 4.7 T zinc including external cooling well. Impeller - graphite, 36 cm diameter with seven radial fins driven by 3.7 KW motor at 400 rpm - 780°K bath temperature.

Recuperators

Surface Combustion Company - refractory tile construction - concurrent flow with three combustion gas passes - all three flues wide - bottom pass four flues deep - upper passes three flues deep - air flow vertically upward. Air preheat - 820°K. Exit flue gas - 1120°K.

Zinc Pumps

New Jersey Zinc Company Design - vertical shaft type with special lift impeller - graphite or special alloy - capacity of 13.5 T/hr and over.

PART D - VERTICAL REFINING

About one-half of the zinc metal produced on the vertical retorts is refined to 99.995 percent purity by means of the continuous, fractional distillation process which was developed at about the same time as the vertical retort process. In the vertical refining process, impurities boiling at temperatures higher than zinc such as lead and iron, are removed in a first stage; lower boiling components such as cadmium, are removed in a second stage. The Depue zinc refinery comprises four first-stage columns and two second-stage columns; the former are normally referred to as lead columns or boilers while the latter are called cadmium columns. 90 T/da refined zinc are produced at Depue. The flow of materials through typical lead and cadmium columns is shown in Figure 6.

Each column comprises a series of about 50 superposed, monolithic, rectangular trays made of bonded silicon carbide. Trays 60 cm x 120 cm are in use at Depue. Each tray is adapted to contain a pool of metal, the height of which is set by an overflow to a rectangular opening near one end of the tray. The trays are installed so that the openings on succeeding trays are 180° apart. Consequently, the metal overflowing from one tray is caught on the one immediately below, the descending flow including a traverse of each tray. The tortuous path for the cascading liquid required by the alternated openings is the only one offered the ascending vapors resulting in more effective contact between vapor and liquid.

Heat is supplied externally to the lower portion of each column by combustion gases. The lower portion of a lead column consists of a series of trays different from those described above in that they have a raised central portion whereby a trough is formed around the periphery of the tray capable of containing a height of metal much greater than that on a flat tray. Increased heat transfer and boiling capacity result from this design which provides for contact of liquid metal with a maximum proportion of heated surface.

The lower part of each column is enclosed by a refractory walled combustion chamber. Natural gas is introduced through ports in the roof along each of the longer sides of the trays. About 15 percent of the combustion air is inspirated through the burner openings. Progressive combustion of the gas for more uniform temperatures is achieved by supplying preheated air at each of three vertical levels through flues and ports in the walls of the combustion chamber. The hot combustion gases are exhausted through refractory recuperators in countercurrent relation to the flow of the incoming air. Preheats at Depue are normally in excess of 1073°K.

As indicated in the previous section, molten zinc overflows from the retort condensers through a launder to a holding pot and thence by a heated trough to the lead column supply pots. The constant level maintained in the trough and supply pots assures uniform feed

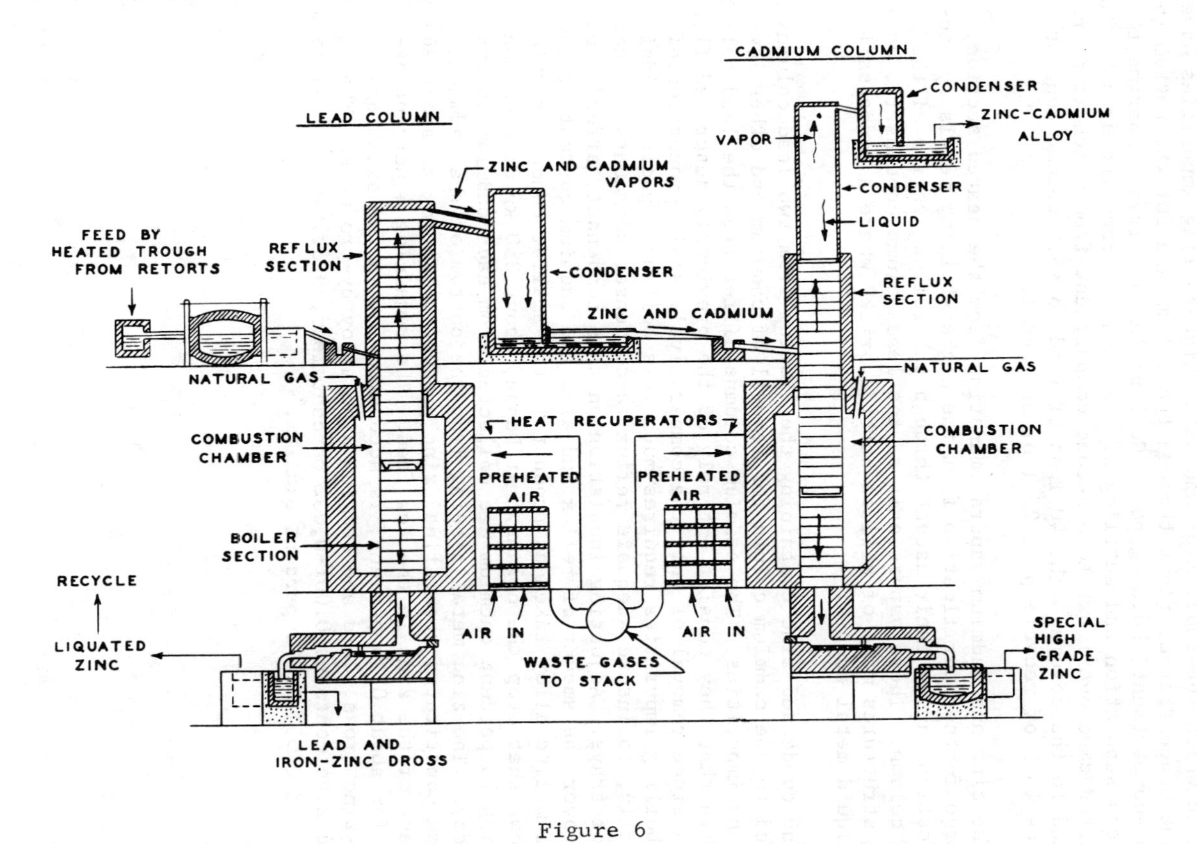

Figure 6

Flow Sheet of Vertical Refining Process

to the lead columns, an essential element for good performance. In each lead column, about 25 T/da of zinc plus essentially all of the cadmium is vaporized from the feed totaling 40 T/da. The remaining 15 T in which the lead, iron and other high-boiling impurities have become concentrated, flows through the column and out the bottom to a two-compartment, holding pot. Cooling in the first compartment effects separation and settling of lead and an iron-zinc dross. The liquated zinc overflows to a second compartment from which it is recycled to the column. The 40 T/da of feed to each column consists of the 15 T of recycle plus 25 T of new metal.

The zinc and cadmium vapors emanating from the heated section, undergo further purification from the higher-boiling metals by rectification during their ascent through the reflux section of the lead column. These vapors exit to the lead column condensers, box-like structures made of silicon carbide brick, where a condensation to liquid metal occurs.

The condensed zinc containing the cadmium from two lead columns is fed to one cadmium column for removal of cadmium and other low-boiling impurities. The cadmium columns differ from the lead columns in that they consist entirely of the previously described flat trays since removal of only the comparatively small proportion of low-boiling impurities requires much less boiling capacity. Additionally, to insure adequate reflux, a condenser surmounts the column of trays. Adjusting insulation on this condenser, affords control over the amount of reflux and also the cadmium content of the cadmium-zinc alloy taken as product in the smaller condenser which follows that atop the column. At Depue, about 350 kg of zinc containing 15 percent cadmium are collected from each cadmium column per day. The zinc metal issuing from the bottom of the cadmium column constitutes the refined zinc product amounting to about 96 percent of the zinc in the new feed. The remaining 4 percent except for about 0.75 percent, is accounted for in the skimmings, iron-zinc dross, lead and cadmium-zinc alloy by-products. The refined zinc contains 0.001-0.002 percent lead, 0.0006-0.0007 percent iron and 0.001-0.002 percent cadmium.

Chapter 20

JOSEPHTOWN ELECTROTHERMIC ZINC SMELTER
OF ST. JOE MINERALS CORPORATION

Monaca, Pennsylvania

R. E. Lund, J. F. Winters, B. E. Hoffacker,
T. M. Fusco and D. E. Warnes*

Abstract

Josephtown Smelter employs the St. Joe-developed electrothermic process for producing zinc metal and zinc oxide. The process uses resistance-type electric furnaces. Flow of current through the sintered ore and coke charge develops the energy required for smelting at the reaction sites. To produce zinc metal, the furnace off-gases bubble through a large "U"-tube filled with molten zinc which condenses the zinc to liquid; the metal is then mechanically cast into slabs. To produce zinc oxide, the furnace vapors burn in air and the resultant powders are collected. The smelter comprises three distinct circuits. One circuit produces American Process zinc oxide and high grade metal; another circuit produces tailor-made alloys of controlled lead and cadmium content; the third circuit produces prime western zinc metal and feedstock which is refined into special high grade metal and French Process zinc oxide. The roasting circuit utilizes multiple-hearth furnaces for deleading the zinc concentrates; fluid bed and suspension roasters are employed for desulfurization. Sintering produces a hard, porous furnace feed. The flexible smelting process is adaptable to consuming various kinds of secondary material. Extensive residue treatment accomplishes high overall zinc recovery. Smelter by-products include sulfuric acid, cadmium, and mercury.

*The authors are respectively Research Manager, Asst. Superintendent Roaster and Acid Depts., Technical Superintendent Sinter and Leach Depts., Technical Superintendent Furnace Dept., and Superintendent Zinc Oxide Dept.

Introduction and History

Josephtown Smelter of ST. JOE Minerals Corporation is one of the world's largest zinc producers. The electrothermic process yields both zinc metal and zinc oxide. Present capacity is approximately 230,000 tons* of zinc equivalent per annum. Plant site borders the Ohio River in western Pennsylvania, approximately 48 kilometers downstream from Pittsburgh.

Early investigators (1, 2) recognized the inherent potential of an electrothermic process for smelting zinc. Developing the thermal energy requirements--which are considerably greater for smelting zinc than for most common metals--by passing electric current through the reactant materials was an enticing possibility. Resistance heating would develop energy precisely at the reduction site and overcome the inefficiency inherent in heating the charge indirectly in the horizontal retort method of producing zinc. Many investigators worked on various types of furnaces, including one which was resistance heated (1), but without commercial success. A major problem until the St. Joe development was that condensing systems were not capable--in a single unit--of transforming many tons of zinc vapor per day into liquid metal.

In connection with its acquisition of zinc mining properties in upper New York State, the St. Joseph Lead Company (now ST. JOE Minerals Corporation) began research on electrothermic zinc smelting in 1926. Process development elaborated on ideas of E. C. Gaskill (3, 4, 5), who had been experimenting with electrothermic zinc smelting, and who became associated with St. Joe. The basic concept comprised a moving bed--composed of approximately equal volumes of sized coke and zinc oxide sinter--as the dynamic resistor in a vertical shaft electric furnace. In late 1926, pilot-scale test work started at the company's Herculaneum, Missouri lead smelter. Commencing with a furnace 46 cm ID, the scale of operations increased to a furnace 12 cm ID and 5 m between top and bottom electrodes. The development wor guided by George F. Weaton and William T. Isbell, was successful in evolving a process for producing large quantities of zinc vapor which could then be combusted with air to make excellent quality American Process zinc oxide.

Development work at Herculaneum concluded in 1929 with the decisio to build a commercial smelter at a site near Monaca, Pennsylvania. The problems of condensing large quantities of zinc vapor to liquid metal had not been resolved at that time. The smelter as commissione in 1930 was restricted to the production of zinc oxide. However, in the initial installation, consisting of five electrothermic zinc oxid furnaces, space was allocated for three additional furnaces for pilot plant experiments to develop a zinc metal producing process.

*Metric units are used throughout this paper.

George F. Weaton and H. K. Najarian spearheaded development of the Josephtown condenser. Several unique problems--such as developing lining materials for the condenser which would withstand the corrosive attack of molten zinc at temperatures close to its boiling point and which would have good thermal conductivity for dissipating the heat of condensation, as well as developing techniques and equipment for cleaning and handling large volumes of carbon monoxide gas at absolute pressures of about one-half atmosphere--yielded solutions to a dedicated development team. The Weaton-Najarian condenser (6) became commercial in 1936. Today--although zinc oxide continues to be an important segment of St. Joe's business--zinc metal exceeds zinc oxide production by the ratio of approximately six to one.

Until about 1940, Josephtown Smelter operated with zinc concentrates from the company's mines in northern New York State. As the plant grew, supplemental sources of concentrates were obtained from both domestic and foreign sources. Today less than half of the smelter's concentrate requirements are met by St. Joe's mines.

The smelter is divided into three distinct circuits. These are termed "High Grade," "Intermediate," and "Prime Western." The High Grade (H.G.) circuit, by means of concentrate selection and by employing unit operations which maximize impurity elimination, supplies the zinc oxide and H.G. metal furnaces with zinc sinter which is relatively free from lead, cadmium, or other deleterious impurities. Zinc sinter produced for the Intermediate (Int.) and Prime Western (P.W.) circuits is controlled in composition to meet the metal specifications which correspond to these grades. Figure 1 shows the smelter flow sheet.

Previous descriptions of various features of Josephtown Smelter have been published (7 - 14). This paper gives an updated description of the entire zinc smelting operation.

Roaster Plant

A distinctive feature of Josephtown Smelter's roasting practice is its use of modified Nichols-Herreshoff furnaces for deleading. By heating the concentrates to 950-980°C in a low oxygen atmosphere, 90-95% of the lead is eliminated as sublimed PbS (15). Preferred practice is to disassociate deleading from desulfurizing (16). Concentrates in the H.G. and Int. circuits, after deleading by heat treatment in the multiple hearth furnaces, are desulfurized in fluidized bed roasters of St. Joe design. In the P.W. circuit, where lead elimination is not a key consideration, a suspension roaster of COMINCO design is employed for desulfurizing concentrates.

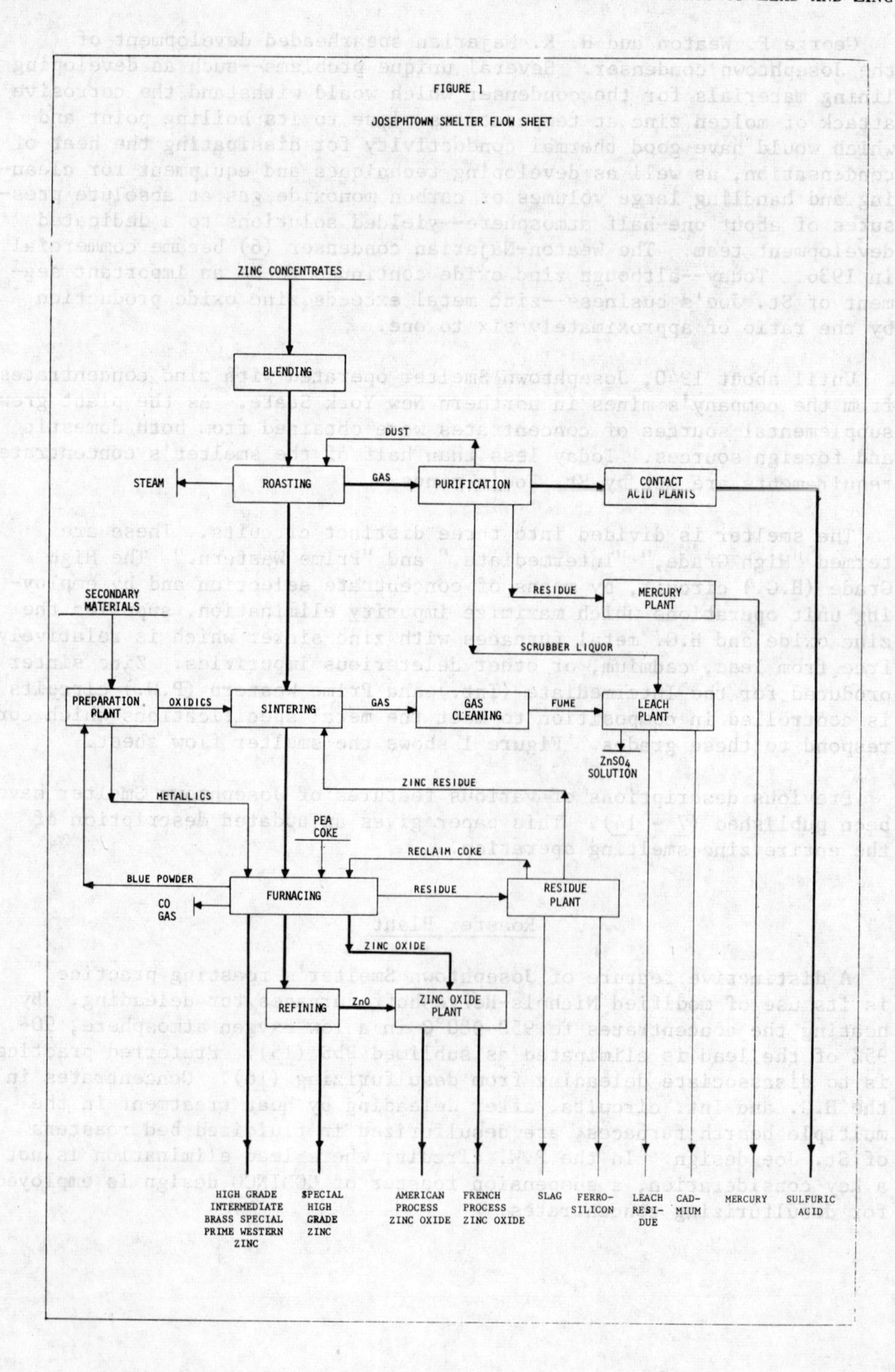
FIGURE 1
JOSEPHTOWN SMELTER FLOW SHEET
ZINC CONCENTRATES
BLENDING
DUST
STEAM
ROASTING
GAS
PURIFICATION
CONTACT ACID PLANTS
SECONDARY MATERIALS
RESIDUE
MERCURY PLANT
SCRUBBER LIQUOR
PREPARATION PLANT
OXIDICS
SINTERING
GAS
GAS CLEANING
FUME
LEACH PLANT
ZnSO4 SOLUTION
ZINC RESIDUE
METALLICS
PEA COKE
RECLAIM COKE
BLUE POWDER
FURNACING
RESIDUE
RESIDUE PLANT
CO GAS
ZINC OXIDE
REFINING
ZnO
ZINC OXIDE PLANT
HIGH GRADE INTERMEDIATE BRASS SPECIAL PRIME WESTERN ZINC
SPECIAL HIGH GRADE ZINC
AMERICAN PROCESS ZINC OXIDE
FRENCH PROCESS ZINC OXIDE
SLAG
FERRO-SILICON
LEACH RESI-DUE
CAD-MIUM
MERCURY
SULFURIC ACID

Principal Equipment

Quantity	Item	Description
1	Thaw House	58 m long x 27 m wide, 15 RR cars, St. Joe design
1	Concentrate Dryer	3.5 m ID x 14 m long, 1.7 rpm, 56 kw
5	Hearth Furnaces	12 hearth, 6.5 m ID, modified Nichols-Herreshoff
1	Flash Roaster	6.9 m ID, 4 hearth, COMINCO design
3	Fluid Roasters	1 unit - 6.1 m ID, 7.9 m freeboard, St. Joe design 1 unit - 6.9 m ID, 7.9 m freeboard, St. Joe design 1 unit - 6.9 m ID, 11 m freeboard, St. Joe design
3	Centrifugal Air Blowers for Fluid Roasters	2 units - 650 m^3/min STP, 41 x 10^3 N/m^2 (31 cm Hg) 1 unit - 470 m^3/min STP, 41 x 10^3 N/m^2 (31 cm Hg)
4	Waste Heat Boilers	3 units - 3 drum Sterling type, B&W 1 unit - 2 drum Sterling type, B&W
3	Ball Mills for Calcine Grinding	2 units - 2.5 m diam, 186 kw 1 unit - 2.1 m diam, 93 kw
7	Hot Precipitators	Combined capacity 3000 m^3/min @ 275°C

Concentrate Handling

Zinc concentrates, received typically from 15 sources, arrive in gondolas, boxcars or river barges. A gantry crane services field storage. A thaw house defrosts frozen concentrates. Ten 910-ton bunkers, under cover, provide short-term storage prior to blending. An overhead clamshell transfers concentrates to four blending hoppers which discharge by apron feeders onto a common collect belt. Concentrates are blended to meet lead, iron, cadmium, copper, manganese, indium, and tin specifications of the H.G., Int. and P.W. circuits. If need be, the concentrates are dried before entering the roaster plant.

Multiple Hearth Furnaces

Concentrate feed rates typically average 200 TPD to each of four hearth furnaces. To accommodate this high feed rate, the original Nichols-Herreshoff roasters, which had been built for desulfurizing, were modified by enlarging drop holes, increasing rabble size, and doubling the shaft speed. To achieve good lead elimination and avoid "snowballing" of concentrates (a condition which accompanies excessive temperatures), the sixth through the tenth hearths (from the top of the roaster) are maintained at 950-980°C. Because gases leaving the roaster have a temperature of only 200-220°C, they do not pass through waste heat boilers, but instead are routed directly to "hot" cottrells.

To maintain desired temperature distribution, a modest amount of natural or carbon monoxide gas is burned on the fourth, sixth, and tenth hearths. It is necessary to continuously monitor the high temperature hearths for plug-ups. Hard accretions which form on the hearths necessitate a routine maintenance maneuver called "plowing," the frequency of which varies from two to three days for the high temperature hearths to two to three months for those operating at low temperatures. Major hearth repairs, necessitating a cold shutdown, are at intervals of five to ten years.

The deleaded product from the hearth furnaces, termed "partially desulfurized concentrate" (PDC), typically contains about 22% S.

Fluid Roasters

The three fluid roasters operate at 950°C. Feed rate to each roaster averages 250 TPD. Twin screws inject feed 30 cm beneath the surface of the fluidized bed. Bed temperature is automatically controlled by injecting water or zinc sulfate liquor. Bed depth is approximately 1.1 m when settled and 1.5 m when fluidized.

Fluidizing air enters the roasters through tuyeres positioned on 20 cm centers and set in 15 cm of castable. Roasters operate at a positive pressure of 10-15 cm water and a freeboard gas velocity of 54-68 cm/sec. The feed/air ratio is regulated by monitoring the oxygen content of cyclone exit gases, which ranges from 2-5% O_2.

Fluid roaster off-gases, before entering waste heat boilers, pass directly into St. Joe-designed hot cyclones for dedusting. The castable lined cyclone on the newest 6.9 m diam roaster has an ID of 2.7 m. Calcine product is evenly split between bed overflow and cyclone heavies.

Routinely, the roasters are off line for about eight hours every three weeks for programmed maintenance of screw conveyors and waste heat boilers. A cold shutdown is necessary at two-year intervals to drill out tuyere accretions.

Flash Roaster

The flash roaster typically operates at 135 tons concentrate feed per day. Feed is ground to 90% minus 0.044 mm. In addition to concentrate, all of the flue, boiler, and cottrell dusts produced in the P.W., Int. and H.G. roasting circuits are fed (via the collect hearth) to this roaster.

Gas Handling

The flash roaster and each of the fluid roasters have individual waste heat boilers which cool the gases from 950°C to about 400°C. Gases flow on a straight line through the boilers. Steam production at 30.6 atm and 300-350°C averages about 600 kg per ton of concentrate. Soot blowers, employing 24 atm air, clean the tubes. Additional cleaning requires a six-hour shutdown at three-week intervals.

Seven electrostatic precipitators, having a combined capacity of 3000 m^3/min, dedust roaster gases before they enter the acid plant purification system. Gas temperature is 250-300°C.

Table I

ROASTER FEEDS AND PRODUCTS

	% Zn	% Pb	% S	% Cd	% Fe	% Cu	% Mn	% Sn	% Hg
H.G. Concentrate	56.0	0.50	31.0	0.22	5.0	0.25	0.20	0.005	0.013
Int. Concentrate	52.0	0.30	31.0	0.25	7.8	0.25	0.12	0.050	0.012
P.W. Concentrate	54.0	0.30	31.0	0.35	7.0	0.40	0.15	0.050	0.004
PDC* Analysis (HG)	59.0	0.013	21.9	0.22	5.3	0.25	0.21	0.005	0.0002
H.G. Calcine	68.0	0.035	1.5	0.22	6.0	0.26	0.20	0.004	0.0001
Int. Calcine	64.0	0.035	1.5	0.25	9.5	0.26	0.15	0.040	0.0001
P.W. Calcine	62.0	1.4	2.5	0.40	7.3	--	0.15	0.060	0.0003
Flue Dust	54.0	1.4	7.0	0.41	7.0	0.40	0.21	0.01	0.03

*Partially desulfurized concentrate (product from hearth furnaces; feed to fluid roasters.)

Calcine Handling

Hot products are conveyed in water-cooled screw conveyors and bucket elevators. Lumps in the product from deleading furnaces are hammer-milled before feeding to the fluid bed roasters.

Final processing in the roaster plant comprises grinding the calcine to 50% minus 0.044 mm. Grinding improves the pelletizing characteristic of the charge for sintering.

Typical analyses of roaster feeds and products are shown in Table I. Impurity eliminations achieved in the H.G. and Int. deleading-roasting circuits are shown in Table II.

Table II

IMPURITY ELIMINATION IN ROASTING

Element	Elimination %	
	High Grade Circuit	Intermediate Circuit
Hg	99	99
S	96	96
Pb	94	90
Sn	34	35
Cd	18	19

Operating Requirements

An 11-man crew on each of three shifts, plus an 11-man utility crew on day shift, operate the roaster plant. A 16-man millwright crew services both the roaster and acid plants. (All figures include salary supervision.) An administrative and technical staff covers both the roaster and acid plants.

At processing rates of 935 tons concentrate per day, total labor averages 0.75 man-hour (including supervision) per ton of feed, composed of 0.49 man-hour for operations, 0.21 for maintenance (which includes utility work), and 0.05 for miscellaneous.

Electrical energy consumption averages 3×10^8 j (88 kwh) per ton of concentrate. Natural gas (39×10^6 j/m^3) consumption average 12.5 m^3 per ton.

Acid Plant

Six Leonard-Monsanto contact acid units, with combined capacity of 820 tons H_2SO_4 per day, convert sulfur in roaster off-gases into sulfuric acid. Production for 1969 totaled 280,000 tons 100% H_2SO_4 equivalent.

An unusual feature of the Josephtown installation is employment of weak H_2SO_4 liquor in closed circuit with a humidifier-scrubber-thickener-cooler combination for cooling and cleaning the gases. Gases from the hot cottrells enter the humidifier, an open cylindrical tower 3.3 m ID x 7.9 m high, where they are partially cooled with sprayed scrubber liquor. A 4.8 m ID x 9.8 m high scrub tower, packed with 15 cm and 7.6 cm diam 4-cell partition rings and irrigated with 2 m^3/sec of liquor, completes the cooling and cleaning. Scrubber liquor, containing 15 g/l H_2SO_4 and 30 g/l Zn, cools the gases to about 35°C. After settling in a 30.5 m diam thickener, the liquor is cooled to 30°C before recirculation to the humidifier-scrubbers. Bleed-off is processed in the leach plant for recovery of zinc and cadmium.

Recovery

The new contact units, which employ four-stage V_2O_5 catalyst converters, transform 98% of the sulfur dioxide into sulfur trioxide. Recovery of sulfur in roaster feed to product H_2SO_4 averages 90%.

Operating Requirements

Three men, including a shift foreman, operate the six contact acid units. An 8-man utility crew, on day shift only, loads acid and maintains equipment. Total operating plus maintenance labor averages 0.23 man-hour per ton H_2SO_4. Power requirements amount to 3 x 10^8 j (82 kwh) per ton H_2SO_4.

Mercury Recovery

Mercury eliminated from concentrates during roasting reports in the gas purification system. A pilot facility for producing metallic mercury commenced operation in 1969. Facilities include an indirect fired kiln, tube-type condenser, soot treating and bottling equipment. Production in 1969 amounted to 9700 kg.

Sinter Plant

The sinter plant, employing the Dwight-Lloyd downdraft process, agglomerates zinc calcines and other zinc-bearing materials into P.W.,

Int. or H.G. feed for the electrothermic furnaces. To produce a strong sinter of relatively uniform particle size requires a silica content of 8-10% and a high recirculating load of sinter fines.

Two-stage sintering in the H.G. circuit promotes impurity elimination. In the first stage, zinc calcines--with no silica addition--are burned to produce a "soft sinter." A rotary slicer removes the top half of the soft sinter cake, which is low in impurities (the bottom half of the cake is recirculated). This top product is sintered a second time with the addition of other zinc-bearing materials and silica sand to produce a high purity hard sinter. The product constutes the zinc feed to the H.G. metal and zinc oxide furnaces. Singl stage hard sintering is practiced on the P.W. and Int. circuits.

In each of the circuits sinter is sized by crushing the hard sinte cakes to minus 76 mm in tooth rolls, screening at 25 mm in trommels, placing the oversize in closed circuit with smooth rolls, classifying product sinter at 6 x 25 mm particle size, and recirculating the minu 6 mm fines to the sinter mix. Particle size distribution of product sinter averages about 45% of 6 x 9.5 mm, 30% of 9.5 x 16 mm, and 25% of 16 x 25 mm.

Equipment

Table III shows the principal equipment used in the sinter circuit

Table III

SINTERING EQUIPMENT

	P.W.	Int.		H.G. Soft	H.G. Hard
No. of Machines Windbox Area/Machine - m^2 Fan Rating* - m^3/min - kw	3 20.4 1270 150	1 20.4 1270 186	1 24.5 1560 336	2 20.4 1270 150	2 20.4 1270 150
Pelletizing Equipment	1 - Pre-mix Drum, 1.2 m diam x 2.9 m, 5.6 kw 3 - Lurgi Discs, 2.6 m diam, 11 kw	1 - Pre-mix Drum, 1.2 m diam x 2.7 m, 5.6 kw 1 Lurgi Disc, 2.6 m diam, 11 kw	1 - Drum, 1.2 m diam x 4.9 m, 11 kw	1 - Drum, 1.8 m diam x 4.9 m, 11 kw	1 - Drum, 1.8 m diam x 4.9 m, 11 kw
Crushing Equipment	1 - Tooth Roll, 76 cm diam x 107 cm, 37 kw 1 - Smooth Roll, 91 cm diam x 41 cm, 18 kw	1 - Tooth Roll, 76 cm diam x 107 cm, 37 kw 1 - Smooth Roll, 107 cm diam x 51 cm, 37 kw		1 - Rib Roll, 70 cm diam x 107 cm, 18 kw	1 - Tooth Roll, 76 cm diam x 107 cm, 39 kw 1 - Smooth Roll, 91 cm x 41 cm, 37 kw
Sizing Equipment	1 - Trommel, 1.2 m diam x 2.4 m, 25 mm openings, 3.7 kw 1 - Dble. Trommel, 1.2 m diam x 2.6 m, 6 x 19 mm openings, 3.7 kw	1 - Trommel, 1.1 m diam x 3 m, 25 mm openings, 7.5 kw 1 - Dble. Trommel, 1.1 m diam x 3 m, 6 x 19 mm openings, 7.5 kw			1 - Trommel, 1.2 m diam x 2.4 m, 25 mm openings, 3.7 kw 1 - Trommel, 1.2 m diam x 2.1 m, 6 x 19 mm openings, 3.7 kw
Soft Sinter Slicer				1 - St. Joe, 1.1 m diam, 25 rpm, 11 kw	

*All fans are rated at 560 mm H_2O and 126°C.

The 61 cm long pallets on the sinter machines contain floating bar seals. The cast iron grate bars formerly used (17) have been replaced on seven of the nine machines with alloy bars containing 29% Cr, 9% Ni, 0.65% C, and 2% Mo. A grate bar knocker (cleaner) removes accretions from the grates (18).

Two types of pelletizers--revolving drum and inclined disc--are used. A premix drum ahead of the disc pelletizer assists in mixing and wetting the raw charge. Swinging rubber spouts distributed the pelletized mix in a configuration which allows the coarser particles to roll onto the grates. Charge depth is maintained at about 33 cm. A gas-fired muffle, using as fuel by-product CO from the zinc condensers, ignites the charge.

Practice

Table IV shows the proportion of feed constituents in typical sinter charges.

Table IV

FEED CONSTITUENTS IN TYPICAL SINTER CHARGES

% of Total Mix

	Calcine	Return Fines	Bag Filter Dust	Fce. Residue	Coke Breeze	Sand	Oxidics	Soft Sinter
P.W.	17.4	60.5	7.0	7.6	0.2	0.6	6.7	--
Int.	25.3	55.8	9.0	6.0	2.0	0.9	1.0	--
Soft H.G.	35.7	48.5	10.8	--	5.0	--	--	--
Hard H.G.	9.8	52.6	--	8.6	2.7	1.0	--	25.3

Representative composition of sinter mix materials (exclusive of calcines which are listed in Table I) are shown in Table V.

Fuel in the charges comprises about 4.5% carbon, part of which originates in furnace residues and bag filter dust, and the balance of which is breeze coke. The oxidics originate from both in-plant and purchased high zinc fines. Zinc sulfate liquor, a by-product of the leach plant, supplies the moisture needed for pelletizing.

The sinter machines typically operate at a speed of 45-70 cm per min and a windbox suction of 35-45 x 10^2 N/m^2 (35-45 cm of water). Production rate in tons per square meter per hour averages 0.39 for

Table V

REPRESENTATIVE COMPOSITION OF SINTER MIX MATERIALS

	% Zn	% SiO_2	% Fe	% C
P.W.-Int. Furnace Residue	23	20	14	13
H.G. Furnace Residue	39	15	13	9
Bag Filter Dust	58	--	--	8
Oxidics	70	--	--	--
Coke Breeze	--	8	4	65
Sand	--	97	--	--
Soft Sinter	60	5	8	--

Zinc Sulfate Liquor:

22 g/l Zn, 12 g/l S, 0.5 g/l Cd, 4.8 pH

H.G. soft sinter, 0.45 for Int., 0.49 for P.W. and 0.71 for H.G. hard sinter. Cadmium elimination is 90% in the P.W.-Int. and 93% in the H.G. circuits. Approximately 70% of the lead is eliminated in the P.W Int. circuits and 80% in the H.G. circuit. Table VI shows typical sin ter composition.

Table VI

PRODUCT SINTER COMPOSITION - %

	Zn	Pb	Fe	Cd	SiO_2	S
P.W.	55.5	0.33	7.9	0.017	9.4	0.15
Int.	57.1	0.037	8.9	0.015	8.8	0.15
H.G. Soft	63.6	0.005	6.8	0.012	5.2	0.36
H.G. Hard	58.6	0.006	7.9	0.006	8.9	0.10

Dust Collection

Three Research-Cottrell electrostatic precipitators, and one bag house filter, all in parallel, clean the sinter machine gases. Each precipatator, rated at 2830 m^3/min, is preceded by a large conditioning chamber which cools the gases to 50 to 60°C by means of water atomized at pressure of 30 x 10^5 N/m^2 (30 atm). Fume recovery by the precipitators averages 90 to 95%.

The bag filter, rated at 4250 m^3/min, has collection efficiency averaging about 98%. The life of the acrylic bags is poor, averaging about 6-1/2 months. Gas temperatures to the filter are automatically controlled between 100-125°C by an auxiliary CO gas burner and by tempering air. The collected fumes from the precipitators and bag filter are treated in the leach plant to recover zinc, lead and cadmium.

Four additional bag filter installations, with a combined capacity of 15,900 m^3/min, collect process dust generated in the sinter, residue and furnace plants. These collectors provide the dual function of conserving valuable material and of maintaining good environmental working conditions. Each of the P.W., Int. and H.G. sinter circuits has its own dust collect system, incorporating return of the dust to the circuit from whence it originated--a feature which enhances impurity control in product sinter.

Residue Treatment

Furnace residues undergo extensive physical beneficiation to recover coke and unsmelted zinc and to segregate slag and low grade ferrosilicon as by-products. Magnetic separators remove high iron particles (low grade ferrosilicon) from the residue. "Air float" pneumatic tables--of St. Joe design, but patterned after those formerly employed in coal cleaning--recover free coke. The air tables reclaim 80 to 95% of the carbon in residue into a 70% C product suited for recharging to the electrothermic furnaces. A heavy media circuit separates the remaining residue into zinc rich and zinc lean fractions. The zinc-rich fraction constitutes one of the feeds to sintering. The zinc-lean slag is sized and sold as ballast.

The heavy media circuit is a unique application of this gravity concentration process (14). The 45 TPH plant of WEMCO design incorporates a prewet screen, a 1.8 m diam x 1.8 m long heavy media drum separator, and two drain and rinse screens 1.3 m wide with combined length of 7.6 m.

Table VII highlights the performance of the heavy media plant.

Table VII

HEAVY MEDIA PLANT PERFORMANCE

	5 x 32 mm Slag	+32 mm Slag
Assay - % Zn in Feed	16.5	6.7
% Zn in Sink	31.5	24.5
% Zn in Float	2.0	2.3
Zn Recovery - %	94.0	73.0
Medium Specific Gravity	2.7	2.9

Coke Preparation

To prepare for furnace feed, pea coke is screened to a top size of 25 mm. Jeffrey ribbed-rolls crush the oversize to minus 25 mm. Fines, removed by screening, are routed to the breeze coke circuit. This fraction, plus purchased breeze coke, is rod milled to serve as fuel in sintering.

Production Requirements

A 14-man crew on each of three shifts operates the sinter plant--including the coke and residue circuits, but exclusive of the heavy media circuit. A 23-man crew on day shift operates the heavy media circuit and performs utility work, which includes general cleanup and maintenance of dust collecting equipment. A 22-man maintenance crew services the sinter plant. All of the figures include salary supervision. An administrative and technical staff covers both the sinter and leach plants.

Performance data for the sinter plant operations (includes sintering, residue treatment, coke preparation, and dust collection) are presented in Table VIII.

Leach Plant

The leach plant treats approximately 19 tons of fume per day from the sinter machines and 125 cubic meters per day of scrubber liquor from the acid plant purification circuit. Modest quantities of cadmium-bearing materials from external sources are also treated. Cadmium metal production--in the form of balls, sticks, and flakes--averages 43 tons per month. Zinc reports in zinc sulfate solution

Table VIII

SINTER PERFORMANCE DATA - 1969

Sinter Produced - tons/yr	400,000
Operating Labor - man-hrs/ton of sinter	0.66
Maintenance Labor - man-hrs/ton of sinter	0.35
Grate Bars Used - kg/ton of sinter	0.16
Breeze Coke Used - kg/ton of sinter	80*
Sand Used - kg/ton of sinter	22
Electrical Energy Used - joules/ton of sinter	19×10^7
- kwh/ton of sinter	54

*Does not include carbon in furnace residue and bag filter dust

which is used for pelletizing sinter mix. Lead--the remaining principal constituent of fume--reports in leach residues as lead sulfate. This residue, termed "lead cake," contains small but significant quantities of gold, silver, and indium. The product is sold.

Typical analysis of the sinter fume treated in the leach plant is 38% Zn, 9% Pb, 10% Cd. The scrubber liquor, which supplies much of the acid required for leaching, contains 30 g/l Zn, 0.2 g/l Cd, and 15 g/l H_2SO_4.

Practice

Prior to leaching, the sinter fume is heat treated at 500°C in a four-hearth, 6.5 m diam, Nichols-Herreshoff type roaster. This patented process (19) selectively sulfates the cadmium and makes about 90% of it water soluble. Water leaching produces relatively pure cadmium solutions containing about 40 g/l Cd and 10 g/l Zn. The addition of 250 g/m^3 sodium bichromate to this pregnant solution removes about 90% of the soluble lead. Cadmium sponge, cemented from solution with zinc dust, is briquetted, melted under caustic, and cast into commercial shapes. Occasionally, for ultra-purity, the metal is distilled in graphite retorts.

The residual solids from water leaching of heat treated fume are batch treated with scrubber liquor, the acid strength of which is bolstered with concentrated acid. Acid leaching solubilizes most of the zinc and residual cadmium, as well as numerous impurities. Cadmium sponge, precipitated with zinc dust from pregnant solutions which contain about 2 g/l Cd, is separated from solution in a hydro-cyclone and dewatered in a centrifuge. Heat treatment of sponge at 650°C in a two-hearth, 3.7 m ID roaster converts the metallic and sulfide cadmium into soluble oxide form and assists in impurity control. A strong acid leach of the oxidized sponge resolubilizes most of the cadmium. Following neutralization and clarification, the cadmium is cemented with zinc dust, briquetted, and melted under caustic. Treatment with zinc ammonium chloride removes thallium. The filter cake derived from the leaching and purifying steps is recycled to the four-hearth roaster employed for heat treating sinter fume.

The residual solids from acid leaching of sinter fume are water washed, settled, and dried. Typical analysis of this leach residue is 32% Pb, 8% Zn, 0.7% Cd, 0.13% In, 0.45% As, 0.30% Cu, 2.3 kg/T Ag, and 4 g/T Au.

Typical analysis of the product cadmium is 0.01% Zn, 0.003% Cu, 0.015% Pb, 0.0001% Ag, less than 0.001% Tl, less than 0.0005% Sn, and less than 0.001% Sb.

Operating Requirements

A five-man crew on each of three shifts operates the leach plant. A ten-man utility crew on day turn casts cadmium metal, services the dust collecting equipment and the cadmium roasters, and performs miscellaneous tasks. A five-man maintenance crew maintains the leach plant equipment.

Table IX sets forth operating requirements and performance data for the year 1969.

Table IX

YEAR 1969 LEACH PLANT PERFORMANCE DATA

Cadmium Production - Tons	520
Lead Cake Production - Tons	1,650
Zinc Sulfate Liquor Produced - m^3	106,000
Operating Labor - Man-hours/kg Cd	0.15
Maintenance - Man-hours/kg Cd	0.04
Natural Gas Consumed - m^3/kg Cd	1.3
Zinc Dust Used - kg/kg Cd	1.03
Caustic Used - g/kg Cd	65
Sodium Bichromate Used - g/kg Cd	7.5
Cadmium Recovery - from feed to Leach Plant -	94%
from zinc concentrates -	67%

Furnace Plant

The furnace plant currently operates 17 electrothermic furnaces. Four produce American Process zinc oxide and the others produce zinc metal. Three of the oxide and four of the metal furnaces are "small" units, being vertical cylinders of 1.75 m ID and 11.3 m high, and having production capability of 16 to 25 tons per day of zinc equivalent. The "large" furnaces have 2.44 m ID barrels, are 15 m high, and produce as much as 100 tons of zinc per day.

The basic operation of the oxide and metal producing furnaces is similar. Preheated coke and zinc-bearing sinter are continuously fed to both furnaces, where the coke serves as the principal electrical conductor. Electricity, introduced through graphite electrodes, develops the heat energy required for smelting. To produce zinc oxide, the furnace vapors are oxidized with air. To produce zinc metal, the furnace vapors bubble through a zinc bath where the zinc is condensed. Residue--composed of slag, coke, globules of ferrosilicon, and some unreacted zinc--continuously discharges from the furnaces and passes to reclamation treatment.

General Description

Figure 2 shows a sketch of the metal furnace. Individual bins, holding coke, sinter, and other zinc-bearing feed, discharge through constant weight feeders. Charge, heated to about 750°C in a 1.6 m ID x 8.7 m gas-fired preheater, enters the furnace through a rotary distributor. The distributor, rotating at 0.4 rpm, positions charge near the furnace wall and seals the top of the shaft. The bottom of the furnace, supported by a refractory-faced, water-cooled steel ring, terminates about 30 cm above a refractory covered discharge table (20) which rotates at 0.03 rpm.

The rotary table, which forms the bottom of the furnace, continuously withdraws some of the spent charge. Automated poker bar machines, however, remove most of the charge. These machines, of St. Joe design, travel on tracks along opposite sides of a furnace. On signal, an air-actuated cylinder rams a heavy bar with an arrowhead point into the charge and withdraws it. Charge height detectors in the upper furnace barrel, comprising a cobalt-60 gamma ray source and receiver, signal a digital control system which regulates the frequency of the table working.

The furnace proper is constructed of a series of short sections, each individually supported by its own skewback (21). At about the midpoint there is an annular ring, termed the "vapor ring," through which the furnace gases are vented to the metal condenser.

For the most part the furnace sections are constructed of 34 cm keys of high duty and super-duty firebrick. Water-cooled steel

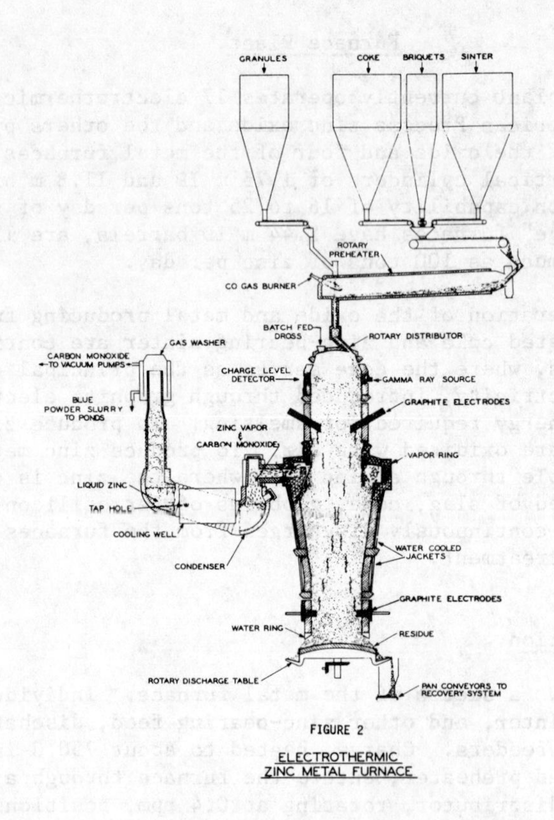

FIGURE 2

ELECTROTHERMIC ZINC METAL FURNACE

jackets encase some of the barrel. Silicon carbide bricks line the interior of the vapor ring, the condenser, and its cooling well.

Eight pairs of 30.5 cm diam electrodes, each pair connected to its individual single-phase transformer and voltage regulator, introduce power into the furnace. Each top electrode has a mate near the botto of the furnace. The arrangement forms a resistance path of about 9 m through the furnace charge. Top electrodes protrude downward into th furnace about 43 cm at a 30° angle from horizontal. Bottom electrode protrude 15 cm horizontally. Power input per electrode circuit range up to 1250 kw, corresponding to a maximum of 10,000 kw per furnace. Voltage can be regulated from 160 to 300 volts; normally it is 200-23 volts.

The condenser is shaped in the form of a "U"-tube with a vertical inlet and outlet, and a 5.8 m long connecting tube inclined at about 22° with the horizontal. The shell, made of 1.9 cm boiler plate, has a cross sectional area inside the silicon carbide brick lining of 2.0 m^2. The condenser and associated cooling well (22, 23) hold about 45 tons of liquid zinc. The gas exhaust leg of the condenser operates under 33-40 x 10^3 N/m^2 (25-30 cm of Hg) vacuum. Gases leaving the furnace at essentially atmospheric pressure bubble through the molten zinc. The head of zinc developed by gas pushing through the condenser causes rapid circulation of metal (about 9 TPM) through the cooling well, which is open to atmosphere. Water-cooled hairpin pipe loops control metal temperatures at 480-500°C. High-velocity impingers water-scrub gases venting the condenser (24). The clean gas, containing 80% carbon monoxide and having a heating value of 93×10^5 j (22×10^2 kcal)/m^3, furnishes fuel for smelter use. The uncondensed zinc (termed "blue powder") in gases from the condenser is recovered by settling the water slurry in ponds; the solids (75-80% Zn) are dried and briquetted for furnace feed.

Refractory-lined launders convey zinc from the condenser cooling wells to gas-fired holding furnaces. Vertical air-driven pumps mounted in the holding furnaces deliver zinc to the casting machines.

Three casting machines are used, all of St. Joe design. Two machines produce slabs weighing 26 kg. The third machine casts ingots weighing 227 kg. Stacking of cast shapes is totally automatic. Selection of different stacking programs permits variation in the number of slabs or ingots assembled in each package. Metal flows continuously to a shallow, rocking tundish of each slab casting machine. Flow rate to the ingot machine is intermittent and directly into the mold. Water sprays on the bottom of the molds accelerate solidification of the liquid zinc. Cast zinc is manually skimmed. The machines are rated at 180 tons per day.

Construction of the zinc oxide furnaces is similar to that of the metal furnaces, except in three of the four oxide furnaces the evolved zinc vapor and carbon monoxide are not collected in a vapor ring but exit the charge through a series of tewels in the furnace wall. Figure 3 shows a sketch of an oxide furnace.

Furnace Operation

Principal feed to the furnaces consists of sinter and coke, but substantial quantities--as much as 25% of total zinc input--of other zinc-bearing materials are also fed. Nominal coke rate is 44% the weight of sinter, which translates into roughly equal volumes of coke and sinter, and approximately 300% stoichiometric carbon relative to zinc in sinter. Other zinc-bearing materials are fed to the furnaces in the form of almond-shaped briquettes, granules, 8 x 25 mm metallic screening, and slab dross. The slab dross is batch fed at two-hour intervals through a chute into the top of the furnaces; the other materials continuously feed into the furnaces through the rotary distributors. Typical daily charge fed to a furnace operating at 10,000 kw comprises 142 tons of sinter, 62 tons of coke, 15 tons of dross, 46 tons of briquettes; or, in lieu of briquettes, 36 tons of granules or screenings. Retention time in the furnace with this charge is about 22 hours.

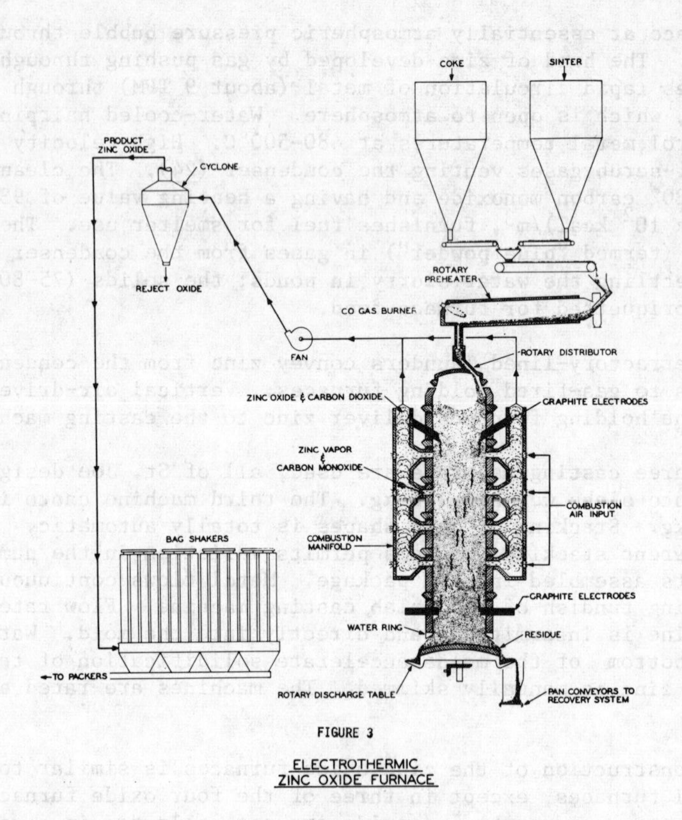

FIGURE 3

ELECTROTHERMIC ZINC OXIDE FURNACE

Both sinter and coke are sized to 6 x 25 mm; the coke, however, contains 75% plus 9.5 mm particles while the sinter contains 55% plus 9.5 mm particles. The rotary distributor positions the charge around the periphery of the furnace shaft. A dish contour in the charge, as shown in Figures 2 and 3, results which permits the larger particles (principally coke) to roll toward the center of the furnace. The selective charge segregation results in about 30% coke in the center of the furnace vs. 15% near the wall and causes the axial region of the furnace to be more electrically conductive than the outer region. This feature helps stabilize electrical characteristics, promotes controlled heating of the charge, and prevents current streaking with associated wall damage.

The furnace charge approximates a 100% resistive load. However, the overall power factor of the transformers, buss bars, voltage regulators, and furnace averages about 94%. Power losses through the traformers and distribution system amount to about 3%.

Top electrodes, consumed at the rate of about 32 mm per day, are repositioned every two or three days. Non-scheduled adjustments are made if thermocouples, inserted in the furnace refractories, detect current excursions along the walls. The lower electrodes do not require repositioning, but are occasionally replaced. Total electrode consumption amounts to 1.1 kg per ton of metal.

At the vapor ring elevation the charge temperature is 900°C near the walls and 1200-1400°C in the main smelting zone. At the bottom electrode elevation, temperatures average about 1300°C. Some liquid slag is present in the spent charge, but the excess of coke makes the charge behave, for the most part, as if it were dry.

Temperature of gases venting the furnace vapor ring averages 850°C. Gas composition is approximately 45% Zn and 45% CO; the balance is nitrogen, carbon dioxide, and hydrogen.

The most powerful factor influencing furnace production is the quantity of electricity introduced into the furnace. Josephtown's newest (and largest) furnace operates at 10,000 kw and produces an average of 91 tons of metal per day. Energy consumption averages 9.3 x 10^9 j (2580 kwh)/ton of metal. About 15% of furnace energy reports in wall losses.

Single-pass zinc elimination averages 92%, with about 7% of the zinc reporting in recirculated residue and 1% reporting in discarded residue. Condenser efficiency varies inversely with production rate; it ranges from 90 to 97%, averaging 93%. Combined single-pass furnace-condenser recovery averages 85%.

Furnace campaigns average 150 days. During the campaign, routine maintenance maneuvers--which consist of repositioning electrodes, removing back reaction (rock oxide) accretions from furnace and condenser gas passageways, and removing blue powder accretions from the condenser off-gas scrubber system--require about 15% power-off time.

A normal rebuild requires ten days. It consists of replacing selected sections of the furnace as needed. Condenser refractories are descaled of rock oxide, but do not require replacing. Total refractory consumption amounts to 10 kg per ton of metal, most of which is for fire clay brick.

Zinc Refinery

To produce Special High Grade (S.H.G.) zinc, we licensed the New Jersey Zinc Company's distillation process. The initial plant, with a capacity of 55 tons per day, came on-stream in 1959. Since then refinery capability has increased to the present output of 160 tons zinc equivalent per day. Product mix is about 82% S.H.G. metal and 18% French Process zinc oxide.

Since the New Jersey Zinc Company's continuous refining process has been described in detail elsewhere (25), no discussion is presented here.

Metal Grades

The consist of metal produced from the furnaces and refinery by major grades is: 11% H.G., 13% Int., 20% B.S. (Brass Special), 25% S.H.G. and 31% P.W. We have about 35 sub-grades with varying chemical specifications.

Operating Requirements

The furnace plant and refinery are managed as one department. A work force of 344 people operate the furnaces and perform the shippin utility, bricklaying, mechanical maintenance, clerical, technical and supervisory work. Table X shows labor distribution and man-hours per ton of zinc equivalent.

Table X

FURNACE LABOR

	Furnace Plant Work Force	Man-hrs/ton Zn Equivalent*
Furnacing	212 (includes 18 supervisors)	2.46
Refining	52 (includes 4 supervisors)	0.65
Metal Shipping	14 (includes 1 supervisor)	0.20
Bricklaying	35 (includes 3 supervisors)	0.29
Mechanical Maintenance	25 (includes 2 supervisors)	0.79
Technical	6 (includes 3 supervisors)	0.13
Total	344 (includes 31 supervisors)	4.52

*For total production of zinc and zinc oxide; includes mechanical and technical labor from other departments.

Zinc Oxide Department

Josephtown Smelter manufactures two distinct types of zinc oxide, the American Process and the French Process. In the American Process, the zinc oxide is made from oxidation of zinc metal vapor produced in the electrothermic furnace by the reaction between zinc oxide sinter and coke. In making French Process oxide, the zinc metal is purified, then volatilized and oxidized to zinc oxide.

French Process Oxide

Smelting - Zinc metal vapor from a boiler is burned in air in a combustion unit of St. Joe design to produce high purity zinc oxide. The fume-laden gases pass through a cyclone to drop out oversize zinc oxide particles.

Collecting - Zinc oxide is filtered from the carrier gases by Dacron cloth bags in a Micropulsaire Collector. Carrier gas for the process is moved by a fan rated at 2237 m^3/min, 47 x 10^2 N/m^2 (48 cm H_2O) positive pressure and 100°C. High-pressure air pulses blow the collected oxide from the bag surface; the oxide drops into collect hoppers underneath the bag units.

Packing - Zinc oxide moves by screw conveyors from the collect hoppers to Orville-Simpson Rotex screens. The screen undersize drops through a rotary magnet, to an H. L. Stoker Company packer. Most of the product is packed in valve-type paper bags, net weight 22.7 kg, which are made up into units of 0.91 ton.

Grades Produced - Seven basic grades of French Process oxide are produced. Three of these are "regular" high purity zinc oxides differing in particle size. The other four grades possess electrostatic and photoconductive properties which are important to the copy paper industry. Differences in particle size and photoconductive properties are achieved by changing combustion conditions.

The three regular grades of French Process zinc oxide average 0.11, 0.18 and 0.30 micron in particle size. They are marketed as untreated powder, as organic coated powder, or as pellets of either type of powder. The four photoconductive zinc oxide grades have average particle sizes of 0.13, 0.18, 0.25 and 0.40 micron.

American Process Zinc Oxide

Smelting - Four electrothermic furnaces have a production capacity of 32,000 tons of American Process oxide per year. Three of the furnaces are 1.75 m in diam; the fourth is 2.44 m. All four have a shaft height of 11.3 m.

In the oxide furnaces, zinc metal vapor and CO gas are produced by the reduction reaction between coke and sinter. These gases pass to vertical, brick-lined manifolds around the furnace periphery. Controlled amounts of air are admitted to the manifolds to burn the CO to CO_2 and the zinc vapor to zinc oxide. High chemical purity is achieved by selecting low volatile cokes for smelting and using H.G. sinter which is low in impurities.

Collecting - The zinc oxide fume-laden gases are conveyed from the furnace manifolds to the bag collectors by six fans, each moving 1270 m^3/min at 34 x 10^2 N/m^2 (35 cm H_2O) positive pressure and 100°C. Normally, one fan services each of the three small furnaces, two fans service the one larger furnace, and one fan is on standby. Fan to duc interchanges are provided to ensure continuous furnace venting for emergency situations or special manufacturing requirements. Tube-typ heat exchangers (water outside the tubes) cool the gases ahead of the fans.

Cyclone separators, 3.0 m ID, downstream of the fans drop out over size particles and foreign material. An automatic system protects th collect bags by injecting cold air if temperatures become excessive.

Zinc oxide is filtered from the carrier gases in cotton fabric bag There are six collect sections, containing a total of 1000 filter bag each 0.51 m diam x 13.7 m high. For a production rate of 88 tons per day, we normally use 85% of the filter capacity. For one minute in every 30 minutes, the flow is dampered off of 50 bags and the zinc oxide mechanically shaken into a stainless steel lined collect hopper below the bags. The oxide, classified according to chemical analyses and particle size, is conveyed and elevated to one of 12 storage bins

Packing - Most zinc oxide is produced in powder form. Grades are characterized by particle size and chemical purity. There are three primary grades, with typical average particle sizes of 0.11, 0.15 and 0.20 micron.

Powder is conveyed from overhead storage bins to an Orville-Simpson rotex. After screening at 0.3 mm, the oxide drops through a magnetic separator to a Fluopacker. The oxide may be densified in a deaerating unit of St. Joe design before packing.

The product is packed in paper, multiwall, valve-type bags. The bags, each containing 22.7 kg of zinc oxide, are built into 0.91-ton units for shipment. Bag specifications or unit sizes may vary to mee a customer's need.

Pelletized Oxide - Soft zinc oxide pellets are formed by squeezing th oxide between two rubber rolls to form pellet nuclei. These preforme particles are then rolled in a rotary drum, with additional feed, to grow round, soft pellets. The pellets are free-flowing and relativel dustless, with a diameter between 0.20 and 1.20 mm. Bulk density is from 0.8 to 1.1 g/cc compared to 0.3 to 0.5 g/cc for unpelletized powder.

Pellets can be made from any of the primary or coated grades. Normally pellets are packed in valve bags (22.7 kg net), although some shipments go in fiber drums (113.3 kg net) or in rubber bags (680 kg net).

Reheated Oxide - Reheating oxide at temperatures of 650 to 750°C causes particle growth and elimination of colloidal fines. All primary grades can be reheated. Reheated grades have average particle sizes of 0.26, 0.31, and 0.41 micron and a narrower particle size distribution than the primary grades.

One type reheater is a 1.5 m ID x 12.5 m rotary stainless steel drum, with removable internal flanges for regulating product residence time, housed in a gas-fired muffle. Two other reheaters are 30 cm diam stainless steel, variable speed screw conveyors, housed in gas-fired muffles. Temperature of combustion gases inside the muffles is controlled below 900°C.

High Sulfur Content Oxide - The sulfur content of zinc oxide affects the curing rate and color of certain rubber compounds in which it may be used.

Clean, dry SO_2 gas is piped from our sulfuric acid plant system, passed through a catalyst converter to oxidize SO_2 to SO_3, and mixed with the zinc oxide-laden gas stream from the electrothermic furnaces. Trace impurities, such as lead oxide, are converted to sulfates. Normal sulfur content (reported as sulfur trioxide) in the product is 0.4%.

Other Grades - St. Joe also produces organic coated zinc oxides. The coating, dispersed over the surface of the oxide, increases incorporation rate in rubber and acts to prevent adsorption of CO_2 and H_2O on the oxide surface.

Zinc oxide granules are produced with an apparent bulk density of 1.2 to 1.5 g/cc. They are free flowing, dense, almost completely dust free, and can be shipped in bulk, in hopper cars, or trucks.

Warehousing and Shipping

The zinc oxide department has warehouse facilities for 3500 tons of zinc oxide. Whenever possible, shipments are made directly from the packing floor. Because of the large number of product specifications, we do maintain a one-to-two month inventory of our most active grades to permit efficient production scheduling.

Shipments are made by commercial truck lines or by rail.

Typical Quality Characteristics

	Amer. Proc. Oxide	French Proc. Oxide
Lead as PbO	0.009%	0.0015%
Cadmium as CdO	0.010%	0.0006%
Iron as Fe_2O_3	0.015%	0.005%
Manganese as MnO	0.002%	<0.0005%
Copper as CuO	0.002%	<0.0001%
+325 Mesh Screen Residue	<0.03%	<0.03%
Brightness; Hunter D-40	93.0 for large sizes	99.0 for large sizes
	91.0 for fine sizes	95.0 for fine sizes

Operating Requirements

Seven-man crews on each of three shifts, supported by a daylight utility group of five men, process and pack the oxide. A four-man millwright crew services the equipment. An eight-man crew warehouses and ships the oxide. All of the figures include salary supervision. An administrative and technical staff manages the operations.

Operating labor requirements (production and shipping)	3.7 man-hrs/ton
Operating maintenance requirements	0.7 man-hr/ton

Secondary Material

An important feature of the St. Joe electrothermic process is its versatility and adaptability in processing a wide variety of zinc-bearing materials. Not only can the process accommodate relatively high gangue and impurity loadings, but it is ideally suited to processing secondary materials in which the zinc is in both the metallic and oxidic state and associated in various combinations with lead, iron, and aluminum. Purchased secondaries consist of skimmings (also termed "ashes") from hot dip galvanizing and die casting, drosses from galvanizing and die casting, and sludges derived from the manufacture of paint and chemicals. Internally generated secondaries include refinery drosses, material derived from vapor ring cleanouts, and blue powder. All of these materials are sorted and processed for introduction at suitable entry points in the zinc plant circuit.

Auxiliaries and Staff Capability

The George F. Weaton Power Station - A 106,000 kw coal-burning plant, commissioned in 1957, provides power for the smelter. The installation comprises two turbines with associated boilers which develop steam at 122 atm and 537°C. Six men (includes one foreman) per shift operate the power plant. Heat rate for 1969 averaged 10.8×10^6 j (2590 kcal) per kwh; 809×10^6 kwh net were generated.

Shops, Maintenance and Process Service - A group generally referred to as the service department, composed of 475 people--headed by the plant engineer, eight general foremen and 36 other supervisors--has responsibility for all facets of mechanical and electrical maintenance, transportation, shop fabrication, materials handling, painting, lubrication and janitorial services. Water pollution control is included in the group's responsibilities. Most of the process replacement equipment for the smelter is built in our own shops. Skilled craftsmen perform these activities, as well as those associated with carrying out comprehensive preventive maintenance programs, considered to be among the best in the industry.

Laboratories - The metallurgical control laboratories play a key role in assuring that smelter products meet customer specifications. Quality control assays of zinc, zinc alloys, zinc oxide and cadmium employ optical emission spectroscopy. Samples, delivered to the direct reading spectrometer by a pneumatic tube system, are analyzed and reported to the furnace plant and zinc oxide departments in 10-12 minutes.

Materials in process throughout the smelter are sampled and composited on a shift or 24-hour basis. An X-ray emission spectroscope performs determinations of zinc, lead, cadmium, iron, sulfur, tin, copper, manganese and silicon. A small computer converts instrument response into percentage of each element reported. A Teletype conveys results to the operating departments immediately upon completion of analysis. In this manner, results can be reported within approximately two hours after completion of the sampling period.

In addition to control analyses, the laboratories make settlement assays and analyze a large number of non-routine samples from research and customer service activities. This chemical analysis group employs classical wet and spectrophotometric methods, as well as the more recent technique of atomic absorption. An analytical development group develops new methods, and provides standard samples for all the instruments used by the metallurgical control laboratories.

Research and Customer Service - A 26-man professional staff, with approximately an equal number of supporting people, performs both process and product research. Process research has developed new methods for treating zinc-bearing materials; improved furnace performance; developed new procedures for treating furnace residues to improve coke, zinc and ferrosilicon recovery; and developed new or improved procedures for recovery of by-products.

Customer service is a fundamental philosophy. Technical service groups for both zinc metal and zinc oxide maintain close contact with customers and aid them in solving technical problems.

Engineering - Responsibility for design and development of plant and production facilities resides in the engineering department. The 40-man staff conducts the necessary investigations to assist management in determining the need for facilities, provides the necessary design drawings, specifications, plans and schedules for construction, and oversees construction and start-up. Industrial hygiene and air pollution control are included in the department's responsibilities.

Purchasing, Accounting, Industrial Relations - Other important service groups include the purchasing department, which oversees all division purchases and administers the storeroom activities. The accounting department is involved in an extensive program of computerized data processing applications--including basic raw material inventory accounting, preparation of concentrate and secondary material settlements, metal and oxide inventory accounting, equipment maintenance cost analysis, and storing and disseminating assays of metallurgical materials. The industrial relations department oversees a wide variety of activities, including training programs for both supervisory and hourly employees. Other programs include apprentice training courses and an engineering technician training program.

Summary

The advantages of the electrothermic process are its flexibility in accommodating zinc concentrates of wide chemical composition, its ease of producing zinc products to close chemical specification, its unique suitability for processing other zinc-bearing materials, and its high zinc recovery. Operating requirements, performance data and capital requirements are highlighted in the following sections.

Operating Data - Summary of operating data for the year 1969 is shown in Table XI.

Manpower - At the end of 1969, 1400 employees, including technical and supervisory personnel, worked at Josephtown Smelter. Total labor requirements for the year 1969 were:

Table XI

OPERATING DATA - 1969

	Tons
Concentrates Used	317,000
Purchased Secondary Materials Used	60,000
Zinc Metal Produced	196,000
Zinc Oxide Produced	32,000
Zinc Equivalent Produced	222,000
Sulfuric Acid (100%) Produced	280,000
per ton of Concentrate	0.88
Cadmium Produced	520
Pea Coke Used	129,000
per ton of Zn Equivalent	0.58
Breeze Coke Used	22,000
per ton of Zn Equivalent	0.10
Silica Sand Used	8,900

	Man-hrs/ton Zn
Direct and Indirect Operating Labor	8.6
Direct and Indirect Maintenance	3.2
Metallurgical Control, Research, Engineering, Miscellaneous	2.2
Total	14.0

Energy - Approximately 80% of the smelter's electrical energy is consumed in the furnaces. Product energy requirements depend upon the amount of metallic vs. oxidic zinc in furnace feed. Approximately 10.8×10^9 j (2990 kwh)/ton of product zinc are required for producing zinc from sinter. Gas and electricity requirements for the year 1969 were as follows:

Electricity	
Furnacing	9.66×10^9 j (2683 kwh)/ton Zn
Total Smelter	12.1×10^9 j (3360 kwh)/ton Zn
Natural Gas (9345 kcal/m^3)	125 m^3/ton Zn
CO Gas (2225 kcal/m^3)	250 m^3/ton Zn

Recovery - High zinc recovery reflects the extensive dust collection facilities, excellent elimination in the electrothermic furnaces, and extensive residue treatment. Since the heavy media plant for treatin furnace residues commenced operation in 1965, Josephtown Smelter's overall zinc recovery has averaged 95.6%.

Capital Requirements - A summary estimate of capital costs (in 1969 dollars) of a new plant producing 120,000 tons per year zinc metal is shown in Table XII.

Table XII

ESTIMATED CAPITAL COST FOR PLANT PRODUCING 120,000 TPY OF ZINC METAL

Land and Site Preparation	$ 2,000,000
Concentrate storage, Thawing, Blending & Drying	1,500,000
Roasting Plant & Boilers	4,500,000
Sulfuric Acid Plant (250,000 TPY) & Storage (18,000 tons)	5,900,000
Sinter Plant, Residue Treatment & Coke Preparation	7,500,000
Furnace Plant, Vacuum Pumps & Compressors	7,500,000
Cadmium Plant	1,000,000
Briquetting Plant	600,000
Air, Water, Electrical, Gas & Other Utilities	3,350,000
Shops & Warehouse	1,000,000
Office, Laboratory & Change House	1,150,000
Engineering, Contractors' Fees & Contingencies	9,000,000
Total --	$45,000,000

References

1. O'Harra, B. M., "The Electrothermic Metallurgy of Zinc," U.S. Bur. Mines Bull. 208 (1922).

2. Landis, W. S., "The Trollhättan Electrothermic Zinc Process," Trans. TMS-AIME, 121, pp. 573-598 (1936).

3. Gaskill, E. C., U. S. Patent 1,743,886 (Jan. 14, 1930).

4. Gaskill, E. C., U. S. Patent 1,743,964 (Jan. 14, 1930).

5. Gaskill, E. C., U. S. Patent 1,775,591 (Sept. 9, 1930).

6. Weaton, G. F. and H. K. Najarian, U. S. Patent 2,070,101 (Feb. 9, 1937).

7. Weaton, G. F., "St. Joseph Lead Company's Electrothermic Zinc Smelting Process," Trans. TMS-AIME, 121, pp. 599-609 (1936).

8. Weaton, G. F. and C. C. Long, "Direct Production of Metallic Zinc by the Electrothermic Process," Trans. TMS-AIME, 152, pp. 316-327 (1939).

9. Weaton, G. F., H. K. Najarian and C. C. Long, "Production of Electrothermic Zinc at Josephtown Smelter," Trans. TMS-AIME, 159, pp. 141-160 (1944).

10. Najarian, H. K., "Weaton-Najarian Vacuum Condenser," Trans. TMS-AIME, 159, pp. 161-175 (1944).

11. Najarian, H. K., "The Improved Weaton-Najarian Vacuum Condenser," Trans. TMS-AIME, 212, pp. 493-497 (1958).

12. Najarian, H. K., K. F. Peterson and R. E. Lund, "Sintering Practice at Josephtown Smelter," Trans. TMS-AIME, 191, pp. 116-119 (1951).

13. Long, C. C., "Josephtown Smelter - St. Joe Lead's Electrothermic Zinc Plant," Journal of Metals, 17, pp. 1351-1352 (Dec. 1965).

14. Lund, R. E., G. E. Welch, J. Ferrighetto and B. E. Hoffacker, "St. Joe Reclaims Zinc with Heavy Media Separation," Mining Engineering, 20, pp. 81-83 (Dec. 1968).

15. Isbell, W. T. and G. F. Weaton, U. S. Patent 1,940,912 (Dec. 26, 1933).

16. Long, C. C. and H. K. Najarian, U. S. Patent 2,847,294 (Aug. 12, 1958).

17. Najarian, H. K., U. S. Patent 1,889,052 (Nov. 29, 1932).

18. Weaton, G. F. and H. K. Najarian, U. S. Patent 1,889,055 (Nov. 29, 1932).

19. Lund, R. E. and D. E. Warnes, U. S. Patent 2,777,752 (Jan. 15, 1957).

20. Weaton, G. F., U. S. Patent 1,932,388 (Oct. 31, 1933).

21. Weaton, G. F., U. S. Patent 1,970,209 (Aug. 14, 1934).

22. Najarian, H. K., U. S. Patent 2,766,034 (Oct. 9, 1956).

23. Najarian, H. K., U. S. Patent 2,766,114 (Oct. 9, 1956).

24. Long, C. C. and G. E. Deeley, U. S. Patent 2,298,139 (Oct. 6, 1942).

25. Miller, E. L., "The Refining of Zinc," Zinc - The Metal, Its Alloys and Compounds, ed. C. H. Mathewson, ACS Monograph No. 142, pp. 334-343, Reinhold (1959).

Chapter 21

NO. 4 I.S.F. SMELTER COMPLEX OF IMPERIAL SMELTING CORP., LTD.
Avonmouth, England

R. M. Sellwood
Manager, No. 4 Smelter Complex
Imperial Smelting Corporation (N.S.C.) Limited

Abstract

The No. 4 I.S.F. Smelter Complex at the Avonmouth Works of Imperial Smelting Corporation (N.S.C.) Limited commenced operation at the beginning of 1968. The furnace rating is 120,000 tons zinc and 40,000 tons lead per annum.

Zinc and lead concentrates are unloaded onto a 1,000 tons per hour capacity conveyor belt and automatically weighed and sampled before receipt into a 48,000 ton capacity raw material store. Distribution is by a reversible boom stacker into 16 x 3,000 ton bays and recovery is by a front end loader. Materials are fed to 16 proportioning bins for feeding via continuous weigh feeders to a 132 square metre effective updraught area sinter machine with a material flow rate of 240 tons per hour over the machine. The required quantity of output lump sinter at up to 800°C is fed to 2 x 600 ton storage bins on the I.S.F. plant. By-product SO_2 rich gas is fed to a conventional wet gas single stream acid plant rated at 600 tons per day utilizing a dry N.T.P. gas volume of 100,000 cubic metres per hour.

The hot sinter and preheated coke (800°C) are automatically weighed and charged to a $27.3m^2$ shaft area I.S.F. fitted with 2 x 5.5 m. wide lead splash condensers. Grade 4 zinc is tapped and transferred to the zinc refinery. Conventional type lead bullion and slag are tapped from the bottom of the furnace through a separation forehearth. The refinery consists of 6 lead and 3 cadmium columns to produce some 52,000 tons per annum of S.H.G. metal. S.H.G. metal and Grade 4 metal is cast into various shapes as required.

Location of Plant

The No. 4 I.S.F. Smelter Complex is situated at the Avonmouth Works of Imperial Smelting Corporation (N.S.C.) Bristol, England, the site of the original experimental and development work for the Imperial Smelting Furnace. The Smelter comprising Raw Materials Store, Sinter Plant, Sulphuric Acid Plant, Imperial Smelting Furnace, Zinc Refinery, Effluent Treatment Plant and Cadmium Recovery Plant commenced operation at the beginning of 1968. The furnace rating is 120,000 tons of zinc and 40,000 plus tons of lead per annum and is at present operating at the originally envisaged production rate of 90,000 tons of zinc and 30,000 tons of lead per annum.

2.1 Conveyor Intake System and Raw Materials Store

The site occupied by the new smelter is approximately 1.5 kilometres from Avonmouth Docks which at present is capable of handling shipping up to about 25,000 tons capacity. A new belt conveyor system including automatic weighing and sampling has been installed from the docks to the new site.

All concentrates used in the United Kingdom have to be imported, consequently the intake system for raw materials is very important. Three kangaroo cranes installed by the Port of Bristol Authority discharge the concentrates at a rate of up to 1,000 tons per hour onto a 1.06 metre wide deep troughed belt conveyor with idlers troughed at 45°. The material is passed through an automatic weighing and sampling system before being stored in a 48,000 tons capacity raw materials store. The conveyor which is also used for other materials is divided into 10 sections and requires a total of 725 H.P. Belt speed is 138 metres/min.

2.2 Weighing and Sampling

The automatic weighing system is a load cell batch system consisting of 2 x 10 ton capacity weigh hoppers. Material is fed from the intake conveyor into one hopper until it is full, when the feed is directed to the second hopper. The first hopper is automatically weighed, emptied and tared ready to receive material from the conveyor. At 1,000 tons per hour this operation is completed in some 36 seconds. The weigh hoppers are fitted with check weights which can be rapidly attached to the hopper to allow the weighers to be checked at frequent intervals. The weights are hung close to the hoppers and when required are raised by electric motors to a position where the required weight is pinned to the weigh hoppers. Additionally, known weights of stone are periodically passed through the whole of the system to check accuracies under operating conditions. Weighing accuracy is better than $\pm \frac{1}{2}\%$ and the weigher has a Board of Trade Certificate.

Material discharged from the weigh hoppers falls into a bin and is discharged by a variable speed belt onto the main conveyor. A sampling cutter crosses the discharge chute of this belt taking a 1% cut of the feed. This material then falls onto a second belt fitted with a similar sampler taking a further cut which is taken for final splitting and assay. The excess material from the second belt falls back onto the main conveyor. See Figure 1.

2.3 Raw Materials Store

The Raw Materials Store is divided into 16 x 3000 ton capacity bays which can be subdivided by moveable concrete sections if required. Distribution is by means of a moveable reciprocating reversible boom stacker which beds the material in the bays and also by virtue of the final shape of the pile makes maximum use of available capacity. There are no vertical supports in the area covered by the stacker so that the ship does not have to stop discharging to allow movement from one bay to another. Recovery is by front end loader into moveable hopper feeders mounted above 760 m.m. wide conveyors running along the wings of the store, which in turn feed inclined conveyors carrying the material to a short reversible shuttle conveyor feeding one of 2 hammer mills or a bye pass chute. Recovery rate and so feed to the sinter plant proportioning bins is up to 250 tons per hour. The hammer mills are of conventional design fitted with reversible swinging hammers. An external high level feed hopper is also available to enable lorries of material from external dump to be fed to the Sinter Plant.

Materials such as sand and limestone are stored in external bins and fed by front end loader through the walls of the building into one of the moveable feed hoppers. See Figure 2.

From the store the materials are elevated and carried by conveyor belts to a reversing conveyor discharging onto 2 reversible shuttle conveyors above the Sinter Plant proportioning bins. These bins are arranged in two parallel rows.

Sinter Plant

3.1 Proportioning and Mixing System. See Figure 3.

The proportioning system consists of 16 bins, 2 for returns and 14 for raw materials. The 2 returns bins have a capacity of 180 tons each, whilst the remaining 14 bins are 75 m^3 capacity and nominally hold 100 tons of material. These 14 bins are cylindrical tapering to a cone which fits into a rectangular boot supported from the conical section of the bin. The boot tapers from the vertical to fit the weigh belt, but is divergent in the line of travel of the belt to enable the material to expand and flow freely. Electric

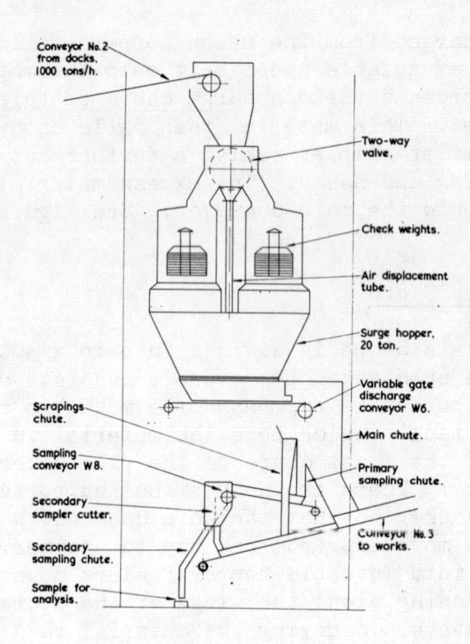

Figure 1 - Automatic weighing and sampling system on Materials Intake Conveyor.

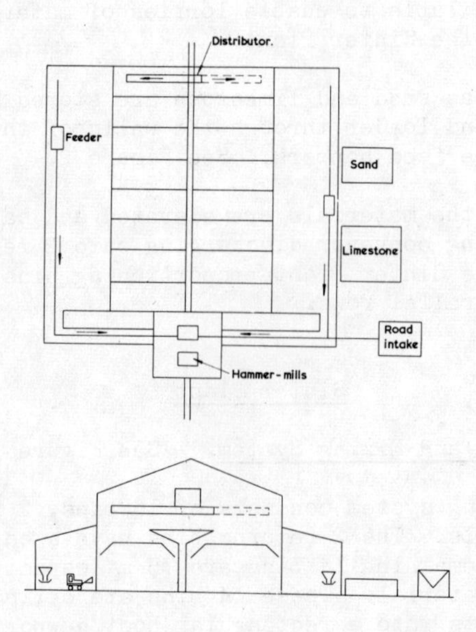

Figure 2 - Layout of Raw Materials Store, capacity 48,000 tons.

vibrators are fitted to the bottom of the conical section to move material should it hang up. Audible and visual alarms are used to inform the operator of any low flows at any time.

The weigh feeders are mounted on load cells, and the speed of the extractor weigh belts are controlled by Kop Variators, the depth of material on the belt being controlled by pneumatically operated control gate. The weigh control system, ganging of bins together and total feed rate to the sinter machine are controlled by the Direct Digital Control Computer which takes the place of conventional instrumentation on the plant. Normally the control gates are set and the belt speed varied to extract the correct weight per length of belt, but if there is a blockage behind the control gate and speed alone cannot control, the control gate will open. The weigh feeders, extractor belts, etc. are sized to various range tonnages to give optimum operation at these rates. Weights delivered by all but the returns bins feeder can be checked by using a diverting flap in the feeder discharge chutes. The returns bins feeders are checked statically by chains of known weight laid on the feed weigher belt.

The new material weigh feeder discharges fall onto 2 collector belts and feed onto a conveyor system which originally passed all new feed through a mixing hammer mill. This is at present out of circuit as it blocks very easily. The sinter returns are then proportioned onto a 760 m.m. wide conveyor carrying the proportioned new material and this feeds to the primary mixing drum at ground level. Feed rate is up to 240 tons per hour.

3.2 Primary Mixing Drum

This is a drum 6 m. long and 2½ m. diameter rotating at 6 r.p.m. and fitted with a paddle shaft rotating at 20 r.p.m. The drive on the drum is through rubber tyres from a 100 H.P. motor whilst the paddle shaft is driven by a 50 H.P. motor. Looking at the discharge end of the drum, it is rotating clockwise with paddle shaft located at 7 o'clock and rotating in an anticlockwise direction. The interior surface of the drum is lined with expanded metal to promote build up of material to prevent wear on the shell and to give better lifting characteristics of the mix. A scraper is fitted at 2 o'clock to prevent excessive build up. A 150 m.m. deep retention weir is fitted on the discharge which gives a retention time of 3 minutes. Moisture is added from a spray pipe inside the drum, the amount added being controlled from a conductivity moisture probe on the output side of the drum. The majority of the moisture is added to this drum, the flow being registered by the computer in the control room; a manual bye pass system is also fitted. After leaving this drum the material is elevated to the 19 metre level and feeds by inclined chute into the secondary or conditioning drum situated above and to one side of the sinter machine.

3.3 Conditioning Drum

A drum of similar size and drive design as the primary drum, but rotating at 8 r.p.m. and with a material retention time of approximately 2 minutes. No paddle is installed, expanded metal is fitted inside and a scraper is installed. Moisture is added through a spray pipe in the drum and the amount is controlled by a conductivity probe working on material leaving the drum and the amount of water being added can be ascertained from the computer in the control room at any time. The water addition can be controlled manually from the control room.

3.4 Feed Splitting and Feed to the Machine

As the updraught sintering technique is used it is necessary to split the feed to ignition and main layers in order to produce a homogeneous product, consequently all the material is fed to the main layer or to the igniter layer. Material from the conditioning drum discharges onto a feed belt on which the moisture conductivity probe is mounted and feeds into an electrically operated shuttle chute controlled from probes in the igniter layer feed board. When feed to the igniter layer is required the chute is pulled across and diverts all feed to a cross belt which feeds a reciprocating conveyor working across the igniter layer. All timings are such that when feed is called for the reciprocating conveyor (normally stationary) moves over the feed board with belt running to its furthest point of travel. The shuttle chute is then moved at a time such that material reaches the discharge point of the reciprocating conveyor at the same time as the conveyor reaches its maximum travel. As the conveyor is retracted an even layer of feed is distributed across the igniter feed board, the conveyor then stopping. The shuttle chute is switched back to the main layer at a time such that feed to the igniter layer feed board stops as the reciprocating conveyor reaches it point of minimum travel.

The remainder of the total feed is fed to a reciprocating conveyor running across the main feed board. The speeds of the belt and the reciprocating action are such that with the quantity of feed material used, an even level of material across the machine is achieved.

A conductivity probe in the top of the igniter layer feed board controls the feed requirement for this layer. Should this fail, three additional probes mounted across the bottom of the feed board in the centre and edges bring up an alarm in the control room if the feed runs out. The feed board slopes at an angle of 68°, and is fitted with a sloped back plate forming a feed hopper. This back plate finishes 250 m.m. above the grate and at a distance of 100 m.m. from the feed board, thus allowing a spill of material at the base. The ignition layer depth is set at 28 - 30 m.m.

The main feed hopper is made up of a sloping feed board angled at 68° with a vertical water cooled back plate extending to within 3 c.m. of the igniter layer. Total bed depth is normally 305 m.m. and the main feed board holds a maximum of 1 minute's feed at full speed of the machine, i.e. 4 tons at a grate speed of 2 m. per minute. The main feed board is mounted on load cells, and the weight indicated in the control room, thus allowing the operator to adjust his proportioning bin feed rates. If the hopper overfills, the feed circuit is automatically stopped and has to be restarted by the operator. This system will eventually be put on the Direct Digital Control computer for control.

The total sulphur content in feed is maintained at approximately 6.5%, i.e. new feed sulphur is controlled at 4.8% in feed mix with returns running at 2.5 - 3.0% of total sulphur.

3.5 Ignition Stove

The ignition stove inside measurement is 2 metres long so that at maximum speed ignition will be for a minimum of 1 minute. Construction is a steel shell with spiggots welded to the shell to hold a rammed refractory lining some 250 m.m. thick. A water jacket runs around the periphery of the bottom of the stove to support the refractory and special heat resistant steel shoes are pinned underneath the jacket to reduce heat loss to the water jacket and to radiate heat back into the ignition layer. Height of the stove is 2 m. and it is fired by 5 Schieldrop oil burners using 950 sec. oil. Consumption is 25 kilograms per ton sulphur eliminated.

3.6 Sinter Machine

A standard Lurgi machine 3 metres wide with swinging discharge end and an effective updraught area of 132 m^2, fitted with grease sealed slide rails and fixed gib plates are installed. The drive motor is a direct current variable speed type of 75 H.P., but under normal operating conditions of 1.7 metres per minute power requirement is approximately 30 H.P. A Bogie flex gearbox is fitted to the drive. The greasing system is of Traborn design with grease points every 0.5 metre along the slide rail, and placed slightly off centre towards the windbox side of the rail, the tendency being with an updraught machine to blow the grease across the rail away from the windbox.

Cast Iron Pallets are one metre long fitted with three rows of pallet bars each 330 m.m. long and spaced at 5 m.m. between bars. The space under each row of bars is completely sealed from the next with the bottom of the partitioning wall being machined to give a tight seal when passing over windbox junctions. Cast Iron wing plates, angled at 3° and 355 m.m. high are fitted. A pallet bar levelling roller is fitted at the feed end of the machine with trip switches fitted above the roller which will stop the machine should a pallet bar fail to be levelled.

The machine hood is approximately domed shaped rising to a height 2.5 metres above the machine grate and fits into a sand seal along the machine at a height of some 1.3 metres above floor level. A rough labyrinth type seal is fitted to prevent fume from collecting in the pallet roller tunnel. Two hood expansion joints are fitted approximately $\frac{1}{3}$ and $\frac{2}{3}$ of the distance along the machine. The rich gas offtake is 8 metres from the feedboard with the recirculation gas offtake at a point over windbox no. 10/11.

The underside of the machine is completely enclosed including the windbox area. All spillage falls into the tapered bottom of the enclosure and is removed continually by a scraper conveyor feeding into the main handling circuit. The igniter windbox is 2 metres long, the remaining 11 windboxes are 4 metres long. Spillage from the igniter windbox is removed continuously by a screw conveyor discharging into a small totally enclosed seal hopper, a minimum fixed depth of material making the seal. High and low level probes are fitted in the hopper and excess material is automatically removed by a screw conveyor discharging into the enclosed underside of the machine. A spring loaded dead plate some 700 m.m. long is fitted between the igniter windbox and the No. 1 windbox.

The main windboxes which are bifurcated to give easy removal of spillage are discharged into hoppers fitted inside the machine underside enclosure. These hoppers are discharged when the machine is operating normally but windboxes are emptied only when the machine and handling system are stopped. The machine operating floor is 12.5 metres above ground level, the scraper conveyor level is 4.5 m. above ground level.

3.7 Gas Circulation System

All gases eventually pass to the acid plant in making up the acid plant volume of 100,000 m^3 per hour at 300 - 350°C and containing approximately 6.5% SO_2. Fresh air is supplied by means of two fans, the first fan being connected only to the No. 1 windbox, the next 5 windboxes being supplied by the second fan. Hot recirculation gases are carried by a main running along the top of the machine hood picking up cold recirculation gas from the machine feed end together with the relatively cold and wet igniter gases. The gases are then passed through a dust collecting chamber and so to the recirculating gas fan. These three fans are driven through variable speed fluid couplings and the volumes are automatically controlled. Igniter windbox gases are automatically controlled by constant suction in the windbox through a pressure control valve. Cold air can be admitted to the recirculating gas system to keep temperatures below 250°C. Fan operating details are given in Table I.

3.8 Sinter Handling

Sinter falls from the machine on to a crash deck and into a pronged breaker with the rails set at 260 m.m. The breaker is driven by a 100 H.P. motor at 3 r.p.m. through a shear pin and is fitted with 3 prongs per section of breaker, each prong being of unequal length. The aim is to reduce the maximum loading on the drive at any one instant and to even out the flow of material to the remainder of the circuit. From the breaker material falls onto a variable speed Schenck feeder feeding a spiked roll crusher which takes the top sizing down to 80 - 90 m.m. The variable speed is provided by a P.I.V. gearbox and speed controls are situated adjacent to the feeder and in the control room. The spiked roll crusher is by Wedag 1500 m.m. diameter by 1500 m.m. wide running at 80 r.p.m. Each roll is independently driven by a 100 H.P. motor and the spring loaded roll is pre-loaded to 90 tons.

From the spiked rolls material falls onto a totally enclosed T.K.V. type pan conveyor and is elevated to the main screen. At this point spillage material from the scraper conveyor is fed via two small schenck conveyors onto the pan conveyor. Material falls from the conveyor onto a 1.5 m. wide x 6 m. long double deck Schenck screen with screen cloths of 100 m.m. and 20 m.m. Lump oversize sinter from both decks can be fed to the furnace or can be diverted for crushing for provision of returns. Lump material for the furnace falls onto a schenck conveyor which in turn feeds a pan conveyor carrying material to the furnace sinter storage bins, or to a quench bin for stock production. Splitting of the output is done from the control room, and is done in such a way as to keep a steady feed to both output and returns circuits. To do this the discharge of the bottom deck of the screen is brought to a 'V' and the diversion flap can be set in any position to give the required split of feed.

The -20 m.m. material from the screen is passed by chute directly to the Schenck conveyor feeding the cooling drum, whilst the excess oversize falls onto a schenck feeder discharging into the coarse roll crusher which reduces over size material to -30 m.m. sizing. Screened undersize material from the furnace is brought back by T.K.V. type pan conveyor and is fed back to the coarse roll crushing circuit or if the plant is on stop, into the quench bin. From the quench bin either lump or fines can be handled by belt conveyor to stock or back into the coarse crusher circuit. The coarse crusher is again by Wedag; 1250 m.m. diameter by 750 m.m. wide running at 89 r.p.m., and driven by a 150 H.P. motor. The moveable roll is preloaded to 65 tons.

All material reaching the cooling drum is -30 m.m. and is all fed via one feeder. At this point, dewatered sludges arising from the

TABLE I

Type of Fan	N.T.P. Dry Vol $m^3/hr.$	m.m. W.G.	Normal Operating Pressure m.m. W.G.	Temperature °C Maximum
Igniter Fan	20,000	250	-60	150
No. 1 Air Fan	17,000	410	250	ambient
No. 2 Air Fan	68,000	410	300	ambient
Recirculating Gas Fan	68,000	500	300	250

Sinter Machine Fan Operating Conditions

TABLE II

Scrubber Type	Volume $m^3/hr.$ N.T.P. Dry	Pressure Drop m.m. W.G.	Water Volume m^3 per minute	Fan Horse Power(s)
Doyles	51,000	250	1.37	300
Venturi	51,000	560	2.7	620

Sinter Plant Ventilation Details

acid plant (lead sludge), Furnace sludges (Blue Powder) and Sinter plant ventilation sludges are also fed to the cooling drum as cooling media. Water is added as required to make up the required moisture control in returns. The cooling drum is 6 m. long x 2½ m. rotating at 6 r.p.m. and fitted with a paddle shaft rotating at 20 r.p.m. A 300 m.m. high weir fitted two thirds of the distance along the drum to help retention time which, at less than 3 minutes, is not sufficient to give adequate cooling of the larger material. It is hoped to replace this drum with a larger one approximately 9½ m. long x 3⅓ m. diameter in the near future and so increase the retention time to 5 minutes. Lifter bars approximately 12 m.m. high and spaced at 375 m.m. around the periphery of the drums and a scraper are fitted. The final moisture content of the cooled material is controlled by a conductivity probe at the outlet of the drum.

Materials leaving the drum fall onto a 760 m.m. wide belt on 25° troughing sets and running at a speed of 55 metres per minute, and are taken by this and other conveyors to two surge bins of 20 tons capacity mounted on load cells. Material is fed to one or other of the bins to two smooth roll crushers, the feed being the same width as the roll crushers. The depth of material on this feed belt is controlled by an air operated gate and is varied according to to the amount of material in the surge bins. As the level in the bin increases, the gate opening increases. The smooth roll crushers again by Wedag are 1800 m.m. diameter x 760 m.m. wide and run at a speed of 75 r.p.m. They are set to give -6 m.m. material with the moveable roll preloaded to 180 tons. Each roll is independently driven by a 100 H.P. motor.

Material discharged from the rolls are fed by discharge belts onto a conveyor feeding the returns bins. Each set of rolls can take two thirds of total throughput rate, i.e. 160 tons per hour.

Originally all main conveyor belts were 760 m.m. wide deep troughed at 53° in order to reduce conveyor costs, maintenance and and conveyor speeds, but on the returns circuit these have been replaced with 25° troughed conveyors. The deep troughed conveyors could not be kept tracked with material varying in moisture content which caused rapid build up in chutes and this altered the point of impact on the next belt continually, causing the belts to turn over very frequently.

Material from the machine has an average temperature of some 800°C, the aim is to feed material from the furnace storage bins to the furnace at some 400°C.

Sinter for stock is passed to an 80 ton capacity quench bin where it is sprayed with water and cooled to a temperature at which it can be handled on a rubber conveyor belt. There is enough heat left in the sinter to dry out on a stock pile without being excessively dusty. The cool sinter is taken to a lump sinter store of 6,000 tons capacity where it is distributed by front end loader. Recovery from the store is by the same front end loader onto a rubber conveyor which passes it to either the feeder and pan conveyor feeding the furnace sinter storage bins, or is fed to the coarse roll crushers for reconstitution. An emergency intake system to the furnace bins is via the furnace coke intake system.

Screened sinter fines from the furnace can be put to the quench bin and thence to stock or the sinter machine circuit when the furnace is operating with sinter plant on stop.

A typical sinter assay is:

Zn%	Pb%	S%	Cu%	Cd%	FeO%	SiO_2%	CaO%
42	20	0.8	0.9	0.05	8.0	3.0	4.8

3.9 Ventilation

As the plant is handling lead containing materials all sections of the plant materials handling equipment are enclosed, except the conveyors between the discharge of the primary mixing drum and the sinter machine, which handle wet mixed materials. Induced ventilation is provided by venturi scrubbers for fine fume from the tip end of the machine and from the cooling drum, while Doyle Scrubbers are used for the coarse dusts arising in the proportioning building, crusher house, and returns system. The Doyle scubbers are situated as close as possible to the point of arising; the venturi scrubber as close as practicable to the cooling drum since there is not problem in ducting the hot fine fume from the tip end of the machine. A rubber lined humidifying tower is provided before the venturi scrubber to eliminate the formation of a wet-dry line, and so build up and blockages. A vertical square rubber stack leads from the discharge of the cooling drum to a short cross over into the humidifying tower to provide easy cleaning of the duct. A control damper is provided in the duct from the tip end of the machine to control distribution of volume to the points of ventilation. Details of scrubbers are given in Table II.

All liquor used on scrubbers is returned to a central 15 metre diameter thickener and after thickening the sludge is returned to the cooling drum via a dewatering hydrocyclone. The clean overflow liquor from the thickener is recirculated to the scrubbers.

The ignition stove area is partially enclosed and some natural and forced ventilation applied.

3.10 Control Room

The Sinter and Acid control rooms are combined and situated close to the feed end of the machine. A Direct Digital Control computer is used instead of conventional instrumentation on the sinter circuit and a slave console of the computer is located in the control room. Sufficient standard instrumentation is installed to allow the plant to be operated on manual control. Sequential starting and stopping of the system is carried out via a mimic panel of the circuit. Print out from the computer is available at fixed periods or can be brought out continually. Control set points can be altered by the operator as required.

3.11 Electrics

All switch rooms are located at various floor levels below the control room. 415 volt motors are used for less than 100 H.P. drives, whilst the 3.3 kilovolt is used for 100 H.P. and over.

4.1 Sludge Handling and Effluent Treatment Plants

All sludges arising on the smelter are returned to the cooling drum of the Sinter plant. As mentioned previously, these sludges arise from the Acid Plant, Blast Furnace and Sinter Plant.

Acid plant sludge is pumped from the thickening circuit to one of three storage tanks 6 m. diameter x 3 m. high each fitted with a stirrer where it is neutralised by Milk of Lime additions. The neutralised sludge is pumped through a ring main to a Sharples continuous centrifuge located above the cooling drum. A pH indicator is fitted in the ring main to ensure the material is correctly neutralised; should the pH drop, the system is shutdown. An automatic control system introduces the sludge to the centrifuge and controls a water flushing out system should the sinter machine stop. The centrifuge is rated at 120 tons per day of solids and is driven by a 180 H.P. motor. The sludge is dewatered from approximately 33% solids to 70% solids and falls into a worm conveyor which carries it with other sludge to the feed point of the cooling drum. The decanted liquor from the centrifuge is pumped to a 9 m. diameter reactivator where it is treated together with other acid plant effluent with Milk of Lime to precipitate all metallics, and ensure complete neutralisation. The precipitated sludge is returned to the sludge holding tanks mentioned above, whilst the overflow liquor is discarded. The pH of the liquor in the reactivator is automatically controlled. The reactivator is by Boby's and dosing agents are used to encourage floculation and precipitation. Standards of cleansing of the liquors are given in Table III, the average rate of flow liquor being 60 m^3 per hour.

Blue Powder from the furnace is pumped to one of two 23 m. diameter Dorr thickeners where it is thickened to approximately 33% solids. The thickened underflow is pumped continuously by Oliver Diaphragm

TABLE III

Total suspended solids	Not more than 40 mgms/litre
Zinc	Not more than 5 mgms/litre
Cadmium	Not more than 7 mgms/litre
Lead	Not more than 2 mgms/litre
Arsenic	Not more than 7 mgms/litre
Cyanide	Not more than 1 mgms/litre

Clarity of Discharged Liquor Effluents

TABLE IV

Sludge	Dry Tons per day	% H_2O before dewatering	% H_2O after dewatering
Acid Plant Sludge	80	70	33
Blue Powder	47	70	33
Ventilation Sludge	60	70 - 80	33 - 50

Sludges returned to Sinter Cooling Drum as Cooling Media

slurry pumps to one of two 6 m. diameter x 3 m. high storage tanks each fitted with an agitator. The Blue Powder is then circulated in a ring main up to a 12 sq. m. rotary Paxman filter and/or to a dewatering hydrocyclone where the moisture content is reduced to 30% H_2O in the filter cake and 45% H_2O in the underflow of the hydrocyclone. The liquor from the filter is returned to an 18.5 m. diameter Boby reactivator whilst the overflow from the hydrocyclone is returned to the thickener. The dewatered material falls onto the screw conveyor system feeding to the intake point of the cooling drum.

Overflow liquor from the thickener passes to the 18 m. diameter reactivator mentioned above where it is treated with Milk of Lime to precipitate metallics. The precipitate is returned to the thickener, whilst the overflow passes to a spray pond where evaporative cooling reduces the temperature to some 30 - 32°C. Some 80% of this clean water is recirculated to the blast furnace gas washing plant whilst the remaining 20% is bled off and discarded. The purity of the discharge is given in Table III. The liquor flow from the blast furnace to the effluent treatment plant is some 410 m^3 per hour and contains on average some 47 dry tons per day of material.

As mentioned previously, the ventilation sludges are also returned to the cooling drum via a hydrocyclone. Tonnages of sludge returned are detailed in Table IV.

The water balance in the cooling drum controls the amount of dewatering required. The addition of sludges is also used as the means of proportioning these returned sludges.

5.1 No. 4 Imperial Smelting Furnace

The operation of the Blast Furnace as such has been the subject of many papers, references to which are given in this paper, and consequently no special design detail or shaft operating mechanisms will be given of the furnace shaft and condensers. See Figure 4.

5.2 Charge Preparation Plant

The charge to the furnace consists of hot lump sinter, preheated coke, and a small addition of hard burnt lime for slag composition control.

The charge is prepared and fed into 2 of 4 charge buckets mounted on a transfer car. The buckets are hoisted in pairs by the autohoist and charged to the furnace. One pair of the buckets are filling whilst the other pair are travelling to and from the furnace.

Hot lump sinter is delivered into 2 x 600 tons capacity insulated double discharge storage bins. When required, sinter is extracted

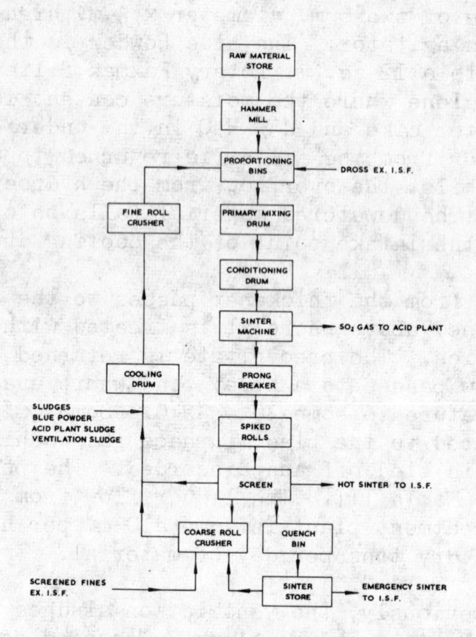

Figure 3 - Flow Sheet of No. 4 Updraught Sinter Plant, No. 4 Smelter Complex, Avonmouth.

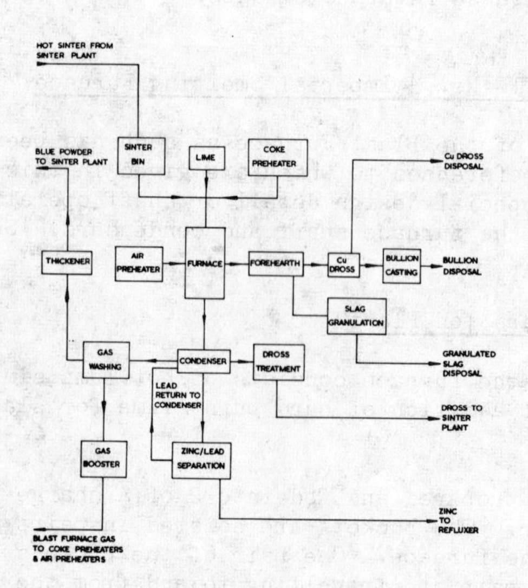

Figure 4 - Flow Sheet of No. 4 Imperial Smelting Furnace, Avonmouth.

at up to 400°C by plate conveyors discharging over 20 m.m. mesh Schenck screens, the oversize passing to weigh hoppers whilst the undersize falls into a 20 ton storage bin from whence it is taken by scraper conveyor and pan conveyor back to the sinter plant. The weight of material required in the weigh hoppers is set from the control room.

Coke of 40 - 90 m.m. sizing and containing 90% fixed carbon is received in 20 ton capacity bottom discharge waggons in 500 ton liner trains and is discharged into an underground feed hopper. A shunting mule is used for handling the wagons. The coke is elevated by conveyor belt to two ready use storage bins each of 200 tons capacity. As required, coke is fed by a Schenck feeder into one of two skip hoists each of which feeds two coke preheaters, a flap switching system controlling which of the preheaters is to receive the charge. The top of the coke preheater must be kept gas tight and this is done by dropping the coke into a space between a slide valve and a bell. The slide is closed before the bell opens and drops the coke into the preheater, the bell then closing. The level in the preheater is controlled by a radioactive detector and source; when there is no detection the coke is above a preset level; when the levels falls, the detector calls for coke.

The coke preheater is a refractory lined shaft containing a column of coke heated by clean Low Calorific Value gas from the furnace, burnt to zero oxygen content in a combustion chamber. The hot products of combustion are mixed with recirculated waste gas from the top of the preheater to control the gas passing into the bottom of the coke column at 800°C. The gas leaving the top of the preheater passes through a water scrubbing tower to remove coke fines and cool the gas before entering the exhaust fan. Most waste gas is put to atmosphere, the remainder circulated to the gas mixing chamber for control of the gas temperature in the mixing chamber. A further control valve in the exit stack keeps the coke preheater at a slight positive pressure to prevent ingress of air. The temperature of coke at fixed positions in the coke column controls the amount of Low Calorific Value gas burnt. When hot coke is required, a gas tight door at the bottom of the preheater is opened, and an extractor roll feeds the coke from the column. The coke drops onto a feeder which delivers into a weigh hopper. The whole sequence is controlled automatically, each operation being sequenced to deliver the correct amount of coke to the weigher. When the correct weight of coke is in the weigh hopper it is discharged via feeders into the rotating charge buckets mounted on the transfer car. The weighed coke from the four coke preheaters is fed to two filling chutes, which match two filling chutes for sinter and lime on the opposite side of the transfer car track. Normally two charge buckets are filled at the same time, but single buckets can be filled, or if one half of the system is out of order, both buckets can be filled from the same point. The time cycle for charging is increased if this is necessary. Hard burnt lime is taken up the coke intake conveyor system and is discharged into the two small bunkers. As required it is weighed out into weigh hoppers and discharged into the charge buckets with the sinter.

The weighers are all fitted with water cooled load cells, and all operations are carried out automatically or semi automatically from the control room situated between the charge preparation section and the furnace. Completely manual operation is also possible but it is slow and cumbersome.

5.3 Charging System

The transfer car has places for four charge buckets which are rotated as the buckets are filled. The transfer car is located for the required positions by proximity switches, the car shunting if necessary for centralising. Solid state switching by Brookhurst Igranic is used for control purposes. When on fully automatic control the system is controlled through the Direct Digital Control Computer, which replaces conventional instrumentation.

At the point of transfer to the autohoist, the car positions with two vacant positions on the transfer car under the hoist. The hoist lowers two empty buckets onto the transfer car which then shunts to position the two full buckets under the hoist. These full buckets are hoisted and once past a preselected height the transfer car moves off for its next load. A Jenny hoist is used for the transfer of buckets to the furnace, i.e. the driving mechanism is fixed and the hoisting and travelling wires hoist the buckets up a guide tower into a travelling carriage which is traversed to the furnace and lowered onto the charging bells.

The furnace charging is carried out through a double bell system. The two buckets lower onto the top of the bells, the top bells opening as the bucket lowers onto a landing ring. The bale carrying the buckets continues to lower allowing the bell forming the bottom of the charge bucket to lower into the top of the furnace bell gear, enabling the charge to discharge into the middle space between the two bells. After a preset time, the hoisting bale lifts the buckets off the landing ring and the top furnace bells close. Once these are closed, the bottom bells are opened with a small delay between each to reduce pressure surges in the furnace and the charge falls into the furnace. The closing of the bells is controlled by timers to ensure the charge has sufficient time to drop clear of the bells. Air cylinders operating at 6 - 7 atmospheres pressure raise the counter weights to enable the bells to open, the counter weights ensuring that the bells always return to the closed position. Air is added to the interbell space except when the bell sequence is taking place to ensure the space is kept at positive pressure in relation to the furnace pressure and that air leakage is always back into the furnace.

5.4 Furnace Operation See Figure 5.

The furnace is the largest size yet constructed I.S.F. with a shaft area of 27.3 m^2 and fitted with 2 x 5.5 m. wide standard condensers each fitted with eight rotors. Detailed descriptions of the shaft operation and mechanisms are described in detail in literature published by Imperial Smelting Processes Limited, the following, however, is a short description of operations.

Some 46,000 m^3 per hour of hot blast air at 800°C and at pressure up to 6,350 m.m. W.G. is blown through twenty water cooled tuyeres into the bottom of the furnace. The coke burns to produce CO_2 + CO, thus providing the heat and reducing agent necessary for melting slag produced and reducing the zinc and lead oxides in the sinter. The reduced lead carrying silver, gold, copper, etc. with it and the slag, pass to the bottom of the furnace and are periodically tapped through water cooled copper blocks into a forehearth. The lead bullion separates to the bottom of the forehearth and runs out through a syphon into a 10 ton capacity lead ladle. The slag runs from the top of the forehearth into a slag granulating launder and so into an elevator pit where the slag separates and is elevated to 2 x 200 ton capacity slag bunkers. The water passes to a settling pond and is then pumped over a cooling tower before being returned to the granulating launders. Full slagging facilities are available at either end of the furnace.

A typical slag composition is:

Zn%	Pb%	Fe%	SiO%	CaO%	Cu%	S%	Al_2O%	MgO%
5-7	0.4-0.8	30-42	16-22	24-30	0.3-0.6	2.5	5.0	1.3

5.5 Condenser and Separation System

The reduced zinc as a vapour passes out of the top of the charge probably around 800°C, where the temperature is increased extremely quickly to around 1000°C, by the injection of preheated air into the area between the top of the charge and the furnace offtakes. The air burns with some of the excess CO present and the increase in temperature reduces the probability of the zinc vapour reacting with CO_2 to revert to zinc oxide. The resultant gases and zinc vapour pass into the lead splash condensers where the gases are quenched by a curtain of lead and reduced to approximately 550°C and at the same time the condensed zinc is absorbed in the hot lead. Each condenser is divided into three stages with four rotors in the first stage, two in the second and two in the third stage, the gas temperature leaving the third stage being about 450°C. Lead at 550°C from the hot end of each condenser runs through an underflow weir forming a gas seal into a pump sump from each of which it is pumped by means of two centrifugal pumps into two lead cooling launders. The cooling launders are made up of a large number of mild steel water jackets enclosed by refractory and steel casing, with a refractory bottom to the launder.

The hot lead with zinc in solution is cooled until the lead becomes saturated with zinc when zinc comes out of solution. The level of metal retained in the launder is controlled by adjustable spades at the end of the launder and the amount of cooling done is controlled by manipulation of the rate of lead pumped through the circuit and the depth of metal retained in the launder. At the discharge of the launder the lead zinc mixture cascades into a flux covered bath, the flux being ammonium chloride, to pick up arsenic contained in the zinc, to remove dross and to reduce oxidation of the metallic zinc. The molten flux layer is removed periodically, broken up and returned direct to the furnace through the bell system, fresh flux being added continuously through a small hopper and screw feeder system. The molten metal mixture passes from the "flux" bath via an underflow baffle into a large separation/liquation bath where the zinc rises to the top of the bath under quiescent conditions and the lead content of the zinc reduces to 1.3% lead. The zinc overflows continuously into a zinc holding and reheat bath, whilst the lead returns at a temperature of about 440°C through an underflow and sealed overflow system back to the cold end (gas exit end) of the condenser. The lead runs by gravity from the feed end of the lead cooling launders back to the condenser, consequently the levels of weirs, etc. through the system is critical. The saturated lead at 440°C contains roughly 2.25% zinc whilst under normal conditions the hot lead leaving the condenser (550°C) contains some 2.5% zinc and as it is unsaturated at this point, mild steel equipment can be used. This means that to produce one ton of zinc, 400 tons of lead must be circulated and consequently to produce the normal furnace output rate of 300 tons of zinc per day, some 120,000 tons of lead per day is circulated through the system. Drosses made in the condenser are removed by dross extractors from the pump sump, and by screw conveyor type dross extractors fitted in the cold end of each condenser. Gas leaves the condenser at approximately 450°C and passes to a Gas Washing Tower where it is completely humidified with recirculated scrubbing liquor and some 40% of the residual fume removed. The gases then pass to Thiessen disintegrators where fresh cold water is added to cool the gas as much as possible, normally to less than 40°C and to give a final gas cleanliness of less than 40mgms. per cubic metre of solids. The cleaned gases from each condenser and Theissen circuit are brought together through a control system which splits the flow of furnace gas equally between each condenser, and which controls the gas pressure throughout the system. The gas with a composition of about 18% CO and 14% CO_2 is passed to a booster fan which increases the gas pressure to 450 m.m. W.G. to allow it to be used for preheating coke and blast air to the furnace. At present, some 50% of the Low Calorific Value gas is used for this purpose, the remainder is discharged to atmosphere. A control system on the Low Calorific Value pressure gas main is used to keep the gas pressure steady, since the requirement of the coke preheaters and cowper stoves varies considerably.

5.6 Main Blower

Blast air to the furnace is provided by a Bryan Donkin Centrifugal blower capable of handling 60,000 m^3 per hour at 6,350 m.m. W.G. driven through a gearbox by a 1450 H.P. motor. The incoming fresh air is passed through an oil filter screen to prevent any dust build up on the fan impellor which could cause out of balance conditions. A blow off to atmosphere valve is provided to prevent surging and overheating conditions on start up. Volume control on the machine is through inlet guide vanes which can be operated from the blower house or from the furnace control room. Special provision has been made to reduce noise level by installation of a silencer pipe in the air line, and to prevent sudden stops by the blower motor due to short voltage drops, the motor overloads have been removed, and a two second delay fitted such that a voltage drop of at least two seconds duration is necessary before the motor cuts out. Two 11 K.V. power lines into the works are provided and all motors of 100 H.P. or over are on 3.3 K.V. supply.

5.7 Cowper Stoves

Two regenerative cowper stoves supplied by Ashmore Benson & Pease 26.0 m. high and 5.1 m. diameter and each containing 200 tons of chequer brick provide the preheat. Dome temperatures in the stoves are at present limited to 1050°C, an ancillary fuel such as oil or natural gas, or preheating of the Low Calorific Value gas is necessary to reach 1150°C. Natural gas pilot lights are used at all times for ensuring ignition of Low Calorific Value gas or of the alternative fuel used, which at present is 250 sec. oil. Flame detectors by Honeywell are fitted and the stoves are interlocked such that Low Calorific Value gas or oil cannot be admitted to the stoves unless the pilot lights are operating. The stoves are at present operating on a 30 minute firing cycle with a 40 minute "on blast" cycle. Changeover of the stoves can be carried out manually, or by semi-automatic or fully automatic systems from the control room. As with all instrumentation on the furnace, fully automatic control is through the Direct Digital Control Computer, but semi-automatic control can be through conventional instruments.

5.8 Soft Cooling Water Circuit

Softened recirculated cooling water is used to the furnace jackets and tuyeres, lead cooling launder jackets, cowper stove valves, furnace dip holes, and blower gearbox. A forced draught cooling tower cools the recirculating water - 2050 m^3 per hour - to some

$40^{\circ}C$ and for constant head feed, the water is pumped by three pumps to a head tank 30 m. above ground level. Circulating water hardness is kept to 50 parts per million total hardness and 1200 parts per million total dissolved solids. Softened water make up is provided from a central softening system on the Complex.

5.9 Compressed Air Services

All plant compressed air, instrument air and breathing air for the Complex is provided from a central compressor house by six Joy-Sullivan two stage compressors with interstage cooling, each capable of delivering 28 m^3 per hour of air at 5.05 atmospheres pressure. The instrument and breathing air is supplied by oil-free compressors, the instrument air being dried to a $-42^{\circ}C$ dewpoint.

5.10 Dross Handling

All drosses from the furnace and refluxer, other than flux bath drosses which are returned direct to the furnace, and furnace accretion, are taken in one ton capacity dross boxes to a dross conditioning plant where they are crushed to - 5 m.m. sizing, conditioned with water and returned to the Sinter plant. The dross boxes are discharged through a rotary tippler fitted with a 150 m.m. grid. All - 150 m.m. material falls onto a scraper conveyor which feeds to a British Jeffrey Diamond hammer mill type crusher. All material feeds from the crusher into an elevator, which feeds a Schenck 5 m.m. mesh vibrating screen. Oversize material returns to the crusher, the undersize falling into a small storage bin from which it is batch fed into a conditioning worm where water is added. The conditioned dross is held in two x 20 ton capacity bunkers until tested for arsine evolution and is then taken back to the Sinter plant in a special container. If arsine is detected the material is held in the ventilated hopper until any reaction is complete. Any large metallics which do not break up are periodically taken out of circuit by a flap at the discharge end of the screen and are fed back to the lead cooling launder inlet boxes or the furnace. The whole of the dross conditioning plant is ventilated by a 17,000 m^3 per hour Doyle scrubber, the sludges from the system being taken to the centralized sludge handling and effluent treatment plant.

5.11 Blue Powder Handling

All dirty liquor from the gas washing towers, theissen scrubbers and ventilation scrubbers is collected in seal tanks under the gas washing towers. Most of the liquor overflows to pump tanks, and dredges in the specially shaped seal tanks move solids which have come out of suspension into a worm classifier, with some of the liquor to remove large particles which may be present. The liquor then overflows into the pump tanks and is pumped by Lee Howl sludge pumps to the blue powder thickeners on the Sludge Handling and Effluent Treatment Plant.

At a zinc production rate of 300 tons per day, carbon burnt is 260 tons per day. At this operating level, dross plus blue powder is produced at approximately 90 tons per day at an assay ranging 35% - 40% lead and zinc.

5.12 Control Room

The centralised control room contains all the control instruments and computer slave console for the plant. It is situated between the furnace shaft and charge preparation system so that operation of the charging system can be seen, at the same time being adjacent to the furnace. The Direct Digital Control computer, an Elliott Arch 2000 Computer with 32,000 word store, handling 96 control loops and scanning 246 plant measurements, is located directly above the control room, the same air conditioning and pressurisation system supplying both rooms. The control room is laid out to group different sections of the plant, the slave console with all alarms, controls, typewriters and mimic panel of the charging system being in the centre of the room. When facing the console, to the left are the semi-auto controls for the cowper stoves, half left front the furnace recorders and manual controls, in front the manual controls for the coke preheaters, half right the weight indicators for the charge preparation systems, and right the mimic panel for the soft and crude water systems. A clear call system is used for communication throughout the plant, all calls having to pass through the control room.

5.13 Crude Water System

Some 80% of the crude water used on the plant is re-used after passing through an effluent treatment plant and cooling pond. The crude water is pumped from the cooling pond to the gas washing towers some 270 m^3 per hour, coke preheaters 46 m^3 per hour and to water cooled moulds on the furnace copper drossing plant 92 m^3 per hour through one of two pumps, the second being a stand-by pump. Some 92 m^3 per hour of fresh cold crude water is added to the theissen disintegrators. The 20% additional crude water overflows from the cooling pond to drain as a steady bleed off. Crude water is also used for emergency slagging water, should the slag water recirculating pump fail during slagging. A pressure switch automatically brings the emergency slagging water into operation.

5.14 Copper Drossing Plant

The ten ton ladles of lead bullion are taken to the copper drossing plant, from the North end of the furnace by crane transfer car and South end crane, from the South end by crane, and tipped into one of four 60 ton capacity lead kettles of prefabricated mild steel. The cranes mentioned are also used for changing forehearths at each end of the furnace. The hot lead is allowed to cool to about 400°C and then stirred with propellor blade stirrers driven by 15 H.P. motors at 250 r.p.m. and treated with sawdust to bring up a fine dry copper dross. The dross is removed by a mechanical shovel - an adapted fork lift truck arrangement - and is eventually shipped to European continental refineries for further treatment. Copper dross assay is about 22% Cu and 58% Pb, but this could be increased to at least 35% Cu by screening to 6 m.m.

After drossing, the bullion is heated and pumped to the casting kettle from which it is pumped to a banjo launder serving 13 water cooled moulds each of one ton capacity. After cooling, the one ton pigs are removed by fork lift truck, weighed, and put to stock for shipment to continental refineries for final refining.

Two or three kettles are used for copper drossing, one kettle is kept as a casting kettle and the fourth kettle can be used for desilverising the bullion with zinc if lead additions to the condenser are required. The silver crusts so produced are returned direct to the furnace shaft.

5.15 Plant Ventilation

Altogether 385,000 m^3 per hour ventilation capacity is provided for the I.S.F. plant, some 85,000 m^3 per hour by three Doyle scrubbers on the charge preparation and dross conditioning plants and the remainder by eight venturi scrubbers. In general, Doyle scrubbers are used for coarse dusts and venturis for fine fume. In both cases as much water as possible is recirculated from circulating tanks, but there is a constant bleed off of dirty liquor to the sludge handling and effluent treatment plant. The pressure drop across the various venturi throats is calculated to give the required scrubbing efficiency and varies from 360 m.m. to 430 m.m.

5.16 Recoveries

Typical recoveries of the No. 4 I.S.F. are:

Zinc metal	92%
Lead in bullion and copper dross	92%
Copper in bullion and copper dross	70%
Silver in bullion and copper dross	92%

Zinc metal produced per ton of carbon burnt = 1.15 tons.

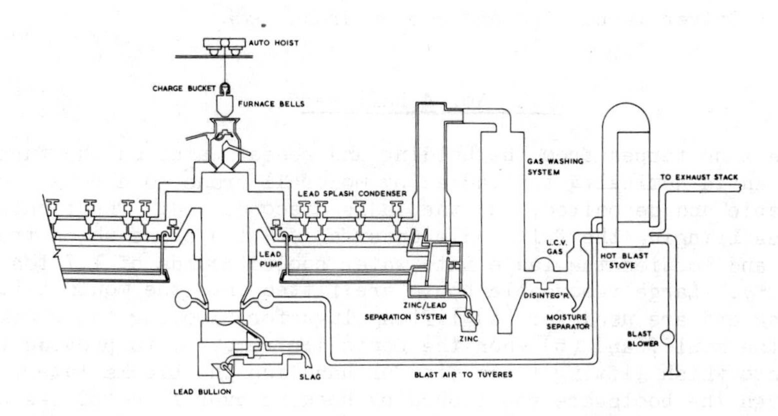

Figure 5 - Layout showing the arrangement of the Furnace Shaft and Condensers, together with Gas and Solids Flow System.

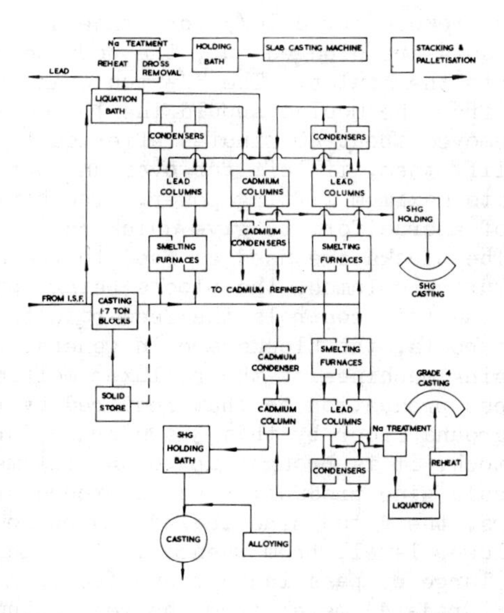

Figure 6 - Flow Sheet of the Metal Handling System on the Zinc Refinery No. 4 Smelter Complex, Avonmouth.

Expected recoveries under full blast operating conditions are:

Zinc metal	93%
Lead in bullion and copper dross	96%
Copper in bullion and copper dross	80%
Silver in bullion and copper dross	98%

6.1 No. 4 Refluxer

The zinc tapped from the holding and reheat baths on the furnace is taken in nominal 4 ton ladles by monorail crane to a rotating turntable and deposited, and the ladle disconnected. The turntable rotates bringing the full ladle under a $7\frac{1}{2}/3$ ton crane which transports and empties the ladle into water cooled moulds of 1.7 ton capacity. Large removeable boots are fitted into the mould before casting and are used for (a) lifting lugs for removing the block from the mould, and (b) when the boots are removed, to provide recesses into which lifting tongs fit for handling the blocks later. Although the boots are positioned by hooking over fixed pieces on top of the mould it is essential to make a clay lute around the edge of the boot to prevent zinc getting in behind the boot and making it difficult to remove from the block.

6.2 Zinc Handling See Figure 6.

The blocks are removed by a 10/3 ton crane and moved to a position where the boots are sledged out, the boot being taken back for refitting into the moulds. The 7/3 ton crane can be used for removing blocks from the moulds should the 10 ton crane break down. If blocks are removed about 40 minutes after casting, little effort is required to lift them, if left for over an hour, the 10 ton crane is required at its maximum lifting power. The bottom of the mould is in the form of a cruciform to give quick cooling in the centre of the block. The blocks are used as feed to the melting baths feeding the refluxing columns, the blocks being lowered and melted at a fixed rate and this controls the feed rate to the column. After removal of boots, the blocks are in general weighed and handled to the charging machines of the refluxer melting baths by a 3 ton crane. Excess production to that required by the refluxer is lowered to the ground floor by this 3 ton crane, or if feed is required from stock, it is brought up to the $11\frac{1}{2}$ metre floor by this crane. Should zinc production be in excess of that required for the refluxers, the 4 ton zinc ladles can be lowered by the $7\frac{1}{2}$ ton crane to a lower level, from whence it is transport by a monorail hoist to a large by pass launder and fed to a liquation bath to join run off (Grade 4) metal from the lead columns of the refinery

6.3 Refluxing Columns

The refinery built to Mechim design consists of six lead and three cadmium columns, arranged four lead and two cadmium in one line, with the other three columns making up the third quarter of a square. Provision is made for the installation of a fourth block of three columns. All columns have trays 1220 m.m. x 610 m.m., the lead columns being of 61 trays, the cadmium columns having 58 trays, including spacer trays in each column. The cadmium condensers are covered externally with insulating brickwork, the lead columns are fitted with moveable shutters for controlling temperature. Insulating bricks are fitted inside the shutters for commissioning of the lead columns and are removed as temperature increases.

The 1.7 ton blocks are weighed and placed on standard Mechim type charging machines ahead of the melting furnaces, a full charging machine containing five blocks, which under normal circumstances is sufficient for four hours. An average rate of feed is 50 tons per day, but the Avonmouth machines can cover a range from 30 - 70 tons per day. The blocks are automatically moved along the charging machine, finally positioning exactly in front of the immersion bath section of the melting bath. An automatic hoist with grab tongs picks up the block, traverse it to the melting bath and lowers it at a predetermined rate into the bath. The automatic control of the charging system is carried out by solid state switching.

The melting bath is a reverberatory type bath with an arched roof 3 m. wide x 4.5 m. long (external measurement with 380 m.m. thick walls) and is fired by a single Schieldrop oil burner. Some 40 kgm. of 3000 sec. fuel oil is used per ton zinc melted to bring the molten zinc temperature to 550 - 570°C. The solid blocks are lowered into a small section of the bath with submerged walls to form a liquid seal between the heated inside and unheated outside well of the bath, and consequently the flame does not impinge on the block, but all melting is done by contact of the block with liquid metal. A certain amount of dross is produced on the bath, and this is removed at intervals. The waste gas from the bath is passed through a metal recuperator for heat recovery by the incoming combustion air. The firing is operated to give a neutral pressure and slightly reducing conditions inside the bath. The rate of lowering of the block controls the rate of melting of the block which in turn controls the rate of overflowing of the bath and so the rate of feed of zinc to the lead column.

The firing of the columns is by 3000 sec. heavy fuel oil, preheated to 95 - 100°C. The oil is stored in three tanks of 160 tons capacity and heated by steam coils to 38°C. Two steam heated pumps, one stand-by for the other, circulate the oil through filters and an electrically traced and lagged ring main to the 11½ m. floor level, where the oil to each individual column is heated in an electrical heater taking the temperature up to 100°C. The oil is then fed via an oil flow meter through insulated pipes to the eight burners on each column. The burners are again of the Mechim drip type design with heated primary air fed with the oil into the burner. An ordinary gate valve is used to control the rate of oil flow which is normally some 12 kgms. per hour per burner. Adjustment of the individual burner and control of its oil flow is critical. The total amount of oil fed to the column is fairly easy to measure but the flow to individual burners to date cannot be measured. The firing of the column and the amount of oil used per burner is critical and is dependant upon the skill of the operator since all burners must be fired eventy. Preheated combustion air is fed to the column through air ports at the top and part way down the column. Products of combustion are taken away from the bottom of the combustion chamber and put through a three pass recuperator for heat recovery. The first two passes of the recuperator are in refractory, whilst the third is in cast iron. Facilities are provided for cleaning of the recuperator tubes. The waste gases pass to a natural draught stack some 55 m. high, the draught and so air to the combustion chamber being automatically controlled by butterfly dampers in the mains between the recuperators and the stack. Sight glasses and lights are also provided in each main to observe any signs of zinc oxide leaving the recuperator. The combustion chambers are fitted with Thermocouples approximately $\frac{1}{4}$ distance down the column and at the base of the column. The aim is to add combustion air at the correct positions to keep the average combustion chamber temperature at a predetermined level, with the minimum temperature gradient between the top and bottom thermocouples, and with 2 - 4% oxygen in waste gases. The average combustion chamber temperature is controlled between 1150 and 1250°C, being increased as the column grows older.

The boil off metal from each pair of lead column condensers feed directly to a cadmium column. Firing is by the same technique as for the lead columns, but temperatures are varied to control the cadmium content of the cadmium zinc alloy from the condenser. This is normally controlled at 7 - 15% cadmium depending upon the amount of cadmium in zinc, it being desirable to always keep not less than a certain minimum of condensate passing into the condenser. This alloy is ladled and cast into special shaped ingots for feeding to a small cadmium refining column.

The run off metal from the first four lead columns is taken to a 100 ton liquation bath for cooling and separation and removal of lead and iron. The bath is partitioned by walls to avoid chanelling and to give maximum retention time of the zinc, thus encouraging best temperature control. The lead coming out of solution in the zinc is removed daily by ladling through a large diameter steel tube immersed through one of the drossing access doors. The lead obtained is cast in one ton ingots and returned to the blast furnace condensers as make up lead. Any zinc taken with the lead is thus recovered through the normal operating channels. Iron is removed as hard metal by ladling from the zinc/lead interface and is cast into 25 kgm. ingots. It is then sold to an associated company for zinc dust production. The assay of this hard metal is approximately 85% Zinc, 2% Iron and 5% Lead.

6.4 Liquation and Arsenic Removal

Metal from the liquation bath overflows at a temperature of approximately 430 - 435°C into a second bath divided into three sections. In the first section the temperature of the metal is increased to 460 - 480°C, in the second section metallic sodium is added for removing arsenic and if necessary antimory from the zinc, in the third section the arsenical dross is removed before the metal overflows into a zinc holding and reheat bath. Approximately 1 kgm. of sodium is used per ton of zinc treated.

6.5 Casting

Zinc in the reheat bath is brought to a temperature of 480 - 500°C and cast either into various shapes of 1 ton, 900 kgm. or 500 kgm. using water cooled moulds, or is cast into 25 kgm. plates on a 160 mould E and J straight line casting machine. Plates are cooled on the machine by water sprays and are discharged into a lowerator which delivers the plates by roller conveyors to an automatic stacking machine. This stacker was built under licence from Vieille Montagne and is pneumatically and hydraulically operated with solid state switching for controlling the movements. The plates are picked up in pairs and moved to the side for stacking on an hydraulically controlled table. As the layers of plates are increased the table is lowered to control levels. When the pallet of plates is completed, the pallet is moved onto a roller conveyor by a hydraulic ram. The pallets are then removed for weighing by fork lift truck and stacked for cooling and strapping; casting rate is up to 16 tons per hour. The large blocks are removed from the moulds by crane and taken for weighing and stacking by fork lift truck, assay of this Grade 4 zinc is 98% Zinc, 1.1% Lead, 0.01% Cadmium and 0.02% Iron.

The Special High Grade metal, generally 99.995% zinc is run into a 20 tons holding bath and is periodically cast into 750 kgm. blocks with the moulds arranged in a semi circle, or is hand cast into 25 kgm. plates as Crown Special Zinc. The 750 kgm. blocks are removed from the water cooled moulds and are stamped, then weighed and stacked using fork lift trucks. Special care is taken to ensure that all blocks are to specification, as this metal is used for die casting.

On the second phase of the refluxer, the Grade 4 metal is treated with sodium before the liquation bath, and the metal is normally cast only into special shaped blocks. If necessary the metal can be taken to the Phase I section for casting by a large transporter and 4 ton ladle.

The special high grade metal on this section is held in a 50 ton holding bath to allow casting on one shift only. The metal can be cast by crane and ladle into 750 kgm. blocks, but is normally cast into 25 kgm. plates on a circular Worswick casting machine. In this case, the zinc is pumped to a travelling and tipping casting bowl and two plates are cast together. The moulds are water cooled and casting rate is 10 tons per hour. Plates falling from the machine discharge onto a metallic conveyor which submerges the plates in a water bath before elevating them to waist level when they are hand stacked. The zinc can be alloyed for casting, and the advantage of this casting machine is that the moulds can be changed in a few hours. On the straight line casting machine it takes many hours to change all the moulds.

Metal is stored in a 10,000 ton capacity metal store and is dispatched by either road or rail. Special 700 ton liner trains with special wagons for easy loading are used for dispatching special high grade metal to the zinc alloy manufacturers for use in die casting.

6.6 Cadmium Refining Column

This is a small column of 72 trays each 410 m.m. x 600 m.m., and is capable of producing up to 300 tons of cadmium per year. If the cadmium loading on the column is low it may be necessary to recirculate cadmium from the condenser to keep the crossover to the condenser open. The combustion chamber temperature is kept at 1130 - 1150°C, and the feed bath metal at 15 - 25% cadmium. The cadmium/zinc alloy ingots from the main cadmium columns are specially shaped to enable them to be fed to the melting feed bath at a constant rate by a low geared motor drive. Run off metal from the bottom of the column is cast into 25 kgm. plates for sale. The condenser metal assays about 98% cadmium and 2% zinc is fed into a heated pot fitted with an agitator. Sodium Hydroxide and Sodium Nitrate is added and the mixture stirred. The caustic slag is removed and sent for leaching with H_2SO_4 and precipitation of the $CdSO_4$ with zinc. The remaining cadmium, some 99.95% purity is cast into ingots and sent for casting into special shapes for sale.

6.7 Ventilation

Ventilation of the plant is provided by four venturi scrubbers each handling 40,000 m^3 per hour. Any fumes collected are returned to the Effluent Treatment plant blue powder thickener and is returned to the Sinter plant.

7.1 No. 4 Acid Plant

7.2 Gas Cleaning

See Figure 7.

The waste gases from the Sinter plant, some 100,000 m^3 per hour normal temperature pressure dry, at 6½% SO_2 and 350°C pass to the Acid plant through a 2.1 m. diameter insulated mild steel main to a 6 m. diameter x 8.2 m. high mild steel lead and acid resistant brick lined humidification tower. They then pass through three venturi scrubbers arranged in parallel followed by cyclonic separators before re-entering a common duct before the wet gas fan. The gas entering the humidifying tower contains some 35 grams per $metre^3$ of dust, mostly lead compound and is scrubbed to 1.0 grams per m^3. The humidification liquor is circulated at 1.4 m^3 per minute and 2.5 atmospheres pressure at a temperature of 52°C to splash plate sprays at the top of the tower. The venturi scrubbing liquor of 0.55 m^3 per minute per venturi and 2.5 atmospheres pressure is passed through strum boxes (rough filters) to splash plate sprays carefully placed at the inlet of the venturi throat. Pressure drop across the venturi throats is 575 m.m. W.G. The run off liquor and sludge returns to a 15 m. diameter thickener constructed in mild steel, lead and acid resistant brick lined for settling of the solids and the liquor returns to the pump tank of the humidifying and venturi scrubber pumps. The rake in the thickener is made in stainless steel.

Gases from the sinter plant are pulled from the machine hood and through the venturi scrubbers by the wet gas fan. To control volume to the Acid plant the dry gas fan situated between the gas drying tower and the converter heat exchangers is set to deliver a constant volume. The wet gas fan controls at constant pressure delivery so that any changes in gas temperature and so adiabatically saturated gas volume do not create pressure surges through the system. The wet gas fan casing is constructed in stainless steel En 58J, with the impellor in Incoloy. The variable speed drive is from a 1050 H.P. motor through a pneumatically operated fluid coupling with the fan capable of developing 825 m.m. W.G. The wet gas fan delivers to a packed gas cooling tower, the delivery into the bottom of the tower being controlled at 25 m.m. W.G.

The gas cooling tower 8.5 m. diameter x 8.5 m. high is packed with stacked rings and irrigated from 6 liquor feed points arranged in circles around the top of the tower. The tower is constructed of steel supported lead and lined with acid resistant bricks. The circulating liquor is indirectly cooled by being passed through shell and tube type liquor coolers, six of these coolers being on the delivery side of the pumps, the remaining three being on the return side from the tower. Cooling water is on the mild steel shell side, circulating liquor being through lead tubes. Gas leaving the cooling tower is maintained at 45°C, by varying the amount of cooling water to the liquor coolers to prevent lead sulphite precipitating to the packing

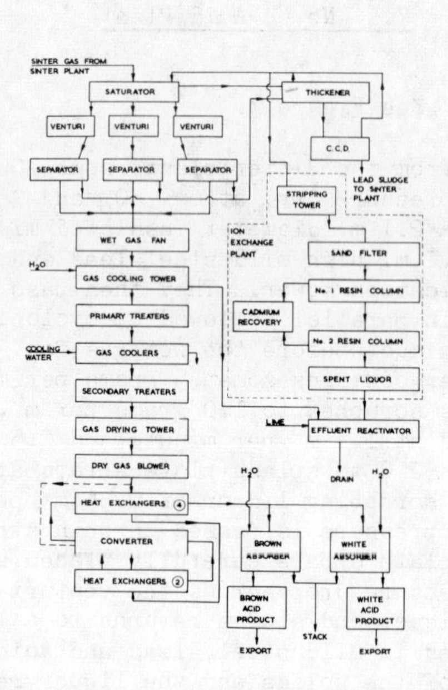

Figure 7 - Flow Sheet of the Acid Plant & Cadmium Recovery Plant, No. 4 Smelter Complex, Avonmouth.

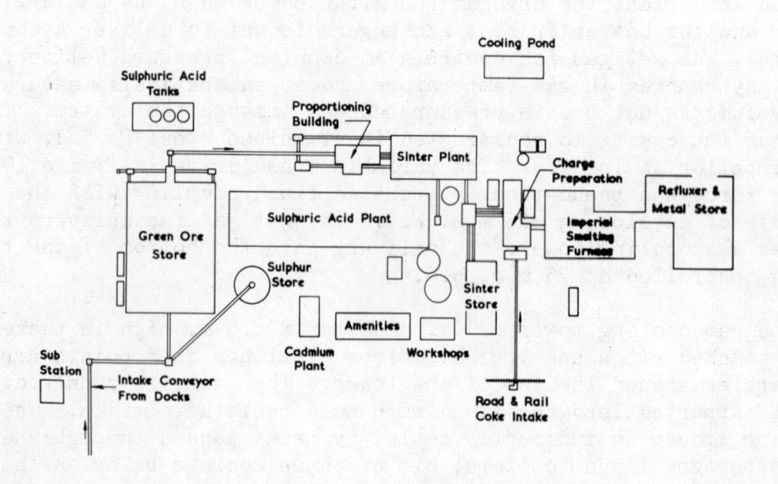

Figure 8 - Schematic Layout of the No. 4 Smelter Complex, Imperial Smelting Corporation (N.S.C.) Limited, Avonmouth.

rings. Additionally, some 900 m^3 per day of softened water is added to the top of the cooling tower to reduce concentrations of lead sulphite, and of fluorine passing on to the converter system.

Water evaporated in the gas in the humidification tower is also condensed in the cooling tower so that the total bleed off of liquor from this part of the circuit is approximately 0.83 m^3 per minute. This liquor is used as make up to the humidifying tower and venturi scrubber circuit, the excess is pumped to the 9 m. diameter acid reactivator on the effluent treatment plant for neutralisation and precipitation of any metals which may be dissolved or carried in suspension.

Some 0.65 m^3 per minute of liquor from the humidifying tower and venturi scrubber circuit is pumped to an SO_2 stripping tower and hence to sand filtration tanks before being passed through Ion Exchange columns for recovery of liquor soluble cadmium.

All spent liquor passes directly to the 9 m. diameter reactivator for neutralisation, from the gas cooling tower the gas at 45°C and a suction of 40 m.m. W.G. passes to three rectangular shaped first stage electrostatic precipitators. These are constructed of lead each oontaining 172 x 255 m.m. diameter tubes 3.9 m. long with an applied potential of 40 k.v. Plastic mesh under the tubes assists gas distribution. Automatic isolation and washing of the treaters is installed, softened water being used for the washing and this, together with treater drips, is collected in a sump tank from which it is pumped to the 15 m. diameter thickener. The gas is then passed through lead constructed interstage hairpin coolers the gas passing around the outside of the tube bundles of lead pipe with softened closed circuit cooling water in the tubes. The amount of water used is controlled by a temperature recorder controller which keeps the outlet gas temperature at 34°C. This avoids rapid fluctuations in the balanced drying tower/absorber acid strength control systems. Leaving the coolers, the gas then passes to three second stage electro-static precipitators of the same size and construction as the primary precipitators. Automatic isolation and washing is not installed, manual control being used. The gas leaving these precipitators is free of mist and optically clear through a distance of 10 metres. Suction at this point is some 305 m.m. W.G. with a safety suction seal set at 380 m.m. W.G. between the second stage precipitators and the inlet of the gas drying tower. All gas and liquor ducts and lines and the venturi scrubber separators are made of P.V.C. reinforced with fibre glass. These have proved very satisfactory when properly designed for the conditions under which they operate.

7.3 Drying System

The gas drying tower is a mild steel acid resistant brick lined tower 7.2 m. diameter x 8.6 m. high containing 5.3 m. of random packed ceramic rings. Distribution of 96% drying acid is by a series of cast iron troughs 0.43 m. high x 0.39 m. wide with distributing pipes 0.69 m. long down into the packing, thus leaving 0.36 m. of dry packing to prevent acid droplet carryover. Altogether some 464 distribution points are fitted. Each distribution point has been fitted with a 75 m.m. high insert to prevent small pieces of dirt and ceramic from entering the distribution pipes. Some 15.6 tons per minute of 94 - 96% drying acid is circulated by two Kestner pumps each driven by 80 H.P. motors through cast iron mains and 6 m.m. filters before entering the distribution troughs in the tower. Hindle cast iron ball valves are fitted in the line to control flow rates. Acid leaves the tower at approximately 56°C and is cooled in 76 m.m. diameter cast iron coolers before returning to the brick lined mild steel circulating tank. A syphon effect is used to improve the pressure head forcing acid through the coolers, but a by pass is fitted from the bottom of the tower to the circulating tank, to prevent build up of acid in the bottom of the tower should excess acid be circulated. Acid return temperature is approximately 45°C. Acid strength is controlled by a Leeds & Northrup conductivity probe fitted at the inlet of the acid coolers. The control probe calls for brown absorber acid as required to maintain the required strength. To control acid levels a pump tank level indicating controller actuates a control valve in a cross bleed line from the delivery of one of the drying tower pumps back to the brown acid absorber pump tank. A small side stream of drying acid also flows to the brown acid product dilution system under he action of a flow indicating controller, the set point of which is automatically adjusted by a similar brown acid flow indicating controller (cascade flow control) to produce product acid at 96%. Dry quench air for control of converter temperatures, some 10,000 m^3 per hour, is dried in a small tower 2.1 m. diameter x 8.6 m. high of similar construction to the gas drying tower. A bleed of 1.1 tons per minute of 94 - 96% acid is taken from the drying acid pumps and it returns direct to the drying acid pump tank. The air is forced through the tower and converter by a fan giving 1,000 m.m. W.G. driven by a 75 H.P. motor.

7.4 Main Blower

This is a 3,000 r.p.m. Davidson fan driven through a fluid-drive variable speed coupling by a 1650 H.P. 3.3 k.v. motor. It is capable of handling 133,000 m^3 per hour at a back pressure of 2485 m.m. W.G. The fluid coupling is set to control at a fixed volume taken from a venturi in the gas main to the gas drying tower. From the outlet of the drying tower through the conversion and absorption system mild steel ducting is used but insulated as necessary, i.e. from first heat exchangers to absorber tower. The plant exit stack 93 m.m. high is made of P.V.C. reinforced with fibre glass.

7.5 Conversion System

Approximately 85% of the gas leaving the dry gas blower is passed through four primary heat exchangers (2 x 2) in parallel where the temperature is raised to 320°C and then through two intermediate heat exchangers in parallel before entering the first stage of the converter. Temperature entering the converter is a minimum of 370°C, the biting temperature of the vanadium catalysts used on the first bed, bed 1A, is normally in the range 430 - 450°C. The heat exchangers are all shell and tube type, the SO_2 gas always being on the shell side. The primary exchangers are each fitted with 2,000 tubes of 43 m.m. diameter and 5.3 m. long. The secondary exchangers contain 1,840 tubes each 41 m.m. diameter and 5.3 m. long.

The converter is recognised as a four stage converter consisting of five catalyst beds 1A and 1B comprising the first stage. Beds 2, 3 and 4 comprising the other three stages. The vessel is 11.2 m. diameter x 9.25 m. high, brick lined around each catalyst bed, and the steel shell is aluminised. Some 150,000 litres of Imperial Smelting Corporation (N.S.C.) Limited Vanadium Catalyst is distributed through the converter as follows:

Bed No.	Litres of Catalyst	Depth of Catalyst
1A	25,800	28 c.m.
1B	21,000	23 c.m.
2	39,000	43 c.m.
3	24,000	27 c.m.
4	40,200	43 c.m.

The preheated gas passes through bed 1A where the temperature is increased to approximately 560°C. Cold gas, some 15% of the total is added and mixed between beds 1A and 1B so that the gas temperature entering bed 1B is some 490°C. Gas leaves bed 1B at approximately 530°C before entering the secondary heat exchangers, where it is cooled by the incoming gas to 450°C, before entering the bed 2. Dried quench air is added between beds 2 and 3 and beds 3 and 4 so that the gas is cooled to 430°C and 420°C respectively. The gas leaves the converter at 420 - 425°C passing through the primary heat exchangers and reaches the absorbers at a temperature of about 170 - 190°C. Plans are in hand for admitting some cold gas between catalyst bed 1B and the inlet of the secondary heat exchangers to keep temperatures down to reasonable levels. Conversion efficiency is better than 98%.

7.6 Absorption System

The absorption system comprises two separate towers, one tower capable of taking full gas flow and making all product acid as brown acid, and one smaller tower capable of taking 20% of the gas flow and producing 20% of the product acid as clean white acid. If gas strengths are low and gas temperatures excessively high, it can be necessary to make all output as brown acid to keep final product strength at 96% acid.

The brown acid absorber tower has the same dimensions as the drying tower and acid distribution is by the same means. The white absorber tower is 8.5 m. high by 3.4 m. diameter and packed with random packed ceramic rings to a height of 5.25 m. Distribution of acid is by the same means as for the other towers.

Circulating acid at 60°C is pumped by two Kestner pumps at 960 tons per hour over the brown absorber tower where absorption of the SO_3 gas increases the acid temperature to 80°C and reduces the waste gas exit temperature to 70°C. The circulating acid is cooled in 26 banks of 14 x 9.75 m. long pipes of 76 m.m. diameter and acid strength is controlled partially by the cross bleed of drying acid and by the addition of water to a dilution pot situated ahead of the acid coolers. A Leeds & Northrup conductivity probe situated in the acid pumping line to the tower controls the circulating acid strength and controls the water addition to the dilution pot.

A similar system is used in the clean acid absorber system, where water only is added for dilution purposes. For cooling, some 8 banks of 14 x 9.75 m. long x 76 m. diameter cast iron coolers are used. Some 208 tons per hour of circulating acid are passed over this tower. The exit gases from both systems are put to atmosphere via the 93 m. high P.V.C. fibre glass reinforced exit stack.

All acid is produced at 96% strength and is controlled in the case of the brown acid by dilution with drying acid and in the case of clean acid by the addition of water. A bleed is taken from the delivery of the pumps set in the circulating lines controls the amount of dilution addition. The product acid is cooled and held in product tanks from which it is pumped to the main acid storage tanks. Level controllers in the product tanks ensure safe working at all times.

7.7 Acid Storage

Three tanks each of 4000 tons capacity, normally two for brown acid and one for white acid, make up the bulk storage. All brown acid is used for the production of Phosphoric acid, whilst the clean acid is sold outside the Company.

8.1 Cadmium Plant

Cadmium is volatilised from the sinter machine as the sulphide, oxide or chloride and consequently a proportion of it is soluble in weak sulphuric acid, such as the scrubbing liquor in the gas scrubbing system. Concentrations in the liquor are normally kept at 1 - 2 grams per litre by bleeding some 0.65 m^3 per minute of liquor to a stripping tower 1.13 m. diameter x 13.3 m. high packed with 25 m.m. diameter polypropylene Pall rings, and is stripped of SO_2 by air pulled through the tower at the rate of 680 m^3 per hour by the acid plant wet gas fan. The liquor is then passed through one of two sand filters to remove any solids before it passes through two ion exchange columns each filled with 68 m^3 of high capacity amberlite base exchange resin of the sulphonated polystrene type acting in the sodium form in which heavy bivalent metals such as lead, zinc and cadmium are exchanged for sodium on the resin. The columns can be run singly or in series depending upon the regeneration cycle. When regeneration is taking place, the remaining column is working singly, when regeneration is complete the fresh unit trails the first column until the first column becomes exhausted, and required stripping and regeneration. The barren liquor leaving the columns is pumped to the effluent treatment plant and so to drain.

The stripping and regeneration of the exhausted column is by pumping a 15% brine solution through the column. The cadmium chloride so produced is then precipitated by sodium carbonate to produce cadmium carbonate plus sodium chloride. The cadmium carbonate is filtered off and the filtrate (brine solution) is recovered for regeneration of the exchange columns. The cadmium carbonate is then taken up in solution by sulphuric acid to produce cadmium sulphate in a solution containing 75 - 100 grams per litre of cadmium. This solution is then taken to another section of the Works Site for precipitation of cadmium by tromelling with zinc in the normal manner. The regeneration and changeover of the columns is entirely automatic or can be operated by manual control.

9.1 Water Softening Plant

The water softening plant serves the whole of the Complex and is capable of softening some 150 m^3 per hour. Towns water is supplied from a break head tank to alkaliminator units which are pressure vessels containing a selective ion exchange resin. The resin removes the temporary or bicarbonate hardness by taking out the calcium and magnesium ions of the bicarbonate. The resin is regenerated by treatment with sulphuric acid and the calcium and magnesium ions removed as sulphates in the waste products. Water from the alkaliminators is passed to a degassifier tower packed with ceramic rings where the CO_2 formed by breaking down of carbonic acid is displaced by a counter current air flow.

The permanent hardness is removed by passing the degassified water through a high capacity ion exchange resin where the calcium and magnesium ions are replaced by sodium ions which form non scaling sodium salts. These columns are regenerated by a brine solution with waste products being put to drain.

10.1 Plant Layout

A block plan of the Smelter Complex is shown in Figure 8.

11.1 Staffing

The Complex acts primarily as a self-contained Smelter with its own canteens, changerooms, offices and workshops. Some 450 craftsmen and process operators, together with 60 staff personnel run the Complex

References

1. S. W. K. Morgan, "The Production of Zinc in a Blast Furnace." Transactions of the Institution of Mining & Metallury, Vol. 66 1956/57. Pages 553 - 565. Vol. 67 1957/58. Pages 127 - 138.

2. S. W. K. Morgan and S. E. Woods, "Avonmouth Zinc Blast Furnace Demonstrates Its Versatility." Engineering and Mining Journal. Vol. 159. 1958. Pages 95 - 99.

3. S. E. Woods and D. A. Temple, "The Present Status of the Imperial Smelting Process." Paper presented at 36th Technical Session of the 8th Commonwealth Mining & Metallurgical Congress, Surfers Paradise, Queensland, Australia. 24th March, 1965.

4. W. Massion, A. Adami and H. Maczek, "I.S.F. Plant and Operation at Berzelius Smelter Duisburg." Presented at the Annual Meeting of the A.I.M.E., New York City, 28th February, 1968.

Chapter 22

IMPERIAL SMELTING FURNACE OF PENARROYA
Noyelles-Godault, France

Jean Bonnemaison, Production Manager

Michel Defonte, Superintendent Zinc Sintering

Albert Lefaucheux, Superintendent Zinc Furnace
Societe Miniere & Metallurgique de Penarroya

Abstract

Societe Miniere & Metallurgique de Penarroya Noyelles-Godault works are located in the northern part of France. The complex includes a lead smelter, a zinc smelter, shops for production of manufactured products and all necessary general services.

The zinc smelting complex described in this paper was designed in 1959 to replace an old horizontal retort distillation furnace and was first operated in May 1962. It includes:

- a sinter plant producing the zinc sinter for the Imperial Smelting furnace : zinc, lead and bulk zinc-lead concentrates are sintered on a Dwight-Lloyd machine with a working area of 80 sq.m. Cadmium sludges are treated by the wet method in a separate plant for recovery of cadmium. Sulphur di-oxide contained in gases goes to a gas washing tower and is subsequently made into sulphuric acid in a plant with a capacity of 550 m.t. per day.

- a smelting plant where the process developed by Imperial Smelting Processes Ltd. is applied : the blast furnace which was modified in 1967 has an area of 17.5 sq.m. at the tuyeres level and a section of 24 sq.m. at the top of the shaft. It has a theoretical zinc capacity of 100,000 m.t. per annum. Air blast is heated by means of cowpers up to the theoretical temperature of 950°C.

Zinc produced is either directly cast into slabs for sale as standard 'good ordinary brand' zinc, or sent to a refining plant where the New Jersey process designed to produce 'special high grade' zinc is in application. Mixes of zinc containing various amounts of lead, cadmium or aluminum are prepared to customer specification in a mixing plant.

Introduction

In 1920, the Penarroya Company which had been previously established in Spain, bought the Noyelles-Godault plant from the Malfidano Company. This plant, built in 1894, was almost completely destroyed during World War I. It consisted of a zinc smelting plant (horizontal retort furnaces) and a small lead blast furnace.

Penarroya rebuilt the plant and completed it :

In 1921, with a plant for lead pipes and lead sheets.
In 1923, with a zinc rolling mill.
In 1924, with a lead shot tower.
In 1925, by restarting the zinc smelting plant with a yearly output of 15 000 tons of GOB..
In 1936, with a lead smelting plant having a yearly output gradually raising to 110 000 tons of lead and 250 tons of silver.

In 1957, the low profitability of the zinc plant and the increasing market requirements compelled the Company to erect a large production unit.

Selection went to the Imperial Smelting Process which had recently been developed. This method, compared to an electrolytic plant, allows the treatment of poorer concentrates, also of lead-zinc bulk concentrates, and this was all the more interesting since a lead refining plant already existed. Finally, a feasibility report showed promising results.

The choice of the site was dictated by the availability of a communication network in the center of a high consumption district, by the proximity of coking plants and by the existence at Noyelles-Godault of a lead smelting plant making it possible to exchange by-products between the two plants so as to valorize metals contained. Finally, the lead refining plant output could easily be increased to 145 000 tons of soft lead and so treat the lead bullion produced by the new zinc smelting unit.

The plant is located on the Deule canal providing rapid inter-communication with the ports of Dunkirk, Ghent and Antwerp where the concentrates are discharged.

A private rail junction connects the plant with the french national railways which are particularly dense in this district. The plant also is 2 kilometers from an access to the Paris-Lille highway which will soon be extended to Dunkirk and Brussels.

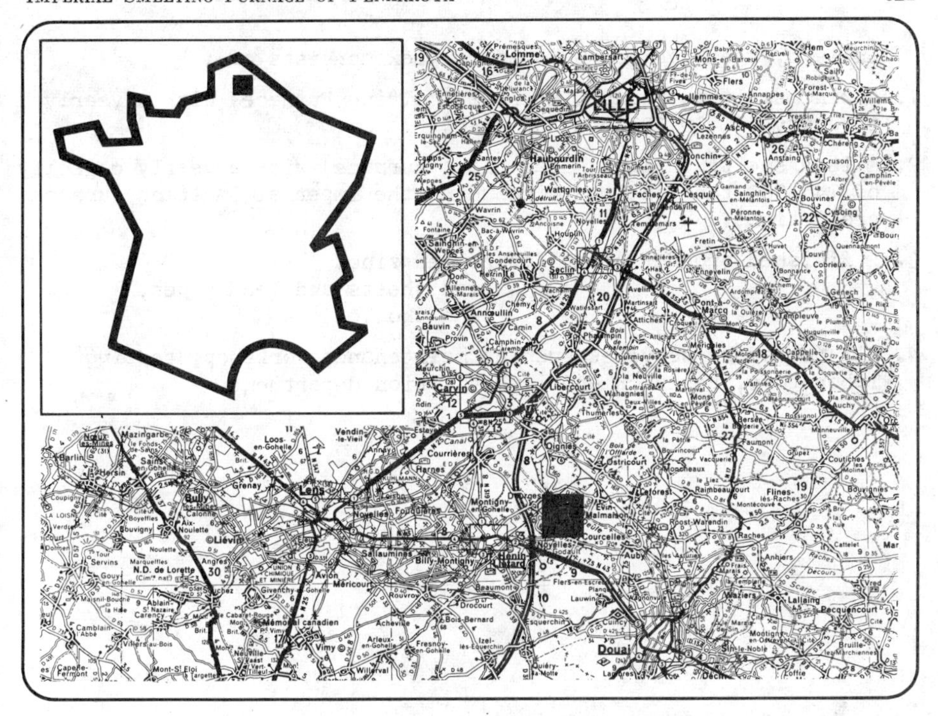

Location of the Noyelles-Godault Plant

The zinc smelting plant receives its concentrates from different countries in the world, mostly from Canada, South America and Africa. European supplies are scarce, Germany and France supplying between them less than ten per cent of the requirements.

The concentrates received are zinc blendes, galena, sulphide or oxide bulk zinc-lead concentrates and also oxidized zinc concentrates.

The 72 000 tons of coke size 40/90mm necessary in 1970 will come from the Drocourt coking plant located a few kilometers from Noyelles-Godault.

Power is supplied through a 90 000 volt network and the plant is equipped with its own transformer sub-station providing the 5 500 V current necessary for the heavy duty motors and the 380 V current for other industrial requirements.

There are two gas supplies : coke oven gas at 4 200 kcal/m^3 and natural gas at 8 000 Kcal/m^3 from Groningen (Netherlands). A feeder passing near the plant supplies the new installations.

Crude water is drawn from the canal by two pumping stations of 1000 m^3/h and 1 500 m^3/h capacity respectively. In warm weather, cooling water is pumped at +15°C from three pits of a total capacity of 300m^3 of water per hour.

In 1970, the Noyelles-Godault complex consists of :

1. A zinc smelting plant (Imperial Smelting Furnace) with a yearly capacity of 100 000 tons of zinc.
2. A lead smelting plant (lead blast furnace) with a yearly capacity of 145 000 tons of lead (including the Imperial Smelting furnace production).
3. A finished product plant for rolled zinc,
   lead sheets and lead pipes,
   lead shot.
4. All necessary services such as maintenance workshop, testing laboratory, research and investigation department.

The Imperial Smelting Furnace at Noyelles-Godault

EVOLUTION OF THE ZINC SMELTING PLANT

DESIGN CHARACTERISTICS

Initially the unit was meant to have a yearly zinc output of 35 000 tons corresponding to the burning of 94 long tons of carbon (95.5 metric tons) per 24 hours. This was at the time of the standard designed Imperial Smelting furnace.

The following installations were erected :

1. A green ore covered store of 15 000 t capacity equipped with an overhead travelling crane.
2. A Dwight Lloyd sinter plant equipped with a 55 m^2 area updraught machine producing 350 tons of sinter (45 % Zn and 20 % Pb) per 24 hours.
3. An I.S.F. charge preparation system consisting in three coke preheaters, four sinter bunkers and two auxiliary bunkers for addition of small loads of drosses, limestone, fluorine materials.
4. An Imperial Smelting furnace of the 94 long tons of carbon per day type (with an area of 11 m^2 at the tuyères) equipped at the bottom end with two rows of water jackets. The condensation system consisted in two condensers according to the technique initially adopted.

The blower could supply the furnace with 24 000 m^3/h of air N.T.P. at the absolute pressure of 1.446 atm.

The blast was heated up to 650°C within a preheater equipped with a metallic network.

Finally, to complete the unit, a plant for the recovery of SO_2 from the sinter plant gases was erected, where sulphuric acid at 78 % and 98 % SMH is produced by the contact process, the catalyser being of the vanadium type.

Plant output : 200 tons SMH per 24 hours from 32 000 m^3/h N.T.P. of gas containing 6.5 per cent of SO_2.

EVOLUTION OF THE CAPACITY

The furnace was started on May 16, 1962.

Right from the very beginning it appeared that the plant output could be superior (45 000 tons of zinc in 1964) and that with minor modifications this output could be increased to 100 000 tons of zinc in 1970 to meet the requirements of the french market.

The following modifications or additions were made :

Green Ore Storage - A second covered store, identical to the first one, was erected equipped with an overhead crane, thus increasing the concentrate storage capacity to 30 000 tons.

Sinter plant - The machine was lengthened by 10 meters increasing the grate area to 80 m^2 and some of the auxiliary equipments (belt, conveyor, crushers) were replaced. This, together with improved techniques makes it possible to prepare the sinter corresponding to the 100 000 tons of zinc.

Furnace - The I.S.F. charge preparation system was not modified. The furnace shaft was redesigned and its cross-section finally increased to 16.18 m^2 at tuyère level.

Most of the water jackets were eliminated and the shaft made of 30 mm thick plating, according to the principles in use in the steel industry (external water trickling).

The number of tuyères was reduced by half to improve draught penetration and burning of the coke into CO.

To take into account the increased gas rate, the condenser cross section was increased and the cooling launders dimensioned accordingly.

At first, a new 40 000 m^3/h (N.T.P.) blower, with an absolute pressure of 2.1 atm. was installed. At a second stage, a turbine was installed and coupled to a fan providing 55 000 m^3 of air per hour at an absolute pressure of 2.3. atm.

The boiler is fuelled with blast furnace gas.

Cowper stoves are now used to heat the blast. They provide a temperature of 950°C at the bustle main by heating the combustion air of the cowper burner. A temperature of 1 050°C is reached by heating both the combustion air and the blast furnace gas before their entering the cowper burner.

Finally, a refining plant was installed to meet the increasing market requirements for special high grade zinc. This refining unit consists in eleven New Jersey type columns and has an annual output of 100 000 tons of SHG.

A new sulphuric acid plant was erected for the recovery of the SO_2 gas in the sinter gases. Though erected on the same principle as the previous one, its characteristics differ : 340 tons of SMH per 24 hours from 53 500 m^3/h N.T.P. of gas at 6 per cent SO_2.

The refrigeration section was however designed to cater for gases at 8 per cent SO_2.

A description will now be given of the two main plants :

1. The sinter plant for mixed zinc and lead concentrates.
2. The Imperial Smelting Furnace (I.S.F.)

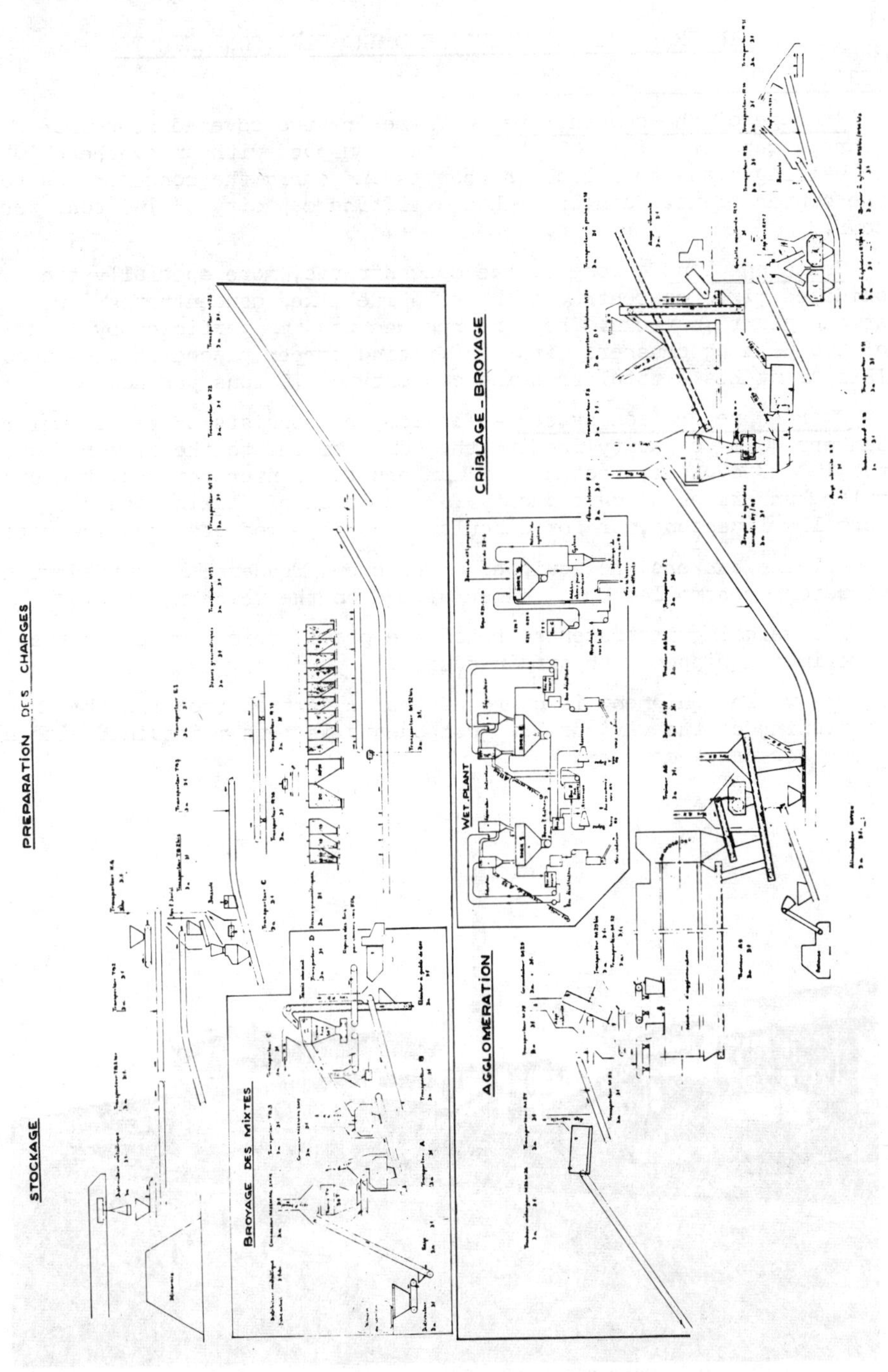

Sinter Plant Flow-sheet

SINTER PLANT FOR MIXED LEAD AND ZINC CONCENTRATES

DESCRIPTION OF THE EQUIPMENT

Storage of the concentrates - There are two covered stores of a storage capacity of 15 000 tons each, equipped with an overhead travelling crane to unload the barges and carry the concentrates to the sinter plant. Each crane has a lifting capacity of 100 tons per hour.

Crushing plant - Some of the concentrates, more specially the oxidized mixed concentrates and sulphide mixed concentrates arrive at the plant in rocks. They are reduced to 4 mm particles by means of two Hazemag crushers with a vibrating screen placed between them. This plant has a total crushing capacity of 10 tons per hour.

Charge preparation system - The complex consists of ten circular bunkers 40 m^3 capacity feeding the concentrates to the sinter plant, two 100 m3 capacity rectangular bunkers for sinter returns, two circular bunkers of 40 m^3 capacity for addition of fluxing agents, normally limestone, or for circulation of by-products at a low rate.

All the bunkers are equipped with Schenk feeders and fitted with vibrators controlled by a feeler placed on the weighing belt.

The weighing instruments are of the gravimetrical type and are sometimes equipped with strain gauges.

The whole equipment is operated from a control room and the proportioning of the various load components is thus maintained within $\pm$ one per cent accuracy.

External view of the sinter plant

Mixing and moisturizing - Our efforts have been directed towards a full pelletisation of the charge so as to obtain a coating of the concentrates on the sinter return particles which already exist in the charge.

The rolling of fine materials into the shape of granules allows the improvement of certain qualities of a charge fed to a sintering machine. These are :

a. Less resistance to the passage of gas streams.
b. Less dust entrainment.
c. Increase in bulk density.
d. Homogeneous distribution of the blast air, thus completely eliminating preferential draughting.
e. Better heat transfer during sintering.
f. Improved mechanical strenght of the pellets.

Until 1966, rolling was carried out in a mixing drum 6m long, 2½m diameter fitted with a water pipe and a paddle-shaft in order to accelerate the discharge of material and to improve mixing.

With the increase in throughput this drum did not work efficiently, resulting into abnormal sintering operations due to frequent variations of blast pressure. This brought about a permanent shifting of the breakthrough point. The pelletising disk was therefore installed at the end of 1966. This is an automatic screening equipment. In effect it only discharges pellets which escape from the centrifugal forces because of their weight and overflow in normal fashion from the disk.

The disk favours compaction of the pellets; the moisture has a tendency to return to the surface which helps the coating of fine particles remaining at the exit of the mixing drum. This is the reason why we do not add any more water at the disk pelletiser. This disk, designed originally for a tonnage of 100 tons/h, must now handle a tonnage of 160-190 tons/h. Also have we attempted to increase the throughput of the mixing drum. The paddle has been completely removed. The water pipe has been replaced by a pipe fitted with sprays which are arranged so that the water is sprayed on to the material cascading in the drum.

This gives four undoubted advantages :

a. We no longer have build-up in the drum.
b. The life of the scrapers has been tripled or quadrupled.
c. The rubber drum discharge belt conveyor no longer suffers any wear following these simple modifications.
d. The feed at the drum exit is already quite well pelletised.

All the water required to moisturise the feed is now introduced in the drum and the moisture content, although indicated in the control room, is controlled manually according to the windbox pressure.

The following table indicates the improvement of the physical quality of the charge treated at Noyelles-Godault.

Evolution of size fractions

0-1mm	1-2mm	2-3mm	3-5mm	Above 5 mm	Porosity test	Grain as percentage
Disk pelletiser discharge						
0.8	5.6	13.4	53.5	26.7	132	30
0.9	4.6	15.6	44.5	34.4	136	32
1.2	7.1	16.9	48.8	26	145	34
Mixing drum discharge						
3.8	9.8	17.2	48.4	20.8	190	
5.8	11	19.1	39.6	24.5	198	
10.9	15.2	13	41	19.9	220	

This obvious improvement of the porosity test obtained by using a disk pelletiser results in much lower windbox air pressures on the sinter machine despite an increase in total bed depth to 34 cm and a draught intensity of the order of 16 m^3/m^2 per min.

Frequently we record pressures less than 200 mm despite an elevated sulphur tenor in sinter machine feed of the order of 7-7.5 per cent.

The advantages of this technique of feed preparation guarantee a uniform operation with a more localised breakthrough point and we think that this is the overriding factor which has permitted us to stop all weak gas recirculation at Noyelles-Godault while maintaining good technical efficiency.

Sinter machine feeding - The disk pelletiser discharges the feed on to a reversible conveyor which feeds alternately one of the two sinter machine feed hoppers via two reversible shuttle conveyors working at right angles to the machine axis. Thus all charge segregation, all unwanted piling-up of feed by means of short drops and all breakdown of the pelletised charge is avoided.

Lurgi type updraught sinter machine

Width	2.5 m
Number of pallets	89 (1 m x 2.5 m)
Number of rows of bars per pallet	3
Number of bars per row	120
Area of ignition windbox area	2.5 m^2
Number of windboxes	16
Updraught area	16x5=80 m^2

Hood for recovery of sulphur dioxide rich gases. This element is partly internally lined with refractory to protect the metal against high temperatures during sintering.

Sintering Machine

Fan characteristics

Ignition fan	volume 160 Nm^3/mn at 208 mm wg 200°C max.
Fresh air fan 1	volume 450 Nm^3/mn at 500 mm wg
Fresh air fan 2	volume 450 Nm^3/mn at 500 mm wg
Fresh air fan 3	volume 800 Nm^3/mn at 520 mm wg 250°C max
Howden type rich gas fan	volume 600 Nm^3/mn at 775 mm wg 350°C max.
Berry type rich gas fan	volume 700 Nm^3/mn at 1050 mm wg 325°C

Machine discharge and Sinter crushing - The hot sinter falls on to a prong breaker which crushes the sinter by revolving between a grid in which the metal bars are separated by 200 mm. Sinter falls into a hopper which feeds a drag link conveyor. This is fitted with a 30 mm bar screen to reduce the load on the spike rolls crusher.

Screening and crushing of returns - The -30 mm fines and the lump sinter crushed to less than 110 mm are conveyed by a drag link conveyor and then by a metallic pan conveyor which feeds a double-deck screen.

Top deck	30 mm screen cloth
Bottom deck	20 mm screen cloth

The +30 mm fraction is conveyed to the blast furnace sinter bunkers.

The 20 to 30 mm fraction is crushed by a corrugated rolls crusher.

The -20 mm fraction recombines with the crushed 20-30 mm fraction and is fed into the cooling drum by a vibrating conveyor.

The cooling drum, 6 m long x 2½ m diameter serves to quench and cool the returns by mixing them with the sludges from the SO_2 rich gases and the blast furnace gases.

The cooled returns are conveyed by a rubber belt to two smooth rolls crushers where they are reduced to -5 mm.

Crusher characteristics :

Spiked roll crusher	diameter	1 400 mm
	width	1 250 mm
Corrugated rolls crusher	diameter	1 200 mm
	width	800 mm
Two smooth rolls crusher	diameter	1 500 mm
	width	1 000 mm

Rich gas cleaning - The sulphur dioxide rich gas is washed in two Pease Anthony scrubbers. Each unit comprises :

a. A saturator - an empty tower into which is sprayed 80 m^3 of water per hour.

b. A venturi throat - fitted with spray nozzles through which the flow, varying from 25 to 80 m^3/h, allows the control of the pressure drop.

c. A separator - an empty tower fed tangentially at its base to separate the liquid phase from the gas.

d. A thickener, 15 mm diameter, in which are extracted the thick sludges and clean water is recycled to the washing circuit.

e. Pumps for conveying the liquids.

The whole installation is either made of stainless-steel or of leaded steel lined with carbon tiles to prevent corrosion by fluoride components.

The efficiency of each of these installations is above 98 per cent with a pressure drop of approximately 500 mm wg.

Wet plant - This plant section allows the return into the circuit of the returns from all the sludges produced at the zinc plant :

a. The acid sludges arising from washing the SO_2 riche gas prior to their transformation into sulphuric acid. These are recycled with the aid of a stainless-steel centrifuge system.

b. Blue powder sludges which are thickened in a hydrocyclone before being sprayed onto the returns.

c. The dust sludges from ventilation of the sinter plant.

d. The sludges from the effluent plant.

Plant ventilation - The equipment consists of :

a. A bag filter with a filtering area through which the volume is 80 000 Nm^3. This filter dedusts all the plant between the sinter breaking and the returns cooling drum.

b. Three wet Lurgi type scrubbers of 18 000 Nm^3/h each which draw off the steam emitted from the cooling drum.

c. Two wet scrubbers of the same type which ventilate the returns crushing section and the return circuit.

Cadmium plant - The cadmium compounds volatilized during the sintering operation are recovered from the sulphur dioxide rich gas clarified cleaning solutions.

After degassing of the dissolved sulphur dioxide, the liquor is treated in three 25 m^3 cylindrical tanks by precipitation of the dissolved metal with sodium carbonate with a 8-8½ pH.

Decantation is improved by addition of flocculent agents while filtration takes place on a press type filter where the cake produced is partly air-dried.

The product thus obtained is sold as cadmium concentrates.

PLANT OPERATION

Typical analysis of crude new charge :

Zn	42.28	%
Pb	17.77	%
S	27.28	%
SiO_2	2.41	%
CaO	0.70	%
FeO	10.35	%
Cd	0.134	%
Cu	0.332	%

Fluxes

Limestone alone is used. The feed is adjusted so that the FeO/SiO_2 ratio in the sinter remains above 1.8.

Typical analysis of sinter

Zn	44.95	%
Pb	16.45	%
S	0.77	%
SiO_2	3.90	%
CaO	4.43	%
FeO	10.93	%
Cd	0.062	%
S_{SO_4}	0.31	%

Dwight Lloyd Feed

	Materials	Hourly tonnage tons	Sulfur content tons
Crude new charge	Zinc concentrates	13.300	4.190
	Sulphide mixed	7.400	1.813
	Oxide mixed	1.600	0.009
	Oxides	1.150	0.006
	Lead concentrates	2.600	0.731
		26.050	6.749
By products and fluxes	Limestone	1.300	-
	I.S.F. dross	0.700	0.009
	I.S.F. sludges	2.500	0.090
	Rich slag	0.400	-
New feed		30.950	6.848
	Acid sludge	2.900	0.336
	Returns	126	4.233
Total feed		159.850	11.417 = 7.14 %

Sinter production

25.6 tons per hour (sulphur content 0.77 % i.e. 0.197 ton).

Operation details

Ignition layer 30 mm
Total bed depth 340 mm
Machine speed 1.5 m/mn

Distribution of air :
Fan 1 250 m^3/mn 15 m^2 (16.6 m^3/m^2/mn) N.T.P.
Fan 2 320 m^3/mn 20 m^2 (16 m^3/m^2/mn) N.T.P.
Fan 3 475 m^3/mn 35 m^2 (13.6 m^3/m^2/mn) N.T.P.

Blast pressure :
N° 1 225 mm wg
N° 2 300 mm wg
N° 3 350 mm wg (this fan ventilating the tip end of the machine the air is at 100°C)

Consumption of gas for ignition : 185 m^3/h 4 500 Kcal/m^3
Production of fume 9.5 per cent of the new feed.

Sulphur burning efficiency :

$$\frac{6.848 - 0.197 \times 100}{6.848} = 97.1 \text{ per cent}$$

Sulphur elimination on sinter machine

Sulphur eliminated per hour	6.651 tons
Sulphur eliminated per day	159.6 tons
Sulphur eliminated/m^2 per 24 hours	2.280 tons
Sulphur eliminated/1 000 m^3 of rich gas handled at the acid plant per 24 hours	2.450 tons

Cadmium elimination

65 per cent of the cadmium is directly recovered from the cadmium cakes.

Rich gas

Average hourly flow to acid plant	65 000 m^3
SO_2 content	7.16 per cent

COMMENTS

There is no recirculation of weak gas at Noyelles-Godault for the present time.

All gases from the sintering machine hood are conveyed to the acid plants as rich gases.

The sulphur in the machine feed is controlled by the proportion of returns so to obtain a smooth and steady sintering operation where the level in the returns bins remains practically constant.

Calculation of the sulphur in the raw feed is made frequently and the machine speed is increased until the breackthrough point is on the one before last windbox.

The sinter thus obtained is obviously very hot but this is the best way to optimize the operation of the D.L.

THE NOYELLES GODAULT IMPERIAL SMELTING FURNACE

INTRODUCTION

The Imperial Smelting Process is based on the same principle as the blast furnace, that is to say, on the reduction of oxides by coke combustion gases.

The main difficulty (re-oxidability of the zinc below 1 000°C in a gaseous mixture containing 9 per cent carbon dioxide and 23 per cent carbone monoxide) has been solved by the following method :

a. Work is carried out with a hot furnace top (950-1 000°C)

b. Reoxidization is stopped by a sudden cooling of the gases in a lead splash condenser.

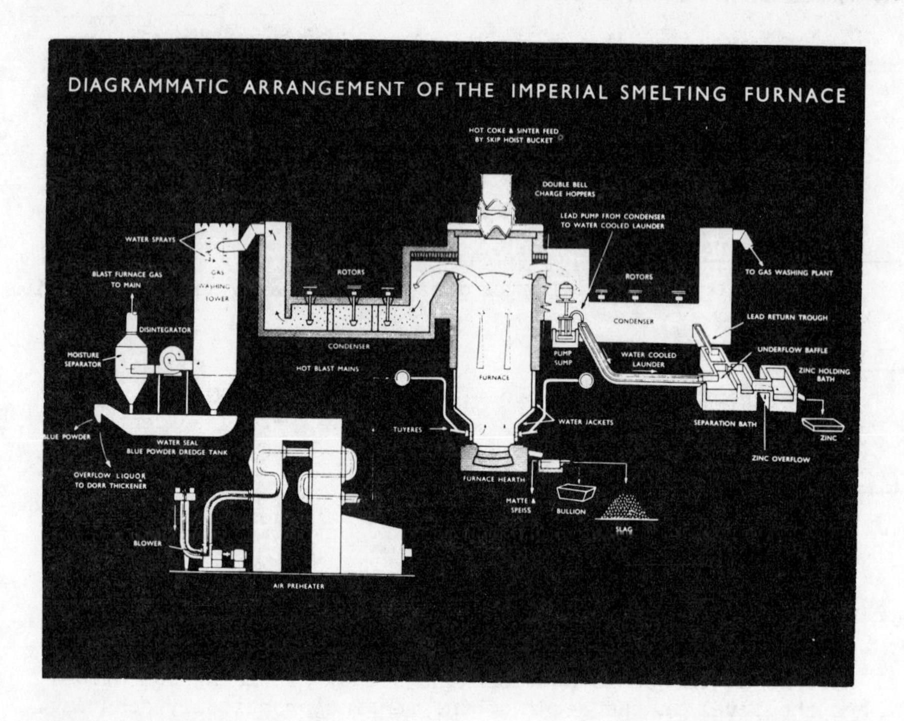

THE SHAFT

Materials charged

a. Sinter - Is obtained by sintering mixed zinc-lead concentrates, zinc blendes and galena over an updraught Dwight Lloyd machine.

   Its sizing must be between 100 mm and 10 mm. Under 10 mm the sinter would be blown into the condensers.

   The chemical composition and physical qualities of the sinter will be dealt with later on. It is to be pointed out that it must be charged into the furnace as soon as produced to avoid disintegration and moistening.

b. Coke - The coke used is metallurgical coke (size 40/90 mm) with low reactivity.

   It is preheated to 750°C in preheaters so as to save calories, avoid water in the furnace and temperature variation at the furnace top. Heating is obtained by burning LCV gas from the furnace.

   Coke is charged at constant weights. The quantity of sinter to be introduced is determined by means of a factor called the "fuel/zinc ratio" which, for normal operation must be approximately 0.80 (meaning that 0.8 kg of dry coke is fed

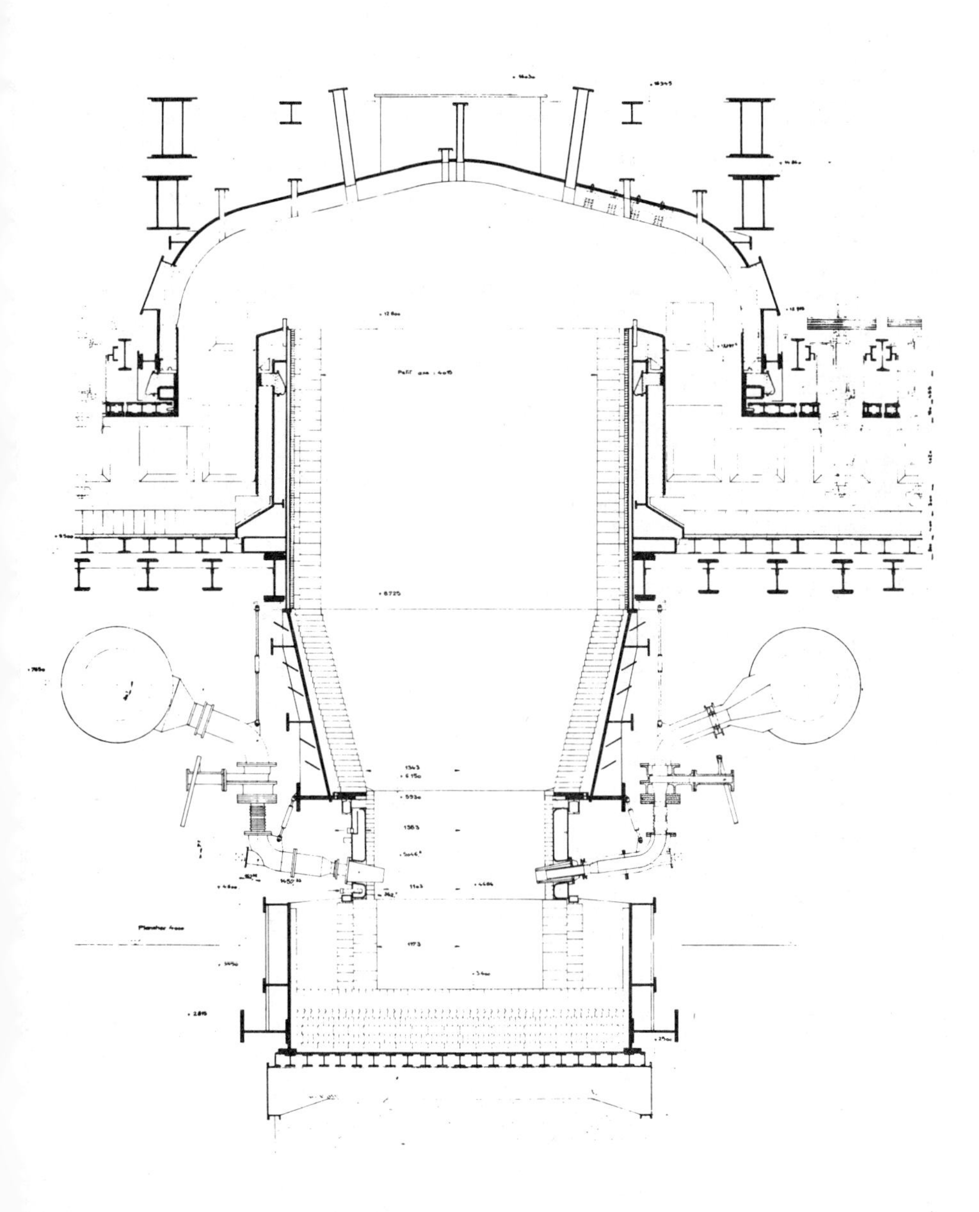

The shaft

to the furnace for each kilogram of zinc introduced). This ratio is altered in function of the quantity of unreduced zinc remaining in the slag which is between 5 and 9 per cent under normal working conditions.

c. Miscellaneous -

Silica - Silica lowers the slag melting point and facilitates its tapping. It keeps the hearth in good condition. However, when the slag melting point is lowered and the CaO/SiO^2 ratio is reduced, silica is no more economical. Nevertheless, silica has been used at the Noyelles-Godault furnace for the past year on a temporary basis.

Limestone - Its purpose is to raise the melting point of the slag and to destroy the zinc silicates. We do not add any at Noyelles-Godault.

Cast iron - This material helps removing occasional accretions in the hearth caused by mattes and is used in some difficult cases.

Fluorine - Is used in small quantities when startup is difficult, to lower the melting point of the slag. Its action is very rapid.

d. Drosses - Drosses of a wide sizing range are produced at weekly cleanouts of the condensers. These drosses are screened and all + 20 mm particles are returned directly to the furnace. Smaller particles are returned to the sinter plant so as not to introduce fine drosses at the top of the furnace.

To avoid formation of arsenious hydrogen whcih might occur if the drosses from the separation bath came into contact with water, these drosses are also returned to the furnace.

e. Charging method - The method used is called the "separate charging method" (two 1 500 buckets of coke are charged on top of two 3 800 kg buckets of sinter). Fluxes are fed with the sinter. The introduction of the coke after the sinter maintains a filtering section on the top of the charge.

At this time, 250 tons of coke are charged per day.

The weight of sinter added varies. It is of approximately 750 tons per day.

25 tons of drosses are recycled daily.

View from the Charge Control Room

Metals - Slag - Blast

The lead and zinc oxides are reduced in the shaft by coke combustion gases. The lead metal is obtained high up in the shaft and goes down towards the bottom. The zinc oxide is reduced in higher temperature zones where zinc vapour is obtained. The zinc follows the same path as the gases and the dust carried by the gases and go to the condensers. The gangue melts in a zone above the tuyères and goes to the bottom of the shaft.

The minor elements contained in the sinter follow either the path of the zinc (cadmium) or that of the lead and the slag (copper, bismuth).

a. Shaft bottom - The blast is introduced into the furnace through 15, 90 mm diameter tuyères (there is a trend to increase this diameter). These tuyères are made of ordinary steel and are lined with jackets. The temperature of the blast is 900°C at this time. This temperature is obtained with two Cowper stoves where the fuel is furnace gas.

Under the tuyères is the hearth which receives the bullion, the slag and the matte or speiss in varying quantities. These products are tapped approximatively every 90 minutes into a forehearth by means of a lined copper tapping block. The orifice of this block is normally blocked with earth and is perforated with an oxygen flame when time for tapping.

The Cowper Stoves

Their specific gravities being different, bullion and slag separate in the forehearth. The bullion is tapped into the ladle and cast into 3-ton ingots.

The slag overflows into a granulation system and is sent to the dump.

The matte and speiss constitute a layer in the forehearth and are removed every 5 or 6 tappings.

The chair shape and the jackets were removed in 1967. The furnace was rebuilt according to the blast furnace principle, using trickling water at the bottom of the shaft. The trickling water is only used during the starting periods above tuyère level while it is maintained under tuyère level throughout the operation.

A tapping block is provided at each end of the furnace but only the one with a forehearth is regularly used.

b. Top of the shaft - The casing of the top part of the shaft is connected to the lower part by means of an expansion joint which was supposed to absorb the movements of the lower part. Spaces between the casing and the refractory were filled with glass to allow expansion of the one part without any incidence on the other, but shaft accretions made this method of no effect.

The roof is dome-shaped. Its refractory lining is made secure with a cement gum. This dome supports a double bell charging system. Cold air is introduced between the two bell valves to avoid leakage. Cold air is also circulated around the lower valves between the bell wall and the dome refractory lining to prevent accretion.

Above charge level and located at equal distances are four top air inlets to raise the temperature of the gases to 1000°C. Hot air is thus introduced into the furnace at a flow rate of 3 500 to 4 500 Nm^3/h. This air burns the carbon monoxide and therefore raises the temperature of the whole gaseous mass by approximately 100°C, the temperature under the charge level being 900°C. This prevents massive reoxidation of the zinc on its way to the condensers.

Two offtakes located opposite each other allow the gases to go to the condensers.

The charge level is maintained at approximately 90 cm below the offtakes. Manual control is made by means of a metal rod.

Reactions within the shaft - Several of the questions raised by the reactions of the zinc blast furnace have not yet been satisfactorily answered. The Imperial Smelting Research Department was the first to formulate a theory to explain the operation. Later on, Professor Rey brought his contribution to this theoretical study. With regards to Noyelles-Godault, the first investigations were undertaken in 1965 and 1966.

The Metallurgical Development Department at Noyelles-Godault continues to study the evolution of the gaseous flow and it is hoped that this approach to the knowledge of the furnace will, in not too long a time, lead to a practical control of the operation.

All studies have established the presence of three zones in the shaft :

1. The upper zone which can be divided into a charge heating zone which does not yet comprise a liquid phase, and a reduction zone where Fe_2O_3 and Fe_3O_4 are reduced to wustite and lead oxide to lead.

   This zone consists of a gaseous phase and a liquid phase (lead). The zinc vapour is partly used to reduce the lead oxide, it is also partly reoxidized by CO_2, the temperature of the gases (900°C-1000°C) making total reoxidation possible theoretically.

   It is to be pointed out that the reduction of PbO and $PbSO_4$ are exothermic.

2. A so-called equilibrium zone, the depth of which depends upon the height of the furnace, the volume of the blast and the fusibility of the sinter.

The temperature in this zone is approximately 1000°C. The difference in temperature between gases, solids and liquids is small, almost inexistent. There is no thermic exchange nor any chemical reaction.

3. A zinc-reduction zone - Reduction of zinc oxide by carbon monoxide partly in solid phase and partly in liquid phase.

This zone is also the seat of the Boudouard reaction :

$$CO + \tfrac{1}{2}O_2 \rightleftarrows CO_2$$

According to the authors, it either extends down to the tuyère level or, on the contrary, is at the limit before tuyère level whe only the combustion of the coke takes place.

The way this combustion occurs is still contested. According to Mr. Lumsden, there is partial combustion to CO_2. On the contrary, Pr. Rey thinks that the reaction is wholly to CO. Mr. Boudier agrees with Mr. Lumsden that the reaction is partly to CO_2 and considers that 20 to 30 per cent of the carbon is thus gasified.

From these studies it follows that two important points have not yet been elucidated :

a. The non-reoxidation of the zinc over the charge level. As already said, at such temperature and taking into account the gas composition, the reaction ought to take place.

b. The non-reduction of the wustite which, according to some authors, is explained either by a partial carbon combustion to CO_2 or by the reduction of ZnO creating a protecting film of CO_2 and preventing the reaction, or even still, by the presence of 5 per cent ZnO in the slag.

Furnace operation - Furnace operation is not continuous. There are three types of offblast periods :

1. The so-called weekly cleanouts inherent to the process, during which time the metal accretions are removed from the furnace and condenser outlets. These cleanouts take place every ten or fifteen days when conditions are favourable, and last 8 to 10 hours.

2. Stoppages for blasting shaft accretions. With some type of charge the shaft gets regularly blocked. These accretions are removed either by vertical or by horizontal dynamiting (through the walls of the furnace). The frequency of these shutdowns depends upon the many origins of shaft accretion :

   a. Water leakage at the tuyère level.
   b. Too fusible a charge (too high lead content in the sinter).
   c. Charging breakdown.
   d. Behaviour of casting block, tuyères, etc.

Sinter Composition - The shaft operates normally when the composition of the sinter is within the following range :

Pb average 18 %
minimum 12 %
maximum 22 %.

The minimum lead content has no metallurgical importance. On the contrary when there is more than 22 % lead difficulties might appear at the top of the furnace as the sinter melts too quickly and blockage may occur. However, normal operation has been obtained with as high as 23 % and even 24 % lead content.

Zn average 40 %
minimum 34 %
maximum 50 %

Minimum and maximum zinc contents are of no metallurgical importance.

Fe average 12 %

The presence of high FeO content makes the slag fluid. In fact, we verify that the FeO/SiO_2 ratio remains above 1.8. Even 3 was reached.

CaO 4 to 6 %

Considerable importance is given to the CaO/SiO_2 ratio which should remain around 1.2. The presence of CaO improves the zinc volatilisation; it also raises the melting point of the sinter but the slag becomes pasty above this figure. Some Imperial Smelting Process licensees add lime to the furnace to adjust the CaO/SiO_2 ratio.

SiO_2

Adjustment is carried out so as to obtain a CaO/SiO_2 ratio which should remain around 1.2 . Silica is directly added to the furnace since it makes the slag fluid, facilitates the operation of the earth and keeps it in good condition. It increases the coke consumption per ton of zinc.

Cu

This element is of minor importance from the metallurgical point of view.

S average 0.9 %
minimum 0.7 %
maximum 1.3 %

As a rule this element must not exceed 1 %. It is partly responsible for accretion formation in the shaft and at the condensers inlets.

BaO 0.9 %

Above this value there are risks of trouble at the bottom of the shaft (separation of a solid phase in the slag).

Fuel/Zinc ratio - This term has been generally adopted to indicate the quantity of coke charged into the furnace per ton of zinc contained. With respect to coke the weight officially considered applies to dry coke. Another fuel/zinc ratio used day by day applies to hot coke.

This ratio fluctuates around 0.78 % and is modified according to :

a. The zinc content of the slag which must be between 4 and 8 %.
b. The temperature of the blast. A temperature increase of the blast of 50°C corresponds to a ratio decrease of 0.02 % and vice versa.

Other factors affecting this ratio are :

1. The CaO/SiO_2 ratio of the sinter.
2. The cleanness of the shaft and of the hearth.

Different values of the zinc charged/coke consumed ratio (ratio we also take into account at Noyelles-Godault) are shown below :

Metallurgical data	1969
1. Slab zinc/zinc volatilized ratio	81.60
2. Zinc volatilized/Zinc in charge ratio	95.08
3. Zinc charge/coke consumed (as payed on N.S. basis)	133.18
4. Coke consumed (as payed on N.S. basis)/work day	216.484 tons
5. Working day/calendar day	84.25
6. Slab zinc/coke consumed (as payed on N.S. basis)	103.34
7. Zinc/dry coke consumed	105.98
8. Zinc/working day	223.714 tons
9. Zinc/calendar day	188.474 tons
10. Slag/calendar day	144.810 tons
11. Zinc in charge/slag	167.73
12. Bullion recovery	76.01
13. Furnace direct zinc recovery	76.57
14. Condensation efficiency	80.53

Slag composition - We have seen that the reduction reactions occur between the reducing gases and the liquid slag. These reactions can be written out as follows :

$$ZnO \text{ (in slag)} + CO \rightleftarrows Zn \text{ (in gas)} + CO_2$$

$$FeO \text{ (in slag)} + CO \rightleftarrows Fe \text{ (in slag)} + CO_2$$

Laboratory studies have been made on the following reaction :

$$Fe(S) + ZnO \text{ (in slag)} \rightleftarrows Zn \text{ (in gas)} + FeO \text{ (in slag)}$$

and its equilibrium constant :

$$K = P\,Zn \frac{A\,FeO}{A\,ZnO} \quad \text{or} \quad P\,Zn = K \frac{A\,ZnO}{A\,FeO}$$

where P Zn is the partial pressure of Zinc
and A FeO and ZnO are the activities of FeO and ZnO in the slag.

To increase P Zn, which is equivalent to increasing the zinc recovery, it is necessary :

a. To increase K which increases with the temperature.
b. To increase the ZnO and FeO activity ratio.

It has also been proved experimentally that this last ratio varies with CaO/SiO_2 ratio, this is a double reason for operating with a high lime/silica ratio since we have already seen that lime increases the melting point of the sinter and therefore of the slag.

Microscope observations having shown that the slag from the furnace is wholly under liquid phase, studies were made of the temperature of the liquidus in the FeO - CaO - SiO_2 - Al_2O_3 and MgO system. With the help of Shairer diagrams it is possible to define the zones giving high-temperature liquidus, thereby satisfactory zinc recovery. Temperature must be above 1250°C. Little is known to this date about the zones above 1300°C.

The relation between the melting point of the sinter and the liquidus of the slag is no simple matter. The importance of a high melting temperature is obvious.

The sinter examined here above gives a slag with the following analysis :

Zn	8 %
Pb	1.1 %
FeO	36 %
CaO	16 %
SiO_2	14 %
Al_2O_3	7 %

Normal furnace operation parameters - The following furnace operation parameters are applied :

1. Pressure at the bustle main. This gives an indication of the porosity of the charge and the condition of the hearth.

2. Physical quality of the slag.

3. Slag analysis. A first appreciation is obtained through visual examination.

4. Sinter analysis.

5. Regularity of the lowering of the charge.

6. Analysis of CO-CO_2 H_2 in gases at the condensers outlets.
   This analysis indicates whether the operation is sufficiently reducing or if there is any water present in the shaft.

7. Percentage of drosses removed from the condensers.

8. Fuel/Zinc ratio.

The various lead and zinc recoveries are also examined daily. Most metallurgical date are shown in the above table.

THE CONDENSERS

Materials

The Noyelles-Godault furnace is fitted with two standard I.S.P. condensers (4 rotors) divided into three stages. These condensers are both washing and cooling units.

Lead is used as washing fluid.

Gases - The leave the furnace offtakes at a temperature of 1050°C which is brought to this value by admission of air through the four top air inlets already mentioned.

The gases have the following composition :

CO_2	10 %
CO	23 %
H_2	1 %
Zn vapour	5 %

They also contain :

- Sinter dust almost of similar composition to that of the sinter.
- Metallic lead particles mechanically entrained at their formation at the top of the shaft.
- Sulphur and volatile sulphides.
- Dust particles from the re-cycling of badly conditioned drosses, which are also mechanically entrained.
- Arsenic.
- Cadmium.

The gases meet the lead spray projected by the rotor blades. They lose most of their zinc content by entrain lead to the washing tower. Thus, with a furnace blast flow rate of 33 000 Nm^3/h, the amount of lead entrained is of 0.9 kg pet Nm^3 of gas containing 30 per cent zinc and 55 per cent lead.

The maximum and minimum temperatures of the gases at the condenser outlet are 470°C and 440°C. The gases pass through the washing system via an insulated pipe called cross-over.

Retention time of the gases within the condensers is increased by two baffles which eliminate the condensation stages.

Lead - This material enters the condenser by its end at a temperature of 440°C. It is saturated with zinc (2.3 %). It flows through the condenser in counter-current to the gas and is projected in fine droplets by the rotors.

During its passage through the condenser the lead carries off some zinc which increases its zinc content by approximately 0.3 %. Its temperature at the outlet of the condenser is maximum 580°C, minimum 510°C. The average temperature adopted at Noyelles-Godault is 540°C.

The volume of lead in circulation is of 2 800 tons per hour.

Leaded Zinc - This material is pumped from the condenser and delivered to the cooling launders where its temperature is reduced from 550°C to 440°C. It then proceeds to the separation baths where the zinc, less soluble at 440°C, liquates and is collected. The lead returns to the condenser via a siphon and goes back into the circuit.

The cooling system adopted at Noyelles-Godault consists of a single launder for each condenser, equipped with jackets. This system completely eliminates the chute which used to occur at the end of the former jacketed launder which had therefore to be left empty during shutdown periods and located on a higher level than that of the baths.

Zinc - Sinc June 1970 both condensers are treated with aluminium and all the zinc is boiled in the New-Jersey columns.

Drosses - They are extracted at the following points :

	Average analysis	Quantities
Pump sump	Pb 44 % Zn 35 %	15 t/day
Separation baths	Pb 33 % Zn 50 %	4 t/day
Condenser (from condenser cleanouts)	Pb 46 % Zn 36 %	50 t/day

Blue powder - The non-condensed materials, part of the reoxidised zinc and of the metallic lead particles mechanically entrained go to the washing system as sludge (approximately 70 tons per day). Their analysis was given above.

Operating hypotheses

Three phenomena take place in the condenser :

1. A thermal exchange.
2. A mass transfer.
3. A washing operation.

Thermal exchange - In the first stage there is mainly a radiation between the gases, the condenser walls and the lead. It has been proved that the exchange is function of $(1050°C - 510°C)^4$ and therefore that radiation is predominant.

In the following stage, the temperatures between gas, wall and lead are about the same and the exchange takes place through convection-conduction.

Mass transfer - The two stages defined above occur in this case too.

In the first stage the gases being very hot there is no saturation and the zinc vapour is directly absorbed by the lead droplets. There is little risk of zinc reoxidation.

In the second stage, the temperature being low, the zinc is condensed into droplets which either dissolve immediately in the lead or reoxidise and are directly entrained to the washing system.

The theories are different with the authors. Some of them say there is no or very little zinc reoxidation. The zinc which has not bee collected escapes from the condenser in metal form and only reoxidises in the washing system.

On the contrary, according to other authors there is reoxidation in conformity with the reversible reaction :

$$Zn + CO_2 \rightleftarrows CO + ZnO$$

$$\text{or} \quad \frac{P\ Zn \times P\ CO_2}{P\ CO} = Ke$$

Ke obviously varies with the temperature but this equation gives no information on the speed of the reaction. The reaction very likely occurs on the cold surfaces :

- Lead.
- Drosses projected by the rotors.
- Condenser walls.

The distinctions made above between the two stages are of a general nature. In fact, when theorizing on micro-particles we find conditions identical in the first stage and in the second stage.

Washing - The lead spray also has a washing effect. Thus are caught a large fraction of the droplets of metallic zinc and the dust particles found in the drosses.

Control Room of the Smelting Plant

Operation of the condensers

Rotors - The rotors are vertical shafts equipped with blades. Lead droplets produced must be small enough so to provide a maximum liquid to gas area. However, they must be sufficiently big not to be massively entrained to the washing system.

For the same reason the lead droplets must be distributed as well as possible.

The size of the droplets and the quantity of lead projected depend upon the following factors :

- The geometrical shape of the blades.
- The immersion of the rotor.
- The rotation speed of the rotor.
- The distance between the lower part of the scoops and the bottom arch of the condenser (on account of the wall effect).

For a given type of rotor with a given rotation speed immersion is an important factor. This will be measured very carefully and maintained constant by addition of fresh lead in the condenser.

Diversity of parameters - The diverse parameters affecting the operation of the condensers are :

a. The temperature of the inlet gases which must be of 1050°C. A lower temperature would cause more reoxidation of the zinc and very quickly a blockage of the condenser inlets by accretions on the walls.

b. The temperature of the gases at the outlet (450°C - 470°C) which must be as low as possible to reduce the zinc vapour pressure and thereby zinc recirculation.

c. The temperature of the lead at the pump sumps (550°C). Too low a temperature might cause mist formation detrimental to the yield of the condenser and to the lead consumption. Too hot a temperature would on the contrary maintain the zinc reoxidation at high level.

d. The temperature of the lead at the return launder which must be approximately 440°C. A lower temperature would cause blockage of the siphon due to freezing of the zinc.

The means to affect these parameters, which furthermore are function of each other, are :

- The quantity of top air above charge level.
- The cooling capacity of the lead launders which varies with the number of immersed jackets.
- the volume of circulated lead, depending upon the number and type of lead pumps in operation.

PRODUCTION

Since 1964, the yearly output has been fluctuating as follows :

	Zinc tons	Lead Bullion tons
1964	45 000	21 000
1965	45 000	18 000
1966	45 000	24 000
1967*	33 000	17 000
1968	49 000	20 000
1969	69 000	30 000

* ten months operation only.

Zinc produced is "GOB" brand (98.5 % Zn).

The lead bullion contains generally 96% lead, the copper and silver tenor depending upon the ores treated.

REFERENCES

Morgan S.W.K. The Production of Zinc in a Blast Furnace. Trans. Inst. Mining and Metallurgy, 66, 1956-57, 553-65, 67, 1957-8, 127-38.

Morgan S.W.K. and Woods S.E. Avonmouth Zinc Blast Furnace Demonstrates its Versatility. Eng. and Mining Journal, 159, 1958, 95-9.

Morgan S.W.K. and Lumsden J. Some Physico Chemical Aspects of Zinc Blast Furnace Operation. Journal of Metals, 11, 1959, 270-5.

Morgan S.W.K. Recent Developments in Zinc Blast Furnace Technology. Journal of Metals. 1964, January 33-36.

Morgan S.W.K. and Greenwood D.A. The Metallurgical and Economic Behaviour of Lead in the Smelting Furnace. Journal of Metals, December 1968.

Chapter 23

THE EVOLUTION OF LEAD SMELTING PRACTICE AT ZAMBIA BROKEN HILL DEVELOPMENT COMPANY
Kabwe, Zambia

B. Barlin, Manager
Zambia Broken Hill Development Company

Introduction

The development of metallurgical practice at Zambia Broken Hill is directly related to the change in mineralization of the deposits as mining progressed from the open pits to underground.

The ore consists of a mixture of lead and zinc sulphide minerals, together with abundant silicates, carbonates and other oxidized minerals of these metals.

The irregularity that characterizes the shape of the orebodies applies equally to their mineral content, which makes ore reserve calculations and the maintenance of a balanced feed to the metallurgical plants, problems of some magnitude.

History

The Rhodesia Broken Hill Development Company was formed in 1904 after an Australian prospector, T. G. Davey, discovered the outcrops in 1902.

In the early years zinc ores were calcined for shipment but this proved uneconomic. Cerussite outcrops were then smelted directly in blast furnaces for the production of lead until 1929 when ore above the water level was exhausted.

At this stage dewatering and underground mining became necessary. During the interim period, however, the production of electrolytic zinc from silicate ores was established, and only sufficient lead for local consumption was produced. Vanadium concentrates were also produced for sale as well as a fused vanadic oxide from low grade vanadium ores. Treatment of underground sulphide and oxide ores started in 1946 when the plants consisted of a concentrator, an electrolytic zinc plant for the treatment of zinc sulphide concentrates and zinc oxide ores and a Newnam Hearth plant for the recovery of lead from the high grade concentrates.

The low level of metal recovery from the underground ores resulted from the dumping of certain flotation plant tailings which contained considerable lead and zinc in oxidised form. These could not be leached due to the high acid consumption, and whose fluorine content caused hard stripping in the cell room. The leach plant residue also contained a high proportion of lead. A lead blast furnace plant was designed and installed in 1953 to treat these materials but did not prove entirely effective. It was closed down again in 1957.

In 1962 the Imperial Smelting Furnace and Sinter plant was designed and installed to improve production by improving the recovery of metal from underground ores and dump materials without increasing the mining rate.

Lead Smelting Practice

During the life of the Mine four different processes for lead recovery have been utilised.

(i) Small blast furnaces for the treatment of carbonate ores.
(ii) Newnam hearths.
(iii) Dwight-Lloyd sintering and lead blast furnace smelting, and
(iv) The Imperial smelting process.

Each plant and process is described.

Future Development

No true tailing from any of the ores treated to date has been produced by any of the processes employed. Studies are proceeding on the application of waelz kilns to the treatment of existing residues dumps and ores, which are not amenable to treatment in the existing plants.

The fume so produced will be utilised to upgrade the feed materials to the electrolytic zinc plant and the Imperial smelting furnace, to increase output and metal recovery.

Introduction

On a plateau some 1,183 metres above sea level in Zambia, Central Africa, are found the deposits of zinc, lead and vanadium ores worked by the Zambia Broken Hill Development Company. Kabwe, where the mine is situated, is 2,137 kilometres by rail from the nearest port of Beira in Mozambique and about 13 degrees south of the equator.

The mineral area was first discovered by an Australian prospector, T.G. Davey, in 1902. He came upon a number of small hillocks or kopjes on the otherwise flat country, which were found to contain minerals of both lead and zinc. (Figure 1). He named it Broken Hill after a similar occurrence of the same name in Australia.

An early photograph of the Broken Hill Kopje (small hill) showing an exploratory adit.

Figure 1.

ZAMBIA BROKEN HILL DEVELOPMENT CO. LTD.

BLOCK DIAGRAM OF 3/4 & 5/6 OREBODIES

SCALE :- 1:12500

FIGURE :- 2

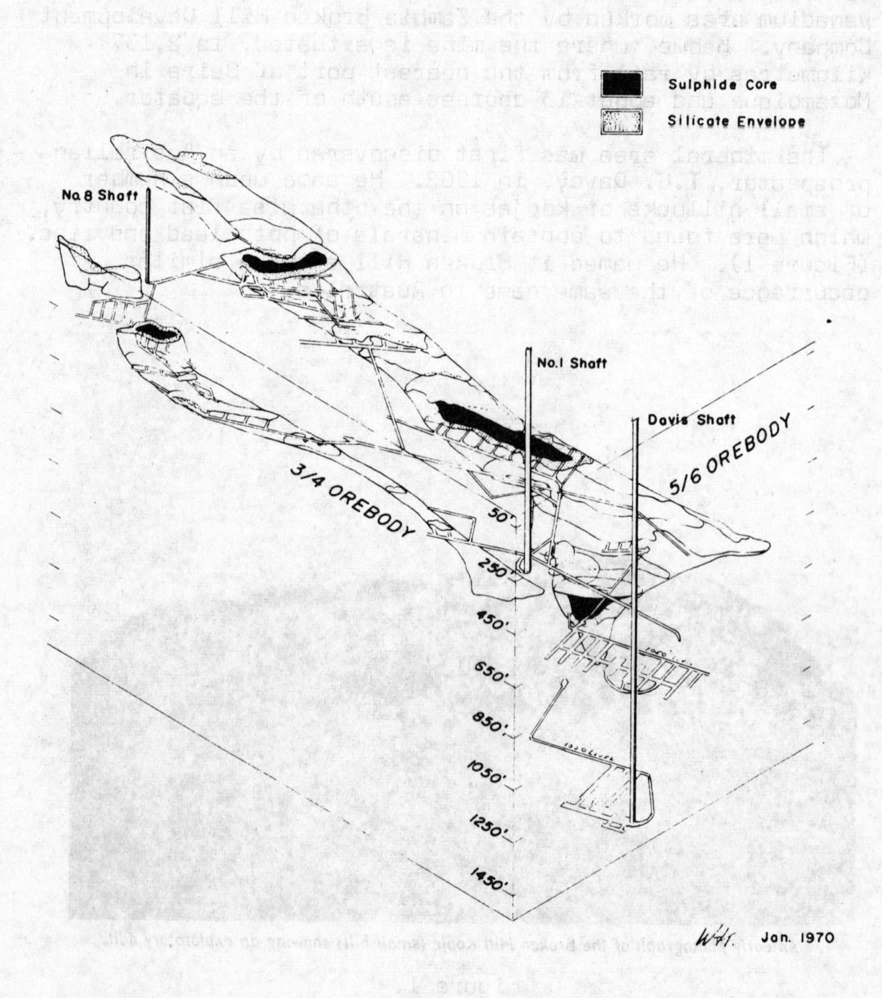

The development of metallurgical practice at Zambia Broken Hill Development Company is directly related to the changing nature of the mineral deposits as mining operations progressed from the surface outcrops to underground.

The irregularity in the shape of the orebodies is also characteristic of their mineral content making ore reserve calculations and the maintenance of a balanced feed to the metallurgical plants problems of some magnitude.

Geology and Mining

The ore deposits occur as pipe like bodies within a massive featureless dolomite. There is no significant alteration of the host rock surrounding these orebodies and their genesis is still a matter of conjecture.

At the time of discovery, the Broken Hill mineral occurrence consisted of four round-topped kopjes up to 20 metres high, with several low flat outcrops. At outcrop, the orebodies were, in the main, completely oxidised whilst in depth they contain a core of massive sulphide surrounded by an envelope of silicate ore. (Figure 2). Between the zinc silicate and the dolomite walls is a zone of more or less broken ground containing a hard clay in which the vanadium minerals occur.

The ore minerals are:

(i) Galena and Sphalerite

(ii) Oxidised lead and zinc minerals notably Willemite ($2ZnO.SiO_2$), Smithsonite ($ZnCO_3$), Hemimorphite ($2ZnO.SiO_2.H_2O$), Cerussite ($PbCO_3$), Anglesite ($PbSO_4$) and Pyromorphite ($3Pb.3P_2O_8.PbCl_2$), but many others are found including some of the rare minerals e.g. Hopeite ($Zn_3P_2O_8.4H_2O$), Parahopeite ($Zn_3P_2O_8.4H_2O$) and Tarbuttite ($Zn_3P_2O_8.Zn(OH)_2$).

(iii) The complex lead vanadium minerals Descloizite ($2PbO.2ZnO.V_2O_5.H_2O$) and Vanadite ($3Pb_3V_2O_8.PbCl_2$).

The oxidised zone of the orebody is famous for its varied rare and extremely beautiful crystallised minerals of which many unique specimens have been presented to several mineral collections.

Several mining methods have been used. Open pit mining was carried on in the earlier days. Underground mining methods, started in 1938, included shrinkage stoping, horizontal cut and fill stoping, square set stoping with full top slicing and long hole drilling from sub levels. This latter method is used exclusively in the present day mining practice.

History

The Mine was first pegged in 1902, and the Directors of the Rhodesia Broken Hill Development Company which was formed in 1904 to work the deposits had to contend with the isolated location of the deposit; even the railway bridge at Victoria Falls, some 626 kilometres to the South of Kabwe, was still under construction. However, with the optimism characteristic of mining men the world over, mining was started and the railway reached Broken Hill in 1906.

At that time the known deposits were of two types - rich oxidised lead minerals with some zinc in No. 1 Kopje and high grade oxidised zinc minerals with some lead in No. 2 Kopje. The decision was taken to treat the zinc ore by calcination in a locally made furnace, and to ship the calcine. By making use of local materials very little was needed to be brought to the site; even the cocopan rails were made of local hardwood.

In all, three such furnaces were built, (Figure 3). These operations continued until April, 1907 by which time 11,000 tons of calcined ore had been produced. However, due to the uneconomic relationship between railage rate and the selling price operations temporarily ceased.

A side view of the first furnace to be constructed at Broken Hill.

Figure 3.

It was then realised that for a mine so far from its markets it was essential to produce finished metal. The only ores available for treatment were the rich zinc ores from No. 2 Kopje, treatment of which had now proved uneconomic, and the high grade cerussite from No. 1 Kopje.

In 1910 the Company was voluntarily wound up and reconstituted with the object of producing lead bullion from the cerussite outcrop above the 33 metre level. After a delay caused by the outbreak of World War I, a small experimental blast furnace, 1.2 metres in diameter, was started in June, 1915 and by November of that year had produced 360 tonnes of lead. The slag from this furnace contained up to 27% ZnO at times, which proved less troublesome to handle than anticipated.

For financial reasons, the property was then leased to the Rhodesia Lead and Zinc Syndicate, which undertook to equip the mine to produce 900 tonnes of lead per month from bigger, water-jacketed blast furnaces.

In June, 1917 the first of these furnaces, 4.9 x 1.2 metres at tuyere level, was blown in by which time the pilot furnace had produced some 2,410 tonnes of lead. The second furnace was blown in in October, 1917 and the fortunes of the Company improved to the extent that in February, 1919 the Syndicate's lease was cancelled. From April, 1916 to February, 1919 the Syndicate had produced 15,629 tonnes of lead and by June, 1919 lead production amounted to 21,000 tonnes. The end of 1919 saw a third furnace operating and by 1920 a fourth was added. Production increased accordingly.

1920 - 14,836 tonnes
1921 - 18,412 tonnes
1922 - 20,829 tonnes

Over this period the charge to the furnace was mostly the cerussite selectively mined from the No. 1 Kopje orebody. The high grade of which is demonstrated by the fact that in 1921 the 18,412 tons of lead produced came from 43,977 tons of ore. But as mining increased below the surface the incidence of sulphide lead (Galena) increased and, as it was being fed directly to the furnaces, production dropped steadily:

1923 - 11,041 tonnes
1924 - 5,929 tonnes
1925 - 3,332 tonnes

In 1924 it was decided to install concentration and sintering plants to improve the feed to the furnaces. This plant after considerable delay in delivery of equipment was started in April, 1926.

All this time, of course, the problem of zinc recovery was being investigated, and this was given extra impetus when Mr. Ross McCartney, who had managed the mine for the Syndicate, took over as Mine Manager when the lease was cancelled in 1919. In 1920 two experienced metallurgists were working on the problem, and in June of that year J.O. Betterton (1) was successful in small scale tests to produce electrolytic zinc.

Zinc fuming tests on the lead blast furnace slags were in progress, in reverberatory type furnaces, and vanadium extraction was also being studied.

In 1923 the decision was taken to erect a one tonne per day pilot electrolytic zinc plant. This would treat oxidised, largely silicate, zinc ore, though it was noted that sulphide zinc was beginning to appear.

By 1924 the pilot tests were sufficiently far advanced to justify the erection of a 15,000 tonne per year electrolytic zinc plant. Cheap power for the process was obtained by the construction of a hydroelectric station, in the gorge of the Mulungushi river, which was officially opened in 1924. The pilot plant tests were supervised by an Australian metallurgist, Mr. R.H. Stevens, who became General Manager in 1925. In the same year Sir Ernest Oppenheimer joined the Board, and Anglo American Corporation of South Africa Limited were appointed Consulting Engineers.

It might be noted here that the mine was closed down for three months in 1918 - 1919 because of a devastating influenza epidemic. It was also flooded, with lost production, for five months in 1925 and another five months in 1926. However, lead production continued for a few years.

1926 - 6,927 tonnes
1927 - 5,255 tonnes
1928 - 2,414 tonnes

But the water level at 69 metres imposed an insuperable barrier, and in July 1929 the lead ore above this level was exhausted, and lead production ceased. The concentrator thereafter was used for concentrating vanadium ores for the production of vanadium concentrate for the market. In that year 4,304 tonnes of ore assaying 5.5% vanadium pentoxide was treated for the recovery of 452 tonnes of concentrate containing 15.0% of V_2O_5. The recovery was approximately 26%.

In the meantime the electrolytic zinc plant, under construction, came into operation in 1928, which was unique in the world for the production of electrolytic zinc from zinc silicate ores. Production rose from 9,732 tonnes in 1928 to 12,315 tonnes in 1929 and 18,194 tonnes in 1930 when the Mulungushi power plant was extended.

Up to this time a certain amount of vanadium ore had been sorted to a high grade (± 15% V_2O_5) and exported with flotation concentrates. A hydro-metallurgical process for the recovery of a fused vanadic oxide from lower grade ores was developed by the mine staff and production began in 1931.

From July, 1931 to December, 1932, zinc production had to be suspended because of low metal prices and operations on the property were carried by vanadium sales alone.

Metal prices, remained depressed, but the Board of Directors agreed to re-start zinc production at the beginning of 1933, again using ore from No. 2 Kopje and oxide ore that had been produced from the concentrator and stockpiled during the years of lead production. With the help of vanadium sales, the mine managed to produce modest profits, but no dividend was paid after 1927 for many years.

The affairs of the Company had reached a critical point. The easily mined and treated ores were all but exhausted and it was essential that ore below the water level should be mined and modern plant installed to recover the metal content.

Diamond drilling had established the existence of substantial ore reserves and that expansion of production was justified. Anglo American Corporation of South Africa, Limited, were appointed Consulting Engineers and Managers in January, 1937, they had been Consulting Engineers since 1925 and had recommended sinking a separate pump shaft under cementation cover and installing a concentrator for the separation of lead and zinc sulphides.

This represented a bold venture into the integrated mining and treatment of the underground ores.

The proposals included the sinking of the dewatering shaft, named the Davis Shaft after Sir Edmund Davis the first Chairman of the Company, and the main ore shaft to the 168 metre level. A second power plant on the Lunsemfwa River, 30 miles distant from Mulungushi was to be installed and a concentrator incorporating a differential flotation plant.

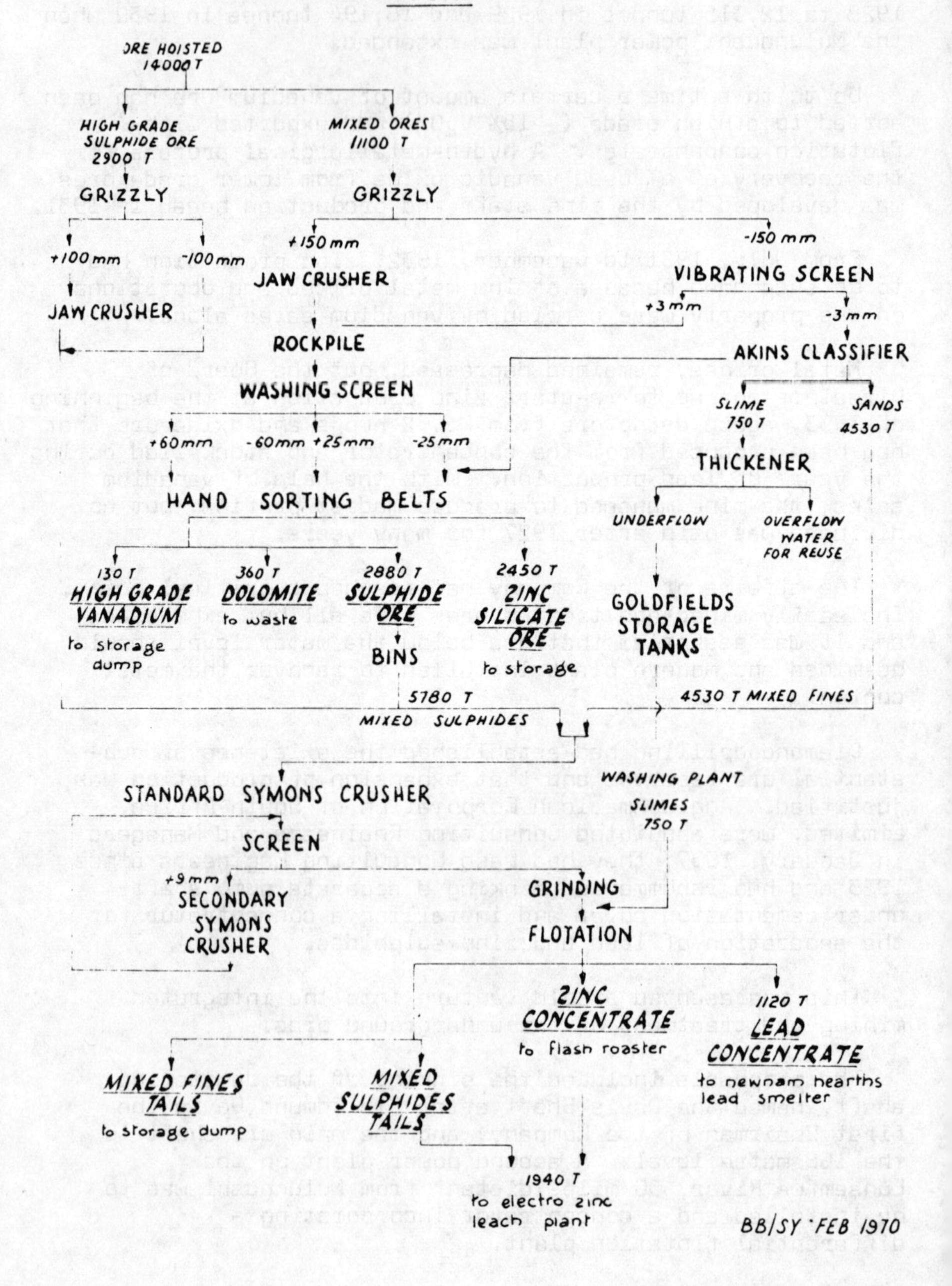
ZAMBIA BROKEN HILL DEVELOPMENT COMPANY LIMITED
DIAGRAMMATIC FLOWSHEET 1946 - 1952
TONNES PER MONTH
FIGURE - 4
ORE HOISTED 14000 T
HIGH GRADE SULPHIDE ORE 2900 T
MIXED ORES 1100 T
GRIZZLY
GRIZZLY
+100 mm
-100 mm
JAW CRUSHER
+150 mm
JAW CRUSHER
-150 mm
VIBRATING SCREEN
+3 mm
-3 mm
ROCKPILE
AKINS CLASSIFIER
WASHING SCREEN
SLIME 750 T
SANDS 4530 T
+60 mm
-60 mm +25 mm
-25 mm
THICKENER
HAND SORTING BELTS
UNDERFLOW
OVERFLOW WATER FOR REUSE
130 T
HIGH GRADE VANADIUM
to storage dump
360 T
DOLOMITE
to waste
2880 T
SULPHIDE ORE
BINS
2450 T
ZINC SILICATE ORE
to storage
GOLDFIELDS STORAGE TANKS
5780 T
MIXED SULPHIDES
4530 T MIXED FINES
WASHING PLANT SLIMES 750 T
STANDARD SYMONS CRUSHER
SCREEN
+9 mm
SECONDARY SYMONS CRUSHER
GRINDING
FLOTATION
ZINC CONCENTRATE
to flash roaster
1120 T
LEAD CONCENTRATE
to newnam hearths lead smelter
MIXED FINES TAILS
to storage dump
MIXED SULPHIDES TAILS
1940 T
to electro zinc leach plant
BB/SY FEB 1970

A Newnam Hearth plant was constructed for the treatment of the sulphide lead concentrate, while a Trail type suspension roaster was installed for the treatment of the sphalerite concentrates. The calcine so produced was to augment the silicate ore feed to the electrolytic zinc leach plant.

The end of World War II enabled plant construction to proceed and in 1946 all new plant was commissioned.

For the first time a substantial tonnage of zinc was won from the zinc sulphides of the orebody while the sulphur content replaced pyrite which had previously supplied the SO_2 necessary for acid manufacture.

However it is interesting to note that, prior to the construction period and during the war years lead had been produced almost entirely for mine use, at the rate of about 300 tonnes per year.

The main reasons for this modest production were the unattractive price of lead and the low grade of the ores. There were inadequate facilities for treating major tonnages of sulphide ores, and the oxide reserves averaged only 6 - 7% lead. However, the increased prices due to the demand for the metal created by the war, resulted in the rehabilitation of the sinter beds and blast furnaces, and once again lead production was resumed.

1940	-	292 tonnes
1941	-	378 tonnes
1942	-	1,118 tonnes
1943	-	1,265 tonnes
1944	-	1,046 tonnes
1945	-	1,747 tonnes

The magnitude of the new development is diagrammatically illustrated by the flowsheet (Figure 4), a description of which is as follows:

Two types of ore were hoisted up to shaft; the first a high grade mixed sulphide ore and the other a mixture of oxides, sulphides, vanadium, muds and dolomite. The high grade portion was crushed to -100 m.m. and stored ahead of secondary crushing.

The mixed ores passed through a primary washing screen and crushed to -150 m.m. It then passed through a secondary stage of washing and split to +25 m.m. material for hand sorting. The -25 m.m. fraction, was again split by an Akins Spiral classifier into a sands and a washing plant slime fraction. The slime was thickened and stored in Goldfields storage tanks ahead of flotation. The sand fraction, or mixed fines, was stored in bins ahead of the crushing plant. The +25 m.m. material was hand sorted, by some 60 labourers, into a high grade mixed sulphide fraction which joined the high grade ore direct from the mine, high grade vanadium ore which was stored separately for leaching or sale, and dolomite waste rock, used for ballast and concrete work.

The material discharged from the end of the belt was a high grade zinc silicate ore, assaying 27% zinc and 6% lead, which was stockpiled for later treatment in the leach plant.

For the next stage of treatment there were three distinct materials.

(i) The high grade mixed sulphide ore containing large proportions of Galena and Sphalerite and lesser proportion of 'oxide' ores of zinc and lead.

(ii) Mixed fines ore containing much larger proportions of oxide ores together with the bulk of the vanadium, and

(iii) The washing plant slime being very similar in mineral composition to the mixed fines.

Each of these was treated separately and intermittently whilst the other two were being stored.

Secondary crushing, grinding and differential flotation followed conventional patterns. From each material treated in the flotation plant was produced a high grade lead concentrate, a high grade zinc concentrate and a tailing. After thickening and filtration the lead concentrate was delivered to the Newnam Hearth plant and the zinc concentrate to the flash roaster.

TABLE I 1952 MONTHLY AVERAGE FIGURES

Materials from Sorting Plant	% Wt.
Silicate ore	17.9
Dolomite waste	5.3
Vanadium ores	1.3
High grade lead carbonate	0.2
	24.7
Ore through Flotation	
Mixed sulphides	39.5
Mixed fines	30.6
Washing plant slime	5.2
	75.3

FLOTATION OF MIXED FINES

Product	% Assay					% Distribution			
	% Wt.	T/Pb	Pb/S	T/Zn	Zn/S	T/Pb	Pb/S	T/Zn	Zn/S
Feed	100.0	17.6	9.4	24.0	10.0	100.0	100.0	100.0	100.0
Pb conc.	10.6	76.8	75.6	5.6	4.6	46.3	85.4	2.4	4.8
Zn conc.	17.8	4.4	3.7	54.6	52.0	4.5	7.0	39.4	91.0
Tails	71.6	12.1	1.0	20.0	0.6	49.2	7.6	58.2	4.2

V_2O_5 in tails - 1.30% and CaO = 4.0%

FLOTATION OF MIXED SULPHIDES

Product	% Assay					% Distribution			
	% Wt.	T/Pb	Pb/S	T/Zn	Zn/S	T/Pb	Pb/S	T/Zn	Zn/S
Feed	100.0	22.5	18.2	31.9	21.8	100.0	100.0	100.0	100.0
Pb conc.	22.2	76.9	76.0	5.6	4.9	75.9	92.5	3.9	5.0
Zn Conc.	39.6	2.9	2.1	54.0	52.0	5.1	4.6	67.0	94.3
Tails	38.2	11.2	1.4	24.3	0.4	19.0	2.9	29.1	0.7

V_2O_5 in tails - 0.60% CaO = 0.5%

Flotation Reagents	grmme/ton ore	
Lead Circuit	Mixed sulphides	Mixed Fines
Cyanide	50	35
Thiocarbonilide	150	100
Ethyl Xanthate	75	65
Cresylic Acid	12	12
Zinc Circuit		
Copper Sulphate	325	175
Ethyl Xanthate	200	125
Aerofloat 25	125	75

The tailings from the flotation of the mixed sulphide ores were treated in the zinc leach tanks together with the calcine from the roaster for zinc recovery while the tailings from the flotation of the mixed fines ore were separately dumped for the possible recovery of zinc, lead and vanadium in the future. The reasons for not including this mixed fines tailing in the leach plant feed was because of its high fluorine content, causing hard stripping in the cell room and the high dolomite content; a high acid consumer.

Table I summarises the concentrator metallurgy for the year 1952.

The gases from the roasting of the zinc concentrates were converted to sulphuric acid in a lead chamber plant. The calcine together with the mixed sulphide tailings were leached together with the acid so produced and spent electrolyte from the cell room. The zinc sulphate solution was filtered off purified for the removal of Cd, Ni and Cl and electrolysed.

The high grade lead concentrates constituted the feed to the Newnam Hearths plant.

No provision was made at the time for lead extraction from oxidised lead minerals. Grey slag from the Newnam Hearths was sintered on the old sinter hearths together with some leach residue and smelted in small cupola type furnaces within the Newnam Hearth refinery building.

While lead recovery was satisfactory from the high grade lead concentrates using the Newnam Hearths, the leach residue which contained a high proportion of lead was still being stockpiled. This lead arose from that contained in the calcine from the roasting of zinc concentrates and the oxidised lead content of the zinc silicates being leached. After considerable test work in Italy it was decided to install a new plant incorporating Dwight-Lloyd downdraught sintering machines and a lead blast furnace to treat this material. The sinter beds, small blast furnaces and the Newnam Hearths were shut down and the new plant was started in January, 1953.

This plant however, did not fulfil its full function. The handling of the leach residue presented an unsurmountable problem. It was for the most part a chemical precipitate, extremely finely divided, clayey in texture and containing up to 60% moisture. The proportion of return sinter required to reduce this moisture to ± 10% for proper pelletisation of the feed to the sinter strands, was extremely high. The result was that the production capacity of the sinter machines was insufficient to satisfy the furnace requirements.

The leach residue also contained considerable silica requiring heavy flux additions of ironstone and lime thus reducing the metal tenor of the sinter, and increasing the slag make.

Considerable effort was expended in attempting to improve the operation, but the only practical way to improve sinter production was to lower the tonnage of leach residue treated. Although in the end the plant operated satisfactorily in that it produced lead it was not achieving its prime objective, the recovery of lead from leach residue.

With high lead prices it was at least profitable to produce lead from the leach residue, but with the fall in prices towards the end of 1957 it became clear that this small quantity of lead was not worth producing and that higher profits could be made on lower lead production by reverting to the Newnam Hearth operation which, on lead concentrate alone, was efficient and cheap.

At the end of 1957, therefore, the blast furnace was closed down and the Newnam Hearths once again became the primary producer of lead, the grey slag being stockpiled.

At about this time test work was initiated into improved methods for the rejection of dolomite from the mixed ore in the sorting plant and to reduce labour costs. Increased production of electrolytic zinc using the dumped silicate ores was also in progress after an extension to the electrolytic zinc plant in 1953. Vanadium production had been discontinued in 1952 as uneconomic and there was no reason to sort vanadium ores, which had almost disappeared from the sorting belts. As a result a Heavy Media Drum Separation plant using ferrosilicon as the medium replaced the sorting plant. Selective mining of the ores was discontinued and ore extraction from the Mine was improved since it was feasible to hoist more dolomite with the ore. The Heavy Media plant sink product, containing all the previously sorted high grade sulphides and zinc silicate ore, now became the flotation feed and the float product the waste dolomite.

The metallurgical complex at this stage was recovering only about 55% of the lead and 65% of the zinc from the ore mined. The losses were tied up in dump stocks of leach residue, in the grey slag produced from the Newnam Hearths and in the mixed fines flotation tailings.

Laboratory and pilot scale tests on the differential zinc/vanadium leach on the stockpile of mixed fines tailing which had accumulated from the treatment of the mixed ores in the new concentrator had proved unsuccessful on a plant scale. Acid consumption was high due to the high dolomite content and the contained fluorine followed the zinc into the cell room with consequent hard stripping. The recovery of vanadium was also unattractive.

Considerable thought was directed towards improving the recovery of metals from accumulated slag and residue dumps. Plans were drawn up to improve the blast furnace plant by increasing sinter capacity. However in the light of recent developments, there were other possibly more effective methods of dealing with the problem.

The treatment of the sulphide minerals presented little difficulty, but it became clear that recovery of metal from the oxidised ores reduced itself to the elimination of silica. Some form of fuming process was indicated and thought was given to the use of a Waelz Kiln for the treatment of dump silicate material and blast furnace slag, discarding the residue. Calculations revealed that the melting point of the charge would be too low and it was considered that ringing of the kiln would result in insurmountable operating difficulty. These plans were abandoned.

Attention was then directed towards slag fuming plants. Such plants usually treated molten slag only, but a certain amount of cold material could also be added. The oxide fume would be collected and leached for zinc recovery and the residue containing the lead returned to the blast furnace.

A project team was set up in 1957 to study operating plants of this type and in the course of their investigation they visited Avonmouth to discuss with Imperial Smelting Processes Limited their new process for the simultaneous production of lead and zinc. Large samples of the materials to be treated were shipped to Avonmouth for testing in their sinter plant and experimental furnace. The test work was highly successful and the project team examined in detail the relative merits of the Imperial Smelting Process and the slag fuming plant. Their findings indicated that both processes yielded similar metal recoveries and profitability, but that the capital expenditure for the fuming plant would be much greater, mainly because of the additional electrolytic zinc recovery plant necessary.

TABLE II

Year	Lead	Zinc	Fused V_2O_5	Cadmium	Silver	Remarks
	Tonnes	Tonnes	Tonnes	Kg	Kg	
1915	427					Experimental blast furnace started.
1916	1,321					
1917	5,312					
1918	9,308					Fourth blast furnace installed
1919	11,392					
1920	14,836					
1921	18,412					
1922	20,829					
1923	11,041					
1924	5,929					
1925	3,332					
1926	3,894					Mulungushi power started
1927	5,951					
1928	4,751	9,732				
1929	1,661	12,315				Electro-zinc plant started
1930		18,194				Lead production ceased
1931	-	7,038	272			Production of fused vandic oxide.
1932	-	-	369			Zinc production suspended
1933	-	18,838	71			
1934	-	19,853	-			
1935	-	20,975	106			
1936	-	21,062	182			
1937	568	14,255	291			Exploration extended.
1938	277	10,378	729			Davis shaft started.
1939	163	12,898	748			Underground Mining.
1940	292	13,401	722			Canadium flotation.
1941	378	13,762	671			
1942	1,118	13,045	755			
1943	1,265	13,619	837			
1944	1,046	14,712	502			
1945	1,747	15,484	431			Lunsemfwa power plant
1946	8,371	17,465	133			New concentrator.
1947	15,890	21,478	110			Newnam Hearths installed.
1948	13,228	22,525	335			
1949	14,168	23,216	298			
1950	13,904	23,078	-			
1951	14,194	22,952	170			
1952	12,801	23,256	84			
1953	11,694	25,735	-			Zinc plant extended
1954	15,240	26,975	-			Lead blast furnace installed.
1955	16,307	28,346	-			
1956	15,443	29,388	-	52,709		Cadmium production started
1957	15,240	29,972	-	56,619		
1958	12,878	30,734	-	17,356	1,702	Silver production
1959	14,630	30,373	-	-	7,990	Blast furnaces shut down.
1960	14,660	30,271	-	26,289	4,297	
1961	15,381	30,339	-	18,913	4,178	
1962	14,088	40,437	-	16,859	1,610	I.S.F. plant started
1963	18,926	49,404	-	14,993	3,455	
1964	13,327	46,756	-	14,631	1,441	Independence of Zambia.
1965	21,427	47,419	-	18,159	420	
1966	19,871	42,317	-	12,093	5,293	
1967	20,169	45,196	-	6,830	4,649	
1968	22,652	53,212	-	11,273	4,590	
1969	23,672	50,165	-	6,046	2,791	
55 yrs	503,410	1,040,570	7,816	272,770	42,418	

The decision was, therefore, taken to install the Imperial Smelting Furnace and Sinter Plant, which was commissioned in January, of 1962. This plant is operating today, together with the electrolytic zinc plant.

In October, 1964 the Republic of Zambia achieved independence from the Federation of Rhodesia and Nyasaland. Northern Rhodesia became Zambia, and the town of Broken Hill was renamed Kabwe.

Table II (2) summarises the metal production statistics and the major developments in the history of the Mine.

Lead Smelting Practice

Throughout the history of the Mine no less than four major types of plant have been utilised for lead production.

Each plant was designed to treat different raw materials or prepared blends of the various ores and residues produced.

1. Early Blast Furnaces

As narrated earlier, commercial production of lead was started in 1916 when a small experimental blast furnace with an output of approximately 100 tonnes per month was in operation. In July, 1917 two larger water jacketed furnaces, each capable of smelting 150 tons per day of ore, were put into commission and in 1920 two additional blast furnaces were installed.

Over the period 1916 to 1922 the lead charged to the furnaces was almost entirely as oxidised ore consisting mainly of cerussite selectively mined from No. 1 Kopje orebody. The depletion of this class of ore as the sulphide zone was approached necessitated the installation of concentration and sintering equipment.

The early concentration plant relied on jigs and Wilfley tables for gravity separation of the valuable minerals and later a flotation plant was added for further recovery from the slimes fraction removed prior to concentration. The flotation plant consisted of standard minerals separation machines with 14 boxes of 150 tons daily capacity.

Double pass sintering was conducted in open hearths; these were set in pits at ground level, each hearth having a grate area of 9.4 metres x 0.3 metres.

The sinter charge consisted of lead concentrates from the

jigs, tables and flotation plant, plus granulated slag and a small amount of oxidised lead ore.

The blast furnace charge then consisted of sinter, limestone, ironstone and Wankie coke, which was transported to the feed floor by inclined haulage. (Figure 5)

Figure 5 : Early blast furnaces - 1920.

Both the sinter hearths and blast furnaces were vented direct to atmosphere with no attempt at fume collection.

The lead bullion from each blast furnace discharged via a lead well to a small wood-fired drossing pot. The bullion was then drossed and moulded into pigs. Lead bullion produced in this manner contained approximately 99.5% lead and dross was re-treated in a small liquating furnace.

The blast furnace slag was tapped to a forehearth which overflowed to a granulator, and the granulated slag was transported to the dump.

The metallurgy of the operation of the plant is demonstrated by the annual figures reported for 1926. (Table III).

TABLE III

	Tonnes	% Pb	% Zn
Feed to the Plants			
Sulphide ore to Concentrator	13,813	25.6	34.6
Oxidised ore	1,915	19.0	34.6
Sulphide slime to flotation	17,959	21.1	33.7
Gravity Concentration Plant			
Sulphide ore milled	13,333	25.8	34.8
Lead concentrate produced	3,084	64.5	12.9
Zinc concentrate produced	6,712	9.6	44.4
Sulphide slime tailing	3,537	22.3	35.0
Flotation Plant			
Sulphide slime treated	17,943	21.1	33.7
Lead concentrate produced	3,522	57.9	13.5
Flotation tails	14,421	12.0	38.2
Sinter Plant			
Lead gravity concentrate	3,084	64.5	12.9
Lead flotation concentrate	3,511	57.9	13.5
Oxidised ore	1,606	16.0	19.3
Hand-picked ore	93	64.5	14.0
Dump slag	2,810	4.6	18.5
Sinter Produced:	11,104	37.9	12.7
Blast Furnace			
Input: Sinter smelted	10,743	37.9	12.7
Oxide ore	308	32.2	26.1
Output: Slag produced	11,495	4.4	15.5
Lead bullion	3,475		

Commercial scale smelting operations were discontinued in 1929 as the lead ore above the water level then established had been worked out and a small production only was maintained for plant use, except during the war years when the blast furnaces were restarted.

2. The Newnam Hearth Plant[3]

Lead production for the market was recommended in 1946 in the newly constructed Newnam Hearth plant, following the completion of an expansion programme for the exploitation of the sulphide ore bodies at depth.

The Newnam Hearth process is suitable only for the treatment of high grade sulphide lead concentrate and is usually used for lead extraction from granular Galena concentrates. It was applied at Broken Hill for the treatment of finely divided flotation concentrates for which efficient dust and fume collection equipment was provided. (Figure 6).

Figure 6 : Newnam Hearth Plant 1946 with sinter beds top right, and cupola type furnace stacks top left.

The plant comprised of five hearths each consisting of a cast iron sump (2.4 metres long x 23 cms. deep - tapering from 42 cms to 25 cms width) which received the lead, and provided with an overflow taphole at one end. The charge rests on top of the lead bath and the smelting zone is enclosed on three sides by water jackets. Tuyeres 25 mm. in diameter are provided on one side and the other side is left open for charging.

The hearth and sloping workplate on the charging side are ventilated by a baghouse. A mechanical rabbling machine with alloy steel poker is provided on the charging side. (Figure 7).

Figure 7 : Newnam Hearth showing workplate and rabbling mechanism.

The moist concentrates are mixed with baghouse and flue dust and fed to the hearths by shovel. Some pea coal is added to the charge to provide the heat necessary to allow the endothermic reduction reactions to proceed. The lead droplets formed coalesce and run into the sump and are periodically tapped off.

The impurities in the concentrate mainly Fe, Zn and SiO_2 form into semifused lumps as the lead is reduced. These lumps are the grey slag assaying approximately 40% Pb, 20% Zn, 10% Fe, 1% Sulphur, CaO 1% and minor amounts of Cu, Ag, Sb and As.

Table IV summarises the metallurgical balance.

TABLE IV

Newnam Hearth Metallurgy (year 1952)

Smelted	Tonnes	% Pb	Tonnes Pb	% Distribution
Lead concs.	17,413	76.7	13,354	97.1
Flue dust	-	-	387	2.9
			13,741	100.0
Produced				
Refined lead	-	-	11,859	86.3
Grey slag	3,375	39.5	1,330	9.7
Copper dross	210	-	145	1.1
Stack loss	-	-	407	2.9
			13,741	100.0

The lead produced was partially refined by sulphur drossing for copper removal, followed by causticizing for the removal of zinc, arsenic and antimony. The resulting bullion contained 99.96+% Pb, 0.005% Cu, 0.025% Ag and minor amounts of Bi and other impurities. This product was acceptable to customers at the time, the chief of whom were South African Cable Manufacturers. The small silver content also helped to make it suitable for chemical plant use and is used to produce lead sheet and pipe in the Company's own rolling mill.

3. Dwight-Lloyd Sinter Plant and Lead Blast Furnace

From 1953 to the end of 1957 lead production was increased by the operation of the new plant incorporating Dwight-Lloyd downdraught sintering and a blast furnace. (Figure 8).

Figure 8 : View of Dwight-Lloyd Sinter Plant and Blast Furnace - 1953.

The two major feed materials to the sinter plant were the high grade lead concentrate requiring little if any flux, and the leach residue containing some 30% SiO_2, requiring considerable flux in the form of ironstone and limestone.

The proportioned concentrates and limestone, ironstone, granulated slag and the required amount of fuel in the form of coke breeze were fed together with return sinter into specially designed paddle mixers.

The reclaimed leach residue was separately proportioned to the mixers. This wet mix passed through the pelletizing drums ahead of each of the three Dwight-Lloyd downdraught sinter machines, before being fed to the sinter strands.

ZAMBIA BROKEN HILL DEVELOPMENT COMPANY L^{TD}
DIAGRAMMATIC FLOWSHEET – SINTER PLANT & BLAST FURNACE
1953 - 1957

FIGURE 9

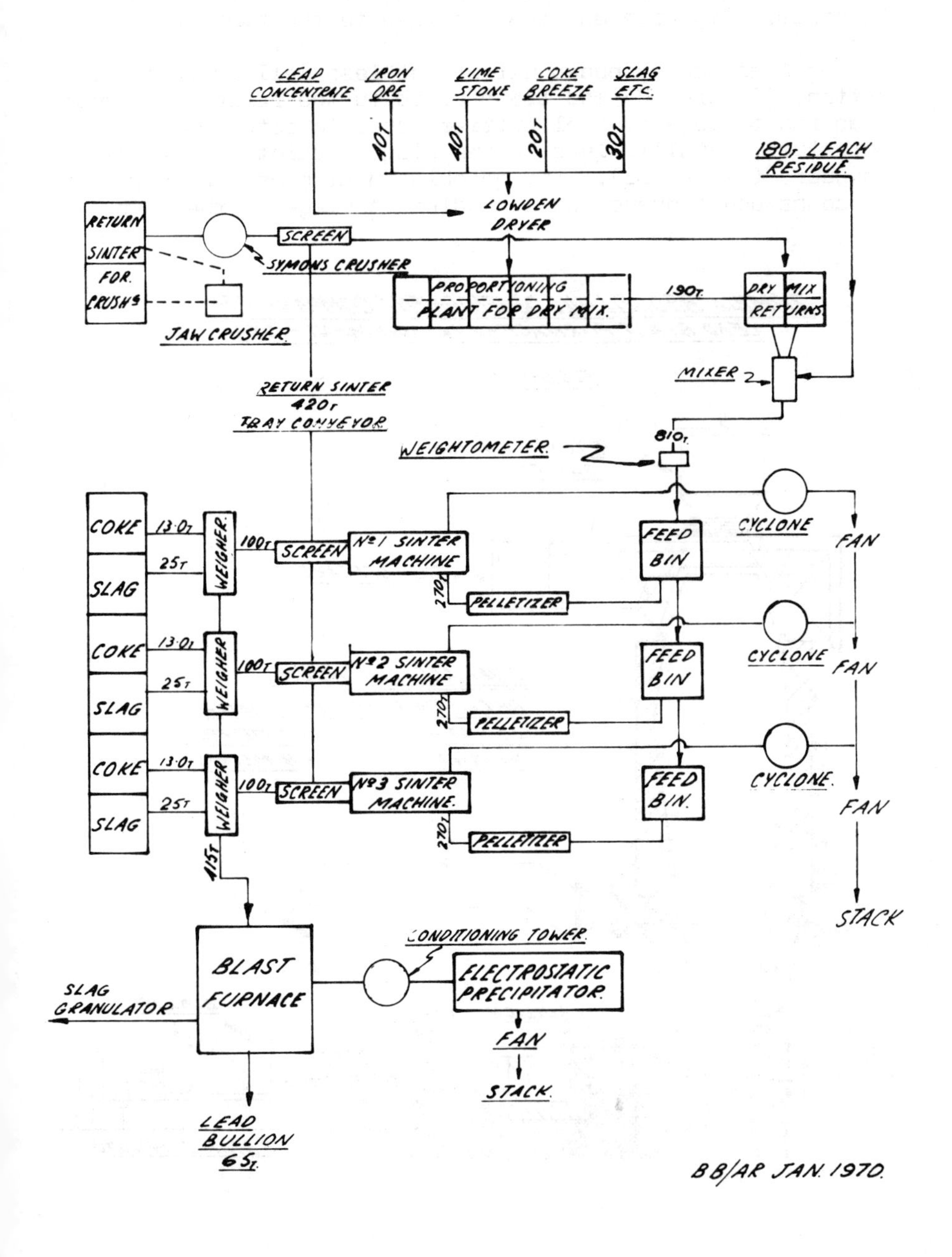

The discharged sinter was screened at 25 mm. the oversize forming the feed to the blast furnace, while the -25 mm. was returned to the proportioning and mixing plant. (Figure 9).

The blast furnace charge consisted of sinter, return settler slag and reclaimed lump slag from the old blast furnaces. Pig iron was also charged to the furnace.

The lead was syphoned out of the lead well in 1½ tonne buttons (Figure 10) and transferred to the refinery. While slag ran through conical settler pots, to catch any entrained, metallic lead in the slag, and into a granulating launder. (Figure 11). The granulated slag was scraped into cocopans and transported by endless haulage to the dump.

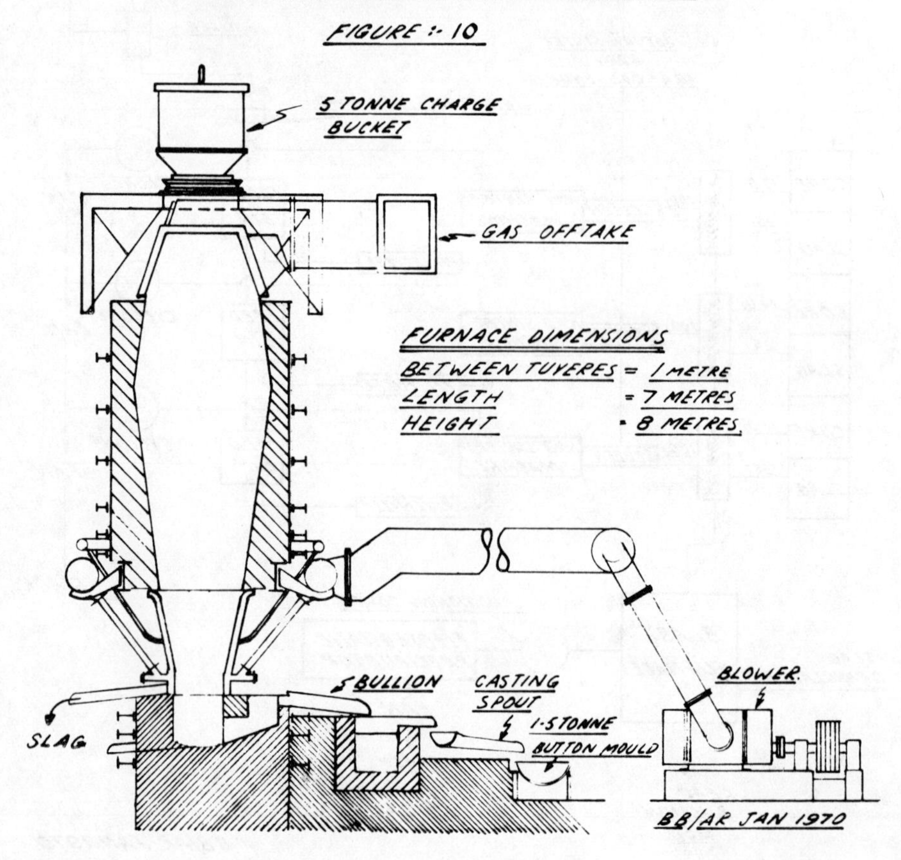

Figure 11 : Slag tapping from the lead blast furnace.

Due to the comparatively low lead grade of the sinter and the consequent low lead fall, the lead well frequently froze through crust formation between the lead and slag interface. The lead well was bricked in and an external forehearth of suitable design installed, which solved the problem.

The poor quality of the sinter caused the rapid development of accretions in the furnace shaft and explosive blasting techniques were employed every five days as a routine to remove them.

Furnace campaigns were indeed short, the longest lasting a little over 100 days. Nevertheless considerable lead was produced and the plant finally closed down at the end of 1957, and Newnam hearth smelting was resumed.

Typical metallurgical results from the Dwight-Lloyd sintering and blast furnace plant are given in Table V.

TABLE V (figures for August 1954)

	Tonnes	% Pb	Pb content Tonnes	% Distribution
Sinter Plant Feed				
Concentrates	1,729	76.8	1,328	
Drosses	349	-	224	
Granulated slag	949	5.2	48	
Gray Slag	94	39.0	36	
Ironstone	190	-	-	
Limesand	1,279	-	-	
Coke	590	-	-	
Total Dry Mix	5,180	31.6	1,636	
Leach residues	2,984	18.5	552	
Drosses	93	62.0	57	
New Feed	8,257	27.2	2,245	
Output				
Total sinter produced	23,084	-	-	100.0
Furnace sinter	7,613	28.3	2,118	18.9
Returns	15,471	-	-	81.1
Blast Furnace				
Smelted				
Sinter	8,533	27.9	2,383	98.1
Lump slag ex dump	207	4.1	9	.4
Return slag	227	3.0	7	.3
Scrap iron	85	-	-	-
Scrap Metallics	36	80.0	29	1.2
Coke 1015 tons @ 29.5% ash	271	-	-	-
	9,361		2,428	100.0
Production				
Lead bullion	-	-	2,302	94.8
Slag	6,980	1.4	98	4.0
Settler Slag	228	3.0	7	0.3
Dust loss	-	-	21	0.9
			2,428	100.0

Plant recoveries	Tonnes		
	Pb Input	Pb Output	%
Sinter plant	2,259	2,152	95.3
Blast furnace	2,428	2,302	94.8
Refinery	2,156	2,032	94.3

The slag analysed: Pb 1.4%, Zn 11.3%, FeO 31.1%, CaO 19.4%, SiO_2 20.8%, Al_2O_3 4.7%, S 1.4%.

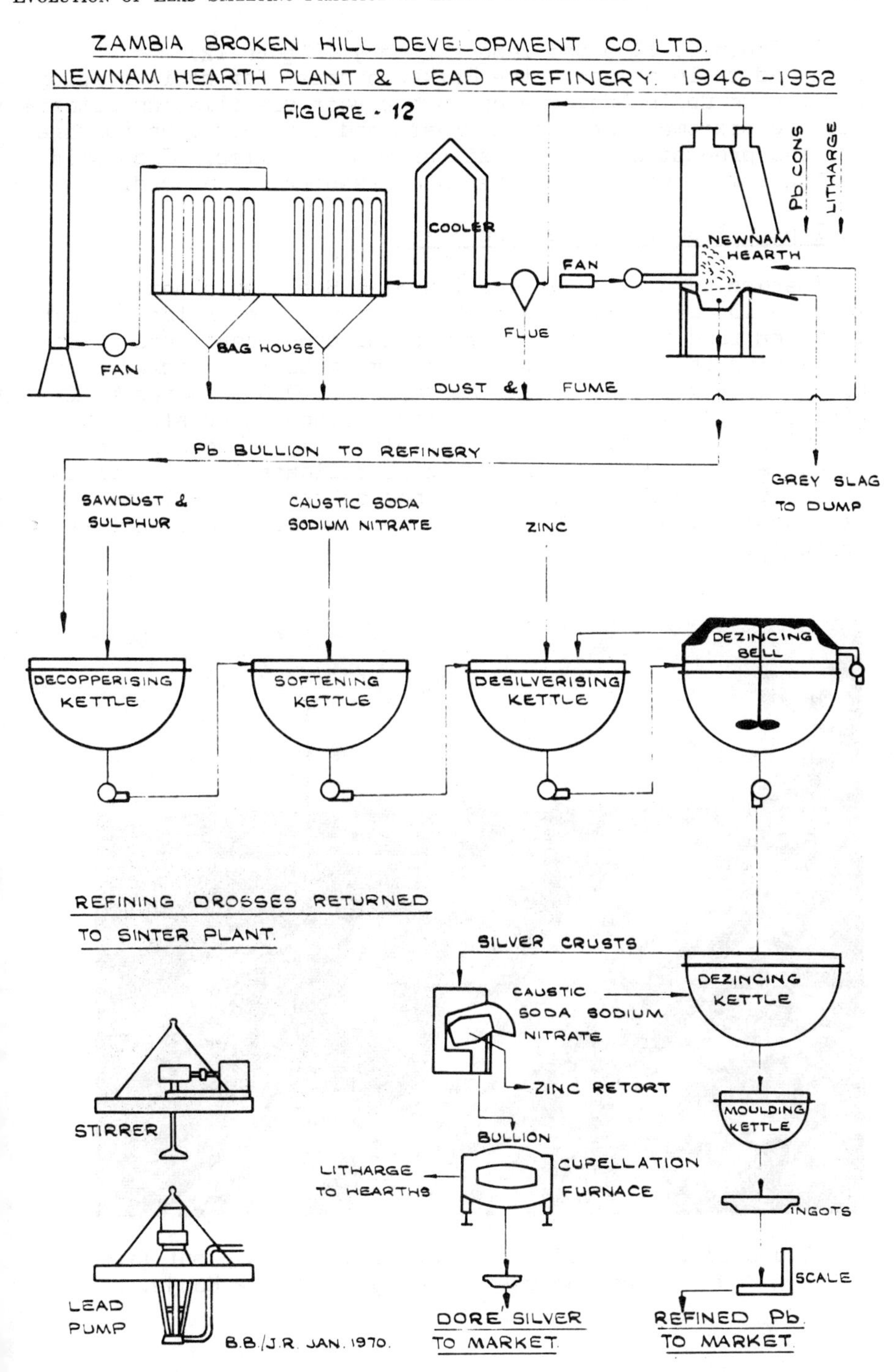
ZAMBIA BROKEN HILL DEVELOPMENT CO. LTD.
NEWNAM HEARTH PLANT & LEAD REFINERY. 1946 - 1952
FIGURE - 12
Pb CONS
LITHARGE
COOLER
NEWNAM HEARTH
FAN
FLUE
BAG HOUSE
FAN
DUST & FUME
Pb BULLION TO REFINERY
GREY SLAG TO DUMP
SAWDUST & SULPHUR
CAUSTIC SODA SODIUM NITRATE
ZINC
DEZINCING BELL
DECOPPERISING KETTLE
SOFTENING KETTLE
DESILVERISING KETTLE
REFINING DROSSES RETURNED TO SINTER PLANT.
SILVER CRUSTS
CAUSTIC SODA SODIUM NITRATE
DEZINCING KETTLE
ZINC RETORT
MOULDING KETTLE
STIRRER
BULLION
LITHARGE TO HEARTHS
CUPELLATION FURNACE
INGOTS
SCALE
LEAD PUMP
B.B./J.R. JAN. 1970.
DORE SILVER TO MARKET.
REFINED Pb. TO MARKET.

In January, 1955 the lead refinery (Figure 12) was extended to incorporate the Parkes process for desilverising and vacuum dezincing. Later in the year destillation retorts for the treatment of Parkes crusts and a cupellation furnace for the production of Dore silver was installed. From this refinery lead of +99.997% has been regularly produced.

4. Imperial Smelting Furnace Plant

The basic function of the Imperial Smelting plant (Figure 13) was to substantially increase production of both lead and zinc from dump materials and underground ore without increasing the mining rate. The dump materials included the mixed fines tailings amounting to some 640,000 tonnes @ 22% zinc and 11% lead, old blast furnace slags, grey slag and leach residues. All these materials were included in the charge except dump and current zinc silicate leach residues. It was decided that these would not be treated until mine ore is exhausted, unless the furnace turned out to have excess capacity.

Figure 13 : View of the Imperial Smelting plant from the opencast workings of No. 2 Kopje.

Since the Imperial Smelting Furnace forms part of an integrated mining and treatment programme, a general description of the flowsheet is necessary. This is detailed in Figure 14 showing data for an average operating month.

5. Concentrator

All the mined ore is hoisted through primary crushing and washing plant. No attempt is made to separate high grade sulphides and mixed ores. The -6 m.m. fraction is screened out and fed to an Akins Spiral classifier which separates a sands fraction from a slime fraction. The sands fraction or mixed fines is transported to the Sinter Plant proportioning bunkers. The washing plant slime fraction after thickening is filtered and blended with dump materials and fed to the drier.

The +6 m.m. portion is treated in the Heavy Media Drum separator to remove the dolomite waste rock. The sink product is crushed, ground and treated in the flotation plant yielding a lead concentrate, a zinc concentrate and a tailing which is in fact a comparatively high grade silicate zinc ore.

As mining has proceeded in depth the incidence of pyrite in the ore has increased to the extent that when floated with the lead concentrate the iron content is too high for optimum I.S.F. slag composition. The concentrator flowsheet (Figure 15) has therefore been modified to remove a pyrite concentrate which is currently dumped.

Table VI shows the concentrator metallurgy.

ZAMBIA BROKEN HILL DEVELOPMENT COMPANY LIMITED.

TREATMENT PROGRAMME FOR AVERAGE MONTH - 1969

FIGURE :- 14

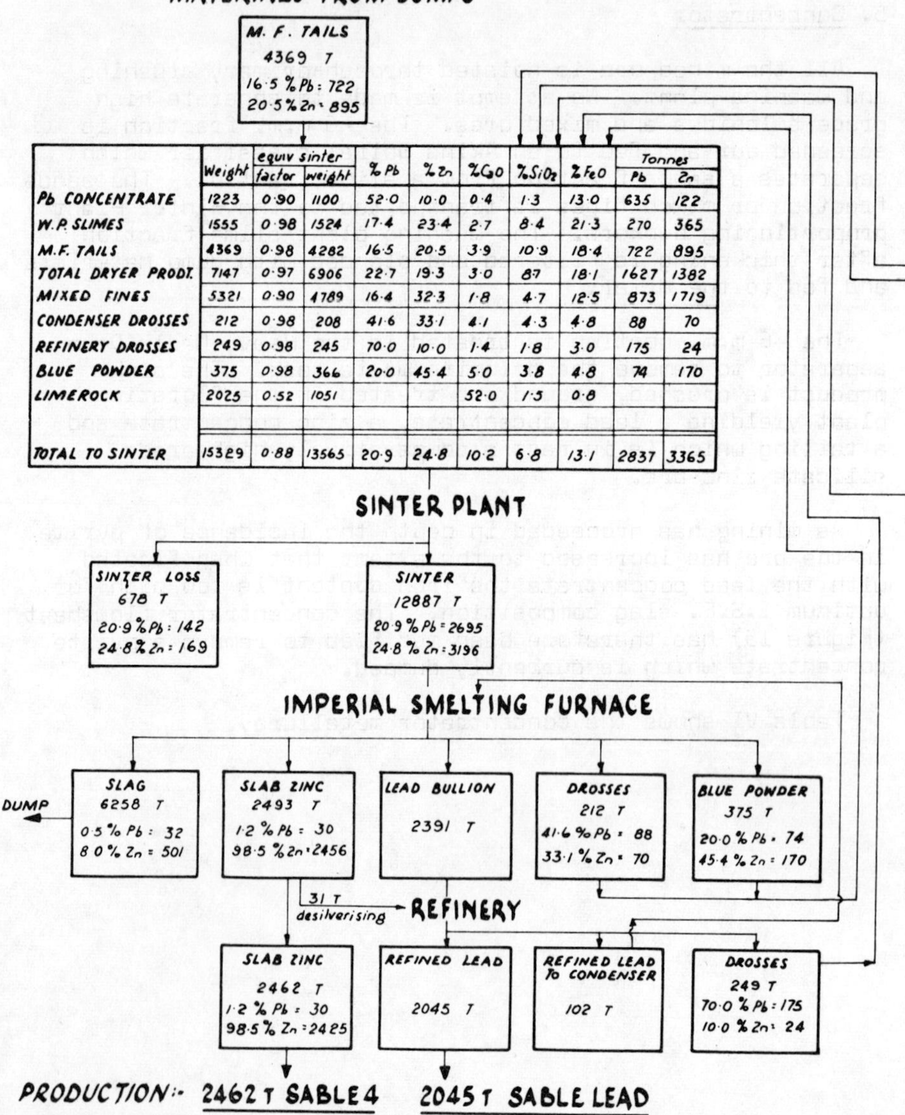

	Weight	equiv sinter factor	equiv sinter weight	% Pb	% Zn	% CaO	% SiO_2	% FeO	Tonnes Pb	Tonnes Zn
Pb CONCENTRATE	1223	0·90	1100	52·0	10·0	0·4	1·3	13·0	635	122
W.P. SLIMES	1555	0·98	1524	17·4	23·4	2·7	8·4	21·3	270	365
M.F. TAILS	4369	0·98	4282	16·5	20·5	3·9	10·9	18·4	722	895
TOTAL DRYER PRODT.	7147	0·97	6906	22·7	19·3	3·0	8·7	18·1	1627	1382
MIXED FINES	5321	0·90	4789	16·4	32·3	1·8	4·7	12·5	873	1719
CONDENSER DROSSES	212	0·98	208	41·6	33·1	4·1	4·3	4·8	88	70
REFINERY DROSSES	249	0·98	245	70·0	10·0	1·4	1·8	3·0	175	24
BLUE POWDER	375	0·98	366	20·0	45·4	5·0	3·8	4·8	74	170
LIMEROCK	2025	0·52	1051			52·0	1·5	0·8		
TOTAL TO SINTER	15329	0·88	13565	20·9	24·8	10·2	6·8	13·1	2837	3365

PRODUCTION :- 2462 T SABLE 4 2045 T SABLE LEAD

RECOVERIES :-

REFINERY	Pb	89·8 %	MELTER	Zn	88·0 %
LEACH	Zn	82·0 %	I.S.F	Pb	85·5 %
				Zn	76·8 %

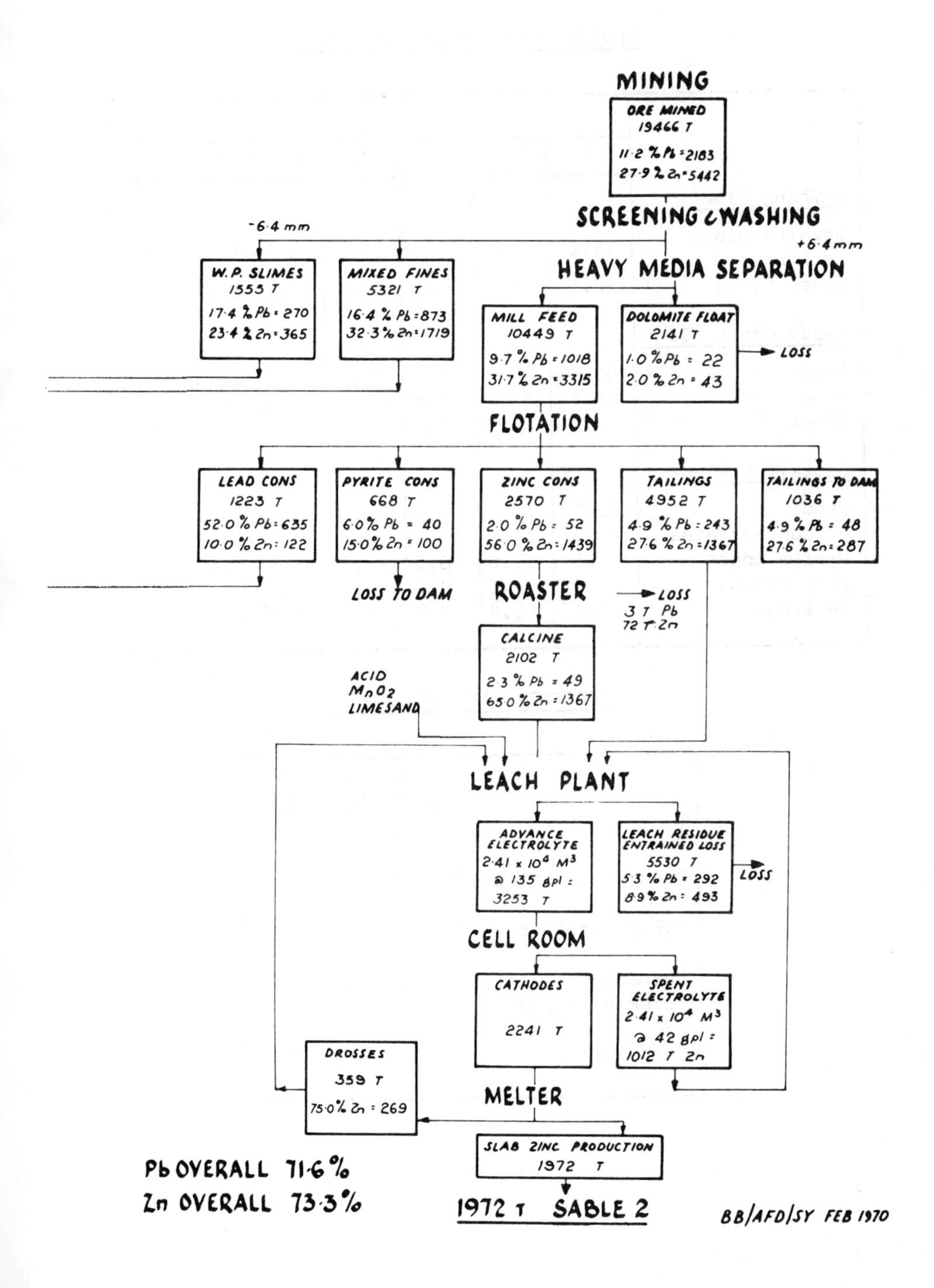
MINING
ORE MINED
19466 T
11·2 % Pb = 2183
27·9 % Zn = 5442
SCREENING & WASHING
-6·4 mm
+6·4 mm
W.P. SLIMES
1555 T
17·4 % Pb = 270
23·4 % Zn = 365
MIXED FINES
5321 T
16·4 % Pb = 873
32·3 % Zn = 1719
HEAVY MEDIA SEPARATION
MILL FEED
10449 T
9·7 % Pb = 1018
31·7 % Zn = 3315
DOLOMITE FLOAT
2141 T
1·0 % Pb = 22
2·0 % Zn = 43
LOSS
FLOTATION
LEAD CONS
1223 T
52·0 % Pb = 635
10·0 % Zn = 122
PYRITE CONS
668 T
6·0 % Pb = 40
15·0 % Zn = 100
ZINC CONS
2570 T
2·0 % Pb = 52
56·0 % Zn = 1439
TAILINGS
4952 T
4·9 % Pb = 243
27·6 % Zn = 1367
TAILINGS TO DAM
1036 T
4·9 % Pb = 48
27·6 % Zn = 287
LOSS TO DAM
ROASTER
LOSS
3 T Pb
72 T Zn
CALCINE
2102 T
2·3 % Pb = 49
65·0 % Zn = 1367
ACID
MnO2
LIMESAND
LEACH PLANT
ADVANCE ELECTROLYTE
2·41 x 10⁴ M³
@ 135 gpl =
3253 T
LEACH RESIDUE ENTRAINED LOSS
5530 T
5·3 % Pb = 292
8·9 % Zn = 493
LOSS
CELL ROOM
CATHODES
2241 T
SPENT ELECTROLYTE
2·41 x 10⁴ M³
@ 42 gpl =
1012 T Zn
DROSSES
359 T
75·0 % Zn = 269
MELTER
SLAB ZINC PRODUCTION
1972 T
1972 T SABLE 2
Pb OVERALL 71·6 %
Zn OVERALL 73·3 %
BB/AFD/SY FEB 1970

TABLE VI

CONCENTRATOR METALLURGY 1969

	Assay						
	% Wt.	T/Pb	S/Pb	T/Zn	ZnS	Fe	CaO
Washing Plant							
Washing plant slime	11.1	18.5	9.6	22.2	13.3	17.3	4.1
Mixed fines	22.1	20.0	15.4	29.4	20.9	13.9	3.3
Heavy Media Plant							
Feed	66.8	9.3	6.1	25.1	10.8	14.6	4.8
Sink	52.8	11.2	7.5	30.8	13.4	16.1	0.7
Float	14.0	2.0	0.7	3.5	0.8	9.0	20.2
Flotation Plant							
Feed	100.0	11.2	7.5	30.8	13.4	16.1	-
Pb concentrates	16.5	44.9	42.1	13.4	9.7	14.1	-
Pyrite concs.	4.8	1.6	0.3	13.3	7.3	36.4	-
Zinc concs.	19.3	1.1	0.9	59.9	56.3	4.1	-
Tailings	59.4	5.8	0.7	27.6	0.9	18.9	0.8

REAGENT GRAMS PER TONNE

	Pb Circuit	Zn Circuit
Soda ash	560	-
Isopropyl Xanthate	90	115
T.E.B. Frother	48	30
Cyanide to lead cleaner circuit	50	-
Copper sulphate	-	370

ZAMBIA BROKEN HILL DEVELOPMENT COMPANY LIMITED
DIAGRAMMATIC FLOWSHEET - CONCENTRATOR - 1969
FIGURE:- 15

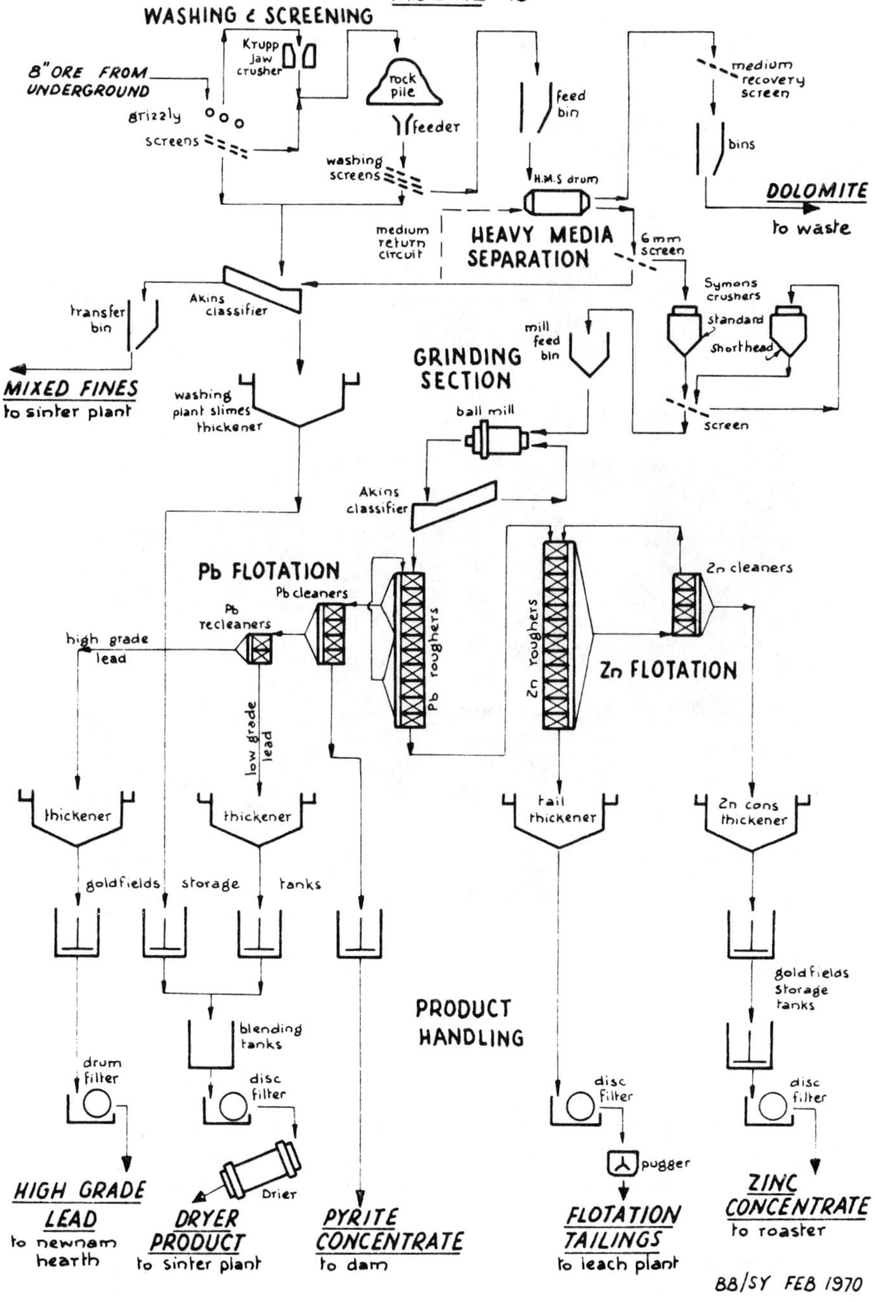

WASHING & SCREENING
8" ORE FROM UNDERGROUND
Krupp Jaw crusher
rock pile
grizzly
screens
feeder
washing screens
feed bin
H.M.S drum
medium recovery screen
bins
DOLOMITE
to waste
medium return circuit
HEAVY MEDIA SEPARATION
6mm screen
Akins classifier
transfer bin
MIXED FINES
to sinter plant
Symons crushers
standard
Shorthead
mill feed bin
GRINDING SECTION
washing plant slimes thickener
ball mill
screen
Akins classifier
Pb FLOTATION
Pb cleaners
Pb recleaners
high grade lead
low grade lead
Pb roughers
Zn roughers
Zn cleaners
Zn FLOTATION
thickener
thickener
tail thickener
Zn cons thickener
goldfields storage tanks
goldfields storage tanks
blending tanks
PRODUCT HANDLING
drum filter
disc filter
disc filter
disc filter
pugger
Drier
HIGH GRADE LEAD
to newnam hearth
DRYER PRODUCT
to sinter plant
PYRITE CONCENTRATE
to dam
FLOTATION TAILINGS
to leach plant
ZINC CONCENTRATE
to roaster

BB/SY FEB 1970

6. Electrolytic Zinc Leach Plant

Although not relevant to the history of lead smelting practice it is interesting to include a short description of electrolytic zinc production to complete the metallurgical picture.

The zinc concentrate produced by flotation is roasted in the flash roaster and the gases converted to sulphuric acid in the lead chamber plant. (Figure 16).

Figure 16 : View of Roaster and Acid Plant left and Leach Plant.

The acid plant first came into production in 1926 when a sulphur burner provided the gases for acid making. Later Herreschoff roasters burning pyrite obtained from the company's Iron Duke Mine in Rhodesia were installed. The flash roaster burning zinc concentrate superseded the Herreschoff roasters.

The roaster calcine and the flotation tailing are combined for leaching and electrolytic zinc production. (Figure 17).

ZAMBIA BROKEN HILL DEVELOPMENT COMPANY LIMITED
DIAGRAMMATIC FLOWSHEET - LEACH PLANT - 1969
FIGURE:-17

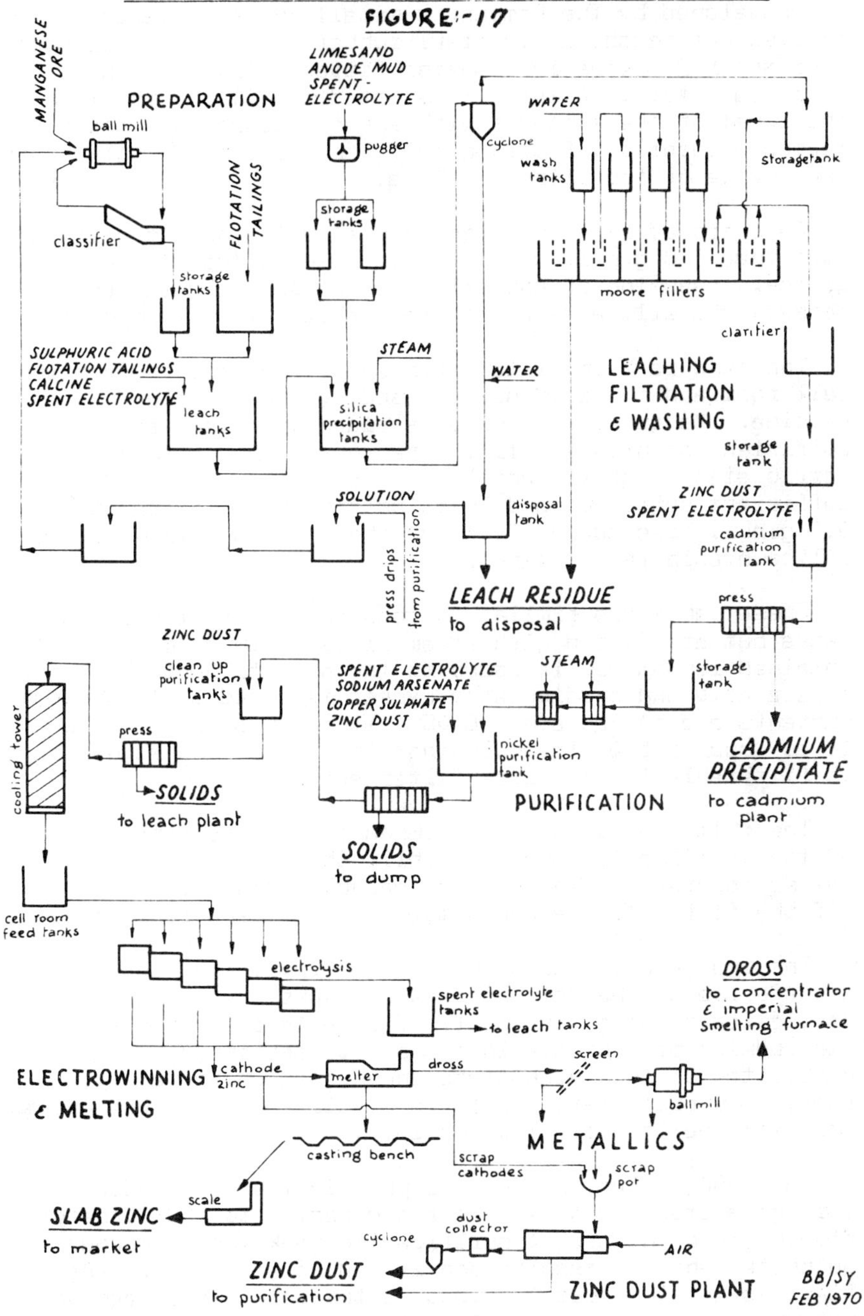

The unique leaching technique (1), which overcomes the problem of the filtration of pulps containing soluble silica was developed by the Company's metallurgists. Leaching is carried out batchwise in steel rubber-lined tanks 5.2 metres deep and 5.2 metres in diameter fitted with Denver high speed agitators. A leach is started by filling the tanks to the level of the agitator with spent electrolytic and a measured quantity of strong acid, followed by 11 to 12 tonnes per charge of flotation tailings.

This procedure ensures an initial acid concentration of more than 300 g.p.l. sulphuric acid which 'dehydrates' the silica. Leaching of the silicates at low acid tenors renders the silica gelatinous and filtration is impossible.

The tank is then filled with spent electrolyte from the cell room and the acid neutralised by the addition of calcine. Manganese ore pulp is added at this stage sufficient to oxidise all the ferrous sulphate to the ferric state. After additional calcine has been added and sufficient agitation and leaching time has elapsed at about 0.5 g.p.l. free sulphuric acid, the pulp is pumped to the silica precipitation tanks.

These tanks are similar in construction to the leach tanks but are fitted with steam lines. Limesand, a locally obtained limestone, is added to the pulp to neutralise the excess acid and a calculated excess is added while the tank contents are heated above 65°C. It is this operation which is so important in 'granulating' the silica and rendering it filterable in the Moore filter section.

The filtered solution is pumped to storage tanks ahead of the purification section, while the filter cake is washed counter currently. The washed residue is hosed off the filter leaves and pumped to the leach residue dumps.

The impure $ZnSO_4$ solution at 130 g.p.l. zinc is transferred to the Cd purification tanks where the Cd is precipitated using zinc dust. The Cd is recovered from the Cadmium precipitate in a separate section by re-precipitation to a high grade and melted under caustic soda. The crude metal cast, is distilled to +99.95% purity. and extruded into pencils for sale.

The $ZnSO_4$ solution after Cd purification is pumped through a steam heat exchanger and heated to +80°C, before flowing into the nickel purification tanks where copper sulphate, sodium arsenite and zinc dust are added. As a final stage zinc dust is added to the solution to remove residual copper and other impurities and after passing over

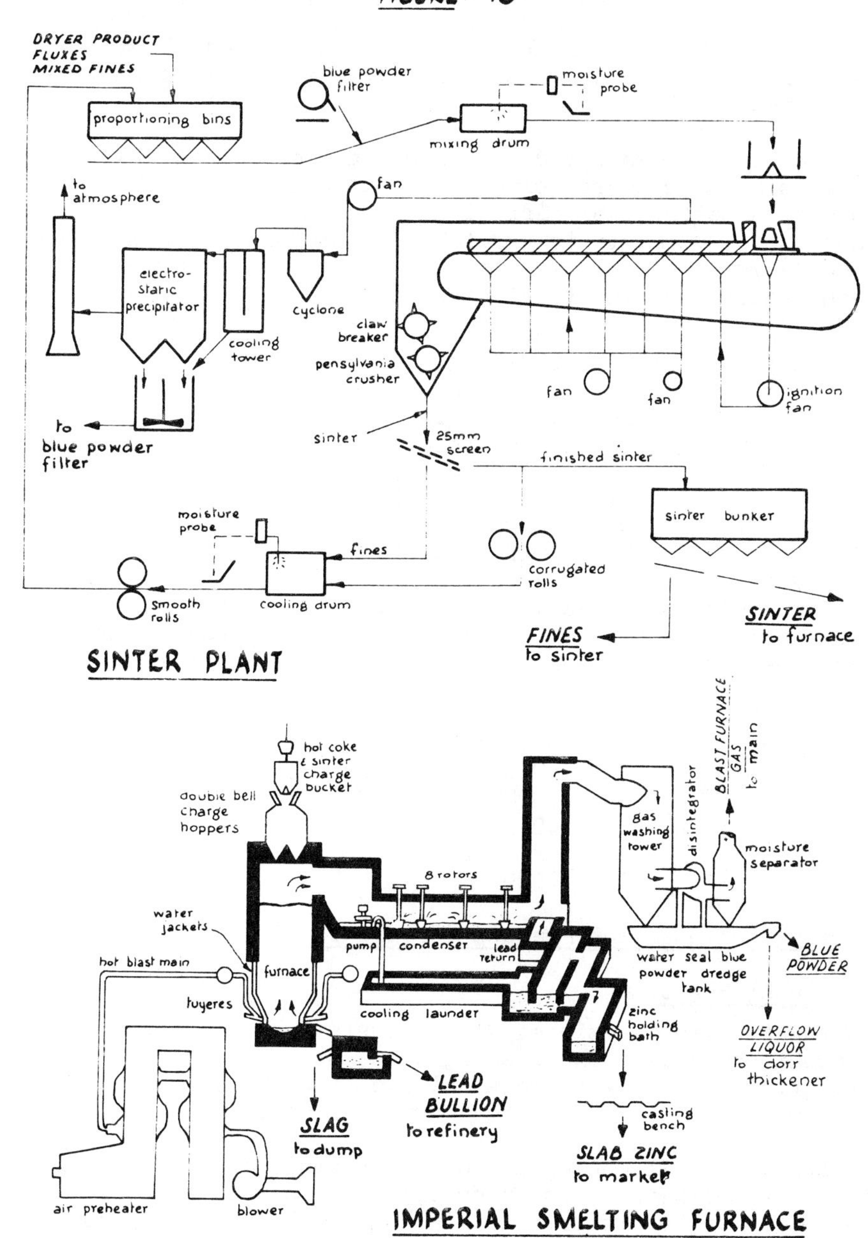
ZAMBIA BROKEN HILL DEVELOPMENT COMPANY LIMITED.
DIAGRAMMATIC FLOWSHEETS - 1962
FIGURE :- 18
DRYER PRODUCT
FLUXES
MIXED FINES
proportioning bins
blue powder filter
moisture probe
mixing drum
to atmosphere
fan
electro-static precipitator
cooling tower
cyclone
claw breaker
pensylvania crusher
fan
fan
ignition fan
to blue powder filter
sinter
25mm screen
finished sinter
sinter bunker
moisture probe
fines
corrugated rolls
smooth rolls
cooling drum
SINTER to furnace
FINES to sinter
SINTER PLANT
BLAST FURNACE GAS to main
hot coke & sinter charge bucket
double bell charge hoppers
gas washing tower
disintegrator
moisture separator
8 rotors
water jackets
pump
condenser
lead return
hot blast main
furnace
water seal blue powder dredge tank
BLUE POWDER
tuyeres
cooling launder
zinc holding bath
OVERFLOW LIQUOR to dorr thickener
LEAD BULLION to refinery
SLAG to dump
casting bench
SLAB ZINC to market
air preheater
blower
IMPERIAL SMELTING FURNACE
BB/SY FEB 1970

cooling towers is pumped to the cell room feed tanks.

Chlorine purification was discontinued early in 1968. The chlorine tenor of purified electrolyte is currently 500 to 600 mgms per litre. The chlorine has had no ill effect on current efficiency, now nearly 90%, or the lead tenor of deposited zinc.

The zinc is deposited in cascading wooden lead-lined tanks on aluminium cathodes using aluminium header bars with copper contacts. The current density is 26 amps per square foot and electrolyte temperature is maintained between 36 - 38°C by water circulating in lead cooling coils fitted in each cell. The electrolyte analyses:

Zn	130	g.p.l.
Fe	.0015	g.p.l.
Mn	9.3	g.p.l.
Cd	.0007	g.p.l.
Cu	.0003	g.p.l.
Cl	.566	g.p.l.
Ni	.0012	g.p.l.
Co	.0008	g.p.l.
F	.015	g.p.l.

The stripping cycle is 48 hours; the cathodes are at present melted in a coal fired reverberatory furnace and hand cast into 25 kg slabs for market, an analysis of which is:

Zn	99.95+	%
Pb	.020	%
Cu	.0007	%
Fe	.017	%
As	Tr	%
Cd	.0007	%

7. Imperial Smelting Process (Figure 18)

Sinter Plant

The feed to the sinter plant consists of the dryer product comprising the washing plant slime, lead concentrate from flotation, mixed fines tailing from the dumps and the -6 m.m. mixed fines from the washing plant.

The materials making up the dryer product are thickened, filtered and blended in predetermined proportions at the concentrator before drying in a Ruggles-Coles drier down to some 5% moisture. They are loaded into a rail wagon, weighed and transported to the sinter plant proportioning bins.

The -6 m.m. mixed fines from the washing plant are also weighed on a weighbridge and transferred via a railway wagon tippler system to the sinter plant proportioning bins. I.S.F. drosses, blue powder and lead refinery drosses are also re-cycled through the sinter plant proportioning system. Pulverised limerock is carefully proportioned to provide the necessary flux.

Coke breeze forms part of the sinter charge to satisfy the deficiency of sulphur fuel. The SO_2 contained in the Cotterel precipitator gases amounts to only 2 per cent which is too low for acid production.

Return sinter is cooled and crushed to 12% plus 4 mesh Tyler and forms 65% of the feed to the sinter strands.

There are two updraught sinter machines each of 28.5 sq. metres grate area. In recent years production rate of sinter has been improved from 8 to 13 tonnes per machine hour and the sulphur content reduced to 0.7%S with a rattler index of over 90%.

Imperial Smelting Furnace

The experimental work at Avonmouth determined that it was possible to successfully smelt a sinter produced from Broken Hill materials containing of the order of 28% lead and 20% zinc and that slags containing down to 2% of zinc could be achieved at acceptable carbon burning efficiencies. On start up in 1962 these results were not achieved and in the first year of operation no less than 9 campaigns were completed with a costly shaft clean out between each. In the second year 5 campaigns were completed, 4 in the third year, 3 in the fourth year and only one campaign per year in the last four years. Campaign 25 lasted 473 days.

It was soon discovered that it was impossible on a large scale to smelt a charge higher in lead than zinc without the rapid build up of accretion in the furnace shaft. The rate of accretion growth was greater than the rate at which it could be removed by blasting. Also, in reducing the zinc in slag to 2% by adjusting the carbon/ zinc ratio in the feed to the furnace, over-reduction occurred with metallic iron freezing in the taphole. To overcome these difficulties, the lead content of the sinter was reduced to below that of the zinc by producing a high grade lead concentrate in the concentrator for smelting in the Newnam hearths, two of which were restarted for the purpose. At the same time changes in sintering techniques were made and with improved quality sinter smelting operations improved.

The Imperial Smelting process has been adequately described in the literature (4) however there are some major differences in feed materials which make the Zambia Broken Hill operation somewhat unique among I.S.F. operators.

Sinter Production

The major constituents of the sinter charge are the mixed fines tailings from the dump and the current mixed fines ore from the concentrator. The composition of these materials with respect to both metal content and slag forming constituents particularly SiO_2 and FeO is extremely variable, which makes blending somewhat exacting. Sufficient limerock flux must be added to the sinter feed to maintain a CaO/SiO_2 ratio in sinter between 1.3 and 1.4, at present FeO levels, in order to produce a CaO/SiO_2 ratio in slag as near to 1.2 as possible.

With the lower grade of materials treated the metal content in sinter is maintained as high as the materials will allow and in all cases the zinc is maintained at a higher level than the lead. The difficulties experienced in the earlier years, were largely overcome when the lead content of the sinter was reduced to 20%, while the zinc content was of the order of 24%. Recent experience, however, has shown that the lead content can be increased to 25% as long as the zinc content is about 1% higher than the lead. Experiments, however, to determine the maximum lead content that can be tolerated in the sinter for smelting continue.

The major diluent in the sinter is silica, but has one advantage in that it makes possible the production of a very hard sinter. This quality is considered highly desirable for good Imperial Smelting furnace performance. Rattler indices of over 90% are not uncommon.

Careful screening of preheated coke and sinter before charging has been practised for some years now. No coke or sinter less than 1" in size finds its way into the furnace charge buckets. The major reason for this practice is to avoid carry over of sinter fines into the condenser, causing heavy dross make. In all charges coke is charged on top of sinter in the same bucket. Charge weights are reduced to the minimum maintaining a high charging rate; this produces more uniform temperature control in the furnace offtake.

Furnace Charging and Shaft Operation

Extensive testing has been carried out on charge and

blast distribution in the furnace shaft. These tests were directed towards reducing shaft accretion build up and avoiding blast channeling.

Some dramatic results were obtained with a plug bell system, designed to distribute the coarser fraction of the charge nearer to the furnace walls, inducing a wall working condition in the furnace. There was no shaft accretion build up, and in fact, the existing accretion was completely smelted away.

Unfortunately at the same time, however, production rates dropped by about 20%. Poor blast distribution was the cause of the poor furnace performance. No other charging equipment or technique yet tested has proved more advantageous than the conventional double bell system.

Perhaps the greatest advance made in controlling shaft accretion growth has been the development of a highly effective explosive blasting technique. By careful and judicious blasting the cross sectional area of the shaft has been maintained at about 85% of the original.

Recent practices indicates that smelting the best quality sinter with respect to hardness, chemical composition and more especially sulphur content, prevention of accretion build up can be achieved to a large degree. It is also believed that the higher the blowing rate in the furnace, the lower the rate of accretion formation.

Condenser Operation

The major problem in condenser operation is to reduce lead return to the condenser to the minimum and to achieve the highest possible condensation and separation efficiency.

The rate of lead return at Zambia Broken Hill is about 120 tonnes per month. This is near the lowest achieved by any Imperial Smelting Furnace operator and is considered to be due to the following.

(i) the use of a 'wet' or molten ammonium chloride flux on the flux bath, which flux, when skimmed off cooled and broken up is returned to the furnace shaft;

(ii) maintenance of good lead circulation in the condenser avoiding short-circuiting of lead between the lead return launder and the pump sump.

(iii) Condenser lead level control is given close attention. Several methods for measuring the level have been used from stopping the pumps once per day and measuring the level at a given point, to observing the level in a port let into the condenser wall. A nitrogen bubbler tube has also been tried. None of these has proven entirely satisfactory and the best method used so far is the measurement and control of the condenser offtake temperature. Depending on the blast rate and the amount of top air used, temperatures of 460 to 470°C appear to be optimum.

Refined lead is added as the temperatures rises above the desired limits.

Gas washing ic also carefully watched to avoid choking the air preheater tubes thus reducing blast preheat.

Slag Composition

The high proportion of slag forming constituents in the sinter and the consequent high slag fall necessitates continuous slag tapping. Lead and slag are tapped directly from a 50 m.m. hole in the tapping breast into a forehearth. The separated slag is granulated as it overflows the forehearth into a strong water jet and pumped to the dump. The lead flows into a 5 tonne ladle and is transported to the refinery.

Operating control of the furnace is maintained by adjusting the carbon/zinc ratio in the furnace charge buckets at a level consistent with smooth slagging operation at the lowest level of zinc in the slag.

Most other Imperial Smelting Furnaces where concentrates only are smelted adjust the carbon/zinc ratio on the basis of the results of rapid analyses of incoming sinter and coke, to produce a consistent zinc content in slag. This is possible because of the comparative uniformity of the feed materials. At Zambia Broken Hill, because of the varying nature of the feed however, the carbon/zinc ratio is adjusted on the basis of the zinc content of the slag. Control is therefore retroactive from rapid two hourly analyses of zinc in slag. This would tend to suggest that the level of zinc in slag would be higher than under more conventional conditions. This is probably true, but it has been found the only practical method to avoid the difficulties of handling over-reduced slags.

Under current conditions it has not been possible to operate with slags containing less than 7% zinc in slag, without running into slagging problems associated with over-reduction. It is important to note that a zinc content of 7% in slag represents a loss of 15% of the zinc in the feed to the furnace, whereas in other furnaces where the slag to zinc ratio is much less, zinc recoveries of 90 - 95% of zinc are common.

In July, 1967 the furnace nearly froze solid when attempting to reduce the zinc content of slag below 9%. Over-reduction of the iron in the slag occurred and metallic iron froze in the furnace hearth and the taphole, giving rise to extreme operating difficulties.

Considerable attention was then directed at the significance of slag composition on furnace operations. As a result of the investigations it is now believed that slag composition is one of the most important single factors in I.S.F. operations.

At the start of operations, problems with slagging did not occur so frequently as the types of slags encountered ran an iron/silica ratio of around unity while the lime/silica ratio was of the order of 1.2:1.0. The zinc content of these slags was about 7%. As operations progressed the materials treated changed and the iron content rose to the point where Wustite type slags were encountered. These were later found to be the most difficult slags to handle.

The operators were reluctant to increase the CaO/SiO_2 ratio for fear of further reducing the metal content of the sinter and increasing the slag loss. It was then decided to reduce the iron content in the sinter by removing some of the pyrite from the feed materials by introducing a flotation step in the concentrator producing a high iron concentrate for discard.

A more comprehensive investigation into slag types has subsequently been undertaken.

A computer programme was developed which converts the chemical analysis of the slags to a zinc free basis and then determines the primary phase of crystallization by reference to the phase diagram; $FeO-SiO_2-CaO$ at 6% Al_2O_3 (Figure 19.)

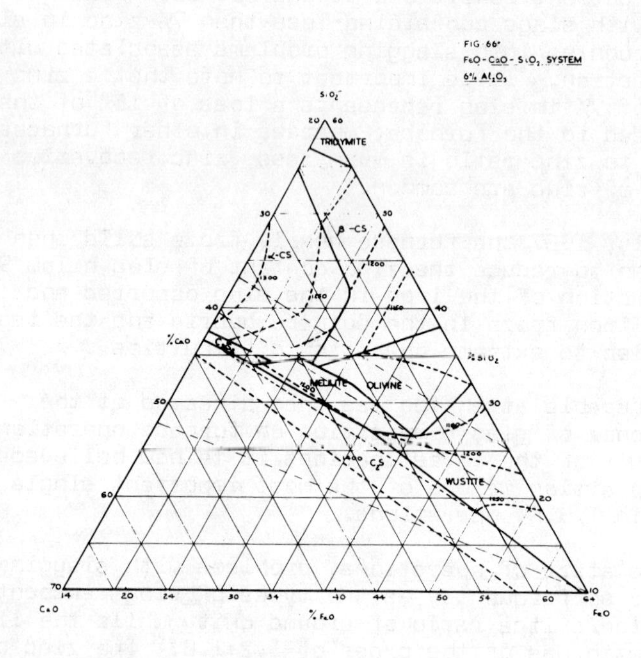

Figure 19.

The accuracy of the diagram was checked by X-ray diffraction analysis of some of the slags chosen.

Two sets of I.S.F. slags were examined. The slag analyses were those obtained on the plant at two hourly intervals in the periods mid September to mid October, 1967 and early July to mid August, 1968. For each time period the average level of zinc in slag was determined for each indicated phase. Table VII shows the results obtained.

TABLE VII

Data Set.	Phase	No. of Observations	% Mean Zinc
1967	Melilite	44	5.81
1967	Wustite	147	10.48
1967	Olivine	18	7.49
1968	Wustite	267	8.78
1968	Dicalcium Silicate	156	7.94

It is interesting to note the wide variety of slags produced from one furnace over so short a period. In fact, some other phases were observed but ignored, because of the small number of occurrences.

These results show that there is a real difference in the level of zinc in slag between the various phases.

The difference in Wustite phases in the two time periods shows that other furnace conditions can alter the level of zinc in slag.

Correlating furnace performance with slag composition over the following months indicated that melilite type slags contained the lowest zinc content, down to 2% zinc in some cases. The I.S.P. factor also improved from the normal 80% to 69% at best.

Dicalcium silicate slags produced similar I.S.P. factors, but the zinc tenor of the slags was somewhat higher. Wustite type slags proved disastrous with respect to both zinc content and carbon utilisation.

The variation in the composition of the feed materials to the sinter plant contributes in the main to the variation in slag composition. It will, therefore be appreciated that control of the slag composition presents a major problem.

Because of the nature of the feed it is not possible to change the composition of the charge sufficiently to produce melilite type slags at all times. However, by reducing the iron as low as possible and increasing the CaO/SiO_2 ratio in slag to 1.2:1 dicalcium silicate slags are possible with improved results.

Table VIII summarises Imperial Smelting Furnace campaign data to date.

Table VIII. Zambia Broken Hill Development Co. Ltd. - Imperial Smelting Furnace Campaign Data

CAMPAIGN	DURATION			SINTER TREATED			SLAG PRODUCED			PRODUCTION		METAL RECOVERY		COKE BURNT			BLAST		ISP	AS % CARBON			ZINC COND. SEP. EFFCY.	C/Zn RATIO
																				DROSS & BLUE POWDER		LEAD VOL RATE		
	START	STOP	DAYS	TONNES	% Pb	% Zn	TONNES	% Pb	% Zn	BULLION TO REFINERY TONNES	SABLE 4 Zn TONNES	% Pb	% Zn	TONNES	TONNES CARBON	PRE HEAT °C	°C	Nm^3/hr	CARBON ESTN.	Pb	Zn			
1	3.3.62	15.3.62	12																					
2	18.3.62	29.5.62	72	24099	25.2	19.4	12791	0.8	6.7	4191	3491	69.0	74.1	7572	6436	544	590	14917	-	-	-	-	-	-
3	8.6.62	6.7.62	28	10512	24.8	19.8	5543	1.2	10.4	1859	1485	71.3	71.4	2933	2493	477	656	17384	89.6	-	-	-	-	1.09
4	10.7.62	17.9.62	69	27636	26.1	21.2	13599	1.2	7.5	5309	3905	73.6	66.7	7637	6491	583	631	18679	87.7	-	-	27.7	81.2	1.13
5	3.10.62	8.11.62	37	12491	27.9	25.3	6876	1.7	10.3	2338	2225	67.1	70.4	3556	3023	537	627	17755	75.8	-	-	46.1	72.0	0.98
6	19.11.62	6.12.62	17	6393	26.2	20.9	3375	1.7	10.6	1001	629	59.8	47.1	1794	1525	474	630	17296	87.8	-	-	41.2	62.0	1.16
7	15.12.62	30.1.63	47	17337	20.3	21.6	10024	1.3	7.4	2564	2615	72.8	69.8	4851	4123	551	618	17444	83.1	-	-	19.7	86.5	1.11
8	7.2.63	17.2.63	10	3553	19.6	22.7	2068	1.3	8.2	549	572	78.8	70.9	1065	905	608	622	17447	86.7	-	-	21.5	87.0	1.12
9	27.2.63	29.3.63	30	11206	19.9	22.9	6160	0.9	8.1	1691	1754	75.8	68.3	3059	2600	560	612	17670	76.6	5.5	9.5	17.5	86.2	0.99
10	2.4.63	11.4.63	9	3781	19.3	22.8	2195	0.7	7.9	609	563	83.5	65.4	1020	866	664	644	17741	75.5	9.6	12.9	12.1	78.0	0.98
11	19.4.63	13.7.63	85	33647	21.3	24.2	18765	0.5	8.2	5916	5820	82.5	78.5	9295	7417	526	647	19539	72.4	13.0	15.4	15.5	86.6	0.92
12	25.7.63	25.9.63	62	30131	20.8	24.6	16499	0.7	7.5	5169	5092	82.5	68.7	7897	6143	507	642	20794	66.7	11.2	15.8	17.1	82.5	0.85
13	5.10.63	5.2.64	123	51981	20.7	25.2	29121	0.8	8.7	8267	9026	76.8	68.9	14433	11587	543	635	19860	72.1	9.8	14.9	21.0	84.3	0.90
14	21.2.64	23.3.64	32	10319	20.0	27.5	5319	0.7	8.7	1360	1810	65.9	63.8	3414	2820	533	634	19894	82.3	22.6	15.3	29.8	63.6	1.15
15	28.3.64	9.6.64	74	32968	20.6	24.3	17781	0.7	7.3	4980	5849	67.8	68.2	9642	8013	514	641	21667	77.4	24.9	19.3	19.7	84.3	1.05
16	18.6.64	16.8.64	59	24055	20.9	31.2	10886	0.9	7.6	3819	5957	69.0	78.4	8380	7023	560	570	22082	78.7	23.2	19.7	16.3	87.9	0.99
17	4.9.64	11.11.64	68	26170	20.2	24.5	14152	0.9	7.8	3292	4384	50.2	66.7	8676	7332	440	622	21453	89.2	43.1	24.7	25.8	80.3	1.11
18	23.11.64	6.2.65	76	31193	20.4	24.5	16692	0.8	7.4	4655	5534	64.4	71.5	8988	7397	636	645	20388	76.3	22.2	15.8	21.5	85.2	0.97
19	22.2.65	5.6.65	105	39796	20.1	24.5	21500	0.8	7.6	6225	7241	75.4	73.3	11923	9808	608	607	21521	79.3	14.2	16.9	8.5	88.2	1.00
20	30.6.65	27.10.65	119	49663	20.8	25.2	25583	0.8	8.7	7372	9231	69.6	71.5	15060	12938	611	587	20643	86.6	18.3	13.5	11.8	90.1	1.00
21	8.11.65	16.3.66	128	49664	20.7	27.6	24494	0.8	9.8	6982	9777	66.6	71.8	15603	13140	606	553	21017	82.7	18.2	13.1	15.2	87.8	0.96
22	4.4.66	22.11.66	224	92180	21.1	26.6	47809	1.0	10.3	13664	15816	68.9	63.8	26244	22691	533	617	20763	78.6	17.8	15.1	16.5	80.0	0.93
23	9.1.67	29.10.67	290	106300	20.1	28.2	54023	0.8	9.5	16428	22383	73.2	73.2	33494	28805	514	534	21117	81.3	10.7	9.4	17.8	88.4	0.95
24	6.11.67	16.5.68	192	66478	20.0	31.1	32359	0.7	9.9	10475	15261	73.2	72.4	22041	19318	382	557	21083	82.6	15.1	12.8	13.3	85.2	0.94
25	13.6.68	29.9.69	473	209023	22.4	27.3	97035	0.7	9.0	39511	43780	81.0	75.7	63251	52876	489	573	23200	77.6	9.2	8.5	16.5	86.8	0.93

Table VIII. Zambia Broken Hill Development Co. Ltd. - Imperial Smelting Furnace Campaign Data

CAMPAIGN	C BURN RATE TONNES 24 hrs	LEAD TO CONDSER TONNES	SINTER								SLAG								REASONS FOR ENDING CAMPAIGN
			CaO	SiO_2	FeO	T/S	Al_2O_3	MgO	CaO/SiO_2	FeO/SiO_2	CaO	SiO_2	FeO	T/S	Al_2O_3	MgO	CaO/SiO_2	FeO/SiO_2	
1																			SLAG IN TUYERES
2	906	257	13·5	10·8	9·3	1·4	-	-	1·25	1·11	28·1	24·0	20·5	1·2	4·0	-	1·17	0·99	SHAFT ACCRETED
3	93·3	114	14·8	10·5	8·9	1·7	-	-	1·41	1·09	28·1	22·5	19·6	1·5	4·0	-	1·25	1·01	SHAFT ACCRETED
4	102·2	83	14·7	10·6	7·7	1·5	-	-	1·39	0·93	27·9	24·4	19·1	2·0	4·0	-	1·14	0·91	SHAFT ACCRETED [E STRIKE]
5	97·6	184	11·9	8·7	8·3	1·5	-	-	1·37	1·23	27·1	22·7	18·9	1·8	4·0	-	1·19	0·97	SHAFT ACCRETED
6	98·3	86	14·2	10·4	9·2	1·5	-	-	1·37	1·13	27·5	23·5	18·6	1·4	4·0	-	1·17	0·92	SLAG IN TUYERES [POWER FAILURE]
7	98·3	163	16·9	12·0	10·2	1·2	-	-	1·41	1·09	28·5	24·9	19·3	1·9	4·0	-	1·14	0·90	SLAGGING DIFFICULTIES AFTER BOMBING
8	101·4	22	14·9	10·8	10·1	1·5	-	-	1·38	1·20	27·0	23·3	19·7	2·0	4·0	-	1·16	0·98	FURNACE ROOF COLLAPSE
9	98·9	115	14·9	10·2	11·8	1·2	-	-	1·46	1·49	27·7	23·5	21·2	1·9	3·9	2·9	1·18	1·05	SLAG IN TUYERES CHARGE BELL FAILURE
10	94·2	61	15·6	10·8	10·6	1·4	-	-	1·44	1·26	28·1	23·0	21·1	1·8	3·6	3·0	1·22	1·07	CONDENSER FLOOR BRICKWORK FLOATED
11	104·9	356	15·4	10·9	9·8	1·4	0·9	1·7	1·41	1·16	29·2	23·0	20·6	2·1	2·1	3·6	1·27	1·04	CRUDE WATER LEAKAGE INTO SOFT WATER CIRCUIT
12	109·4	283	15·2	11·6	9·8	1·5	1·2	1·4	1·31	1·09	29·0	23·3	20·6	2·1	3·0	3·7	1·24	1·03	SHAFT ACCRETED
13	110·9	1139	16·0	11·8	9·9	1·2	1·0	1·4	1·36	1·08	29·8	23·5	20·6	1·7	4·5	3·4	1·27	1·02	SHAFT ACCRETED
14	112·1	192	14·1	10·5	8·9	1·2	-	-	1·34	1·10	28·2	22·8	18·6	-	-	-	1·24	0·95	BLOW HOLE FORMATION IN SHAFT
15	123·6	678	16·1	11·8	9·0	1·2	0·8	2·4	1·36	0·98	30·6	24·1	20·9	1·7	5·0	4·4	1·27	0·87	SHAFT ACCRETED
16	124·3	506	12·4	9·2	7·9	1·0	0·8	1·7	1·35	1·10	27·6	24·2	22·6	1·9	6·2	4·0	1·14	0·95	SHORTAGE OF COKE. BLOW HOLE IN SHAFT
17	122·0	1255	16·0	11·8	9·1	1·2	1·4	1·3	1·36	0·99	29·2	24·6	24·3	1·5	6·0	3·4	1·15	1·12	SHAFT ACCRETED
18	112·9	856	14·5	10·8	10·2	1·0	1·8	1·1	1·34	1·21	27·2	24·7	22·3	1·3	5·7	3·5	1·10	1·04	CONDENSER LEAD LEAK
19	115·4	249	13·9	10·2	11·1	1·1	1·4	1·1	1·36	1·40	26·1	23·3	24·5	1·5	5·4	3·7	1·12	1·21	AIR HEATER TUBE BANK FAILURE
20	124·3	170	13·7	10·1	11·1	1·0	1·3	1·1	1·36	1·42	26·2	23·1	24·3	1·6	5·1	3·3	1·13	1·21	REPAIRS TO LEAD COOLING LAUNDER
21	119·7	213	12·2	9·1	11·3	0·9	1·5	1·0	1·34	1·59	24·7	22·0	25·9	1·8	5·9	3·3	1·12	1·35	REPAIRS TO CONDENSER LEAD LEAK
22	114·9	322	12·5	9·3	12·2	0·8	1·1	0·9	1·34	1·69	24·0	21·8	23·4	1·7	5·6	3·2	1·10	1·41	REPAIRS TO CONDENSER LEAD LEAK
23	120·0	1134	11·9	8·8	12·7	0·8	0·8	-	1·35	1·85	24·0	21·7	24·8	1·5	5·5	2·8	1·11	1·47	LEAKING TUYERES
24	121·6	1051	10·8	8·1	13·2	0·8	-	-	1·33	2·10	22·7	20·9	28·0	1·6	5·6	-	1·09	1·62	COLLAPSE OF ROOF TILES AT CONDENSER INLET
25	130·5	1991	10·5	7·2	11·9	0·7	-	-	1·46	2·13	24·0	19·5	29·1	1·5	5·3	-	1·23	1·65	GENERAL MECHANICAL OVERHAUL

The Future

In some 65 years of operation a tailing worthy of the name has never yet been produced at the Mine from any of the metallurgical processes that have been used. The high grade of the ore, almost entirely mineral, coupled with the varied association of the lead and zinc minerals are the major contributors to this phenomenon. The problem today is still the same as it has always been; the separation of the lead and zinc from silica. The problem is also complicated by the physical properties of the dump materials, which consist of large tonnages of:

leach residues analysing	7.5% Pb	9.1% Zn
old blast furnace slags containing	3.3% Pb	12.6% Zn
I.S.F. slags containing	0.9% Pb	9.4% Zn

In addition to these, several other minor orebodies in the area consisting mainly of zinc silicate ores are available for treatment by some other means.

Investigations have revealed that the only existing process offering the flexibility of treatment necessitated by the chemical and physical properties of the dump materials is the use of Waelz kilns.

Fuming by this means has been considered on several occasions during the history of the Mine, but was discarded due to the low melting point of the feed materials. It is this property of the dump materials that gave rise to the fears of the earlier investigators who considered that serious ringing of the kilns would result. This tendency has been largely overcome in modern times by the use of excess fuel in the form of coke breeze on the charge. It is also possible by the adjustment of the CaO/SiO_2 ratios in the feed materials to effect reduction of the iron oxides to metallic iron if desired. It is hoped that the use of this process will finally produce the tailing that has eluded Broken Hill metallurgists for so long. This development is being studied in detail from both the technological and economic aspects, the results of which study will determine whether the next phase in the treatment of the Zambia Broken Hill ores will proceed.

Acknowledgements

The Author wishes to thank the Anglo American Corporation for permission to publish this paper and Imperial Smelting Processes Limited for their permission to publish those sections of the paper dealing with the Imperial Smelting Furnace. Thanks are also due to the Mine staff, particularly the Technical Assistant, the Drawing Office, Geology Department and the Survey Office for their assistance in compiling the data and drawings.

References

1. J.O. Betterton - Soluble Silica in the Preparation of Zinc Sulphate Solution for Electrolysis. New York Meeting, A.I.M.E., February, 1923.

2. K.C.G. Heath - Mining and Metallurgical Operations at Rhodesia Broken Hill, Past, Present and Future. Transaction of the Institute of Mining and Metallurgy, Vol. 70, Part 12, 1960 - 1961.

3. A.J. Perry - Lead Smelting and Refining at Broken Hill, Northern Rhodesia - Technical Proceedings of the 7th Commonwealth Mining and Metallurgical Congress - South Africa, 1961 - Northern Rhodesia Section.

4. S.W.K. Morgan - The Production of Zinc in a blast furnace. Transactions of the Institute of Mining and Metallurgy, Vol. 70, Part 2, 1960/1961.

SECTION VI

LEAD SMELTING AND REFINING

Chapter 24

THE HERCULANEUM LEAD SMELTER OF

ST. JOE MINERALS CORPORATION

Herculaneum, Missouri

Donald H. Beilstein
Chief Metallurgist, Lead Smelting Division

Abstract

The St. Joe Minerals Corporation Lead Smelter and Refinery have been in continuous operation at Herculaneum, Missouri since 1892 as the Herculaneum Lead Smelting Division. Over the years, the plant has undergone many changes to increase production, improve the technology, reduce the cost of operations, and produce the highest grade of primary lead.

The latest alterations were begun in 1960 and completed in 1970 and have resulted in the Herculaneum Smelter capacity being increased to in excess of 200,000 tons per year (180,000 metric tons). This increase has made the Herculaneum Smelter the largest in the United States, and second largest in the world.

This paper will describe the Herculaneum Smelter equipment, processes, and material balances. Particular emphasis will be given to the McDowell-Wellman 10' x 100' (3 x 30 meter) up-draft sinter machine and ancillaries; to the new Heavy Smelting Department (blast furnaces and drossing section); to the new Lead Refinery and its automatic casting equipment and to the gas handling system including the 340 tons per day (305 metric) Sulfuric Acid Plant utilizing a four pass converter.

The description will include photographs, flow sheets, tonnages and assays where applicable.

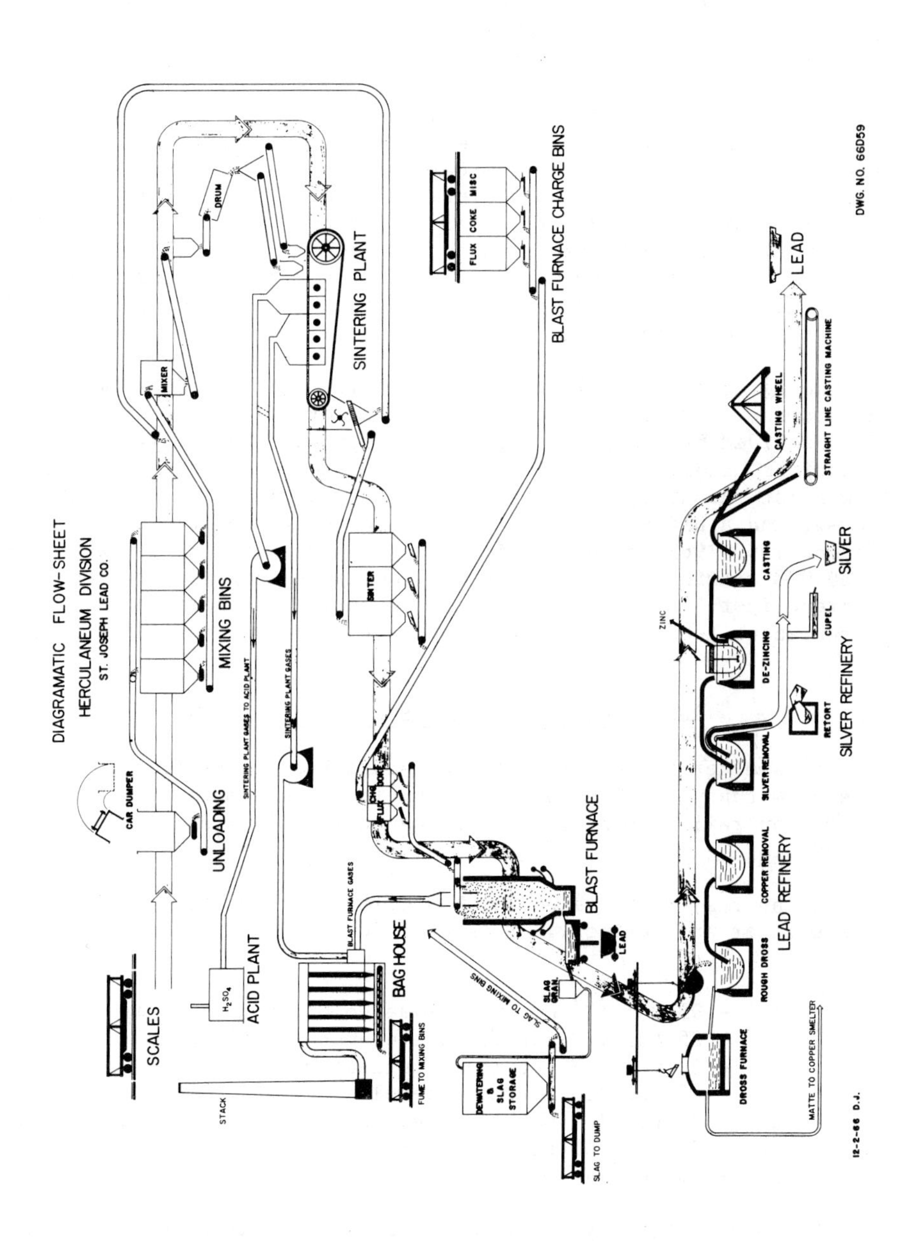

Figure 1. Herculaneum Smelter Flow Sheet

Lead mining in the Southeast Missouri area dates back to the early 1700's. Lead metal production followed mining, primarily at the mine site. Herculaneum, Missouri, approximately 25 miles (40 km) south of St. Louis on the west bank of the Mississippi River, was the site of shot towers in the early 1800's, using lead from the Southeast Missouri mines and smelters.

In 1892, the present smelter was established and has been in continuous, expanding operation ever since. As technology has changed, the smelter has changed - from Calcine furnaces, to Savelsburg converters, to small down-draft sinter machines, to a modern up-draft sinter machine; from 36" diameter (.92 meter) cupolas to 36" x 100" (.92 x 2.54 meter) blast furnaces, to modern 66" x 336" (1.68 x 8.53 meter) blast furnaces; from matte roasters to modern drossing practice; from rudimentary refining processes to present refining practice, resulting in 99.99+% lead.

The Herculaneum Smelter was practically rebuilt, department by department, during the 1960's, with much of the design and engineering provided by Treadwell Engineering Company, New York. A new materials handling-receiving section, a new up-draft sinter section, new blast furnaces, a new Drossing Plant, a new Refinery, a new baghouse, and a new Sulfuric Acid Plant, were all constructed in the decade 1960-1969, resulting in a designed capacity of 200,000 tons (180,000 metric) per year. The following descriptions represent current installations, practice, metallurgy and operations at the Herculaneum Lead Smelting Division of the St. Joseph Lead Company.

RECEIVING AND MATERIALS HANDLING SECTION

The smelter is served by the Missouri Pacific Railroad, which has a switch yard adjacent to the smelter. All materials are received by rail, except for minor tonnages of flux and miscellaneous materials.

An internal rail system, with 9 miles of track (14.5 km), serves the smelter and refinery. Equipment for the rail system consists of:

1 - 95 ton (85 metric) diesel-electric locomotive
1 - 25 ton (23 metric) diesel-mechanical crane
1 - 30 ton (27 metric) diesel-mechanical crane
1 - 40 ton (36 metric) diesel-electric crane
25 - 70 ton (63 metric) steel side/bottom dump hopper cars
12 - 70 ton (63 metric) gondolas
3 - 50 ton (45 metric) flat cars

The latter three types of cars are used for in-plant materials. A 150 ton (135 metric) railroad scale is used for all in-bound, outbound, and internal transfers. The engine crew consists of three

St. Joe Minerals Corp.
Herculaneum, Missouri, USA
Chapter 24, page 702

Amax-Homestake Lead Tollers
Buick, Missouri, USA
Chapter 25, page 738

American Smelting & Refining Co.
Glover, Missouri, USA
Chapter 26, page 777

Broken Hill Associated Smelters Pty., Ltd.
Port Pirie, So. Aus., Australia
Chapter 27, page 790

N.V. Metallurgie Hoboken S.A.
Hoboken, Belgium
Chapter 28, page 824

Mitsubishi-Cominco Smelting Co.
Naoshima, Japan
Chapter 29, page 853

Air Photograph by Aero-Lux, Frankfurt/Main
Released by Reg. Praes. Wiesbd. Nr. 704/67

Norddeutsche Affinerie (N.A.)
Hamburg, Federal Republic of Germany
Chapter 30, page 867

Cerro de Pasco Corp.
La Oroya, Peru
Chapter 31, page 891

men. The self-propelled crane crew is made up of an operator plus helper.

Concentrates are received from the Southeast Missouri lead mines in 100 ton capacity (90 metric) gondolas. Weighing and sampling is performed immediately upon arrival. Excess receipts, after weighing and sampling, are held in the plant switch yard. Two thaw houses are in use - an old brick and wood unit with a 6-car capacity, and a new steel unit with a 24-car capacity. Loaded cars are also stored here for protection from the rain in mild periods. During the winter months these units function as true thaw houses, fired by two 4 x 10^6 Btu/hr (1 x 10^6 kg-cal/hr) forced air furnaces.

All gondolas, after weighing and sampling, are taken to the Rota-side car tippler. This unit handles one car at a time; rotates the car and track approximately 150°, vibrates the car until empty, and returns it to the down position. The complete cycle is about 6 - 8 minutes, which includes car movement and dumping.

Figure 2. Rota-side Car Tippler

The Rota-side car tippler is a Stephens-Adamson unit (built to Strachan & Henshaw Ltd., U.K. design) capable of handling a 150 ton (135 metric) gross weight gondola. It is powered by a 100HP, 720 r.p.m. motor. Braking is via a D. C. twin magnetic type brake. Limits are controlled by a travelling nut type switch. Photo-electric eye safeguards are provided to ensure proper car location.

Material is dumped into a four compartment bottom-discharge hopper, where it is fed on to a conveyor belt for transfer to a tripper located over the sinter preparation (mix room) bins. On a normal day, 10 concentrate cars and 4 - 5 miscellaneous material cars are unloaded and delivered to the bins. A three-man crew, working day shift only, operates the unloading system.

In addition to the above, blast furnace coke and excess sinter production is handled by bottom-dump cars to the blast furnace railroad trestle for dumping into the trestle bins.

SAMPLING SECTION

A new sample room was built in 1969 and is equipped with the following:

1 - 8" x 10" Denver Jaw crusher (20 x 25 cm)
2 - #00 Sturtevant automatic coal crushers, which are basically 20 1/2" (52 cm) cone crushers, max. feed 3" (7.6 cm)
1 - Bedeck Gyratory crusher, max. feed 1" (2.5 cm)
3 - Bico-Braun model UA disc pulverizers with 8" (20 cm) discs
1 - Massco/McCool pulverizer - 9" (23 cm) discs
2 - Michigan Oven Company #334 drying ovens - 71" x 48" x 93", rated at 110,000 Btu/hr, natural gas fired (180 x 120 x 235 cm, rated at 27,500 kg-cal/hr)

Sampling and sample preparation is handled by five men working day shift. In addition to incoming and outgoing materials, all the slag, matte, dross, fume and dust, and other internal miscellaneous materials are sampled for assay.

YARD

The Yard Department supplies a general labor pool, and is responsible for rubber-tired transportation, change house and laundry facilities, janitorial service, watchman service, railroad track repairs, and a garage for servicing and light repairs.

SINTER PLANT

The new Sinter Plant at Herculaneum, which went on stream in January, 1966, is of the up-draft design, replacing five smaller down-draft machines. Design considerations were to increase capacity, produce high grade SO_2 for acid production, produce more sinter more economically, and improve hygiene conditions. All of these requirements have been met by the new installation.

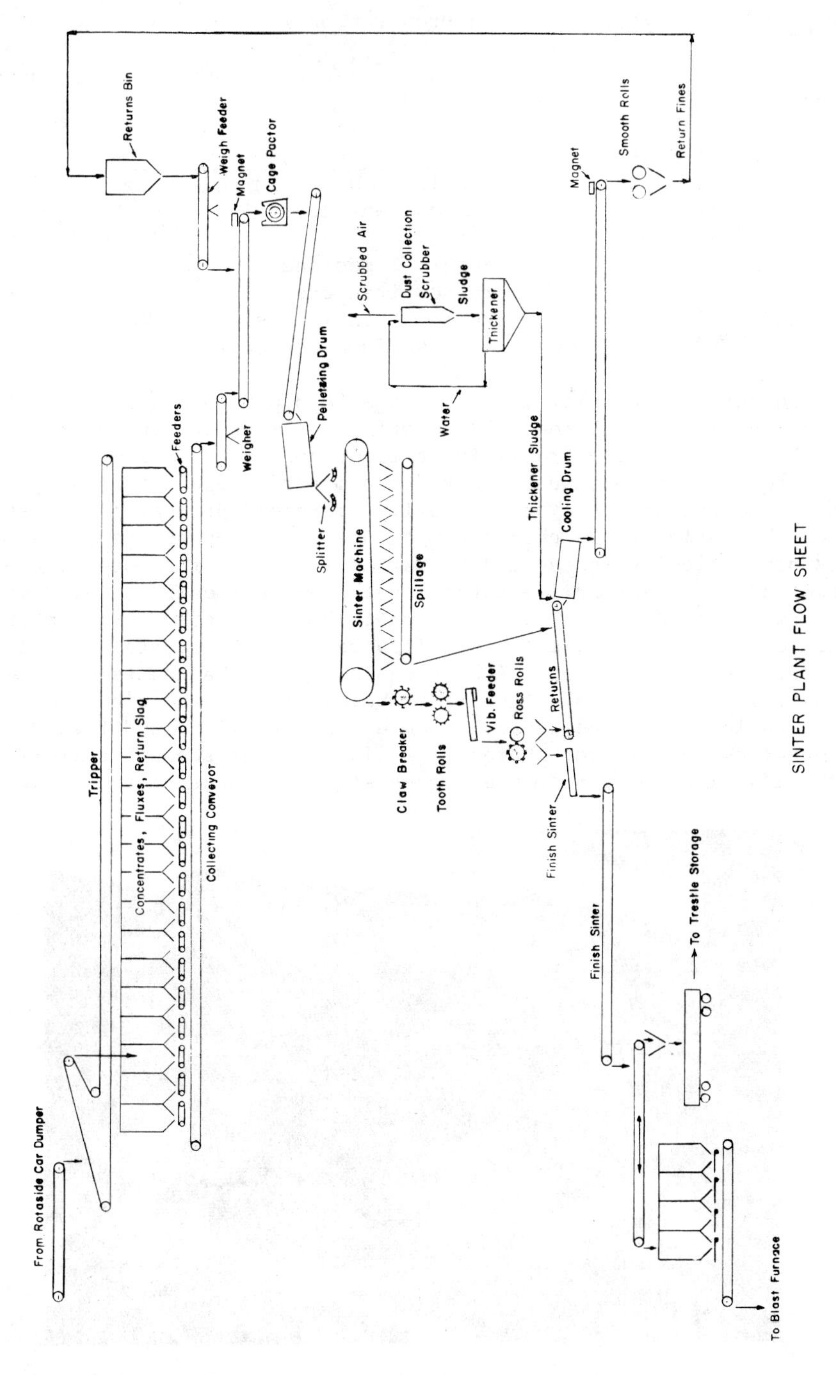

Figure 3. Sinter Plant Flow Sheet

Proportioning System and Feed Preparation.

The mix room (proportioning system) has 23 concrete, vee-bottom bins as follows:

No.of Bins	Contents
5	Granulated blast furnace slag
12	Lead concentrates
1	Sand
1	Crushed limestone
1	Crushed iron ore
1	Secondary materials (in plant)
2	Baghouse fume and dust

Concentrate capacity in these bins is 3,000 tons (2,700 metric); slag capacity is 850 tons (770 metric). All materials enter the bins via an overhead travelling tripper conveyor. Below each bin, an apron feeder continually withdraws material and discharges it onto a collector conveyor. Manually operated, pre-set gates determine the ratio of the charge components. The tonnage delivered by the proportioning system can be varied by means of remote control frequency regulated drive motors on the apron feeders. The weight of the raw feed proportionately controls the weight of return sinter fed from a separate 150 ton (135 metric) bin located within the sinter machine building. A belt scale weighs the raw feed and electronically controls a weigh feeder below the returns bin according to a ratio set by the control room operator. The mixed feed enters a Gundlach Cage-Paktor where it is mixed and crushed to approximately 85% -1/4" (.6 cm). From the Cage-Paktor, the mixed feed is moistened

Figure 4. Pelletizing Drum

and partially pelletized in a 9' x 30' (2.75 x 9.15 meter) Allis-Chalmers variable speed drum. The pelletizing drum is fitted with adjustable water sprays and a reciprocating cutter bar.

Machine Feed and Sintering.

The mixed feed, leaving the pelletizing drum, is directed by an electrically positioned flop gate into one of two divergent chutes. The smaller portion (10%), containing somewhat smaller pellets, is fed onto a hydraulically operated reciprocating belt feeder which discharges into the 10' x 2' ignition layer hopper (3 x .61 meter). The balance (90%) is similarly fed into a 10' x 4' (3 x 1.2 meter) main layer hopper. The ignition layer is cut off and levelled by a stainless steel back plate at approximately 1 1/4" (3.2 cm).

Down-draft ignition is accomplished in 84 inches (2.13 meter) of travel through a natural gas-fired muffle, 9' x 10' x 4'(2.75 x 3 x 1.2 meter), using four burners. After ignition, the main layer is laid down and levelled to 10" - 14" (25 - 35 cm) by a stainless steel back plate. Up-draft sintering starts immediately and burn-through is accomplished in about 30'(9.15 meter). The remaining 70' (21.4 meter) are used to cool the cake with up-draft air.

Figure 5. Sinter Machine Hood and Off-takes

Sinter gases from the first 30' (9.15 meter) of the sinter machine containing 6% - 8% SO_2 by volume, are sent to the Acid Plant. The balance of the gases go to the regular baghouse.

Crushing and Returns System.

Sinter drops off the pallets at the discharge end of the machine as a large cake, onto a railroad rail crash deck. The cake slides on to an 8" (20 cm) grizzly, through which it is crushed by a claw breaker, with 18" (.46 meter) claws. A Traylor 42" x 48" (1.0 x 1.2 meter) toothed roll reduces the material to -5" (12.7 cm). A Ross Rolls screen is used to control the amount of return sinter. The aperture is remotely controlled and is usually set at 2". Final sinter, +2" (5 cm), then travels by conveyor belt to one of three sinter storage bins (see Lead Blast Furnace Department). Excess sinter production goes to railroad cars for discharge on the blast furnace charge bin trestle, or yard storage.

Figure 6. Sinter Machine Operating Floor

Return sinter, -2" (5 cm), which was separated by the Ross Rolls, is conveyed to a 7' x 20' **(2.14 x 6.1 meter)** Louisville cooling drum. Thickened scrubber sludge is used to cool the return sinter. The cooled returns are further crushed to -1/2" (1.2 cm) by a Traylor 42" x 36" (1.0 x .92 meter) smooth roll before being conveyed to the 150 ton (135 metric) return sinter bin. Rotating paddles in the bin indicate bin level to the operator in the control room, and guide his setting of the Ross Rolls opening.

Typical Operating Data.

Chemical Analysis

Material	Lead %	Sulfur %
New feed	40-45	9-13
Returns	43-45	1.2-1.7
Machine feed	40-45	4.7-7.0
Finish Sinter	45-50	1.0-1.5

Typical Finish Sinter Analysis - %

Pb	Cu	Insol	SiO_2	FeO	CaO	S
48	1	10	9	15	5	1.4

Sizing

Material	% Returns	% Machine Feed
+1" (2.5 cm)	3	-
+3/4" (1.9 cm)	8	3
+.37 (.94 cm)	15	4
+3 mesh	17	7
+6 mesh	20	15
+14 mesh	20	20
+35 mesh	15	30
-35 mesh	2	21

Typically the Sinter Plant Operates with:

New feed	50%
Returns	50%
Machine feed	100%

Machine Operating Data

Pallet speed	45-55"/min (114-140 cm/min)
Ignition bed depth	1 1/4" ± 1/8" (3.2 cm ± .3 cm)
Total bed depth	10-14" (25-35 cm)
Down-draft area (including dead-plate)	70 sq.ft. (6.5 sq.meter)
Up-draft area (including dead-plate)	1040 sq.ft. (96.7 sq.meter)
No. of up-draft windboxes	13
Total number of pallets	104

Operating Tonnages

	Tons Per Hour (metric)
Total machine feed	160 - 180 (145 - 160)
Finish Sinter	75 - 100 (68 - 90)

Air Distribution

Windbox No.	Volume	Pressure - Inches Water Gauge
1	8000 cfm (226 cu meter)	15 (38 cm)
2	8500 " (240 ")	20 (51 ")
3	9000 " (254 ")	20 (51 ")
4	15000 " (425 ")	20 (51 ")
5	15000 " (425 ")	15 (38 ")
6	15000 " (425 ")	10 (25 ")
7	15000 " (425 ")	10 (25 ")
8	7000 " (200 ")	5 (12 ")
9	7000 " (200 ")	5 (12 ")
10	Not in use at present	
11	"	
12	"	
13	"	
Down-draft	7200 cfm (204 cu meter)	-2 to -3 (-5 to -7 cm)
Total	106,700 " (3024 ")	

Fuel Requirements

Natural gas (ignition) 85,000 Btu/ton finished sinter (19,400 kg-cal/metric ton)

Labor Requirements

The Sinter Plant operates with six men and one foreman on each shift. In addition, there are ten men in the maintenance crew who work day shift, five days a week. Maintenance is performed, on schedule, for eight hours each Monday and Wednesday. Additional maintenance personnel are available, as needed, from the main shops. Minor spare parts, such as vee belts, pulleys, idlers, etc., are kept within the Sinter Plant, while larger parts are kept in central stores.

Instrumentation.

The Sinter Plant control room has many instruments and the information provided by them has been a major factor in reaching the present high level of operation. The control room console contains:

1. Mix room bin starvation alarms and recorders, with local alarms in the mix room.
2. Feed rate indicators and totalisers for new feed, returns and finish sinter.
3. Returns ratio controller.
4. Air volume controllers and recorders on each windbox and blower.
5. Windbox pressure recorders, with a controller only on the down-draft windbox.
6. Temperature controllers on acid and exhaust gases which operate water sprays via step-controlled solenoid valves.
7. Miscellaneous temperature recorders.
8. Ross Rolls aperture controller.
9. Level monitors on the returns bin and a high level monitor on the finish sinter bin.
10. Water volume recorder and pressure indicator for the machine hood sprays.
11. Cooling and process water controllers.
12. Electrical interlocks, ammeters, speed controllers and other electrical monitors throughout the plant.
13. Continuous recorder for SO_2, O_2, and N_2 in Acid Plant gas via an L & N chromatograph.
14. Various pressure and temperature alarms.

Dust Control.

Every effort has been made to minimize the contamination of the area by dust. All transfer points and major dust producers are hooded and vented to an elaborate scrubbing system. There are six wet scrubbers, with a total capacity of 185,400 cfm (5,250 cu meter/min). Total installed horsepower for these units is approximately 650. Scrubber effluent is thickened in a 20' (6.1 meter) Denver thickener. Thickened sludge is pumped to the returns cooling drum, and overflow water is returned to the scrubbers.

General Equipment Data.

Conveyor Belts. All conveyor belts are 30" (.76 meter) wide, except the collector belt in the mix room which is 24" (.61 meter), and the belts between there and the machine, which are 36" (.92 meter). Belt speeds are usually 150' per minute (46 meter), using Falk reducers. Conveyor belting is generally 4 ply, 1/4" top (.63 cm) and 1/16" bottom (.16 cm).

Weighers. All weighers are "ABC" by McDowell-Wellman.

Feeders. Feeders in sinter preparation are all 3' x 5' (.92 x 1.5 meter) apron feeders.

Sinter Machine. The sinter machine is a Dwight-Lloyd type supplied by the McDowell-Wellman Engineering Company. The machine pallets are 10' wide (3 meter), and up-draft length is 100' (30 meter). The machine structure is independent of the building.

There are thirteen up-draft windboxes - twelve 10' x 8' (3 x 2.4 meter), and one 10' x 6' (3 x 1.81 meter). (The down-draft windbox, in the ignition section, has a 10' x 4' [3 x 1.2 meter] opening.) Access doors for periodic cleanout are provided in each windbox. The down-draft windbox and the discharge end of the machine have a screw conveyor for spillage removal.

Pallets are ductile iron, and the grate bars are malleable cast iron. The pallet wheels are so arranged that front and rear wheels describe separate arcs at the end curves, resulting in a "roll" action at pallet-to-pallet contact, rather than sliding action, which minimizes wear. A sliding seal is provided by wear plates on the machine rails and the underside of the pallets. These replaceable plates are lubricated automatically by high temperature, high pressure grease.

There is a 9' (2.75 meter) dead plate provided between ignition and up-draft sections; an 18" dead plate (.46 meter) between each up-draft windbox; and a 6' dead plate (1.8 meter) at the end of the machine. All are 3/4" thick (1.9 cm).

A grate bar leveller is installed in front of the ignition hopper, as well as a lifted grate bar alarm. On the underside of the return strand there is a grate bar rapper to clean the grates. A pallet retarder, on the return strand, eliminates pallet gap at the discharge end.

Machine speed is continuously variable between 20" and 80" per minute (50 - 200 cm/min) by a frequency regulated drive.

A collecting hopper and conveyor belt runs the length of the machine, below the return strand, to collect any spillage and deliver it to the returns circuit.

LEAD BLAST FURNACE DEPARTMENT

The Blast Furnaces and Blast Furnace Operations at Herculaneum are classical examples of lead smelting practice. The copper, antimony, and arsenic contents are low and do not produce furnace matte or speiss. The zinc content is sufficient to make a normal zinc-bearing slag, but not so high as to require any special consideration.

Storage System.

The main storage system for sinter and coke is in bins below the high line railroad trestle. In addition, these bins store fluxes and secondaries. Storage capacity is 1600 tons of sinter (1400 metric), 350 tons of coke (310 metric), and 500 tons of miscellaneous materials (450 metric).

Each bin is constructed of concrete with a steel vee bottom leading into a reciprocating plate feeder. These plate feeders are hydraulically operated, individually or in pairs, by four hydraulic power units. The reciprocating action is controlled by a pilot valve actuated by the travel of the feeder pan. All reciprocating feeders discharge on to the main collector conveyor belt. Only one type of material is fed at any time.

Additionally, there is live sinter storage in the sinter plant, consisting of three steel bins with steel vee bottoms. Each has a capacity of 350 tons (310 metric). These bins discharge, by vibrating feeders, to a cross conveyor belt which empties onto the main collector belt.

Charge System.

The charge system has three bins which contain, respectively, 150 tons of sinter (135 metric), 30 tons of coke (27 metric), and 30 tons of gravel or secondary material (27 metric). These bins are fed from the top by a shuttle belt which receives material from an extension of the main collector belt. The shuttle belt, in one position, feeds the coke bin, and, in another position, can feed either the sinter or gravel bin using a flop gate. The three bins are filled intermittently as needed.

Below the coke bin is a vibrating feeder, discharging onto, and controlled by, a belt weigher. When the pre-determined weight of coke has been delivered, the vibrating feeder stops. The material is delivered, by conveyor belts and a travelling tripper, to the proper side of whichever furnace has been designated. Upon arrival

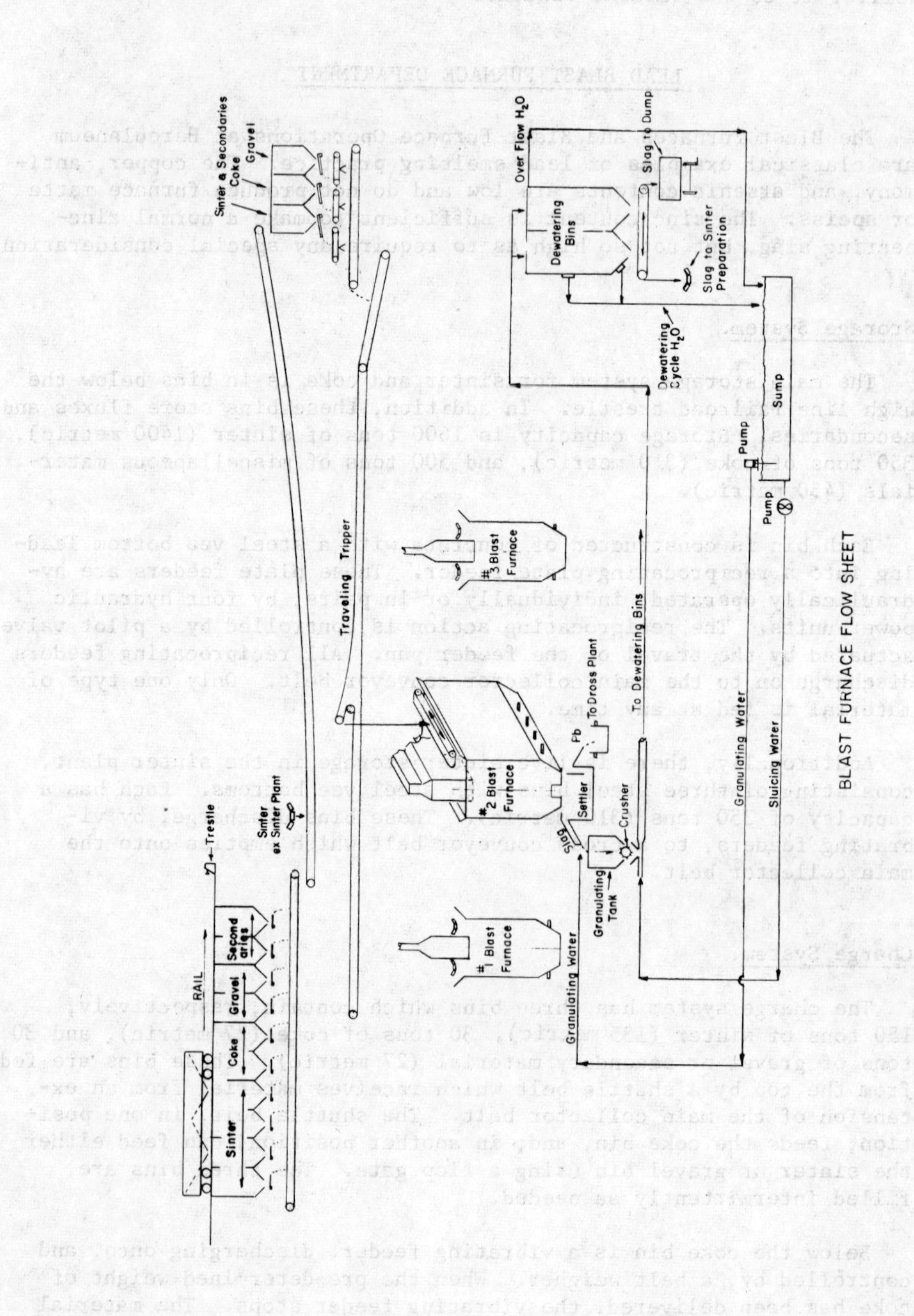

Figure 8. Blast Furnace Flow Sheet

at the furnace, the charge is delivered to a shuttle conveyor which travels back and forth over the length of the furnace distributing the charge in a minimum of three passes. In like manner, sinter is also fed to the furnace. The charge man initiates the complete cycle by pushing the button. Manual override for shuttle travel is provided to cater for charge distribution and irregular charge descent. Charge make-up is determined and set in the system control cabinet by supervision.

Blast Furnace.

The present plant consists of three blast furnaces, two of which are usually in operation. No two furnaces are alike in dimensions or construction, reflecting a continual program to develop the most efficient design. All furnaces are of the "Australian" type with two rows of tuyeres. Dimension details are as in Table I.

All furnaces have 6" thick (15 cm) water cooled steel (thermosiphon) jackets within 5' (1.52 meter) of the charge floor. Above the jackets, the furnaces are fireclay brick, 13 1/2" thick (.34 meter). The off-take from each furnace is of the thimble type and is water cooled. It discharges centrally to a circular steel gooseneck, 72" in diameter (1.83 meter), which connects to the main flue system.

Each furnace operates with a continuous slag tapper, the outlet of which flows into a 9' x 3'6" x 3' (2.75 x 1.07 x .91 meter) gas-fired settler lined with firebrick. Molten slag overflows the settler into a granulating system. Furnace bullion leaves the settler, via a leadwell, into a 10 ton (9 metric) refractory-lined transfer ladle on a wheeled motorized carriage. The leadwell is served by a "Y" track, with one ladle and carriage in place and a spare sitting on one arm of the "Y". The ladles are moved to the drossing section by one of two 20 ton (18 metric) P & H overhead cranes.

Some typical analyses are as follows:

COMPONENTS	SINTER	B.F.SLAG	COKE
Pb	48	3.5	-
Cu	1	.25	-
Insol	10	22	-
SiO_2	9	20	-
FeO	15	33	-
CaO	5	9	-
S	1.4	1	-
MgO	-	4-5	-
Al_2O_3	-	5	-
Zn	-	15	-
Volatile	-	-	1.4
Ash	-	-	7.6
Fixed Carbon	-	-	91.0

BLAST FURNACE DIMENSION DETAILS

	Furnace 1	Furnace 2	Furnace 3
Crucible Depth	18" (.46 meter)	24" (.61 meter)	24" (.61 meter)
Width at top tuyeres	10'6" (3.20 meter)	10'6" (3.20 meter)	10'6" (3.20 meter)
Width at bottom tuyeres	66" (1.67 meter)	66" (1.67 meter)	66" (1.67 meter)
Length	28'1" (8.55 meter)	24'2" (7.30 meter)	28'1" (8.55 meter)
Height	18'3" (5.5 meter)	16'9" (5.10 meter)	15'3" (4.65 meter)
Number of tuyeres	44	38	44
Diameter of tuyeres	4 3/4" (.12 meter)	4 3/4" (.12 meter)	4 3/4" (.12 meter)
Area at bottom tuyeres	155□' (14.4□ meter)	133□' (12.4□ meter)	155□' (14.4□ meter)

TABLE I

Typical furnace operating data are shown below:

	Furnace 1	Furnace 2
Tons sinter smelted/24 hours	900 (803 metric)	850 (770 metric)
Size of charge, sinter, tons	10 (9 metric)	10 (9 metric)
% coke on charge	9.0	9.0
Air volume cfm	10,500 (298 M^3)	9,000 (255 M^3)
Air blast oz (kg per sq. cm)	35 (.154 metric)	45 (.198 metric)
Tons sinter/sq.ft/day (Metric tons/sq. meter/day)	5.8 (55.7 metric)	7.2 (68.0 metric)
Tons sinter/1000 cfm (Metric tons/100 M^3/day)	90 (28.4 metric)	95 (30 metric)
Sinter size	+2" -5" (+5 -12.7 cm)	
Coke size	+1" -4" (+2.5 -10.0 cm)	

Air blast is supplied by three Rootes Connersville centrifugal blowers, each rated at 15,000 cfm (425 cu meter) @ 63 oz/sq. in. (.277 kg/sq. cm), and driven by a 350HP motor. They are interconnected by a manifold and valve system. For the upper row of tuyeres, air is supplied by Allis-Chalmers centrifugal blowers rated at 6,000 cfm (170 cu meter) @ 48 oz/sq. in. (.210 kg/sq. cm) driven by a 100HP motor.

Slag Handling System.

Since the slag handling system at the Herculaneum Smelter evolved in several stages, it is somewhat unusual. A detailed description follows.

Each furnace has its own cylindrical granulating tank with a cone bottom. A toothed disc type crusher-feeder, mounted horizontally operates within the cone bottom, discharging vertically downward into a horizontal line, just upstream from a venturi. Overflow settler slag, which has been granulated by water (1,000 gpm at 60 psig; 3750 litre/min at 4.2 kg/sq. cm), falls into this crusher in the cone bottom.

Sluicing water at 880 gpm and 275 psig (3300 litre/min and 19.3 kg/sq. cm) flows through this horizontal line and venturi, picking up the granulated and crushed slag. This thin slurry is carried by abrasion resistant piping to one of two elevated dewatering bins.

In normal operation, the slurry flows into the dewatering bins and slag falls to the bottom. Overflow water returns to the concrete sump of the water circuit (25,000 cu ft. capacity or 707 cu meter). Adequate baffling in this sump provides water to each of the three sluicing water pumps. Overflow water from this sump also supplies the granulating water pumps.

When a sufficient amount of slag builds up in the bin, the slurry is directed to the other bin, and the dewatering cycle commences. Dewatering is on a scheduled, automatic cycle. Numerous screened ports on the sides and conical bottom of the dewatering bin pass the drainage water back to the sump when the drain valve is automatically opened. When drained, a hydraulically operated seal gate at the bin bottom is opened and the dewatered slag is presented to a reversible belt feeder. This discharges on to a conveyor system either to the Sinter Plant mix room, or to a railroad car for disposal on the slag dump. When the dewatering bin is empty and ready for normal operation, the seal gate and the drain valve are closed; slag slurry flows into it, and the overflow cycle begins again. Various portions of the cycle can be performed manually, if necessary. The system was supplied by, and is the design of, United Conveyor Corporation.

When necessary, molten slag can be drawn from the settler to wheeled slag pots, and then hauled to a dump site by an electric locomotive.

Figure 9. Dewatering Bins

DROSSING SECTION

The drossing section consists of four 250 ton (225 metric) capacity hemispherical steel kettles, three of which are used for blast furnace bullion, and one of which serves for final decoppering of the product of the first three. Dross is smelted in a reverberatory furnace, 12' x 25' (3.65 x 7.6 meter), water jacketed at the slag line. The furnace arch and sidewalls are chrome-magnesite; the invert is super duty fireclay and chrome-magnesite. Two furnaces are installed; only one is in use at any time.

A modified soda ash process is used. Bullion is stirred with soda ash, sand, and coke until cooled to below 950°F (510°C). The dry dross is removed by a perforated scoop, using an overhead crane, and charged directly to the dross reverberatory. The drossed metal is then transferred, by bailing in a 10 ton (9 metric) steel bucket, to the fourth kettle, where final decoppering is done with sulfur. This dross is returned to one of the primary drossing kettles. Occasionally, some refinery high-copper products from the desilvering operation are also returned to these kettles.

Figure 10. Drossing Kettles and Reverberatory in Background

The drosses smelted in the reverberatory yield matte, bullion, and a small amount of slag. Occasionally, a layer of nickel-bearing material (which has built up slowly at the matte-lead interface) is also tapped out. The matte, slag, and nickel products are granulated, and either sold or recirculated. Lead metal is tapped into one of the drossing kettles, either direct or via a 12 ton ladle (10.7 metric).

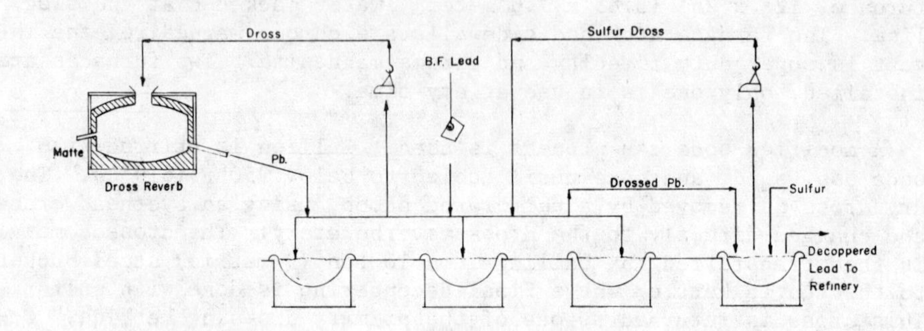

Figure 11. Drossing Plant

Typical Assays of Dross Section Feed and Products

	Reverb. Bullion	Copper Matte	Ni Matte	Dross	Lead
% Pb	-	15	35	60	-
% Cu	1.4	60	35	13	.010
% S	-	20	-	4.5	-
% Ni	-	-	15	3	.004
% Insol	-	-	-	3	-
% FeO	-	-	-	1.5	-
% Zn	-	-	-	4.3	.001
% Co	-	-	-	0.5	-
% Cd	-	-	-	-	.0000
% Bi	-	-	-	-	.0000
% Ag	-	-	-	-	.031

Some typical operating data are shown below:

Weekly Summary of Reverberatory Operations

Material Charged	Tons (Metric)	% of Charge
Dross	835 (750)	92
Soda Ash	45 (40)	5
Coke breeze	16 (14)	2
Silica sand	10 (9)	1
Material Tapped		
Lead bullion	590 (525)	65
Copper matte	164 (146)	18
Slag	81 (73)	9
Ni bearing material	10 (9)	1

Natural gas is used for fuel. The reverberatory furnace consumes 500,000 cu ft/day (14,150 cu meter), and the drossing kettles consume 90,000 cu ft/day (2,550 cu meter).

LEAD REFINERY

The Herculaneum Lead Refinery was rebuilt during the years 1960-1964, incorporating 250 ton (225 metric) kettles throughout. All are arranged in line from the #1 receiving kettle to the #11 casting kettle. The increase in kettle capacity and the number of kettles has enabled the Refinery to process in excess of 23,000 tons (21,000

Figure 12. Typical Refinery and Dross Plant Kettle Installation

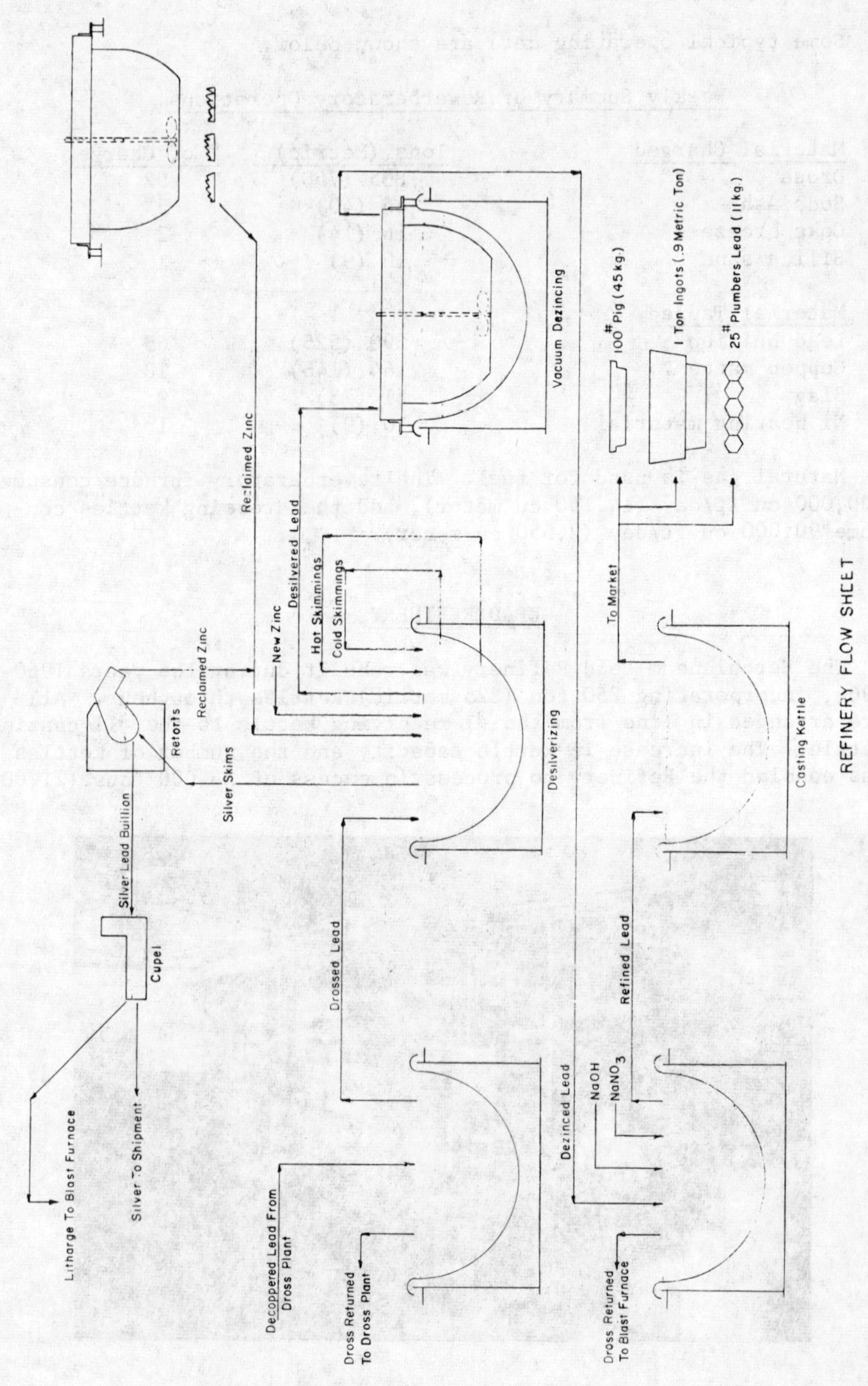

Figure 13. Refinery Flow Sheet

metric) of lead in a calendar month. In addition to the "Doe Run" and "St. Joe" brands, various alloys are produced. A small separate alloy plant was constructed in 1969 for specialty alloys.

A silver section, using retorts and a cupel, operates intermittently to produce semi-refined silver.

Lead metal is cast as 25 lb. (11 kg) plumbers lead links, 100 lb. (45 kg) pigs, 1,000 lb. (450 kg) ingots, and 2,000 lb. (910 kg) ingots. Silver is produced as a granulated product.

Crane service in the Refinery is by two 15 x 3 ton (13.5 x 2.7 metric) and one 25 x 5 (22 x 4.5 metric) Shaw Box cranes, and two 25 x 5 ton (22 x 4.5 metric) P & H cranes. All cranes operate on the same overhead rails.

Finished metal is shipped by rail, truck, and occasionally, by barge on the Mississippi River.

Equipment.

Kettles. The kettles in the Refinery are constructed of grade C firebox steel (ASTM A-285), 1 1/4" (3.2 cm) thick. Kettles are hemispherical with a 6'9" (2.06 meter) radius, surmounted by a 12" high (30.5 cm) cylindrical section, capped with a rolled lip of 5 3/8" radius (13.6 cm). Kettles are stress-relieved at 1,600°F (870°C) by the manufacturer.

Each kettle setting is a steel shell, lined with 4 1/2" (11.4 cm) of insulating brick, with another 4 1/2" (11.4 cm) of firebrick on the fire face. The bottom of the setting is formed by a 5" (12.7 cm) tamped layer of mixed asbestos and cement on top of reinforced concrete. A layer of rammed refractory, at least 5" (12.7 cm) thick, constitutes the bottom fire face. The bottom slopes toward a drain hole. The low point of the kettle is 30" (76 cm) above the refractory.

Heat is provided by three Maxon Premix burners per kettle, set at 120°, and firing tangentially. Each burner is 24" (61 cm) above the bottom and is rated at 2.6 x 10^6 Btu/hr (655 x 10^3 kg-cal/hr) using natural gas. Provision is also made for emergency fuel oil firing. Safety pilot lights and automatic temperature controls are installed on each kettle.

Stirrers, Pumps, Dezincing and Casting Machines. All stirrers use four bladed impellers, vertically mounted on a frame that sits on the kettle rim. Power is supplied by a 40HP motor. The impeller is 22" in diameter (56 cm) and operates within a 30" diameter basket-type shroud (76 cm). The basket is 34" (86 cm) high and extends upward from the lowest point of the impeller.

All lead pumps are centrifugal, with curved impellers. Three sizes of impellers are in use: 6" diameter, 8" diameter, and 8 3/8" diameter (15 cm, 20 cm, and 21 cm). The peripheral discharge of the impeller is to 1" or 1 1/4" (2.5 or 3.2 cm); 2" (5 cm); and 3" (7.6 cm) pipe, respectively. Drive motor size is varied, depending on impeller and discharge pipe sizes. The larger pumps are used for transfer from one kettle to another, at a rate of 300 tons per hour (270 metric), while the smaller pumps are used for feeding lead to the various casting machines at a much lower rate.

Vacuum dezincers are of the well-known St. Joseph Lead Company design - a submerged bell and water cooled condensing top. Impeller size is similar to stirrers, but a 60HP motor is used. Sealing of the impeller shaft is accomplished by a vertical tube dipping into the lead bath. Vacuum is provided by a 14" x 14" (36 x 36 cm) Kinney DVD vacuum pump, driven by a 25HP motor. Vacuum lines are steel pipe and reinforced rubber hose, both 3" (7.6 cm) in diameter. Oil reclamation is done with a locally designed unit.

Finished metal is cast on either Newnam wheels or straight line machines. One ton (.9 metric) ingots are cast on a 26' diameter (7.8 meter) wheel containing 25 molds. Vacuum lifters remove the ingots after a mechanical stamper has identified the metal. A 19'9" diameter (6 meter) wheel is equipped to cast 100 lb. pigs (45 kg). Pigs are removed by a mechanical picker after the lot number has been stamped. A Sheppard straight-line casting machine is used to cast plumber's lead in 25 lb. (11 kg) links. A Treadwell designed, straight-line casting machine for 100 lb. (45 kg) pigs has also been installed. The machine casts four pigs at once, using a four-trough tundish synchronized with mold travel. After casting and skimming, the pigs are cooled by running the molds half-submerged through a water bath contained in a pan underneath the mold strand. After lot number identification, the pigs are automatically stacked in batches of 25, 5 tiers of 5 each, with alternate tiers placed at 90° to each other. By proper programming, stacks of 4, 5, 6, or 7 tiers may be made, and alternate pigs may be inverted. After the stack is formed, it is delivered automatically to a fork-lift pick-up station. Capacity of the unit is 60 tons (54 metric) per hour.

Silver Section. The silver recovery section at Herculaneum produces fire refined silver. Silver skims are retorted in four tilting furnaces using No. 11 graphite retorts and cast iron condensers. The retort furnaces are 5' x 6 1/2' high x 4' deep (1.5 x 2.0 x 1.2 meter). Each is fired by two natural gas burners rated at 750 x 10^3 Btu/hr (190 x 10^3 kg-cal/hr). The furnaces are lined with 4 1/2" (11.5 cm) firebrick, backed up by 2" (5.1 cm) of asbestos.

The cupel pan, 44" x 132" x 7" deep (112 x 335 x 18 cm), has a cast steel plate bottom, water-jacketed sides, and is completely lined with magnesite brick. The pan is enclosed in a firebrick-lined furnace which is fired with two natural gas burners rated at

1.5 x 10^6 Btu/hr each (378 x 10^3 kg-cal/hr). Bullion is sidecharged through a trough. Approximately 2,500 cfm (71 cu meter) of cupellation air is supplied by a Sturtevent #4 blower, powered by a 10HP motor. The depth of the bath is controlled by a chain block which tilts the furnace, using the tapping end as the fulcrum.

Material Handling. All lead shapes are handled by fork-lift truck after casting. Loading equipment consists of eleven battery powered or gasoline-electric units.

A major portion of the lead production is banded to customer specifications, using 3/4" x .025" high tensile steel strapping (1.9 x .063 cm), which is zinc coated.

Operations.

Two major brands of lead are produced at Herculaneum - "St. Joe" and "Doe Run". The "St. Joe" brand lead, containing copper and silver as the major alloying elements, is the naturally occurring alloy of lead smelted from unblended ore. The "Doe Run" brand is fully refined lead of 99.99+% purity (see Table II).

St. Joe Brand Lead. The St. Joe brand lead requires very little refining. A normal sulfur treatment for copper removal to 0.05% Cu is sufficient. Silver content is satisfactory with no treatment.

Figure 14. Retorting Operation

This metal is given a final stirring with a caustic soda and nitre mixture (4:1) and is ready for casting into the desired shape.

Doe Run Brand Lead. Bullion is received from the dross plant with .010% or less copper, and about .030% silver. The silver content has been raised to this level by recirculation of refinery residues and other miscellaneous material.

Desilvering is accomplished by use of a modified Parkes process, which involves recirculation of silver skims within the Refinery. High temperature silver-deficient skims and low temperature zinc-rich skims are recirculated. A "middling" skim, high in silver, 800 - 1,000 oz/ton (approximately 3% Ag) is removed and stocked. When a sufficient quantity has accumulated, it is batch-treated in a kettle, and high grade silver skims are produced for retorting, assaying about 1,500 oz/ton (5% Ag). Desilvered lead contains approximately .0003% Ag. New zinc consumption is about 21 lbs./ton, or 1%.

Desilvered metal is pumped to one of the dezincing kettles, heated to 1,050°F (565°C) and vacuum dezinced at 50 microns Hg. for about five hours. Feed to the dezincing operation assays 0.55% Zn, and dezinced lead contains about 0.05% Zn. The dezincing bell is used only once and the deposit is removed for re-use.

The residual zinc and other remaining impurities are removed in the casting kettles by multiple additions of 100 lbs. NaOH plus 25 lbs. $NaNO_3$ (45 kg, 11 kg).

The metal is now ready for casting, or alloying, as customer needs dictate.

TABLE II

Typical Analysis of Lead

	Doe Run (%)	St. Joe (%)
Silver	.0003 - .0005	.0085 - .0095
Copper	.0000 - .0001	.045 - .055
As + Sb	.0000 - .0001	.0001 - .0002
Zn	.0000 - .0001	.0000 - .0001
Fe	.0000	.0000
Bi	.0000 - .0001	.0000 - .0001
Ni + Co	.0000 - .0001	.0035 - .0045
Cd	.0001 - .0005	.0000 - .0001

Treatment of silver skims follows general industry practice. Charges to the retorts are 1,200 lbs. skims (550 kg) and 5 lb. coke breeze (2.3 kg). Zinc is distilled off at 2,000°F (1,090°C) and reused in the desilvering operation. Bullion, containing more than

Figure 15. Finished Lead Storage and Shipment Area

2,000 oz/ton (7%), is cast for cupelling. The retort cycle is 8 - 10 hours.

When enough rich bullion has been accumulated, with a content of about 200,000 oz. of silver (6.0 metric tons), the cupel is started. Charging and litharge removal proceed as rapidly as possible. When the silver assays 900 fineness or better, cupellation is halted and the metal is granulated. The granules are dried and then packaged in 1,500 oz. capacity buckets for shipment (46.5 kg).

Maintenance.

Maintenance in the Refinery is lighter than that performed in the heavy smelting sections of the plant. Kettles are welded as cracks develop, and have a useful life of about four years. The desilvering kettles take the worst punishment, and after repeated cracking and repair, are used for other less rigorous operations in the Refinery. Pumps, stirrers, and fork-lift trucks require high maintenance, while other units require somewhat less. The Refinery maintains all fork-lift equipment in its own repair shop, but all other maintenance is provided by the main shops.

FUME AND DUST COLLECTION

The Herculaneum Smelter utilizes baghouses to collect dust and fume. Two baghouses, containing 9,360 bags, handle process gases.

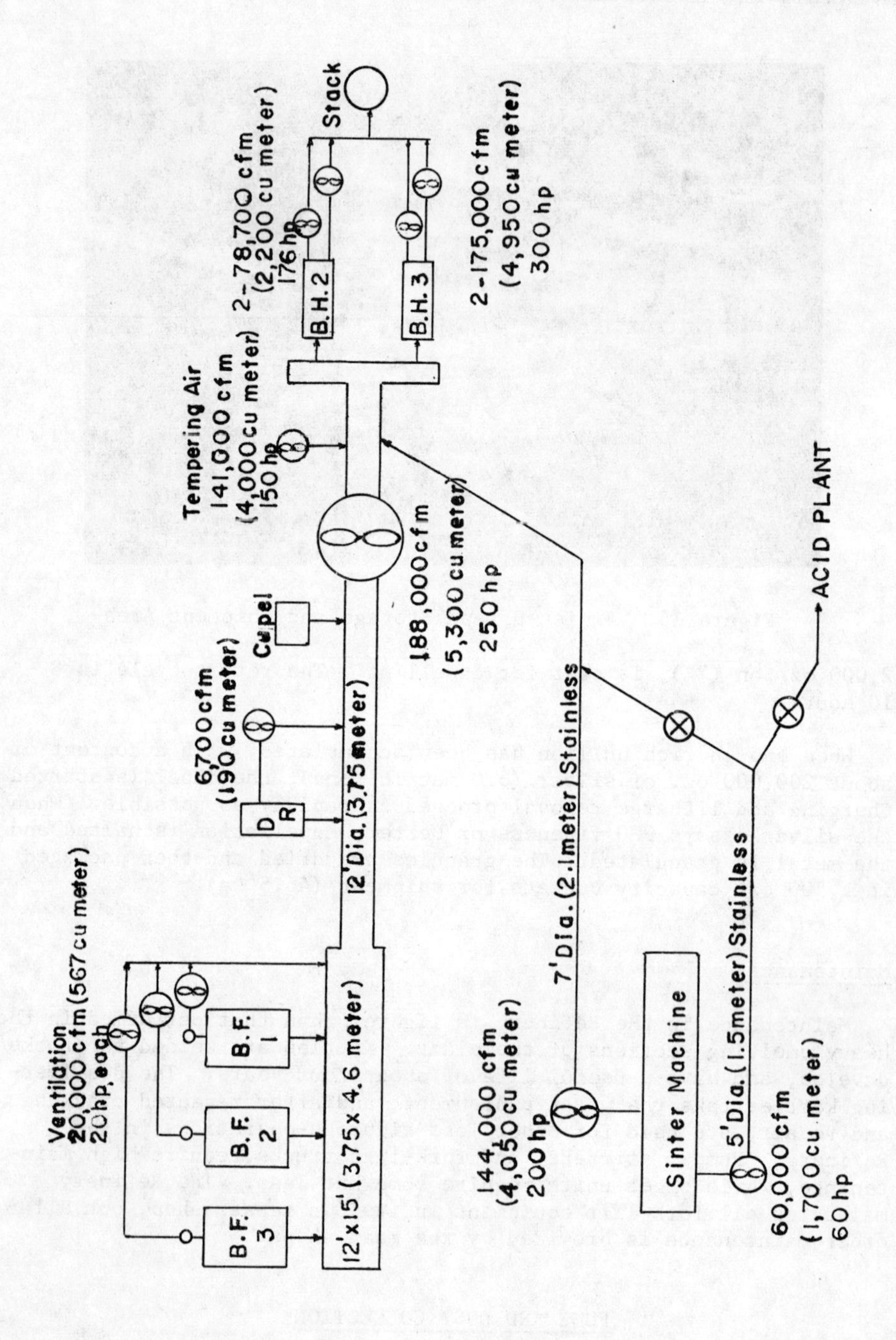

Figure 16. Gas Handling Flow Sheet

A third baghouse handles high-SO_2 gases from the sinter machine, through 1,152 bags, prior to entering the Acid Plant circuit. The gas handling flow sheet illustrates the circuit.

Number 2 baghouse contains 4,752 bags, 5" in diameter x 9'6" long (12.7 cm x 2.9 meter), in 12 cells of 396 bags per cell. Number 3 baghouse contains 4,608 bags, 8" in diameter x 21'6" long (20 cm x 6.55 meter), in 12 cells of 384 bags per cell. Number 4 baghouse contains 1,152 bags, 8" in diameter x 21'6" long (20 cm x 6.55 meter), in 6 cells of 192 bags per cell. All bags are acrylic 2 x 2 twill with an original porosity of 55-65 cfm per 1/2" water gauge pressure (156-184 cu meter per minute per 1.27 cm water pressure). All baghouses were designed and built by the Wheelabrator Company.

Number 2 baghouse, built in 1954, contains 59,675 sq. ft. of cloth area to filter 136,000 cfm of gas (5,500 sq. meters; 3,850 cu meter/min), for a gas:bag ratio of 2.29:1. Two fans, each rated at 78,000 cfm (2,200 cu meter/min) at 7" water gauge (17.8 cm) running at 1,200 r.p.m. handle clean gas and keep the baghouse under suction. The shaking cycle and outlet damper operation are automatically controlled by a programmed timer. Dust is collected in inverted cone bottom hoppers and removed through a rotary valve and 12" (30.5 cm) screw conveyor.

Number 3 baghouse, built in 1962, contains 185,856 sq. ft. of cloth to filter 350,000 cfm (17,300 sq. meter; 9,900 cu meter/min) for a gas:bag ratio of 1.89:1. Two fans, rated at 175,000 cfm at 8" water gauge (4,950 cu meter/min, 20.3 cm), running at 880 r.p.m. exhaust clean gas and provide suction. A repressurizing fan, running at 2,380 r.p.m., provides 17,000 cfm at 11" water gauge (480 cu meter/min, 28 cm). Operation of the outlet dampers, shaking, and repressurizing are controlled as in Number 2 baghouse. Hopper construction and dust removal are also similar.

Number 4 baghouse, built in 1969, contains 42,240 sq. ft. of cloth to filter 60,000 cfm (3,940 sq. meter; 1,700 cu meter) for a gas:bag ratio of 1.42:1. The Acid Plant blower provides the necessary suction. Shaking operations and dust removal are similar to Numbers 2 and 3 baghouses.

There is no Number 1 baghouse; it was abandoned and removed in 1963.

Dust product handling is by screw conveyor from vee bottom hoppers, through a rotary valve, into collection screw conveyors which move the dust to a double shaft, bladed pugging unit. Water, in sufficient quantity to prevent dusting, is added to the pugger. The dampened dust is bottom-discharged into a railroad car for transport to the sinter preparation section via the rotary car dumper.

Periodic assays of dust-make are performed. If the cadmium content is sufficient, the material is reserved for cadmium recovery elsewhere.

Typical assay of dust:			
	Pb	-	60%
	Cd	-	3-5%
	Zn	-	10%

All baghouse outlet fans discharge into the base of a brick stack, 352' high with a diameter of 20' (108 x 6.1 meter).

ACID PLANT

The new Sulfuric Acid Plant went on stream in July, 1969, and is operating at its designed rate, producing up to 340 tons (305 metric) per day of 100% H_2SO_4 from sinter gas. The flow sheet illustrates the equipment and process.

The conditioning chamber of reinforced concrete, 50' x 20' x 12' high (15 x 6.1 x 3.66 meter), is equipped with automatic high pressure water sprays to control the temperature. The sprays operate at 20 gpm and 500 psig (78 litre @ 35 kg/sq. cm). The baghouse is described previously, but it should be noted here that the internal construction features a double wall, with clean filtered gas passing

Figure 17. Acid Plant

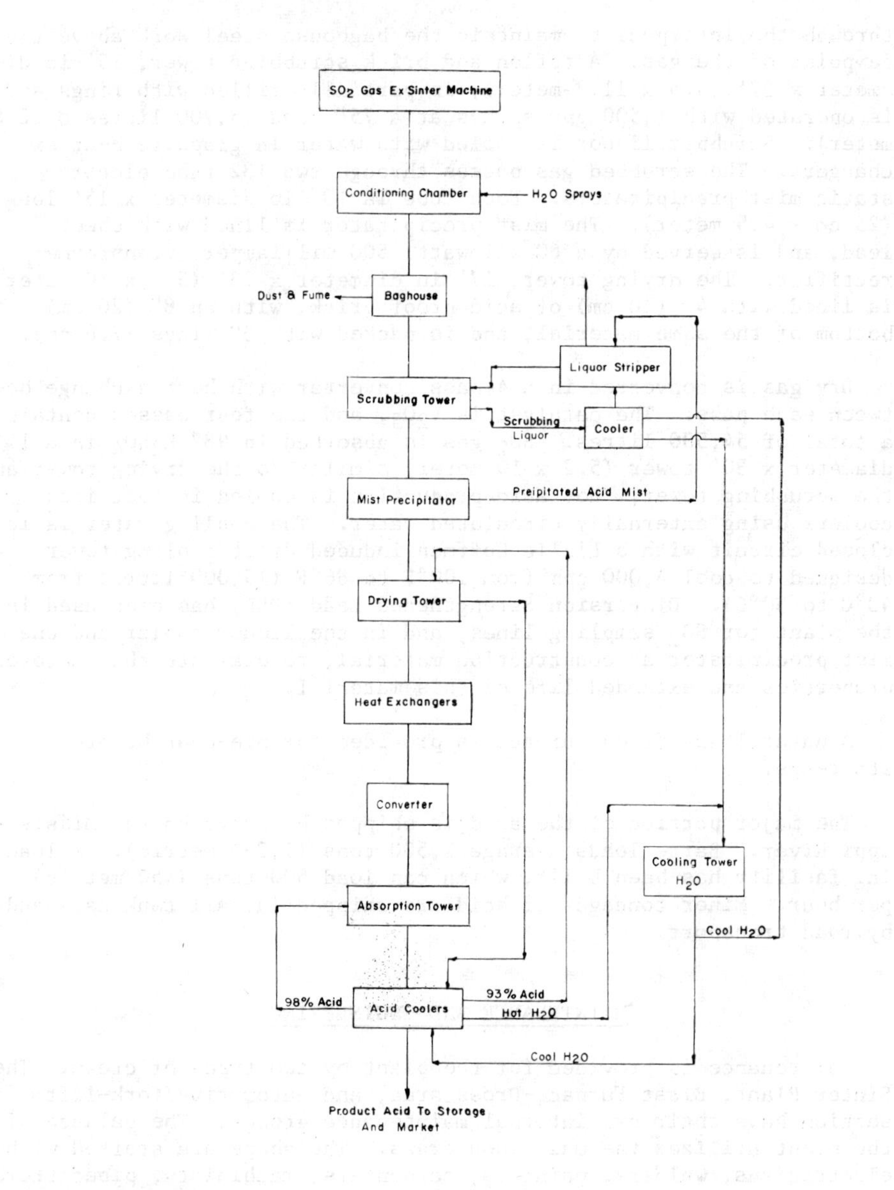

Figure 18, Acid Plant Flow Sheet

through the interpace to maintain the baghouse steel work above the dewpoint of the gas. A teflon and brick scrubbing tower, 15' in diameter x 37' (4.5 x 11.3 meter), is partially filled with rings and is operated with 1,500 gpm sprays at a 75' head (5,700 litres @ 22.8 meter). Scrubber liquor is cooled with water in graphite heat exchangers. The scrubbed gas passes through two 132 tube electrostatic mist precipitators. Each tube is 10" in diameter x 15' long (25 cm x 4.5 meter). The mist precipitator is lined with sheet lead, and is served by a 60 kilowatt, 500 milliampere transformer rectifier. The drying tower, 17' in diameter x 33' (5.2 x 10 meter), is lined with 4" (10 cm) of acid proof brick, with an 8" (20 cm) bottom of the same material, and is packed with 3" rings (7.6 cm).

Dry gas is converted in a 4-pass converter with heat exchange between each pass. The catalyst is V_2O_5, and the four passes contain a total of 54,500 litres. SO_2 gas is absorbed in 98% H_2SO_4 in a 17' diameter x 30' tower (5.2 x 10 meter) similar to the drying tower and the scrubbing tower. Hot acid production is cooled in cast iron coolers using externally circulated water. The cooling water is in closed circuit with a Lillie Hoffman induced draft cooling tower designed to cool 4,000 gpm from 100°F to 86°F (15,000 litres from 43°C to 30°C). Dispersion Strengthened Lead (DSL) has been used in the plant for SO_2 sampling lines, and in the liquor cooler and one mist precipitator as construction material, to evaluate the improved properties and extended life of this material.

A natural gas fired furnace is provided for pre-heat before start-ups.

The major portion of the acid is shipped by barge on the Mississippi River. Barge loads average 1,500 tons (1,350 metric). A loading facility has been built, which can load 500 tons (450 metric) per hour. Minor tonnages of acid are shipped in rail tank cars and by road transport.

MAINTENANCE AND ENGINEERING

Maintenance is provided for the plant by two types of crews. The Sinter Plant, Blast Furnace-Dross area, and automotive/fork-lift section have their own internal maintenance groups. The balance of the plant utilizes the main shop crews. The shops are staffed with electricians, welders, painters, carpenters, machinists, pipefitters, blacksmiths, and sheet metal men. A comprehensive apprenticeship program provides the needed trained personnel on a continuing basis.

Scheduled maintenance is performed in the Sinter Plant and Blast Furnace-Dross areas, augumented, as needed, by shop personnel, while the balance of the plant operates on a "work request" basis. Afternoon and night shifts are catered for by a small crew on each of these shifts.

The Sinter Plant has instituted a "Planned Maintenance" schedule incorporating preventive maintenance and corrective replacement of units. The replaced units are renewed in the shops and are available for the next changeover. This program has enabled the Sinter Plant to operate in excess of 90% of available time.

Engineering studies are performed provided they are not too large. An engineering and drawing office is available to make engineering drawings. Large scale projects are generally contracted with outside consultants and engineering service companies.

LABORATORIES

All chemical laboratories at the Herculaneum Smelter are housed in one building. Besides office and storage areas,there are rooms for the spectrometer, the assay-furnace, the atomic-absorption apparatus and the analytical balances. There are two wet-chemistry laboratories - the larger laboratory performs most of the production analyses, while the smaller laboratory handles special analyses.

Four graduate chemists and five technicians work day shift, seven days a week, to provide the smelter operating personnel with the information necessary to control the plant processes and the quality of the finished products.

In addition to the conventional wet-chemical techniques, the laboratory force makes use of a Baird-Atomic, 3 meter, model HB-2, Direct-Reading Spectrometer, with a model RS-1 Readout Console and a teletype print-out; a model 303 Perkim-Elmer Atomic Absorption Spectrophotometer with a Perkin-Elmer Recorder Readout and a Honeywell Electronik-19 Recorder; and a "fire-assay" furnace which uses natural gas as fuel.

All incoming raw materials are assayed as necessary. Past experience dictates whether every lot is analyzed or if only an occasional analysis is necessary. Concentrates get the greatest amount of attention; each lot is analyzed for lead. Monthly composites of each type of concentrate are analyzed for minor elements. Special attention is given to the slag-producing elements and those elements which may contaminate the finished metal.

Chemical control of the blast furnace, dross furnace, and sintering plant is maintained by analyzing the slag, matte, and sinter daily. Weekly and monthly composites of the daily samples provide an internal check on daily analysis, as well as providing information for metallurgical balance.

The refinery process is almost exclusively controlled by utilizing the spectrometer. Silver, zinc, and copper contents are closely watched. Finished metal is also analyzed for arsenic, antimony, tin, bismuth, cadmium, and iron. Analysis of the alloying elements is done on the spectrometer or by wet-chemistry, whichever provides the necessary accuracy in meeting customer's specifications. Development work is constantly being done to improve analytical curves and sampling procedures in order to increase spectrometer performance. Initial work has indicated that sinter, matte, and slag can be run on the spectrometer. Having the ability to run such materials quickly and precisely will increase the control of plant operations.

RESEARCH

The Research Department is made up of graduate engineers and technicians. The scope of their activities should perhaps be described as development and pilot plant work, rather than pure research, because their projects are closely tied-in to the operation of the plant.

In recent years, the research group has conducted investigations into various aspects of plant metallurgy, including up-draft sintering, moisture control of the Sinter Plant charge, gas analysis, and sampling systems. Other investigations include determining the forms of lead in blast furnace slag and modifications of practice in such refinery operations as decoppering, desilvering, dezincing, etc.

A full scale research and development program was carried out on direct smelting of concentrates to produce metallic lead in a one step converter operation. This included a pilot scale operation of the process and resulted in Patents being granted for the process.

The Research Department, in addition to turning out small quantities of specialty alloys where the amounts involved are too small for regular plant facilities, supplies standard alloys for the spectrograph in the analytical laboratory. A metallographic and mechanical testing laboratory is used for in-plant control and product development.

The research group runs gas volume surveys in various trails about the plant, in addition to running dust burdens and analyses of the gas streams. A series of ambient air monitoring stations surrounding the plant is maintained by the Research Department, as well as a small network of in-plant air sampling stations.

GENERAL

The Herculaneum Lead Smelting Division is the only lead smelting operation of the St. Joe Minerals Corporation.

The total complement is approximately 540 - - 80 salary and staff employees; 460 hourly paid employees. The smelter operates seven days per week, on a 24-hour-per-day basis.

In 1969, the first full year of operation at expanded capacity, the plant produced 223,000 tons (201,000 metric) of refined lead.

ACKNOWLEDGEMENT

The author wishes to thank the St. Joe Minerals Corporation for permission to publish, and the staff at Herculaneum for their assistance.

Chapter 25

THE BUICK SMELTER

OF AMAX-HOMESTAKE LEAD TOLLERS

F. W. Gibson

Smelter Manager, Missouri Lead Operating Company

Boss, Missouri

ABSTRACT

A detailed description of the smelting and refining operations of the Amax-Homestake Lead Toller's smelter at Buick, Missouri.

This is one of two completely new lead smelting and refining operations to go into operation in the United States in over forty years. Incorporated into the operation are the new methods and equipment which have been developed and lend themselves to the particular metallurgy of this plant.

The text, as well as the statistical data presented, represent actual current practice after 22 months of operation, and although the metallurgy is considered to be relatively simple, several metallurgical problems unique to Missouri concentrates are discussed.

INTRODUCTION

The Buick smelter is located in the "new lead belt" area near Bixby, in Iron County,Missouri.

The facility consists of a lead smelter, refinery and sulfuric acid plant with a nominal annual capacity of 100,000 tons of high purity (99.99%) refined lead and 53,000 tons of 93% sulfuric acid.

Small amounts of copper matte and a silver rich retort bullion are produced as secondary products and at present are shipped elsewhere for refining.

The plant, one of the first completely new lead smelting operations built in the United States in 40 years, went into operation in July of 1968. The first nine months were spent in training crews and going through the operational and metallurgical problems that plague most new plant start-ups. These were gradually worked out and the Buick smelter has been operating at design capacity or better for some time.

Both the smelter and refinery were designed and built to treat the concentrate production from the Amax-Homestake Lead Companies Buick mine and the Magmont mine of Cominco American-Dresser Ind.

These concentrates are typical of those produced in southeast Missouri. They contain high lead, low silver and copper, and are free from the impurities usually associated with lead concentrates such as arsenic, antimony, bismuth and tin. This permits a comparatively simple metallurgical operation for the production of lead that is 99.99% pure, known in the trade as "Four Nine" lead.

The following text describes in general the various phases of the operation of the Buick smelter along with details of some of the metallurgical problems found in smelting and refining the southeast Missouri lead concentrates. In most cases operating data and equipment sizes are summarized and tabulated as "Operating Data" at the end of each of the sections covered.

RECEIVING AND HANDLING

Incoming material, including coke, fluxes and concentrates from the Buick mine, is received in dump bottom railroad cars. The Magmont concentrates are delivered in 30-ton dump trucks. Each is weighed over the railroad or truck scale before being unloaded into its proper bin in the unloading and storage area, which consists of nine covered individual storage bins for concentrates and fluxes, one open storage bin for coke and an adjacent storage yard for plant retreatment products.

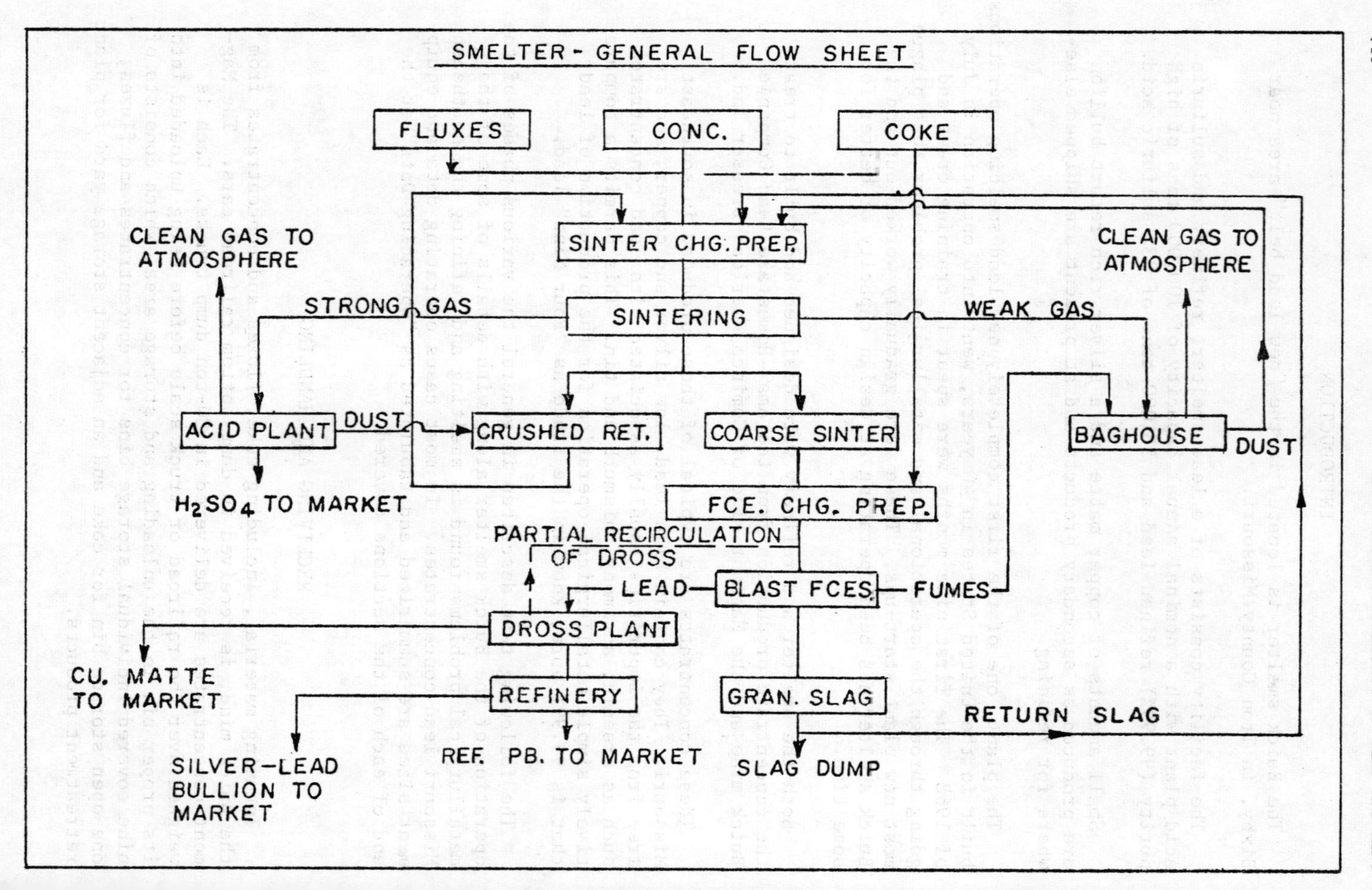
SMELTER - GENERAL FLOW SHEET
FLUXES
CONC.
COKE
SINTER CHG. PREP.
CLEAN GAS TO ATMOSPHERE
STRONG GAS
SINTERING
WEAK GAS
CLEAN GAS TO ATMOSPHERE
ACID PLANT
DUST
CRUSHED RET.
COARSE SINTER
BAGHOUSE
DUST
H_2SO_4 TO MARKET
FCE. CHG. PREP.
PARTIAL RECIRCULATION OF DROSS
LEAD
BLAST FCES.
FUMES
DROSS PLANT
CU. MATTE TO MARKET
REFINERY
GRAN. SLAG
RETURN SLAG
SILVER-LEAD BULLION TO MARKET
REF. PB. TO MARKET
SLAG DUMP

Plant secondaries for retreatment such as granulated slag, storage sinter, refinery drosses, coarse slag, etc., are handled by front end loader and dump trucks to the storage area.

The Buick concentrates are received in specially designed 100-ton drop bottom gondolas furnished by the Frisco railroad. These cars are modifications of the railroad cars developed by Balwin-Lima-Hamilton for copper concentrate service in the Southwest. They are so designed that the body sets between the trucks rather than over them as in the standard design. The bottom of the body is essentially two air operated doors hinged from the sides of the car. Air applied to the actuating cylinder opens and closes the doors easily and rapidly, allowing a 100-ton load to be dumped in a matter of minutes with little or no car cleanup required.

All fluxes and coke received by rail are delivered in standard hopper bottom gondolas which are unloaded with the aid of a side mounted car shaker.

Materials for the sintering operation, namely concentrates, individual fluxes, and granulated slag are reclaimed from their bins by means of a front end loader, dumped into an underground feed hopper and discharged onto an inclined belt conveyor. This belt carries the selected material to the top of the sinter charge preparation plant where it is distributed to the proper bin by a tripper conveyor and reversible wing conveyor.

Materials for the blast furnace, namely coke, coarse slag, refinery drosses and storage sinter are reclaimed in a similar manner and delivered to the blast furnace feed bins by a separate feeder and conveyor system.

OPERATING DATA

1. Storage Capacity

Material	Bins	Tons
Concentrates	2	400 tons each
Concentrates	2	1300
Limerock Flux	1	600
Iron Flux	1	800
Silica Flux	1	500
Coke	1	1200
Granulated Slag	1	600
Storage Yard	-	20,000

2. Analysis of Materials

Percent	Pb Conc.	Iron	Lime	Silica	Slag
SiO_2	1.0	33.0	1.0	88.0	22.9
Fe	3.0	38.0	-	0.5	31.0 (FeO)
CaO	1.9	-	55.0	-	17.0
MgO	0.5	-	0.2	-	3.5
Zn	1.3	-	-	-	11.5
S	15.9	-	-	-	1.0
Pb	74.2	-	-	-	3.5
Cu	0.4	-	-	-	0.10
Ag g/t	80.	-	-	-	-

3. Labor Force

One Shift Operation	
Unloading	2
Sampling	2
Sample Preparation	2
Reclaiming	3
General Labor	10
Total	19 Per Day

SINTERING

PROCESS DESCRIPTION

The preparation of lead concentrates into a suitable feed for the blast furnace is accomplished by agglomerating the fine material and simultaneously burning off most of the sulfur in the concentrates. The resulting product is called sinter, which is the principal constituent of the blast furnace charge.

It is necessary that the sinter composition be such that a liquid, free-flowing slag is formed at the operating temperatures of the blast furnace. This requires that the chemical makeup of the slag be within close limits, and is best obtained by the proper blending of the individual slag forming constituents and diluents with the concentrates before sintering.

For convenience the description and data presented on the sinter plant operation at the Buick smelter are separated into three subjects, namely:

1. Charge Preparation
2. Updraft Sintering
3. Sinter Crushing

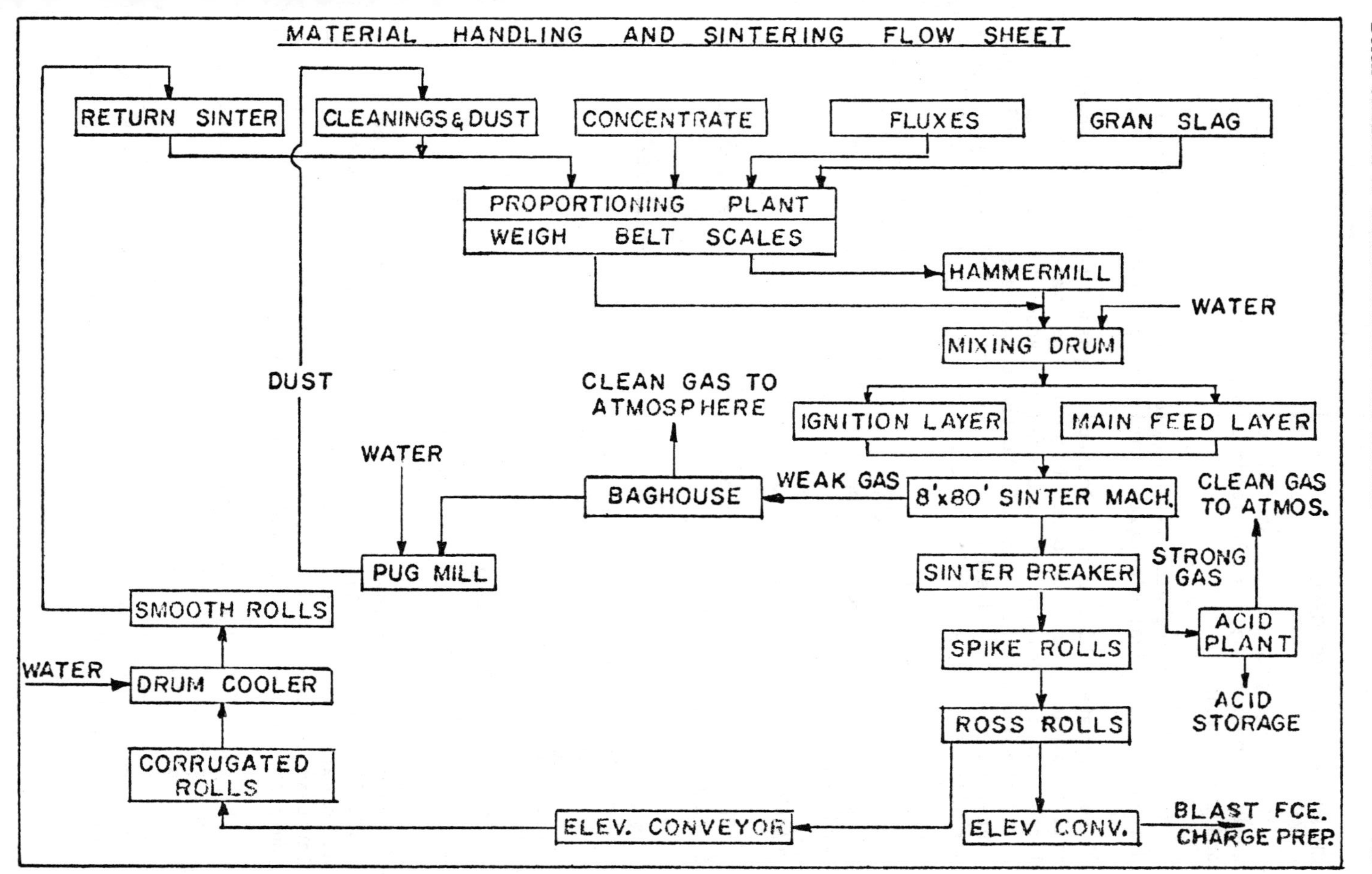
MATERIAL HANDLING AND SINTERING FLOW SHEET
RETURN SINTER
CLEANINGS & DUST
CONCENTRATE
FLUXES
GRAN SLAG
PROPORTIONING PLANT
WEIGH BELT SCALES
HAMMERMILL
WATER
MIXING DRUM
DUST
CLEAN GAS TO ATMOSPHERE
IGNITION LAYER
MAIN FEED LAYER
WATER
BAGHOUSE
WEAK GAS
8'x80' SINTER MACH.
CLEAN GAS TO ATMOS.
PUG MILL
SINTER BREAKER
STRONG GAS
SMOOTH ROLLS
ACID PLANT
SPIKE ROLLS
WATER
DRUM COOLER
ROSS ROLLS
ACID STORAGE
CORRUGATED ROLLS
ELEV. CONVEYOR
ELEV CONV.
BLAST FCE. CHARGE PREP.

CHARGE PREPARATION GENERAL

The charge preparation system consists of ten individual bins, their respective belt-scale feeders, collector belts, hammer mill and mixing drum.

Material from the bins is fed over belt scales with the belts driven by individual electric motors through eddy current clutches.

Concentrates, fluxes and cleanup are passed through the hammer mill to break up any lumps and blend the new material feed. Granulated slag and crushed return sinter are added to the collector belt after the hammer mill. All of the constituents of the feed to the sinter machine then discharge onto an inclined belt conveyor equipped with a scale, which is the control for the total feed.

The blended charge is then fed into a drum mixer for moisture conditioning and further mixing. Another conveyor belt delivers the conditioned charge from the drum mixer to the sinter machine feed system.

CHARGE PREPARATION DETAILS

The normal feed to the sinter machine, with only slight variation, is made up as follows:

Material	Percent	Feed Rate Tons Per Hr.
Concentrates	26.0	24
Iron Flux	4.0	3
Lime	2.0	2
Silica	1.0	1
Return Slag	15.0	14
Dust and Cleanup	2.0	2
Return Sinter	50.0	44
	100.0	90

As return sinter is the largest single constituent of the sinter feed, it is used as the primary unit in the feed control system. All other constituents of the sinter machine feed are set and regulated as a percentage of the return sinter by means of the Bristol control system on the individual belt feeders.

The rate of feed to the sinter machine is controlled manually from a remote control panel, located at the sinter machine. The belt scale on the incline collector belt senses the rate of feed supplied to the sinter machine and, by means of the master controller, increases or decreases the speed of all the collector belts simultaneously to correct for any change in the desired feed rate.

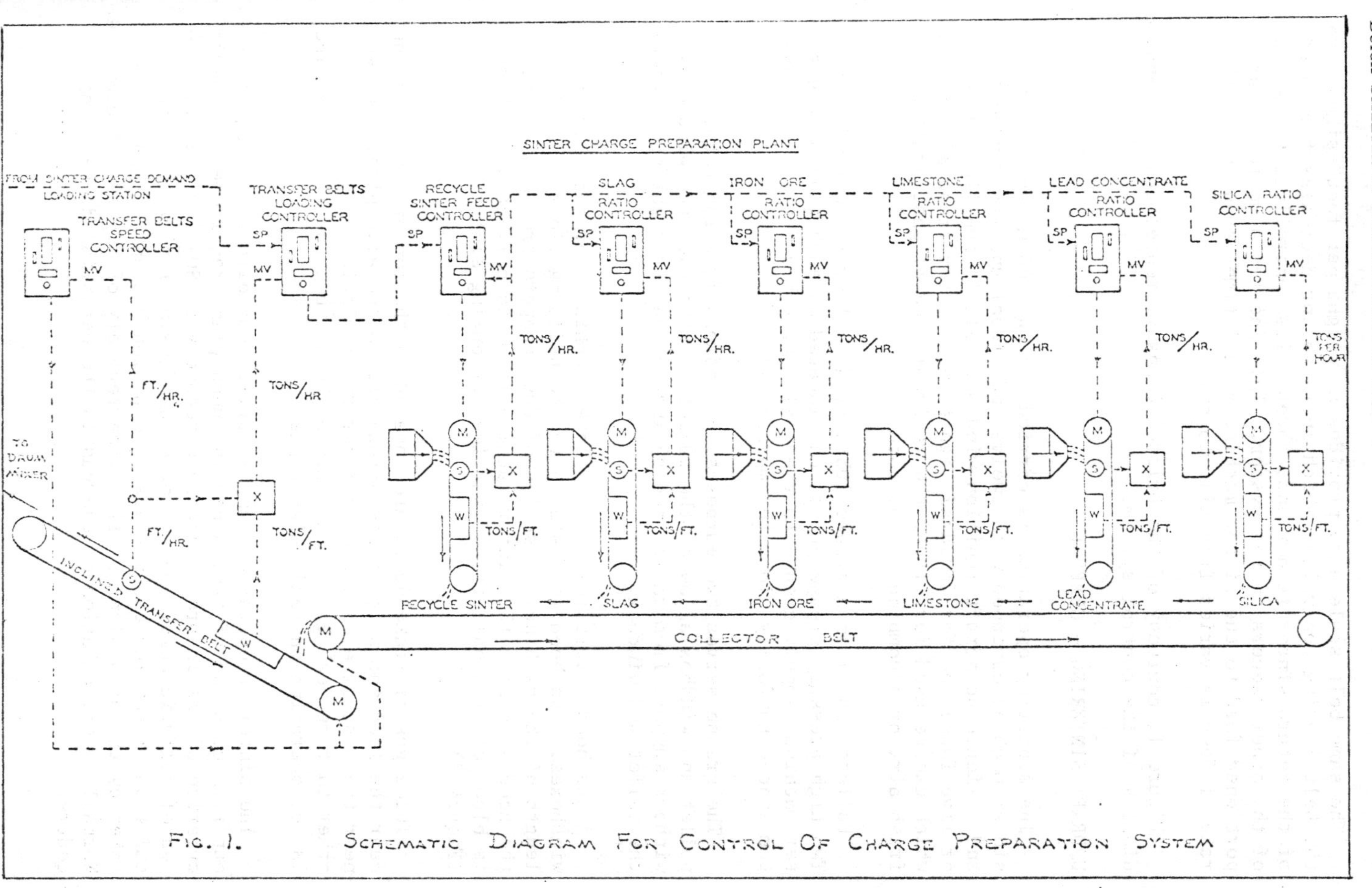

FIG. 1. SCHEMATIC DIAGRAM FOR CONTROL OF CHARGE PREPARATION SYSTEM

The same belt scale also provides a "weight per foot" signal to the belt loading controller which increases or decreases the speed of the return sinter feeder and, through its controller, the speed of the other feeders in the system. This insures a uniformly proportioned feed to the sinter machine at all times even though the rate of feed is varied from time to time.

Figure 1, courtesy of the Bristol Company, represents a schematic diagram of the control system.

UPDRAFT SINTERING - GENERAL

The sintering operation is carried out on a 60 m^2 Lurgi updraft sinter machine equipped with twelve individual updraft windboxes and a single downdraft ignition windbox. Air is supplied by means of five fans; one for downdraft ignition, two for fresh air and two which can be used for either the recirculation of gas, additional fresh air, or a combination of both.

Pallets travel on a grease lubricated seal over the windboxes. Two high pressure grease pumps, one located on each side of the sinter machine, supply grease to the seals through a distribution system spaced uniformly along the machine seal.

The grease serves two purposes, a) reduces friction between the pallet and windbox allowing the pallet to move over the windboxes without support from rails, and b) insures an air tight seal between the pallet and windbox.

A gas hood covers the entire sinter machine over the updraft windboxes. The hood is fastened to the building floor along the length of the machine. A series of dust hoppers are located under the hood alongside the sinter machine frame to collect dust which is blown off the pallets and settles out during sintering. (Figure 2)

Three gas off-take ducts are located in the top of the hood; one near the feed end which takes strong gas to the acid plant and two near the discharge end, one used for recirculation of gas and the other to take weak gas to the main baghouse when the sinter machine is not operating on recirculated gas.

The sintering operation can be carried out either with or without recirculation of gas, depending upon plant requirements. Recirculation of gas insures a complete recovery of SO_2 for the production of sulfuric acid. On the other hand, sintering with no recirculation of gas increases sinter production but as the gas volume taken by the acid plant is fixed, the recovery of SO_2 is not complete. Normally, recirculation of the gas is the established operating procedure.

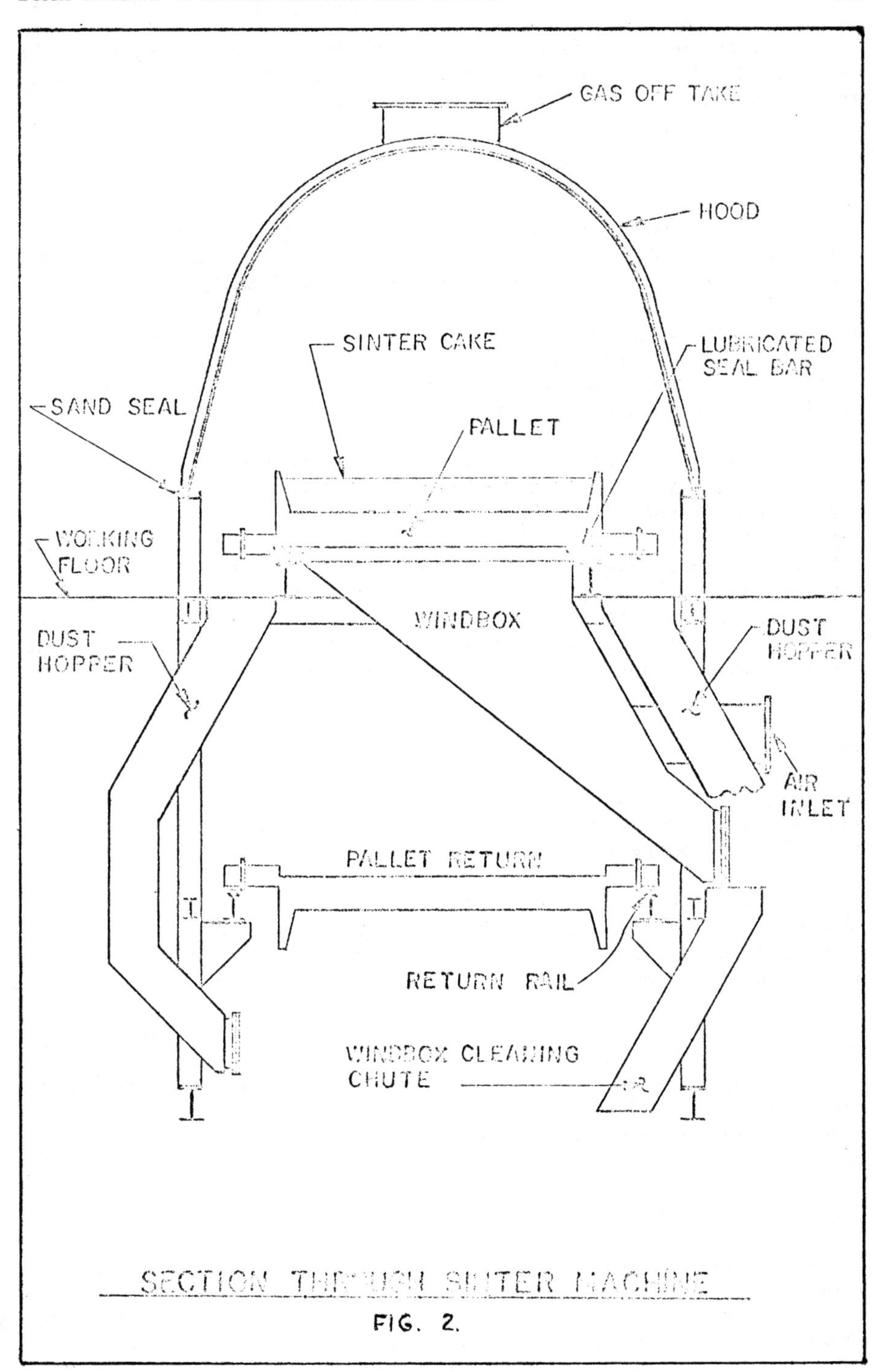

SECTION THROUGH SINTER MACHINE

FIG. 2.

Sulfur is the only fuel in the sinter feed. Fine coke, commonly used in many lead sintering operations, is not necessary for the production of good quality, low sulfur sinter at Buick.

SINTERING DETAILS

Feed The sinter machine feed system, Figure 3, consists of the main feed hopper, a small surge hopper and the ignition feed hopper. A shuttle conveyor belt (S1) traverses longitudinally over both the main feed hopper and surge hopper. A variable speed cross conveyor belt (S2) connects the surge hopper to a shuttle conveyor belt (S3) which traverses longitudinally over the ignition feed hopper. Both shuttle belts are actuated pneumatically, with limit switches controlling the distance of travel.

The conditioned feed is delivered by conveyor belt to the shuttle conveyor (S1) over the main feed hopper. This shuttle conveyor not only feeds the main feed hopper constantly but also feeds the surge hopper intermittently at the end of its traverse. The surge hopper with its variable speed belt (S2) insures a uniform feed to the shuttle conveyor (S3) which feeds the ignition hopper constantly. The amount of feed to the ignition feed hopper is controlled by a limit switch which regulates the overrun of the S1 shuttle belt into the surge hopper and by the speed of the cross conveyor (S2).

Both the ignition and main feed hoppers are equipped with high and low level alarms to indicate the feed level in each hopper.

Ignition The ignition layer, 3.1 cm deep, is laid on the grates and passes under a gas fired muffle located between the ignition and main feed hoppers.

A downdraft windbox is located directly under the muffle. The volume of air pulled through the ignition layer is automatically controlled by a damper in the duct connecting the downdraft windbox to the ignition fan.

As the ignition layer passes under the muffle, the heat ignites the sulfur in the charge and starts the roasting. The object is to obtain an incandescent layer of burning material as it passes under the main layer feed hopper. This is the critical step in the updraft sintering operation and requires consistant and uniform ignition if a good sinter is to be produced.

ROASTING AND SINTERING

As the hot ignition layer passes under the main feed hopper the bulk of the sinter feed is superimposed upon it, resulting in a total bed depth of 28 cm. Experience over the past two years has shown this to be optimum for the production of good quality low

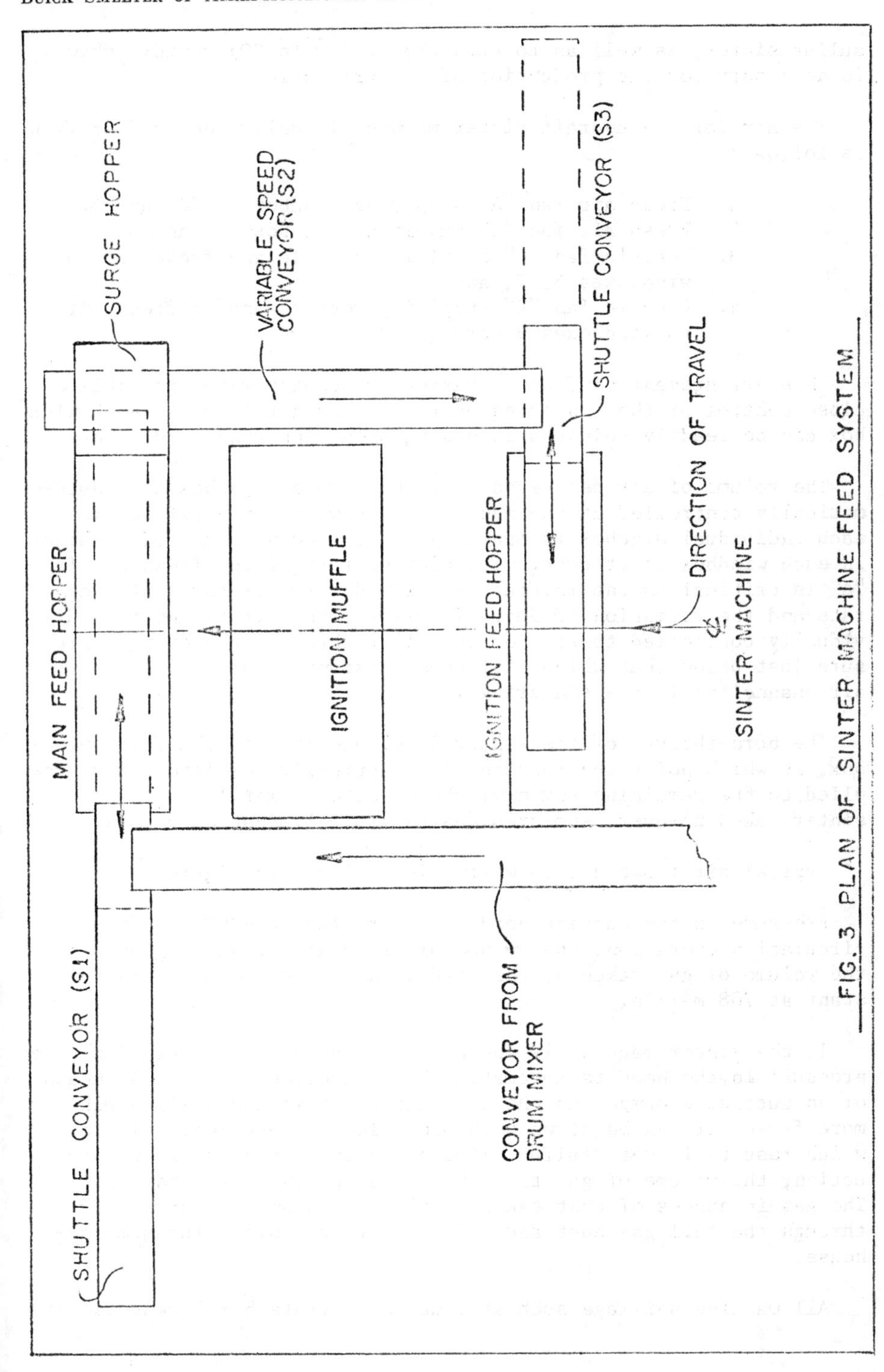

FIG. 3 PLAN OF SINTER MACHINE FEED SYSTEM

sulfur sinter, as well as to burn the sulfur to SO_2 rapidly, which is necessary for the production of sulfuric acid.

The air for the updraft sinter machine is delivered by four fans as follows:

1. Fresh air fan "A" supplying windboxes 1,2, and 3.
2. Fresh air fan "B" supplying windboxes 4 and 5.
3. Recycle fan "C" supplying recycle and fresh air to windboxes 6, 7, and 8.
4. Recycle fan "D" supplying recycle and/or fresh air to windboxes 9 through 12.

This arrangement of fans to various windboxes makes possible a close control of the sintering operation, as air flow to each windbox can be readily adjusted depending upon sintering conditions.

The volume of air delivered to each group of windboxes is automatically controlled at the fan inlet. However, the air volume to each individual windbox is manually controlled by means of a damper in each windbox inlet duct. The blowing rate of the fresh air fan "A" is critical as the initial air flow determines the sintering rate and the formation of SO_2. Therefore, the air volume is individually controlled to each of the first three windboxes at a pressure just below that which will cause disruption of the charge or air channeling in the sintering layer.

The burn-through of the sinter layer occurs over the fifth windbox, at which point the roasting is practically complete. Air supplied to the remaining seven windboxes acts primarily to cool the sinter cake; however, some residual sulfur elimination occurs.

Typical air flows are shown in Figure 4 and in Figure 5.

Pressure in the machine hood is controlled at -6mm H_2O. On a recirculation operation, the volume of fresh air blown is governed by the volume of gas taken by the acid plant, which normally is constant at 708 m^3/min.

If the sinter machine is operated without gas recirculation, the pressure in the hood is automatically controlled at -6 mm by means of an automatic damper in the tail gas off-take duct. Although more fresh air can be blown when operating without recirculation, which results in more sulfur elimination and a higher sinter production, the volume of gas taken by the acid plant is constant. The gas in excess of that taken to the acid plant is drawn off through the tail gas duct and delivered to the blast furnace baghouse.

All machine spillage such as fine feed, grate bar leakage, dust

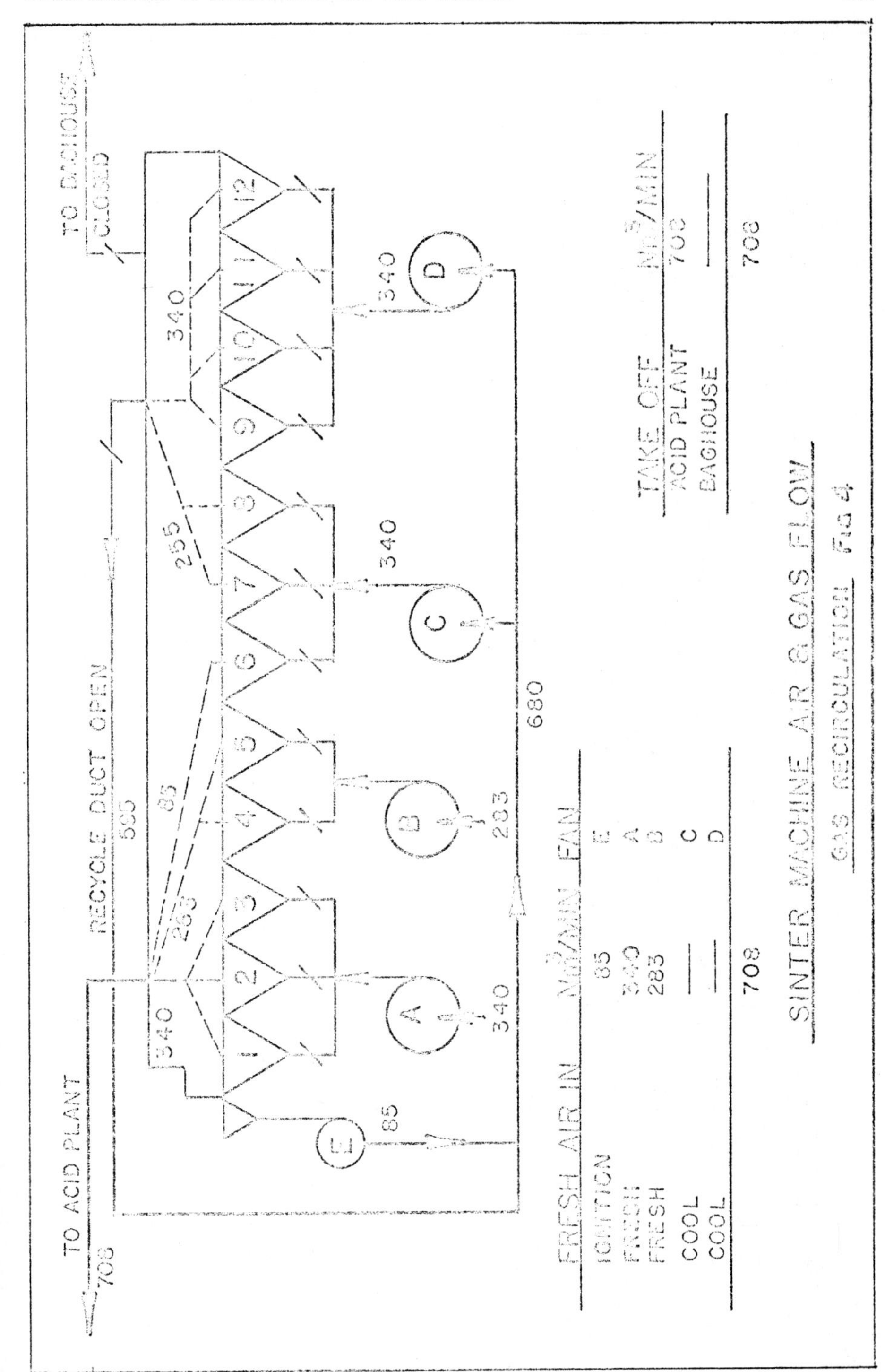

SINTER MACHINE AIR & GAS FLOW

GAS RECIRCULATION FIG 4

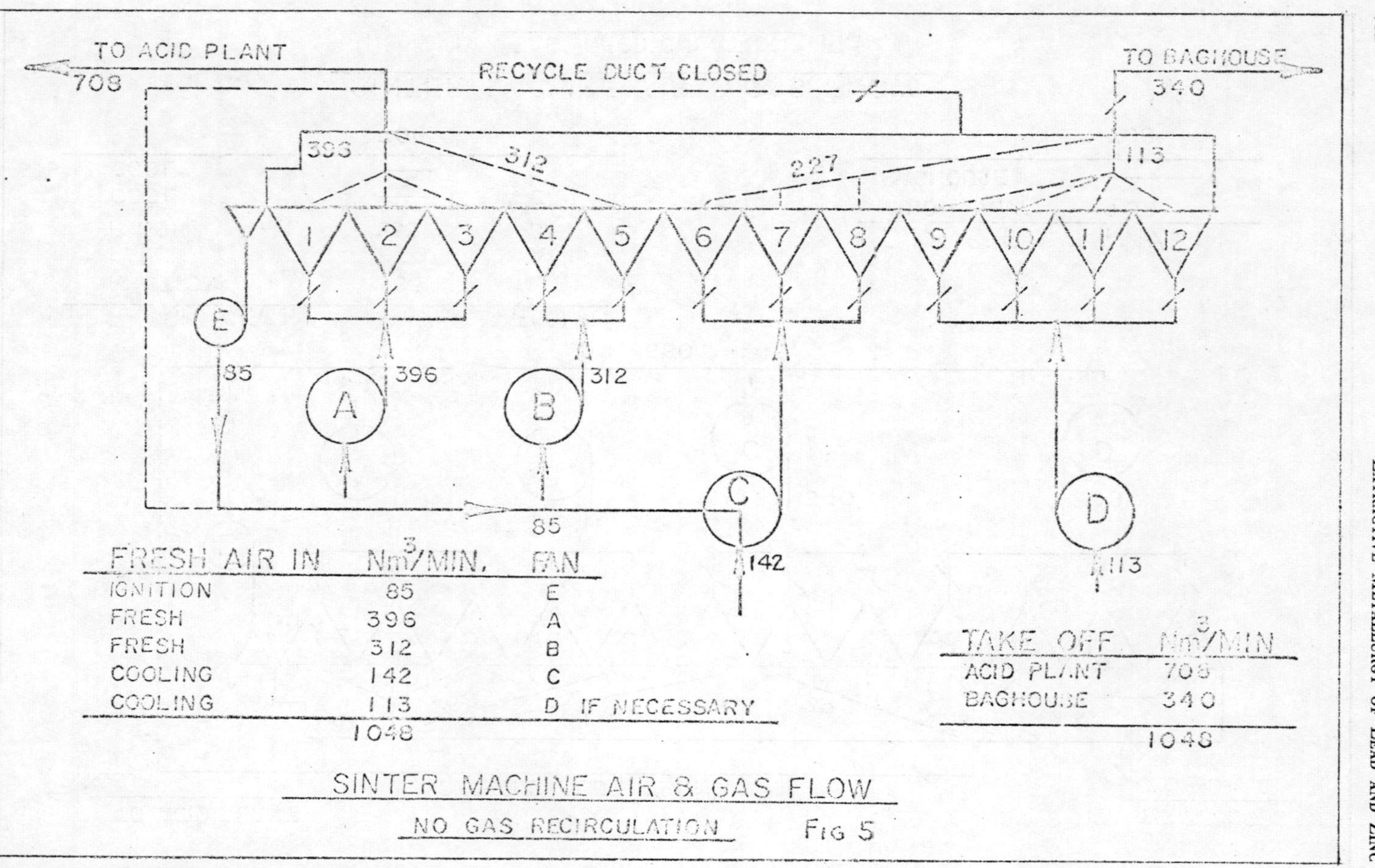

SINTER MACHINE AIR & GAS FLOW

NO GAS RECIRCULATION   Fig 5

blown through in sintering and grate bar cleanings is collected in a hopper running the length of the sinter machine beneath the return strand. This material is transported continuously by drag conveyor for blending in the return sinter circuit.

No water is used for cooling of gas in the hood. The dust generated at the machine discharge is adequately vented to the main baghouse through the weak gas flue.

SINTERING CRUSHING - GENERAL

The sintered product from the sinter machine is discharged in a solid mass approaching the size of the machine pallet. This is too large, and must be broken up into smaller sized lumps to be suitable as blast furnace feed.

Also, as return sinter makes up from 45-55% of the sinter machine feed, a substantial portion of the sintered product has to be continually returned to the sinter charge preparation plant.

The size reduction and separation of the sintered product is as follows:

1. The sinter drops from the machine pallets onto a heavy rail grizzley and claw breaker which reduces the sinter cake to a maximum of 20 cm.

2. This is fed at a uniform rate by means of an oscillating feeder into a set of spiked rolls where the sinter is reduced to 10 cm.

3. A vibrating bar grizzley removes all -5 cm material to the return sinter conveyor, while the +5 cm material is fed into a set of Ross Rolls which acts as an adjustable screen for the separation of coarse and fine sinter.

4. The oversize from the Ross Rolls falls into a pan conveyor to bin storage for the blast furnace. The undersize falls into another pan conveyor and blends with the fines from the vibrating grizzley and machine spillage and is fed into a 35 ton surge bin.

The opening or "set" of the Ross Rolls is adjusted according to the return sinter requirements of the sinter feed. The set can be reduced to a minimum of 2.5 cm for low return production or opened up to a maximum of 10 cm for high return production.

Normal "set" varies between 6-8 cm and is regulated from a control located at the control console at the sinter machine.

The sizing and separation arrangement insures that only well sintered material, varying in size from 5 cm to 10 cm, is taken as blast furnace feed. All of the fine, partially sintered material is separated out and passes to the return sinter circuit.

SINTER CRUSHING - DETAILS

The surge bin is equipped with high and low alarms and a variable speed pan conveyor. The variable speed pan conveyor is the means by which a uniform feed rate is maintained to the "fine crushing" system consisting of corrugated rolls, cooling drum and smooth rolls. The speed of the pan conveyor is manually controlled from the control console located at the sinter machine and is adjusted according to the alarm signals.

The uncrushed return sinter is fed into a set of corrugated rolls which reduces all the material to minus 2 cm. This discharges to a short inclined drag conveyor feeding a drum cooler where the sinter is cooled and moistened with water.

Water addition is done manually by the crushing plant operator as the automatic system originally installed did not prove satisfactory.

Dust from the acid plant baghouse is fed into the drum cooler by drag conveyor. In this manner the dust in moistened and blends with the return sinter, eliminating a dusty handling problem.

From the drum cooler the material is transported by a series of five conveyor belts to a set of smooth rolls which reduces the sinter to a maximum size of 0.6 cm. The crushed sinter is then transported by conveyor belt to the return sinter bin in the charge preparation plant.

OPERATING DATA

1. Sinter Feed

Material	Wt.	Percent Pb	Percent S
Pb Conc.	26	74.1	16.5
Iron Flux	4	-	-
Lime Flux	2	-	-
Silica Flux	1	-	-
Gran. Slag	15	3.5	1.0
Dust and Clngs	2	50.0	8.0
Return Sinter	50	50.0	2.8
	100	46.0	6.0

Analysis	Percent Feed	Final Sinter
SiO_2	10.3	11.2
Fe	12.2	13.3
CaO	9.2	10.0
MgO	0.8	0.9
Zn	5.1	5.6
S	6.0	1.1
Pb	46.0	50.0
Cu	0.3	0.4
Approximate tons per hour	100	45

2. Charge Preparation

(a) Feed Bins

Feed Bins	No of Bins	Tons Cap.	Feeder Width mm	Tons/Hr - Range Low	High	Norm.
Concentrates	3	1050	914	3.3	26.0	24
Iron Flux	1	100	609	0.7	6.0	3
Lime Flux	1	100	609	0.7	6.0	2
Silica Flux	1	100	609	0.3	2.0	1
Slag	2	300	762	2.0	16.0	14
Dust and Cleanup	1	60	609	2.0	16.0	2
Return Sinter	1	150	914	15.0	120.0	44

(b) Weigh Belts & Scales

P.V.C. belting to avoid material sticking to belt surfaces. Thayer Type RF scales, sized and calibrated to range shown in the above table.

The belt feeders are electrically driven through Wer eddy current variable speed drives.

(c) Hammer Mill

Pennsylvania Impactor, model CD9-38. Speed 1200 RPM
200 H.P.

(d) Drum Mixer

Make	Bartlett Snow
Size	2.6 mD x 7.9 mL
Slope	6.2 cm/m
Speed	9 RPM
H.P.	125

3. Lurgi Updraft Sinter Machine

Grate Width	2.5 m
Grate Length	24.0 m
Effective Updraft Area	60.0 m^2
Grate Speed ±	1 m/min
Bed Depth (ign)	31 mm
Bed Depth (Total)	280 mm
Sinter Production	1060 t/day
Sulfur Burning Rate	1.37t/m^2/D
Gas Volume to Acid Plant	708 m^3/min
Gas Strength - percent SO^2	5.0 - 5.5
Operating Time	75%

4. Sinter Machine Fans

		Ignition	Fresh Air		Recycle	
		"E"	"A"	"B"	"C"	"D"
Make:	Buffalo Forge					
Type:		60 MW	730-L-25		R	
Capacity	Nm^3/min	255	480		340	
	mm H_2O	-254	+508		+432	
Operating	Nm^3/min	85	340	283	340	
	mmH_2O	-152	+382	+356	+305	+300
RPM		1300	1600		1600	
H.P.		25	75		100	

5. Sinter Crushing Equipment

	Mfg.	Size Diam X Face
Sinter Breaker	Lurgi	1.33 m -
Spike Rolls	Wedag	1.25 m x 1.00 m
Ross Rolls	Ross Eng. Co.	0.69 " x 0.67 "
Corrugated Rolls	McLanahan	1.25 " x 0.67 "
Smooth Rolls	Traylor	1.53 " x 0.67 "
Drum Cooler	Same Specifications as drum mixer	

6. Labor Force

Three shift operation

Charge Preparation Plant	3
Sinter Machine Operator	3
Sinter Curshing Plant	3
Labor	6
Total	15 Per Day

SULPHURIC ACID PRODUCTION

PROCESS DESCRIPTION

Apart from the generation of a suitable SO_2 laden gas from the sinter machine, which has already been discussed, the manufacture of sulfuric acid in a "metallurgical" type plant consists of three principal steps:

1. Cooling and purification of the SO_2 gas from the sinter machine.
2. Conversion of SO_2 to SO_3.
3. Absorption of the SO_3 gas in sulfuric acid.

COOLING AND CLEANING OF SO_2 GAS

The SO_2 laden gas from the sinter machine contains dust, metallic fumes and water vapor. It is first cooled in a spray chamber in which the gas temperature is reduced by means of high pressure water sprays. The cooled gas is passed through a baghouse for removal of essentially all particulate matter by the filtering action of the bags.

The temperature of the filtered gas is further lowered and most of the remaining impurities are removed from the gas by scrubbing with weak acid (5% H_2SO_4) in a packed tower. In this tower the gas flows countercurrent to the flow of weak acid which is recirculated through indirect coolers. Water, acid and solid impurities are removed from the tower as an effluent, neutralized with lime and discarded.

A final cooling of the gas takes place in two vertical heat exchangers connected in parallel before it enters a mist precipitator where all remaining impurities are removed.

After leaving the mist precipitator the gas passes through a drying tower countercurrent to a flow of 93% sulfuric acid for removal of all water vapor.

The clean dry gas is then forced through the balance of the plant by the main blower.

CONVERSION OF SO_2 TO SO_3

The conversion of SO_2 to SO_3 takes place in a "three pass" converter containing vanadium pentoxide as a catalyst. The function of the catalyst is to accelerate the reaction between SO_2 and O_2 to form SO_3.

As the SO_2 is converted to SO_3, heat is evolved by the reaction

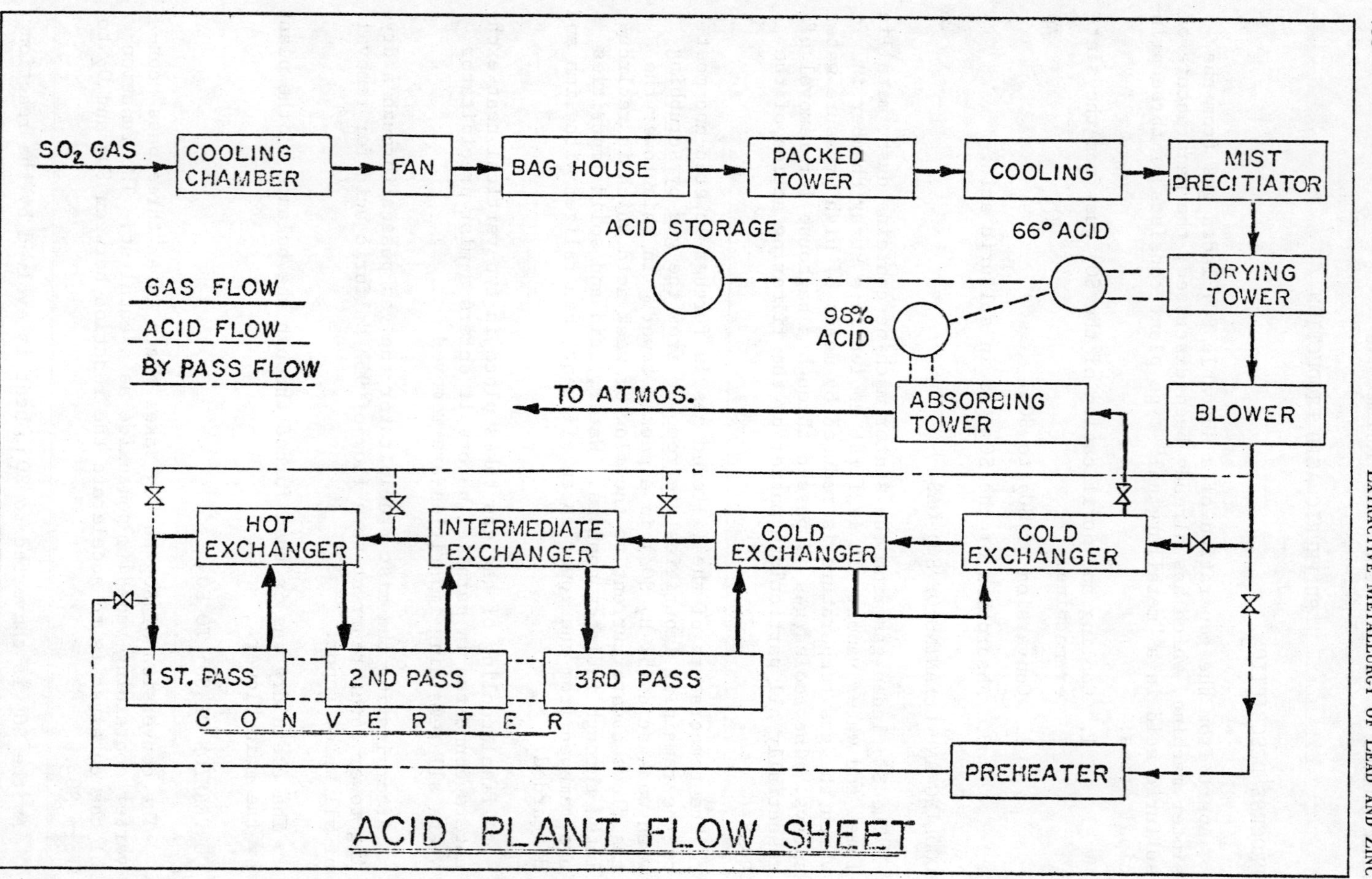

ACID PLANT FLOW SHEET

and the gas temperature increases. If the temperature is allowed to rise excessively only partial conversion can be obtained. Therefore the gas is taken from the converter after each pass, cooled in external heat exchangers and returned to the next section of the converter. The heat removed from the converter gas is used to heat up the cold SO_2 gas before it enters the first pass of the converter, as conversion of SO_2 to SO_3 will not start below 415° C.

By-pass valves are provided around the heat exchangers so that the required temperatures can be controlled.

Upon leaving the final pass of the converter the gas is cooled to the proper temperature for admission to the absorption system.

ABSORPTION OF SO_3 GAS

Even though adequately cooled, the SO_3 gas produced in the converter will not combine directly with water, but must be combined indirectly by dissolving it in 98-99% sulfuric acid. This operation is carried out in the absorbing tower where the SO_3 gas is scrubbed with 98-99% sulfuric acid.

The acid in the absorbing system is strengthened by the absorption of SO_3 while the acid in the drying tower system is weakened by the water vapor removed from the SO_2 gas. The drying tower is maintained at proper strength (93%) by the constant addition of acid from the absorbing tower system. The absorbing tower acid is maintained at proper strength (98-99%) for absorption of SO_3 by the addition of acid from the drying tower system and fresh water.

The continual absorption of water vapor, SO_3 and water in both the drying and absorbing systems materially raises the temperature of both acids. Therefore, both acids are pumped through separate radiator type coolers before delivery to their respective towers.

The constant transfer and cross-flow of the drying and absorbing acids which are combining with water vapor, SO_3, and fresh water increases the amount of acid in the system. Therefore the cross-flow pumping rate is adjusted so that this excess acid is maintained at 93.2% (66° Be') which represents production and is pumped to storage.

OPERATING DETAILS

Normally an updraft lead sintering operation produces a gas with an SO_2 content of five to six percent. However, often there are extended periods when the SO_2 concentration will be as low as four percent or as high as eight percent. Therefore the size of the acid plant has to be designed to produce a 93% acid under these extreme conditions. The acid plant at Buick is designed to produce a 93% acid when treating gas in the range of 595 Nm^3/min at 4.5%

SO_2 and 708 Nm^3/min at 5.0% SO_2.

With low SO_2 concentrations, a larger gas cooling system is required to insure sufficient condensation of water vapor in the gas stream.

On the other hand, eight percent SO_2 in the gas from a lead sintering operation results in a deficiency in the oxygen required to convert SO_2 to SO_3. Therefore, the gas is diluted to about six percent SO_2 by the addition of dried atmospheric air. This dilution increases the volume of gas handled and the equipment from the mist precipitator on is sized accordingly to avoid excessive gas velocities and pressures. The deficiency of oxygen is caused by not only the oxygen required to oxidize sulfur to SO_2 but also the oxidation of the metals present in the sinter feed.

The acid produced from a sintering operation is coal black in color. This discoloration is due primarily to unburned organic flotation reagents in the concentrates being sintered. There are several methods by which the black acid can be partially clarified using hydrogen peroxide, persulfuric acid, or ozone but none have produced a water white acid at a reasonable cost. Therefore, the sulfuric acid produced from a lead sintering operation is used principally in the manufacture of fertilizers and in acid-bake leaching operations.

OPERATING DATA

1. Production

Vol. Nm^3/m	595
Av SO_2 (% by Vol.)	5.0
Production (100% Basis) tons	200
Conversion Eff.	96%

2. Temperatures - Pressures - Flows

Gas		Temp°C	S.P. mm H_2O
Sinter Machine Hood		345	-6
Spray Chamber	IN	330	-76
Spray Chamber	OUT	115	-117
Baghouse	IN	113	+102
Packed Tower	IN	110	+25
Gas Coolers	IN	41	-50
Mist Precipitator	IN	32	-381
Drying Tower	IN	30	-432
Main Blower	IN	35	-533
1st Pass Converter	IN	420	+762
1st Pass Converter	OUT	566	+655
2nd Pass Converter	IN	443	+586
2nd Pass Converter	OUT	493	+485

3rd Pass Converter	IN	435	+381
3rd Pass Converter	OUT	448	+277
Absorbing Tower	IN	250	+157

Acids		Temp°C.	Flow Lt/Sec.
Absorbing Acid Tower	IN	82	40
Drying Acid Tower	IN	54	40
Weak Acid (Karbate)	IN	41	85
Weak Acid (Karbate)	OUT	36	85

Cooling Water		Temp°C.	Flow Lts/Sec
Supply Water		25	25
Water Cooling Tower	IN	38	380
Water Cooling Tower	OUT	29	-
Acid Coolers	IN	29	140
Weak Acid Coolers	IN	29	50
Weak Acid Coolers	OUT	41	-

Cooling Water Distribution	Temp°C.	Flow Lts/Sec
Supply	25	25
Cooling Tower Makeup	25	17
Spray Chamber	25	2
Acid Dilution & Misc	25	1
Return to Smelter	36	5

3. Labor Force

Three Shift Operation		
Operators	3	
Utility	1	
Total	4	Per Day

SMELTING

PROCESS DESCRIPTION

Sinter and coke, with additions of refinery and low copper drosses make up the feed to the blast furnace. The coke supplies the fuel for the melting and reduction of the charge. Air for combustion is blown into the furnace through a series of pipes located on each side near the bottom of the furnace.

Three products are made in the blast furnace operation; impure lead bullion, slag and fume. Both lead and slag are continuously removed from the bottom of the furnace into a settler where the lead is separated from the slag.

The lead, containing various impurities such as copper and silver, is siphoned continuously from the settler and taken to the

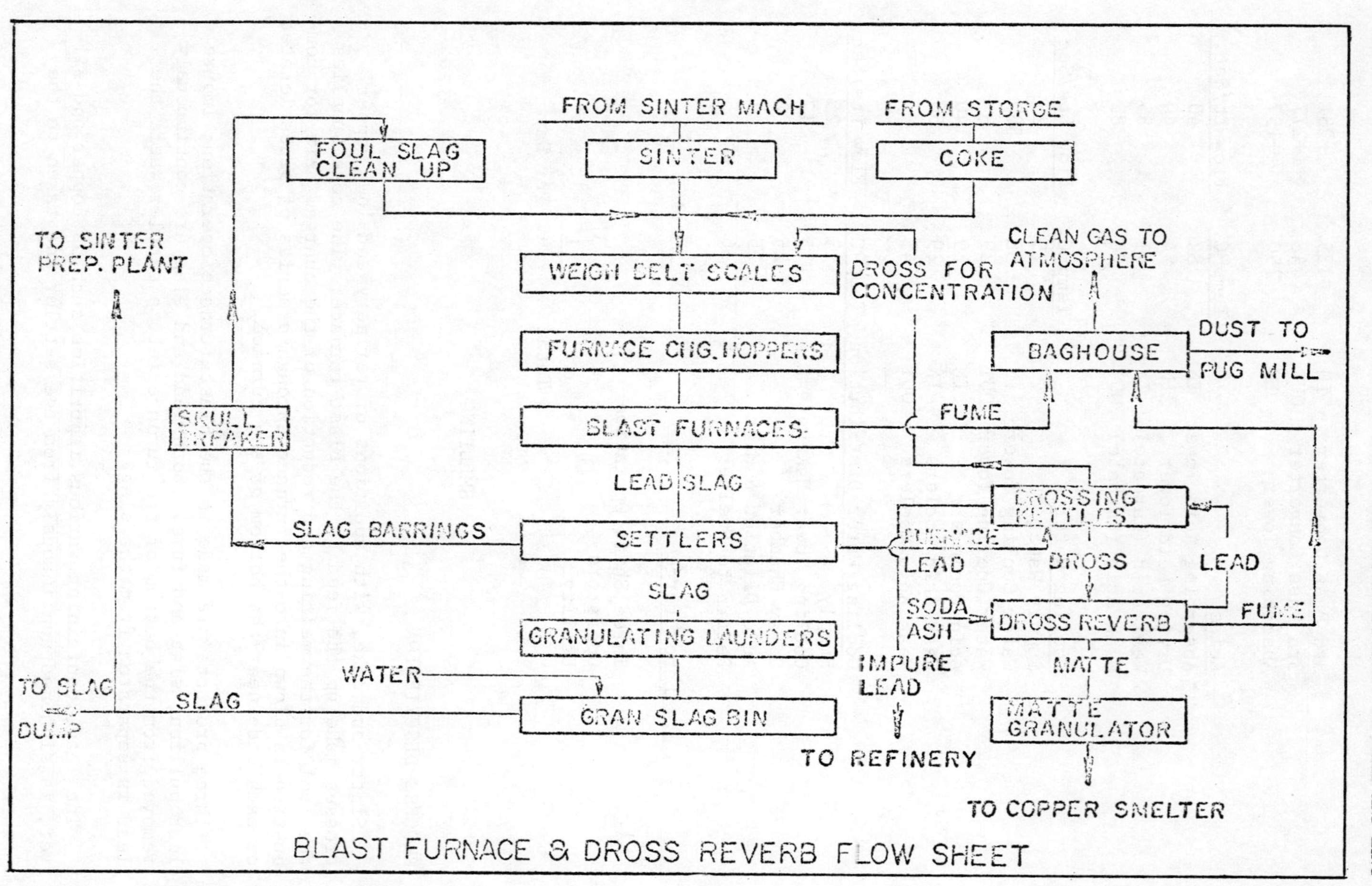

BLAST FURNACE & DROSS REVERB FLOW SHEET

drossing plant for further treatment.

The slag overflows from the settler into a stream of water, is granulated and stored for future use or discarded.

Dust and fumes produced in the operation are collected from the top of the furnace, cooled and filtered through a baghouse. The clean gas is then exhausted to atmosphere through a stack.

FURNACE FEED SYSTEM - GENERAL

The feed system consists of ten individual bins, their respective vibrating feeders and five weigh belts.

The bins and feeders are arranged in pairs so that each pair of bins feed the same material to an individual weigh belt. The material from the individual weigh belts is discharged onto a collector belt, and then to an inclined transfer belt to the top of the blast furnace, where it is dumped from a shuttle conveyor into feed hoppers located on each side of the furnace top.

FURNACE FEED SYSTEM - DETAILS

The normal feed to the blast furnace is made up of sinter, low copper dross, refinery dross and coke. The furnace feed is a batch operation, with all constituents being fed simultaneously, and is handled by the feedman from a control station located on the furnace feed floor. The feed system is put in operation by setting the desired tonnage of each of the materials to be fed on a controller (WC) which controls the weight over the individual feed belts in the system. Separate recorder controllers (WRC) regulate the rate of feed of each material by means of powerstats which control the vibrating feeders. When the preset tonnage has passed over the individual belt scales the vibrators and belts shut down, automatically stopping the feed.

The individual vibrating feeders for sinter and dross etc., are interlocked with the coke weigh-belt scale so that the entire system is shut down on a failure of coke feed.

The feeding procedure is carried out as often as is necessary to keep the furnace full of charge. Normal feeding is in ten ton batches at a feed rate of 50 tons per hour.

BLAST FURNACE

The two blast furnaces, one of which is in operation and the other on standby, are essentially the Port Pirie or "Australian" type of furnace with chair jackets and a double row of tuyeres.

Figure 6 shows the general arrangement of a furnace.

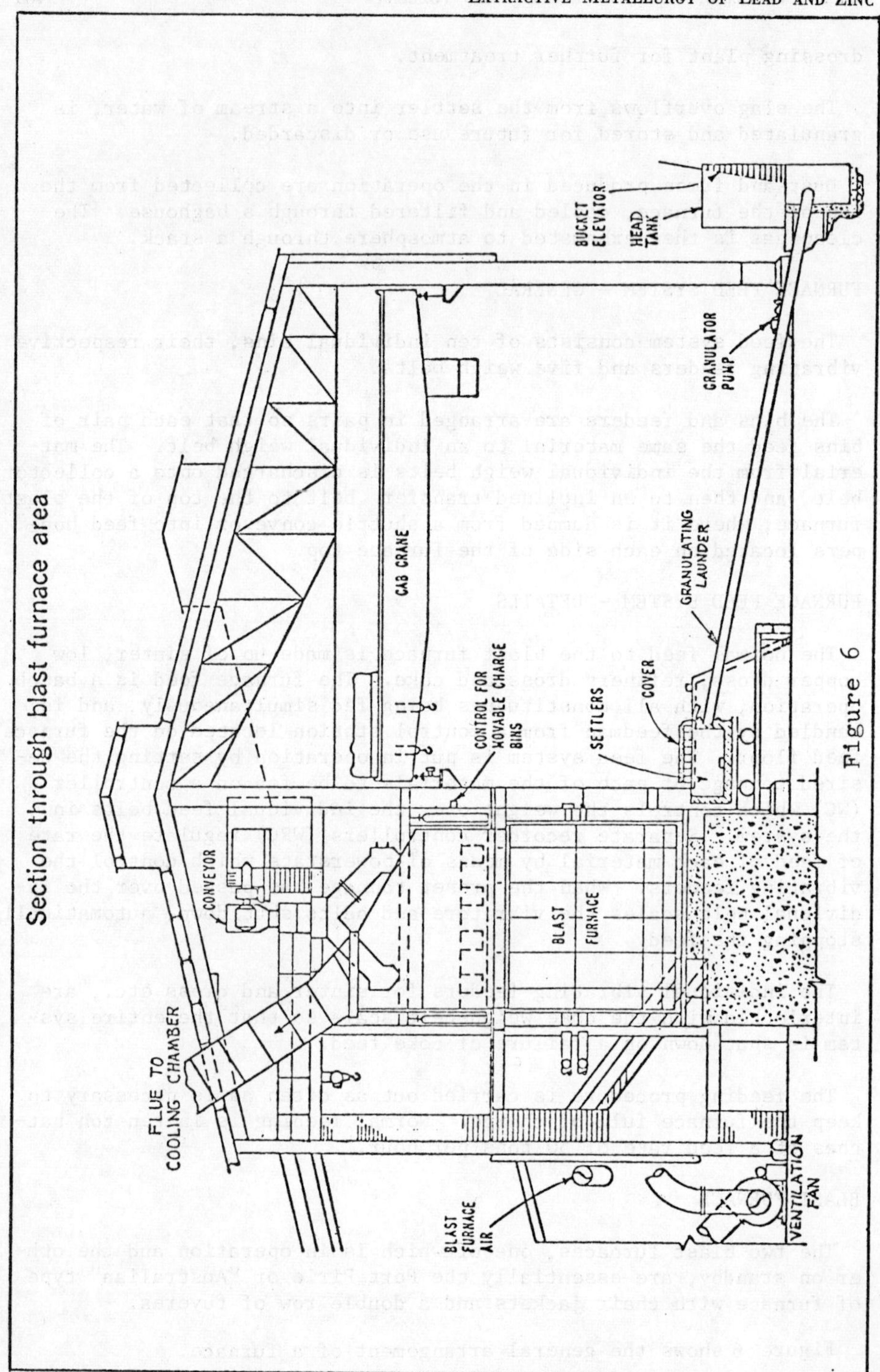

Section through blast furnace area
FLUE TO COOLING CHAMBER
CONVEYOR
CAB CRANE
CONTROL FOR MOVABLE CHARGE BINS
BLAST FURNACE
SETTLERS
COVER
GRANULATING LAUNDER
GRANULATOR PUMP
HEAD TANK
BUCKET ELEVATOR
BLAST FURNACE AIR
VENTILATION FAN

Figure 6

The air supply for each furnace is delivered by separate blowers. The air mains from the blowers are interconnected by valves so that air can be supplied to either furnace by either blower. An automatically operated damper in the air main controls the volume delivered to the furnace, while a manually operated valve is used for the distribution of air between the upper and lower tuyeres. Air to the upper tuyeres is controlled by positioning the valve to an opening of thirty percent. Under these conditions approximately 25 percent of the total air volume is put through the upper tuyeres, with a pressure of from 30 to 35 cm below the pressure on the lower tuyeres.

The tuyeres are kept open by hand punching at regular intervals; the lower tuyeres every hour and the upper tuyeres once a shift.

All molten material is removed at the bottom of the furnace and flows into a settler through a continuous tapping device known as a "Roy Tapper". This method of tapping a lead blast furnace was developed by ASARCO at the East Helena smelter in the late fifties. Essentially it is a method of removing molten material from the blast furnace as fast as it is made. This is accomplished by installing a box-shaped trap with an adjustable weir around the furnace tap hole. The height of the weir is governed by the operating conditions of the furnace and is maintained at such a level as to counteract the hydraulic head produced by blast pressure and molten metal inside the furnace. In this manner the air blast cannot escape from the tap hole nor will molten material build up inside the furnace, but flows out in a constant stream.

A cast steel, brick lined settler is used for separation of lead and slag flowing from the furnace. The settler is covered with a brick lined water jacket which serves both as a cover and working platform for the front of the furnace. Three gas burners located in ports on the cover keep the slag from chilling in the settler.

Lead continuously siphons into a 15-ton brick lined transfer pot through a lead well located on the side of the settler and is taken to the drossing plant by an overhead crane. Slag, overflowing from the settler, is granulated with a stream of water in a cast iron launder and sluiced to an elevator pit.

The granulated slag is transported to a 500 ton bin by means of two bucket elevators, one of which is an installed spare. These are conventional belt elevators enclosed in a wooden housing. The housing acts as a stack to remove the steam formed in the granulating operation.

Granulated slag is trucked from the bin to storage in the unloading area for use as diluent in the sinter feed or is discarded on the slag dump.

Water for slag granulation is in a closed circuit system consisting of a head tank, pumps to the granulating nozzles, a launder system to settling pits, a spray cooling pond and pumps back to the head tank. Make-up water for the system comes from the cooling tower blow-down and neutralized effluent from the acid plant.

OPERATING DATA

1. Furnace Dimensions

Length	6.40 m
Width (lower tuyeres)	1.52 m
Width (upper tuyeres)	3.04 m
Tuyere Area (lower)	9.75 m^2
Height of Column	5.9 m
Number of Tuyeres (lower)	28
Number of Tuyeres (upper)	38
Diam. of Tuyeres (lower)	102 mm
Diam. of Tuyeres (upper)	76 m
Jacket Water Volume	44 lt/sec
Jacket Water Temp. in	38° C
Jacket Water Temp. out	55° C

2. Average Performance - 30 Day Period

Tons Per Day	755
Tons Per m^2 Per Day	77.5
Vol. Air Blown (total) Nm^3/min	315
Pressure (lower Tuyeres) cmH_2O	156-200
Tons Bullion Per Day	371
Percent Coke on Furnace Charge	9.7
Percent Fixed Carbon	8.7
Gas Offtake to Baghouse M^3/min	1130
Top Temperature °C	121
Draft cmH_2O	-6

3. Blowers (2)

Make: American Standard Centrifugal	
Rated Volume m^3/min	425
Pressure cmH_2O	335
Drive	Direct
H.P.	350
R.P.M.	3600

4. Slag

(a) Analysis

SiO_2	FeO	CaO	MgO	Zn	S	Al_2O_3	Pb	Cu
22.9	31.0	18.0	3.5	11.5	1.0	5.8	3.5	0.1

(b) Granulation Water	lts/sec
Volume to Nozzles	96
Volume to Head Tank	192
Temperature at Nozzle	73°C
Temperature at Settling Pits	85°C

5. Labor Force

Three Shift Operation		
Furnaceman	3	
Tapper	3	
Feeder	3	
Craneman	3	
Slag Truck	1	
Labor	6	
Total	19	Per Day

DROSSING OF LEAD BULLION

PROCESS DESCRIPTION

Lead bullion produced in the smelting process contains varying amounts of other metals. In order to reduce these to the required limits for refined lead, the bullion is subjected to a series of refining steps.

Copper and silver are the only metallic impurities present in the blast furnace bullion produced at Buick. The bulk of the copper is removed by cooling the hot bullion down to near its freezing point because solubility of copper in lead decreases as the temperature falls. The cooling produces a copper rich dross which separates out on the surface in a semi-liquid form. After removal of the dross, the bullion contains from 0.05 to 0.08% copper. Normally the copper content is further reduced to 0.008% by stirring sulfur into the bullion at a temperature of 330° C before it is transferred to the refinery. However, due to the low silver content and the absence of other impurities such as antimony and tin, sulfur does not remove copper. Therefore zinc is used in place of sulfur and the final decopperization is carried out in the refinery rather than in the drossing plant.

DROSSING DETAILS

Molten bullion is transferred from the blast furnace in 15-ton pots to one of the three receiving kettles. When a kettle is full a stirring machine is set in place and the molten bullion is stirred continuously until the dross on top of the kettle is free of large lumps. Soda ash and coke breeze are added before and during stirring to aid in forming the dross.

The dross is then removed from the kettle by a cast steel scoop operated from an overhead crane and is charged directly to a small reverberatory furnace. When the reverberatory is not operating the dross is granulated in a tank of water and returned to the blast furnace for concentration.

The rough drossed bullion is then bailed or pumped to another kettle for further cooling and final drossing. Only forty to fifty tons of bullion are transferred from the receiving kettle to the final drossing kettle at any one time. This serves three purposes:

1. Avoids extreme temperature changes in the kettle caused by the addition of large amounts of hot bullion.
2. The remaining large heel in the kettle will accelerate the cooling of the hot bullion brought from the furnace.
3. Only a relatively small amount of dross will be formed. This not only facilitates the skimming operation but also will allow the dross to be charged into the reverb without overloading.

The bullion in the final dross kettle is stirred continuously and cooled to close to the freezing point of lead. The dross is skimmed off clean and returned to the receiving kettles. At this point most of the copper has been removed and the copper content ranges between 0.05% and 0.08%.

The clean drossed lead is then heated and pumped to a holding kettle in the refinery for the final decopperization and subsequent refining.

DROSS FURNACE OPERATION

The dross furnace is a small reverberatory type furnace equipped with two "pre-mix" propane gas burners located in the front wall.

Dross from the kettles is charged to the furnace in approximately four-ton batches. Normally soda ash and coke have been mixed with the dross in the receiving kettle. However, occasionally either or both of these fluxes are added directly after charging dross in order to improve furnace bath conditions.

As the copper content of the sinter feed to the blast furnace is very low, averaging only 0.4% Cu, only a small amount of dross is formed on the drossing kettles. In spite of continuous stirring and fluxing with soda ash and coke breeze the dried dross will average only five to eight percent copper. This is not enough copper to satisfy the sulfur in the dross and if it is charged directly into the reverberatory furnace the resulting matte will be a high-lead, low-copper product. (35% Pb - 38% Cu)

This is overcome by recirculating dross back through the blast furnace, which increases the copper content of the furnace feed to about one percent. This, in turn, results in a kettle dross containing 16% Cu with no increase in dross production. At 16% Cu there is sufficient copper to satisfy the sulfur in the dross and the resulting matte from the reverberatory furnace is a low-lead, high-copper product. (15% Pb - 53% Cu)

Lead, matte and a small amount of an alloy of lead, nickel and copper are the products of the furnace, the latter tending to form a refractory layer between the matte and lead in the furnace bath.

Lead and matte are tapped separately from the furnace on each shift. The matte is granulated in a stream of water into a settling pit from which it is removed by means of a drag conveyor to a storage bin for subsequent shipment to a copper smelter.

Lead is tapped directly into the No. 1 receiving kettle in the dross plant.

Once a week the lead-nickel-copper alloy is tapped out of the furnace and granulated after all the matte has been removed from the bath. This material is very refractory and if allowed to build up and remain in the furnace it tends to form a solid layer between molten lead and matte which eventually closes up the furnace bath.

OPERATING DATA

1. Production

	Tons/Day
Dross	50
Matte	14
Lead	35
Pb-Ni-Cu Alloy	1

2. Analysis*

	Pb	Cu	Fe	S	Ni	Co
Dross	65.0	16.0	0.7	5.0	0.8	0.3
Matte	15.0	53.0	1.5	16.0	1.5	0.6
Pb-Ni-Cu Alloy	50.0	14.0	0.1	8.0	18.0	1.2

* Based on recycle of dross through blast furnace.

3. Dross Reverberatory Furnace

Size (L X W)	2.1 m x 6.4 m
Bath Depth - Total	101.6 cm
Normal Bath Matte	25.4 cm
Normal Bath Pb	76.2 cm
Fuel Consumption	.88 million Cal/ton

Soda Ash	3.0%	
Coke Breeze	0.5%	

4. Labor Force

Three Shift Operation		
Furnace Operator	3	
Kettleman	6	
Craneman	3	
Laborers	3	
Total	15	Per Day

LEAD REFINING

PROCESS DESCRIPTION

A small amount of copper and some silver are the only impurities in the bullion delivered to the refinery after drossing. These are reduced to the acceptable limits in the refined lead by the use of metallic zinc. The bulk of the zinc remaining in the lead after decopperization and desilverization is removed by vacuum dezincing and the use of caustic and niter. The final product, being at least 99.99% pure lead, is cast for marketing.

REFINING DETAILS

The refining operation is a batch process in which individual lots of lead approximately 180 tons each are processed in the following sequence:

1. Decopperization with zinc from the desilverizing step.
2. First step desilverization with new zinc.
3. Second step desilverization with residual zinc from the first step.
4. Vacuum dezincing.
5. Refining with caustic and niter.
6. Casting into market shapes.
7. Recovery of silver.

Decopperization The drossed bullion from the drossing plant is heated in a 200-ton kettle to 440-460 °C and stirred to mix in any crust or dross from the previous charge along with refinery scrap. One zinc head from the first desilverizing operation is stirred in and the kettle cooled to 350 °C to allow a crust to form on the top of the lead. The lead is then pumped from beneath the crust into a 250-ton kettle for the first desilverization.

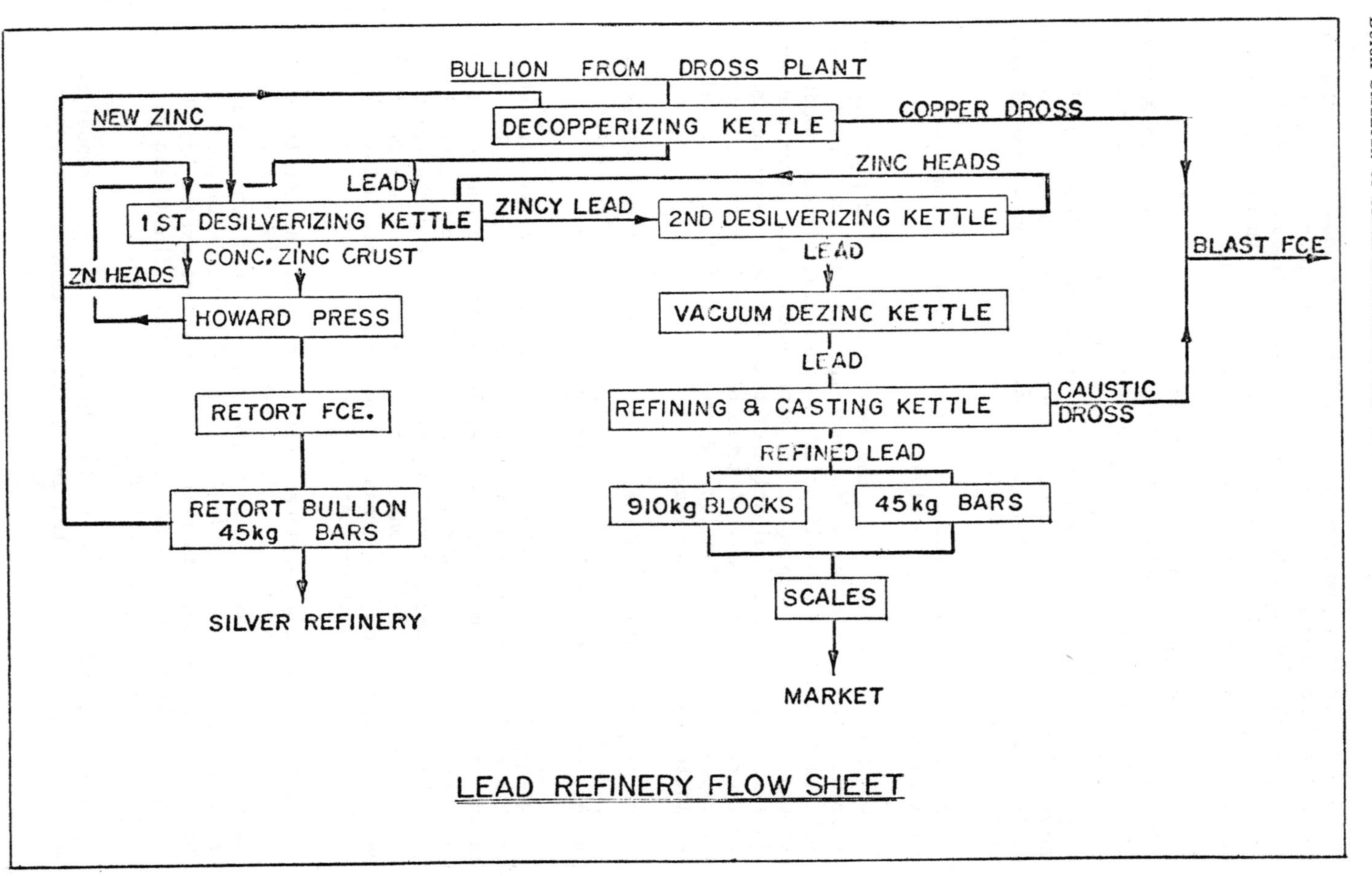

LEAD REFINERY FLOW SHEET

In order to conserve zinc and reduce dross production to minimum, three lots are treated in this manner. On the fourth lot, the lead is stirred continuously with a small addition of caustic to form a dry dross instead of the crust. The dross, containing copper and zinc, is removed and returned to the blast furnace.

Desilverization - 1st Step The decopperized lead is heated in a 250-ton desilverizing kettle to 450-460° C and stirred with approximately 725 kg of zinc along with one zinc head from the second desilverizing kettle. The lead is then cooled to 400° C and the resulting zinc dross is skimmed off into cast iron molds. Usually three 2.5 ton heads are removed on each lot. One is used to decopperize the subsequent lot and the remainder are reused several times in this step in place of new zinc.

The lead is further cooled to 360° C and pumped from under the crust to the second step desilverizing kettle.

Two samples are taken from the kettle; a "cold" sample which by its zinc assay indicates sufficient zinc has been used and a "pumping" sample which by its silver assay indicates correct pumping temperature. Also, samples of the zinc heads removed from the desilverizing kettle are indicative of both the decopperizing and desilverization operations. A ratio of four silver to one copper indicates good decopperization. A ratio of four zinc to one silver indicates correct zinc usage.

The silver gradually builds up, and when the zinc heads assay two percent silver, with a silver-copper ratio of five to one or better, they are set aside for further concentration.

Desilverization - 2nd Step The second step desilverizing kettle has a zinc crust frozen from the preceding charge. This is rapidly melted by preheating the kettle and pumping the lead from the first desilverizing kettle in on top of the crust. Once the crust has been melted and well stirred into the lead the temperature is lowered to 350° C and two heads of approximately two tons each of a mushy zinc-lead dross are skimmed off into molds for use in the first step desilverization.

A large steel plug is placed in the center of the kettle to keep a hole open in the crust for a pump and the lead is further cooled to 335° C. The plug is pulled, a preheated pump is set in place and the desilverized lead is pumped to the dezincing kettle. The pumping temperature is critical and must not exceed 335° C or excessive silver will be carried over and the refined lead will not meet the .0015% Ag specification.

A sample is taken while pumping which indicates the copper and silver content to be expected in the refined lead.

Dezincing The desilverized lead, containing 0.55 - 0.65% zinc is heated in a 200-ton kettle to about 500° C. Any dross which forms is removed and returned to the decopperizing kettle. Then a vacuum bell is set in the kettle and connected to a vacuum pump. Meanwhile, the temperature of the lead is raised to 600° C. At this temperature the vacuum pump is started and when the pressure in the bell has dropped to 0.1 mm (100 microns) the agitator is started. Both temperature and pressure are held constant at 600° C and 100 microns respectively while stirring for a period of eight hours. The vacuum is then released and the bell removed. At this stage over 90% of the zinc content of the desilverized lead has been removed.

The vacuum bell is essentially a bell-shaped hood open at the bottom and water cooled on top. A mechanical agitator of sufficient length to extend into the bath of molten lead when the bell is set in the kettle, is centrally mounted on the water cooled top.

The zinc is vacuum distilled from the lead and condenses in form of crystals on the underside of the water cooled top. The condensed zinc is removed after every third charge, weighed and returned as metallic zinc to the first step desilverizing kettle.

Refining and Casting After dezincing the lead is bailed to the refining and casting kettle. At this point the lead contains approximately .05 to .06% zinc. This residual zinc, along with any traces of antimony and arsenic, are removed by stirring the lead with caustic and niter for a period of two hours at a temperature of 480° C. The caustic dross is then removed and returned to the blast furnace.

The refined lead is cooled to 425° C and cast into 910 Kg blocks on a stationary, water cooled, semi circular casting ring or into 45 kilo bars on a continuous straight line casting machine. The bars are stacked and strapped into bundles of 25 bars for the market.

Recovery of Silver The zinc heads, containing two percent silver, are concentrated by returning them to the first desilverizing kettle. The resulting heads contain more than five percent silver, with a silver-copper ratio of 15 to 1. About every six months there are enough of these heads on hand to go to a final concentration by stirring them into the lead in the first step desilverizing operation and removing and pressing the resultant dross with a Howard Press.

The pressed dross is then melted in a retort furnace in batches of 700 Kg at a temperature of 1150-1200° C for a period of six hours. The zinc is distilled off, collected in a condenser and is tapped into bars to be used again in the desilverization operation. The bullion is then tapped into a brick lined ladle and cast into 45 kilo bars for shipment to a silver refinery for further treatment.

OPERATING DATA

1. Analysis

	Percent Cu	Percent Ag	Percent Zn
(a) Decopperizing			
Lead Bullion to Refinery	0.080	0.009	-
After Decopperization	0.004	0.010	0.30
Dry Dross Removed	5.70	0.034	21.20
Zinc Head to Kettle	0.56	2.040	12.50
(b) 1st Desilverization			
Lead to Kettle	0.0040	0.010	0.30
"Cold" Sample	0.0003	0.0007	0.60
"Pumping" Sample	0.0003	0.0023	0.70
Zinc Heads Removed	0.50	2.04	12.50
Zinc Heads Concentration	0.40	2.50	10.00
(c) 2nd Desilverization			
To Dezincing	0.0003	0.0007	0.57
(d) Dezincing			
To Final Refining	0.0003	0.0007	0.06

(e) Refined Lead to Market (%)

Ag	Cu	Zn	As Sb Sn Bi	Pb
0.0007	0.0003	0.0003	Nil	+99.99

(f) Silver Concentration

	Cu	Ag	Zn
Zn for Concentration	0.40	2.50	10.0
Conc. Heads	0.34	5.5	8.0
Pressed Dross	1.00	9.0	10.0
Retort Bullion	1.5	12.0	1.2

2. Reagent Use

	Kg/Ton Refined Pb
New Zinc	4.9
Reclaimed Zinc	2.0
Caustic	.5
Niter	.1

3. Kettles

Process	No	Ton Cap
Decopperizing	1	200
Desilverizing	3	250
Dezincing	2	200
Refining & Casting	2	200

4. Vacuum Pumps

2 Model KT 300

1 Model KT 500

5. Labor Force

Three Shift Operation

Craneman	3	
Furnace Operator	3	
Kettlemen	9	
Caster	3*	
Lead Loading	2	
Labor	6	
Total	26	Per Day

* Casting on one shift only

DUST, FUME AND GAS HANDLING SYSTEMS

Dust, fume and gas produced in the various operations are handled in three separate systems:

1. Strong SO_2 gas from the sintering operation is treated in a sulfuric acid plant.
2. Fumes and gases produced from the blast furnace and dross reverb, as well as weak gas from the sinter machine and hygiene fumes from the blast furnace are collected and filtered in a 14 compartment baghouse and the clean gases are discharged to atmosphere through a 66 m concrete stack.
3. Hygiene ventilation in the sinter crushing and furnace charge system is handled in two separate, three compartment baghouses.

The sulfuric acid plant has been detailed previously and as the hygiene ventilation baghouses are essentially miniatures of the main baghouse, only the latter will be discussed here.

The baghouse consists of two sections in parallel, each containing seven individual compartments with 416 bags per compartment. Gases from the various sources are combined in a centrally located cooling chamber where they can be cooled to 110° C with outside air and a water spray system, before being moved through the baghouse by means of two forced draft fans. Automatically controlled dampers on each fan inlet balance the load across each of the two sections of the baghouse.

Overall dust and fume recovery is in excess of 99% and there is no visible plume or "flag" from the stack.

The baghouse operation is fully automatic. Temperature is controlled primarily by the addition of atmospheric air through a damper located in the cooling chamber. A series of high pressure sprays are also installed to supplement the air cooling in cases of extreme temperature.

Shaking of the bags in each compartment for the removal of dust is set on a five minute time interval, thus each compartment is shaken once every seventy minutes. Dust is removed continuously from hoppers under each compartment by means of screw conveyors and is transported to a pug mill where the dust is pugged with water and then returned to the sinter feed system.

OPERATING DATA

1. Main Baghouse

Make	Wheelabrator
No. of compartments	14
No. of bags - total	5824
Bag size (D x L)	20.3 cm X 6.1 m
Bag material	Filtron 260-50
Vol m^3/min at temp. (max)	12750 at 110° C
Vol m^3/min (normal)	8300 at 90° C
Air to cloth ratio m^3/m^2	.59:1
Operating Pressure mm H_2O	100 - 150
Normal dust loading g/m^3/min	1.26

2. Hygiene Baghouses

	Sinter Crushing	Furnace Charge
Make	Pangborn Type CT	
No. of compartments	3	3
No. of bags - total	312	456
Bag size (D x L)	12.7 cm X	3.4 m
Bag material	Wool	
Vol m^3/min at temp. (max)	380 at 45°C	580 at 45°C
Vol m^3/min (normal)	-	-
Air to cloth ratio m^3/m^2	.90:1	
Operating Pressure mm H_2O	250	
Normal dust loading g/m^3/min	-	

3. Main Baghouse Fans

Type	Sturtevant-Double Inlet
Size (D x W) 2 Fans	2m x 4m each
Rated cap at temp each	6650 m^3/min at 110° C
Static pressure (mmH_2O)	355
H.P.	800
R.P.M.	900

4. Operating Labor

Three shift operation includes dust pug mill.

Operator	3	
Labor	1	
Total	4	Per Day

Chapter 26

THE GLOVER LEAD SMELTER AND REFINERY

of

THE AMERICAN SMELTING AND REFINING COMPANY
Glover, Missouri

Robert B. Paul, Manager

This paper describes the new lead smelter and refinery recently completed by the American Smelting and Refining Company in Southeast Missouri.

The Glover Plant is located in Iron County, Missouri about one hundred miles south of St. Louis. It is surrounded by timber land and cattle grazing areas with the setting rather typical to rural Ozarkian Missouri. This location was selected in preference to several others after an extensive survey, with the site choice being made because of the accessibility to transportation, both rail and truck, the availability of both natural gas and electricity, the closeness to the main concentrate supplier, Ozark Lead Company and because there are rural communities within reasonable commuting distance. Further advantage was realized by the contour of the land which enabled the production buildings to be put on gentle slopes. Property for the plant was first optioned in May, 1964 and plant design work proceeded by Asarco personnel. In April 1966, Kaiser Engineers were chosen as the principal engineers and construction contractor. Actual on site work was started in September 1966. In February 1967, M. W. Kellogg Company was awarded a contract for a 186 meter stack. In April 1968 the first cars of concentrates were received, sampled and unloaded. Sinter plant operations were begun in May, and the blast furnace and refinery operations followed in June with the first shipment of refined lead in early July 1968.

Smelter facilities accommodate either rail or truck delivery. The truck receipts are unloaded into plant owned dump bottomed cars at a specially designed facility for subsequent sampling and unloading. Railroad receipts are spotted for sampling and then transferred to the unloading track which is in the building containing the receiving bins and is the first step in processing new material. All intraplant switching is done by a plant owned 110 metric ton Baldwin locomotive. Open top cars are unloaded by a 2.3 cubic meter bucket crane, while box cars are handled with a small front-end loader. The major portion of the concentrates, from the Ozark Lead Company, are via truck with the truck dumping facilities designed to receive around the clock. This feature allows Glover personnel to service this portion of the operation at their convenience. A thaw house for handling frozen receipts runs part time from November through March as needed. The unloading bins are located under a railroad track so that all cars can be dumped directly in an appropriate bin.

Storage bin area showing receiving bins with sinter proportioning bins on the right.

This area consists of a building housing elevated railroad tracks set above 12 concentrate receiving bins with a 23 cubic meter bucket crane for car unloading and for transferring material to sinter plant proportioning hoppers or to blast furnace feed hoppers. The unloading area is designed specifically to unload bottom dump cars directly into an appropriate bin. Solid bottom gondolas are unloaded by the bucket crane while box cars are handled with a small front-end loader.

Sinter plant charge components, usually consisting of concentrates, silica flux, iron flux, coke breeze, plant secondaries and miscellaneous purchased material are proportionally fed to a collector belt by variable speed DC driven feed belts. The collector belt discharges into a Pennsylvania Impactor which blends this material as well as sinter plant cleanup. The blended product is then discharged onto a common collector belt where it is joined by similarly proportioned amounts of recirculated granulated slag and return sinter. This represents the full charge to the sinter machine and is fed in series through two 3.05 meter by 9.15 meter mixing drums where moisturing and feed conditioning is performed. The feed is then conveyed to a splitter chute which separates the ignition and main feed layer fractions to the 2.44 meter wide machine. The ignition layer is passed through a vibrating grizzly so that oversize material is returned into the main feed hopper. Shuttle conveyors operated by a hydraulic system distribute the feed evenly across the width of the machine, with sensor elements in these individual hoppers providing level control. A baffle plate diverts the feed to either direction in the splitter chute with the ignition layer getting first call and the main layer taking the total feed when the demand of the ignition feed hopper is satisfied. The ignition layer passes through the gas fired ignition muffle which is over a downdraft windbox with the main bed then being laid on top of this ignited layer. The full bed then advances to the updraft section of the machine, which is 29 meters in length and consists of twelve windboxes each 2.44 meters long. Beginning here and continuing for the rest

Ground level view of sintering machine showing fan ducts and lower level of machine.

of the machine the air is reversed, being blown through the bottom of the pallet up through the sinter bed where burning progresses down the length of the machine with the last several feet of the updraft section being used for a cooling zone so that the cake will not collapse nor will metallic lead run out of the sinter to blind the pallet grate bars. The sinter is discharged from the machine onto a breaker, thence via a variable speed pan to a spiked roll and up a pan conveyor to a Ross Classifying Roll. The oversize goes to sinter storage bins for feed to the furnace. The undersize discharges into a surge bin so that a cooling drum is supplied at an even and consistent rate by a variable frequency vibrating conveyor. The sinter is quenched so that the discharge can be handled by rubber conveyor belts and is first transferred to corrugated rolls, then to smooth rolls, and into the return sinter storage hopper.

Sinter plant control room.

Composition of the sinter plant feed:*

27.5%	Concentrates
1.4%	Fluxes
7.0%	Purchased and Generated Secondaries
16.3%	Granulated Slag
47.8%	Return Sinter

* These and all subsequent statistics are for the last half of 1969.

Analysis:

Ag%	Pb%	Cu%	SiO_2%	Fe%	CaO%	Zn%	S%
0.05	43.0	1.0	10.6	11.3	7.1	5.4	5.1

Composition of the final sinter:

Pb%	Cu%	S%
46.3	1.08	1.7

Tons feed to sinter plant per operating day - 1125.

Ventilation and cleanup systems were designed for single handling of material. Sinter machine spillage, windbox cleanings, as well as spillage from the sinter breaker, the spike roll, and the two apron conveyors is automatically conveyed to a cleanup hopper. Provision is also made for floor cleanup and baghouse dust by the utilization of a grizzly over the final collector belt which takes the cleanup to the dust and cleanup feeder bin.

Two small individually packaged baghouses provide ventilation for main feed and return systems. These baghouses automatically discharge directly onto the collector belt carrying sinter machine feed.

The sinter machine and the subsequent sinter handling system up to the Ross Roll Classifier are all vented through the sinter spray chamber into the sinter plant baghouse. Gas discharge from the sinter machine is initially controlled to a specified temperature (205° C.) by automatically controlled 35 kilograms per square centimeter water sprays. The gas is then further cooled in the spray chamber by another set of 35 kilogram per square centimeter sprays which are actuated by a completely independent sensing element than that used in the machine hood. The cooled gas (125° C.) then passes through the fan into the sinter plant baghouse. This baghouse consists of nine separate chambers each containing 204 orlon bags, 30 centimeters in diameter and 7.3 meters long. The baghouse is designed to be automatically shaken at a preset pressure. The fume is collected

Sinter plant spray chamber, baghouse and base of stack.

in cellars which are periodically cleaned by a front-end loader. The clean gas discharges into a 186 meter concrete stack to provide dispersion. The control center of the automated baghouse is located in the sinter plant control room with routine baghouse procedures performed on day-shift.

THE BLAST FURNACE OPERATION

Charge components for the blast furnace are stored in bins adjacent to and in line with the sinter plant hoppers. Each component is automatically weighed when it is added to the charge car. Final sinter can be either directly fed into the sinter feed hoppers or into a large sinter storage area. Reclaimed sinter and other furnace charge is transferred into these feed hoppers by the bucket crane serving both this and the sinter plant.

Feed for the blast furnace is accumulated in a charge car positioned on a transfer car that receives sinter, coke, sinter reverts and direct smelting charge. The shuttle car moves forward under an automated gantry crane that lifts the charge car and elevates it, advances over the furnace and drops the charge.

Automated charging crane dumping charge into blast furnace.

The variation in charge levels within the car accommodates for differences in smelting rate within the furnace shaft with a dumping lever controlling the side of the furnace charged. The furnace proper is 7.6 meters long, 1.5 meters wide at the lower tuyeres and 3.0 meters wide at upper tuyeres. The water jackets are thermo syphon with heat loss by steaming. Water for the system is softened and treated with sodium sulfide to prevent oxygen corrosion. Air for the furnace is supplied by a blower that will deliver 510 cubic meters per minute at .26 kilograms per square centimeter and a proportioning controller allows distribution of the air between the lower and upper tuyeres. The furnace is a typical thimble top design and the front of the

Spray chamber and baghouse for blast furnace gases.

Lower level of furnace showing end of lead settler, lead discharging into transfer ladle with slag granulating launder in near background.

furnace accommodates a Roy Tapper* which continuously discharges into a settler at right angle to the furnace. The slag is granulated by a fishtail nozzle placed above a sluicing nozzle and flushes the granulated slag into an elevator pit, with the slag transported to a pair of wooden silos for dewatering. Upon discharge from the silo the slag can be delivered via conveyor belt to the sinter plant storage bin or deposited into a truck for transport to the waste area. The granulating water is pumped from sumps, immediately adjacent to the elevators, to a settling tank where entrained slag is removed in the underflow. The overflow discharges into two cooling towers in parallel and these flow through weirs into the basin containing the suction lines of the granulating water booster pumps. This closed system was used to minimize water consumption.

Blast Furnace slag produced:

Pb%	Cu%	SiO_2%	Fe%	CaO%	Zn %	Al_2O_3%	MgO%
3.8	0.26	23.5	24.6	12.1	10.8	4.4	5.0

Rough Dross Produced:

Pb%	Cu%
62.3	20.48

Tons smelted blast furnace per operating day - 665
Tons lead produced from blast furnace per operating day - 310

Lead from the furnace is received in cast steel ladles and transported by a 27 ton crane to a rough drossing kettle where the temperature is maintained at 540° C. The copper dross is skimmed and the lead is transferred to a second drossing kettle where the temperature is lowered to about 425° C., with the dross from the kettle being returned to the first kettle. The lead is then bailed to the refinery for decopperizing. The drossing and refinery kettles all have a 286 metric ton capacity. When the decopperizing kettle is filled with lead, cooling is accomplished by adding frozen lead blocks or by water on the surface of the metal bath. As the lead is cooling to the freezing temperature wet blocks of dross are skimmed and these are returned to the rough drossing kettles. Because of very low silver content of the bullion, efficient copper removal is essential and the lead is decopperized to a copper content of 0.01% or less. The decopperizing dross is dried and skimmed off

* Patented by American Smelting and Refining Company

General view refining area - top floor.

and returned to the sinter plant charge. After the kettle is skimmed clean the lead is transferred to the desilverizing kettle.

The first desilverizing kettle is the high silver kettle. The silver zinc blocks produced in this kettle are recycled to produce a zinc crust of over 2,000 oz. Ag/ton. Howard presses are used to produce a high grade silver zinc crust. Since the silver intake is quite low relatively little zinc crust is produced. The crust produced is retorted in a single annual campaign.

After pressing the kettle, enough zinc is added to produce a final desilverized product containing less than .15 oz/ton. the zinc added is in the form of purchased zinc spelter, vacuum zinc or retort zinc. After stirring in this zinc, the kettle is cooled and drossed down to approximately 700° and transferred to the low silver kettle. The lead transferred to the low silver kettle never contains more than 1 oz Ag/ton.

In the low silver kettle, the lead is drossed and cooled down to freezing. A 3" rim is formed and pulled at the freezing point. This rim is returned to the next charge in the low silver kettle. All other dross off the low silver kettle is returned to the high silver kettle where they are used to help cool the kettle down.

The desilverized lead, approximately 2.1 grams/ton Ag is then transferred to another kettle for vacuum dezincing employing the rapid dezincing procedure developed and patented by ASARCO. Vacuum zinc produced during this operation is returned to the high silver kettle as required. After dezincing the lead is transferred to either of two kettles for refining with caustic and nitre and then casting of refined lead.

Cu in bullion during decopperizing:

Before	0.13% Cu
After	0.008% Cu

Ag in bullion during desilverizing:

Before	110 gms/T
After	2.3 gms/T

Analysis of pressed zinc cake:

Kilos Ag/T	Cu%	Zn%	Pb%
89.0	1.35	43.0	45.9

Analysis of retort bullion:

Au/T	Ag/T	Pb%	Cu%
28 gms.	114 Kilos	75.0	1.3

Analysis of refined lead produced:

Ag/T	Cu%	Bi%	Sb%
46 gms.	0.0002	0.0008	0.001

Lead is cast as either 100 pound pigs or one ton blocks. The pig casting machine is ASARCO developed and was built at the Omaha Refinery. Block casting is done in a semicircular arc with water cooling on the bottom of the moulds. Casting rate for pigs is normally 50 tons per hour and for blocks 75 tons per hour.

Refined lead one ton block casting.

Both battery and gasoline driven fork lift trucks are used for warehousing and loading lead shipments. Since shipments are made in both boxcars and gondolas, a craneway over the loading track alongside the refinery storage area provides loading where fork lifts cannot be used. The automatic stacker provides versatility via an indexing dial to accommodate various stacking patterns that are normally five bars per layer and four layers tall. These stacks are normally tied by at least two wires to secure the bundles.

Glover lead is typical of that produced from Missouri ores and intake is monitored to protect this quality.

Chapter 27

LEAD SMELTING AND REFINING AND SLAG FUMING AT THE BROKEN HILL ASSOCIATED SMELTERS PTY. LTD.
Port Pirie, South Australia

G. C. Hancock, Lead Production Superintendent

D. H. Hart, Zinc Production Superintendent

L.A.H. Pelton, Technical Assistant to the Manager

Abstract

The operating plant of The Broken Hill Associated Smelters Pty. Ltd. is situated at Port Pirie in South Australia and it treats to finality the whole output of lead concentrates from the mines of The Zinc Corporation Ltd., North Broken Hill Ltd., and Broken Hill South Ltd. at Broken Hill, New South Wales. Lead bearing ores from other sources are also purchased for treatment and lead scrap and residues are treated on a toll charge basis. The present output of the plant is approximately 200000 tonnes of refined lead per annum and there is a substantial production of by-products including refined silver, gold, cadmium, antimonial lead alloys, copper matte and sulphuric acid.

Recently the Company commenced the production of zinc by slag fuming and electrolysis from a six million ton dump of lead blast furnace slag, which has been accumulating at Port Pirie for over fifty years. The slag fuming plant contains two furnaces of conventional design, but features a high degree of pre-heat for the blast air and this is obtained by the use of all-metal recuperators. The raw zinc oxide fume produced by the plant is roasted in a rotary kiln prior to treatment in the leaching and electrolysis sections, which follow conventional practice for high current density plants. Present output is approximately 36000 tonnes of electrolytic zinc per annum.

Introduction

The development of the lead and zinc industry at Port Pirie dates from the discovery of the rich lead-silver-zinc mining field at Broken Hill, Australia, in 1883. As the nearest seaport to Broken Hill, Port Pirie provided a natural outlet for the products of the field and a lead smelting plant was built there in 1889. Refining facilities were subsequently established and the operations integrated under the control of The Broken Hill Proprietary Company Limited (B.H.P.), which remained the sole owners of the plant until 1915, when the present company, The Broken Hill Associated Smelters Pty. Ltd., took over all operations and immediately embarked on an expansion program which made the B.H.A.S. works the largest single lead smelting and refining plant in the world. Port Pirie is situated on the eastern shore near the head of Spencer Gulf in South Australia, approximately 230 kilometers from the State capital, Adelaide, and 400 kilometers from the inland city of Broken Hill in New South Wales.

High grade lead sulphide concentrates containing more than 70 per cent lead provide over 95 per cent of the input to the lead plant and these are delivered from The Zinc Corporation Limited, North Broken Hill Limited and Broken Hill South Limited mines at Broken Hill. Additional lead bearing materials entering the plant include lower grade products recovered from the retreatment of dumps at Broken Hill, battery scrap and other residual lead materials, and concentrates and ores from small scale mining operations in various parts of Australia. The production of zinc is based on the treatment of a 6M. tonne dump of granulated lead blast furnace slag containing about 18 per cent zinc, which has accumulated adjacent to the Works. Most of this is being brought back through the lead smelter system and delivered molten to the Slag Fuming Plant, but about 20 per cent is fed direct to the slag fuming furnaces.

The products of the Port Pirie plant include refined lead, antimonial lead and cable sheathing alloys, silver, gold, cadmium, copper matte, sulphuric acid, high grade and special high grade zinc and galvanizing alloys. The metallurgical operations are carried out by the Lead Production Division and the Zinc Production Division and their activities are described below. The plant operates 24 hours per day in three shifts seven days a week throughout the year and the operating labor force is divided into four rotating gangs or shifts each working a five day week averaging 42 hours, with overtime rates applying to the two hours in excess of the nominal standard Australian working week.

Lead Plant flowsheets are shown in Figs. 1 and 2 and the Slag Fuming Plant flowsheet in Fig. 3.

Lead Production

Concentrate Handling

Broken Hill concentrates are delivered to Port Pirie in 55-tonne open rail wagons operating on the standard gauge rail system which links the two centres. The concentrate traffic on this line amounts to approximately 850000 tonnes per year and of this amount some 300000 tonnes of lead concentrates are treated by B.H.A.S. and the remainder, consisting mainly of zinc concentrates, is shipped inter-state or overseas for treatment. All concentrates are unloaded at a central tippler installation operated by B.H.A.S. The tippler is of the side-dump type and was designed by Strachan and Henshaw. It incorporates a 100-tonne weighbridge for automatic gross and tare weighing of the trucks and this is recorded by a punch card system along with details concerning source and type of concentrate, date and time of discharge, destination, and eventually, moisture content, net dry weight and metal assay. There is, therefore, a complete card record, for each truck tipped.

As the wagons are tipped, the concentrates fall into four hoppers which in effect divide the wagon into four equal lengths and feeder belts at the base of these hoppers discharge onto a reversible col-lector belt which delivers the concentrates to wharf stockpiles for shipment or to the B.H.A.S. concentrate storage bin system. Four samplers are set up to obtain samples of the concentrates as they fall from the feeder belts to the collector belt and at least 80 separate 454g. samples are taken automatically by this method from each wagon.

The lead concentrates for treatment at Port Pirie are delivered by belt conveyor to 20 bins each of 250 tonnes capacity where the concentrates from each mine and also the subsidiary lead bearing materials received from Broken Hill are kept separate. Discharge from these bins is by feeder belts driven by hydraulic motors equipped with variable speed controllers so that a pre-determined proportion of each component can be delivered to the Mixing Plant ahead of the updraught sintering machine. This constantly propor-tioned feed is passed through a hammer mill type disintegrator to eliminate lumps and to provide a primary mix before being sampled by a two pass slot sampler on its way to a 1000-tonne storage bin. The lead bearing materials delivered to this bin constitute a batch of feed and an assay is available for the batch before it is passed to the Mixing Plant bins. This is of considerable assistance in determining the flux requirements. A typical analysis of a batch of mixed concentrate is shown in Table 1.

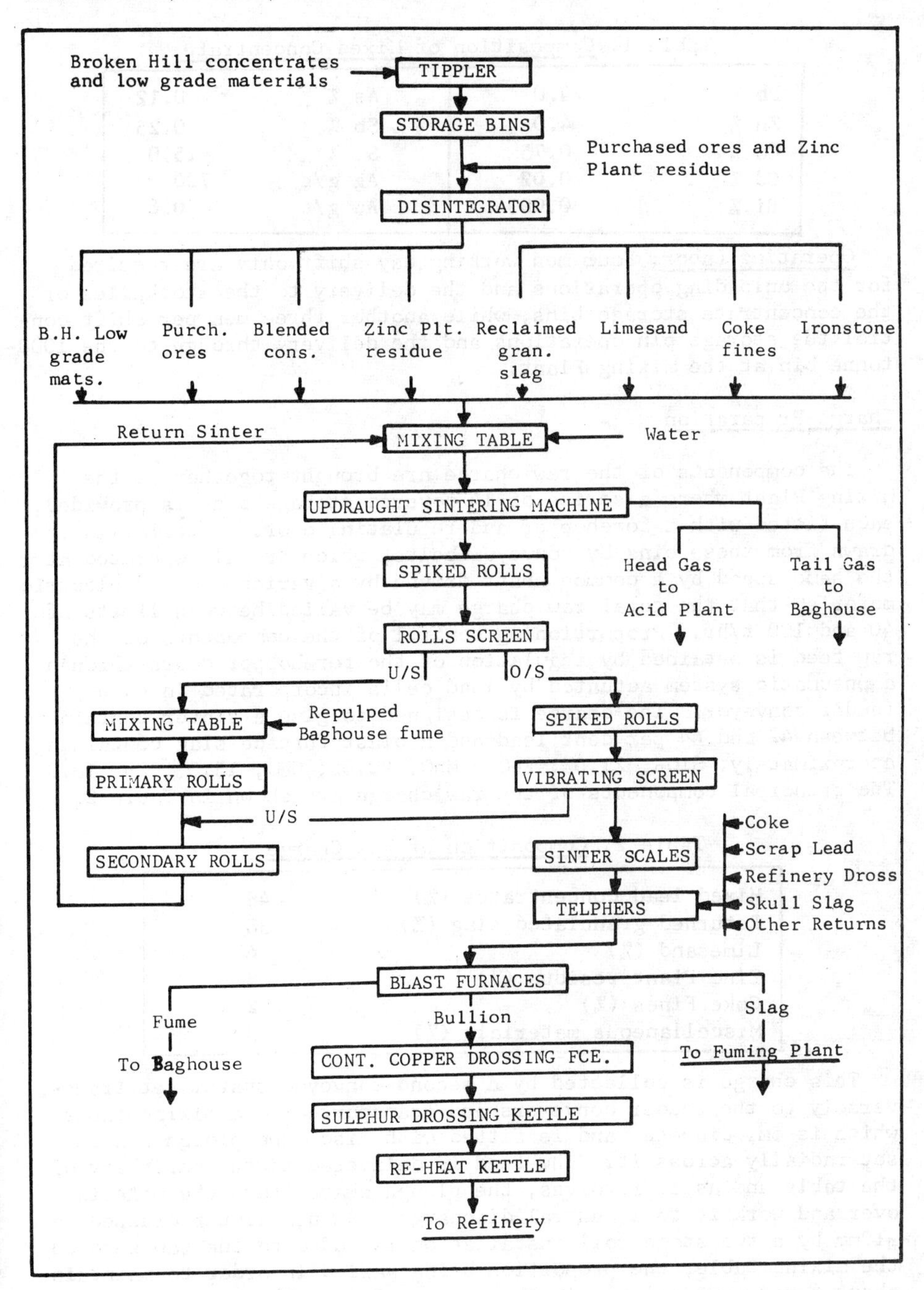

Fig. 1. Lead Smelter Flowsheet of The Broken Hill Associated Smelters Pty. Ltd.

Table 1. Composition of Mixed Concentrate

Pb %	74.0	As %	0.12
Zn %	4.0	Sb %	0.25
Cu %	0.75	S %	15.0
Cd %	0.02	Ag g/t	700
Bi %	0.003	Au g/t	0.6

Operating Labor: Four men working day shift only are required for the unloading operations and the delivery to the stockpiles or the concentrate storage bins, while another three men per shift control the storage bin operations and the delivery through to the 1000-tonne bin at the Mixing Plant.

Charge Preparation

The components of the raw charge are brought together at the Mixing Plant where a series of 14 covered storage bins is provided, each fitted with a forehopper and regulating door. Material is drawn from these bins by conveyor belts, which are all operated at the same speed by a common shaft driven by a variable speed electric motor so that the total raw charge may be varied between limits of 40 and 100 t/hr. Proportioning control of the components of the raw feed is obtained by regulation of the forehopper doors through a pneumatic system actuated by load cells incorporated in each feeder conveyor. The charge is designed to give a sinter containing between 42 and 44 per cent lead and a blast furnace slag containing approximately: SiO_2, 21.0%; FeO + MnO, 30.0%; CaO, 15.0%; Zn, 18.0%. The principal components of the raw charge are shown in Table 2.

Table 2. Composition of Raw Charge

Mixed lead concentrates (%)	48
Returned granulated slag (%)	38
Limesand (%)	4
Zinc Plant residue (%)	5
Coke Fines (%)	2
Miscellaneous materials (%)	3

This charge is collected by a second conveyor system set transversely to the feeder conveyors and transported to a mixing table which is 5m. diameter and is fitted with disc type plough shares set radially across it. The feed is delivered to the periphery of the table and as it revolves, the plough shares turn the material over and work it to a central discharge. Return sinter crushed to -10mm by a two stage roll installation is added to the raw feed on the mixing table, the proportion being varied in order to maintain about 6 per cent sulphur in the machine feed. This usually means about equal parts of raw feed and returns. Water is also added on the mixing table to provide a constant optimum moisture level of

5-6 per cent. The addition is made automatically and the requirement is signaled from a moisture probe located on the discharge conveyor from the table. This conveyor delivers the mixed feed to the updraught sintering machine.

Operating Labor: The operation of the Charge Preparation section requires one man per shift.

Updraught Sintering

The development of updraught sintering on a Dwight Lloyd type machine was pioneered at Port Pirie and has already been described in published information. (1) (2). Only the main features of the machine and current practice will be described here.

The Machine: A single machine is used which is 30.18 m. long and 3.05 m. wide over the windboxes, of which there are nine, each 3.05m. square with 30.5 cm. deadplates in between to give an effective roasting area of 920m.^{2}. Even at the maximum capacity of the lead plant, only about two-thirds of this area is utilised. The pallets are 1.07 m. long and are fitted with two sets of grate bars, each 53.5 cm. long and 4.3 cm. wide with an aperture between the bars of 5 mm. Each set has two locking bars with alternate loose elongated holes to permit a 16 mm. vertical scissor action to clear the grates on the return run. Side walls are 30 cm. high and have a five degree taper. The machine is driven by a 7-35 h.p. variable speed motor through reduction gearing to give a grate speed of 5 cm. to 30 cm. per minute. Four pressure fans each capable of supplying 1420 m^3/min. of blast air at 50.8 cm. w.g. deliver to a common header fitted with dampers which permit a flexible windbox pattern to suit the machine speed. Sealing of the pallets to the windboxes and the hood is achieved by rubber strips.

Feed Delivery and Ignition: An oscillating conveyor pivoting around a fixed point at the head of the machine is used to give uniform feeding across the width. It discharges into two feed hoppers, one for the ignition bed and the other for the main roast bed. Attached to the discharge end of the conveyor is a screen, which is automatically rapped to keep it clear, and this ensures that neither lumpy material nor trash is delivered into the ignition hopper. An adjustable knife-edged plate attached to this hopper maintains a 32 mm. ignition layer, which is then passed under the ignition stove, placed between the ignition hopper and the roast hopper. This stove is down-draughted and is fitted with five Major, high pressure, wide angle, atomising oil burners. An automatically controlled damper regulates the volume of air used through the ignition layer and a spring loaded flexible dead plate is used to provide a seal between the ignition downdraught box and the first windbox of the updraught section. The normal ignition downdraught is 196 m^3/min. at 9 mm. w.g. The roast hopper discharge is designed to place a loosely packed layer of feed onto the burning carpet of the ignition layer so as to give a total bed depth of up to 30 cm., but the normal operating depth is 26 cm.

Sinter Discharge and Screening: At the tip end of the machine the sinter cake slides from the pallets and drops 3.7 m. onto three breaker bars set at 76 cm. centres and the broken cake then enters the hopper of a reciprocating plate feeder, which discharges into a set of spiked rolls set at 70 m.m. aperture, this measurement being made from the tip of a spike to the boss of the opposite roll. From the spiked rolls the sinter is conveyed by a Locker-Traylor type HM4 vibrator feeder to a rolls screen of local design, which has an adjustable aperture to separate the proportion of sinter required for the returns circuit. The oversize from the rolls screen is delivered by conveyor belt to a second set of spiked rolls, which are set to control the size of sinter required for the blast furnaces. The product of these spiked rolls is screened by a vibrating screen to provide a blast furnace feed with a predominant lump size of 75 mm. x 25 mm. This sinter contains approximately 43 per cent lead and 1.5 per cent sulphur and is delivered by belt conveyor to the sinter storage hoppers ahead of the blast furnace section.

Returns Crushing and Sizing: Undersize from the rolls screen (above) passes to a vibrator feeder delivering onto the returns mixing table where it is quenched and moistured by the addition of repulped fume collected from the sintering and smelting plant baghouses and the first stage of the acid plant purification train. This fume is pulped at the appropriate sections of the plant and pumped to an Oliver disc filter positioned above the returns mixing table. The filtrate is delivered to the cadmium plant and the cake from the filter is repulped and sprayed onto the table. The sinter returns discharged from this table are delivered by belt conveyor to a set of 122 cm. x 41 cm. smooth faced crushing rolls set at a gap of 19 mm. and the product of this unit is conveyed to a surge bin of 50 tonnes capacity. A variable speed conveyor then delivers the returns from the surge bin to a second set of smooth faced rolls which are 140 cm. x 61 cm. and these are set at 10 mm. Undersize from the blast furnace sinter vibrating screen is also delivered to the surge bin and passed through the secondary rolls. The -10 mm. return sinter, which contains about 60 per cent -3 mm. material, is delivered to the mixing table ahead of the updraught sintering machine as has been described previously.

Gas Handling and Disposal: The gas collecting hood above the updraught windboxes is suspended from arch trusses mounted on rollers. There are only two off-takes from the hood, a 1.5 m. diameter flue for the acid plant gas situated 3.0 m. from the feed end of the machine and a 2.5 m. diameter flue at the discharge end of the machine, which delivers the balance of the gases to the baghouse system. At the normal production rate, the Acid Plant takes approximately

623 m^3/min. of gas containing about 6.5 per cent SO_2 and the remainder of the hood is maintained under constant suction sufficient only to remove the roast gases. This is controlled by a pneumatic servo-motor operated damper in the baghouse flue so that the suction is maintained at 2-5mm. w.g. High pressure water sprays are used in the machine hood to maintain the off-take temperature of the Acid Plant gas at about 160°C and the Baghouse gas at 120°C.

Hygiene: All units at the discharge end of the machine such as the spiked rolls, rolls screen and vibrator conveyors are draughted to three National type wet scrubbers, each with a capacity of 250 m^3/min. and the pulp from these is thickened and returned to the circuit with the repulped baghouse fume.

Instrumentation: A central, air-conditioned control room is located on the machine floor. All plant units are controlled by start-stop buttons on a main control panel with each drive motor having an individual indicating ammeter and speed indicators are provided for variable speed motors. All units in the plant are connected in a sequence circuit controlled by a Telechron relay system, so that in starting the plant each unit begins operating in the correct time sequence and should one unit stop, the whole sequence stops. For convenience, some units such as the spiked rolls, plate feeder, vibrator conveyors, rolls screens and crushing rolls can be operated out of sequence. Essential control points are connected to the control room by a public address system.

Maintenance: This is normally carried out during three scheduled stoppages each week, one of 8-12 hours duration and the other two of about 1½ hours duration. With effective maintenance control, an operating time efficiency of 85-90 per cent is achieved.

Operating Labor: Three men per shift are required to operate the updraught sintering machine and another three men per shift are employed on the tip end operations, including all crushing, screening, hygiene control and delivery of the sinter to the storage bins ahead of the Blast Furnace Department.

Blast Furnace Smelting

The blast furnace installation consists of three furnaces arranged with the long dimension in line for ease of servicing with an overhead telpher system for charging and a crane bay at the bottom floor level for handling of the furnace products. All furnaces are water jacketed, with two rows of tuyeres and the stepped, or chair jacket development, described by White (3). Two furnaces, Nos. 3 and 4, are 7.78 m. in length and have a conventional siphon tap for the bullion and a water cooled breast for intermittent tapping of slag at each end; whereas the third furnace, No. 2, is 10.67 m. in length and is provided with an Asarco continuous tapper and a forehearth placed centrally at one side of the furnace.

Furnace capacities in terms of base bullion for 24 hours are:-

No. 2	530 tonnes
No. 3	350 tonnes
No. 4	350 tonnes

The principal dimensions of the furnaces and related data are shown in Table 3.

Table 3. Principal Dimensions of the Blast Furnaces

Dimension	No. 2	No. 3	No. 4
Width at top of shaft (m.)	3.05	3.00	3.00
Width at tuyeres			
Top row (m.)	3.05	3.00	3.00
Bottom row (m.)	1.52	1.52	1.52
Length (m.)	10.67	7.78	7.78
Height			
Base of jackets to C/L bottom tuyeres (cm.)	33	61	61
Base of jackets to C/L top tuyeres (cm.)	132	152	152
Base of jackets to top of shaft (m.)	5.06	5.84	5.84
Number of tuyeres			
Top row	46	40	40
Bottom row	42	30	30
Internal diameter of tuyeres (cm.)	7.62	7.62	7.62
Rows of jackets	3	3	3

Water jackets are of 9.5 mm. mild steel plate with a 7.62 cm. water space, and each set is in series vertically and operated on the thermo siphon principle using closed circuit corrosion inhibited fresh water cooled by seawater in a heat exchanger. All jackets can be isolated and the top row jackets are fitted with fusible plugs.

Charge Handling: All charge materials are handled by a Telpher system comprising high and low level units with storage facilities. The installation was brought into operation in 1929 and the high level runway is in three sections.

No. 1 Section: Runs parallel to the water front and is so located that coke, which is discharged from ships by 7½-tonne Luffing Jib cranes can be delivered to stockpile or to the coke screening plant which is under the command of this section of the Telpher system.

No. 2 Section: This section operates at right angles to, but is connected with both No. 1 and No. 3 sections, and spans the main storage bin system and the operating skip floor in front of the discharge bins of the Sintering plant.

No. 3 Section: This section operates in a direction parallel with No. 1 section but is some 150 metres distance from it and spans the line of blast furnaces.

The storage bins have a total capacity of 2270 tons, made up as follows:-

Sinter	1600 tonnes
Coke	170 tonnes
Chilled Slag	200 tonnes
Dross	300 tonnes

These bins can discharge from either side into the low level Telpher skips, which are bottom discharging and operate on an ancillary runway, to the side of, and above the high level Telpher skip floor.

During normal operations, crushed and screened sinter direct from the sintering machine is delivered by conveyor belt to storage bins adjacent to the high level Telpher skip floor and is then automatically weighed into the skips, which are pushed into position on a two-station suspended platform scale installation below the bins. The skips are then moved under the low level Telpher runway and receive from its skips the appropriate amount of coke to smelt the unit sinter charge. The high level Telpher system is then used to convey the skip containing the combined sinter and coke charge to the blast furnace hoppers. Sinter produced in excess of blast furnace requirements is handled by the high level Telpher system to the previously mentioned storage bins, from which it can be reclaimed by the low level system for use when the Sintering Plant is down for maintenance.

The standard blast furnace charge consists of:

Sinter	3000 kg.
Coke	225-275 kg.

The fixed carbon content of the coke is normally 83 per cent and it is screened into two sized fractions (-7.6 cm. + 3.8 cm.) and (-3.8 + 1.3 cm.) and these are used in the proportions of about two parts to three. The objective is to get a match with the sinter sizing to provide optimum shaft conditions.

Other materials charged direct to the blast furnaces include Refinery drosses, chilled settler slag, copper drossing furnace slag, and battery scrap. These are conveyed in the high level Telpher skips in 3000 kg. lots.

Furnace Operations: On each blast furnace, the charge hopper is placed above the draughting hood and in the case of No. 2 furnace it is fitted with eight manually operated quadrant doors, controlled by rack and pinion gear. The two smaller furnaces have six similarly operated doors. The charge material is fed from these doors onto the periphery of the draughting hood and rills from there into the open furnace top. Around the top of the shaft are fenders which permit the furnace to be fed closed (that is with charge material covering the edge of the draughting hood), or open. Normal practice is to run with the ends open, but the side feeding depends on furnace conditions. Blast air for the furnaces is supplied by an installation of four Rootes-Connersville blowers, each with a capacity of 240m^3/min., but normally only two, or at the most three, of these units is used. Blast pressure at the furnaces is 190-220 g/sq.cm. in the case of No. 2 furnace and 140-160 g/sq.cm. for Nos. 3 and 4 furnaces. Control of the blowing rate is by pressure adjustment.

Bullion and slag flow together from No. 2 furnace through the Asarco continuous tapper to a forehearth, where separation takes place. The bullion flows via a lead well into a launder from which it can be directed to any one of three 11-tonne capacity ladles, lined with castable refractory, which are filled in turn. The ladles are covered and draughted to reduce fume emission. Slag produced by No. 2 furnace is directed from the forehearth to 11-tonne cast steel ladles for transport to the Slag Fuming Plant, or if not required for this plant, it is granulated. With No. 3 and No. 4 furnaces, separation of slag and bullion takes place within the crucible and the bullion runs continuously through a lead well to a ladle, while the slag is tapped intermittently through a breast at the end and is run via a settler to the slag fuming ladles or is granulated. Granulating launders on all furnaces deliver to bucket elevators which discharge into overhead bins for drainage before being transported to the reserve dump. Typical analyses (in rounded terms) of lead bullion and slag are shown in Table 4.

Table 4. Composition of Lead Bullion and Slag

Lead Bullion		Slag	
Cu %	1.00	Pb %	2.3
As %	0.20	SiO_2 %	21.0
Sb %	0.50	FeO %	25.6
Ag g/t	1430.60	MnO %	4.3
Au g/t	1.20	CaO %	14.7
Fe %	0.20	ZnO %	23.0
Bi %	0.003	(Zn) %	18.4
S %	0.25	MgO %	0.9
Pb %	Remainder	Al_2O_3 %	5.7
		S %	1.7
		F %	0.1

Two overhead travelling cranes service the blast furnace tapping floor for handling slag ladles to the slag fuming train and bullion ladles to the Continuous Copper Drossing Furnace.

Operating Labor: With No. 2 furnace in operation, the labor allocation for the blast furnace smelting section is as follows:-

Skip floor attendants and Telpher drivers	8 men/shift
Top floor feeders	2 " "
Bottom floor furnacemen	4 " "
Crane drivers and chaser	3 " "

Copper Drossing

The removal of copper from the lead bullion is the first stage of the refining process, but for convenience it is carried out within the Blast Furnace Department. The operation is conducted in two stages, firstly by passing the bullion through the Continuous Copper Drossing Furnace, and secondly by sulphur treatment in an open oval-shaped kettle.

Continuous copper drossing was introduced at Port Pirie in 1962, superseding the manual pan drossing process previously used. The development of the process has been described by McNicol (4) and by Peck and McNicol (5). The furnace used is an oil-fired reverberatory unit, which is 6.00 m. long, 1.73 m. wide and 1.42 m. deep. It is divided into four compartments by submerged walls which control the movement of bullion within the furnace and help to direct the flow to an external cooling system on one side and a discharge pot on the other. The operation is essentially one of cooling the incoming hot bullion and thereby causing it to reject copper in the form of mixed sulphide and arsenide crystals, which float to the top of the bath and are liquified by the oil burners to form a copper matte. Lead and iron are also present in the matte and silica sand is added to the furnace to form a slag with the components that are oxidised.

The matte and slag are tapped intermittently into a tilting ladle, where a liquid separation takes place and these products are then cast into moulds and when solidified, tipped onto the breaking and sorting floor, the matte to be collected and further crushed before disposal to copper smelters and the slag to be returned to the blast furnaces. As each ladle of blast furnace bullion is charged to the furnace, a corresponding amount of cooled bullion containing about 0.06 per cent copper overflows to the discharge pot through a channel communicating to the coolest and most quiescent zone of the bottom of the furnace. An immersion heater in the discharge pot raises the temperature sufficiently for this bullion to be pumped to a 200-tonne storage kettle ahead of the sulphur treatment section.

From this storage kettle the bullion is pumped to a 90-tonne open kettle where it is stirred until cooled to approximately 320°C at which temperature yellow lump sulphur is added in an amount equal to about one kilogram per ton of bullion. This is stirred in over a period of about 30 minutes and the kettle is then skimmed, the dross being returned to an empty bullion ladle. The bullion is then pumped to a second 90-tonne kettle for reheating to about 450°C before being transported in a 15-tonne ladle car to the Refinery. Typical analyses of the products of the copper drossing section are shown in Table 5.

Operating Labor: Two men per shift are required to operate the Continuous Copper Drossing Furnace and another two men per shift are employed on the sulphur drossing operations.

Table 5. Products of the Copper Dressing Section

Matte		Bullion		Slag	
Cu %	50.0	Cu %	0.004	Pb %	47.5
Pb %	30.0	Sb %	0.50	Zn %	10.0
S %	15.0	As %	0.15	Cu %	4.5
As %	0.9	Ag g/t	1430.0	SiO2 %	10.0
Fe %	0.4	Au g/t	1.2	FeO %	4.5
Ag g/t	960.0	Bi %	0.003	Ag g/t	78.0
Au g/t	0.3	Pb %	Remainder		

Lead Refining

In 1932, B.H.A.S. brought into operation the world's first continuous lead refinery and many of the features which were pioneered then are incorporated in the present plant, which was commissioned in 1959. The principles and practice of continuous softening and desilverising have been described previously by Williams (6), (7) and by Green (8); the background to the development of continuous vacuum dezincing by Davey (9) and the first operating V.D.Z. plant by Davey and Williams (10). The complete operation of the new Refinery has been described by Heggen (11). A flowsheet of the Refinery is shown in Fig. 2.

Bullion Delivery: Decopperised bullion is delivered to the Refinery in a 15-tonne capacity, refractory lined ladle mounted on a rail bogey pulled by a battery truck. It is pumped to the first of two 100-tonne storage kettles and then to the second, from which it is again pumped to the softening furnace, the first of the continuous refining units. The flow rate may be adjusted between 18 and 34 tonnes per hour.

Softening: The softening furnace is a reverberatory unit, lined with chrome-magnesite bricks and water-jacketed at and above the slag line. The hearth measures 1.52 m. x 4.57 m. and bullion enters

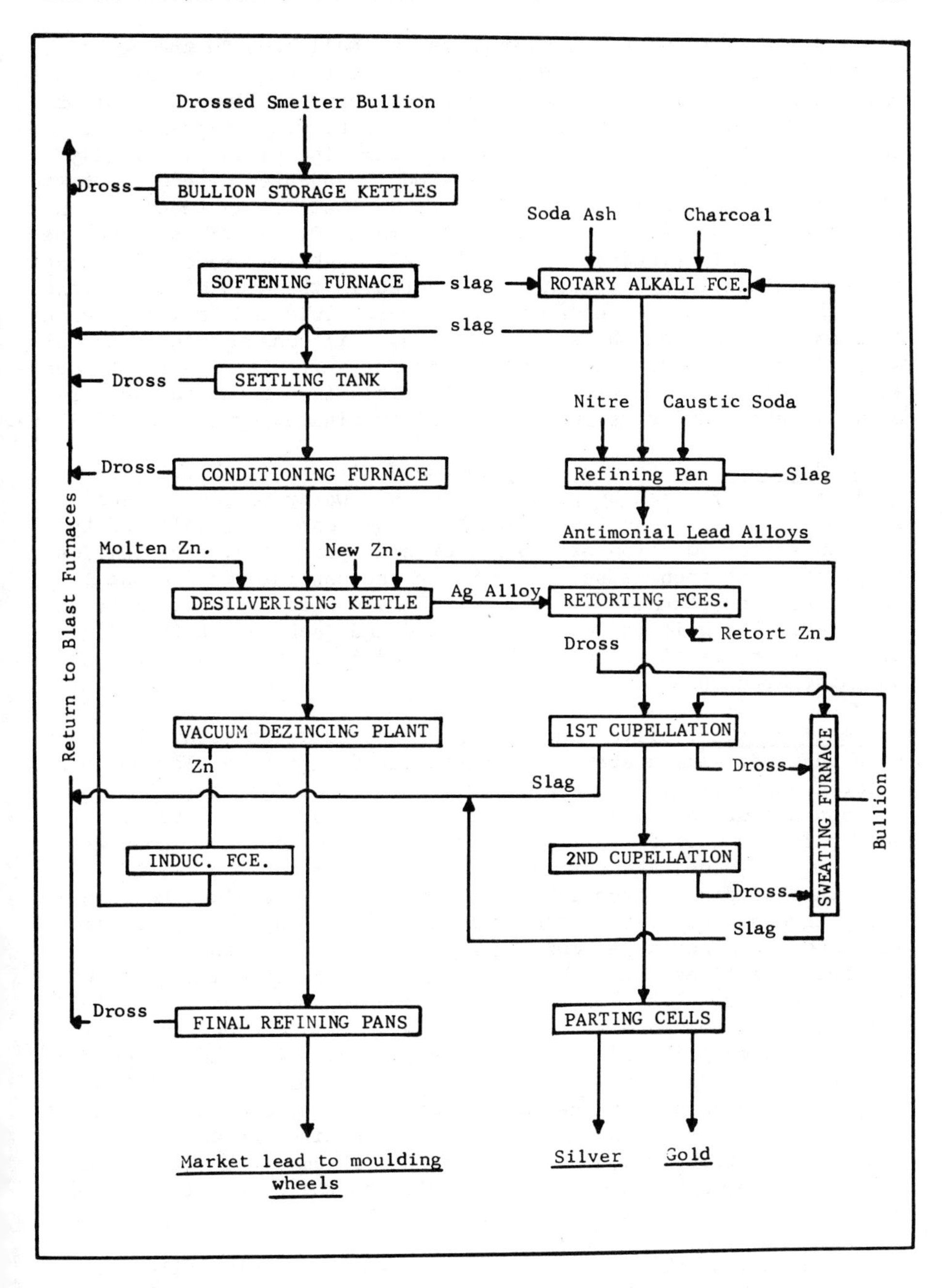

Fig. 2. Lead Refinery Flowsheet of The Broken Hill Associated Smelters Pty. Ltd.

the furnace at about 420°C through an end wall beneath the jacket. Softened bullion and slag flow through outlets at the opposite end, which are respectively 30 cm. and 36 cm. above the lowest point of the hearth. Oxidation is brought about by blowing compressed air into the bath through a 2.5 cm. I.D. steam pipe placed vertically through the arch. The volume delivered is adjusted depending on the bullion composition and treatment rate so that the antimony content of the softened bullion is held in the range 0.02-0.05% Sb. and the temperature maintained at 700-730°C. Although the process is largely self-sustaining, an oil burner is mounted in the arch of the furnace near the inlet end to render the slag more fluid and to melt accumulations of slag from the walls and arch. Oil consumption is normally 40-55 litres per hour and only one man per shift is required to operate the unit, irrespective of output. The life of the furnace is normally about 200 days and is usually terminated by a jacket failure.

Conditioning: Before passing to the desilverising kettle, the bullion is deoxidised by passage through a water-cooled section of launder and a settling tank of eight tonnes capacity, followed by the continuous addition of 1.5 kg. of zinc per tonne. The bullion temperature is then raised to 650°C in the conditioning furnace, which has a hearth area 1.52 m. x 4.57 m. and is filled to a depth of 22 cm. The unit is refractory lined and jacketed at the slag line only and is oil-fired at the rate of 60 l/hr. by a burner at the discharge end.

Desilverising: Silver and gold are removed together by the continuous desilverising process in a specially designed kettle, which has a total depth of 7.09 m. and a maximum internal diameter of 3.05 m. It consists of four cast iron sections which are bolted together and sealed by welded flexible joints. The sections are known as the top, the cone, the straight and the bottom and the kettle is contained within a firebrick structure, which is divided horizontally into six hearths, three of these surrounding the bottom section and the other three corresponding with each of the three remaining sections. Each hearth has provision for oil firing and the No. 2 hearth (that is the one surrounding the cone section) is provided with forced draught air cooling. The top section casting is the most complicated one as it has provision for the inflow of the bullion via a dross trap and the outflow through the siphon pipe and an opening for the introduction of zinc and the removal of the silver enriched zinc alloy. The siphon pipe, which is also made of cast iron, reaches almost to the bottom of the kettle and discharges through a leg at right angles to the centrally located pipe.

In operation, the top casting is almost completely filled with the zinc rich layer which is maintained at a temperature of 530-580°C. The incoming bullion passes through this layer before mixing with that in the remainder of the kettle and the flow is then to the bottom of the kettle and up and out through the siphon pipe.

Careful control is maintained over the temperature gradient in the kettle so that a pad of solid lead is maintained on the bottom of the kettle. Overall control of this temperature gradient and the free flow of bullion through the kettle is mainly exercised by continuously firing the top hearth, air cooling the second hearth, and occasionally firing the No. 6 hearth of the bottom section.

The bullion as it gradually descends and cools in the kettle rejects crystals rich in silver and zinc which float to the top and are absorbed in the zinc rich layer. When the silver content reaches the point where solidification commences, the heterogeneous layer is dipped out and cast into pellets of about 3 kg. weight for delivery to the Silver Yard. The layer is then re-constituted with zinc and some low silver returns, which arise from the weekly routine firing of the straight section (No. 3 hearth) to clean up the kettle. This firing is necessary to release accumulated banks low in the kettle and a plant stop of 10-12 hours is then necessary to cool back the contents to the normal operating condition.

Three men handle all operating work associated with the conditioning furnace and the continuous desilverising kettle. Typical operating lives of the individual castings of the kettle are top, 120 days; cone, 150 days; straight, 500 days; bottom, 1000 days. All castings which come in contact with the zinc rich layer are of grey iron with a minimum combined carbon content.

Vacuum Dezincing: In passing through the desilverising kettle, the bullion picks up about 0.56% Zn and the bulk of this is removed by vacuum dezincing in a virtually continuous process. The bullion is discharged from the siphon pipe of the C.D. kettle at about 340°C and this is heated to 600-630°C in a tubular lead heater before being drawn into the vacuum vessel. The operation of this equipment in the new Refinery has already been described in the literature (10) and only a brief summary will be repeated here.

The vacuum vessel is cylindrical in shape with a diameter of 2.18 m. and is open at the top and has a dished bottom with provision for the connection to the vacuum pump and the outlet pipe for the dezinced lead. A removable water cooled condenser sits within the vacuum vessel and is sealed to it by a specially designed rubber ring. In operation, the lead is drawn into the vacuum vessel, which is maintained at about 50 microns of mercury absolute pressure and rises in an annular space formed between the vessel and the spreading surface. It then overflows a weir before cascading down the spreading surface to the outlet at the bottom and then away through a lead pot which serves as a barometric seal. Both the spreading surface and the condenser are in the shape of truncated cones and are positioned so that an annular space exists between them across which predominantly horizontal distillation takes place. The process is not completely continuous in that the vacuum must be broken and the zinc laden condenser removed after about 250 tonnes of lead have been dezinced, but this operation and the replacement by a clean condenser takes only about three minutes and the capacity in the system avoids any necessity to interrupt the refinery flow. Lead leaving the vacuum vessel contains about 0.05% Zn and this is then passed to the final refining pans for caustic treatment.

The columnar crystals of zinc deposited on the condenser are readily removed by barring and are then melted in a Major "Tama" induction furnace of 3-tonnes capacity, the molten zinc being returned as required to the desilverising kettle. The operating life of both the tubular lead heater and the vacuum vessel is usually about 200 days.

Final Refining: This is carried out on a batch basis in 200-tonne capacity kettles fabricated from 32 mm. mild steel plate. These have not required any maintenance since the plant was installed in 1959. After partial drossing, flake caustic soda equivalent to 1 kg. per tonne of lead is gradually added as the kettle is stirred, the temperature being maintained at about 480°C. Spectrographic analysis, with a supplementary check on antimony by the Hofman test, is used to ensure that the final lead complies with the specifications required. Simple alloys containing nominally 0.0025% Sb, 0.075% Sb and 0.85% Sb are also made in the final refining kettles by the addition of lead-antimony master alloy. Three men handle all operations associated with vacuum dezincing, final refining and the preparation of special alloys.

Typical assays at various stages of the refining process are shown in Table 6 and these assume that the input bullion is of the same approximate analysis as that given in Table 5.

Table 6. Typical Assays at Various Stages of the Refining Process

Element	Bullion ex Softener	Slag ex Softener	Lead ex C.D. Kettle	Lead ex V.D.Z. Unit	Market Lead
Cu %	0.004		0.00006	0.00006	0.00006
Sb %	0.04	12.8	0.04	0.04	0.00015
As %	0.003	4.5	N.D.	N.D.	0.0001
Bi %	0.003		0.003	0.003	0.003
Sn %	Nil		Nil	Nil	Nil
Zn %	N.D.		0.56	0.06	0.0004
Ag g/t	1430		1.8	1.8	1.8
Au g/t	1.2		Nil	Nil	Nil
Pb %	R.	73.0	R.	R.	99.996+

Moulding: Final refined lead is pumped to a 200-tonne moulding kettle where it is held at a controlled temperature before being pumped to the moulding wheels. A pair of Newnam wheels are used for moulding 25.5 kg. pigs and a specially designed wheel for moulding 909 kg. pigs in block form. Carefully controlled cooling is practised to ensure the uniformity and soundness of the small pigs and to provide a near flat surface on the large pigs. All moulding is performed by a contract team of seven men and it is basically a manual operation. Electric fork lift trucks are used to handle the products to the weighbridge and then to the storage area adjacent to the shipping wharf.

Antimonial Lead Production

Slag from the softening furnace provides the input to the antimonial lead section and this is tapped into a 3.5 tonne capacity tilting ladle and treated in 7 tonne batches in a 3 m. short rotary furnace lined with a high chrome refractory. Additions are made of 5% soda ash, 7% charcoal and 6% caustic slag, the latter being returned from the subsequent refining operation. The charcoal is added in two stages, the first of 2½% yielding a 2-3% antimonial lead alloy, which is returned to the circuit ahead of the softening furnace; and the second addition of 4½% yielding a 25-30% antimonial lead alloy containing about 85% of the available antimony. The slag, containing typically 2.6% Pb and 3.0% Sb, is tapped after each cycle and returned to the lead blast furnace. The furnace is oil-fired at about 60 l/hr. and a typical lining life is 100 days. Two men per shift operate the unit.

The crude metal is cast into butts and selected for refining according to the grade of metal required. The butts are melted in an 80-tonne capacity kettle and refined by stirring in caustic soda in an amount approximately equal to twice the weight of arsenic to be removed. After adjustment of the composition the market alloy is cast into 25.5 kg. bars. Two men operate the refining section, but four are required when casting.

Recovery of Silver and Gold

Silver and gold are recovered from continuous desilverising kettle alloy by the standard methods of retorting, cupellation and electrolytic parting.

Retorting: The 3 kg. pellets of alloy from the C.D. kettle are hand charged into clay-graphite bottles held within oil-fired tilting furnaces. Five units are available and usually three or four are in operation at any one time. The standard charge is 1680 kg. and the retorting operation usually takes 19 hours. An addition of 8 kg. of crude calcium borate is used with each charge to inhibit blue powder formation. Zinc, which distils from the retorts, is collected in air-cooled condensers sealed to the necks of the bottles. The liquid zinc is tapped every two hours into half tonne moulds for return to the C.D. kettle. When distillation is completed, the condenser is removed and the furnace tilted so that the contents of the bottle (lead-silver-gold alloy) may be cast into bars for cupellation.

Cupellation: This operation is performed in two stages in oil-fired furnaces of identical design, each holding approximately two and a half tons of metal. Three furnaces are available, each with a chrome-magnesite hearth area of 3.6 m.^{2} and a maximum depth of 13 cm. Two are used for the first stage and for the treatment of drosses and the third for working up the metal to Doré grade for parting. One man attends each of the furnaces which consume about 55 l. of fuel oil per hour.

In the first stage operation, oxidation is promoted by blowing low pressure air across the bath and by the addition of chilled softener furnace slag, which also has the effect of increasing the fluidity of the cupellation slag. This is run off continuously as additional bars of retort bullion are added until eventually the silver content of the bath is such that reaction almost ceases. The resulting metal known as high grade concentrate is then cast into bars and subsequently re-cupelled in the Doré furnace, where sodium nitrate equivalent to 35 kg. per tonne is progressively rabbled into the bath. When a cast sample exhibits a persistent oxygen "blow" the metal is cast into rectangular plates weighing about 8 kg.

Doré Parting: The parting plant is equipped with 80 Balbach Thum cells constructed of P.V.C. plastic. The anode plates (four per cell) are held within an open bottomed cradle on a synthetic cloth supported by plastic coated aluminium rods. Two anode contact pieces cast from Doré bullion rest on the plates which are partly submerged in 40 l. of electrolyte containing typically 250 g/l of silver and 35 g/l of copper. The cathode is cut from stainless steel and rests on the bottom of the cell. The effective area is 4350 cm.^{2} while that of the anodes is 2100 cm.^{2}. The cells are connected in two parallel groups of 40 in series and a potential of 120-140 volts is applied to both groups from a common D.C. source. The cathode deposit is removed as frequently as necessary to limit the current to about 100A. Concentrated silver nitrate solution is added to maintain the silver content of the electrolyte, while the copper content is controlled by regularly discarding de-silverised solution.

Cathode silver collected from the cells is washed, dried, melted under charcoal and cast into 23.3 kg. bars, or is granulated. Anode sludge from the cells, is removed on a twenty day cycle and worked up for the recovery of gold.

Typical assays at various stages of the silver recovery process are shown in Table 7.

Table 7. Typical Assays at Various Stages of the Silver Recovery Process

Element	C.D. Kettle Alloy	Retort Bullion	Dore Metal	Market Silver
Zn %	62.0	5.9	N.D.	0.00025
Pb %	24.0	63.0	0.06	0.0040
Cu %	0.4	1.1	0.13	0.0035
Ag %	12.0	29.5	99.70	99.99+
Au g/t	120.0	270.0	900.0	1.80

Operating Labor: Six men per shift are required for the silver and gold operations and with the fourteen for lead refining and moulding, and the four for antimonial lead production, this makes a total crew of twenty four per shift for the whole of the Refinery Department, with an additional two men required when antimonial lead alloys are being moulded.

Zinc Production

Slag Fuming Plant

Process and Design Considerations: The production of zinc from lead blast furnace slag at Port Pirie had been envisaged for many years before a decision to proceed with the design of a plant was made in 1964. After considering the various processes in use throughout the world, it was decided to construct a slag fuming plant, in which the lead blast furnace slag would be treated for the production of zinc oxide fume, and an electrolytic zinc plant of conventional design for the production of metallic zinc.

As pointed out by Butcher (12), the slag fuming furnace itself presents no major design problems, but the choice of ancillary equipment, particularly that involved in handling the fume laden gases from the furnace, requires careful consideration, because the effective utilisation of waste heat is essential for the economic success of the process. Due to local conditions, the use of waste heat for power generation was not feasible at Port Pirie, and an investigation was made of the possibility of applying the heat contained in the off-take gases for pre-heating the blast air delivered to the furnaces. The results of this investigation have been described by Blaskett (13) and showed that preheated blast would give higher furnace output and greater fuel economy for a fixed rate of coal consumption.

Further detailed examination of the process design revealed that the use of waste heat boilers for limited steam production was justified; to provide steam for driving sootblowing air compressors in the Slag Fuming Plant, for processing operations in the electrolytic zinc plant, and to reduce furnace gas temperatures to a level suitable for the operation of metal recuperators.

The Slag Fuming Plant which was commissioned in June, 1967, was designed to provide for the production of 40000 tonnes of zinc per year, of which approximately 15000 tonnes would be obtained from the zinc content of lead concentrates treated by the Lead Production Division and the balance from retreatment of the accumulated reserves of blast furnace slag in a dump adjacent to the Works. A flowsheet of the plant is shown in Fig. 3.

Furnace Operations: In practice, the slag fuming process is a batch operation consisting of four stages viz. charging, heating, fuming and tapping. In the heating phase, pulverised coal with an excess of combustion air is injected through the tuyeres beneath the surface of the bath of molten slag to melt any solid slag present and to bring the bath up to the operating temperature of approximately 1200°C. In the fuming phase, only some 60 to 75% of the theoretical air required for complete combustion is provided with the result that carbon monoxide is available to reduce the lead and zinc oxide present in the slag to metal. These metals vaporise, and additional or tertiary air is introduced above the bath to reoxidise them. The coal has to supply the conflicting requirements of a high carbon monoxide concentration for a high zinc elimination rate and a heat release matching the highly endothermic heats of reaction and the loss to the walls of the bath, in order to maintain the molten slag at the required operating temperature. Preheating the combustion air to the bath provides part of the heat requirements and permits operation at a lower air to fuel ratio, resulting in considerable economics in coal consumption. The coal and air rates used during the heating cycle are 41 kg/min. and 340 Nm^3/min. respectively and during the fuming cycle 55 kg/min. and 260 Nm^3/min.

Production of molten slag from the lead blast furnaces is insufficient to supply two slag fuming furnaces operating continuously and some cold granulated slag is added to make up the 45 tonne charge. When cold slag is added, the length of the heating cycle has to be increased, resulting in an increase in the overall cycle time per charge. The practice adopted at Port Pirie is shown in Table 8.

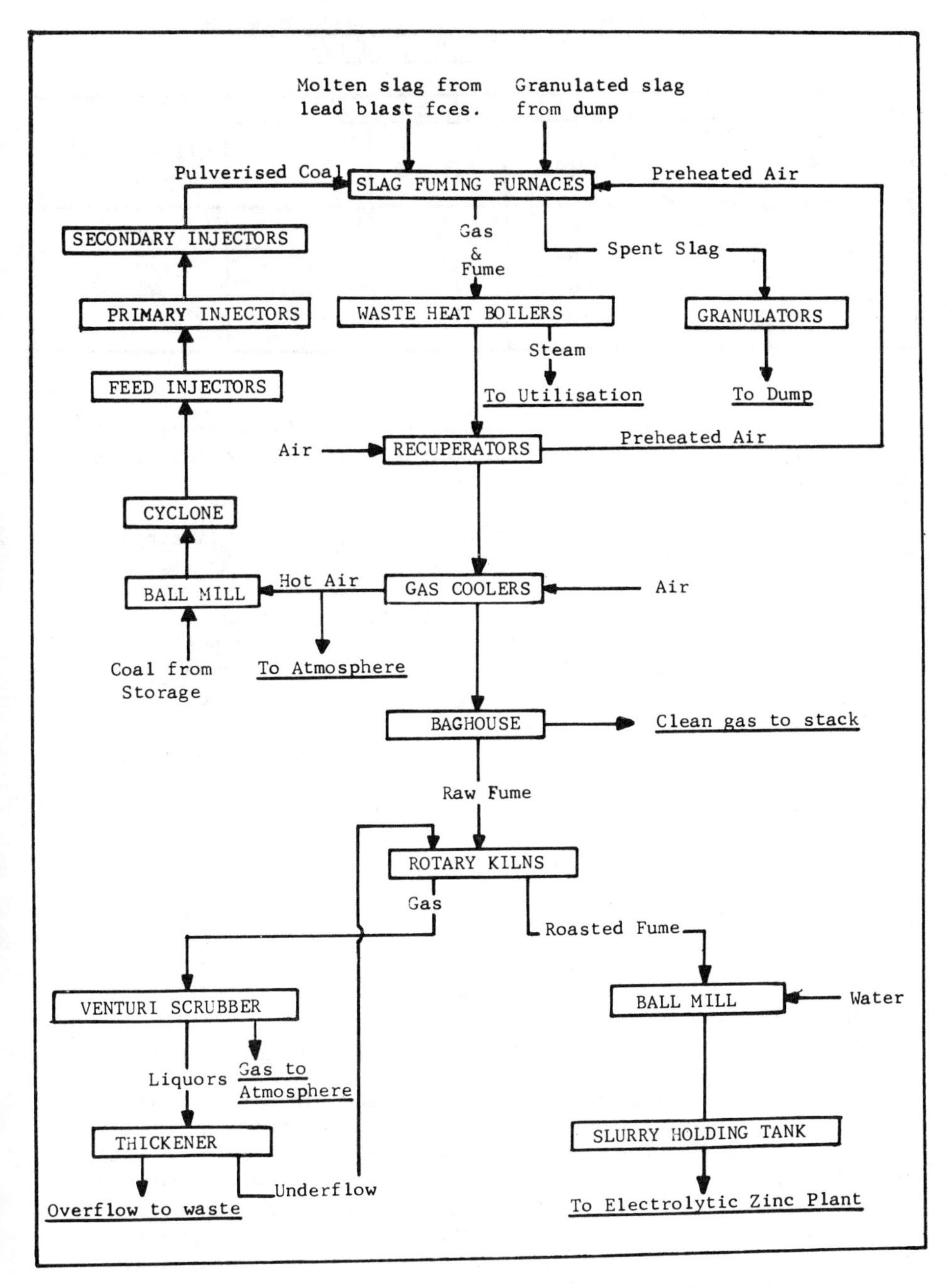

Fig. 3. Slag Fuming Plant Flowsheet of The Broken Hill Associated Smelters Pty. Ltd.

Table 8. Effect of Hot Slag on Cycle Time and Zinc Elimination Rate

Hot Slag on the Charge %	Cycle Time (min.)				Zinc Elimination kg/min.
	Charging & Heating	Fuming	Tapping	Total	
100	20	90	15	125	58
75	40	90	15	145	50
50	60	90	15	165	44
25	80	90	15	185	39

Under the above operating conditions, the zinc in spent slag is reduced to 3.3% representing approximately 86% zinc elimination from the input slag.

Typical operating results for a seven day week for a single furnace are shown below.

Molten slag treated (incl. skull) tonnes	2276
Granulated slag treated (tonnes)	598
Total slag treated (tonnes)	2874
Number of charges	62
Average weight per charge (tonnes)	46.3
Average cycle time (minutes)	147
Operating time efficiency (%)	90.2
Coal consumption (tonnes)	457
Coal rate (kg. per minute)	50.3
Average zinc in input slag (%)	18.3
Average zinc in spent slag (%)	3.3
Zinc elimination (%)	85.7
Average lead in input slag (%)	2.6
Average lead in spent slag (%)	0.03
Est. weight of fume produced (tonnes)	670
Zinc elimination rate (kg/min)	50.0
Av. coal per kg. of zinc eliminated (kg)	1.02

The two slag fuming furnaces are identical in construction, the hearth dimensions being 4.57 m. x 2.44 m. The shafts are water jacketted to a height of 6.40 m. made up of three tiers of jackets each 2.13 m. x 91 cm. To retain a layer of slag on the furnace jackets, studs which are 38 mm. x 13 mm. (diam.) are welded on the jackets at 75 mm. centres. These studs burn back to approximately 15 mm. length in the course of time. In order to minimise slag build up at the charge chutes, the second tier of jackets on the end wall immediately beneath the chute is not studded.

The furnace floors are also water cooled and each is made up of five panels of alternate 5 cm. O.D. tubes and 15.2 cm. x 1.6 cm. bar iron on edge. Cooling is by a low pressure steam vapourisation system with the steam condensed in air-cooled condensers and returned to header drums on each side of the furnaces. Circulation through the side and end walls is by thermo syphon action, but forced circulation is used for the floor and charge door, also the tap-hole jackets.

Combustion air and pulverised coal are injected into the slag bath through 30 tuyeres, 15 on each side at 30.5 cm. centres and located 16 cm. above the furnace floor. Tuyere inserts are 56 mm. I.D. cast Ni-Resist alloy. Their projection into the furnaces was initially 17.8 cm. but this was later reduced to 10 cm. After the installation of new inserts, rapid burning back to the jackets occurs and a life of up to nine months is obtained with the inserts virtually flush with the jacket face. Little wear from coal abrasion occurs on the inside of the inserts.

Secondary (combustion) air requirements for each furnace are supplied by a Demag, single stage blower of 350 Nm^3/min. capacity at a pressure of 620 mm. Hg. The blowers are driven by Siemens Cascade drives with a control ranging from 860 to 1480 r.p.m. If the secondary air flow falls below the normal minimum due to a power failure or other reasons, emergency air is admitted at a controlled pre-set rate to the secondary air mains to prevent slag entering the tuyeres. At the same time, coal injection to the tuyeres is stopped. The supply of emergency air is limited and the furnaces are tapped out immediately if there is a failure of the secondary air supply.

Molten slag from the lead blast furnaces is run into 11 tonne capacity ladles and hauled to the slag fuming plant on rail bogeys drawn by a tractor. The ladles are lifted from the bogies by an overhead electric crane and after knocking against a block to break the slag skull they are charged to the furnaces through full width charge chutes at one end. When insufficient molten slag is available to make up the 45 tonne charge weight, cold granulated slag is delivered from a storage bin by a bucket elevator and belt conveyor system to each furnace, entering through a deflector jacket immediately above the charge chute. The weight of cold slag is recorded by an integrator linked with a weigh feeder mounted at the top of each furnace.

Spent slag is tapped through mild steel water cooled tapholes (two per furnace) and these are tapered from 14 cm. to 15.2 cm. diameter, and located at the end opposite the furnace charging chutes. The tapholes were initially set at the furnace floor level to drain the charge completely, but it is now considered necessary to hold a heel of slag in the furnaces to reduce flame action on the opposite tuyere jackets during the period between tapping and re-charging, and the taphole centre lines are now 16 cm. above the floor. At the conclusion of the fuming cycle, the full charge of spent slag amounting to approximately 36 tonnes per furnace is tapped in 12-15 minutes and granulated by salt water jets operating at four atmospheres pressure. A total of 320000 litres of seawater are used per charge to granulate, chill, and convey the slag over cast Ni-hard screens into concrete pits, from where is pumped to dewatering hydrocyclones and collected in a 400 tonne capacity bin before being carted to waste.

Coal Supply and Handling: Coal is shipped from Coalcliff, New South Wales, and is unloaded by wharf cranes into motor lorries and dumped on a storage area of approximately 12000 tonnes capacity, adjacent to the Slag Fuming Plant. The coal is a non-coking fuel type of the following approximate composition:-

Fixed carbon (%)	64.0
Volatile hydrocarbons (%)	18.0
Ash (%)	18.0
Calorific Value (k cal/kg)	6650
Moisture (%)	5.0
Grindability (Hardgrove index)	77.0
Sizing (cm)	-2

The coal is reclaimed from the storage heap by a front end loader and delivered to a stacker conveyor feeding a 1000 tonne stockpile. This stockpile is located above three chutes which feed the coal by vibrator conveyors to a Redler conveyor which carries the coal through a 2.14 m. diam. Armco tunnel and elevates it to the coal grinding plant. The coal discharges into a surge bin positioned above a table feeder delivering into a 1.83 m. diam. x 2.44 m. cylindrical Hardinge ball mill, loaded with 20 tonnes of 5 cm. balls. This is driven at 20 r.p.m. by a 275 h.p. motor and is air swept by hot air from the gas cooler system, diluted with cold air so as to enter the mill at 95°C. The moisture content of the coal is thereby reduced to a maximum of one percent. The air current through the grinding mill conveys the ground coal to a double cone classifier, where the oversize is separated and returned to the mill. Coal of the desired sizing leaving the classifier is recovered in a 2.44 m. diam. cyclone and falls into two fine coal hoppers. Excess air bled from the system is filtered in a Wheelabrator baghouse containing 720 terylene tubular bags 12.5 cm. diam. and 3 m. long.

It is generally recognised that to obtain efficient furnace operation, coal should be ground so that at least 80% is -200 mesh (B.S.S.). On the other hand, excessive quantities of very fine sizings cause problems in the pneumatic conveying of the coal in the injection system, and an upper limit of not more than 65% -300 mesh (B.S.S.) has been set at Port Pirie.

Pulverised Coal Injection: Following the decision to use preheated blast up to 600°C to the furnaces, considerable thought had to be given to the design of equipment for injecting pulverised coal to the furnaces. The practice in most slag fuming plants of using combustion air to convey the pulverised coal could not be adopted for safety reasons, and a coal conveying and injection system designed by Petrocarb Inc. of New York was installed. This system, which has been described in detail by Brett (14), uses less than 0.1 m^3 of conveying or primary air per kg. of coal, that is, only 1.5% of the total combustion requirements, and this allows a high degree of preheat to be introduced into the furnace as secondary air.

Two coal injection systems are provided, one for each furnace. Coal collected in the fine coal storage hoppers is delivered by screw conveyor to a vibrating screen (1.5 mm. aperture) and then to a storage pressure vessel known as the feed injector. The coal mass in this vessel is fluidised by air and transferred in 1500 kg. batches to a similar vessel known as the primary injector located adjacent to each furnace. The primary injector has attached to it six small fan shaped vessels, known as secondary injectors, which further subdivide the inlet coal stream into five smaller streams, each feeding one furnace tuyere through a 1 cm. diam. lance. Both the feed and primary injectors are supported on load cells and transfer of coal from the coal bunker to the feed injector and thence to the primary injector is automatic. The system is designed to inject coal at any selected rate from 35 to 75 kg/min. against a variable bustle main pressure, and uniformly to the 30 tuyeres on each furnace.

A feature of the Petrocarb system is that no moving mechanical parts are used in the coal distribution equipment and operation has been relatively trouble free. However, abrasion of the stainless steel coal lances by the pulverised coal has been high, particularly at points of direction change, and of the various materials which have been tried, Ni-hard, cast around the bends, has been the most satisfactory.

Waste Heat Boilers: Each furnace has its own gas train leading to the Baghouse and the gases pass first through a membrane wall water tube boiler superimposed above the furnace, but supported independently of the bath. The membrane walls consist of 7.5 cm. tubes at 10 cm. centres. Water circulation is from the main drum by external downcomers to the lower headers, then by the riser tubes of the membrane walls back to the drum . The design capacity of each boiler is 23000 kg. of steam per hour at 30 atmospheres pressure. Actual steam production rate varies throughout the charge cycle, but lies within the range 7000-18000 kg/hr. Each boiler is fitted with a pendant superheater of 5 cm. diam. tubes having an effective area of 51m^2. Gas temperature at the boiler exit varies from 800-1050°C. Each boiler is equipped with two Major oil burners for starting after a shutdown and together they consume 100 l/hr. of oil. Instruments record steam flow, and record and control feed water level, steam drum pressure, storage tank level, and the operation of the recirculating pumps and the feed water pumps.

Boiler feed water is supplied by a two stage Permutit demineralising plant situated at the electrolytic zinc plant. Steam generated by the boilers is used to drive four compressors providing air at 17 atmospheres for sootblowing. Steam passing through the turbines of these compressors is reduced to 5 atmospheres pressure to provide the process requirements of the electrolytic zinc plant.

Build up of fume on the boiler and superheater tubes is limited by the use of ten automatically controlled Diamond sootblowers, four being long retractable units covering the full width of the boiler, and six blowing the membrane walls.

Blast Air Preheaters and Gas Coolers: Gases leaving each boiler pass through a section of brick flue before entering a set of five metal recuperators, arranged in parallel. These units are 68.6 cm. in diameter, 9.14 m. high and contain 18 closely spaced fins, in the form of flat air tubes, positioned radially and connected at the top and bottom to annular headers. Total heating surface per unit is 75 m^2. Fume laden gases, controlled to 900°C by the use of water sprays and dilution air in the brick flue, pass around the outsides of the fins at high velocity, providing good heat exchange conditions and limiting fume deposition. A central rotating core fitted with automatically controlled soot blowing nozzles assists in keeping the fin surfaces clean. Cooling air supplied from the secondary air blowers passes at high velocity through the fins, countercurrent to the direction of the process gases, being preheated to 500°C before entering the slag fuming furnaces.

Process gases leaving the recuperators at 500°C enter a set of six gas coolers in parallel, designed to reduce the temperature to 200°C prior to its entry into the baghouse. Each unit is 99 cm. in diameter, 12.2 m. long, and has a total heating surface of 155 m^2. The coolers originally contained 46 fins per unit, but despite the fitting of sootblowers in the central core, complete blinding of the narrow gas spaces between each fin occurred as accretions of fume built up on the fin surface. The cleaning of this accretion proved tedious and expensive and the number of fins per unit was reduced to 36 to increase the clearance between adjacent fins. As the result, the period between cleanings has been increased substantially, and the work has been further expedited by the use of high pressure water at 300 atmospheres. Cooling air for the gas coolers is provided by a Richardson fixed speed fan, rated at 1800 m^3 at 50 mm. Hg. With the exception of the first cooler in each train, which provides hot air for coal drying, no heat recovery is obtained from the air, which is vented to atmosphere at 150 to 200°C.

The recuperators and gas coolers were designed by H. Escher Pty. Ltd. of Sydney and manufactured in Australia. Material of construction is predominantly mild steel with the exception of the top half of the recuperator fins which are in 321 stainless steel.

Baghouse: Draught at the slag fuming furnaces is maintained at approximately 1 mm. Hg suction by two process gas fans, one on each gas handling train, and located at the outlet from the gas coolers. The fans are rated at 1980 m^3/min. at 200°C and 30 mm. Hg. Each fan is driven by a variable speed motor under automatic control to maintain the pre-set furnace suction. Gas is delivered by the fans to two balloon flues which join in a common header at the inlet to the baghouse.

The baghouse consists of seven insulated chambers, each containing 232 Nomex bags, 22.8 cm. in diameter, and 8.5 m. long. The Nomex cloth is plain weave, 300 g/m^2 weight, and each bag has a filter area of 6.2 m^2. The chambers are automatically isolated and shaken in sequence on a time cycle which may be varied according to baghouse conditions. Normally each chamber is shaken every 75 minutes. Fume dislodged from the bags is collected in two hoppers beneath each chamber, and removed by screw conveyors delivering to a common collector conveyor. Although Nomex cloth is relatively expensive in comparison with other fabrics used for filtering metallurgical gases, its property of withstanding continuous exposure to temperatures of 200°C, allows the size of the baghouse and gas handling system to be reduced with consequent savings in capital and operating costs.

Gas from the baghouse is discharged to atmosphere by a centrifugal fan driven by a variable speed motor controlled to give a slight suction at the inlet to the baghouse. Gas volume up the stack is 3000 m^3/min. at NTP and filtration efficiency in the baghouse exceeds 99.9%.

Raw Fume Treatment: The high fluorine and chlorine contents of the raw fume make it unsuitable for direct treatment in the electrolytic zinc plant, and these elements are reduced to acceptable levels by roasting in a rotary kiln. The fume collected in the baghouse and gas train is handled by screw conveyor and bucket elevators to two 200 tonne bins which act as buffer storage prior to kiln treatment. Further intermediate storage is provided by an "A" frame shed of 600 tonnes capacity. The feed rate from the bins to the kiln is controlled by a weighfeeder delivering to a bucket elevator and screw conveyor system.

Following pilot plant work, a 27.5 m. long, 2.44 m. diameter Kennedy van Saun kiln was constructed, lined with 15 cm. to 22.5 cm.

thick refractory. Kiln slope is 4 cm. per metre, and the kiln is driven by a 30 h.p. electric motor through a Heenan Dynaspeed water cooled magnetic coupling to a Sonnerdale triple reduction gearbox. Final drive is by a cast steel spur gear and forged steel pinion and this system allows the kiln speed to be varied within the range of 0.6 to 2.5 r.p.m. A 5 h.p. electric motor, served by the emergency diesel generator, provides the emergency drive to maintain rotation of the kiln to prevent shell distortion in the event of a power failure.

The kiln is oil fired to maintain a product discharge temperature of 1150°C, oil consumption being 450 l/hr. at a pressure of 10 atmospheres. Primary air is supplied by a turbine blower and secondary air is introduced via the product cooler, where it obtains some preheating. The kiln refractory consists of a 15.25 m. long section of 15 cm. thick 40% alumina brick at the feed end, followed by 9.15 m. of 22.5 cm. thick special duty 40% alumina brick in the hot zone of the kiln, and 1.1 m. of castable refractory at the discharge end. The hot zone was originally lined with 15 cm. thick 70% alumina brick, but experience showed that this material suffered penetration by lead oxides and relining became necessary after the treatment of 28000 tonnes of raw fume. A trial panel of 15 cm. thick special duty 40% alumina brick showed slightly better resistance, and it was then decided to increase the refractory thickness to give improved service life.

Roasted fume from the kiln is discharged via a firebick transfer chamber to a rotary cooler 9.75 m. long by 1.83 m. diam., of the direct air-indirect water spray type. Cooler slope is 4 cm/m. and speed 6 r.p.m. The first 2.75 m. of the feed section is refractory lined followed by an unlined mild steel section with lifters. The shell is stainless steel clad externally and cooled by fresh water from an overhead launder. This water is circulated in a closed system and cooled by salt water in a tubular heat exchanger.

Gases leave the feed end of the kiln at 500°C and pass through a two stage venturi scrubber system, irrigated by fresh water at the rate of 72 l/min. in the first stage and 270 l/min. in the second stage. The gases are cooled to 60°C and pass to a cyclone separator with the liquors and suspended solids. Clean gas is removed from the separator via a flue and fan system and discharged to atmosphere, while the slurry is discharged from the bottom conical section via a seal pot to a launder feeding an 11 m. diameter thickener. Overflow from the thickener is sent to waste while the underflow, containing 50 to 60% solids, is pumped to the feed end of the kiln and re-treated. Recovered solids represents approximately 5% of kiln feed. Composition of the kiln input and output materials is shown in Table 9.

Table 9. Composition of the kiln input and output materials

Element	Raw Fume	Roasted Fume	Solids in Thickener U/F
Zinc %	66.0	68.0	47.0
Lead %	12.5	12.0	25.0
Fluorine %	0.25	0.005	0.5
Chlorine %	0.20	0.02	0.3

The treatment of raw fume containing high fluorine and chlorine contents to obtain an acceptable product at the required feed rates has been difficult in a single kiln, and a second kiln of identical dimensions will be commissioned late in 1970.

The baghouse installation initially installed to handle gas from the kiln (15) did not have the capacity to handle the volume necessary for efficient halogen removal. Furthermore, the retreatment of the dust and fume recovered in the kiln baghouse resulted in a high circulating load of fluorine and chlorine, and to prevent a further reduction in kiln throughput, this retreatment was suspended at the expense of reduced zinc and lead recovery. A redesigned gas handling system incorporating the venturi scrubbing system previously described was designed and installed, and has allowed the recovery of lead and zinc values in the solids in the thickener underflow. At the same time approximately 80% of the fluorine and chlorine eliminated from the kiln, are carried in the thickener overflow as soluble salts, and are removed from the circuit.

Typical kiln operating data are shown below:-

Raw Fume treated (tonnes per week)	1263
Operating time efficiency (%)	91.3
Average feed rate (tonnes per hr.)	8.2
Zinc content of product (tonnes per week)	888
Fuel oil per tonne of fume roasted (litres)	58
Gas volume through kiln (m^3/min. at NTP)	140

Roasted Fume Handling: Roasted fume, discharged from the kiln cooler at temperatures less than 100°C, is conveyed by screw conveyors and a bucket elevator to two 350 tonne storage bins. Surplus roasted fume can be diverted via an overhead distributor screw to an "A" frame storage shed of 3500 tonnes capacity and is returned to the bins as required by a front end loader feeding a hopper mounted above the kiln discharge screw conveyor system.

From the storage bins, the roasted fume is fed through screw conveyors and a weigh feeder to an Allis Chalmers Centrix ball mill 2.44 m. long by 1.52 m. diam. The mill is driven at 29.6 r.p.m. by a 100 h.p. motor and carries a load of 7.5 tonnes of 5 cm. diameter balls. Feed rate to the mill varies from 6 to 8 tonnes per hour depending on zinc plant requirements, and weak wash water, returned from the leaching plant, is added to the feed chute to the mill to produce a 70% W/W solids slurry. Slurry discharged from the mill is pumped to a holding tank with a capacity equivalent to 100 tonnes of dry fume. The sizing of ground roasted fume varies significantly with the feed rate of the mill. Table 10 gives a comparison of the sizing before and after grinding at feed rates of 6-8.5 tonnes/hr.

Table 10. Roasted Fume Sizing before and after Grinding

Before Grinding		**After Grinding**	
Mesh B.S.S.	**%**	**Mesh B.S.S.**	**%**
+ 4	8	+ 48	0.5 - 2.0
+ 10	40	+ 100	16 - 20
+ 48	85	+ 150	26 - 34
+ 100	92	+ 200	38 - 50
- 200	1 - 2	- 200	50 - 62

Slurry is pumped to the leaching section of the Zinc Plant by two-stage Warman pumps delivering a pressure of 14 atmospheres at a rate of 400-500 l/min. through a 7.5 cm. I.D. mild steel pipeline 1100 m. long. Pumping is intermittent, each batch comprising approximately 70000 litres of slurry is followed by some 5000 litres of flushing water to prevent solids settling and blocking the pipeline between successive batches.

Operating Labour: Seven men per shift are required for the operation of the two slag fuming furnaces including charging, tapping and control room duties. One man per shift attends to the operation of the coal handling, grinding, classification and pulverised coal storage systems. The operation of the waste heat boilers, feed water and steam handling system is controlled by two certificated boiler attendants on each shift. These men are also responsible for the operation of a standby boiler which has been installed to provide process steam for the electrolytic zinc plant, when both slag fuming furnaces are shut down. The gas handling and baghouse system is controlled by one man on each shift. Finally, two men per shift control the kiln operation, including handling and grinding of the product, and pumping the ground slurry to the Zinc Plant.

Electrolytic Zinc Plant

The recovery of zinc from the roasted fume follows conventional practice for high current density electrolytic zinc plants. The roasted fume slurry is leached in two 135000 litre stainless steel tanks and the resultant pulp is filtered in Burt filters. The zinc sulphate filtrate is then subjected to zinc dust purification and pumped to the cell room for electrolysis. The residue from the Burt filters is re-slurried and washed by countercurrent flow through two 11 m. diam. Eimco thickeners and filtered on a belt-filter 3.27 m. long by 2.44 m. diam. The filter cake is dried in a rotary drier to approximately 10% moisture and returned to the Lead Production Division for recovery of its lead and silver contents. Cathode zinc produced in the cell room is melted in two 800 kW. Ajax induction furnaces and cast into 25.5 kg. slabs or 1 tonne ingots depending on market requirements.

Typical results for one week's operation of the Zinc Plant are shown below:

Fume leached (tonnes)	1300
Equivalent market zinc in purified solution (tonnes)	742
Zinc dust used relative to zinc produced (%)	3.8
Leach residue produced (tonnes)	413
Leaching efficiency (%)	96.9
Purification residue produced (tonnes)	15.1
Average cell room current (A)	22270
Average current density (A/m^2)	6.24
Current efficiency (%)	84.5
Cathode zinc produced (tonnes)	812

Annual Production

Works production for the period 1st January, 1969, to 1st January, 1970, is shown below.

Soft lead including that used in antimonial lead and other alloys (tonnes)	193763
Refined silver (kg.)	246534
Fine gold (kg.)	163
Copper matte (tonnes)	4127
Refined cadmium (tonnes)	34
Antimonial lead (tonnes)	6287
Lead sheathing alloys (tonnes)	12209
Antimonial lead master alloys (tonnes)	566
Zinc - S.H.G., H.G. and alloyed (tonnes)	32086
Sulphuric acid - calculated to 100% (tonnes)	60929

References

1. Burrow, W.R., Development of a Continuous Updraught Sintering Process, Proc. Aust. Inst. Min. Met., No. 162-3, 1951, pp 267-292.

2. Burrow, W.R., Ridley, K.L., and Adams, F.C., Updraught Sintering at Port Pirie, Proc. Aust. Inst. Min. Met., No. 180, 1956, pp 179-206.

3. White, L.A., The Development of the Lead Blast Furnace at Port Pirie, South Australia, Trans. A.I.M.M.E., Vol. 188, October, 1950, pp 1221 - 1228.

4. McNicol, J.H., The Development of a Continuous Copper Drossing Process for Lead Bullion, Proc. Aust. Inst. Min. Met., No. 207, 1963, pp 53-73.

5. Peck, W.H. and McNicol, J.H., An Improved Furnace for Continuous Copper Drossing of Lead Bullion, Journal of Metals, Vol. 18, No. 9, September, 1966, pp 1027-1032.

6. Williams, G.K., Description of Continuous Lead Refinery at the Works of The Broken Hill Associated Smelters Pty. Ltd., Port Pirie South Australia, Proc. Aust. Inst. Min. Met., No. 87, 1932, pp 75-133.

7. Williams, G.K., Continuous Lead Refining at Port Pirie, South Australia, Trans. A.I.M.M.E., Vol. 121, 1936 (Rocky Mountain Fund Volume), pp 226-263.

8. Green, F.A., The Refining of Lead and Associated Metals at Port Pirie, South Australia, Inst. Min. Metall., Symposium on the Refining of Non-ferrous Metals, London, July, 1949, pp 281-325.

9. Davey, T.R.A., Vacuum Dezincing of Desilverised Bullion, Trans. A.I.M.M.E., Vol. 197, Journal of Metals, August, 1953, pp 991-997.

10. Davey, R. (T.R.A.) and Williams, K.C., Continuous Vacuum Dezincing Plant at The B.H.A.S. Pty. Ltd., Port Pirie, Proc. Aust. Inst. Min. Met., No. 180, 1956, pp 207-217.

11. Heggen, K.R., Features of the New Lead Refinery at Port Pirie, Proc. Aust. Inst. Min. Met., No. 207, 1963, pp 25-51.

12. Butcher, A.J., The Recovery of Zinc from Lead Blast Furnace Slag at Port Pirie, Conference Papers, Chemical Engineering Conference, Adelaide, 1968, pp 81-85.

13. Blaskett, D.R., Effects of Preheated Blast on Fuel Consumption in a Slag Fuming Operation, Ninth Commonwealth Mining and Metallurgical Congress, 1969, Mineral Processing and Extractive Metallurgy Section, Paper No. 3.

14. Brett, I.D., Pulverised Coal Injection in Slag Fuming Furnaces at Port Pirie, South Australia, Institute of Fuels, Conference on Combustion and Combustion Equipment, Canberra, 1968, Paper No. 15.

15. Anon, The B.H.A.S. Slag Fuming Plant, Australian Mining Vol. 60, June, 1968, pp 16-19.

Chapter 28

LEAD SMELTER OPERATION
AT N.V. METALLURGIE HOBOKEN S.A.
Hoboken, Belgium

Jean L. Leroy
Assistant General Manager, Metallurgie Hoboken

Pierre J. Lenoir
Assistant Manager of the Hoboken Plant

Louis E. Escoyez
Metallurgical Engineer in charge of the
Refinery Division at the Hoboken Plant

Abstract

The Lead Smelting works of Metallurgie Hoboken S.A. are located on the banks of the river Scheldt a few miles South of Antwerp. Lead refining began at Hoboken in 1887, when it was restricted mainly to desilverizing lead bullion from Central America. Since then, various changes have been made to develop the works into a comprehensive and integrated custom smelter and refinery.

Multiple hearth roasting furnaces, down-draft sinter machines and blast furnaces of standard design are used for the treatment of "complex" lead ores and secondary materials. A lead refinery based on the Harris process, with Parkes desilverizing followed by vacuum dezincing and Kroll Betterton debismuthizing was commissioned in 1967. Facilities for the recovery of precious metals, bismuth, antimony, arsenic and sulfuric acid are available.

Special problems arise from the presence of large quantities of copper in the materials treated.

Introduction

The ores and secondary materials produced throughout the world are almost limitless in their range of physical properties and chemical composition. Custom smelters process a great part of these materials, and therefore have to be located suitably in relation to the sources of ores, taking transport into account, and to the markets for refined metals. A custom smelter has to be able to accept a great variety of materials, extending from run of the mine ore, through concentrates, to impure crude metals that need only refining. If located within an industrially developed area, such a smelter will also need to recover metals from all sorts of secondary and scrap materials. For successful operation flexibility is essential both in regard to the nature of the materials treated, and to variations in available quantities.

Economical operation of a custom-smelter demands a scale of operation which makes it essential to have a number of sources of supply.

With such sources there follows the advantage of being able to treat complex materials by appropriate blending.

With these principles in view, the smelter at Hoboken has been remodeled throughout the last twenty years to meet all the foregoing prerequisites. It has now become a comprehensive and flexible plant, based on well tried and up to date processes, suitably adapted to the changing nature of input material.

History

In 1887 at Hoboken, Belgium, a German company was operating a desilverizing and refining plant for lead bullion. From the early 'nineties and until World War I, they smelted lead and mixed copper-lead ores.

At the end of World War I, the plant at Hoboken was taken over by the Belgian Government as reparations, and then sold in 1919 to the predecessor of the present company called "Compagnie Industrielle Union". This company was later renamed "Société Générale Métallurgique de Hoboken" and it remained unchanged until 1963 when it was changed to "METALLURGIE HOBOKEN". In 1926, a plant for the recovery and production of precious metals was erected, followed in 1927 by a complete renewal of the lead refining plant, based on the "Harris" process. At the same time the Petersen acid plant was built.

By World War II the Hoboken works had become a well integrated smelter treating principally copper-lead ores from Africa and South America. But then followed more than four years of inactivity, until the works resumed operations in 1946 and a program of major rebuilding or remodeling of older plant was initiated.

Changes were made as follows :

1951 : Remodeling of the n° 3 and 4 water-jacket blast furnaces bringing the total capacity to 1000 t of charge daily.

1956 : Construction of two new down-draught straight line sintering units with recycling of gases.

1957 : Addition of one multiple-hearth roasting furnace to ore preparation plant.

1960 : Construction of refining furnace for the production of arsenic trioxide.

1966 : Addition to the sulfuric acid plant to increase capacity to 12,000 t per month.

1968 : Commissioning of new lead refinery to bring lead refining capacity to 100,000 t per year.

1968 : Construction of reverberatory furnace for production of antimony metal.

1969 : Addition to precious metals plant to bring silver capacity to 150 t per month and conversion of P.G.M. treatment plant to nitric acid cycle following a long programme of research and development.

The present layout of the Hoboken plant is shown on fig. 1.

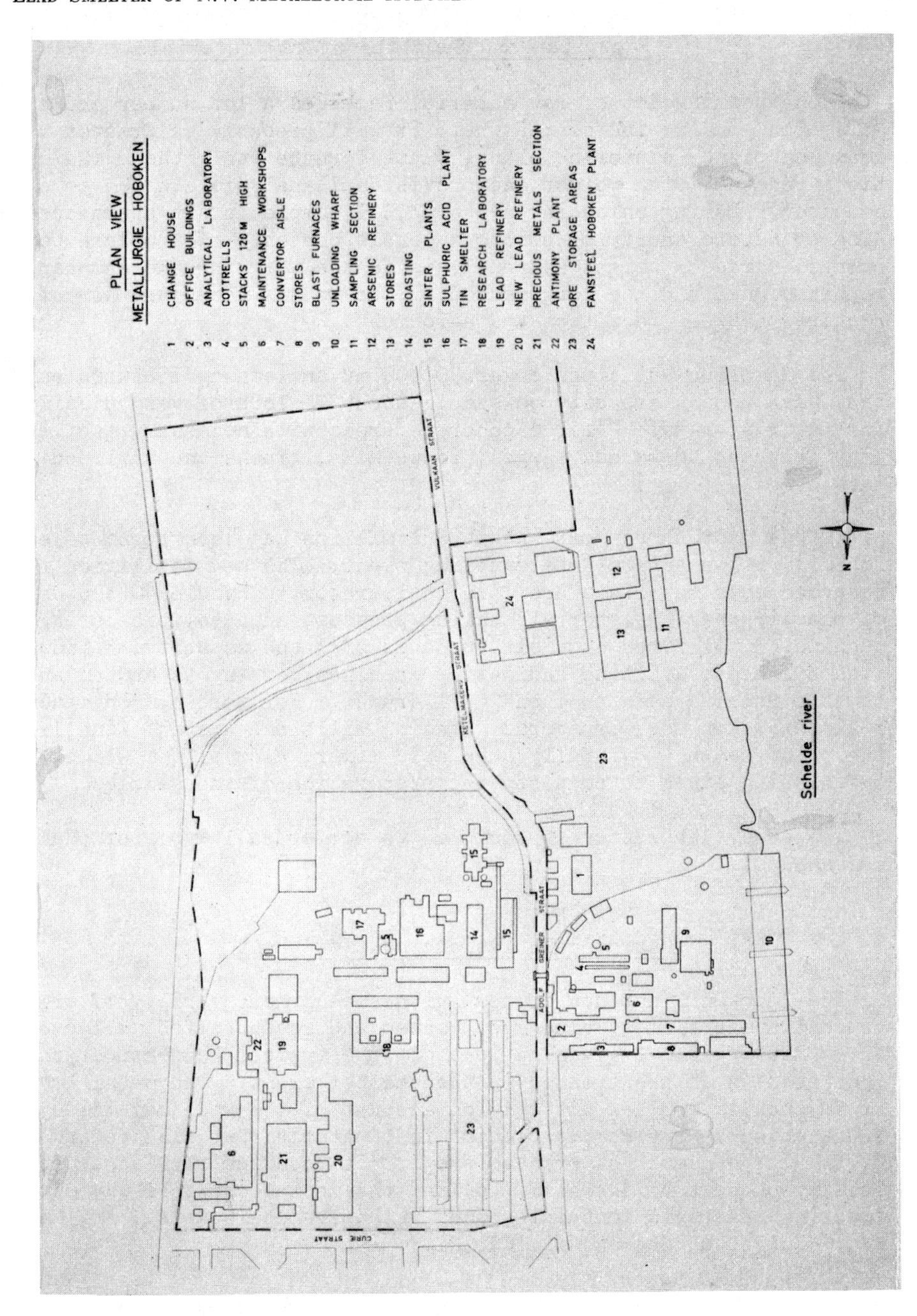

Fig. 1 - General layout of the Hoboken Plant.

Reception and Sampling of raw materials

Each incoming lot of raw material receives a lot number and a "dispatch" index, indicating where it will probably be treated : roasting plant, sintering plant, blast furnace etc.; these indications together with weight and provisional analysis are fed to a computer. During unloading a 5 to 100 % sample is set apart according to heterogeneity or precious metals content. Not before both parties agree on weight and analysis is the weighing and sampling report signed and the lot treated. Four to six weeks are normally required between reception and agreement.

The Sampling buildings cover 50,000 m2 and employ 150 workmen; they have enough capacity to sample about 25 lots of very dissimilar material a day; 2 large concrete areas with necessary facilities are used to unload barges, containers, trucks and railroad cars.

In the last three years about $ 1 million has been spent to equip Hoboken with an up-to-date sampling plant. The new facilities for heterogeneous materials are : an incinerator to handle 40 t a day of plastic-bearing material, baling presses, an automatic coring machine, 3 oil-fired crucible furnaces of 1 ton capacity, 3 induction furnaces, drilling and sawing machines for ingots and an automatic machine made to open 200 l drums . For more common materials, Hoboken uses crushers, grinding mills and sieves. Finally the plant has a 400 l fully automatic mixer, a dryer for slimes and 5 finishing lines to complete the preparation of the samples.

The assay laboratory is equipped to perform all types of chemical analysis.

Charge calculation and flow-sheet

The Hoboken Plant has to deal with an enormous variety of ores, concentrates, slimes, flue dust, scrap and residues from all over the world. Table 1 gives an idea of some typical lead-copper concentrates which are treated in the smelter plant. The metallurgy at Hoboken is complex not only on account of the wide day-to-day fluctuation in the composition of feed material but also because of the large number of process steps. It requires skill and flexibility on part of the staff to find the most economical way of treating materials containing such valuable metals as Ag, Au, Pt, Pd, Rh, Pb, Cu, Sb, Sn, Bi, Cd, Ni.

Purchasing, mixing and smelting are coordinated by a 360/30 IBM computer. The computer is programmed with a technical and economical model of the overall production flow-sheet. In the process of simulation by the mathematical model, materials or concentrates can be introduced simultaneously in 4 different ways into the condensed flow-sheet shown in fig. 2 : i.e. into roasters, sintering plant, blast furnaces, and converters.

Table 1. Typical Lead Copper concentrates

H_2O	Ag	Pb	Cu	Bi	As	Sb	Zn	CaO	SiO_2	Fe	S
%	g/t	%	%	%	%	%	%	%	%	%	%
12,0	120	24,7	7,4	0,001	1,3	-	3,65	10,4	11,5	1,35	7,04
6,1	920	31,6	5,4	0,09	0,35	0,10	8,0	0,6	1,5	19,7	29,4
9,5	810	41,0	6,9	0,001	1,5	0,9	4,9	0,35	4,2	9,1	18,6
5,5	300	38,1	8,8	0,001	1,4	0,36	1,7	1,8	2,76	3,57	6,8
12,6	2.400	13,6	4,7	0,003	0,08	-	16,3	0,8	1,5	26,0	36,0
6,5	2.920	37,9	10,3	0,07	0,6	1,05	11,5	0,2	0,60	11,6	25,5
5,4	550	58,0	2,6	0,02	0,06	-	14,4	0,2	0,4	4,0	20,2
8,1	470	32,3	0,7	0,04	0,36	-	9,6	-	0,8	18,6	29,9
0,1	1.200	57,5	0,3	0,004	0,03	0,3	11,2	1,60	7,6	1,95	15,9
3,2	5.570	37,0	1,0	0,120	0,80	2,6	7,9	-	13,0	8,1	18,4
8,5	184	44,28	10,34	-	1,76	-	5,7	4,68	5,44	1,61	15,33

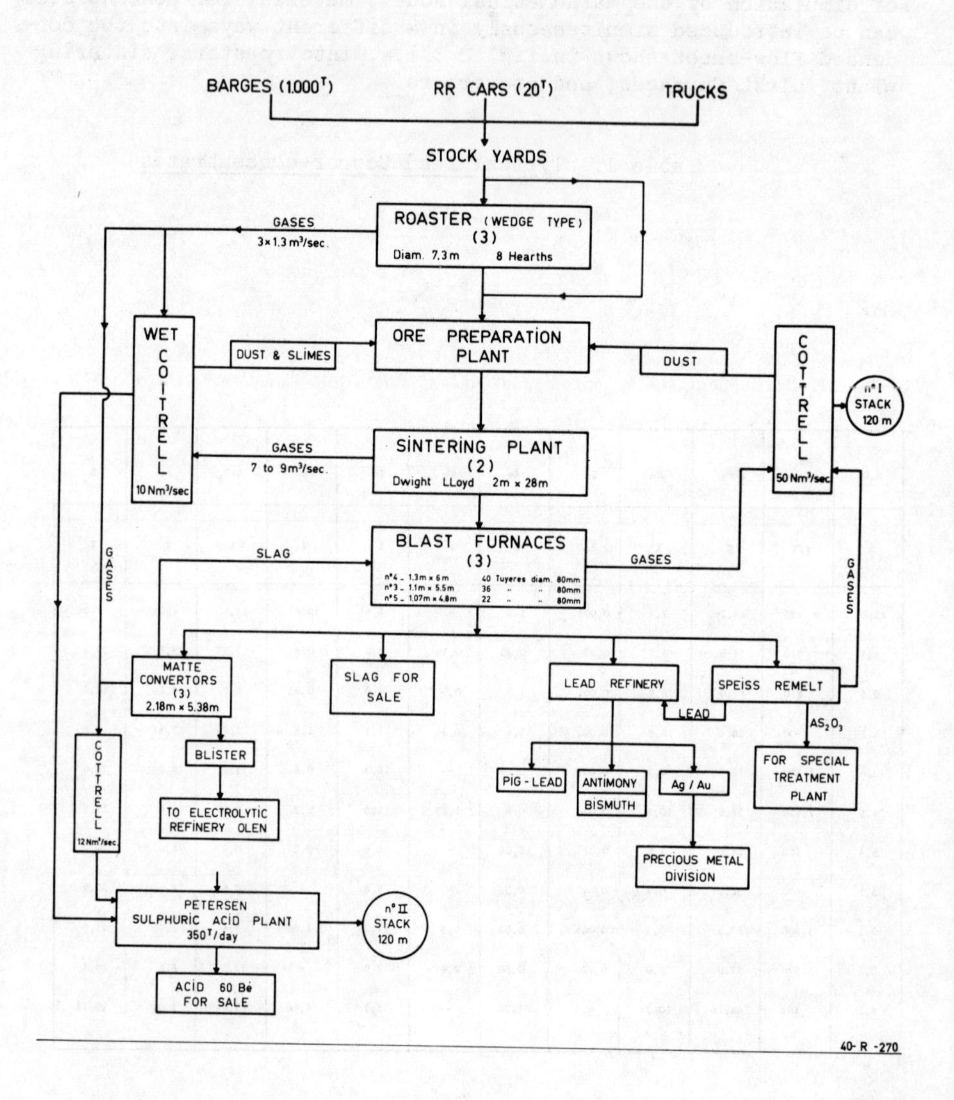

Fig. 2 - Simplified flow-sheet for the Hoboken Plant.

At first the computer calculates for each metal or gangue component the total content introduced along each route. It automatically simulates various ways of possible metallurgical treatment. For each theoretical charge there is a system of 24 equations, each one corresponding to the balance of a particular metal or material. Parameters of the equations are taken from balances obtained from previous carefully studied charges.

The computer solves the equations system corresponding to the optimal flow-sheet that has been retained. It calculates for instance

- the times of operation of the roaster's and D.L. machines
- the quantity of sulfuric acid to be produced
- the quantity and composition of the sinter for the blast furnace
- the partition schedule for Pb, Cu, Ni, As, S and Cd in the lead blast furnace phases : bullion, matte, speiss, slag, dust and dross

The last part of the program calculates the provisional cost for material reception, flux additions, roasting, sintering, smelting and matte blowing, refining of lead and precious metals, sulfuric acid production.

Roasting

The Hoboken Plant is provided with three 7 hearth Wedge furnaces having a capacity of 60 to 100 t per day depending upon the material being treated. Roasting is autogenous. The critical factors at this stage of the operations are

1) Melting point of the concentrate. For leady materials the temperature should be kept as low as possible.
2) Rate of sulfur elimination. Gas removal per furnace is 1.3 Nm3 per sec. and the sulfur dioxide content of exhaust gas is 7 - 8 % for a concentrate with 30 % sulfur, although some mixtures can contain as little as 15 % sulfur.
3) As and Sb volatilisation.

Gases from the Wedge furnaces are cleaned in a dry Cottrell followed by wet Cottrell, and then sent to the sulfuric acid plant.

The wet Cottrell, which also treats gases from the sintering plant, consists of four double sections in parallel. Each section has 10 plates of 6 sqm area, so the total plate area is 960 sqm. Details are as follows :

- Distance between plates	250 mm
- Number of tantalum wires	110 per section
- Gas volume	12 to 13 Nm3/sec.
- Water supply	2.3 m3/h per section
- Operating voltage	50.000 V
- Discharge Operating Current	100 mA.

Normally, liquors coming from the wet Cottrell are used for moistening the sintering plant charge. Sometimes liquors are filtered, the cake being stored for further treatment.

Generally a concentrate containing more than 20 % S is roasted before sintering on the D.L. machines. For example :

	weight	% Pb	Cu	Bi	SiO2	Fe	S	SO3
Crude concentrate	1000	36.2	14.4	0.43	2.1	17.1	23.7	2.5
Calcine	875	38.5	15.3	0.46	2.3	18.2	10.3	3.1

Other characteristics of the multiple hearth roasters are :

Outside shell diameter	6.7 m
Firebrick lining	35 % Al2O3
Total hearth area	216 sqm
Layer thickness	3 to 8 cm
Driving rate	0.2 to 0.5 rpm

Feed preparation and crushing section

The first mixing of material is made by crane according to calculated requirements. The most important factors determining a mixture are slag viscosity, slag volume and partition of metal values during the smelt. Once roughly mixed, the feed is loaded into railcars which are later lifted by a 10 t crane and discharged into 4 bins of 150 t at the top of the crushing plant. The crushing and mixing section comprises two main circuits; one for fine materials one and the other for coarse. Very fine materials can be discharged from one of the 150 t bins by a Robson Belt conveyor directly into 4 hoppers of 120 t located ahead of the sintering plant feeding system. Fines and fine size return sinter can also be discharged from one of the 150 t bins into a conveyor which feeds the hammer mill. The discharge of the hammer mill is delivered by conveyor belts and elevator into one of 8 bins of 80 t capacity ahead of the sintering plant feeding system or into a 480 t, 24 outlet cellular bin for mixing of products. Many materials such as matte and return sinter require crushing; first they pass on roller screens, so that oversize falls into one of the two 120 HP jaw crushers, and then into 60 HP roll crushers. Undersize from the roller screens and output from the roller crushers is screened on a rotary screen and conveyed into the cellular bin or directly to the sintering plant's feeding bins. The return sinter is crushed to 6 mm, so as to avoid as far as possible, particles under 1 mm.

Fig. 3 - Crushing mixing and sinterplant flow-sheet.

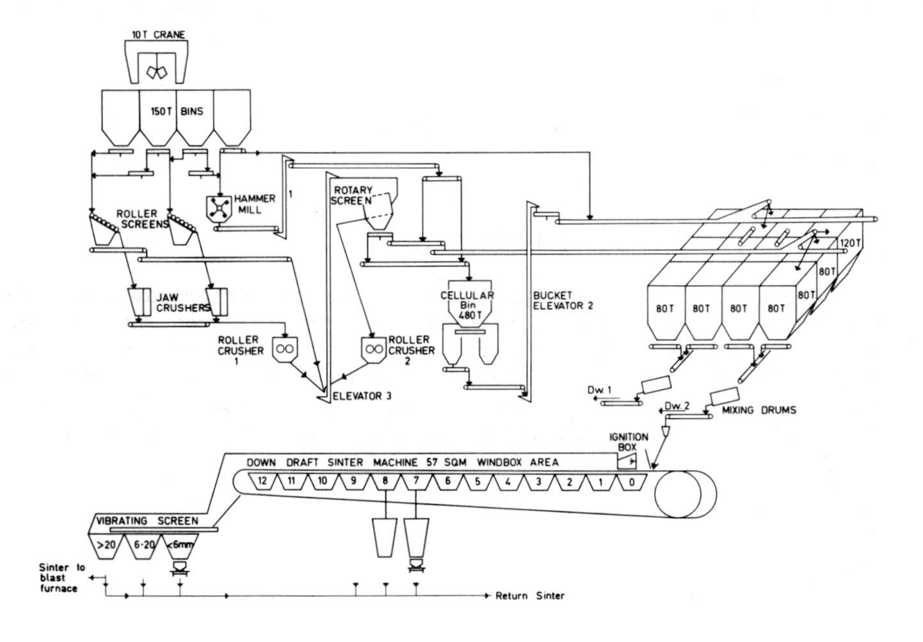

In the crushing plant motor starters are electrically interlocked so that machines are started in the correct sequence. When the plant is running the stopping of any unit will stop any preceeding unit. Lubrication of all crushing units is carried out from one central pumping station.

The complete process equipment is vented to control dust in the working area, and the ventilating gases are filtered through a baghouse.

Characteristics of the crushing plant

Roller grate area	1,5 sqm
Corrugated roll diameter	242 mm
Space between rolls	20 mm
Minimum jaw crusher opening	20 mm
Hammer mill	4 series of 7 hammers of 15 kg each
Primary roll crusher 1 - Space between rolls	18 mm
Secondary " " 2 - " " "	5 mm
Rotary screen	octagonal cross section
Screen area	12 sqm
Diameter of openings	8 mm
Angle of tilt	10°

Sintering Plant

The charge consists of concentrates, various other raw materials and fluxes. In addition, finely crushed sinter is returned and added to the charge in the proportion of 100 to 200 % of raw feed to improve the roasting and sintering characteristics and to bring the sulfur content to 7-8 %. When siliceous ore is not available, the silica is supplied by the use of siliceous sand or by-products.

A typical raw feed charge is

Mixed lead-copper concentrates	30 %
Calcine	14 %
Siliceous ore	10 %
Lime flux	18 %
Return dust and purchased dust	18 %
Miscellaneous	10 %

Moisture content is brought to 6-7 % in two small mixing drums by addition of Cottrell liquors or water. Retention time in these drums is 20 sec., and the drums serve also to homogenise the feed. Moisture is controlled by hand. As shown on fig. 3, the charge proceeds to the respective D.L. machines from each of the twelve feed hoppers by a system of belt conveyors. The Dwight Lloyd plant consists of 2 sintering units 2 m wide by 35 m long. The downdraft two pass method is used, 1 machine being used for first pass and 1 for second pass or final sintering. Fine coke breeze (1 to 1.5 %) is normally added to the second pass to promote lead prereduction. Each strand has 12 windboxes plus an ignition box fired with natural gas. Gases from the first two and the last six boxes average 1-2 % SO_2 and are recirculated above the middle windboxes, which are separated from the other boxes by dead plates.

Emerging gas 4.5 - 5.5 % SO_2 is cleaned in Venturi scrubbers, washing towers and a wet Cottrell (as described in the section on roasting) before passing to the acid plant. By recirculating the gases, at least 99 % of the sulfur eliminated can be recovered.

The agglomerate is passed over a vibrating screen as it falls from the strands. Pieces larger than 20 mm are accepted for blast furnace feed and their sulfur content is about 2 %. The undersize is loaded into railcars and lifted by crane to the top of the crushing building. The production of windbox lead does not occur because of the relatively low lead and high copper content of the charges. This is one of the reasons why Hoboken has continued to use the downdraft process in spite of its slower production rate.

The demand for sinter at the blast furnaces frequently exceeds supply, for their capacities have been substantially increased by the introduction of oxygen enriched blast. This shortage is commonly offset by direct additions of smelting materials and lead refinery drosses to the blast furnace.

D.L. machine operating details

Machine speed	0.5 - 2.5 m per minute
Total windbox area	114 m2
Pallet size	2 m by 0.68 m
Number of pallets per machine	116
" of grates per pallet	50
Grate alloy	13 % Cr steel
Rich gas windbox area	37 m2 (boxes 2-3-4-5)
Recirculated gas windbox area	77 m2 (other boxes)
Bed depth	10 to 16 cm
Sinter production rate	750 ton per day
Exhaust gas volume	
- rich gases	5 - 6 Nm3 per sec per machine
- poor gases recirculated	8 - 9 Nm3 per sec " "
Ignition box area	1.8 sqm
Natural gas consumption	2.4 Nm3 per t sinter
Driving motor	29.5 HP

Blast furnace section

Two of the three blast furnaces smelt Pb agglomerate. The third blast furnace is normally used to smelt copper-bearing materials.

The sinter is mixed with coke, low grade matte (if sulfur is required), lead drosses and converter slag in a bedding operation carried out by mechanical shovels. The prepared charge is lifted to the top of the furnace in long buckets of 1500 kg capacity. The Pb-Cu furnaces smelt 1100 to 1200 t/d of charge having approximately the following composition :

	Typical lead charge %	Typical lead-copper charge %
Sinter	60 - 65	50 - 60
Return converter slag	-	15 - 20
Scrap iron	1	-
Lead drosses	10 - 15	10 - 15
Miscellaneous scraps	5 - 10	5 - 10
Return slag etc.	14 - 19	8 - 10
Low grade matte	-	2 - 5

Coke consumption varies from 10 - 14 % of total charge (90 % fixed carbon). It depends mainly on the charge composition which varies widely with the nature of sinter and other components.

Lead bullion production is equal to 15 to 25 % of the input charge. On lead-copper charges, which contain also some arsenic, matte production is approximately 5 - 15 % of the input and the speiss 5 - 10 % of input. The bullion, matte and slag are tapped together into a forehearth at 1150° to 1200°C, and from this, three phases, slag, matte and bullion (with speiss) are recovered separately. The bullion is tapped from the forehearth into 1200 kg ingots and is then sent by rail to the Lead Refinery. Slag contains 10-12 % Zn, 1,5 % Pb, 0,5 % Cu, 26 % SiO_2, 17 % CaO, 22 % Fe and is sold in large lumps to dam builders. Matte containing 20 % Pb, 40 % Cu, 20 % S, 10-15 % Fe is passed to the converter aisle for blowing. Speiss containing As, Sb, Cu, Ni is treated for volatilisation of the As. The blast furnace dust is partly returned to the sinter-plant, and partly treated for cadmium extraction.

The top gases are cleaned in a dry electrostatic Cottrell and sent to a 120 m high stack. Exhaust gases from forehearth, hoods and working areas are vented with high draft to ensure clean air for the personnel and then cleaned in separate baghouses.

Table 2 - Dimensions of the lead blast furnaces

Blast furnace	Nr 3	Nr 4
Nr of tuyeres	36	40
Tuyeres diameter	80 mm	80 mm
Width at tuyeres	1.13 m	1.30 m
Length at tuyeres	5.55 m	6.00 m
Smelter column height	3.81 m	4.60 m
Furnace blast volume	9,000 to 10,000 Nm^3/ h	10,000 to 12,000 Nm^3/h
Blast pressure	170 to 200 cm Water	180 to 200 cm Water
Fore hearth	2.2 by 1.1 m	2.2 by 1.1 m

Oxygen enrichment of the blast

Oxygen enrichment was extensively tested in 1968 and 1969. It appears to be very beneficial for all types of charges but gives greater advantages in particular cases.

Some results are summarised below.

% Oxygen in blast	Relative enrichment	Coke consumption	Smelting Rate
20,9	100	100	100
23	110,6	97,4	112,5
25,1	120	94,5	121,7
26,5	126,7	90	135

In addition to its efforts on coke consumption and smelting ra-te oxygen

- a reduction in dust production and a lower temperature of the top gases
- hotter and clearer tuyeres which facilitate the running of the furnace
- less accretion formation in the shaft.

At present, oxygen enrichment is current practice and the injection of fuel through the tuyeres is under study.

Matte blowing in "Siphon" converter

Our converters which have been described fully elsewhere (Ref. 1), are of original design and have several special features. In particular a gas rich in sulfur dioxide (8 - 10 %) is produced by preventing indraught of air between converter and flue : at the same time the escape of noxious converter gases into the works atmosphere is virtually eliminated. An inverted "U" flue is bolted to one end of the converter and a patented seal, which is fitted around the end bearing, connects to a stationary flue. Draught is provided by a variable speed fan which the operator adjusts to give zero pressure at the converter mouth throughout all phases of the blowing cycle. A converter can be charged while blowing without escape of sulfurous gases, and this permits the addition of large quantities of cold copper scrap.

There are three 10 ft. x 20 ft converters, each able to hold 45 - 50 tons of copper. Air is introduced through the seventeen tuyeres of 1 1/2 inch diam. at a rate of 180 Nm3 per min. The time for one cycle is approximately twelve hours. Leady matte is added at regular intervals so that the exhaust gas has a consistent SO_2 content. As soon as blowdown is over, the following converter starts its cycle and a steady flow of rich gas is obtained.

The converters produce 90 t per d of a 98-99 % blister copper with one converter on blow and 150 t per day with two converters simultaneously on blow. The blister copper is cast into 2 ton blocks for shipment to the electrolytic refinery at Olen.

Lead Refinery

Since 1927 Metallurgie Hoboken has been treating the blast furnace bullion in a lead refinery built for the Harris process which removes arsenic, tin and antimony with sodium hydroxide. In 1964, when modernization and increased capacity were required, the Harris process was retained in order to insure both a good recovery of the tin and the flexibility required for the widely varying bullion produced at Hoboken.

With the new plant commissioned in 1968 the following monthly outputs can be reached :

- fine lead production 10,000 t
- silver extraction from lead 50 t
- bismuth extraction from lead 40 t
- arsenic + tin + antimony extraction 400 t

The capacity to extract arsenic, tin and antimony is unusually large and is a most important characteristic of the Hoboken Lead Refinery. To develop this capacity an extended research program on the metallurgy and chemistry of the Harris process was required. A complete layout of the refining plant is shown in fig. 4.

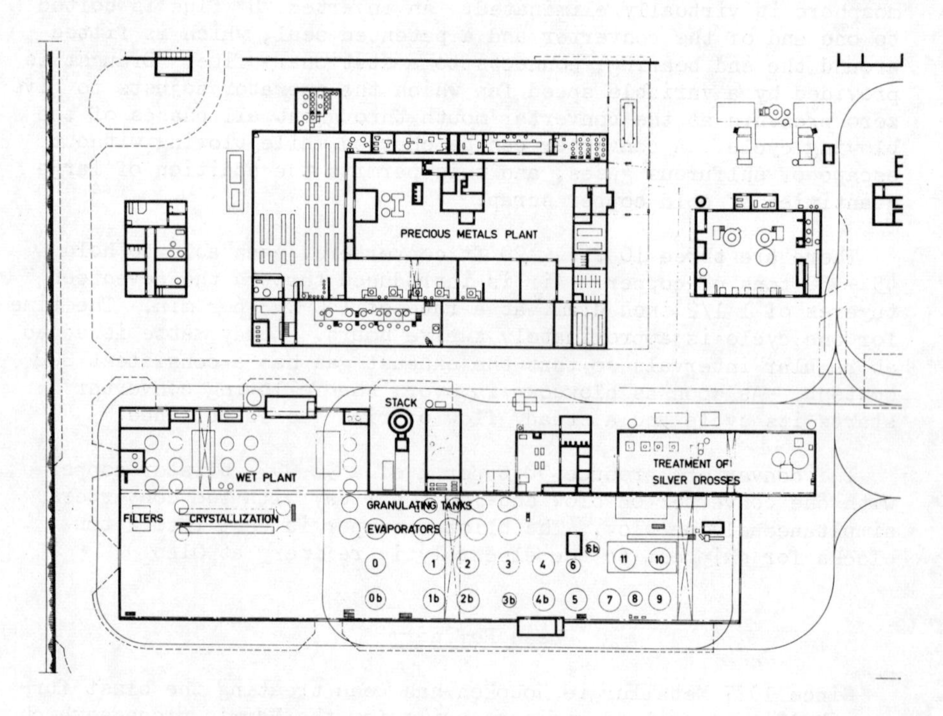

Fig. 4 - Layout of the lead refining plant.

The main building measures 150 m by 30 m and contains 18 lead kettles, 6 evaporators and the granulating tanks for the Harris salts. Two overhead rolling cranes, one with two hooks 20 and 5 t capacity and the other a 10 t weighing crane, service this building. A second building, 60 m long and 20 m wide, contains the wet plant and is also equipped with an overhead crane. A third building, 50 m by 15 m, equipped with a 5 t overhead crane, contains the liquating equipment for the silver drosses, the zinc distillation furnaces and a cupellation furnace. In separate buildings are offices, compressors and fan rooms, fuel oil tanks and pump station.

1. Drossing

The lead bullion, predrossed at the blast furnaces, arrives at the refining plant in 1.2 t blocks and is remelted in 2 welded steel pots of 225 t capacity, numbered 0 and 0b on fig. 4. In order to retain the tin and antimony as far as possible in the lead there is no sulfur addition and drossing is achieved at 400° by stirring some dry pitch into the lead bath. The copper content of drossed lead is about 0.1 % : Other impurities vary widely and depend on the bullion composition. Assays vary within the following typical ranges :

Silver	1,000	to	12,000 g per t
Bismuth	.015	to	1.00 %
Arsenic	.010	to	1.5 %
Tin	.020	to	4.0 %
Antimony	.5	to	6.0 %

Drosses assaying about 25 % copper and 65 % lead are retreated at the smelter.

2. Softening of lead

The Harris process depends on the tendency for arsenic, tin and antimony oxides to react with sodium hydroxide and form sodium arsenates, stannates and antimonates; oxides are thus held in the salt melt at reasonably low activities and fast rates of softening can be obtained.

The oxidizing agents are sodium nitrate and/or air. Air alone is a weak oxidiser and the rate of reaction is low. Selective oxidation of arsenic and tin with respect to antimony can be obtained because the oxidation rate is less than the exchange rate, across the salt + metal interface, between the antimony and the tin or arsenic. With sodium nitrate a faster rate can be obtained, but oxidation is not selective so this method is used when the lead contains antimony only.

The "Harris machine" used for these processes, is shown in fig. 5. It consists essentially of a reaction cylinder, 2 m in diameter with a cone-shaped bottom, at the vertex of which there is an outlet valve : this can be closed to check the lead flow. There are two pumps, each with an output of 1000 t lead per hour. The cylinder and pumps rest on a frame built on top of a 225 t pot so that the bottom of the cylinder dips into the lead.

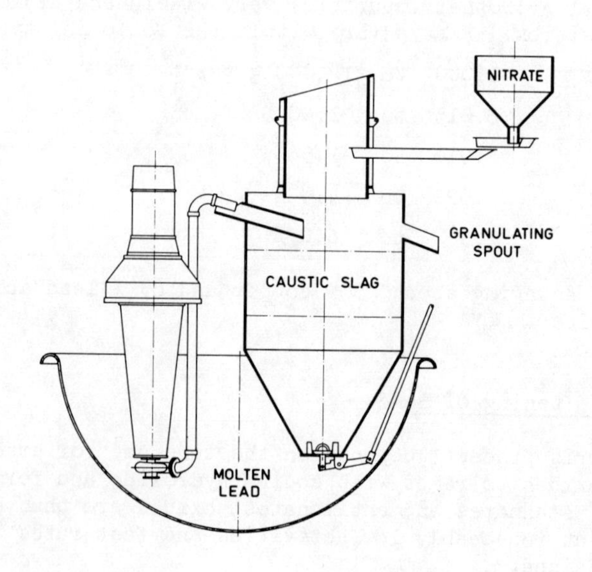

Fig. 5 - Sketch of a Harris machine.

Softening begins with the pouring into the reaction cylinder of some 4000 kg of molten sodium hydroxide; then the pumps are started. They draw the lead from the pot and disperse it through a specially designed nozzle, into the caustic slag. The lead returns to the pot through the valve. Each time it flows into the Harris machine, some of the lead is oxidized by air or by sodium nitrate which can be continuously added by means of a small shuttle conveyor. Arsenic, tin and antimony react with the lead oxides to form sodium arsenate, stannate and antimonate within the caustic slag. This slag becomes thicker and when it contains about 20 % of one or more of these salts, the valve is partly closed, and the outward flow of the lead checked; the slag level and the lead level in the reaction cylinder both rise and the thick salt runs out through the granulating spout. A new batch of 4000 kg of molten sodium hydroxide is poured into the Harris machine and another cycle begins. In a number of cycles, depending upon the impurities, all the arsenic, tin or antimony is removed and the lead is pumped to the next pot.

The Hoboken lead refinery has four such Harris machines. Two marked 1 and 1b on fig. 4 extract arsenic and tin; the other two extract antimony. With a well controlled program in which oxidation is started with air and finished with sodium nitrate, and with a continuous lead assay, the operator can obtain caustic salts with arsenic and tin and very little antimony in the first two Harris machines and slags with antimony and no tin or arsenic in the latter. Treatment of the caustic slags is described later under "Wet plant".

Owing to modernization, remote control and effective damp exhaust, working conditions of operators are much better than with earlier Harris machines. There is an air-conditioned instrument room from which all controls can be operated and measurements made.

3. Decopperizing of softened lead

Drossing leaves 0.1 % copper in the lead, so further decopperizing is needed to avoid unnecessary zinc consumption during desilverizing. This is done in the 225 t pot numbered 3 in fig. 4. Two kg of sulfur are added per ton of lead at 330°C into the vortex of the stirrer. The decopperized lead contains about .02 % copper and is pumped to the next kettle. The dry dross obtained assays 5 % copper and is returned to the smelter.

4. Desilverizing of decoppered lead

It is normal practice at Hoboken to use the Parkes' process in two steps with cold pumping of desilverised lead. Two pots marked 4 and 4b on fig. 4 are used for this purpose. Two Howard presses of 30 t capacity, press entrained lead out of the silver rich crusts; after pressing these contain about 10 % silver and their further treatment is described in section 10. The 225 t pot n° 5 on fig. 4 is used as a holding tank between desilverizing and dezincing. The 80 t pot n° 12 is only used to keep the desilverizing pumps hot.

5. Dezincing of desilverized lead

The first dezincing equipment used at the Hoboken lead refinery was based on the St Joseph design. A steel cylinder extension has now been welded on top of the two 125 t lead pots (marked 6 and 6b on fig. 4). On the upperpart of this collar a watercooled ring has been fixed to support the rubber seal of the cover. (fig. 6). A 20 cm diameter pipe is welded to the shell of the pot itself and connected to the vacuum pumps. The most important advantages of these improvements over the original design are firstly that coupling to the vacuum pumps is permanent and secondly that zinc can be recovered from the cover very easily and with no hazards : the cover is almost flat and there is no hindrance from side walls when removing the condensed zinc as can be seen on fig. 6.

The lead is heated to 600°C and stirred whilst a .05 mm Hg vacuum is maintained inside the kettle for 4 to 5 hours; at least 98 % of the zinc is recovered and reused for desilverizing.

Fig. 6 - Dezincing kettle during removal of the cover

6. Debismuthizing of dezinced lead

Most of the lead produced at Hoboken has to be debismuthized to meet commercial specifications, Bi $\leq$ .025 % or Bi $\leq$ .010 % ("Crystal" quality). The Betterton calcium and magnesium process is used.

The normal batch process yields crusts which are 10 times richer in bismuth than the dezinced lead. But with improvements which have been introduced at Hoboken crusts are obtained which are 17 to 20 times richer in bismuth than the lead.

Equipment for debismuthising includes three lead pots marked 7, 8 and 9 on fig. 4; in pot n° 7 (225 t capacity) calcium and magnesium are added at the vortex of a stirrer; pot n° 8 1.30 m in diameter and 4.5 m in depth, is fitted with a removable cover and placed in a hearth divided into four superposed sections. Each section can be heated by 3 natural gaz burners (flat flame burners) or cooled by introducing cool air through adjustable openings. A siphon pipe is fixed in the axis of the pot with a lateral outlet pipe passing through the shell of the pot and directed to pot 9.

The process takes place as follows. In the first pot a minimum of 150 t lead is held at 480°C and dezinced lead is added in batches of 50 to 60 t as needed. For each batch a calculated quantity of metallic calcium and magnesium is added according to the concentration of bismuth. A small lead pump with variable speed and an output from 8 to 20 t per hour continuously pumps the mixture into pot n° 8. The top of this pot is heated to 500/550°C, the other sections are cooled so that the lead flowing downwards is very near its solidification point when it reaches the bottom. A bismuth-calcium-magnesium-lead alloy crystallizes from the cooling lead and rises to the top of the pot. As it rises the alloy absorbs more bismuth from the incoming lead. Rich bismuth crusts are formed, skimmed off manually and removed in 1 t blocks that are treated later in the bismuth refinery to produce 99.9 or 99.99 % Bi. Debismuthized lead from the bottom of pot 8 flows up through the siphon pipe to kettle 9. It has an assay in bismuth varying from .014 % to .008 % depending of the quantities of reagents added. By regulating the input of the lead through the pump and the output of the lead through the siphon by a needle valve, stable operation can be obtained for outputs between 200 and 450 t/day.

7. Final refining of debismuthized lead

Most of the calcium and magnesium left in the lead after the debismuthizing is washed out in pot n° 9, by stirring caustic soda into the lead bath. The calcium and magnesium is then brought lower to less than 1 ppm in pot 10 in fig. 4. The dross produced at this step must be dry but not powdery and is retreated at the smelter.

8. Casting of fine lead

The Hoboken lead refinery is equipped with a continuous fully automatic straightline casting machine producing standard 45 kg pigs with an output of 45 t/hour. Lead is fed to this machine by a vertical pump placed in pot n° 11 (see fig. 4) which is of 225 t capacity. The ingot moulds fastened to Reynold chains circulate whilst dipping into a water tank; ingots are skimmed, trimmed, removed from the moulds and stacked automatically. Stacks comprise 25 or 50 pigs, they are transferred on a roller conveyor to a weigh-bridge (accuracy ± 200 g) and stamped with a reference number. Each weighing is reported on a weighing note and also on a punch card which is used for computer control of the fine lead stock. One weigher and one helper are needed to operate the casting machine.

9. Wet plant and retreatment of the Harris salts

A fundamental program has been carried out to determine accurately the solubilities of arsenic and tin as sodium arsenate and sodium stannate in aqueous solution in function of temperature, and also of the free sodium-hydroxide and the other metals present. The best conditions for precipitating calcium stannate and calcium arsenate have also been determined. These studies have made it possible to simplify the flow-sheet of the classical Harris process, to increase the yield of tin and antimony recovery and to improve the quality of the different products. The improved flow-sheet can be seen on fig. 7.

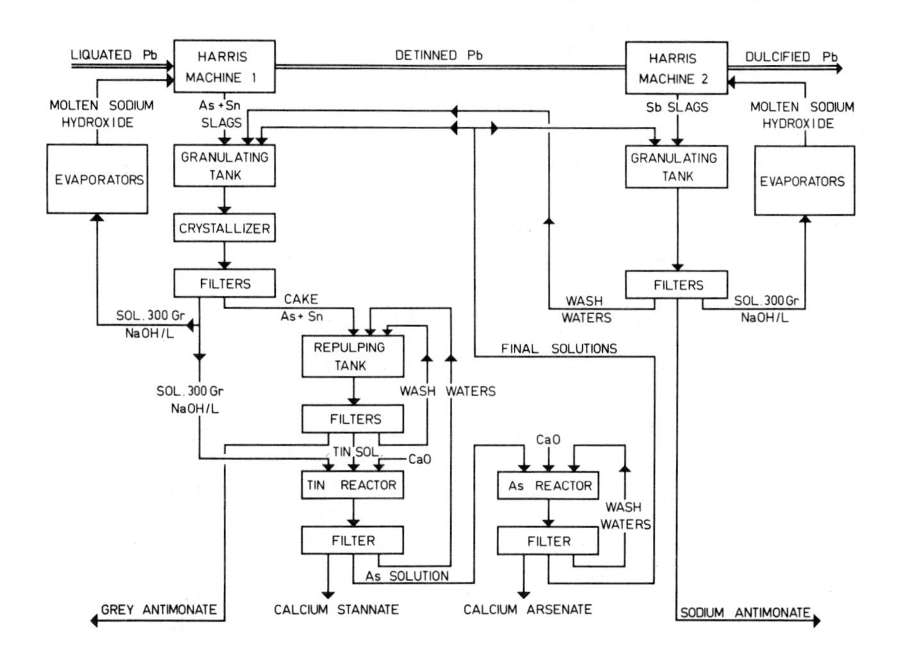

Fig. 7 - Flow-sheet of the wet plant.

The caustic salts from the Harris machines 2 and 2b which extract antimony, are granulated into the waste solutions which remain at the end of the wet process and which contain about 100 g/l free sodium hydroxide and 1 to 2 g/l arsenic. During granulating the free sodium hydroxide content of the solution increases to 300 g/l NaOH. Sodium antimonate in suspension in these solutions is then filtered, washed and dried on two Funda filters, type R, each with 30 m2 filtering area.

The caustic salts produced in the Harris machines 1 and 1b which extract arsenic and tin, are granulated in waste solutions in the same way as the antimony salts above waste solutions. When the solutions have reached a free sodium hydroxide content of 300 g/l, they are cooled to 25°C on a water cooled stainless steel moving trough; during cooling, all of the sodium arsenate and sodium stannate crystallize. The salts are then filtered and dried to give an arsenic-tin cake which is leached in washwaters to yield arsenic-tin solutions containing 50 to 70 g/l free sodium hydroxide. This solution is first filtered on two Funda filters type R with 10 m2 filtering area each. The solids remaining are called grey or impure antimonate. To the clear solution concentrated sodium hydroxide solution (300 g/l) is added; tin in solution is then precipitated at 95°C by adding calcium oxide. The calcium stannate is filtered, washed and dried on a fully automatic filter-press, with a filtering area of 67 m2. Detinned solutions have a free sodium-hydroxide content of 120 g/l and are diluted with washwaters so as to obtain 100 g free sodium-hydroxide per liter after precipitation of the arsenic, which is effected by adding more calcium oxide.

The different products of the wet plant are :

- sodium antimonate assaying 45 to 46 % Sb, which is sent to the antimony refining plant for smelting and refining to make 99 % antimony
- calcium stannate assaying 40 to 42 % Sn
- calcium arsenate which is without value but is non-toxic, and can be dumped
- grey or impure antimonate produced from purification of arsenic-tin solution. This collects most of the impurities of the wet plant such as copper, lead and tellurium together with some tin and the antimony extracted with the arsenic and tin in the first Harris machine due to incomplete selectivity.

The sodium hydroxide used in the Harris machine is recovered. Solutions with 300 g/l free sodium hydroxide originating in the filtering of the granulating solutions are evaporated to 1500 g/l in 6 evaporators shown on fig. 4 and are so re-used in the Harris machines. Another part of the sodium hydroxide is returned to the granulating tanks in the final solutions with about 100 g/l free sodium hydroxide. The soda contained in sodium antimonate is not recovered.

10. Treatment of silver rich drosses

Pressed silver drosses from the Howard presses are liquated in four cast iron pots called "coffee pots". These are conical with a tapping hole on one side near the top, and on the other side a siphon to allow the lead from the bottom to flow out when the lead level in the pot is higher than the siphon outlet. The coffee pots are placed in special hearths, heated with two natural gas burners, so that the upper part of the pot is warmer than the bottom. An eutectic mixture of calcium and sodium chloride is melted on the lead bath to protect it from air oxidation and to collect the zinc and lead oxides present in the pressed drosses. Silver drosses are charged through the chloride slag and some lead flows from the siphon outlet; a cast iron cover is put on the pot and the silver drosses melt.

Because of miscibility gaps in the ternary Pb-Ag-Zn diagrams, two liquid layers are formed in the pot : the lower consists of liquated lead assaying around 1500 g per t silver which is returned to the desilverizing and the upper, (under the chloride slag) is a ternary alloy assaying about 5 % lead, 35 % silver, 60 % zinc. The alloy is tapped when all the drosses are melted and new drosses are then charged. The lead content of the ternary alloy is then raised to 40 % and the mixture is retorted in two Leferrer furnaces to recover the zinc. In these furnaces which are heated to 950° to 1050°C with carbon resistors and kept under vacuum (10 mm Hg), zinc is distilled and condensed in a specially designed condenser: liquid zinc is tapped, cast in 40 kg ingots and returned to the desilverizing plant. Retort bullion assaying 30 % silver and 70 % lead is cast in 40 kg pigs and sent to the precious metals plant.

Precious Metals Plant

Raw materials for the precious metals plant are retort bullion, anode slimes from the copper refinery and other bullions and scrap treated on a toll basis. The average feed thus varies markedly and the equipment has to be versatile, with large potential capacities in the separate refining sections. Capacities of the precious metals plant are :

fine silver	150 t/month
fine gold	3000 kg/month
platinum	1000 kg/year
palladium	6000 kg/year

Copper anode slimes, retort bullion and most of the foreign materials are cupelled with production of doré metal and litharge which is returned to the smelter. There are 3 cupellation furnaces, two are stationnary and have an inside diameter of 2.25 m; the third is tilting and has an inside diameter of 3.25 m. Dust recovered from the flues and baghouses is retreated to produce selenium.

Doré metal is cast into anodes and parted in 154 Moëbius cells, with mechanical rabbling of the stainless steel cathodes. The silver crystals are washed on movable filters by automatic equipment, and then dried and melted in 1 t crucible furnaces. Fine silver is cast in standard 30 kg ingots or granulated in water to produce granules or flakes. The assays run from 99.9^{+} % to 99.97 % Ag according to purchaser's requirements.

Anodes slimes recovered in the anode bags from the parting plant, are retreated in a plant as described previously (Ref. 2). The flow-sheet is shown on fig. 8.

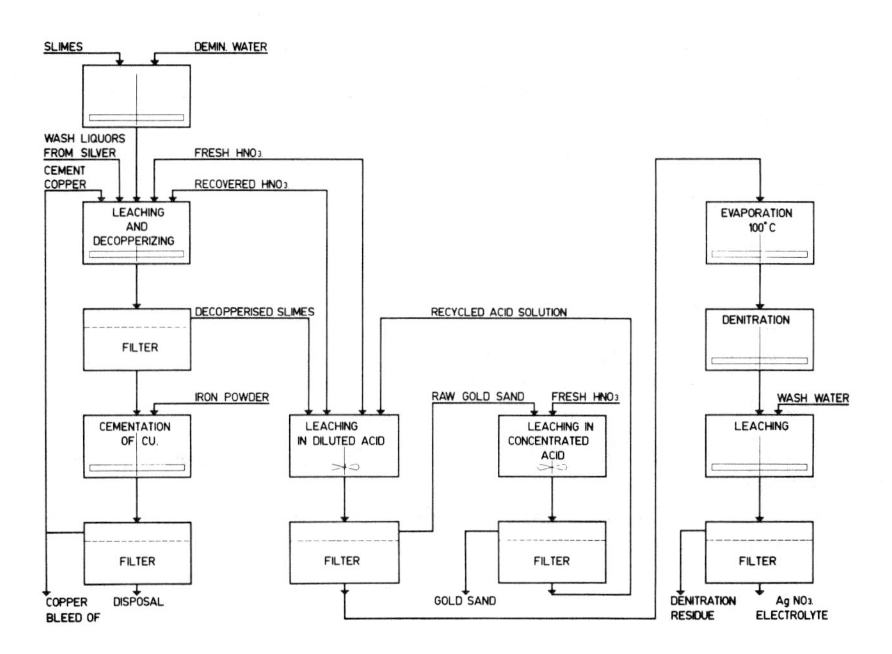

Fig. 8 - Flow-sheet of the treatment from the slimes of the silver parting plant.

The products from the treatment of anode slimes are goldsand, denitration residues and silver electrolyte which is needed to make up for electrolyte losses in the parting process. The denitration residues are treated for production of 99.95 % Pd as described previously (Ref. 2). The palladium is sold as sponge. The goldsands are melted, chlorinated to extract silver and cast into anodes. 16 Wohlwill cells are used to produce fine gold 99.99 %. The electrolyte from those cells collects platinum which is precipitated as ammonium chloroplatinate and refined in the classical manner to give platinum sponge assaying 99.95 % Pt.

References

-1- J.L. Leroy, P.J. Lenoir
"Hoboken type of copper converter and its operation"
Proceedings of the Symposium on advances in extractive metallurgy ,
The Institution of Mining and Metallurgy, London, April 1967
p.p. 333 - 343.

-2- Tougarinoff B., F. Van Goetsenhoven and A. Dewulf,
"Recovery by a nitric acid cycle of gold and platinum metals from the anode slimes arising from the electrolysis of doré metal"
Proceedings of the Symposium on advances in extractive metallurgy,
The Institution of Mining and Metallurgy, London, April 1967
p.p. 741-758.

Chapter 29

THE MITSUBISHI-COMINCO LEAD SMELTER

At Naoshima, Japan

T. Suganuma
Assistant Superintendent, Mitsubishi-Cominco Smelting Company
Naoshima-Cho, Kagawa-gun, Kagawa-ken, Japan

and

R. Melenka
Development Engineer IV, Metal Production
Cominco Ltd.,
Trail, British Columbia
Canada

Abstract

Mitsubishi-Cominco Smelting Co. is a joint venture of Mitsubishi Metal Mining Co. Ltd. (M.M.M.) of Japan and Cominco Ltd. of Canada. The smelter, which is located alongside M.M.M.'s Naoshima copper smelter, was completed in May, 1966 and has a capacity of 36 000 metric tons per year of refined lead.

The concentrate feed for the smelter from Pine Point Mines Ltd. is high grade with low impurities; particularly silver, bismuth, antimony, and arsenic, which facilitated a simple plant layout and operation. Concentrate, fluxes, recycle granulated slag and return sinter are drawn from bins by automatic control over weigh belt feeders, sintering is carried out on a 20 m^2 Lurgi updraught sintering machine, furnacing in a 3.0 m x $1\frac{1}{2}$ m water jacketed blast furnace equipped with an Asarco continuous tapper, refining in four 120 metric ton kettles and casting on a 25 metric ton/hour automatic casting machine. The SO_2 gas from sintering is cleaned in a high temperature baghouse utilizing glass bags and is then delivered to the M.M.M. copper smelter acid plants. The furnace gases after cleaning in a low temperature baghouse are vented to atmosphere.

Location

The smelter is situated on Naoshima Island in Japan's Inland Sea approximately three kilometers from the mainland and 750 kilometers southwest of Tokyo.

At Naoshima, Mitsubishi Metal Mining Co. Ltd. operates a copper and tin smelter along with a sulphuric acid plant.

Some of the main reasons for building the joint Mitsubishi-Cominco lead smelter at Naoshima are as follows:

1. Available capacity of the existing acid plant to treat SO_2 gas from the new smelter.
2. Use of the existing berth capable of handling 20 000 metric ton ships.
3. Availability of experienced smelter personnel.
4. Existence of a stack available for waste gas disposal.
5. Nearness to market.
6. Fluxes and coke obtainable within 300 kilometers by barge.

Operating History

Production of refined lead bagan July, 1966 and in 1967 reached 30 000 metric tons. For 1968 production was also 30 000 metric tons rising to 31 000 metric tons in 1969.

Some minor changes have been made in the physical plant during these years and more ventilating equipment added but the overall plant operation has changed little from that envisaged in the design stage with the major exception of the refining process.

Due to the low impurity level of the concentrate, particularly in Ag and Sn, de-copperizing using sulphur was ineffective; therefore a method was developed using Al-Zn as the reagent. Figure 1 outlines the flow sheet of the smelter.

Sintering

Feed Preparation

Fluxes which include silica, limestone and iron ore are trucked or loaded by front end loader to a dump pocket and transferred by conveyor belt and tripper car to three separate bins each of $52 m^3$ capacity. Granulated slag is loaded into a fourth bin with miscellaneous material such as fine dross and dust charged to a fifth bin. The bins are equipped with belt weightometers controlled by variable speed drives to give set point control. Fluxes and

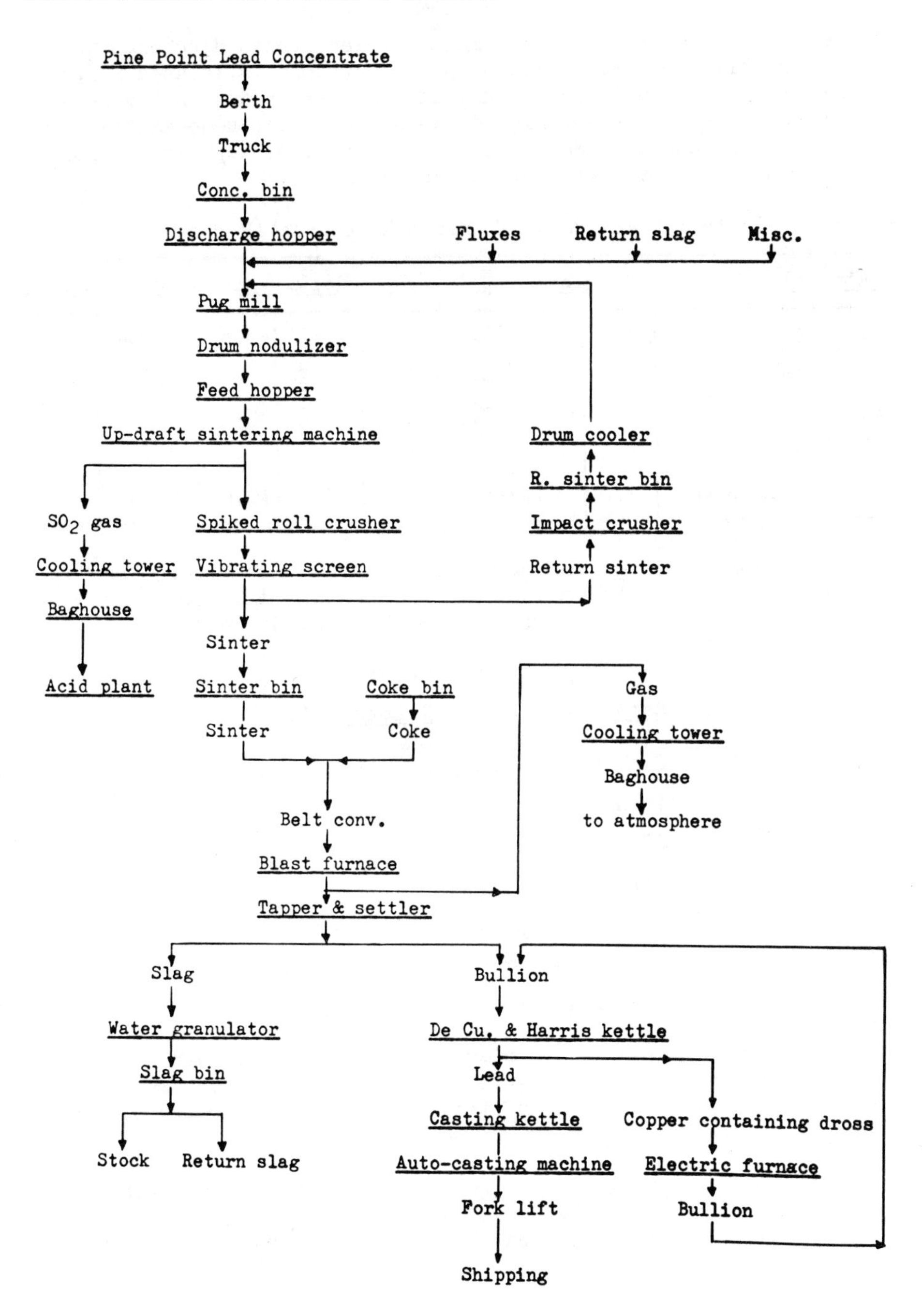

Fig. 1 - Flow Sheet of Mitsubishi-Cominco Smelter

granulated slag are 90% — 3 mm. All feed belts discharge to a common collector belt and the control console is located in the sinter machine building along with the other plant instruments. Instrumentation and weighing devices are of Japanese manufacture with the Kubota Iron Works Co. being the major supplier. Table 1 shows typical analysis of charge materials.

Table 1 - Analysis of Charge Materials (Per cent)

Material	Pb	S	CaO	Fe	SiO_2	Zn	Cu	Al_2O_3
Pine Point Conc.	73.2	16.8	0.5	3.2	0.2	3.6	0.004	0.6
Iron Ore	-	-	0.2	61.3	3.2	-	0.005	3.9
Silica	-	-	0.5	2.0	88.6	-	-	1.0
Limestone	-	-	54.9	0.3	0.5	-	-	0.2
Granulated Slag	2.0	0.7	21.3	26.5	23.0	10.6	0.007	5.3

The charge is calculated based on the desired production and slag composition with the amount of return sinter for sulphur control added on. A typical charge is shown in Table 2.

Table 2 - Typical Charge

Material	Kilograms/Min.
Pine Point Conc.	122.5
Iron Ore	5.9
Silica	7.0
Limestone	11.1
Granulated Slag	55.9
Return Sinter	242.9
Miscellaneous	26.3

As with all lead sinter plants the amount of return sinter required can be quite variable. Generally sufficient return sinter is added to maintain sinter machine feed S between 6 and 7 per cent.

Return sinter 85% — 6mm from a 70 metric ton surge bin is fed to a drum cooler then is conveyed on a belt to the pug mill where it is joined by the combined flux and concentrate feed.

Concentrate is trucked from the dock to a 4000 metric ton storage bin equipped with an overhead travelling clamshell. Concentrate is reclaimed from the bin with the clamshell then transferred to two 75 metric ton capacity current bins. These bins are equipped with belt weightometers and variable speed drives. From the bins concentrate is conveyed to a discharge hopper joining the flux belt and the layered charge is then conveyed to the pug mill where it joins the return sinter. Lumpy concentrate is broken down by a rotating drum with its outer circumference serrated. The drum is set approximately 20 mm above the concentrate belt.

From the pug mill the mixed fluxes, concentrate and return sinter discharge into a drum nodulizer with a capacity of 25 metric tons per hour. The nodulizer is 1.8 m in diameter x 4.5 m long and is equipped with a variable speed drive giving variations in r.p.m. to a maximum of 16. Also the nodulizer can be declined from 0 - 4 degrees. Water is added to the nodulizer to maintain 4.5 per cent moisture in the pelletized product.

Return Sinter Circuit

The concentrate to return sinter ratio varies between 1:1.5 and 1:2.5. Return sinter is obtained by screening the product of the sinter machine claw breaker through an adjustable screen feeder where the undersize ranging from —12 mm to —25 mm, depending upon the amount required, is scalped for return sinter. Sulphur content of return sinter varies between 2 and 3 per cent.

This material is conveyed by natural frequency conveyor to two parallel impact crusher circuits. The conveyors delivering the return sinter to the crushers are equipped with slotted sections set at 8 mm enabling —8 mm material to go directly to the return sinter surge bin.

The +8 mm material passes through the impact crushers in an open circuit thence to the 70 metric ton surge bin. The impact crushers are 1.05 m in diameter by 0.87 m long and are equipped with six hammers; motor power is 37 KW. Return sinter screen analysis is shown in Table 3.

The hot return sinter from the surge bin damaged the original belt conveyor system and to overcome the problem a cooling drum was installed at the surge bin outlet. The inclined belt conveyor transporting return sinter to the pug mill is equipped with a weightometer which monitors the rate of return sinter conveyed. The return sinter rate can be manually adjusted by altering the rotation of the screw conveyor feeding return sinter from the surge bin to the drum cooler. Also a load cell has been installed on the surge bin indicating amount of return sinter in the bin.

Table 3 - Typical Return Sinter Screen Analysis

	%
+ 6.7 mm	15.1
+ 4.0	15.8
+ 2.4	18.9
+ 1.7	21.3
+ 1.0	8.0
- 1.0	20.9
	100.0

Sinter Machine

Sintering is carried out on a Lurgi-designed, Hitachi-built updraft machine 2m wide by 10m long. Nominal feed rate is 21 metric tons/hour. A shuttle conveyor feeds either the main or ignition hopper. There are five updraft windboxes and the downdraft ignition windbox. Fresh air is blown through the first two windboxes and 6.0% SO_2 gas withdrawn through the hood above the bed at this point. Gas from the last half of the machine and the downdraft windbox is re-circulated. Figure 2 below illustrates gas flow and volumes.

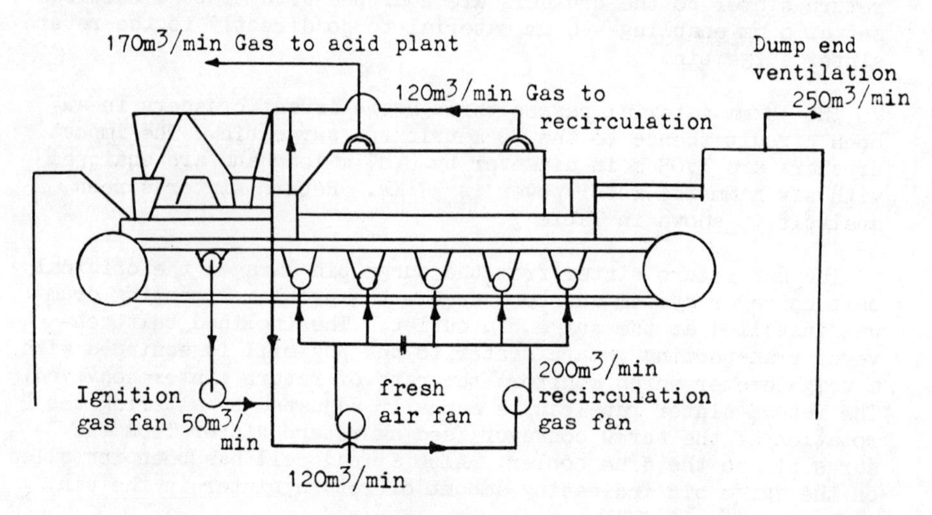

Fig. 2 - Sinter Machine Gas Flow

The normal ignition layer is 30 mm and ignition is accomplished using oil burners burning Bunker C. The main bed varies between 200 - 250 mm and the machine speed is 0.3 - 0.4 m/min. which can be varied through the variable speed drive. There are forty-one, 2m wide x 1m long pallets with three hundred, 19mm wide x 300mm long grate bars per pallet made of ductile cast iron.

Normal pressure drops and temperatures along the windboxes is shown in Table 4 below:

Table 4 - Windbox Pressure Drop and Temperatures

Wind Box No.	Pressure N/m^2	Temperature °C
Downdraft		60
1	2450 2940	150
2	" "	300
3	3430 4410	550
4	" "	600
5	" "	550

Sinter at the discharge end falls on a wear plate and slides into a spiked roll sinter breaker with spacing between stationary bars set at 100 mm. The breaker is driven by a 30 KW motor coupled to a double helical three stage reducer. Shear pins are used for protection.

From the sinter breaker the — 100 mm sinter is conveyed by an electro vibrating feeder to the adjustable screen type feeder where the undersize mentioned previously is scalped. The oversize sinter normally assaying 49 - 50% Pb and 1.0 - 1.5% S is conveyed by natural frequency conveyor to a bucket elevator of 40 metric tons/hour capacity. From the bucket elevator sinter discharges into one of two 150 metric ton sinter storage bins. Spillage from the sinter machine is conveyed by belt conveyor to the return sinter circuit.

Blast Furnace Plant

In addition to the two bins for final sinter storage there is a coke bin of 45 metric tons capacity which is filled by means of a front end loader dumping to a hopper that feeds a bucket elevator. The coke is stored in the yard and is screened through a —6 mm screen before loading into the bin. Screenings are currently sold but a program is underway to add screenings on the sinter plant charge.

Each sinter bin is equipped with a pan feeder feeding a common grizzly feeder which screens out the — 12 mm final sinter fraction. These fines are returned to the return sinter circuit by belt conveyor. From the grizzly feeder +12 mm sinter is conveyed on a belt conveyor trnasporting the charge to the furnace feed floor. Coke is weighed on a separate belt weightometer fed by a pan feeder.

The sinter and coke charge is layered into the furnace after presetting the weight of sinter then presetting the amount of coke required. Both the sinter and coke weightometers are equipped with totalizers.

The furnace is a thimble top design, totally water jacketed, 1.64m wide at the tuyeres, 6m high at top of the thimble, and 3.0m long inside the jackets. A shuttle conveyor, controlled automatically or manually, receives the sinter or coke from the belt conveyor and spreads the charge evenly across the furnace. The flexibility of the system is such that any part of the furnace can be fed as desired. The thimble extends into the furnace 1.1m from the top of the water jackets. Figure 3 shows a front and side view of the furnace.

Blast air is supplied by a three stage turbo blower manufactured by Dengyosha Co.rated at 140 m^3/min. at 22 554 N/m^2 pressure. A tube type preheater is provided capable of heating the blast air to 250°C. There are twenty-four, 75 mm diameter tuyeres on the furnace individually valved for blast air control. Distance from the tuyere centre line to bottom of taphole is 500 mm and with the sloping crucible the distance between the tuyere centre line and crucible decreases to 350 mm at the back end.

An Asarco continuous tapper is employed with a settler from which the slag is granulated and the bullion caught in one of two 120 metric ton capacity bullion kettles. Granulated slag is settled in a catch basin and recovered by means of a bucket elevator discharging into a bin. From the bin slag is trucked to the sinter plant and/or storage. Fresh sea water is used for furnace jacket cooling and slag granulation.

Blast furnace slag analysis is as follows:

	Pb	Fe	CaO	SiO_2	Zn	Al_2O_3
%	2.0	26.5	21.3	23.0	10.6	5.3

Coke on charge is normally 9 - 10% and the furnace is run down and barred using dynamite three to four times a month.

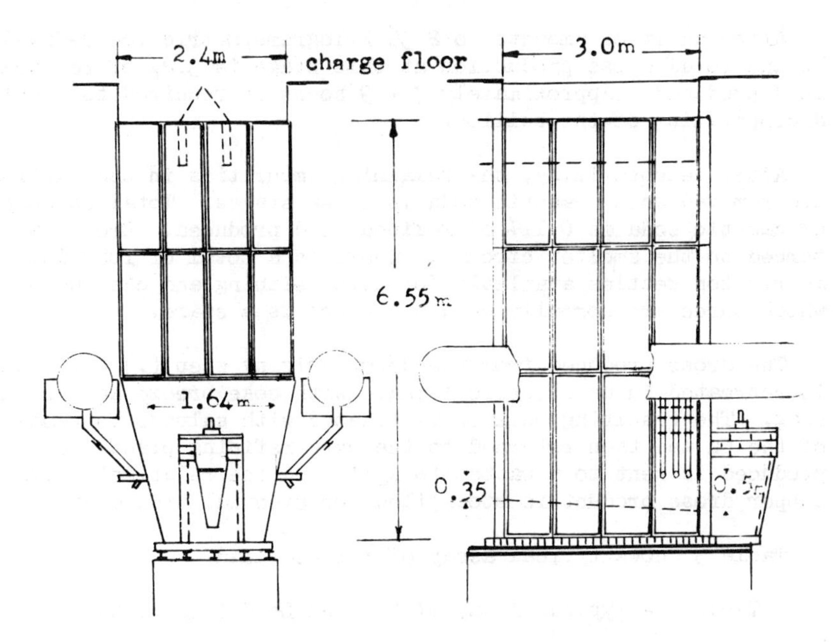

Fig. 3 - Blast Furnace

Drossing and Refining

After one of the two bullion kettles is full, usually 24 hours of furnace production, the bullion flow is diverted to the other kettle and drossing commences on the full kettle. As the rate of bullion production is relatively low, bullion from the furnace has cooled sufficiently during filling of the kettle that most of the dross can be skimmed immediately after the flow is stopped. Prior to skimming the bullion is stirred for 1/2 to 1 hour.

An overhead crane equipped with a grab bucket is used to skim the dross which is then screened with −25 mm fines returning to the sinter plant and the +25 mm lump material sent to the blast furnace. Tonnage of dross skimmed off at this stage is 0.05 tons per ton of refined Pb. Temperature of bullion after skimming is 480°C and typical Cu assays of bullion after skimming are 0.010 - 0.020 per cent Cu. The dross analysis is Cu - 0.030%; S - 5.3%; Pb 89.4%.

After the first dross is removed from the bullion,decopperizing is accomplished using Al-Zn alloy (30% Al, 70% Zn). The alloy is added to the bullion which is stirred by an agitator for approximately two hours. The temperature of the bullion is maintained between 450 - 470°C during agitation. The dry black powder dross produced is skimmed and the bullion agitated further with the resulting dross again skimmed.

Alloy addition amounts to 2.56 kilograms/metric ton refined Pb and total dross production at this stage is 3.2% of refined lead produced. Approximately 7 - 9 hours is required to complete decopperizing of the bullion.

After decopperizing, the remaining impurities in the bullion are removed using caustic soda in three stages. Total consumption of caustic soda is 0.11% of refined lead produced. Dross is returned to the smelter circuit. There is a total of four 120 metric ton kettles available for pyro-refining and casting of which three are normally used the other is a spare.

The dross produced from the decopperizing step (.4 - .9% Cu) is retreated in an electric furnace with coke breeze and granulated slag. The resulting bullion is treated with sulphur to remove most of the Cu and then returned to the pyro-refining plant. Slag produced is sent to a waste stockpile and the relatively high copper dross product is stockpiled for eventual treatment.

Table 5 shows typical assay of refined lead.

Table 5 - Typical Assay of Refined Lead (Per cent)

Ag	Tr
Cu	0.0008
Zn	0.0002
Fe	0.0002
As	Tr
Sn	Tr
Sb	Tr
Bi	0.0002
Pb	99.998 up

Casting

After caustic clean-up refined Pb is cast on a straight line casting machine designed and built by Tamagawa Machinery Co. and rated at 25 metric tons/hour. There are 178 molds on the strand producing 50 kilogram pigs.

Refined lead pigs are automatically stacked and weighed on a five by seven pattern using photoelectric cells to control stackir

Gas Handling

Sinter Plant

The SO_2 rich gas at 450°C from the first two-three windboxes passes through a duct to a cooling tower (10m high and 2.9m in diameter) where it is cooled using water sprays to a temperature of 250°C. The gas then goes through a six compartment glass bag Wheelabrator type baghouse. Bags are cleaned by the reverse air method with one compartment down for 35 seconds every 330 seconds. Individual bags are 133 mm in diameter by 3000 mm long.

Total number of bags is 864 with cloth area amounting to 1080 m^2. Dust is collected in the hopper and pumped by Fuller Kinyon pump to the sinter plant ventilation baghouse hoppers. Dust caught is 4.0 metric tons/24 hours.

Typical analysis of dust is Pb - 65.89%; Zn - 0.43%; Cd - 0.20% and S - 10.55%.

The pressure drop through the baghouse is 1960 - 2450 N/m^2 and there are two fans in the system both manually or automatically controlled, one between the cooling tower and baghouse, the other between the baghouse and the M.M.M. acid plant.

Sinter Plant Ventilation

There are two baghouses handling sinter plant ventilation gas. Fume and dust emission from the dump end of the sinter machine, natural frequency conveyors transporting final and return sinter and impact crushers is collected in the No. 1 ventilation baghouse. This is a five compartment baghouse with 350 Dacron bags in total. Cloth area is 690 m^2 and volume of gas treated is 700 m^3/min.

The No. 2 baghouse handles dust from the final sinter bucket elevator, final sinter bin discharge hoppers and final sinter transfer points to the furnace. There are four compartments in this baghouse with 216 Dacron bags giving 418 m^2 of cloth area. Volume of gas handled is 400 m^3/min.

Dust from both baghouses is collected in their respective hoppers then sent to the return sinter belt conveyor by means of screw and chain conveyors. Total dust catch amounts to 1 - 2 metric tons/24 hours.

These units are Wheelabrator type baghouses manufactured by Shinto Kogyo in Japan and employ mechanical shaking.

Furnace Plant Ventilation

Furnace top gas from the water cooled thimble passes through a 1.0m diameter balloon flue fitted with high pressure water sprays. The gas then flows through a duct to the top of a cooling tower 10m high by 4.28m in diameter. Here water sprays capable of delivering 0.13 m^3/min. at 2 000 000 N/m^2 pressure are used to cool the gas to 120°C before entering the baghouse. A tempering air damper is provided at the cooling tower outlet set to open at 135°C. Fans are located at the cooling tower outlet and baghouse outlet. The Wheelabrator type baghouse contains five compartments with 144 Dacron bags per compartment. Total cloth area is 990 m^2.

The collecting and shake cycle is 2 mins. catch; 15 secs. shake. Dust from the unit hoppers is conveyed by screw conveyor to a chain conveyor which transports the dust to the return sinter belt at the sinter plant. Analysis of the dust is: Pb - 74.5%; Zn - 6.13%; Cd - 0.04%; S - 8.0%, and dust catch amounts to 5.0 metric tons per 24 hours.

From the baghouse the waste gas travels up an inclined flue, 100m long built along the slope of a hill to a stack which is 30m high.

Furnace and Refinery Ventilation

Fume from the blast furnace tapper, settler, lead launders and refinery kettles is collected in a Wheelabrator type baghouse containing four compartments. Each compartment is equipped with 144 glass bags and total cloth area is 740 m^2. Volume treated is 400 m^3/min. Dust amounting to 3 metric tons per 24 hours is conveyed by screw and chain conveyors to the sinter plant.

Manpower Requirements

Operating Crew

The smelter is on a 3 shift, 7 day per week schedule. There are six scheduled national holidays during which the plant is shut down. Table 6 below shows the number of men employed in the operation.

Table 6 - Mitsubishi-Cominco Operating Crew

Job Description		No. of men/day
Sinter Plant		
	feed plant	6
	sinter machine	9
	relief	3
		18
Furnace Plant		
	feeder	6
	furnace	6
	refining	6
	day shift	1
	relief	3
		22
Other		
	casting	3
	yard crews	7
	shift bosses	5
	clerks	2
		17
	Total	57
	Staff	8

Maintenance

Practically all maintenance is contracted out with material supplied by both the company and the contractor. A preventative maintenance program is underway at the sinter plant whereby 8 hours per week is set aside to carry out planned maintenance.

The trades employed on maintenance with approximate manshifts per month are as follows:

Mechanical maintenance	210 manshifts per month
Electrical maintenance	15 manshifts per month
Civil maintenance	30 manshifts per month

Materials Handling

Movement of materials is contracted out and the amount moved per month is as detailed in Table 7 below.

Table 7 - Material Handling

No. of Tons moved (Tons/month)	
Lead concentrate	3,800 T/M
Coke and fluxes	1,360 "
Slag	2,740 "
Miscellaneous	830 "
Dump truck	40 hrs/M
Shovel loader	140 "
No. of man-shifts used	120 man-shifts/M

Summary

The Mitsubishi-Cominco smelter may be relatively small compared to other smelters, however, most of the recent innovations in lead smelting have been incorporated into the design of the smelter. The main features of the plant are listed below:

1. Updraft sintering
2. Acid production from sinter machine gas
3. Continuous tapping of lead and slag
4. Compactness
5. Pyro-refining
6. Extensive use of front end loaders and other wheeled vehicles
7. Hot gas baghouse cleaning of sinter machine gas
8. No crane handling of furnace products other than skimming dross

Chapter 30

LEAD REFINERY AND AUXILIARY BY-PRODUCT RECOVERIES AT NORDDEUTSCHE AFFINERIE (N.A.) Hamburg, West Germany

Klaus Emicke
Chief Metallurgist

Gerhard Holzapfel
Superintendent Lead Refinery

Elmar Kniprath
Research Chemist

Abstract

The paper describes the lead refining process operated at Norddeutsche Affinerie (N.A.). Incoming materials are different grades of lead with varying percentages of impurities: Cu, Te, As, Sn, Sb, Bi, precious metals. The facilities are designed for charge-wise operation.

After drossing, generally Te, As, Sn and Sb are removed substantially by the Harris Refining Process using fused NaOH. A certain selectivity during refining is achieved by controlled addition of $NaNO_3$. Another refining step is decopperizing by means of elemental sulfur. Complete separation of Te, As, Sn and Sb is accomplished by chemical methods in a leaching plant. A Howard Press is used in the Parkes Process for desilverizing. After vacuum dezinking in kettle, Bi is removed, if required, by means of Ca and Mg. In an end refining step Ca, Mg and Zn are removed by having the lead melt treated with NaOH and $NaNO_3$. The refined lead as such, or in the form of special alloys, is cast by an ingot casting machine into 50-kg ingots.

Zinc which is used as a precipitant in the Parkes Process is recovered by distillation from the high grade Ag-Zn-Pb crystals in Faber du Faur retorts while the Pb/Ag alloy is fed to the cupellation furnace. Ca and Mg are removed from the Ca-Mg-Bi crystals formed in the course of Bi removal, and the Bi-bearing lead is cast into anodes. The electrolytic lead refining facilities at N.A. are operated largely for the purpose of separating Pb and Bi. These facilities are also used particularly for the refining of Bi-bearing lead which had gone through the above process, but from which Bi has not been removed by Ca and Mg.

Introduction

Norddeutsche Affinerie, a company founded in 1866, started in 1912 a lead refinery with a reverberatory furnace, located in Hamburg's industrial district of Peute (air photograph). Since 1925, lead had been produced by the Harris Process in a plant built by Lurgi (Frankfurt/Main, West Germany), and in 1926, after a number of reconstructions and mechanical improvements, an electrolytic lead refinery was added for the treatment of Harris pre-refined bismuth-rich lead. Today the capacity of the lead refinery is approximately 45,000 tons of bullion per year and the electrolytic capacity some 8,000 tons a year of bismuth-rich lead.

In keeping with the concept of a custom smelter, the layout of the lead refinery at N.A. is such as to enable it to take in different types of lead bullion with varying percentages of impurities. The refining process has to deal with copper, tellurium, arsenic, tin, antimony, bismuth, and precious metals. Nickel and cobalt play a subordinate part. The purity of the lead leaving the refinery conforms to the standard requirements of a whole number of applications.

The refining of lead bullion is essentially partial oxidation, precipitation reactions, compound formation and physical separation, with the differences in solubility and specific gravity playing the main part.

Figure 1 shows the lead refining stages as practised by Norddeutsche Affinerie.

Kettle Plant and Labor Requirements

Kettles of unalloyed steel, Type ASTM-A284-55 T are available for the refining process.

The steel assay for a kettle with good lifetime is as follows:- C: 0.16%; Si: 0.06%; Mn: 0.5%; P: 0.045%; S: 0.016%; Al: 0.004%; Cu: 0.05%; Mo: less than 0.01%.

The average grain size of the steel is approximately 1400 μm^2. The structure is coarsely ferritic with evenly distributed pearlite.

Dimensions of the kettle:

Inside diameter	3440 mm
Cylindrical part	1540 mm high
Concave bottom	875 mm deep
Walls	30 mm thick
Capacity	200 tons of lead.

The advantage of this diameter is that 1 cm height of the cylindrical part equals 1 ton of lead.

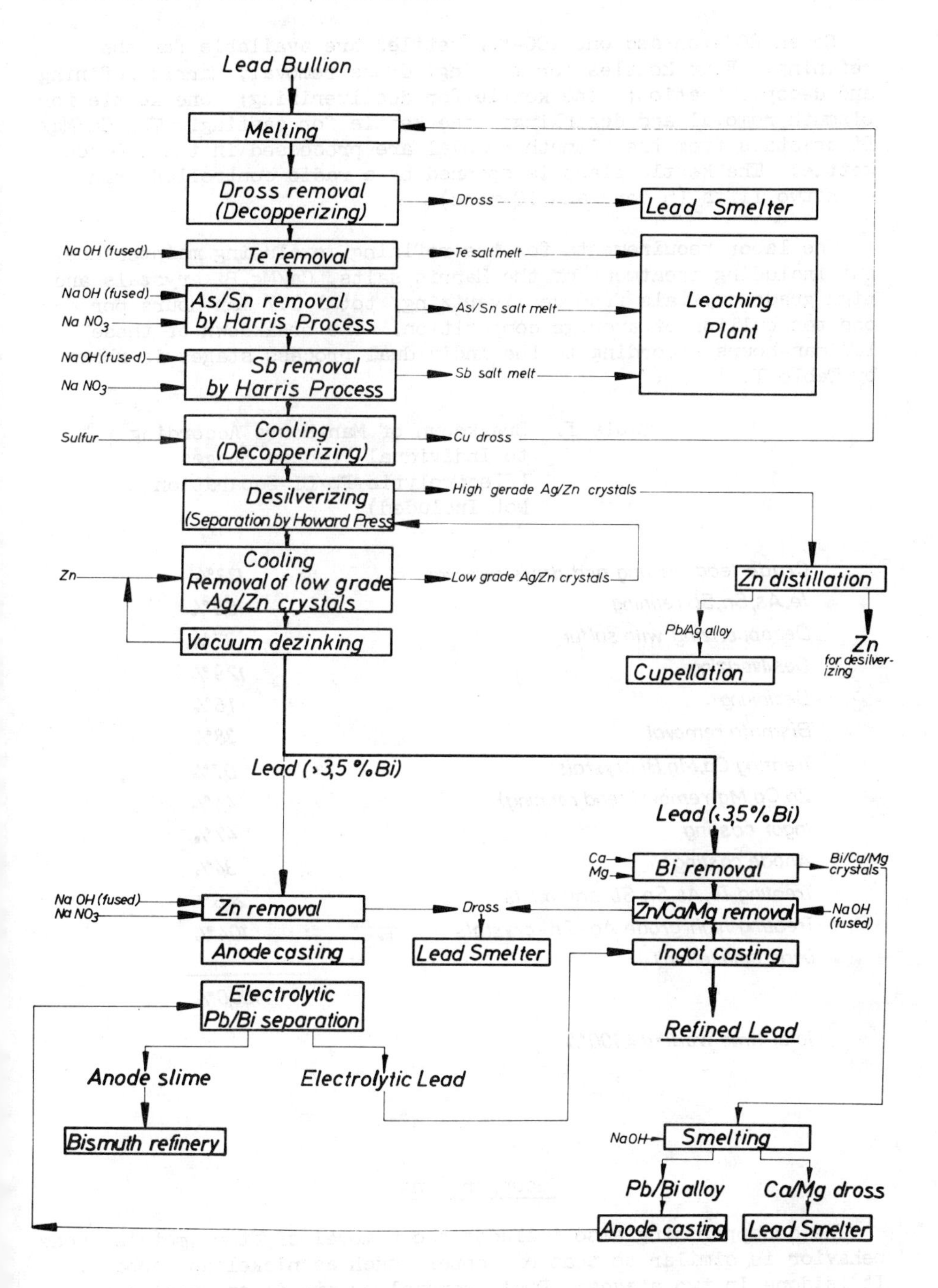

Fig. 1 - Plant Flow-Sheet, Lead Refinery.

Seven 200-ton and one 100-ton kettles are available for the refining: Four kettles for melting, dross removal, Harris refining and decopperization; one kettle for desilverizing; one kettle for bismuth removal and dezinking; one kettle for casting. The Ca/Mg/Bi crystals from the bismuth removal are processed in the 100-ton kettle. The kettle plant is spanned by a radio controlled crane with two lifts (5 tons and 10 tons).

The labor requirements for the refining, excluding maintenance, but including treatment of the Harris salts, Ca/Mg/Bi crystals and high grade crystals from desilverizing, total 1.7 man-hours per one ton bullion of average composition. The breakdown of these 1.7 man-hours according to the individual process stages is shown by Table I.

Table I. Breakdown of Man-Hours According to Individual Process Stages (Electrolytic Pb/Bi Separation Not Included)

Crude lead melting and dross removal	:	*13,3%*
Te,As,Sn,Sb refining	:	*16,5%*
Decopperizing with sulfur	:	*3,7%*
Desilverizing	:	*12,9%*
Dezinking	:	*1,6%*
Bismuth removal	:	*3,8%*
Treating Ca,Mg,Bi crystals	:	*0,7%*
Zn,Ca,Mg removal (end refining)	:	*4,4%*
Ingot casting	:	*4,7%*
Anode casting	:	*3,4%*
Treating Te,As,Sn,Sb salt melts	:	*24,6%*
Treating high grade Ag-Zn-crystals (zinc distillation)	:	*10,4%*
		100,0%

Total time worked = 100%

Decopperizing

The decopperizing also includes the removal of other metals whose behavior is similar to that of copper, such as nickel and cobalt. It is done in two stages: Dross removal or pre-decopperizing and decopperizing with sulfur.

In the course of dross removal, the Cu_2S-rich phase segregates and rises to the surface as dross[1]. The decopperizing with sulfur is done by the Colcord Process (1923) [2]. Assays of different bullions (Types A, B, C) with corresponding drosses, and of decopperized lead are shown by Table II. Yields relate to bullion input.

Table II. Assays - Lead Bullions, Copper Drosses, Decopperized Lead.

Bullion Assays	Type A		Type B		Type C	
% Cu	2,28		2,04		1,52	
% As	0,61		0,17		0,43	
% Sn	2,00		0,06		0,96	
% Sb	2,50		0,29		3,33	
% Bi	0,62		0,04		6,99	
% Te	0,13		—		0,27	
g/t Ag + Au	5 465		1 063		19 575	
Copper Dross (kg/t lead)	165		95		130	
	Assay	Yield	Assay	Yield	Assay	Yield
% Pb	55,6	—	65,4	—	59,5	—
% Cu	13,1	94,8	20,6	95,6	10,6	90,8
% As	2,7	72,6	1,4	73,9	2,5	75,5
% Sn	7,2	58,9	0,5	84,7	3,7	50,3
% Sb	4,3	28,7	1,6	50,9	4,8	18,6
% Bi	0,3	8,8	<0,1	10,5	3,2	6,0
% Te	0,3	35,3	—	—	0,9	44,8
g/t Ag+Au	3 247	9,8	637	5,7	14 950	9,9
Decopperized Lead						
Assays % Cu	0,05		0,06		0,05	
% As	0,20		0,05		0,12	
% Sn	0,99		0,01		0,55	
% Sb	2,12		0,16		3,18	
% Bi	0,68		0,04		7,56	
% Te	<0,01		—		<0,01	
g/t Ag+Au	5 900		1 110		20 270	

Stage 1 - Dross Removal: After charging solid bullion and the copper dross from the second decopperizing stage into the kettle, the lead is melted and heated up to a temperature of approximately 420°C. It is then agitated by a mechanical stirrer (155 rpm) until a dross is formed consisting of sulfides and oxides with metal entrainments. This dross is skimmed off by means of a pneumatic grab (capacity: 0.25 m^3). To get a dry dross, the lead is agitated and heated up to about 480°C.

The final copper content after dry dross is removed is about 0.13% to 0.15%. Contrary to the subsequent decopperizing with sulfur, Stage 1 of decopperizing involves unintentionally a considerable loss of arsenic, tin and antimony. So, about 70% of the arsenic input, 60% of the tin input and 30% of the antimony input go into the copper dross (presumably as Cu_3As, Cu_3Sn, Cu_2Sb) [3].

Stage 2 - Decopperizing with Sulfur: As a rule, the bullion, from which dross is removed, is decopperized after the removal of tellurium, tin, arsenic and antimony, such decopperizing being done with sulfur according to the Colcord Process ("cold decopperizing").

The lead is first cooled to 320°C whereupon some 300 kg sulfur are stirred in rations into the melt (charge size now approximately 180 to 190 T. lead) over a period of about twenty minutes followed by another fifteen minutes of stirring to make sure that the sulfur is thoroughly mixed with the lead. After about thirty minutes liquation the metallic, "wet" dross is removed from the lead by means of a grab.

The efficiency of copper removal ranges from 50% to 80% depending on the type of lead used. NA's own tests have corroborated the frequently stated assumption that the efficiency rate varies considerably depending on how much tin and/or arsenic is present[4].

The quantity of dross removed in Stage 2 and recycled to Stage 1 is about 5% of the lead input. The Colcord dross contains some 1.7% to 2% Cu. The decopperizing with sulfur does not cause any appreciable changes in arsenic, tin and antimony contained in the lead.

In Stage 2, the behavior of tellurium is influenced by the presence of copper before sulfur is stirred in. We have observed that, if the percentage of tellurium is comparatively high (e.g. 0.5%), up to 90% of the tellurium is being removed together with copper. To prevent this tellurium returning into the dross of Stage 1, before proceeding to Stage 2, lead charges with higher tellurium contents are subjected to a tellurium removing process described later.

In practice, the decopperizing just described does not result in a quantitative removal of copper from the lead. Residual copper contents of some hundred ppm are retained throughout the entire process and finally removed from the lead with the Ag/Zn crystals (see below).

Harris Process

According to Harris[5], tellurium, arsenic, tin and antimony can be removed from the bullion with molten sodium hydroxide, sodium nitrate being used as an oxidizing agent, and transferred into the alkaline salt melt. The equipment used is the so-called "Harris Cylinder"[6]. Its performance naturally depends on the operating conditions of a given plant (assay of the lead input, pump efficiency, surfaces of the reacting phases, retention time etc.). The separation of the impurities removed through the salt melts is accomplished by a combined metallurgical and hydrometallurgical process.

The following short review is merely given for better explanation of the chemistry of the process. Full details may be found in publications by Lauterbach[7], Pawlek et al.[8], and Winterhager a. Paschen[9].

Chemical Reactions in the Harris Process

Under the conditions of the Harris Process, tellurium may be removed from the lead into the NaOH melt either chemically or physically. According to the phase diagram Pb-Te[10], tellurium has a relatively low solubility in lead at 400°C - 450°C, the temperature of the Harris Process. When the tellurium contents are higher than 0.25%, PbTe enters the NaOH melt and can be identified as such in the tellurium cake by X-ray diffraction. To prevent this undesirable reaction, at N.A. tellurium is removed at a temperature of about 460°C. The principal chemical reactions are as follows:-

$$3\ Te + 6NaOH \longrightarrow 2\ Na_2Te + Na_2TeO_3 + 3H_2O \qquad (1)$$

$$x\ Te + Na_2Te \longrightarrow Na_2Te_{x+1} \qquad (2)$$

Tellurium reacts with NaOH so quickly that there is no need to add $NaNO_3$. The lead is brought into contact with air through pumping and, as a result, tin, arsenic and antimony are partly oxidized:-

$$2\ As + 2.5\ O_2 + 6NaOH \longrightarrow 2Na_3AsO_4 + 3H_2O \qquad (3)$$

$$Sn + O_2 + 2NaOH \longrightarrow Na_2SnO_3 + H_2O \qquad (4)$$

$$2\ Sb + 2.5\ O_2 + 6NaOH \longrightarrow 2Na_3SbO_4 + 3H_2O \qquad (5)$$

Finally, arsenic and tin can also react with water whereby hydrogen is released:-

$$2\ As + 3Na_2O + 3H_2O \longrightarrow 2Na_3AsO_3 + 3H_2 \qquad (6)$$

$$Sn + Na_2O + H_2O \longrightarrow Na_2SnO_2 + H_2 \qquad (7)$$

When tellurium is removed from the lead with NaOH, the NaOH salt melt contains, besides tellurium, also arsenic, tin and some antimony. The salt melt is then granulated with water and elemental tellurium precipitates by reverse reaction (1):-

$$2Na_2Te + Na_2TeO_3 + 3H_2O \longrightarrow 3Te + 6NaOH \qquad (8)$$

$$2Na_2Te_x + Na_2TeO_3 + 3H_2O \longrightarrow (2x + 1)Te + 6NaOH \qquad (9)$$

At the same time, Na_2TeO_3 is reduced by Na_2SnO_2 formed by reaction (7):-

$$Na_2TeO_3 + 2Na_2SnO_2 + H_2O \longrightarrow Te + 2Na_2SnO_3 + 2NaOH \qquad (10)$$

As a result, the solution usually retains an excess of Na_2Te_x which accounts for its red color. An introduction of air will cause these polytellurides to be oxidized readily to elemental tellurium and thus precipitated:-

$$Na_2Te_x + 0.5\ O_2 + H_2O \longrightarrow xTe + 2NaOH \quad (11)$$

Through decanting washing, the tellurium containing precipitate is freed from alkali. After filtration, there remains a tellurium cake containing up to 65% Te from which pure tellurium is recovered hydrometallurgically.

For the refining of arsenic, tin and antimony out of the lead, $NaNO_3$ as oxidizing agent is added to the NaOH melt. Besides the reactions expressed in equations (3) through (7), the following reactions occur:-

$$2As + 2NaNO_3 + 4NaOH \longrightarrow 2Na_3AsO_4 + N_2 + 2H_2O \quad (12)$$

$$5Sn + 4NaNO_3 + 6NaOH \longrightarrow 5Na_2SnO_3 + 2N_2 + 3H_2O \quad (13)$$

$$2Sb + 2NaNO_3 + 4NaOH \longrightarrow 2Na_3SbO_4 + N_2 + 2H_2O \quad (14)$$

At the same time, As^{III} and Sn^{II} formed through reactions (6) and (7) are oxidized by $NaNO_3$ to their highest valence.

The oxidizability of the elements decreases in the order As > Sn > Sb > Pb. Antimony is only partially oxidized as long as the lead still contains arsenic and tin. Once these two elements are separated, the oxidation rate of antimony increases. Noticeable oxidation of lead does not begin until antimony is removed.

The NaOH salt melts contain arsenic, tin and antimony in the form of sodium salts. Of these only Na_3AsO_4 has certain solubility in fused NaOH[7], [11], whereas Na_2SnO_3 and Na_3SbO_4 are suspended in the melt. Most of the NaOH, therefore, acts as a matrix for suspended metal oxides. In the process of refining, the viscosity of the NaOH salt melt increases along with increasing concentration of the sodium salts suspended in the salt melt. The melt is regarded as "saturated" at the point when its consistency is still just viscid; this is when it has to be granulated. To continue the refining, the Harris cylinder is filled with fresh or regenerated NaOH. This operation is repeated until all of the arsenic, tin and antimony is removed from the lead.

A time flow-sheet of the Harris refining process for arsenic, tin and antimony is shown in Figure 2. It makes clear how the antimony content of the salt melt increases granulation-by-granulation. In the chosen example, the refining of arsenic and tin is completed after the fifth granulation (Cylinder V). The salt melts of the subsequent granulations are practically free from arsenic and tin.

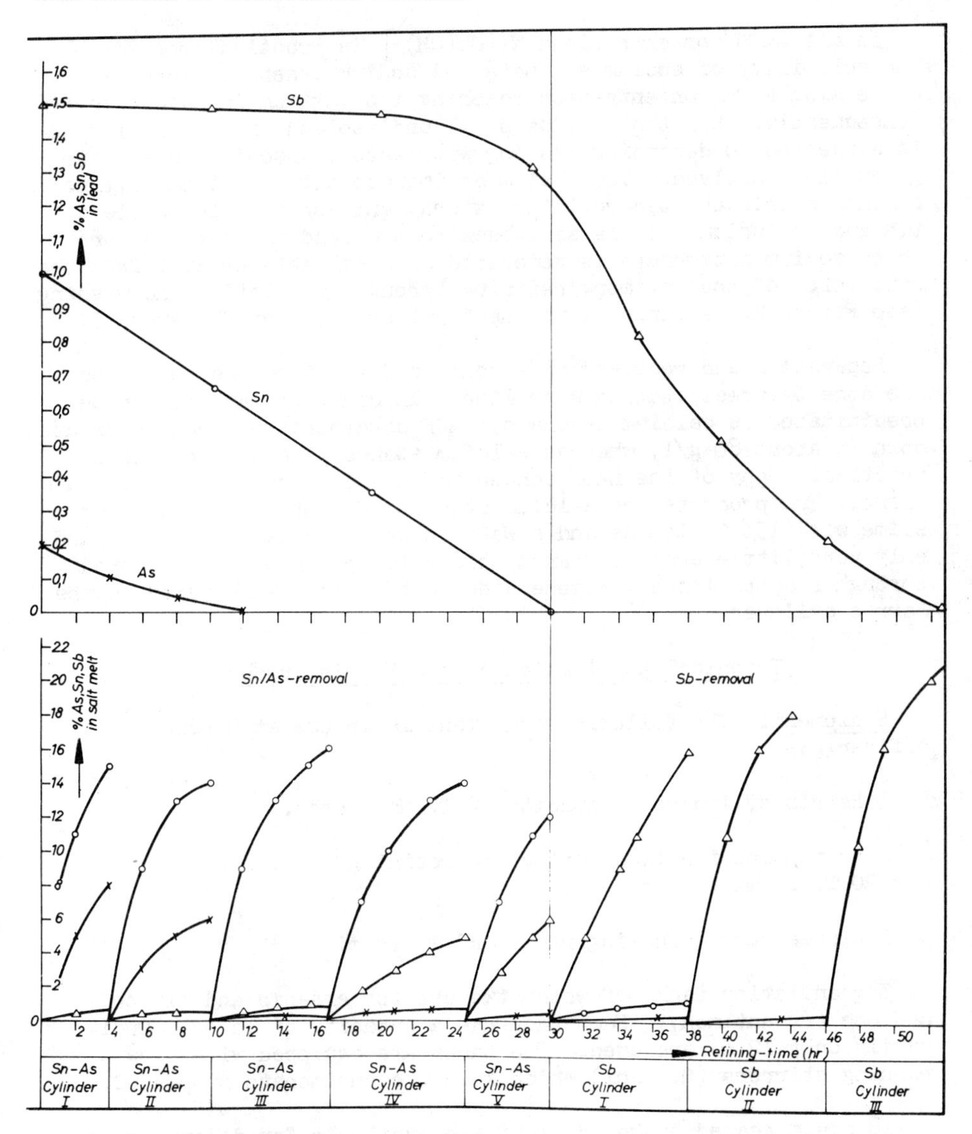

Fig. 2 - Time Flow-Sheet, Harris Refining Process for As, Sn, Sb.

The suspensions formed through granulation with water contain some 300 g/l free NaOH. Arsenic is still present as Na_3AsO_4; whereas, stannate and antimonate are being converted into the corresponding hydroxo complexes:-

$$Na_2SnO_3 + 3H_2O \longrightarrow Na_2[Sn(OH)_6] \quad (15)$$

$$Na_3SbO_4 + 4H_2O \longrightarrow Na[Sb(OH)_6] + 2NaOH \quad (16)$$

In all NaOH concentrations $Na[Sb(OH)_6]$ is practically insoluble. The solubility of sodium stannate and sodium arsenate increases with decreasing NaOH concentration reaching its maximum in pure water[12]. Consequently, when the residue still undissolved after granulation is subjected to decanting washing with water, arsenic and tin are gradually dissolved. The sodium antimonate obtained from salt melts of the arsenic and tin refining is gray and contaminated by lead, tin and tellurium. It is sent back to the lead smelter. A pure white sodium antimonate is recovered as a saleable product from the salt melts of the antimony refining through granulation and washing (see Figure 2, beginning with the first cylinder of Sb removal).

Separation and recovery of arsenic and tin from the solutions are done by precipitating with lime. In order for arsenic to be precipitated as calcium arsenate, NaOH concentration must be diluted down to about 80 g/l, whereas calcium stannate is not soluble in practically any of the NaOH concentrations occurring in the leaching plant. End products are calcium stannate $Ca[Sn(OH)_6]$, a calcium slime with 15% to 18% As and a NaOH solution containing no tin and only very little arsenic. From this solution, NaOH is recovered through evaporation as "regenerated salt" which is recycled to the Harris cylinder.

Technical Application of the Harris Process

Equipment: The following equipment is in use at Norddeutsche Affinerie:-

3 Harris cylinders. Capacity: 2 T. NaOH each.

2 twin pumps for lead during the refining. Pumping rate: 2 x 20 T. Pb/min. each.

1 single pump. Pumping rate: 20 T. Pb/min.

3 granulation tanks of which two are for arsenic and tin only, and one for antimony. Each tank has a capacity of 16 m^3. Ordinarily only 12 m^3 are used. The tanks are equipped with slow-running stirrers (0.8 rpm) which keep the antimonate suspended.

18 steam heated jacketed tanks are available for decanting washing and the precipitation of tin and arsenic. Capacity: 16 m^3 each.

Transportable stirrers (720 rpm) are used for agitating. Likewise transportable centrifugal pumps (pumping rate: 25 m^3/h) are used to pump solutions and suspensions from tank to tank or to the suction filters.

In the leaching plant, the precipitates are separated from solutions on 4 suction filters having a filter area of 9 m^2 each. (Supplier of filter bricks: Schumacher, Bietigheim, W. Germany).

Sodium antimonate and calcium stannate are dried on rack cars in 3 steam heated drying chambers at 110°C (Type HN 14, Supplier: Haas, Remscheid, W. Germany). One chamber has a capacity of 2 tons dry material.

The white antimonate is milled by a hammer mill (Type HM 3a, Supplier: Siebtechnik, Mühlheim/Ruhr, W. Germany), milling rate: 12 T./h, and sieved on a Variator sieving machine (Supplier: Engelsmann, Ludwigshafen/Rhein, W. Germany). The machine is equipped with a stainless steel screen, mesh size 60 μm, area 600 x 1200 mm, sieving rate 300 kg/h.

The screened sodium antimonate is filled in bags by hand.

Prior to evaporation, the NaOH solution is stored in 6 steam heated storage tanks (capacity: 15 m^3). From there it goes into 2 pre-evaporators with about 8.5 m^3 capacity each, equipped with an anchor stirrer (14 rpm). These are heated by the waste heat from the salt kettle heating system. The solution is pumped from the pre-evaporators into 3 salt kettles by means of a centrifugal pump (pumping rate: 12 m^3/h). Each kettle has a capacity of 8.2 m^3. The fused "regenerated salt" is agitated at the rate of 14 rpm and pumped out to the Harris cylinder by a centrifugal pump at the rate of 15 m^3/h.

All equipment is steel comparable to ASTM Designation: A 284 - 55 T.

Removal of Tellurium: Normally, tellurium is removed from lead which contains more than 0.01% Te after drossing. Depending on the tellurium content of the lead, a small quantity of fused NaOH is charged several times to the Harris cylinder: For each 0.05% Te in lead about 425 kg "regenerated salt", equivalent to about 7 kg NaOH per kg tellurium in the cake (see Figure 3). The lead is then circulated through the salt melt in the Harris cylinder at 460°C by a single pump. The refining time is 25 to 45 minutes depending on the tellurium input. The efficiency of tellurium removal is in the range of 60% to 90%.

Since the quantities of salt melt with 15% to 17% Te are comparatively small, the melt instead of being charged to a large tank, is poured into molds forming 500-kg blocks. These are sent to the adjacent leaching plant and leached in a wash tank with water or weak NaOH solution at 80° to 90°C, as shown in Figure 3.

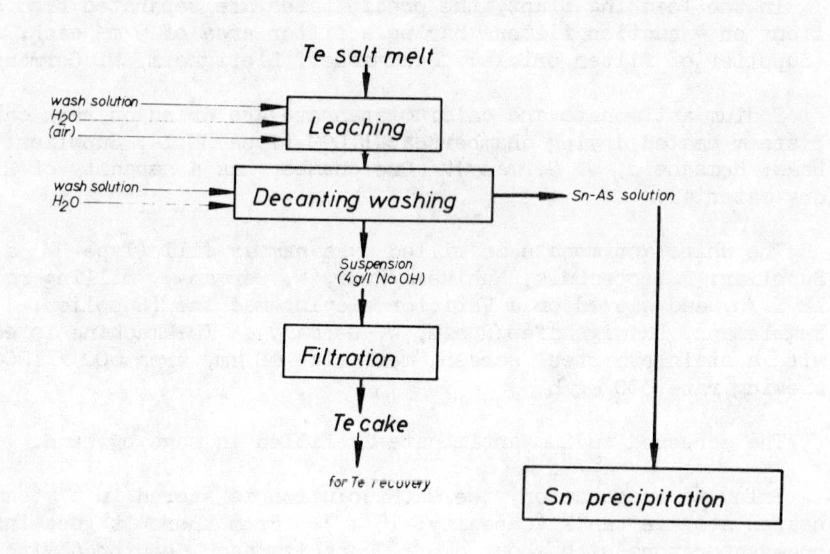

Fig. 3 - Leaching of Tellurium Salt Melt.

Tellurium remains in the residue while most of the tin and arsenic is leached. NaOH is removed from the residue by decanting washing and the tin-arsenic solutions are treated to recover tin and arsenic as described later.

When tellurium salt melts are leached, the solubilized sodium polytelluride often causes the solutions to turn red. From these the soluble tellurium is precipitated as elemental tellurium by air injected into the solution.

After decanting washing and filtration some 1.5 T. to 2 T. of a black tellurium cake with 50% to 65% Te are obtained per one ton of tellurium. A typical assay of the cake: Te 61-62%, Sn 5-6%, As 0.5-1%, Sb 5-6%, Cu 8-9%, Pb 5-6%, CaO 3-4%. This cake goes to the tellurium plant.

Removal of Tin and Arsenic: After tellurium is removed, lead cools down to about 430°C. About 2 T. fused "regenerated salt" are charged to the Harris cylinder and either a single or a twin pump is used depending on the rate of oxidation. Whenever fresh NaOH is used, it is added in 250-kg blocks to the cylinder where it melts through the contact with molten lead. During the process of tin and arsenic removal, 50 kg $NaNO_3$/h are added to the salt melt by hand. Once the melt is "saturated" (see page 8), the bottom valve of the Harris cylinder is closed and the lead level in the cylinder is raised by keeping the pumps going. Now the salt melt flows out of the cylinder, over the granulation launder and into the granulation tank. The saturation point is determined by visual inspection only without the knowledge of the real contents of tin and/or arsenic in the salt melt flowing into the tank. The salt melt may, for instance, contain 15% Sn and 8% As, while lead which is free from arsenic but contains tin may give salt melts with 20% Sn, and lead free from tin but containing arsenic may give salt melts with 20% As. During the removal of tin and arsenic, the antimony contents of the salt melts increase from 0.5% - 1% in the first cylinder to about 6% in the last Sn-As cylinder (see Figure 2). Normally, about 70 kg Sn + As are removed each hour, but the rate of removal, also for antimony, depends on the size and design of the equipment used. Chemicals required per one kg Sn + As: 0.38 kg $NaNO_3$ and 3.48 kg NaOH of which 0.12 kg (about 3.5%) are lost in the gray antimonate and in the calcium slimes.

The operation is repeated until less than 0.05% As and less than 0.01% Sn are retained in the lead (see Figure 2, Cylinders I - V). Another 400 kg NaOH are then charged to the last cylinder in order to clean the refining equipment from salts of tellurium, tin and arsenic before removing antimony from the lead.

Prior to granulation, 10 m^3 water or weak NaOH solution from the leaching plant are filled into the granulation tank (see Figure 4).

The NaOH solution with suspended salt melt residues is circulated by pumping from the granulation tank, over the granulation launder, and back to the tank. Every time two Harris cylinder batches have been handled in this manner, the suspension in the granulation tank has a concentration of about 300 g free NaOH per liter. Lead which has been carried over to the granulation tank settles on the bottom and is periodically removed from there by hand. Undissolved salts are kept suspended by slow-running stirrers.

The suspension is pumped into a wash tank and the residue washed countercurrently free from NaOH. It is separated from the last wash water and sent to the lead smelter as "gray antimonate". It consists mostly of sodium antimonate. Approximate assay: Pb 6%, Bi less than 0.1%, As 1%, Sb 32%, Sn 8%, CaO 6%, Se 0.1%, Te 1%, precious metals 300 g/T. Depending on the type of lead bullion, up to 25% of the antimony are recycled as "gray antimonate".

For the precipitation of tin as calcium stannate, the Sn-As solutions from the washing procedure are pumped into a wash tank filled with water in which about 600 kg lime are suspended. After stirring for one hour at 90°C, the precipitate settles. The clear, tin-free (less than 0.1 g/l Sn) solution is decanted and goes to arsenic precipitation. More Sn-As solution is added to the residue and the process repeated until no more lime is left for the tin.

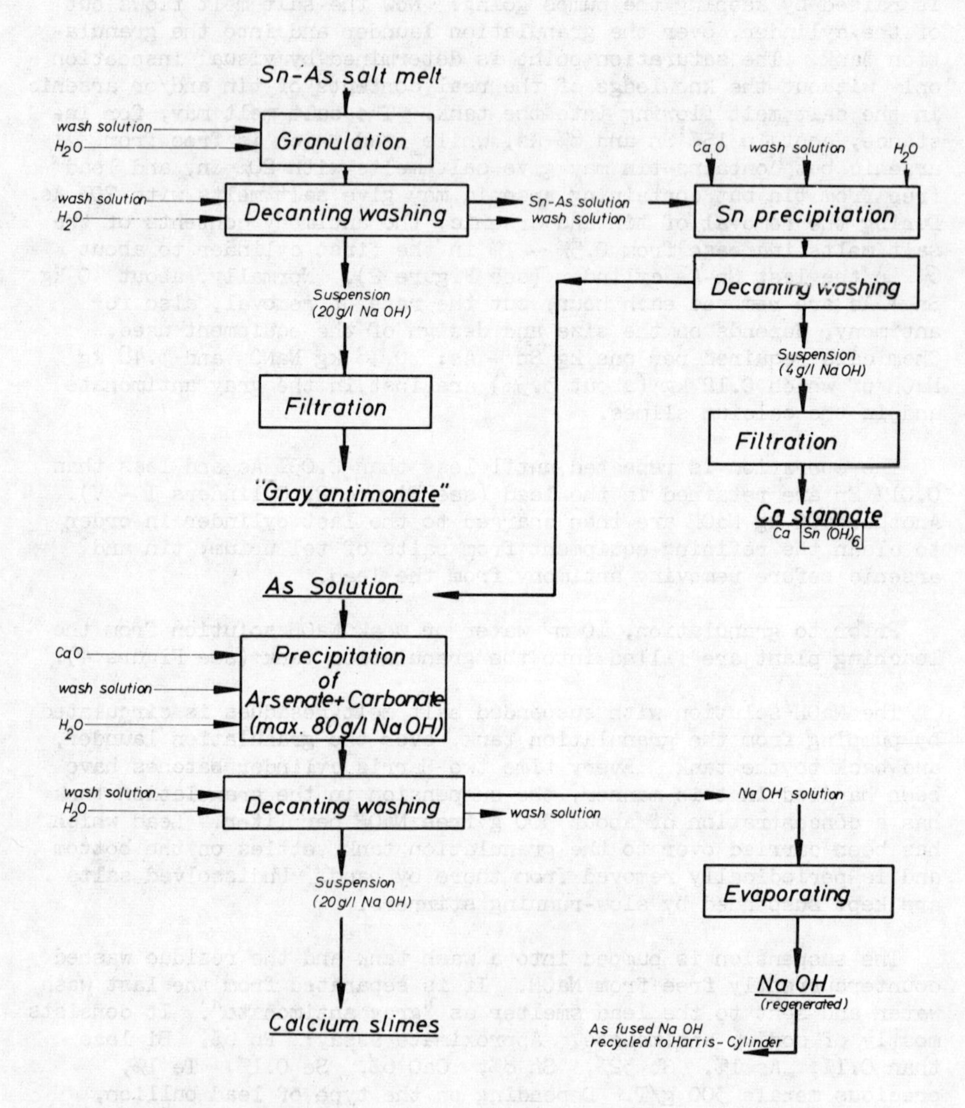

Fig. 4 - Leaching of Sn-As Salt Melt.

Lime consumption for the stannate precipitation is approximately 0.5 tons per one ton of tin. The resultant calcium hexahydroxo stannate $Ca[Sn(OH)_6]$ is freed from NaOH by being washed first with weak Sn-As solution and then with water. After filtering and drying, a calcium stannate is obtained assaying approximately: Sn 40%, Pb less than 0.2%, As less than 0.3%, Sb less than 1%, Ca 15%. It is used for the production of solder alloys.

The precipitation of arsenic with lime is only possible in concentrations not exceeding 80 g total NaOH per liter. Therefore, the arsenic containing solutions are normally diluted after tin is precipitated as stannate. The method of arsenic precipitation is similar to that of tin precipitation. In the course of arsenic precipitation, a parallel reaction occurs represented by the following equation:

$$Na_2CO_3 + Ca(OH)_2 \longrightarrow CaCO_3 + 2\ NaOH \qquad (17)$$

This means that a greater or lesser surplus of lime is required depending on the composition of the solution. The calcium slimes saturated with arsenic lose their NaOH by decanting washing. After filtration, the calcium slimes assaying As 15% - 18%, CaO about 40%, Sn less than 0.5%, Sb less than 2%, are discarded. The filtrate contains 0.1 to 3 g As/l and is evaporated. For economic considerations, the precipitation of arsenic is sometimes cancelled when arsenic concentrations are low. The disadvantage in such case is that there is more arsenic in the "regenerated salt".

Removal of Antimony: The same method as for the removal of tin and arsenic is used for antimony. At about 420°C, $NaNO_3$ is added at the rate of about 75 kg/h while the rate of antimony removal decreases with decreasing antimony content of the lead. N.A. calculates an average removing rate for antimony at about 110 kg Sb/hour. Before granulating, the salt melt contains about 25% Sb. It is granulated in a tank used specifically for the antimonate. Chemicals required: 0.61 kg $NaNO_3$ and 2.12 kg NaOH per one kg Sb. Of these 15% (0.32 kg) are needed for $Na[Sb(OH)_6]$.

The dry Harris refining process is completed when oxidation of lead occurs. It can be seen by the golden-yellow opalescent shine of the salt melt. Finally the lead is treated once more with about 500 kg NaOH. The resultant salt melt is recycled to a new charge for the removal of arsenic and tin.

The suspension from the granulation tank is freed from NaOH by decanting washing in a wash tank and the solutions are evaporated (see Figure 5).

White antimonate is obtained after filtration and drying. Before sieving, it is treated in a hammer mill. The saleable end product has a particle size of about 60 μm and assays: Sb 48%, Na 8%, Pb 0.15%, As less than 0.1%, Sn less than 0.3%, Sb_2O_3 less than 0.05%.

The leaching of antimony salt melt is shown in Figure 5.

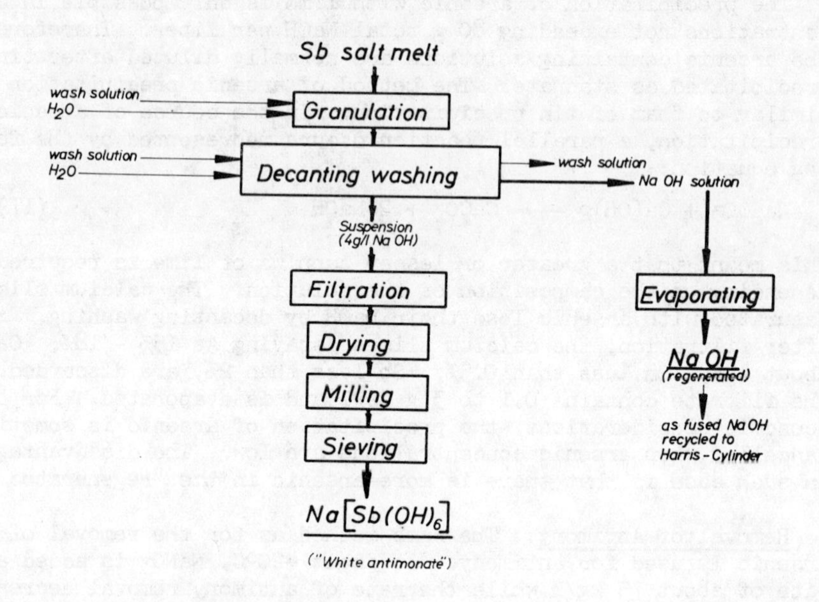

Fig. 5 - Leaching of Sb Salt Melt.

The percentagewise distribution of arsenic, tin and antimony in the products obtained through the Harris refining operation is shown by Table III.

Table III. Distribution of As, Sn and Sb in the Products of the Harris Refining Process.

Product	Yield %As	Yield %Sn	Yield %Sb
Calcium stannate	0,5	76,8	0,6
Calcium slimes	95,3	5,4	2,6
Gray antimonate	2,8	15,4	19,3
White antimonate	1,4	2,4	77,5
Total	100,0	100,0	100,0

Recovery of NaOH: The arsenic- and tin-free solutions containing between 70 g and 300 g NaOH per liter are stored in tanks at about 110°C and pumped from there into the pre-evaporators. These operate at a temperature of about 120°C. The solution leaves the pre-evaporators with a NaOH concentration of about 160 g/l and goes to the salt kettles for further concentration. The salt kettles contain fused NaOH at a temperature of about 400°C. The water of the incoming solution evaporates instantly. The bottom of the salt kettles is covered with a layer of molten lead which improves the heat transfer from the fire box (Bunker C Oil).

The composition of the "regenerated salt" may vary considerably. A typical assay, for instance, is: Total NaOH 70%, free NaOH 58%, Cl^- 7.5%, Na_2CO_3 10%, SO_4^{2-} 1.75%, NO_3^- less than 0.02%, NO_2^- less than 0.02%, Cu 0.03%, Pb 0.6%, As 5%, Sb 0.6%, Sn 0.5%, Zn 0.1%, Ca 0.01%, Se less than 0.1%, Te less than 0.1%.

Desilverizing

The Harris refining operation is followed by the Parkes Process[14]. It is practised at N.A. in several stages depending on the quantity of the incoming silver. Normally, two stages are sufficient. Where precious metal contents are higher than 6,000 ppm, the operation is done in three, occasionally in four stages.

When zinc is added to the molten silver-containing lead, Ag/Zn crystals are precipitated and, while the melt is cooling, rise to the surface with lead entrained. These intermetallic compounds have a higher melting point and a lower specific gravity than the lead melt and are practically insoluble in lead saturated with zinc.

For the first desilverizing stage, a kettle is charged with low grade Ag/Zn crystals. Afterwards the lead is pumped into the kettle at a rate of about 20 tons per minute, heated to about 460°C and stirred for a short time. Care is being taken that the crystals floating to the surface do not oxidize. A Howard Press is used to separate the entrained lead and the resultant silver-enriched crystals are removed.

For the second desilverizing stage, zinc as spelter, from Faber du Faur retorts and from vacuum dezinking is added to the lead melt which is stirred at 450°C for about fifteen minutes. Part of the low grade Ag/Zn crystals which are formed while the lead is slowly cooling down to about 320°C, attach themselves to the kettle walls from which they are scraped and then skimmed off the surface by a grab. The low grade Ag/Zn crystals are thrown into molds and left to solidify. After solidifying, the blocks are used for the next charge of the first desilverizing step. The quantity of zinc added at the second stage of desilverizing is calculated to provide sufficient zinc for the next charge of the first desilverizing stage.

The desilverized lead having a temperature of about 320°C is pumped at a rate of about 20 T/h into the next kettle for the purpose of dezinking.

The desilverized lead contains less than 10 ppm silver and less than 3 ppm copper. The crust from the Howard Press assays approximately as follows: Ag + Au 9% - 10%, Cu 1%, Zn 20% - 25%. The process data of the desilverizing operation are shown by Table IV.

Table IV. Process Data for Desilverizing.

Average silver contained in lead: 4 600 g/t	
Zinc added as:	
Spelter	*26% ≙ 4,4 kg/t Pb ≙ 0,98 kg/kg Ag+Au*
Zn from Faber du Faur retorts	*36% ≙ 6,1 kg/t Pb ≙ 1,36 kg/kg Ag+Au*
Zn from vacuum dezinking	*38% ≙ 6,5 kg/t Pb ≙ 1,41 kg/kg Ag+Au*
Total	*100% ≙ 17,0 kg/t Pb ≙ 3,75 kg/kg Ag+Au*
High grade Ag-Zn crystals from Howard Press:	*39 kg/t lead*
Low grade Ag-Zn crystals	*: 120 kg/t lead*

Dezinking

The desilverized lead contains about 0.5% to 0.6% Zn. A water cooled vacuum vessel is dipped into the lead melt. The required vacuum of about 5 x 10^{-3} torr is produced by a pump unit consisting of a surplus gas pump for the pre-vacuum and an oil injector which is connected with a supporting pump. The zinc content of the lead charge is reduced to 0.03% - 0.04% by vacuum distillation over a period of six hours during which time the temperature of the lead is raised to 520° - 580°C.

Further vacuum dezinking of the lead melt would be uneconomical and the final zinc removal is, therefore, done during the end refining stages (see below) before casting the refined lead.

Debismuthizing

Depending on the bismuth content of the lead, two different methods are used at N.A. to remove bismuth. The Kroll-Betterton method(15) is used for lead containing between 0.05% and 3.5% Bi. Where bismuth contents exceed 3.5%, bismuth is separated electrolytically.

According to the Kroll-Betterton Process, bismuth can be removed down to a content below 0.01% through having calcium and magnesium added to the charge whereby $CaMg_2Bi_2$ is formed as a precipitate and liquated. The practice at N.A. is a one-step and batch-wise operation.

To prevent oxidation, lumpy calcium metal is dropped by means of a bell into the agitated lead melt having a temperature of 420°C. Thereafter, the required quantity of magnesium in ingot form is stirred into the lead at the same temperature. Another hour of stirring is followed by a two-hour liquation period while the temperature decreases at a rate of 20°C/h and the lead-bearing Ca-Mg-Bi crystals float to the surface and are skimmed off. When the temperature is down to 380°C, the walls and bottom of the kettle are scraped and the crystals floating to the surface are also skimmed off. Shortly before solidifying (about 320°C), the bismuth-free lead is pumped into the next kettle for end refining. The process data of bismuth removal by the Kroll-Betterton Process are shown by Table V.

Table V. Process Data for Debismuthizing - Kroll-Betterton Process.

Bi contained in lead before Bi removal	
Average bismuth contained in Ca-Mg-Bi crystals	: 0,05-3,5%
Quantity of Ca-Mg-Bi crystals	: 110 kg/t Pb
Rate of Bi removal	: ~98%
Calcium requirements	: 0,15 kg/kg Bi ≙ 0,90 kg/t Pb
Magnesium requirements	: 0,39 kg/kg Bi ≙ 2,30 kg/t Pb
Ca and Mg contained in Pb before end refining	: 0,03% Ca; 0,1% Mg

End Refining

All lead having passed the refining steps described above is now subjected to an end refining operation in a holding kettle before it is cast into ingots. The residual contents of zinc (0.03% - 0.04%), calcium (0.03%) and magnesium (0.1%) must be removed from the bismuth-free lead, and likewise the residual zinc content from the lead that has not been treated by the Kroll-Betterton Process.

While adding small quantities of NaOH and $NaNO_3$, the lead melt having a minimum temperature of 400°C is agitated until a dry dross is formed which is then skimmed off by a grab. A sample taken from the lead melt at this stage must retain a bright surface until just before it solidifies.

The NaOH consumption for lead from the Kroll-Betterton Process is about 3.5 kg/T. and for lead from the Parkes Process about 1.9 kg/T. The $NaNO_3$ consumption is 2.1 kg/T. and 1.8 kg/T., respectively. The dross yield averaging 29 kg per ton of lead is sent to the lead smelter.

Ingot Casting

After the end refining, the lead melt having a temperature in the range 420°C to 480°C is cast into 50-kg ingots by a straight-line casting machine:-

Supplier:	Sheppard, Bridgend, England
Distance from axis to axis:	16.75 m
Number of molds:	234
Casting rate:	about 25 T/h
Speed:	1.25 m/min

Variable speed reducer.

The grades of lead cast by this machine are listed in Table VI.

Table VI. Lead Grades Produced by N.A.

Type	*Grade*	*Alloy components*
Pig lead *Soft lead* *Corroding lead*	99,9 99,94 99,97 99,985	——
Acid Copper lead	99,985	Cu
Lead alloys	99,9	Cu, As, Sn, Sb, Te
Electrolytic lead	99,99	——

Treatment of Pressed Silver-Zinc Crystals

The silver-zinc crust pressed by the Howard Press is charged to the Faber du Faur retort[16] without prior liquation. It contains in the average 9% - 10% Ag+Au, 20% - 25% Zn, 1% Cu, balance Pb. The crust is charged by hand to a retort heated up to about 800°C. One charge consists of about 600 kg crystals. The evaporating zinc condenses in an allonge, is tapped continually and cast into blocks. When the zinc evaporation comes to an end, the process is completed and the melt now consisting of a lead/silver alloy is poured from the Faber du Faur retort into a steel ladle and cast by hand into blocks weighing about 50 kg each. These are fed to a cupellation furnace for precious metals recovery. For further process data see Table VII.

Table VII. Process Data for Treatment of Ag/Zn Crystals from Howard Press.

Duration of charge	8 hours
Zinc recovery	12 kg/hr
Life of retorts	45-50 charges
Yield distribution	wt.-% of Ag/Zn crystals
Pb/Ag alloy	70
Zn	15
Dross	15

	Ag+Au %		Zn %		Cu %	
Product	Assay	Yield	Assay	Yield	Assay	Yield
Pb/Ag alloy	13,0	93,5	1,1	3,0	0,8	60,0
Zinc	0,1	0,1	95,0	62,5	0,2	3,5
Dross	3,0	6,4	50,0	34,5	2,0	36,5
Total [%]		100,0		100,0		100,0

Treatment of $CaMg_2Bi_2$ Crystals

The Ca-Mg-Bi crystals are melted in a kettle of 100 T.capacity. To speed up the melting process, some 40 tons of lead/bismuth alloy from the preceding charge are left in the kettle to which the crystals are fed in portions of about 20 tons. After adding NaOH salt melt (about 17 kg per ton of crystals), mainly calcium and magnesium oxidize. The forming dross is skimmed off by a grab and the whole operation repeated until the kettle is filled. The melting temperature is about 400°C. During oxidation with NaOH the temperature rises (without additional heating) up to 600°C and sometimes higher. The dross yield is about 180 kg per ton of $CaMg_2Bi_2$ crystals.

Normally lead is added to reduce the resultant lead/bismuth alloy to about 8% Bi. The alloy so obtained is cast into anodes at 450°C by a casting wheel. It is frequently mixed with Type C lead containing more than 3.5% Bi (see Table II) which had passed through all refining steps except for the Kroll-Betterton Process. The casting wheel has a diameter of 7.20 m and carries 15 molds.

Its casting rate is about 15 T/h. The anodes are then sent to the electrolytic lead refinery for the separation of bismuth from the lead. Process data of the tankhouse practice at N.A. are shown by Table VIII.

Table VIII. Data on Lead Tankhouse.

Cells: 71 — *Inside dimensions* : *2 400 x 700 x 960 (mm)* = *Length x width x depth*

Capacity : *1,5 m^3 electrolyte*

Sizes and Weights of Anodes and Cathodes:

Electrode	Length (mm)	Width (mm)	Thickness (mm)	Area (m^2)	Submerged Depth (mm)	Weight kg
Blanks	1 140					7,1
Cathode	900	600	15	0,9	750	~ 80
Anode new	700	530	50	0,82	685	~ 200
Anode rest	690	520	2,5 - 5,0	0,72	680	~ 60 (~ 30%)

Tankhouse Operation

19 Anodes per cell, 18 Cathodes per cell } Distance : 12 cm

Space between anode and cathode surfaces : 3,5 cm

Current: 2,6 KA ≙ 160 A/m^2 cathodic ≙ 176 A/m^2 anodic (new) ≙ 200 A/m^2 anodic (old).

Current efficiecy approx. 90% Anode lifetime 12 da; Cathode lifetime 6 da.

Cell voltage I. Cathode period ~ 400 mV; II Cathode period ~ 600 mV.

Flapping cathodes: 8 hr after cathode under current.

Scraping anodes : every 2-4 days (per hand).

Electrolyte circulation: in 40°C; out 32°C (cascade). Electrolyte flow: 15 l/min.

Glue consumption: 300 g/t electrolytic lead.

Output: electrolytic lead ~200 kg/da cell; tankhouse slime ~ 20 kg/da cell.

Assays:
- *Anodes approx. 0,005 - 0,01% Cu; 4-8% Bi; 50 g/t Ag*
- *Cathodes approx. <3 g/t Cu; 10 g/t Bi;*
- *Tankhouse slime 0,06% Cu; 88-90% Bi; 2-4% Pb*
- *Electrolyte (g/l) 70 Pb, 80 F; 20 B, <0,002 Cu; <0,002 Bi*

Labor: 17 operators divided in 3 shifts per day + 1 replacement shift of 4 men + 1 day-shift of 1 man.

Work distribution
- *Day shift: blank casting, lead sampling, electrolyte supervision*
- *Rotating shifts: one of the 4 shift workers acts as "first man".*

Jobs:
- *Cathode fixing, weighing, charge and discharge of cells.*
- *Crane operating, cathode flapping, anode scraping, current control.*
- *Short circuit detection, electrolyte supervision, preparing and adding additives, washing and drying of tankhouse slime, removing Bi from wash solution.*

References

1. Tafel, V., Lehrbuch der Metallhüttenkunde, 2nd ed., Vol. II, Leipzig, 1953, pp. 137-140.

2. Colcord, F., U.S. Smelting and Mining Co., U.S.Pat. 1,523,980, 1923.

3. Krysko, W.W., and Drinkwater, J., "Die Entkupferung des Bleis", Teil VIII, Erzmetall, Vol. 20, No. 4, 1967, pp. 171-173.

4. Kleinert, R., "Über die Entkupferung von Hartblei", Metall und Erz, Vol. 42, 1945, pp. 18-20.

5. Harris, H., Brit.Pat. 142,398; 184,639; 189,013.

6. Gmelin, Handbuch der Anorganischen Chemie, 8th ed., p. 41.

7. Lauterbach, H., "Beiträge zur Bleiraffination nach dem Harris-Verfahren", Metall und Erz, Vol. 28, 1931, pp. 317-326.

8. Behl, M., Gerlach, J., Pawlek, F., and Wuth, W., "Zur Kinetik des Harris-Verfahrens", Erzmetall, Vol. 21, 1968, pp. 411-415.

9. Paschen, P., and Winterhager, H., "Die Raffination von Blei mit Ätznatron", Erzmetall, Vol. 21, 1968, pp. 14-20.

10. Elliot, R.P., Constitution of Binary Alloys, First Supplement, New York, 1965, pp. 724-725.

11. Urazov, G.G., Lovchikov, V.S., and Lipshits, B.M., Izv.Vysshikh Uchebnikh Zavedenii, Tsvetn.Met., No. 4, 1958, pp. 96-102.

12. Reiff, F., and Toussaint, S.M., "Untersuchungen über Beständigkeit und Löslichkeit des Natriumstannates", Zeitschrift für Anorganische Allgemeine Chemie, Vol. 241, 1939, pp. 372-380.

13. Tafel, V., Lehrbuch der Metallhüttenkunde, 2nd ed., Vol. I, Leipzig, 1951, pp. 97-119.

14. Davey, T.R.A., "Entsilberung und Entwismutierung von Blei", Erzmetall, Vol. 10, 1957, pp. 53-60.

15. Kroll, W., "Fortschritte auf dem Gebiete der Metalltrennung", Metall und Erz, Vol. 35, 1938, pp. 252-254, pp. 282-286.

Betterton, J.O., and Lebedeff, Y.E., "Debismuthizing Lead with Alkaline Earth Metals, Including Magnesium, and with Antimony", Transactions of The Metallurgical Society of AIME, Vol. 121, 1936, pp. 205-225.

Davey, T.R.A., Transactions of The Metallurgical Society of AIME, Vol. 206, 1956, p. 341.

16. Tafel, V., Lehrbuch der Metallhüttenkunde, 2nd ed., Vol. I, Leipzig, 1951, pp. 116-118.

Chapter 31

ELECTROLYTIC LEAD REFINING AS PRACTICED BY THE CERRO DE PASCO CORPORATION AT LA OROYA, PERU

Carlos A. Aranda

Supt. Lead & Copper Refining Div., Cerro de Pasco Corp.

Philip J. Taylor

Metallurgist, Lead Refinery, Cerro de Pasco Corp.

Abstract

The Smelting and Refining Department of Cerro de Pasco Corporation is located at La Oroya at an altitude of 3,720 meters (12,205 feet) in the Peruvian Andes. Producing lead, zinc and copper as well as twelve by-product metals and chemicals, the smelter is among the world's most complex. With the intake of high-bismuth ores in 1934, electrolytic lead refining by a modified Betts process was piloted and the plant went into commercial production in 1937 at a nominal capacity of 100 M.T. per day. After expansions in 1950 and 1963, nominal capacity has increased to 250 M.T. per day.

Anodes spaced at 10.8 cm centre to centre and starting sheets are both set into the cells by overhead cranes. The asphalt-lined concrete cells are arranged in a Walker side-by-side configuration, and the electrolyte, circulating at 13 l/min./cell, is a solution of locally-produced hydrofluosilicic acid and lead fluosilicate. The corrosion cycle is limited to four days due to high impurity content of the bullion, which has successfully been treated at contents of up to 9% impurities.

The cathodes are melted, drossed, and cast into blocks and pigs assaying 99.997 + % lead. The anodes with the blanket of slime adhering, are washed with electrolyte and condensate make-up water to remove the concentrated lead fluosilicate entrapped in the slimes. The slimes are then removed with high-pressure water sprays, centrifuged and sent to another plant for recovery of silver, gold, bismuth, selenium, tellurium, and antimony.

Introduction

Established in 1902, the company, which became known as the Cerro de Pasco Copper Corporation, first engaged in the mining and smelting of high grade copper ores and silver-bearing copper ores with two smelters producing blister copper containing silver and gold. By 1922, a new smelter, located at La Oroya, 190 kilometers northeast of Lima, Peru, went into operation with a design capacity of 50,000 M.T. of blister copper per year.

As the grade of the copper-silver ores slowly declined, more attention was paid to the lead-zinc-silver ores of the mining properties. With the introduction of selective flotation the concentrators were changed over from gravity methods to flotation methods and started to produce lead-silver concentrates. A lead circuit was incorporated into the smelting operations in 1928 and had an annual capacity of 160,000 M.T. of concentrates and fluxes. Commercial electrolytic lead refining followed in 1937, subsequently requiring the development of a process for the recovery of silver, gold, bismuth, antimony, selenium and tellurium from anode slimes.

Lead ores and concentrates are received at La Oroya by rail and road, 70% from Corporation concentrators and 30% from over thirty different private miners. After bedding with fluxes, cottrell dusts, and refinery antimony slag, the process follows the conventional sequence of sintering on straight-line machines and smelting in blast furnaces. The crude bullion is treated in drossing kettles to remove copper and is then cast into anodes averaging 96% Pb, 1.0% Bi, 1.5% Sb, 0.4% Ag, 0.0003% Au, 0.3% As, and 0.04% Cu.

The electrolytic process employed is based on the original Betts method (1) for lead refining, but has been adapted to local conditions in order to treat the very impure bullion mentioned above, while still obtaining a first class refined product of 99.997% lead. This is accomplished by using a short anode cycle. A second modification consists of a countercurrent washing system for anode slimes, extracting entrapped electrolyte before the slimes are removed from the anode cores.

History of the Lead Refinery

During the first years of operation of the Oroya smelter the low grade lead ores of Cerro de Pasco were entirely disregarded since the Company's main activity was the recovery of blister copper carrying some gold and silver. Generation of dusts and fumes posed a difficult problem of atmospheric pollution, which after some years of experimentation, was satisfactorily resolved by installing a Cottrell electrostatic precipitation plant for handling and treating all the smelter dust and fumes.

The amount collected by this Cottrell plant was so large that it called for more facilities for its treatment. These dusts contained 40% lead and so lead blast furnace smelting was decided upon. But the preparation of a normal charge required other materials: namely, concentrates, ores and fluxes. This led to the purchasing of custom lead ores and concentrates and the recovery of lead and companion metals on a large scale.

By 1928, it was evident that, due to the high proportion of copper smelter dusts in the blast furnace charge, the bullion would be very impure. The necessity of recovering large quantities of antimony, bismuth, silver, gold and arsenic led to the consideration of electrolytic lead refining.

Research and Pilot Plant Testing

Metallurgical testwork in 1928 showed that pyrometallurgical refining of lead bullion containing such high amounts of antimony, silver, bismuth and arsenic would be too expensive.

The Betts electrolytic lead refining process at that time could not economically treat bullion carrying less than about 97.5% - 98% lead, but partial softening of the bullion followed by Betts refining seemed to offer a better approach. The 1929 - 1931 financial crisis, low metal prices and labor trouble slowed down lead smelting operations from 1930 to 1936. Meanwhile, T. E. Harper and G. Reinberg (2) developed their outstanding modifications of the Betts process which permitted the economical treatment of bullion assaying 80% - 95% lead with lower acid losses than other Betts plants experienced when treating 98% - 99% lead anodes. Furthermore, the Harper-Reinberg process produced exceptionally pure lead.

The pilot plant (3) was put into operation in June 1934 with a daily capacity of 25 M.T. of refined lead and consisted of 64, asphalt lined, concrete electrolytic cells, 2.69 m long, 79 cm wide and 1.17 m deep inside, arranged in four rows according to the Walker system and serviced by an electric monorail hoist of 3 tons capacity.

There were 24 anodes, 66 cm wide by 91 cm long, and 25 cathodes, 69 cm wide by 94 cm long, in each cell, and power from a synchronous motor-generator set was provided at 5 000 A and 30 V. Electrolyte at 37 ºC temperature was circulated at 11.3 liters/minute per cell. The total hydrofluosilicate concentration was normally kept between 100 and 150 grams per liter with lead between 60 and 100 grams per liter, equivalent to 60 to 80 grams of free acid per liter.

Additional pilot plant facilities consisted of four, 70-ton, oil-fired kettles, two for melting bullion and two for melting cathodes, and two mechanical casting wheels, the bullion wheel with 12 molds for anodes and the refined lead wheel with 12 five-pocket molds for 45.4 kg bars. There were 16 concrete cells for anode washing and electrolyte recovery.

This plant was operated in a similar way to standard Betts plant practice as known at the time except for the main modifications which, briefly, may be summarized as follows:

1. The anodes were cast thinner and replaced at more frequent intervals, thus limiting the anode corrosion period and preventing the voltage drop across the adhering slime blanket from exceeding a certain critical value above which impurities dissolve from the slimes blanket and contaminate the cathode deposit.
2. Anode slimes were washed by a system of counter-current dipping, prior to their removal from the surface of the anode scrap, thus recovering the entrapped electrolyte and reducing expensive acid losses.

Operations were carried out from 1934 through April 1937 with the following results:

1. A current density of 1.51 - 1.61 A/dm^2 was required for bullions containing over 90% lead and having an approximate anode corrosion period of four days.
2. A cathode of high purity was ensured by limiting the period of anode corrosion and was essentially independent of anode impurities content. Typical assays were (3):

	% Pb	% Cu	% As	% Sb	% Bi	% Ag
Anodes	90.1	0.12	1.9	3.3	4.4	0.14
Cathodes	99.998	0.0001	0.00005	0.0004	0.0005	0.000008
Slimes	19-20	0.8	12-13	23-24	30-31	1.0

3. Acid losses were about 0.9 kg of 100% hydrofluosilicic acid per ton of lead produced and independent of the amount of impurities in the original bullion.
4. Impure bullion was treated directly without pre-softening or other pre-refining steps, except tin removal to prevent cathode contaimination.
5. Accumulation of slimes in the cells was minimum.
6. The standard lead fluosilicate-hydrofluosilicic acid electrolyte operated satisfactorily over a wide range of concentrations between 100 and 150 grams of lead fluosilicate per liter with lead between 60 and 100 grams per liter, equivalent to 60 to 80 grams of free acid per liter.

Commercial Operations in the Past

Based on pilot plant operating data a commercial scale refinery was constructed and placed into operation early in 1937 at a daily capacity of 100 metric tons.

Bullion, containing 94% to 96% lead and varying amounts of silver, gold, bismuth, antimony, arsenic, copper, selenium and tellurium, was cast in the smelter into anodes, 66 cm wide by 91 cm long by 22 mm thick, exclusive of lugs, weighing 130 kg for four-day corrosion cycles.

Starting sheets, 68 cm wide by 94 cm long, were cast from refined lead on an inclined table in the usual manner but supporting rods were made of copper-plated steel formed with a dovetail slot into which the sheet was integrally cast to ensure a better electrical contact.

Reinforced concrete cells, "Harvel" lined, 2.69 m long by 79 cm wide by 1.17 m deep inside, were arranged in four rows according to the Walker system, 24 anodes and 25 cathodes to a cell, spaced 10.2 cm center to center. There were 256 electrolytic cells, 64 cells for anode washing and 4 cells for cathode dip washing.

Power was supplied by a General Electric synchronous motor-generator set with a rated output of 6 000 A at 120 V. Current density employed was 1.90 A/dm^2 and initial voltage on a newly set cell averaged 0.4 V increasing to 0.6 V by the final day.

Electrolyte composition was maintained at about 130 grams of total hydrofluosilicic acid per liter and 74 grams of free hydrofluosilicic acid per liter. Fresh acid, produced in a batch retort plant, was added in proportion to operating losses which varied from 1.5 to 2.0 kg per metric ton of refined lead. Electrolyte lead content had a tendency to increase and was controlled by sulphuric acid additions in a separate tank where lead sulphate was settled out and clear solution returned to the main circuit after centrifuging. Glue and "Bindarene" as addition reagents were daily added to the circuit at the rate of 0.75 to 1.0 kg per metric ton of refined lead produced.

An electrolyte total working volume of 520,000 liters was circulated from storage sumps containing about 7% of this total through hard rubber lined, steel piping by means of "Worthite" centrifugal pumps to the outer rows of the commercial cells. After passing through the cells (top inlet and bottom outlet) solution cascaded to the two inner rows and returned to the sumps through launders. The circulation rate was kept at 15 liters per minute per cell and the electrolyte temperature at about 37 ºC without any heat exchanger.

Cell changing operations were carried out on the basis of four-day anode and cathode cycles. Working cells were cut out two at a time to limit downtime, corroded anodes removed, packed together in sets of 96 and placed in the counter-current dip-washing process for a four-day period. Anodes were first washed in circulating electrolyte for a period of 24 hours, after which they passed through a series of three additional tanks in which they met a small flow of wash water travelling in the opposite direction to anode movements. After the fourth day wash, anodes, containing negligible amounts of electrolyte, were sent to the adjacent anode residue plant for manual removal of slimes.

Cathodes were dip-washed prior to melting, transported by a narrow-gauge, battery-operated tram to the kettle house, dropped into the melting kettles by overhead crane and supporting rods skimmed from the molten metal surface. There were four 70-ton, oil-fired kettles, two for melting cathodes and two for melting scrap anodes. Refined lead pigs of 45.4 kg and anodes of 130 kg were cast on mechanical wheels of similar design.

After melting, cathodes were heated to 500 ºC and stirred with a high-speed stirrer for a short period to remove any small quantities of antimony, arsenic or tin and also to circulate the melting drosses and separate entrained metal. Pigs cast at about 425 ºC were stacked in bundles of 25 and loaded into shipping cars. Refined lead assayed approximately 99.997% Pb, 0.0004% Cu, 0.0007% Sb, 0.0020% Bi, and 0.0004% Ag, with traces of arsenic.

Refining operations were carried out in this first commercial Betts plant up to March 1951, though moving to a new refinery building began in November 1950. The full-scale plant performed well between 1937 and 1950 with anodes averaging 92% to 96% lead, producing refined lead of good quality and proving, both economically and metallurgically, the soundness of the modifications made to the original Betts process. A summary of operating data from this first commercial plant is shown in Table I.

For the period 1946 to 1950 considerable trouble was experienced in maintaining acceptable current efficiency and acid loss values. Main factors contributing to this situation were the poor condition of circulation piping, cathode deposit deterioration caused by glue of inferior quality, increased resistance due to progressive damage of copper-plated cathode cross-rods and frequent failures of cell linings causing solution spillages. All these operating problems and the condition of the tankhouse required a complete revamping at a substantial cost. Moreover, the nearby zinc pilot plant had to be expanded and more additional area was urgently needed. Consequently, the decision was taken to use available facilities at the copper refinery site.

Table I. Data from 100 M.T./Day Plant

Year	Bullion Assays Pb	Sb	Bi	As	Lead Produced	Current Density	Current Efficiency	Acid Loss	Organic Reagents
	%	%	%	%	M.T.	amp/dm²	%	kg/M.T.	kg/M.T.
1937	92.6	3.8	1.2	1.8	19 053	1.50	84.9	1.30	0.37
1938	93.5	3.2	1.2	1.2	26 004	1.53	90.4	1.17	0.41
1939	94.4	2.2	1.4	1.1	24 311	1.52	90.0	1.50	0.41
1940	94.0	1.8	1.8	1.5	31 131	1.40	90.7	0.99	0.45
1941	95.7	1.9	1.6	0.2	32 871	1.47	86.4	1.50	0.52
1942	95.8	2.2	1.2	0.5	37 915	1.89	76.1	1.83	0.75
1943	95.6	2.4	1.1	0.5	43 171	1.85	87.5	1.89	2.92
1944	95.1	2.9	1.1	0.5	38 906	1.79	85.7	2.07	1.00
1945	95.4	2.9	0.9	0.5	39 990	1.83	83.0	2.59	1.06
1946	95.5	3.0	1.0	0.1	36 478	1.80	77.0	2.71	1.21
1947	95.3	3.3	0.9	0.1	32 809	1.75	76.1	5.18	1.15
1948	95.3	3.2	0.9	0.1	34 297	1.68	79.1	2.73	1.19
1949	94.8	3.7	0.9	0.1	36 014	1.77	78.9	3.31	1.00
1950	94.5	3.7	1.0	0.4	31 608	1.65	76.9	3.62	0.97

The Huaymanta Lead Refinery

One half of the new copper refinery building was converted to lead refining in 1950 with a relatively modest capital expenditure and refining capacity was thus increased from 36 000 to 45 000 metric tons per year. Operations started on November 12, 1950 using a common electrical equipment with the copper refinery which consisted of two General Electric Ignitron mercury arc rectifiers, connected in parallel, capable of supplying D.C. power at 7 200 A and 260 V to 416 electrolytic cells in the copper refinery and 7 200 A and 200 V to 320 electrolytic cells in the new lead refinery tankhouse. All cells were arranged in series on the same rectifier circuit (4), which made this installation unique in the electrorefining industry for many years until April 1969 when the copper refinery circuit was separated.

Table II gives operating data from the Huaymanta plant for typical years. Since a detailed description of the present lead refinery operations is given in the following sections of this paper, a review is now made of the most important changes that have taken place during the period 1951 to 1969, namely the following.

Table II. Data from the Huaymanta Refinery

	1951	1957	1961	1964	1969
Production, M.T.	44 482	68 853	76 147	88 443	77 540
Current Density, Amps/dm^2	1.37	1.55	1.58	1.58	1.55
Current efficiency, %	92.80	97.60	97.30	92.50	90.20
Kg lead/Kw-day	127.60	137.30	121.30	132.50	127.40
Acid loss, kg/M.T.	3.50	1.30	1.90	1.90	3.90
Glue added, kg/M.T.	0.32	0.31	0.35	0.49	0.56
Goulac added, kg/M.T.	0.23	0.31	0.34	0.43	0.52
Lead in electrolyte, g/l	73	85	73	78	66
Free acid in electrolyte, g/l	65	61	74	63	69
Anode scrap returned, %	-	47.10	47.20	49.60	48.80
Bullion grade, % Pb	-	-	-	97.10	96.70
Bullion antimony, %	-	-	-	1.37	1.51
Bullion bismuth, %	-	-	-	0.89	0.94
Labor efficiency, kg/man-hr.	-	278.50	316.40	302.80	314.80

The refining capacity was gradually increased to 68 000 M.T. per year by raising rectifier capacity from 6 700 A in 1951 to 7 200 A in 1954; then to 75 000 M.T. per year at 7 500 A in 1956. Finally, expansion to 90 000 M.T. per year was attained in 1963 by closing electrode spacing from 12.7 cm to 10.8 cm, center to center, by increasing anodes and cathodes from 33 and 34 to 40 and 41 respectively, and by incorporating a motor-generator set at 1 600 A into the mercury rectifier busbar system.

Lead bullion anodes were changed in weight from 135 kg to 155 kg so as to endure the increased corrosion. Several trials were conducted for refining heavier anodes with five-day corrosion cycles with little success, since grade of lead bullion was too low and bismuth in final refined lead bars was high. Vertically cast anodes were satisfactorily refined though mechanical casting problems have thus far limited ample supply for a commercial scale operation.

Different reagents such as Aloes, Orzan "A", chesnut extract, sulphonated tannin extracts, Aerosol OT, etc., were tested alone or in combination with glue and goulac without attaining too much success in improving cathode deposit.

Current efficiencies were impaired by current leakages through damaged cell asphalt linings and corroded concrete of cells and supporting columns. This problem became so serious that an intensive campaign had to be carried out without delay for renewing all cell linings. Also current efficiency and acid recovery were adversely affected by closer spacing and low bullion grade.

Slimes removal from anodes posed a difficult problem when the manual operation was unable to handle 2 560 anodes per day which required a large labor crew. After several attempts, a cleaning machine was satisfactorily designed and constructed by the Oroya engineering department based on the use of high pressure water sprays operating at 100 kg/cm^2 pressure and cleaning scrap anodes at the rate of one anode per 15 seconds.

Slimes dewatering operations were originally started with thickeners and steam drum dryers which gave high losses of dust containing silver, bismuth and antimony. Dryers were replaced by filter presses, which reduced slimes losses, but yielded a filter cake with excessive moisture content besides the frequent problems caused by slurry leakages through corroded plates and frames. Finally, continuous, high speed, solid bowl centrifuges were installed and the dewatering problem was partially solved, since slimes losses are nil and all material is rapidly handled,although slimes moisture is still somewhat high.

Melting and casting of refined lead had to be improved in order to eliminate both ingot cavities and excessive drossing on remelting. Our Research department thoroughly investigated this problem and established the required techniques which have been described in detail in the literature (5) and do not need to be elaborated upon here. In brief, the process consists firstly in treating the fast-drossing lead with caustic soda at 480 ºC, thus reducing antimony content to less than 1 ppm and secondly, in the installation of an adjustable top heating device mounted above the straight-line casting machine and facing downwards. The heating intensity of 0.33 kW/m^2 keeps the top surface of the bar molten for several minutes after casting and allows a uniform cooling from the bottom upwards thus ensuring cavity-free bars.

A melting kettle life of one year was considered to be unduly short and one of the main difficulties was elongation. A supporting ring placed on the bottom of the furnace setting reduced this failure and the number of repairs as well, although total life was not greatly extended. In 1961, an "Orange Peel" type of kettle was put into service with good results, as the first leak developed after 14 months of operation, and the kettle lasted 4 years with minor repairs.

Present Operations

Equipment and Materials Handling

Building and Services: The lead refinery is housed together with the electrolytic copper refinery in a steel-framed building of which an area of 27.5 m by 244 m is occupied by the lead refinery. A wall separates the two refineries. The lead refinery tankhouse basement, where the sumps, pumps and pipework are located, has an asphalt-covered concrete floor which slopes to a launder for recovery of spillage. The cells rest on reinforced concrete beams and pillars and each cell is insulated from ground with four porcelain insulators. The cells are cast locally of reinforced concrete with an asphalt lining and internal dimensions of 4.52 m by 92.6 cm by 1.14 m deep. They are arranged in twelve blocks, each consisting of a double row of sixteen cells in the Walker side by side configuration. Ten of the blocks are used for lead refining and two for anode washing. The aisles surrounding each block have wood block floors covered with asphalt. All other floors are concrete, asphalt-covered where there is danger of electrolyte spillage.

Electric power is generated by the Company's hydro-electric plants and supplied as 50 000 volt A.C. power. This is transformed to 11,000 volts by the refinery substation, transformed to 6 000 volts by a General Electric 2.4 MVA autotransformer and converted to 280 volt D.C. power by a General Electric hexaphase rectifier-transformer. From there a General Electric twelve-tank mercury rectifier supplies 7 600 A to the tankhouse. The remaining current, usually 1 600 A is produced by a pair of General Electric motor-generator sets, one of which is a stand-by. Separate transformers supply the plant with 440 V and 110 V A.C. power for machinery, lighting, etc. A schematic representation of the power supply can be seen in the general flowsheet of figure 1.

Some 35 m^3 per day of soft water is supplied to the plant as condensate from the copper refinery steam heat exchangers. This water is used where it will enter the electrolyte; that is, for the manufacture of electrolyte acid and for washing anodes and cathodes, as the salts in hard water react with the electrolyte. Also some 250 m^3 per day of hard river water are used in the slimes plant and by the air compressors.

Compressed air is supplied to both refineries at 0.07 kgf/mm^2 by three Ingersoll-Rand compressors with a total capacity of 60.7 m^3/min.

Anode Handling: Decopperized bullion is cast on horizontal wheels in the smelter with an average weight of 153 kg* and a

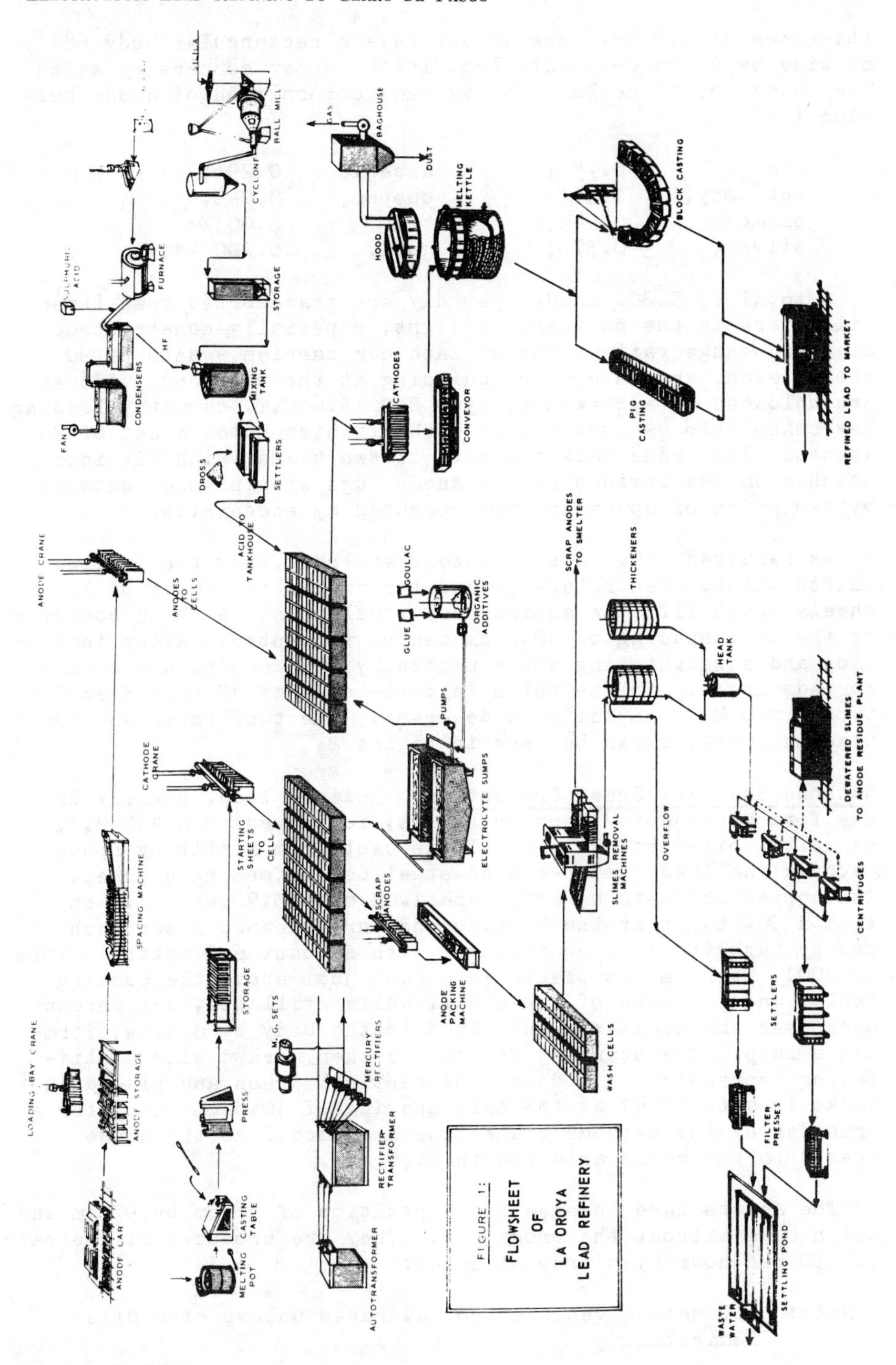

FIGURE 1: FLOWSHEET OF LA OROYA LEAD REFINERY

thickness of 2.5 cm. The anodes have a rectangular body 68 cm wide by 91 cm deep with lugs in the upper corners by which they hang in the cells. The average composition of anode bullion is:*

lead,	96.75%;	arsenic,	0.29%;
antimony,	1.51%;	copper,	0.04%;
bismuth,	0.94%;	tin,	0.003%;
silver,	0.37%;	gold,	0.000 411%.

A total of 3 200 anodes per day are transported some three kilometers to the refinery in eight, especially-constructed, standard-gauge railway cars. Each car carries 4 sets of 90 anodes each, and enters the building at the west end. Anodes are unloaded by a Shaw-Box, type BRC, 13.6 M.T. capacity loading bay crane into 44 steel racks each of which holds a set of 90 anodes. The crane bale consists of two beams which fit into notches on the insides of the anode lugs when pressed outwards by two pairs of spreader arms operated by eccentrics.

As required, the sets of anodes are hung from two inclined shafts which, when rotated, feed the anodes to a pair of lug wheels which lift the anodes individually onto a chain conveyor at the cell spacing of 10.8 cm centre to centre. After inspection and straightening where necessary, the anodes are transported directly to the cells in cell-loads of 40 by a Shaw-Box, type S, 10 M.T. capacity anode crane. The two cranes and the spacing conveyor can be seen in figure 2.

Cathode Starting Sheet Production: Refined lead, usually in the form of rejected bars or blocks, is melted in a 4.5 M.T. capacity, oil-fired kettle. It is cast from a tilting spoon onto an inclined, water-cooled steel table forming a sheet. The copper cross-rods, which are 1.08 m by 3.7 cm by 1.2 cm with a 90º twist at the contact end, are cleaned after each use by tumbling in a rotary drum with sawdust and water in lots of 800. Each bar is placed in a rack just above the casting table, and the ears of the sheet, while still hot, are thrown back over the cross-rod and fixed to the body by a blow, forming a loop. The starting sheets are then marked with a stiffening impression in a door-type vertical press and placed in racks in sets of 41 at the cell spacing of 10.8 cm ready for transfer by the cathode crane (the same model as the anode crane) to the cells as shown in figure 3.

The sheets have an area for deposition of 76 cm by 97 cm and weigh 8 kg without the cross-rod. They are produced at the rate of 250 per hour by a crew of 5 men.

* Note: All data given are 1969 averages unless otherwise indicated.

Fig. 2 - The photograph shows anodes being loaded into the spacing machine by the storage bay crane and the spaced anodes being transported to the tankhouse by the anode crane.

Fig. 3 - Here the starting sheets are being transported to the cells by the cathode crane.

Cell Setting: The plant operates on a four-day cycle for both anodes and cathodes, dictated by the high impurity content of the bullion and consequent heavy slimes formation. Each day, one-quarter of the tankhouse, 80 cells or 2-1/2 blocks, are changed on two shifts. The cell to be changed is shorted out with two laminated copper jumper bars. The sets of 40 anodes and 41 cathodes are removed by crane, the starting sheets are set by crane after manual straightening and, finally, the anodes are set between the cathodes. After minor adjustments are made to the spacing and the electrode contacts are checked, the jumper bars are removed and the cell is back in operation. Cell changing takes about 6 minutes per cell with a crew of 2 cell tenders and 2 crane operators.

<u>Electrolyte:</u> The electrolyte is an aqueous solution of 69 g/l of locally produced hydrofluosilicic acid (H_2SiF_6) and 66 g/l lead in the form of lead fluosilicate ($PbSiF_6$) which is slowly produced due to the difference between anode and cathode current efficiencies. The content of fluosilicate radicle, commonly called total acid, from both constituents is 115 g/l expressed as hydrofluosilicic acid. The minor constituents and impurities in the electrolyte are as follows:

HF,	5.9 g/l;	H_2SO_4,	0.17 g/l;
Ca,	2.1 g/l;	Zn,	0.12 g/l;
Fe,	1.44 g/l;	Sb,	0.08 g/l;
Al,	0.46 g/l;	Ni,	0.01 g/l;
Mn,	0.46 g/l;	Tl,	$<$0.01 g/l;
Mg,	0.27 g/l;	As,	0.002 g/l.

The lead content of the electrolyte is controlled at the desired level by liberator cells with insoluble carbon anodes and lead cathodes which give the following reactions:

Anode reaction: $H_2O - 2e^- = 2H^+ + 1/2\ O_2\uparrow$

Cathode reaction: $PbSiF_6 + 2H^+ + 2e^- = H_2SiF_6 + Pb^o$

Total reaction: $PbSiF_6 + H_2O = H_2SiF_6 + Pb^o + 1/2\ O_2\uparrow$

Electrolyte is pumped from the sumps by one of two 4.5 m^3/min. Worthington pumps with 25 hp. (18.6 kW) Louis-Allis motors. It passes through a 30.5 cm line to a 25.4 cm distribution line to 10.5 cm I.D. feed lines running down each block between the two rows of cells. Electrolyte enters at the solution line of each cell at the rate of 13 l/min. and is discharged from the bottom of the cell at the other end through a 5.4 cm I.D. pipe. (There is no detectable change in electrolyte composition as it flows through the cell; the purpose of electrolyte recirculation is mixing.) The electrolyte from the cells passes through a 25.4 cm by 12.7 cm concrete channel lined with asphalt and integral with the floor and running between the blocks and then through a 30.5 cm return line to the main sumps. All pipework is of rigid P.V.C. construction. The sumps are 15.25 m long by 3.15 m wide by 1.43 m deep. The total volume of electrolyte is 1 500 m^3 at a temperature maintained without external heating at 40 - 43 ºC. A third and smaller sump is used to settle solids from spillage collected from the basement floors.

Organic Additives: Animal bone glue from England, and Goulac, a solid, impure form of calcium lignin sulphonate from the United States, are added to the electrolyte to give a smooth deposit. These materials, in the amounts of 117 kg of glue and 110 kg of goulac per day (503 g of glue and 472 g of goulac per metric ton of refined lead produced), are dissolved in water at 50 - 60 ºC in a steam-heated, 8.77 m^3, stirred, steel tank. The solution is then fed at a constant rate to the electrolyte circuit at the main sump inlet by a 7.6 l/min. Mil-Royal-A metering pump.

Electrolysis: An average current of 9 000 A (range: 8 500 A to 9 800 A) is applied to the 10 blocks of the electrolytic tankhouse through 25.1 cm by 3.8 cm copper busbars. The current passes from the busbar at the end of the block to a 17.8 cm by 6.4 mm copper transfer plate lying along the long edge of the cell and insulated from the cell by a pressed asbestos strip. From there, current flows through the anodes, through the electrolyte to the cathodes and thence to the transfer plate and anodes of the next cell and so on to the end of that half-block where a busbar carries it to the next half-block. This path can be followed in figure 4. A current of 9 000 A gives a current density of 1.54 A/dm^2 at the anode and 1.34 A/dm^2 at the cathode.

During the four days of electrolysis, short circuits develop between anodes and cathodes due to bent or misaligned cathodes and due to nodular deposition (trees) on the cathode, especially when the organic additives are not quite right. Short-circuiting and current loss to ground are essentially the only forms of loss of current and of current efficiency. A crew of four men with a supervisor are employed in correcting and preventing short circuits. Firstly, when the starting sheets are stiff with a four-hour deposit, each sheet is lifted and straightened if necessary. Secondly, at least once per shift all the cross-rods are checked to see if they are hot, in which case the cathode is lifted and the fault corrected.

The supervisor of the crew also detects short circuits and bad contacts using a voltmeter. The normal range of cell voltage is from 0.50 volts at the beginning of a cycle to 0.70 volts at the end of the cycle. (The voltage increases due to resistance of the slime blanket). Cell voltages which differ from the normal, either being lower due to short circuits or higher due to poor contacts, are checked and put right.

Fig. 4 - An electrolytic cell. From right to left, the current flows from the bus-bar to the transfer plate to the anodes through the electrolyte to the cathodes and thence to the next transfer plate.

The average current efficiency in 1969 was 90.2% with a range in monthly figures of 86.0% to 94.8%. The average current efficiency corresponds to 0.190 kWh per kg of lead and 127.3 kg lead per kW-day. (Current efficiencies have increased to 95% during 1970 and a lower amperage of 8 500 A is in use.)

Refined Lead Melting and Drossing: Cell-loads of cathodes such as shown in figure 5, each of about three metric tons of refined lead, are removed from the cells, brushed to remove any adhering slime, dipped in a tank of hot water to wash off electrolyte, and placed on a small chain conveyor. Here the cross-rods are slipped from the loops and the cathodes charged to one of four 140 M.T. oil-fired kettles. The firebox steel kettles, of 3.3 m I.D. at the top by 2.2 m inside depth, are of "orange peel" construction; that is, segments of the hemisphere are electrically welded together so that all welds are vertical. The kettles are ventilated with a portable hood and a flue to a Norblo 12-bag dust arrester.

After melting and raising the temperature to 450 ºC, the melt of 130 M.T. of lead is agitated and a vortex created with a 50 hp. (37.3 kW) stirrer for one to one and a half hours. The melt-down dross is removed and the temperature raised to 480 ºC whereupon 20 kg of caustic soda is added to the bath. Stirring is continued for one hour or until a blue-film formation test shows that antimony has been reduced to 1 ppm. This test is performed by heating a sample of the lead to 400 ºC in an iron crucible, skimming the surface and noting the time required for the blue oxide film to re-cover the surface (5). The melt is considered ready for casting when the blue-film formation time is over 300 seconds. The blue-film formation time for metal cast in 1969 was 354 seconds.

Fig. 5 - Cathode being removed from a cell. Note the jumper bars which bridge the cell and the two dark cathodes which have been short-circuited.

Antimonial lead, C. de P. Electrospecial brand, which contains 0.0020% to 0.0040% antimony, is made by dissolving antimony metal in the melt. Smaller quantities of a 45% antimony alloy are also produced.

Refined Lead Casting: Molten lead or alloy at 475 ºC is pumped with 5 hp. (3.7 kW) centrifugal pumps either to a platform where 2,000 lb. (907 kg) blocks are cast or to an 18 M.T./hour Treadwell pig-casting machine. Pigs weighing 100 lb. (45.5 kg) are cast at the rate of 350 per hour, skimmed of dross and stacked in piles of 25 with a jib crane and air hoist. After weighing, marking and strapping, the pigs are stored until spectrographic analysis confirms that the lot meets specifications and then shipped by rail to the company's port facilities in Callao.

Blocks are cast in iron molds, cooled with water, and lifted from the molds by one of four 2.5 M.T. capacity Hyster fork-lift trucks by means of two slotted steel lugs cast into the sides of each block. The lugs are knocked off and the blocks weighed, marked and shipped. Production of refined lead was 77 850 M.T. in 1969 with an average composition as follows:

Lead,	99.9975 %;	Thallium,	<2 ppm;
Bismuth	11 ppm;	Arsenic,	2 ppm;
Antimony,	<2 ppm;	Tin,	2 ppm;
Silver,	2 ppm;	Iron,	2 ppm;
Copper,	2 ppm;	Zinc,	2 ppm.

Scrap Anode Handling: It can be seen in figure 6 that the bullion is made up of a lead-rich (dark) phase, the major phase, and a minor, intergranular (light) phase probably, as it would appear from figure 7, an eutectic mixture of an antimony-rich (white) phase and a lead-rich (dark) phase. Thus, during electrolysis, the lead-rich phases are mainly dissolved away, leaving a skeletal network of impurities, the slimes.

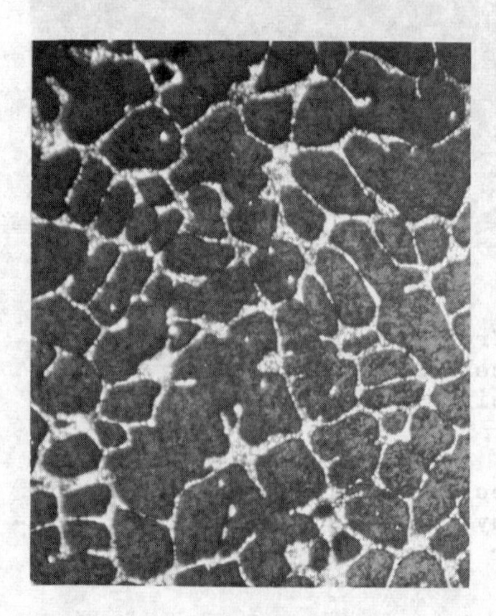

Fig. 6 - Bullion containing 96.6% Pb, 1.60% Sb, 1.05% Bi. Mag. 100 x; etch, acetic acid - hydrogen peroxide.

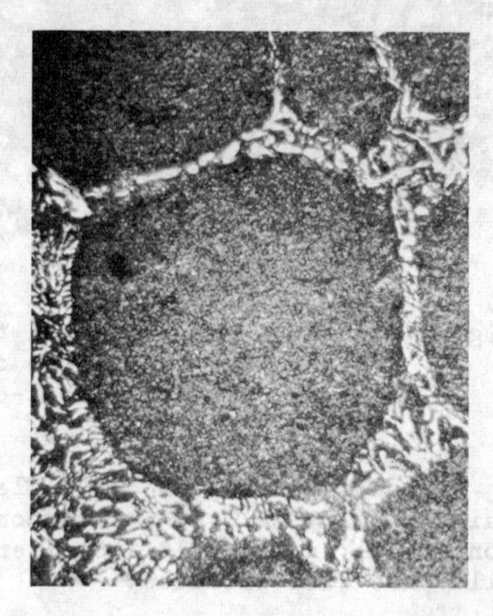

Fig. 7 - Bullion as in figure 6. Magnification, 1000 x; etch, acetic acid - hydrogen peroxide.

The slimes form an adherent blanket over the anode about 6 mm thick which contains in its pores a rich solution of lead fluosilicate. Because of the high impurity levels in the bullion and the resulting hardness of the slimes, the solution can be removed by dip washing the slimes while still on the anodes. Corroded anodes are shown in figure 8. To prepare them for washing, the anodes are pushed together into sets of 133 with a face to face separation of 3 to 4 mm. This is done by an anode packing machine in which the anodes are pushed along rails by a chain-operated bar. They are then placed by crane into the wash section.

Fig. 8 - Corroded anodes leaving the electrolytic cell.

The wash section comprises four half-blocks of 17 regular-sized cells each, which are arranged in the same manner as the electrolytic cells. In each half-block is performed one stage of a four-stage, counter-current wash. Soft, condensate water at 50 - 60 ºC enters the fourth stage cells at the rate of 30 m^3 per day divided evenly among the 17 cells. From the bottom of these cells, the liquor flows by gravity to the corresponding third stage cell, from the bottom of which the overflow runs to a small concrete surge tank in the basement. From the surge tank the liquor is recirculated through the second stage by a 3 in. Labour centrifugal pump at the rate of 8 l/min. per cell and a small part of the liquor bled off to the electrolyte circuit. The first stage wash liquor is electrolyte supplied by the main pumps at a rate of 12.5 l/min. per cell.

The anodes enter the first stage wash containing a lead fluosilicate solution in the slimes layer of some 400 g/l. The anodes remain in each wash section about 15 hours and finish the fourth stage with about 28 g/l lead in the slimes layer solution for a recovery of approximately 93%.

The loss of hydrofluosilicic acid, most of which is lost as lead fluosilicate in anode slimes, was 307 M.T. in 1969 or 3.94 kg of acid per metric ton of lead produced. These figures are exceptionally high; a more normal loss would be half this amount.

Slimes Removal: After washing, the anodes are moved by crane to one of two locally constructed slimes removal machines. Here the sets of anodes are hung from a pair of rotating inclined shafts which feed the anodes to a pair of lug-wheels. The lug-wheels pick up each anode individually and place them on a stainless steel chain conveyor which carries them upwards through a cabinet between two sets of sprays at the rate of 9 anodes per minute. The slimes are removed by the impact of high pressure water supplied by two 946 l/min., 0.63 kgf/mm^2, Worthington piston pumps. The scrap anodes are deposited in a rack from which sets of 90 are picked up by the loading bay crane and placed in the anode cars for return to the smelter. The weight of scrap returned in 1969 was 48.8% of the original anode weight.

Slimes Treatment: The slimes slurry drops into a sump from which it is pumped by a 3 in. Worthington sand pump to two 3.65 m diameter thickeners in the slimes plant. The slurry is thickened to 16% to 20% solids and the overflow runs to a settler. The pulp is pumped to a head tank from which it flows to four Sharples model P-2000 centrifuges. The centrifuge product at 35% moisture falls through a chute into a special railway car in which 30 W.M.T. lots are transported to the anode residue plant for recovery of antimony, bismuth, silver, gold, selenium and tellurium. The 1969 production of slime was 3 577 D.M.T. with the following composition:

Antimony,	35.01%;
Bismuth,	21.83%;
Lead,	14.31%;
Silver,	9.14%;
Gold,	0.103%.

Both the overflow from the thickeners and the centrifuge liquid discharge each flow into a separate wooden settler, 7.34 m by 3.05 m by 1.85 m deep, from which the overflow is pumped to a pair of Shriver No. 30 plate and frame filter presses. The filtrate, with a volume of 220 m^3 per day flows to a 15 m long by 6 m wide settling pond from which 10 D.M.T. of material containing 53% lead were removed in 1969.

Hydrofluosilicic Acid Plant: Fluorspar of 97.5% CaF_2 is imported from England in 45.4 kg bags. Some 840 kg of this material is charged to a 3 m long by 2 m diameter, externally oil-fired, steel rotary furnace. The furnace is rotated and 1.14 M.T. of 98% sulphuric acid of local manufacture added over four hours at temperatures rising from 70 ºC to 120 ºC. After all the acid is added, the temperature is raised to 200 ºC for two hours to drive the reaction to completion:

$$CaF_2 + H_2SO_4 = CaSO_4 + 2HF \uparrow$$

Hydrofluoric acid gas leaves the furnace via a steel pipe in the furnace axis and is absorbed in counter-current fashion in cold, condensate water in two water-cooled lead tanks equipped with baffles and agitators. The resulting solution, containing 320 g/l hydrofluoric acid, 20 g/l hydrofluosilicic acid and 2 g/l sulphuric acid, flow to a lead-lined steel tank where fine silica is added. The high-purity silica is ground from -1/4 mesh to 80% -200 mesh with a Hardinge conical air-swept ball mill with air-classifier and collected by a 1 m diameter cyclone. To each batch of acid, 245 kg of silica is added and mixed for 7 hours producing hydrofluosilicic acid:

$$6\ HF + SiO_2 = H_2SiF6 + 2\ H_2O$$

The slurry, containing excess silica, flows to one of two asphalt-lined concrete tanks and is air-agitated for two hours with 35 kg of lead kettle melt-down dross to precipitate any sulphuric acid carried over from the furnace:

$$PbO + H_2SO_4 = PbSO_4 + H_2O$$

The slurry is then settled for 3 hours and the clear liquor, containing approximately 450 g/l hydrofluosilicic acid, 7 g/l hydrofluoric acid and 5 g/l lead, is pumped to the electrolyte circuit of the tankhouse. The plant operates around the clock, producing two or three charges per day according to requirements. The plant operated 280 days in 1969 to process 632 charges and produce 298.5 M.T. of hydrofluosilicic acid. The average fluorine conversion efficiency was 91.1%.

Manpower: The normal complement of the lead refinery is close to 100 men divided in their duties as shown in Table III. The table does not include bull-gang labour nor men who replace others on their days off.

Metallurgical Development

Current Efficiency: The effects of operating variables on current efficiency have been studied with computer multiple regression analysis. The results shown in Table IV are from a regression on 66 monthly average data from 1963 to the present time.

Table III. Manpower

OPERATION	MEN PER SHIFT	SHIFTS PER DAY	MAN-HR.PER DAY
New anode handling	2	2	32
Starting sheet	5	2	80
Cell setting	4	2	64
Circulation	1	1	8
Short correction	4	3	96
Cathode handling	1	2	16
Melting and casting	5	2	80
Shipping	1	1	8
Scrap anode handling	1	2	16
Slimes plant	1	3	24
Acid plant	1	3	24
Maintenance	12	1	96
Supervision	2	3	48
Administration	2	1	16

Table IV. Effects of Operating Variables on Current Efficiency

SIGNIFICANT VARIABLES					
	Tankhouse Current	Electrolyte Temperature	Tankhouse Operating	Electrolyte Total Acid	Electrolyte Lead Tenor
Units	A	°C	%	g/l	g/l
Average	9 196	42.4	97.0	116.7	72.1
St.Dev.*	320	2.3	5.9	3.2	6.3
Effect**	-1.25 %	+ 1.14 %	- 2.03 %	+ 0.71 %	+ 0.51 %
Limits +	∓0.30 %	∓ 0.31 %	∓ 0.26 %	∓ 0.33 %	∓ 0.32 %

NONSIGNIFICANT VARIABLES			
	Electrolyte Free Acid	Glue Added	Goulac Added
Units	g/l	kg/day/block	kg/day/block
Average	66.3	13.1	11.3
St.Dev.	3.8	1.4	3.2

* Standard deviation of independent variable.

** Effect on % current efficiency of an increase of one standard deviation of the independent variable.

\+ Limits determined by one standard deviation of the multiple regression coefficient. They cover 66% of the probable range.

The equation from which these data were taken is given below. It explains 45% of the variation in current efficiency.

Current Efficiency, % = $\left[100 \div \text{antilog}_e (2.3405 + 2.1285 \times 10^{-5} \text{ Tankhouse current, A} - 2.6585 \times 10^{-3} \text{ Electrolyte Temperature, }^{o}\text{C} + 9.4930 \times 10^{-4} \text{ Tankhouse Operating, \%} - 1.2059 \times 10^{-3} \text{ Electrolyte Total Acid, g/l} - 4.4329 \times 10^{-4} \text{ Electrolyte Lead Tenor, g/l})\right]^2$

An attempt is made below to briefly rationalize the relationships shown by the equation. It is not suggested that these explanations are either complete or proven. Current affects current efficiency adversely because increased current gives a thicker cathode and so more short circuits occur between cathode and anode. Thus an increase in current has not given the expected increment in production due to higher current losses. Electrolyte temperature shows a strong beneficial effect, but the temperature in the plant is limited by the softening of asphalt cell linings. A temperature of 45 ºC or more would require installation of P.V.C. cell linings. Percentage tankhouse operating apparently owes its effect to the extra time available for inspection and correction of short circuits when the plant is not operating at capacity. With 9 of the 10 blocks working, there is 17% more time available for this work and with 8 blocks operating, 38% more time is available. This situation is expected to improve shortly with the installation of a pneumatic gang press for straightening cathode starting sheets mechanically before setting or after a few hours deposition. The electrolyte, according to the regression, should be increased in total fluosilicate (total acid) and lead, and, moreover, other results have shown that this can be done at the expense of the free acid content, i.e., within the range of data given in Table IV, increases of total acid and lead would be expected to improve current efficiency even if free acid is decreased.

The rather poor fit of the equation and the failure of the amounts of organics added to enter the equation is attributed in part, at least, to the variable effects of the organics. Goulac is a residue from the making of paper and as such would not be expected to have a very constant composition nor a consistent effect on deposition. Figure 9 shows the effects of two lots of goulac at different concentrations. For this reason, work is being started at present on analytical determination of organics in electrolyte and on measurement of the effects of organics on the polarization voltage at the cathode.

Product Purity: Multiple regression analysis has also been performed on the impurity content of refined lead, using 63 monthly average data from 1963 to the present. The correlations obtained were not very strong and only 20% of the variation in total impurity content and 20% of the variation in bismuth content was explained. Qualitatively, the regression showed that increasing antimony in bullion has a beneficial effect on refined lead quality under prevailing conditions, especially on bismuth in refined lead. This effect may be mechanical, as there would be less carry-over to the cathode of a hard, high-antimony slime, or the quantity of antimony in the bullion might affect the distribution of bismuth in the different bullion phases. Also, as would be expected, bismuth in refined lead is proportional to bismuth in bullion. Finally, the impurity content of refined lead was found to be directly proportional to current efficiency, probably through a common relation with another variable such as electrolyte composition or temperature.

Refined Lead Cathode using Goulac from old stock March 10, 1970
Refined Lead Cathode using Goulac from new stock March 26, 1970
Refined Lead Cathode After Adjusting Goulac Additions to 0.9 Lbs/S.T March 30, 1970
(a)
(b)
(c)

Fig. 9 - Showing the different deposits obtained with:
a) Goulac, lot 1, at 532 g/M.T. lead produced (current efficiency - 95.1%),
b) Goulac, lot 2, at 532 g/M.T. lead produced (current efficiency - 85.8%), and
c) Goulac, lot 2, at 408 g/M.T. lead produced (current efficiency - 93.2%).

Acid Losses: As previously mentioned, acid losses have been high for several years and in 1969 was double the normal for the period up until 1967. Considerable work is being done on the problem, but no final solution has yet been found. One promising line of attack being followed at present is slow-cooling of anodes. By air cooling as long as possible and giving anodes more time for freezing slowly, the slimes structure becomes more coarse and diffusion of lead fluosilicate is facilitated, reducing acid losses by some 15 - 20 %, according to preliminary results. This innovation, along with better regulation of wash water volumes, improved wash cell flow patterns, and increased wash time in the first stage should shortly reduce acid losses to the normal value, less than 2 kg hydrofluosilicic acid per metric ton of lead produced.

Acknowledgements

The permission of the Management of Cerro de Pasco Corporation to publish this paper is gratefully acknowledged. The help and advice of colleagues in preparing this paper is greatly appreciated.

References

1. Betts, Anson G., "Lead Refining by Electrolysis", John Wiley and Sons, 1908.

2. Harper, T.E. and G. Reinberg, U.S. Patent 1913985, 1933.

3. Harper, T.E. and G. Reinberg, "The Betts Process at Oroya, Peru", Transactions of the Metallurgical Society of AIME, Volume 121, 1936, pp. 283.

4. Barker, I.L., "Complex Metallurgy by Cerro de Pasco", Journal of Metals, August, 1956.

5. Jacobi, J.S. and B.H. Wadia, "Betterments in the Quality of Refined Lead", Transactions of the Institution of Mining and Metallurgy, Vol. 67, part 4, 1958, pp. 141-161.

SECTION VII

UNIQUE PROCESSES FOR LEAD AND ZINC

Chapter 32

WAELZ TREATING OF COMPLEX ZINC-LEAD ORES,

KILN PRODUCTS LIMITED, BERG AUKAS, SOUTH WEST AFRICA.

Harry E. Cross
Consulting Metallurgist, Gold Fields of South Africa Limited,
Johannesburg, South Africa.

and

Frank O. Read
Deputy Consulting Metallurgist, Gold Fields of South Africa Limited,
Johannesburg, South Africa.

Abstract

Kiln Products commissioned a Waelz kiln 4 metres in diameter by 75 metres long, in South West Africa in March, 1969, to recover zinc in a form suitable for the production of electrolytic zinc. The raw material consists of a mixture of zinc silicate concentrates and zinc rich tailings purchased from an adjacent zinc mine - the mixture containing 20% to 25% zinc. The chemical composition of the ore is tabulated and the initial test results are described. Due to the comparatively low temperature at which the ore starts softening the kiln has certain unusual features to enable the temperature to be controlled within the necessary limits. A detailed description of the kiln, the starting-up problems and present operating conditions and results are presented.

Introduction

The South West Africa Company Limited have operated a mine at Berg Aukas, approximately 21 kilometres north-east of Grootfontein in South West Africa since 1959. Lead-zinc vanadate concentrates and lead and zinc sulphide and zinc silicate concentrates are produced by froth flotation.

The zinc silicate (willemite) concentrate produced is of high grade but the percentage recovery is low as an appreciable amount of the zinc silicate is in the form of a fine slime not amenable to froth flotation.

An associated company, Kiln Products Limited, have now commissioned a Waelz kiln on the same property, to recover the zinc from both the zinc silicate concentrate and an accumulated dump of zinc bearing tailings. The resultant zinc oxide fume is transported some 2 800 kilometres by road and rail, to another associated company, Zinc Corporation Limited, situated near Johannesburg, as a source material for the production of electrolytic zinc.

Description of ore mined at Berg Aukas

Zinc occurs in the ore mainly as the mineral willemite $2ZnO.SiO_2$. Minor quantities are present in the form of sphalerite and descloizite.

The gangue material is predominantly dolomite.

Treatment of Ore

Approximately 13 000 tons of ore are delivered to the reduction plant monthly. Approximately 1 000 tons of barren waste are discarded by manual sorting and the remaining 12 000 tons are crushed and milled in ball mills to a grind of approximately 70% minus 74 microns. After thickening, a lead sulphide concentrate is produced by flotation with xanthate and Aerofloat 25, the zinc being depressed by the addition of zinc sulphate and calcium cyanide. The zinc is then activated by the addition of copper sulphate to produce a zinc sulphide concentrate. The tailings from this flotation are conditioned with lime and calcium cyanide and again subjected to flotation with a mixture of amyl and ethyl xanthates and Aerofloat 25, to produce a lead vanadate concentrate.

The resultant tailings, amounting to some 10 000 tons per month are deslimed in a 522 mm cyclone in closed circuit with a 13 m diameter thickener. The cyclone overflow product discharges into the thickener. The fine slime overflowing the thickener amounts to about 2 500 tons per month containing about 18% zinc and about 4% lead. This is impounded in a temporary slimes dam for later treatment in the Waelz kiln.

The thickener underflow joins the feed to the cyclone. The cyclone underflow is subjected to 2 stages of flotation to produce a lead carbonate (cerussite) concentrate and a zinc silicate concentrate amounting to about 3 000 tons per month.

For cerussite flotation, sodium hydro-sulphide, is used in conjunction with amyl xanthate, Aeromine 3037 and T.E.B. frother while willemite is floated with further additions of the same reagents but excluding the xanthate.

The flotation tailings containing about 6% zinc are discarded. The cerussite concentrate is small in quantity and is mixed with the lead sulphide concentrate.

As zinc silicate concentrates are not popular with smelters and fetch a much lower price per unit of contained zinc than do zinc sulphide concentrates, it was decided to investigate the feasibility of treating these concentrates along with an existing tailings dam in a Waelz Kiln to produce a zinc oxide fume suitable as a feedstock for an electrolytic zinc plant.

The Waelz Process

The Waelz process has its origin in a process patented in 1910 by Edward Dedolph of British Columbia. However, it was not until 1923 that Krupp Grusonwerk in collaboration with Metallgesellschaft A.G. started developing the process to the stage where it could be applied on a commercial scale for the first time at Luenen in Upper Silesia in 1925. In 1957, according to M. Bogacz[1], 28 Waelz Kilns were operating in Poland treating over 3 000 tons of ore per day.

The process which has been well described in the literature 2, 3, 4, 5, 6, 7 consists in outline of treating zinc bearing materials with coke or anthracite in a horizontal rotary kiln at temperatures ranging from 1000°C to 1500°C. The zinc is reduced, volatilized, oxidised to zinc oxide and finally separated from the exhaust gases by means of bag filters or electrostatic precipitation.

It is commonly accepted that the following reactions occur:-

1. $ZnO + C \rightarrow CO + Zn$ (vapour)
2. Zn (vapour) $+ CO + O_2 \rightarrow ZnO + CO_2$
3. $C + O_2 \rightarrow CO_2$
4. $ZnS + CaO + C \rightarrow Zn$ (vapour) $+ CaS + CO$
5. $ZnS + FeO + C \rightarrow Zn$ (vapour) $+ FeS + CO$
6. $2\,(Zn, Fe, Mn)O + SiO_2 \rightarrow 2(Zn, Fe, Mn)O.SiO_2$
7. $2(Zn, Fe, Mn)O.SiO_2 + Fe \rightarrow Zn$ (vapour) $+ 2(Fe,Mn)O.SiO_2$
8. $ZnO + Al_2O_3 \rightarrow ZnO.Al_2O_3$

9. $ZnO.Al_2O_3 + Fe \rightarrow Zn\ (vapour) + FeO.Al_2O_3$
10. $3\ ZnO.Fe_2O_3 + 3\ C \rightarrow 3\ ZnO + 2\ Fe_3O_4 + 3\ CO$
11. $ZnS + Fe(2\ Cu) \rightarrow Zn\ (vapour) + FeS\ (Cu_2S)$
12. $2\ ZnO.SiO_2 + 2\ C \rightarrow 2\ Zn\ (vapour) + SiO_2 + 2\ CO$
13. $ZnO + CO \rightleftarrows Zn\ (vapour) + CO_2$
14. $2\ ZnO.SiO_2 + 2\ CO \rightarrow 2\ Zn\ (vapour) + SiO_2 + 2\ CO_2$
15. $C + CO_2 \rightarrow 2\ CO$

Fig. 1

It is obvious, however, from the work of Bodenstein[6], that no chemical reaction takes place directly between solids as shown in equations 1, 3 or 4. Simultaneous reactions actually occur in the gaseous phase as shown in equations 13 and 15 and by analogy 14 and 15. The progress of these particular reactions was critically examined by Truesdale and Waring[8] to determine which reaction was rate controlling. They concluded that in the temperature range 900°C to 1200°C reaction 13 proceeded rather more rapidly than reaction 15, while reaction 14, the reduction of willemite by carbon monoxide, was by far the slowest. This is illustrated in Fig.1 below.

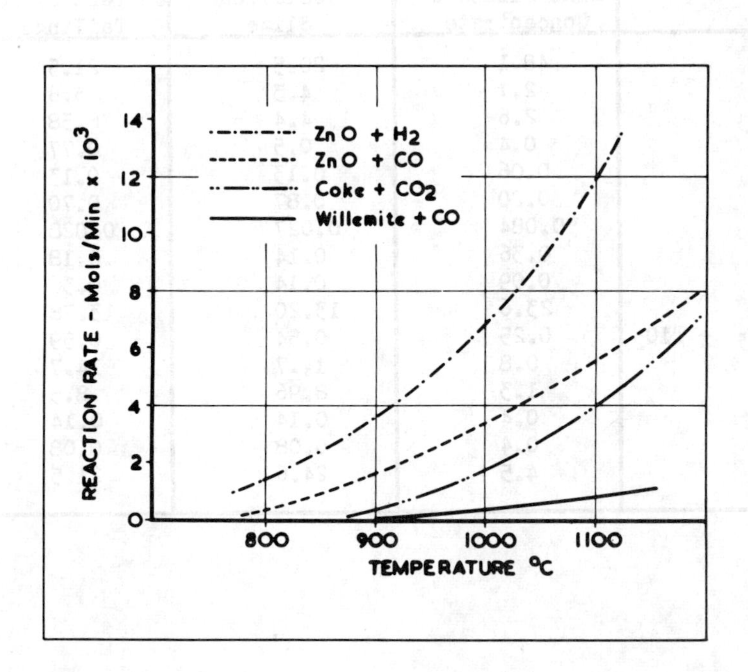

Pilot Plant Waelz Kiln Tests

After preliminary laboratory scale tests, Messrs. Fried Krupp Industriebau were commissioned to conduct a pilot plant scale investigation in their test kiln at Rheinhausen near Duisburg in West Germany. For this purpose approximately 70 tons of current slimes tailings, 40 tons of material reclaimed from the high grade dump, 2 tons of zinc silicate concentrate and 30 tons of washed anthracite duff from the Vryheid area in Natal, were shipped to their pilot plant.

Chemical analyses of the zinc silicate concentrate, reclaimed slime from a high grade dump, and current slimes tailings used for the test are shown in Table 1 below:-

Table 1. Chemical Analyses of Zinc Bearing Feed Materials (%)

	Zinc Silicate Concentrate	Reclaimed Slime	Current Slimes Tailings
Zn	48.1	20.5	21.5
Pb	2.1	4.3	3.6
Fe_2O_3	2.6	4.4	6.58
FeO	0.4	0.5	0.77
MnO	0.06	0.13	0.13
V_2O_5	0.20	0.87	0.70
As	0.084	0.027	0.028
P_2O_5	0.36	0.14	0.18
S	0.09	0.14	0.36
SiO_2	23.6	13.20	13.78
As_2O_3 + TiO_2	0.25	0.54	0.59
CaO	0.8	14.7	14.7
MgO	1.3	8.96	8.5
Na_2O	0.4	0.14	0.14
K_2O	0.4	0.08	0.08
CO_2	4.5	24.6	21.5

An analysis of the anthracite duff used is shown in Table 11 below:-

Table 11. Analysis of Anthracite Duff

Fixed Carbon (%)	86.0
Volatiles	5.6
Ash	8.4
Total Sulphur	1.17
Screen analysis + 10 mm	0.0%
+ 5 mm - 10 mm	5.7
+ 3 mm - 5 mm	23.7
+ 1 mm - 3 mm	50.0
- 1 mm	20.6
Calorific value cal/g	7.4
Ash analysis (%)	
SiO_2	40.3
As_2O_3 + TiO_2	31.6
CaO	3.5
MgO	2.7
Fe_2O_3	16.7
Ash softening temperature	1110°C
Ash melting point	1250°C
Ash flow point	1360°C

Krupp's test kiln was 1.2 metres in diameter by 14 metres long with an effective volume of 8.2 cubic metres. The kiln was equipped with 6 thermocouples fitted through the shell and 2 shell fans with suitable ducting to permit additional air to be introduced at any of 5 different points. The inclination used was 2% and the speed of rotation could be varied from 0.5 to 1 rev/min. The charge to the kiln consisting of the zinc bearing ore, anthracite and recycled zinc oxide ('preoxide') was homogeneously mixed in batches in a concrete mixer and the moisture content adjusted to about 10% before being fed to the kiln.

The exhaust gases passed through settling chambers to permit entrained gangue material to settle with some of the zinc and lead oxide in the form of 'preoxide', which was recycled. The oxide fume was collected in a bag filter.

Test work was conducted over a period of 4 weeks during which time over 60 tons of zinc bearing material averaging 21.7% zinc and 3.8% lead were treated in the kiln. The residue discharged averaged 2.03% zinc and 0.01% lead. The Waelz oxide produced averaged 63.3% zinc and 10.2% lead, with a magnesium content ranging from 0.4% to 1.0%. A typical analysis is shown in Table 111

Table 111. Typical analysis Waelz Oxide produced in Krupps pilot plant

	%
Zn	63.2
Pb	10.1
Fe	0.6
V_2O_5	0.04
As	0.086
Cl	0.07
F	0.025
SiO_2	1.5
Al_2O_3	0.3
CaO	1.8
MgO	1.2

Anthracite duff was used as the reductant at the rate of approximately 30% of the weight of the new zinc bearing feed. The following conclusions were reached:-

(a) the burden started softening at about 1100°C

(b) thus to avoid excessive formation of accretions the operating temperature should not exceed 1100°C

(c) it was possible to volatilize at least 90% of the zinc present without exceeding 1100°C

(d) as a source of additional heat, gas would be preferable to either oil or powdered coal, due to the softer flame obtainable.

(e) although accretions were to be expected, it should be possible to treat the raw material tested by the Waelz Process, provided operating conditions could be sufficiently carefully controlled.

As the Waelz oxide produced in the test kiln had a bulk density of only 0.83 g/cm^3 it was obvious that bulk transport by normal road and railway vehicles would present considerable problems. It was therefore decided to pelletize the oxide using a disc pelletizer and adding a small quantity of water only. The bulk density was thereby increased to about 1.7 g/cm^3.

A bulk sample of this pelletized material was returned to South Africa for testing purposes in a pilot electrolytic zinc plant. Test work showed that although the magnesium and fluorine might prove troublesome, good zinc recoveries could be expected and no insuperable difficulties were likely to be encountered.

As a result of the above, the decision was taken to install a kiln at Berg Aukas, with a nominal capacity of 10 000 tons per month of new zinc bearing feed.

Kiln Products - Description of Waelz Plant

Messrs. Lurgi (S.A.) (Proprietary) Limited were commissioned to design, supply and erect a kiln capable of treating 120 000 metric tons per annum of new zinc bearing feed consisting of 20 000 tons of zinc silicate and 100 000 tons of tailings of analysis similar to those shown in Table 1.

Location

The plant is situated adjacent to the Berg Aukas mine at an altitude of 1 450 m above sea level. Maximum ambient temperature is 40°C and the average annual rainfall is 625 mm essentially within the 3 months of summer. The nearest railhead is 21 kilometres distant.

A flow plan of the plant installed is shown in Fig. 2.

Kiln

The kiln itself is 4 metres in diameter by 75 metres long. The shell is fabricated of welded mild steel plate, quality BSS.1501/151 Grade 28A, 29 mm thick reinforced to 60 mm for the four running tyres and the driving gear sections.

The running tyres, 5 160 mm in diameter and 770 mm wide are of cast steel, BSS.592/1950 Grade B quality, welded to the reinforced sections of the shell. The eight supporting rollers, 1 300 mm in diameter are also made of cast steel and run on roller bearings which are mounted on concrete pedestals approximately 4 metres above ground level.

The kiln is mounted at an inclination of 2½% to the horizontal. The first, third and fourth sets of supporting rollers numbered from the feed end are adjusted such that the supporting surfaces of each pair are parallel to each other but are inclined to the face of the riding ring by an amount of about 0.15 mm. This has the effect of causing the kiln to move up the slope towards the feed end. A pair of horizontal rollers rotating about a vertical axis are rigidly mounted at No.2 riding ring, one on each side of it, to restrict the maximum horizontal movement of the kiln to about 50 mm. When No.2 riding ring reaches the top position, oil is applied to numbers 1, 3 and 4 riding rings, which causes the kiln to slip back to the lower position. By wiping off the excess lubricant, the kiln begins to climb again towards the upper position. This complete cycle is performed once daily.

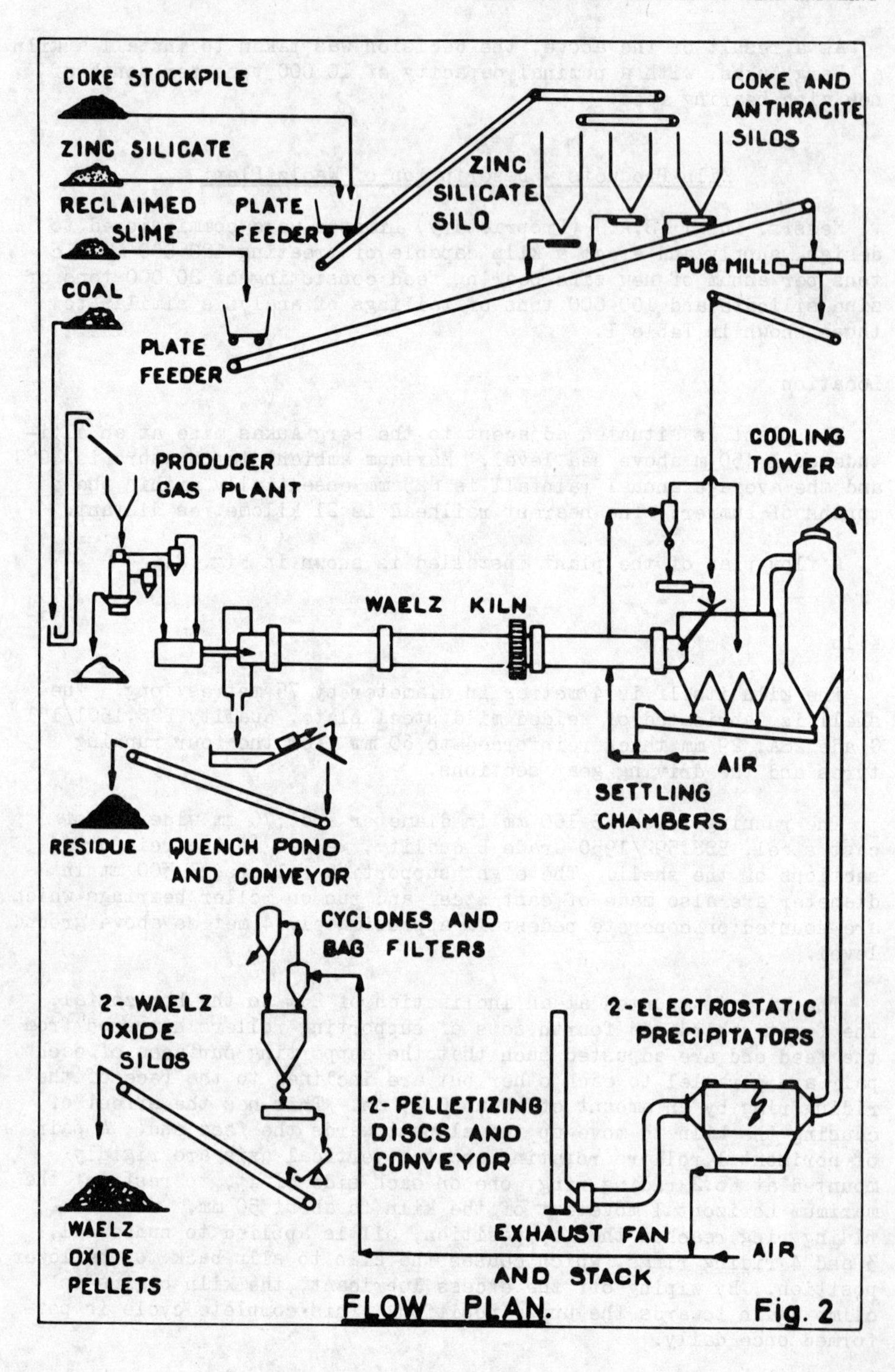
COKE STOCKPILE
ZINC SILICATE
RECLAIMED SLIME
PLATE FEEDER
COAL
PLATE FEEDER
ZINC SILICATE SILO
COKE AND ANTHRACITE SILOS
PUG MILL
COOLING TOWER
PRODUCER GAS PLANT
WAELZ KILN
AIR
SETTLING CHAMBERS
RESIDUE
QUENCH POND AND CONVEYOR
CYCLONES AND BAG FILTERS
2-WAELZ OXIDE SILOS
2-ELECTROSTATIC PRECIPITATORS
2-PELLETIZING DISCS AND CONVEYOR
WAELZ OXIDE PELLETS
EXHAUST FAN AND STACK
AIR
FLOW PLAN.
Fig. 2

The kiln inlet section is tapered over the first 1.1 metres from an opening of 1.9 metres. This tapered portion was originally lined with specially shaped tapered Lusite firebricks, but due to severe spalling, these were later replaced by castable refractory approximately 150 mm in thickness which has since given good service.

The feed to the kiln is introduced by gravity via an inclined steel tube about 5 metres long and 500 mm in diameter with a wall thickness of 25 mm. Sealing air is blown down the feed tube to prevent the escape of hot kiln gases, by means of a 4 kW fan capable of delivering 2 000 Nm^3/h at a pressure of 200 mm wg. The actual amount used is controlled by manual adjustment of a calibrated butterfly valve.

Sealing of the rotary kiln inlet end is achieved by means of 2 slip rings, of cast iron and cast steel respectively, sliding against each other. One ring is attached externally to the periphery of the kiln and the other, which is stationary, consists of separate segments held up against the rotating ring by means of 16 pneumatic pistons.

The kiln outlet section is double walled and provided with a labyrinth type seal cooled by means of a 10 kW fan. The shell diameter is reduced by 610 mm in two steps over the last 4 metres and as the brick-lining thickness is maintained at 229 mm throughout, the internal diameter of the discharge end of the kiln is reduced to 2.87 metres.

Eight air fans were originally installed on the shell of the kiln at 19, 25, 33, 37, 42, 46, 50 and 56 metres respectively from the feed end, for blowing additional air into the kiln via tubes of special heat resistant steel containing 25% chromium and 12% nickel.

The tubes are approximately 400 mm in diameter with a wall thickness of 20 mm. The discharge nozzle is 200 mm in diamter and designed and positioned so as to ensure that the air is directed horizontally at the centre of the kiln, counter-current to the main gas flow, i.e. towards the kiln discharge end. Sight glasses were subsequently fitted on the bends on the airducts between the fans and the tube to permit visual examination of the tube during operation. Each fan has a rated capacity of 2 000 Nm^3/h at a pressure of 200 watergauge, and is driven by a 4 kW motor, power being supplied by means of copper sliprings attached to the kiln. The actual amount of air blown in at each point can be controlled by manual adjustment of a calibrated butterfly valve.

The kiln was originally provided with 6 platinum-rhodium thermocouples fitted through the shell and protruding a maximum of 50 mm inside the brick-lining. These were connected to sliprings near the feed end of the kiln from where impulses were transmitted to a 12 point temperature recorder in the control room. The transmission times and the positions of the thermocouples were so arranged that each thermocouple produced 2 recordings per revolution - once when the thermocouple was embedded in the burden at about a 7.0 o'clock position and the other when in the diametrically opposite position. By this means it had been hoped to obtain both a burden temperature and a gas temperature. However, it was soon obvious that the two temperatures recorded were practically identical as there was insufficient time between readings for the thermocouple to reach equilibrium. It was decided later to intersperse 5 additional thermocouples and at the same time alter the design so that the thermocouple could be allowed to protrude up to 360 mm within the kiln, if desired. Thermocouples are therefore sited at the following positions from the feed end:-

8, 20, 29, 34, 40, 44, 47, 50, 53, 59 and 67 metres. The thermocouple at 8 m still recorded burden and gas temperatures - all the rest recorded burden temperatures only.

The kiln outlet head is of welded steel construction lined with heat resistant refractories and is mounted on an undercarriage with castors to enable it to be moved back out of the way when necessary. A large hinged door provides ready access to the kiln. As the kiln is operated with this door closed, two 100 mm diameter sight glasses are provided for viewing the contents of the kiln during operation.

Kiln Drive

The kiln is driven by a cast steel BSS.592/1950 Grade C girth gear 400 mm wide, made in two sections and attached to the shell by 12 tangential spring plates. Two synchronized variable speed d.c. motors each 70 kW, with thyristors and diodes for voltage regulation, operate separate reduction gearboxes which enable the kiln speed of rotation to be varied over the range 0.25 to 1.0 revolutions per minute. Two additional emergency 22 kW motors, powered by a Deutz diesel operated 80 kVA synchronous generator, operating through additional gearboxes are capable of rotating the kiln at 0.0625 revolutions per minute. Suitable instrumentation ensures that this unit comes into operation automatically in case of a power failure, to keep the kiln rotating and to keep certain other essential services in operation.

Residue Disposal

The residue discharged from the kiln drops down a transverse inclined chute lined with firebrick, into a quench pond from where it is raked up an inclined steel covered slope by means of a manually controlled motorized scraper winch, and discharged via a 50 mm grizzley onto an inclined rubber conveyor belt, 610 mm in width. The scraper bucket has a volume of 0.7 m^3 and the total lift is about

9 metres. The winch is powered by a 35 kW motor.

As originally designed, the discharge chute was open to the atmosphere, which in effect left the discharge end of the kiln also completely unsealed and permitted an uncontrollable amount of air to be drawn into the kiln. This was eventually remedied by sealing the discharge chute by means of hinged horizontally overlapping steel slats each about 500 mm wide, continued down to below the water-level in the quench pond.

An elevated steel walkway runs the entire length of the kiln on one side, to provide access to the shell fans and the shell thermocouples, etc.

Gas Producer

The producer gas plant, operating on bituminous coal nuts, nominally 25 mm to 40 mm in size is capable of delivering 2 000 Nm^3/h of gas at 300°C to 350°C with calorific value of approximately 1 800 $kcal/Nm^3$, i.e. a maximum of 3.6×10^6 kcal per hour, to a burner centrally positioned at the discharge end. Flexible connections permit the angle of the burner to be altered relative to the axis of the kiln. Primary combustion air is delivered to the burner by a separate fan with a maximum capacity of 3 500 Nm^3/h at 600 mm water gauge, driven by a 10 kW motor. The actual volume can be varied by manual adjustment of a calibrated butterfly valve, and is recorded in the control room. The coal is screened immediately prior to use through a 19 mm screen to remove any fines which are used as a reductant and mixed with the coke and anthracite. Maximum coal consumption is about 20 tons per day. A typical analysis of the coal used is given in Table 1V below:-

Table 1V. Typical Analysis of Bituminous Coal (Air Dry Basis)

Calorific value	**6 950 cal/g**
Ash	**10.1 %**
Volatile material	**25.9 %**
Fixed Carbon	**61.2 %**
Total Sulphur	**0.6 %**
Ash fusion temperature	**1380 °C**
Moisture	**2.8 %**

The producer gas has a typical analysis as shown in Table V below:-

Table V. Typical Analysis of Producer Gas

	%
CO_2	5.4
CO	25.2
H_2	14.5
O_2	0.2
CH_4	5.0

Fig. 3

A general view of the kiln showing the driving gear, the air inlet ducts and the gas producer plant in the back ground is shown in Fig.3.

Brick Lining

The bricks used for lining the kiln measure 229 mm by 152 mm by 76 mm tapering down to about 69 mm and are laid end on to give a lining 229 mm thick. Two qualities of bricks were used originally; 'Superlin' for the first 30 m from the feed end and 'Lusite' for the remaining 45 m. Subsequently 'Jumbo' bricks were also used as replacements. Typical analyses are shown in Table Vl

Table VI. Typical Analyses of Superlin, Lusite and Jumbo Bricks

	Superlin	Lusite	Jumbo
SiO_2%	53 - 55	44 - 46	53 - 55
Al_2O_3%	42 - 44	51 - 53	42 - 44
Fe_2O_3%	0.8 - 1.0	1.2 - 1.7	0.8 - 1.0
TiO_2%	1.5 - 1.7	0.5 - 0.7	1.5 - 1.7
CaO%	0.2 - 0.3	0.3 - 0.5	0.2 - 0.3
MgO%	0.2 - 0.3	0.3 - 0.5	0.2 - 0.3
Alkalis	0.4 - 0.5	Trace	0.4 - 0.5
Porosity %	10 - 15	14 - 18	6 - 11
Bulk density g/cm^3	2.32	2.40	2.42
Permeability (c.g.s. units)	0.05	0.10	0.03
Cold crushing strength kg/cm^2	350 - 630	350 - 850	350 - 700

Steel rings made of 25 mm flat mild steel 100 mm deep were welded into the shell at about 4 to 5 metres intervals to prevent movement of the bricks relative to the shell. A cardboard expansion joint 3 mm thick was inserted at approximately 1.5 metre intervals. Relining is now done by the plant operators at the rate of 2 metres per 2 bricklayers per 8 hour shift, provided they are not kept waiting for materials. The lower half of the kiln is lined first. These bricks are then kept in position by means of mechanical jacks while the kiln is rotated sufficiently to allow the rest of the bricks to be laid.

Recovery of Oxide from Exhaust Gases

The gases emerging from the feed end of the kiln pass through settling chambers to remove entrained solids, a cooling tower to reduce the temperature and electrostatic precipitators where the oxide is precipitated, before finally being discharged to atmosphere via a stack.

Settling Chambers:

The three flue gas settling chambers are each approximately 5 m long by 7 m wide by 6 m high with hopper type bottoms. They are constructed of steel plate and the walls are lined with 23 cm of normal duty firebrick containing about 38% Al_2O_3. The roof is flat and is insulated by about 23 cm of heat resistant mortar, held in place by means of stainless steel reinforcing mesh. Three large doors are fitted for providing access for inspection and there are eight hatches each about 0.5 m^2 in size which are designed to blow off in case of an explosion in the chamber. Preoxide was discharged originally from each compartment via a star feeder into a pneumatic transfer system delivering into a storage silo which in turn discharged via star feeder on to the main feed belt immediately ahead of the pugmill.

This system which had been designed to operate under vacuum gave so much trouble due to blockages in the delivery line that it was later altered to operate as a pressure system. This was still unsatisfactory and as result of continual blockages and large dust losses, was abandoned until it was eventually modified to function as a pressure system embodying the various refinements described later in the paragraph dealing with pneumatic transfer.

Air is provided by a Rootes type blower with a displacement of 1500 m^3/h at a pressure difference of 0.41 kg/cm^2. The delivery duct is 125 mm in diameter with reinforced bends. Approximately 95% of the dust is collected in a 17° cyclone, approximately 550 mm in diameter, the remaining 5% finally being removed in a bag filter, all this dust being discharged into the storage silo ahead of the pugmill. The bag filter contains 28 socks with a total filtering area of approximately 40 m^2. The maximum operating temperature for the type of bags used is approximately 150°C.

Cooling Tower: After leaving the settling chambers the flue gases are cooled in an evaporative cooler by the controlled injection of spray water. The cooling tower is 6.5 m in diameter and approximately 24 m in height, constructed of 8 mm mild steel plate.

The cooling tower was designed to cool a maximum of 65 000 Nm^3/h of gas from an inlet temperature of about 550°C to an outlet temperature of about 200°C - i.e. a temperature gradient of about 350°C. Seven sets of sprays each containing 6 nozzles are fitted at the top. The nozzle design is such that excess water which is not sprayed into the tower is bypassed back from the nozzle into a return water manifold. The amount of water sprayed into the tower is controlled by adjusting the opening of a valve on the return manifold, thereby increasing or decreasing the pressure on the nozzles. This control is effected automatically from the temperature of the gas leaving the cooling tower. Two other automatic controls are provided to operate in an emergency, viz:-

(a) if the temperature of the exhaust gas exceeds 300°C an emergency flap at the top of the tower operated by means of a motorized winch opens to atmosphere, to avoid damage to the electrostatic precipitators.

(b) if the volume of gas passing through the exhaust stack drops below 30 000 Nm^3/h or if the temperature of the gas at the inlet to the cooling tower drops below 220°C, the water supply to the nozzles is shut off completely to prevent the accumulation of unevaporated water in the tower, and a signal light flashes in the control room. The amount of water consumed here is normally about 110 litres per minute - maximum output of the pump is 250 litres per minute at a maximum operating pressure of 40 kg/cm^2. Settled dust drops into a screw conveyor, the trough of which has a hinged flap at the base, to facilitate cleaning. By changing the direction of rotation of the screw, oxide which settles in the tower can be diverted either to the preoxide pneumatic transfer system or to the Waelz oxide system, depending on its quality. Provision is also made for discharging the dust on to the floor in case of emergency.

Electrostatic Precipitators: Two horizontal electrostatic precipitators designed and supplied by Lurgi are installed for normal operation in parallel, for a maximum gas flow of 85 000 Nm^3/h. In emergency either precipitator can be isolated and the full gas stream routed through the other. Collection efficiency of 99.5% is guaranteed for an inlet gas dust content of above 50 g/Nm^3. At a lower inlet gas dust content, the cleaned gas dust content is not to exceed 300 mg per Nm^3. With only one precipitator on line the collection efficiency drops to about 95%.

Each precipitator is 17.5 metres long and 5 metres wide and is constructed of 5 mm steel plate with suitable stiffeners to withstand a negative pressure of 120 mm wg. The positively charged grounded collecting electrodes are of the plate type about 5 metres in height and spaced about 250 mm apart with the negatively charged discharge electrodes suspended centrally between them at about 160 mm intervals. Mechanical rapping devices are provided for both positive and negative electrodes. Each precipitator contains three electrostatic fields connected in sequence. Each power pack is rated at 95 kVA and has a cabinet type switchboard with thyristor control and automatic power control.

The precipitated dust collects in the hopper type bottoms from where it is removed continuously by means of Redler conveyors. As originally supplied, these Redlers each discharged via individual star feeders into a pneumatic transfer system operating under vacuum. This arrangement gave endless trouble due to blockages and was later modified as described in the paragraph dealing with the pneumatic transfer system.

Air for the pneumatic transfer system is provided by a 1 500 m^3/h Rootes blower powered by a 30 kW motor. The dust delivery column is 125 mm in diameter and is constructed of mild steel with suitably reinforced bends. Approximately 95% of the dust is collected in a cyclone and the remaining 5% in a bag filter with a total filtering area of 40 m^2. Both products gravitate into either of two conical bottom storage silos, each with a nominal capacity of 100 tons.

Exhaust Fan: An axial flow exhaust fan with vane control and servo motor is installed between the precipitators and the final stack, which is 2.2 metres in diameter and 26 metres in height.

The fan was supplied by Kühnle, Kopp and Kausch of Frankenthal-Pfalz and has a rated capacity of 175 000 m^3/h at 200°C and 131.5 mm wg - it is driven by a 100 kW motor. Inlet vane control operates in conjunction with the automatic draught controller.

Fig. 4 below shows the cooling tower in the centre with the electrostatic precipitators and settling chambers on either side.

Fig. 4

Pelletizing Plant: Waelz oxide is discharged from each silo via a star feeder and screw conveyor to two pelletizing discs 4 metres in diameter. By the addition of about 10% of water, as a fine spray, the powder is turned into pellets ranging from about 6 mm to 20 mm in diameter - no other additives are found to be necessary. The "green" pellets, as produced, without any drying, have a crushing strength of about 15 to 20 kg per pellet. Each disc is fitted with a 30 kW motor. The angle of inclination can be altered in the range 30° to 60° by operating a handwheel, and the angle normally used is 45° to the horizontal. The discs are operated at a speed of 6 revolutions per minute and this can be varied only by changing pulleys. The rate of output is approximately 8 tons per hour per pelletizing disc. The pellets are discharged on to a conveyor belt for delivery to a storage shed and are subsequently handled by means of front end loaders.

Control Room

An air-conditioned control room is provided with a mimic flow diagram of the plant, and the necessary indicating lights, recorders, switches, alarms, etc. to enable the plant to be remotely controlled from this position. In particular the following instruments are provided:-

(a) A Schenk belt weighing machine for new zinc bearing feed, which records in the control room, and integrates the tonnage.

(b) 2 Schenk reductant proportioning weigh feeders and recording and integrating equipment.

(c) Kiln draught controller and recorder.

(d) 12 point kiln temperature recorder.

(e) Kiln rate of rotation indicator and recorder.

(f) Kiln main drive kilowatt recorder.

(g) Airflow rates, pressure and temperature recorders, etc. for producer gas plant.

(h) Recorder of oxygen in kiln exhaust gas.

(i) Recorder for gas temperatures at inlet and outlet of cooling tower with control equipment.

(j) Indicating instruments for milli amps and voltages in electrostatic precipitators.

(k) Exhaust gas temperature indicators.

(l) High level indicators for Waelz oxide bins.

Operation

Reductants

Unwashed anthracite duff from the Vryheid area in Natal and coke fines from ISCOR (IRON & STEEL CORPORATION) at Van der Bijl Park are used as reductants. Current analyses are shown in Table V11

Table VII. Typical Analyses Unwashed Anthracite Duff and Coke Fines

Size Analysis	Unwashed Anthracite duff	Coke Fines
+ 5 mm	13%	11%
- 5 + 3 mm	22	11
- 3 + 2 mm	18	11
- 2 + 1 mm	21	24
- 1 + 0.5 mm	11	18
- 0.5 mm	15	25
Proximate analysis (Air dried basis)		
Ash	9.7%	16.6%
Volatiles	10.5	1.1
Fixed Carbon	78.2	81.6
Ash fusion temp.	1400°C	1400°C
Calorific value cal/g	7 500	7 000
Bulk density kg/litre	0.88	0.69

These products are railed in bulk approximately 2 800 kilmetres to Grootfontein, the nearest railhead to the kiln, and then transferred to road trucks by means of Caterpillar 622B front end loaders, to traverse the final 21 kilometres to the kiln. Both products are stockpiled in bulk in the open, the height of the stockpile being about 3 metres. As required, the reductant is removed by means of front end loaders and dropped onto a variable speed plate feeder with an effective width of 1 metre, which discharges onto an inclined conveyor belt 610 mm wide and delivers onto an elevated reversible conveyor at a maximum rate of 20 tons per hour, which drops the product into either of 2 storage silos, each with a capacity of 150 tons. Each storage silo is equipped with a Schenk weigh feeder which can be set to automatically deliver a preset percentage of the weight of the new zinc bearing feed material passing over the belt weightometer on its way into the kiln. Alternatively each weigh feeder can be adjusted from the control room to deliver reductant at a steady pre-selected rate. Each weigh feeder indicates, in the control room the tons per hour being fed, and integrates the tonnage. The reductant drops on the zinc bearing feed material on the main feed belt which discharges into a pugmill to provide homogeneous mixing of the reductant with the ore.

Zinc bearing feed

Zinc silicate concentrate is delivered daily to an open stockpile, using a Shawnee-Poole tractor-trailer unit with a carrying capacity of 10 tons. The product as delivered contains about 12% moisture. It is removed from the stockpile by means of a front end loader as required and dropped on the same plate feeder as used intermittently for reductant, for delivery into the zinc silicate storage silo with a capacity of 450 tons. The silo is equipped with a 2 metre diameter table feeder, rotating at 0. 9 revolutions per minute, capable of delivering up to 10 tons per hour on to the main feed belt to the pugmill.

Slime is reclaimed from the slimes dam some 500 metres from the kiln by means of front end loaders digging in from the side. The dam is about 6 metres in height and periodically it has been considered prudent to collapse the face when it becomes too nearly vertical, by blasting. The front end loaders deliver into Shawnee-Poole tractor-trailer units as used for the zinc silicate concentrate, and deliver to a daily stockpile under cover, alongside the zinc silicate plate feeder. The bin above the feeder has a capacity of 90 tons and is filled periodically during the course of each shift from the stockpile alongside, using a front end loader. The plate feeder can be adjusted to deliver at a steady rate ranging from about 5 to about 25 tons per hour, on to the main feed belt.

The main feed belt is equipped with a weightometer which records the rate of feed in tons per hour and integrates the total tonnage.

The mixture of zinc silicate, reclaimed slime, reductant and preoxide is delivered on to a grizzley which permits the fines to drop into a pugmill while the plus 50 mm lumps, stones and foreign bodies are bypassed directly on to feed belt receiving the mixed product from the pugmill. The pugmill was supplied by Karl Handle and Sons and is about 2.5 m long by 0.7 m wide. It is equipped with two parallel shafts carrying blades which rotate in opposite directions to produce a mixing and propelling motion. It is driven by a 30 kW motor.

Start up procedure

Drying out of the brickwork was commenced on 19th February, 1969. The following procedure was adopted:-

(a) The kiln was rotated one quarter turn every twenty minutes, using the auxiliary drive only, i.e. rate of rotation:- 0.0625 rev/min.

(b) Producer gas was burnt at the discharge end using the standard burner, at a rate sufficient to raise the temperature of the brickwork at Numbers 1 and 3 thermocouples 67 and 59 m respectively from the feed end to 150°C in 24 hours, and the temperature was then held steady at 150°C for 5 days.

(c) Temperature was then increased at the rate of 50°C per hour to 200°C and held there for one day.

(d) Shell fans were started up and sufficient air admitted to maintain the air tube temperatures at 200°C.

(e) When the temperature in the settling chambers reached 200°C, it was maintained there for 4 days.

(f) Cooling tower flap was opened and the main fan started and adjusted to its minimum delivery rate.

(g) Kiln temperature was steadily increased at the rate of 50°C per hour until the brickwork at Nos. 1 and 3 thermocouples reached 700°C.

(h) Kiln was then rotated continuously on auxiliary drive.

(i) Temperature was raised to 900°C at the rate of 50°C per hour.

(j) Anthracite was then fed into the kiln followed by zinc bearing feed when the temperature had reached 1000°C.

The above programme took 13 days to complete. Once the brickwork had been thoroughly dried out the subsequent starting up procedure was streamlined to enable zinc bearing feed to be introduced approximately 18 hours after starting preheating.

During the first year of operation it was necessary to cool the kiln down and cease operations on 13 occasions. Current start-up procedure, if there is no brickwork that requires slow drying out, is as follows:-

(a) The cooling tower flap is left open.
The ducts to the precipitators are closed.
The shell fans are operated with butterfly valves sufficiently open to allow only a trickle of air to pass.
The main fan is stationary.
The kiln is rotated $\frac{1}{4}$ turn every 20 minutes on auxiliary drive.
The gas burner is started up at about half maximum capacity.
By gradually increasing the gas burning rate and closing the cooling tower flap, the temperature of the gas at the inlet to the cooling tower is raised to 200°C over a period of about 6 hours.

(b) The kiln is then rotated continuously on main drive at minimum rate of 0.25 rev/min.
The flap on the cooling tower is closed completely, the ducts to the precipitators are opened, the shell fans are opened one or two notches and the main fan is started up with inlet vanes opened less than 10% initially.

Anthracite duff is fed to the kiln at the rate of 2 tons per hour.

(c) About 5 hours later the anthracite reaches the discharge end of the kiln where it is ignited by the gas burner. The temperature then rises rapidly and when the gas temperatures at the inlet to the cooling tower reaches 650°C, zinc bearing feed is introduced, at an initial rate of 5 tons per hour, with 50% by weight of anthracite and coke. This is usually about 18 hours after the initial lighting up.

(d) The feed rate is gradually increased over the following 12 hours to maximum rate.

Results of Operation

Operating results obtained to date are summarized in Table V111.

Zinc bearing feed containing about 14% zinc was introduced into the kiln for the first time on 10th March, 1969. Difficulty was experienced in maintaining the temperature, which eventually after 7 days dropped so low that it was decided to cool down and inspect the kiln. Except for some spalling of bricks in the feed cone and some physical damage to some of the thermocouples, the kiln was in good condition. During this campaign the feed to the kiln consisted of 8 tons per hour of reclaimed slime and 15 to 20% of washed anthracite.

During the next 3 months there were 5 further campaigns ranging from 4 days to 27 days in length. In each case the kiln was eventually closed down due to excessive buildup of accretions. On various occasions shock treatment was tried whereby the kiln was rapidly cooled for a couple of hours and then heated up again as rapidly as possible in an attempt to cause the accretions to crack and drop off. Some success was achieved with comparatively short rings, but where the accretions extended over a few metres or more, the treatment was quite ineffective. In these cases the kiln had to be cooled down completely to enable the accretions to be removed manually. The worst accretions occurred during the fourth campaign in May, 1969, when one particular accretion was found to be over 8 metres long ranging in thickness from 1 to 1½ metres. The total weight of accretions removed from the kiln on this occasion exceeded 450 tons. A typical view of accretions prized off, alongside an internal air tube, is shown in Fig. 5

Table VIII. Summary of operating results

Campaign No.	From date	To date	Duration (days)	Tons Zn bearing feed	% Zinc in feed	% Lead in feed	% Zinc in Waelz oxide	% Lead in Waelz oxide	% Zinc fumed off	% Lead fumed off	Reductant added (% of feed)	Reductant actually consumed (% of feed)	% H_2O in feed to kiln	Speed of rotation rev/min	mm WG at kiln outlet	Temp. No.11 Thermocouple °C	Temp. Cooling Tower inlet °C	Temp. Cooling Tower outlet °C	Temp. Exhaust gas to stack °C
1	10/ 3/69	16/ 3/69	7	1270	13.8	3.1	-	-	69.0	69.2	26.6	-	6.0	0.50	+1.1	359	390	232	205
2	20/ 3/69	23/ 3/69	4	720	21.7	2.8	65.0	8.0	90.8	88.5	20.6	-	8.0	0.57	+4.3	457	502	242	207
3	4/ 4/69	13/ 4/69	10	2570	13.7	3.4	60.1	9.2	68.5	74.0	24.7	12.3	6.8	0.41	+1.7	287	394	230	207
4	28/ 4/69	7/ 5/69	10	1276	24.2	6.2	60.5	8.9	80.1	80.7	21.9	12.7	7.5	0.48	+1.8	286	336	235	205
5	19/ 5/69	14/ 6/69	27	3590	24.8	3.4	57.2	7.9	62.0	55.3	32.9	11.0	7.4	0.35	+1.6	363	441	231	210
6	19/ 6/69	25/ 6/69	7	576	22.3	3.2	55.6	8.4	32.0	25.0	30.9	6.2	9.9	0.33	+0.7	187	273	209	191
7	29/ 6/69	6/ 8/69	39	4895	23.2	2.7	59.0	7.5	54.0	45.0	22.0	5.1	7.7	0.43	+1.2	334	362	241	217
8	15/ 7/69	25/ 9/69	42	8350	23.8	3.0	53.3	6.0	72.0	63.0	43.8	17.7	9.9	0.73	-2.7	395	455	242	208
9	1/10/69	15/10/69	15	3060	24.8	3.2	60.3	4.8	77.8	68.0	58.2	22.9	11.0	0.80	-3.2	391	474	238	212
10	22/10/69	25/11/69	35	5204	25.4	2.3	60.3	5.1	72.5	47.0	56.5	19.5	11.5	0.72	-2.1	411	462	247	218
11	10/12/69	27/12/69	18	1940	27.7	2.4	60.5	6.0	66.2	52.5	62.1	17.6	11.8	0.60	-0.4	455	474	247	216
12	30/12/69	5/ 1/70	7	700	29.4	2.7	63.9	6.0	70.5	58.0	57.5	11.0	10.6	0.60	-1.4	469	503	250	229
13	10/ 1/70	5/ 2/70	27	3745	28.2	2.3	57.5	6.3	73.1	69.3	58.0	14.5	11.7	0.51	-4.2	483	544	260	234
14	11/ 2/70	14/ 3/70	32	7465	21.0	2.5	54.7	7.6	81.2	58.0	59.7	13.8	12.7	0.66	-1.8	440	531	242	217

Fig. 5

The thicker the accretions the longer the kiln takes to cool off sufficiently to start work inside. This period ranges from about 36 hours with a comparatively clean kiln to 3 days or more. Even after 3 or 4 days of cooling, the thicker accretions are still red hot inside. 'Jack hammers' and 'tommy bars' have to be used for prizing off the accretions which are then trundled along to the kiln discharge end in a wheel-barrow, for disposal.

During this period, characterized by the formation of accretions, the amount of reductant used ranged from about 15% to about 25% by weight of the zinc bearing feed. For most of the time the discharge chute was open to atmosphere which rendered it practically impossible to prevent an excessive volume of air from being drawn into the kiln and cause the formation of accretions near the discharge end. Constant trouble was also experienced with mal operation of the cooling tower, resulting in a flood of water pouring into the cooling tower oxide, turning it into a paste which could not be handled by the screw conveyor or the star feeder.

Both pneumatic transfer systems also continually blocked and rendered steady operation impossible. Dust and precipitator oxide were continually being either dumped on the ground or blown into the atmosphere making it impossible to obtain any semblance of a metallurgical balance.

At this stage discharge chute was then effectively sealed, the percentage of reductant added was increased and the temperature of operation was deliberately kept low in an endeavour to prevent the formation of accretions. This resulted in higher zinc values in the residue but did prolong the length of the campaigns. The cooling tower and both pneumatic transfer systems continued to give trouble.

During campaign No.8 which started during July, 1969, the quantity of reductant added as a percentage of the new zinc bearing feed was increased substantially to over 50%. This enabled higher operating temperatures to be used without a rapid buildup of large accretions. From this period onwards kiln stoppages were brought about almost entirely by mechanical breakdowns of one type or another, and not primarily by the necessity to remove accretions. It was found that although accretions still tended to form, they were very friable and brittle and generally fell down of their own accord when they grew too big because the burden contained so much unburnt coke. This raised another problem, however, which periodically caused an increase in the zinc content of the residue and also reduced the percentage zinc in the Waelz oxide produced. If a ring formed anywhere, the burden dammed up behind it until the ring collapsed when the accumulation rushed through the kiln and was discharged before getting hot enough for the zinc to be volatilized. Furthermore, as a result of the additional agitation, a great dust cloud was formed, much of which was swept out with the exhaust gases and polluted the Waelz oxide.

At this stage pelletizing of Waelz oxide was temporarily suspended at the request of Zinc Corporation, who were having considerable difficulty in handling and dissolving the pellets supplied. At least 50% of the pellets had broken down to powder by the time the product had been off-loaded at their silos. Furthermore, there were a certain number of oversize pellets up to 50 mm in diameter and hard lumps of agglomerated material. The moisture content was about 7%. At Kiln Products, as a temporary procedure, the Waelz oxide from the storage silos was discharged onto the final pellet conveyor belt bypassing the pelletizing discs, dropped onto the ground and loaded into a 24 ton tipping truck by means of a front end loader, for transport to the railway siding at Grootfontein. Here the product was tipped onto the loading platform and loaded into open railway trucks, lined with 0.15 mm polythene sheeting, with the aid of a front end loader. The trucks were covered with waterproofed tarpaulins prior to despatch. The powder was found to have a bulk density of about 1.25 g/cm^3, which was considerably higher than had been anticipated from the original pilot plant work, when the bulk density was only 0.83 g/cm^3. Despite the primitive handling facilities for this product, dusting and dust losses were not nearly as serious as had been expected.

Due to continual blockages in both the pneumatic transfer systems and the resultant interference with production, Lurgi undertook to redesign both systems. As this could not be implemented for several months, various temporary arrangements had to be made, in order to keep producing. All preoxide, cooling tower oxide and precipitator oxide were discharged onto the ground and handled by means of front end loaders, the first two products being returned to the kiln feed with the reclaimed slime while the precipitator oxide was despatched without being pelletized. The preoxide from the settling chambers was discharged at a temperature in excess of 500°C and presented the biggest problem. It was found necessary to deposit this product on an intermediate stockpile to allow it to cool, and then spray water onto it to wet it before returning it to the feed belt. Otherwise when the hot dust was dropped onto the reclaimed slime containing about 10% of moisture so much steam was generated that a large dust cloud resulted.

At the beginning of November the pneumatic transfer system for the precipitator oxide was overhauled and recommissioned temporarily, and the product was again pelletized. Two important alterations were made to the pneumatic system which eliminated most of the earlier trouble, viz:-

1. Oxide was delivered into the system at one point only, in the first instance, by operating only one precipitator at a time and later when operating both precipitators in parallel, by fitting a time switch which allowed oxide from only one precipitator to be discharged into the system at a time, by stopping alternate Redler conveyors at the bottom of the precipitators for 15 minute spells.

2. A pressure switch was installed in the air duct adjacent to the blower which tripped out the Redlers whenever the pressure rose too high, to allow time for the system to clear itself. As soon as this happened the pressure dropped and the Redler automatically started up again.

With a bit more experience and perseverance it was found possible to produce pellets of relatively uniform size and by careful supervision of the handling, to prevent excessive subsequent breakage of the pellets.

At about the same time temporary arrangements were made to spray sufficient water onto the dust emerging from each of the 3 settling chambers and from the cooling tower, to turn the product into a watery slurry which was allowed to gravitate into a submerged sump and pumped into settling paddocks nearby. After settling and drying for a few days, the preoxide was reclaimed by means of front end loaders and returned to the circuit with the reclaimed slime. This system, although it necessitated double handling and rendered it more difficult to calculate the percentage recovery, worked reasonably satisfactorily until February when it started raining heavily. The whole settlement area became a bog and it was impossible to use the front end loader. It then became necessary to revert to the earlier system of dropping the hot dust onto the floor. For a few days, however, a temporary pneumatic transfer system was introduced to recycle the cooling tower oxide only, by discharging the dust plus carrier air directly down the feed chute into the kiln with the new feed. Mechanically this worked satisfactorily but it was noted during this time that the zinc content of the Waelz oxide produced was consistently less than 60%, possibly due to excessive recirculation of dust.

During campaign No.13 it became progressively more difficult to maintain a negative pressure at the discharge end of the kiln, until eventually it was necessary to stop production and close down. Typical pressures at various points in the circuit measured by means of water manometers immediately prior to the end of campaign No.13 are shown in Table lX, with typical pressures subsequently obtained during campaign No.14.

Table lX. Water Gauge Pressures - mm wg

	Main fan suction	Inlet to Precipitators	Cooling Tower	Settling Chambers	Kiln Discharge
Towards end Campaign No.13	- 110	- 90	- 90	- 10	- 4
Campaign No.14	- 35	- 20	- 15	- 10	- 4

It was found that the duct delivering the gas from the settling chambers to the cooling tower was completely blocked with dust which had settled on the baffles within the uppermost bend.

A few days after the start of campaign No.14 it became necessary to stop the feed and allow the kiln to cool down sufficiently for a few days to enable a large accumulation of oxide to be removed from the cooling tower. This had deposited in the tower presumably over a long period of time, in the form of a stalagmite, the base of which blanked off more than half the base of the cooling tower. The deposit was about 10 metres in height and had consolidated to such an extent that it took 4 days to remove, using shovels and pickaxes. The total weight removed was nearly 200 tons.

Much of the trouble experienced in controlling the temperature in the cooling tower is caused by the hardness of the water used. A typical water analysis is shown in Table X.

Table X. Analysis of Process Water at Kiln Products

Total dissolved solids	459 milligrams per litre
Total alkalinity, as $CaCO_3$	439
Total hardness, as $CaCO_3$	406
Calcium, as Ca	7.8
Magnesium, as Mg	92.7
Fluorine, as F	0.3
Chloride, as Cl	0.1
Sulphate, as SO_4	0.1
pH	7.1

Scale accumulates in the entire system which in the first instance reduces the volume of water available at the nozzles. Correct functioning of the nozzles is hampered not only by the buildup of scale in the nozzles themselves, but also by loose bits of scale lodging in the inlet ports. When this happens, large drops of water are discharged which do not vaporize fast enough to prevent the accumulation of water at the base of the tower. This wets the oxide and turns it into a paste which cannot be transported by the equipment provided. It then becomes necessary to open the flaps below the screw conveyor and drop the product onto the floor. While operating with the flaps open much of the cooling tower oxide is aspirated into the precipitators thus lowering the zinc content of the Waelz oxide.

Steps are now being taken to soften the water by the controlled addition of lime, followed by filtration.

Kiln Gun

As it is common practice in the cement industry to use kiln guns firing lead slugs to break down rings, a Western Ringblaster kiln gun was purchased. This gun has a bore of approximately 23 mm and fires 85 gram solid lead slugs at a muzzle velocity of 500 metres/second. It is mounted with recoil springs on a substantial gun support. It has been found that comparatively narrow rings up to about 1 m in width can be effectively collapsed by cutting a longitudinal slot right through the ring. This usually requires at least 500 rounds of ammunition. The gun is quite ineffective with rings which are either much wider than this or more than about 20 metres from the discharge end of the kiln.

Comments on Difficulties Encountered

Accretions

Samples of accretions removed were submitted to the laboratory, with samples of the willemite concentrate and reclaimed slime being charged to the kiln, for determination of the temperature at which these products started melting. The softening points are shown in Table Xl below:-

Table Xl. Softening temperature of various products

Product	Softening Temperature °C
Willemite concentrate	1150
Reclaimed slime	1150
Accretion sample A	1120
Accretion sample B	1200
Accretion sample C	1300
Kiln residue	1150

Portion of one typical accretion approximately 14 cm thick was examined mineralogically. It was found to have a layered structure marked by texture and also compositional differences. The specific gravity ranged from 3.26 for the layer adjacent to the kiln lining, to 3.68 for the surface layer. The corresponding zinc contents were 8.25% and 28.0% respectively. The chief minerals identified were diopside, melilite, periclase and calcium oxide, with unconverted willemite and globules of metallic zinc in the layers nearer the surface. Periclase and calcium oxide are obviously the formation products of dolomite at elevated temperatures. Diopside and melilite are complex silicates of calcium, magnesium and aluminium. Diopside probably begins to form at a temperature between 650°C and 800°C and is stable up to about 1350°C. Melilite is a high temperature mineral and begins to form at around 800°C to 900°C and is stable up to a temperature of about 1400°C.

Pneumatic transfer systems

The pneumatic transfer systems were designed to work under suction at a maximum vacuum of about 0.5 atmospheres. In each case a Rootes blower evacuated the warm air from a bag filter and discharged to atmosphere. Air was allowed to be drawn into the conveying pipeline immediately behind the furthermost dust feeding points. In the case of the preoxide, dust was fed via star feeders into the settling chambers. The dust collected in the cyclone was fed into a screw conveyor and moistened with water before also being dropped down the feed chute. Two such systems were installed, one as a standby. The preoxide bag filter which thus became redundant was re-installed as a standby unit in the Waelz oxide circuit.

Thus modified, the preoxide pneumatic transfer system has worked smoothly. However, the screw conveyor under the cooling tower proved to be under capacity and tripped out several times on overload before the shaft eventually broke, after less than two weeks in operation.

The modified precipitator oxide system was still not capable of operating at the required capacity of 8 tons per hour without frequent choking. Consequently the following further modifications were carried out during April, 1970:-

(a) The cross Redler, newly installed between the two precipitators, was removed and installed below the cooling tower in place of the screw conveyor.

(b) Each electrostatic precipitator was provided with a completely separate pneumatic transfer system.

Air inlet tubes

The original air inlet tubes were constructed of a 25% chromium, 12% nickel alloy in 3 parts, viz:-

(a) the end portion approximately 60 cm in length with the discharge nozzle

(b) the tubular middle section approximately 130 cm long, which was spun cast and

(c) the flanged end section approximately 40 cm long.

These three portions were welded together.

The air inlet tubes started failing from about August, 1969, when No.1 air tube was found to have a circumferential crack just over half a metre from the end parallel to the original weld. as can be seen in Fig. 6

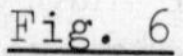

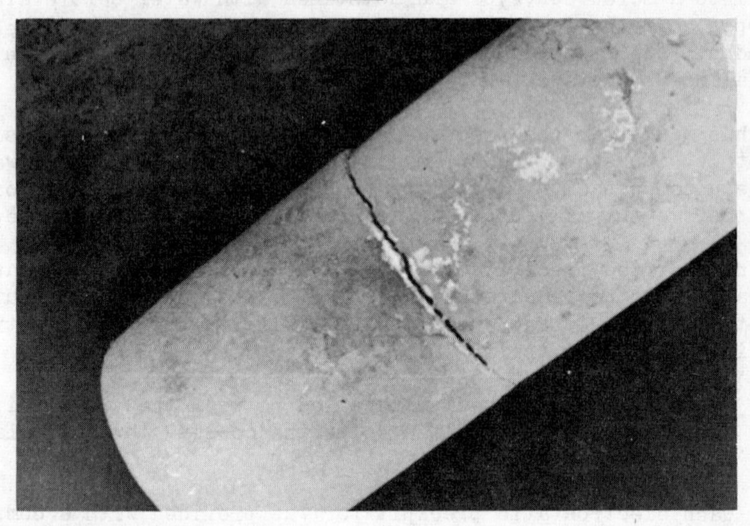

This was welded in position, but by the end of campaign No.8 about a month later, the crack had opened up again and the metal was so severely crystallized that it became necessary to remove the tube, after 146 days in actual operation. This tube was not replaced at this stage.

No.3 air tube actually broke off somewhere near the weld at the base during No.9 campaign and was also not replaced - it had been in operation for 161 days. By this stage both Nos. 2 and 4 air tubes had developed circumferential cracks similar to No.1 and had to be welded. The next stoppage was brought about by the breakage of No.4 air tube. It and No.2 and 5 air tubes were removed after 196 days in actual operation. No.2 had cracked circumferentially but No.5 had actually abraded away to such an extent that a hole had appeared near the extremity.

Two new tubes of somewhat different design, cast in one piece by Scaw Metals from an alloy containing 25% chromium and 20% nickel were fitted in the Nos. 2 and 5 positions while positions Nos. 1, 3 and 4 were blanked off. No.2 Scaw tube had to be removed after only 25 days of operation due to severe cracking both longitudinally and circumferentially. The No.2 position was then also blanked off.

After a further 27 days of operation it became necessary to stop the kiln due to brick damage at the feed end and also a severe blockage in the duct to the cooling tower. No.5 Scaw tube appeared to be in good condition but No.6 original tube after 248 days in use had developed a small circumferential crack and a bulge. It was, however, decided to operate one more campaign before replacing it.

Nos. 7 and 8 tubes were still apparently in good condition. It was decided to put back one tube nearer the discharge end to facilitate better distribution of air. As an experiment a new Lurgi tube was installed in the No.1 position with the air inlet port rotated through 180° so that the discharge was directed towards the feed end. As no rings developed anywhere near No.1 fan, it was decided at the end of campaign No.14 to operate with Nos. 1, 2 and 4 fans discharging towards the kiln feed end and Nos. 7 and 8 fans discharging in the opposite direction. By this stage No.6 air tube had failed completely, after 280 days in operation. Scaw tube No.5 after 84 days in use also had to be removed due to metal failure.

It is of interest to note that Komley and Gareev[7] recommend, as result of an investigation at the Chelyabinsk Waelz Kiln, 40 m in length treating leach plant residues, that it is highly desirable that air should be introduced into the kiln stagewise in proportion to the oxygen demand in the particular zone. In the case of the above kiln, they consider that 20% to 25% of the total air should be supplied at a point 21 metres from the feed end and that additional air is also required at 27 to 30 metres from the feed end. Kubyshev et al[9] report that in the treatment of oxidized zinc ores in a kiln at Achisaisk, improved results were obtained by introducing 1 800 to 2 500 m^3/h of air at a pressure of 7 to 8 atmospheres, at the discharge end of the kiln, the high pressure being required to ensure that the air travelled well down the kiln before the oxygen could be depleted.

Brick Lining

Right from the start trouble was experienced with the brick-lining in the feed cone to the kiln. Initially these bricks spalled rather severely and then started dropping out. Patching was quite ineffective and eventually at the end of November, 1969, the conical portion was cast in position using refractory material REFCAST S.P., with typical properties as shown in Table X11. The first 3 rows of bricks adjacent to the cone were also replaced using Superlin bricks. After 52 days the cast material still appeared to be in good condition but the bricks had all fallen out again and had to be replaced.

Table XII. Refcast S.P. - Typical Properties

Chemical analysis (%)			
SiO_2	33.8	CaO	14.9
Al_2O_3	42.4	MgO	0.1
Fe_2O_3	6.9	Loss on ignition	0.5
TiO_2	1.5		
Brick density			
Air dried			2.24 g/cm^3
Fired to 1250°C			2.08 g/cm^3
Cold Crushing Strength			
Air dried			425 kg/cm^2
Fired to 1250°C			140 kg/cm^2
Linear change after firing to 1250°C			0.5 to 1%

The first signs of brick failure in the main body of the kiln were noticed after 196 days of operation. The zone extending from 42.5 metres to 49.6 metres from the feed end was then replaced using Lusite bricks as before but including 2 rows of Superlin as a test. The Lusite bricks that had to be replaced had all failed in the middle. The top 5 of 10 cms of each brick were still extremely hard, but had acquired a purplish colour and the zone 5 to 10 cms deep, in contact with the steel shell had turned a greyish-black colour but was also still hard. The middle portion was completely friable and impregnated with slag, globules of metal and carbon. This is illustrated in Fig. 7 below - the surface of the bricks in contact with the burden can be seen in the top left hand corner and the steel shell of the kiln in the bottom right hand corner.

Fig. 7

After a further 25 days another 1.5 metres were renewed from 49.6 metres to 51.1 metres from the feed end. 27 days later 1.6 metres were renewed from 42.5 metres to 40.9 metres from the feed end.

At the end of campaign No.14, 1.4 metres of the lining, viz. from 42.5 to 43.9 metres from feed end, which had previously been renewed after 196 days in operation, had to be replaced for the second time after 84 days in operation. This time Superlin bricks were used.

The two test rows of Superlin bricks previously fitted in this same zone superficially still appeared to be in good condition. This was confirmed by test drilling, as shown in Table X.

Using a diamond drill, approximately 30 mm in diameter, 6 test holes were drilled in bricks at selected points in the kiln and the bore cores examined. The results are tabulated in Table X11l

Table X111. Bore Cores from Brick Lining

Sample No.	Metres from feed end	Type of brick	Days in use	Conditions of core
1	70	Lusite	280	Greyish colour, hard, and condition generally good.
2	60.6	Lusite	280	Greyish colour, hard, and condition generally good.
3	53	Lusite	280	Only half core obtained. Greyish in colour tending towards black - suspect carbon impregnation.
4	42.2	Superlin	84	Light grey with mauve tinge - core broken, but no sign of carbon impregnation.
5	32.5	Lusite	280	Dark grey in colour, but no sign of carbon impregnation.
6	22	Superlin	280	Light grey with mauve tinge - no sign of carbon impregnation

From a critical examination of the type of brick failure, it appears that the damage has been caused by the penetration of gases followed by some chemical and or physical changes within the body of the brick. Normally the surface of the brick in contact with the burden will have a temperature in the region of 1000°C to 1200°C while the end in contact with the shell is at a temperature of 200 to 300°C.

The carbon deposition reaction is well known and may occur in the temperature range 400°C to 700°C as follows:-

$$2\ CO \longrightarrow C + CO_2$$

This reaction appears to be catalysed by the presence of iron oxides and could result in the deposition of carbon along the joints and in the pores of the bricks, setting up stresses which cause cracking of the lining.

Zinc vapour could also penetrate the bricks to a point where the temperature is sufficiently low to cause condensation of the vapour. The presence of globules of metallic zinc in the centre of the bricks is clear proof that this has occurred.

A further reaction involving zinc vapour is possible. The CO_2 produced by the carbon deposition reaction, while diffusing back into the kiln could react with the zinc vapour penetrating the bricks and cause re-oxidation by the reaction.

$$Zn\ (vapour) + CO_2 \longrightarrow ZnO + CO$$

The zinc oxide produced by this reaction would also deposit within the brick and behave in the same fashion as the carbon produced by the carbon deposition reaction.

Further laboratory work is at present being conducted to confirm the above assumptions. However, it is significant to note that the Superlin bricks in the 42 m (from feed end) zone have stood up much better than the adjacent Lusite bricks which had to be replaced after 84 days. In future Jumbo bricks will be used as these have still lower porosity and permeability characteristics and a lower iron content, as can be seen from Table V1.

Thermocouples in Kiln

The only thermocouple in the kiln that has continued to provide reliable readings is No.11 which is approximately 8 metres from the feed end, where a temperature of 400°C to 500°C is recorded. It is suspected that this reading is probably higher than the true temperature of the burden and lower than the gas temperatures at this point. It does, however, provide a useful guide for operational purposes.

The other thermocouples very rarely record a reliable temperature for more than a few days; thereafter they either become embedded in an accretion and then record an erroneously low temperature or they become physically damaged by large lumps of fallen accretion rolling around. A portable thermocouple is used for determining the temperature of the residue discharge from the kiln. At hourly intervals it is inserted, for a few minutes, through a guide tube suitably positioned to allow the residue to cascade over the end of the thermocouple. This has been found to be more reliable than using an optical pyrometer, due to the interference often caused by excessively dusty conditions within the kiln.

The sheaths of the thermocouple are fabricated from a 26% Cr, 5% Ni alloy and there has been no evidence of the sheaths either being abraded or eroded away nor of any actual metal failure.

Supporting rollers

In mid January, 1970, one of the rollers supporting the third riding ring stopped rotating with the kiln. It was found that the shaft had sheared. The kiln was operated without this roller for a week, without any apparent deleterious effects, while a new shaft was being fitted. During April, about 3 months later, the same roller again stopped rotating. It was found that the roller had moved on the shaft, so the whole assembly was renewed. Investigations are proceeding to establish the cause of the failure.

at 4 different points, into one common conveying pipeline which discharged into a cyclone, the overflow from the cyclone being filtered in a bag house. In the case of the Waelz oxide, oxide was delivered into the conveying pipeline at 2 different points via star feeders, and was collected in either of two dust cyclones each situated immediately above a storage silo. The cyclone exhaust gas was filtered in a bag filter. The systems suffered from the following defects:-

(a) the conveying pipelines choked frequently

(b) thebends and the cyclone were very rapidly abraded away particularly in the case of the preoxide

(c) the cyclone dust outlet choked frequently

(d) the dust outlet from the filter choked frequently

(e) the filter bags themselves charred brown and appeared to shrink and pull off the fittings.

(f) the filter bags actually burst, often at the seams

(g) as no star feeders were fitted between the cyclones and the respective storage silos, these silos became part of the vacuum system and caused a great deal of inertia in the circuit. Hence if any incipient blockage occurred at the feed point into the system, there was a considerable time lag before the vacuum in the system increased sufficiently to clear the blockage. Before this happened, the circuit had invariably blocked up completely. This was particularly bad in the case of the Waelz oxide circuit due to having the two 100 ton silos as part of the vacuum system.

As a first modification the suppliers of the equipment decided to alter both systems to work under pressure instead of under vacuum, as this would overcome the time lag problem. However, as most of the star feeders had not been designed to work under pressure, this scheme did not work either, as sufficient air leaked back through the star feeders to interfere with the discharge of the dust into the conveying system. Dust also escaped through the various seals and discharged copiously into the atmosphere.

During March, 1970, a cross Redler was installed to pick up the oxide from the two Redlers under the electrostatic precipitators and deliver it via a Möller pump into the pneumatic system operating under pressure. At the same time one Redler was installed to collect the preoxide from the 3 settling chambers and also the cooling tower oxide and deliver the combined load into the pneumatic system at one point. This also worked under pressure and discharged into a dust collecting cyclone positioned immediately above the feed end of the kiln. The gas leaving the top of the cyclone was discharged back in.

Recovery of coke from the residue

In order to maintain a granular, free flowing discharge from the kiln it has been found necessary to maintain a free carbon content of about 35% in the residue. Even if accretions do form at isolated spots due to localized overheating, accretions with this amount of surplus coke, are usually sufficiently friable to break away of their own accord from time to time. Under normal conditions over 90% of the residue will pass through a 6 mm screen. As can be seen from Table V11l, the amount of reductant actually consumed in the kiln is of the order of 15 to 20% of the weight of new zinc bearing feed, whereas, the actual addition is in the range of 50 to 60%. Pilot plant scale jigging tests conducted on the residue showed that if the residue were reduced to all minus 6 mm in size it should be possible to recover 75% of the carbon in the residue into a product containing 70 to 75% carbon, which could be re-used in the kiln if this could be attained on a plant scale the loss in the residue would be equivalent to about 10% of the weight of the new feed which would reduce the overall consumptions of new coke or anthracite to about 25 to 30%.

As a temporary expedient a second-hand 1 metre square twin hutch Yuba jig was installed in February, 1970, to recover as much coke as possible. Due to inadequate screening facilities, insufficient hutch water and various other obvious drawbacks, this plant has operated very inefficiently but has nevertheless managed to recover up to 50% of the carbon in the residue into a product containing about 70% carbon. This has been fed back into the kiln without any deleterious results. In the light of the experience gained, a full scale plant is now being designed.

Statistical Data

Volume of gas discharged

Under normal operating conditions, it is estimated that the distribution and source of gases are approximately as follows in Table X1V:-

Table XlV. Source of Gases Exhausted up the Stack - Typical Conditions

Source	Nm^3/h
Sealing air fan delivering down feed chute	2 000 Nm^3/h
Producer gas consumed	1 330
Water vapour ex feed	1 620
CO_2 from decomposition of carbonates in feed	1 280
Water vapour ex sprays in cooling tower	6 360
Air introduced via shell fans	17 170
Air introduced as combustion air	Nil
Air drawn in through end of kiln as result of draught	16 610
Miscellaneous air leaks nominally estimated	2 000
Total gas exhausted up stack	48 370

The actual volume of gases passing through the kiln, from the above figures would be 38 000 Nm^3/h. Assuming an average gas temperature of say 1000°C, the volume of gas passing through the kiln would be approximately 176 000 m^3/h, equivalent to a linear velocity of approximately 5.3 m per second.

Oxygen content of kiln gases

No facilities are available for measuring the oxygen content of the gas within the kiln itself. The figures shown in Table XV below refer to the gas in the settling chamber and the gas discharged up the stack respectively. As can be seen from Table XlV the gas in the settling chamber includes about 2 000 Nm^3/h of air blown down the feed chute, which dilutes 38 000 Nm^3/h of gases emerging from the kiln and would account for approximately 1% of oxygen in the mixture.

Table XV. Typical Analysis of Exhaust Gases

	Settling Chamber	Stack
% O_2	5.3	7.0
% CO_2	17.1	15.0
% CO	Trace	Trace

Labour requirements

The plant operates with the following labour complement:-

Manager	1
Plant foreman	1
Secretary/Storekeeper	1
Part-time Typist/Clerk	1
Shift Operators (2/shift)	7
Dayshift Operators	2
Relief Operator	1
Foreman Mechanic	1
Other Mechanics	4
Manual Labourers	60

Water, electric power and producer gas consumption

When operating at the rate of 10 000 tons of new zinc bearing feed per month the consumption of water, electric power and producer gas are as shown in Table XVl below:-

Table XVl. Water, electric power and producer gas consumption

	per month	per ton new feed
Water (tons)	12 000	1.2
Electric power (kWh)	270 000	27
Producer gas Nm^3	1 800 000	180

Preoxide and cooling tower oxide and Waelz oxide

There is no ready means of determining the tonnage of the first two products, but spot checks from time to time have indicated that the preoxide (from the settling chambers) amounts to about 4 tons per hour and the cooling tower oxide about 2 tons per hour. Typical metal contents are shown in Table XVll below:-

Table XVll. Typical analyses of preoxide and cooling oxide (%)

	Zinc	Lead	Mg	Ca
Preoxide	32.8	6.9	3.2	5.3
Cooling tower oxide	44.0	8.3	2.7	4.6

A typical analysis of Waelz oxide currently produced is shown in Table XVlll below:-

Table XVlll. Typical Analysis of Waelz Oxide (%)

Zn	64.00	F	0.028
Pb	9.09	Co	0.001
Ca	2.40	Fe	0.41
Mg	1.54	Ge	<0.006
SiO_2	1.95	Ni	<0.02

Conclusions

One year of operating experience has shown that a satisfactory elimination of zinc can be achieved without excessive trouble due to the formation of accretions, that a satisfactory grade of Waelz oxide can be produced, and that the life of the refractory brick lining will be within the expected limits.

The fact that neither the designed rate of production nor the anticipated percentage recovery have been maintained is due largely to the inadequacy of the pneumatic transfer systems. Vigorous steps are now being taken to remedy this position.

Acknowledgment

Thanks are due to Mr. R.R.M. Cousens, Technical Director of Gold Fields of South Africa Limited, for permission to publish this paper.

References

1. Bogacz M., "Fire-refining of Zinc-Lead ores in Poland," from Materials of the 'Technical Conference in Warsaw on Questions of Production Techniques for Zinc, lead and Associated Metals,' Moscow 1957, pp. 129 - 149.

2. Johannsen F., "The Advance in the development of the Waelz Process," Metall und Erz, 1927, 24 (17) 425.

3. Hoffman R., "The Waelz Process," Transactions of the American Institute of Mining and Metallurgical Engineers, Vol. 76, 1928.

4. Harris W.E., "The Waelz Process," American Institute of Mining and Metallurgical Engineers Transactions, Vol.121, 1936, Rocky Mountain Final Volume on Metallurgy of lead and zinc.

5. Jensen C.W., "The Waelz Process," Mining Magazine, Vol. 92, 1955, pp. 73 - 79.

6. Bodenstein M., "The Mechanism of the Metallurgical production of Zinc," Transactions of the American Electrochemical Society (1927), 51, 449.

7. Komlev G.A. and Gareev V.N., "Chemism of the Waelz method of processing Zinc Cakes," Tsvetnye Metally The Soviet Journal of Non-ferrous Metals, March 1964, pp. 22 - 29.

8. Truesdale E.C. and Waring R.K., "Relative Rates of Reactions involved in Reduction of Zinc Ores," AIME Transactions, Institute of Metals Division 152, 1942, pp. 303 - 315.

9. Kubyshev et al., "Waelz treatment of Achisacsk oxidized zinc ores in high capacity furnaces," Tszvetnye Metally, Vol. 9, September 1968, pp. 36 - 40.

Chapter 33

ROTARY HEARTH PROCESS FOR SMELTING LEAD ORES AND BATTERY SCRAP OF BLEIBERGER BERGWERKS UNION, A.G.
Arnoldstein, Austria

Dr. Herbert Dlaska - Works Manager, Lead Smelter
Dipl. Ing. Odo Notzold - Works Manager BBU

Abstract

The BBU - rotary hearth treats lead concentrates and battery scrap by the roast-reaction process. It corresponds in principle to the long-known Newnam hearth, however its hearth-basin is not straight but curved to a closed ring. In operation this annular hearth is filled with liquid lead and rotates around a central blast-box. The charge, heated to a glowing-red, floats on top of the lead bath, into which air is blown from the blast-box through a horizontal slot-type tuyere.

Ore pellets and brown coal are continuously charged onto the reacting mass from two storage bins. Lead is set free by the roasting reactions and trickles through the charge into the lead bath from where it is tapped from time to time. The reacting mass is continuously stirred by a mechanical agitator and backed, by a mechanical shovel, against the water-jacketed wall of the blast-box.

The gangue of the charge forms lumps of scorified character, the so-called hearth slag or grey slag, which are discharged from the hearth. The waste gases are collected in a hood and conducted to a baghouse from where the fumes and dust are automatically transported to the pelletizing installation and are re-cycled with new material.

The daily output of lead bullion depends mainly on the lead content of the charge. With lead concentrates containing 74%

lead, about 24 tons of lead bullion per day are produced on the hearth at a direct lead recovery of about 89 per cent.

Approximately 10 per cent of the lead content of the new material passes into the hearth slag from where it can be recovered in a blast furnace or in a rotary furnace.

For small lead smelters the BBU-process represents the most economical way of smelting high-grade lead concentrates. The process requires a relatively small capital investment, consumes little fuel, utilizes cheap fuel and is very flexible. Further, of great importance, is the fact that battery scrap can be treated by the BBU-process with very good results.

1. History and locale of the BBU plant.

The lead smelter of the Bleiberger Bergwerks Union at Arnoldstein (Gailitz) has existed since 1882 and has always treated silver-free galena concentrates from its own mines by the roast-reaction process.

The type of the smelter employed has, of course, changed several times in the run of the years. At first American-type ore hearths were used, and later for some time, the so-called Belgian reverberatory furnaces were used.

Until shortly before World War II, three Newnam hearths were in operation, plus a small blast furnace for smelting hearth slag and lead sludges and ashes.

In 1936 a rotary hearth, after the patent of F. v. Schlippenbach, was installed, which, however, proved to be inoperable. During the following years this apparatus was further developed, until finally in 1942 it could be used for production. Since that time the rotary hearth furnace has been continuously improved and, after the introduction of the pelletizing method, flotation concentrates also could be charged onto the hearth without previous sintering.

Today two BBU- hearth furnaces treat all the ore and battery scrap provided to Arnoldstein and produce about 14,000 tons of crude bullion per year.

Beside the lead smelter the works of Arnoldstein comprise an electrolytic zinc plant, a sulfuric acid plant and chemical works.

Arnoldstein is situated in the southmost part of Austria near the Italian border.

2. Theory of the process.

The basis of the BBU-rotary hearth process is the roasting and reaction process. This is the oldest known process of lead smelting and is based on the precipitation of metallic lead after the reaction of lead sulfide with its roasting products.

By blowing air into a glowing mass, rich in lead sulfide, some of the lead sulfide is roasted. The resulting lead oxides and lead sulfates react with undecomposed lead sulfide and this gives metallic lead and sulfur dioxide. A certain amount of the lead oxide is directly reduced to lead by the coal which is added to the process.

The reactions which may occur during the roasting of galena are manyfold and have been the aim of numerous investigations[1-7]. The results of these investigations, however, differ so that the true explanation of the reactions still is not entirely clear.

Greatly simplified, the reactions taking place in the ore-hearth can be described by the following equations:

$$2\ PbS + 3\ O_2 = 2\ PbO + 2\ SO_2 \quad ..equ.\ 1$$

$$PbS + 2\ O_2 = PbSO_4 \quad ..equ.\ 2$$

and

$$PbS + 2\ PbO = 3\ Pb_{(L)} + SO_2 \quad ..equ.\ 3$$

$$PbS + PbSO_4 = 2\ Pb + 2\ SO_2 \quad ..equ.\ 4$$

These equations can be regarded only as summary reactions. For example, in the roasting process primarily various basic lead sulfates such as $PbSO_4.PbO$, $PbSO_4.2PbO$ and $PbSO_4.4PbO$, are formed, rather than simple PbO or $PbSO_4$. In addition to this, also occurring in the hearth are the various reactions of the lead compounds with the gangue components of the ore, whereby lead silicates, lead ferrites, etc. are formed, which also can decidedly influence the run of the roast-reactions.

After more recent investigations of the system PB-S-O the stable formation of PbO is only possible at a temperature range where the lead compounds are already liquid. The liquation of the charge must, however, be absolutely avoided in the hearth process.

On the other hand a stable equilibrium between PbS, PbO, Pb and SO_2 corresponding to equ. 3 is not possible after the thermodynamical rules (see Fig. 1, phase diagram for Pb-S-O after G. Fischer[5]).

G. Fischer[5], however, shows in his work that this is only true for the pure system Pb-S-O. If slag-forming components and roast gases containing 80% N_2 are present, as is always the case in the hearth furnace, the phase field of PbO expands to all directions and point B moves to the phase boundary of PbS, so that a univariant equilibrium between PbS, Pb, PbO and SO_2 (equ. 3) becomes possible.

With increasing proportions of slag components, however, the phase field of Pb is shifted to higher temperatures so that for a certain proportion of slag the minimum temperature of formation of liquid lead exceeds the temperatures admissible in the hearth furnace. For this reason the slags of the hearth

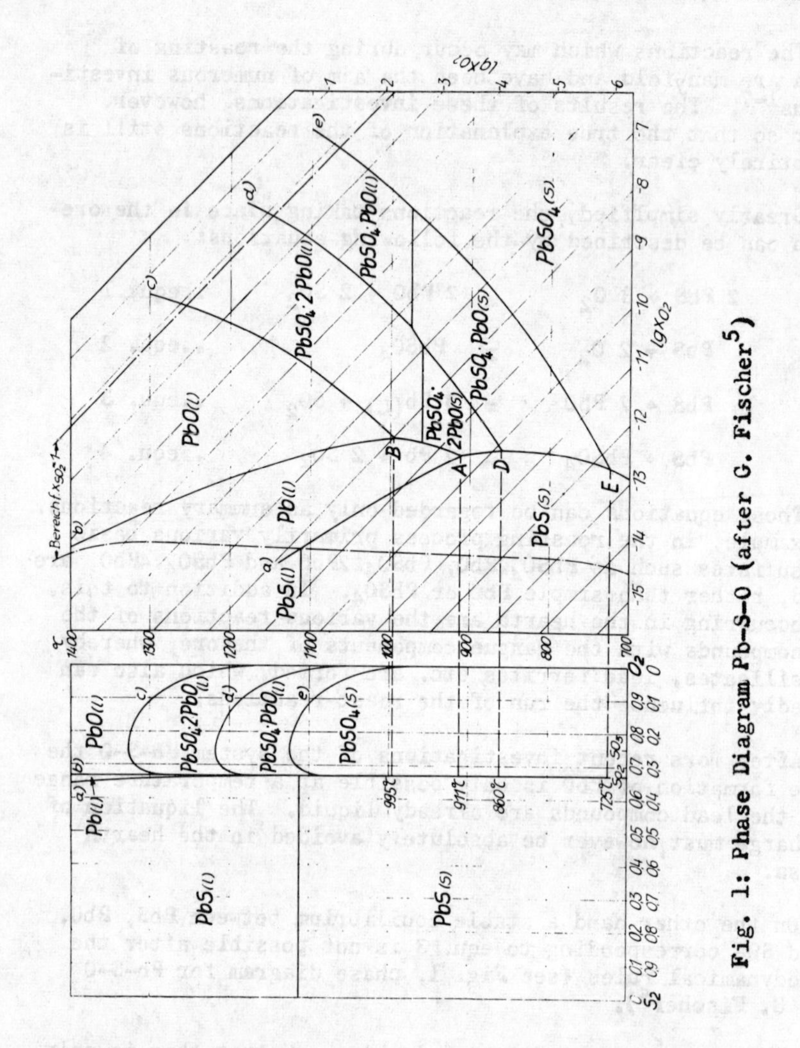

Fig. 1: Phase Diagram Pb-S-O (after G. Fischer[5])

process are necessarily very rich in lead.

An inherent advantage of the hearth process is the fact that the heat which is set free during the roasting process (equ. 1 and 2) can be utilized directly for the heat-consuming reactions (equ. 3 and 4). The addition of a small quantity of coal is however necessary to heat up the raw galena to ignition temperature and to compensate heat losses.

The roast-reactions are strongly dependent on temperature. After calculations of equilibria in the system of Pb-S-O G. Fischer[5] indicates the temperature interval from 830 to 900° C.

to be the optimal range of operation for the hearth process. At lower temperatures the reactions proceed too slowly and mainly $PbSO_4$ and basic lead sulfates are formed instead of lead. Higher temperatures are objectionable because of the increasing volatilization of Pb and PbS and the danger that the charge will liquate and complex lead compounds will be formed that cannot be decomposed in the hearth.

At these working temperatures the mass in the hearth is in a pasty condition. To obtain kinetically tolerable conditions of reaction, it is therefore necessary to stir the charge mechanically.

For the same reason, only high-grade lead concentrates can be treated in the hearth furnace. The reactions which lead to lead precipitation can only attain sufficient velocity if the reacting substances are in intimate contact and are not separated from one another by inert components.

For economical reasons a lead content of 70% in the concentrate must be regarded as the lower limit for the hearth process. Even poorer lead concentrates give metallic lead but then the lead recovery is very unsatisfactory and the proportion of lead in the hearth slag is unbearably high.

The composition of the gangue also plays an important role. Generally speaking, gangue components which raise the melting point of the charge, as for instance CaO, MgO and ZnS, have a favorable effect on the hearth process as they help to maintain the charge in a pasty state. All components which lead to liquation of the mass as CaF_2, SiO_2, Fe_2O_3 are undesirable and their portion must not exceed certain critical values. In a later part of this paper this will be dealt with in more detail.

3. Description of the BBU-rotary hearth process.

Principally the BBU-rotary hearth process corresponds to the old hearth process as it has been applied in the form of the so-called Newnam hearth in many places.

These Newnam hearths consisted of a cast-iron basin about 2.5 m long, 0.5 m wide and 0.3 m deep with water jackets flanged onto it to form the back and side walls of the hearth. The back water-jacket was cored to accomodate 12 to 36 tuyeres of 25 to 50 mm diameter.

The front of the hearth had to be open over the entire length of the hearth to enable the necessary operations like charging of ore and coal, stirring and shoveling back of the

Fig. 2: General view of the BBU-rotary hearth plant at Arnoldstein.

mass, to be carried out. The tuyere holes had to be kept free by frequent stirring with a long bar.

With the exception of the stirring, which was effected by a mechanical apparatus, all these operations had to be carried out by hand and in great heat. Work at Newnam hearth, therefore, was very hard and because of the outpouring gases and lead fumes very unhealthy.

In the thirties, F. v. Schlippenbach had the idea of building the hearth ring-shaped and to make the annular hearth rotate around this axis. With this construction it is possible to let the charge pass by stationary installations for charging and stirring and to obtain a continuous process. By covering the complete hearth with a large hood to carry off the fumes, leaving free only a small working door, the exhaust of fumes can be controlled and the radiation of heat can be reduced to a minimum.

After the patent of v. Schlippenbach a rotary-hearth furnace was built at Arnoldstein. In the proposed mode of construction, this furnace was not operable. During a period of development lasting several years, many essential parts of the rotary-hearth were altered and finally, after many discouraging failures, brought to successful operation.

One of the main difficulties was the fact that the tuyere holes through which the blast was blown in from the central body of the furnace always plugged. There was a star-shaped system of pegs to keep the nozzles free but they were quickly distorted and became ineffective.

By the invention of a slot-type tuyere with a stationary nozzle tongue, this problem was overcome in an ideal manner.

3.1. The Rotary-hearth furnace

Fig. 2 gives the overall view of the rotary-hearth plant in Arnoldstein.

The construction and mode of operation of the hearth furnace shall be explained by the help of Fig. 3, which represents a longitudinal section of the furnace:

Around a central body (1) an annular trough (basin) (2) of 3,650 mm external diameter is placed. The inner diameter of the hearth basin is 1,530 mm, the maximal depth is 360 mm. With its undercarriage the basin rests on six roller-bearings (4) and is driven over a toothed rim (3) by a motor.

The back-wall of the hearth is formed by the water-filled

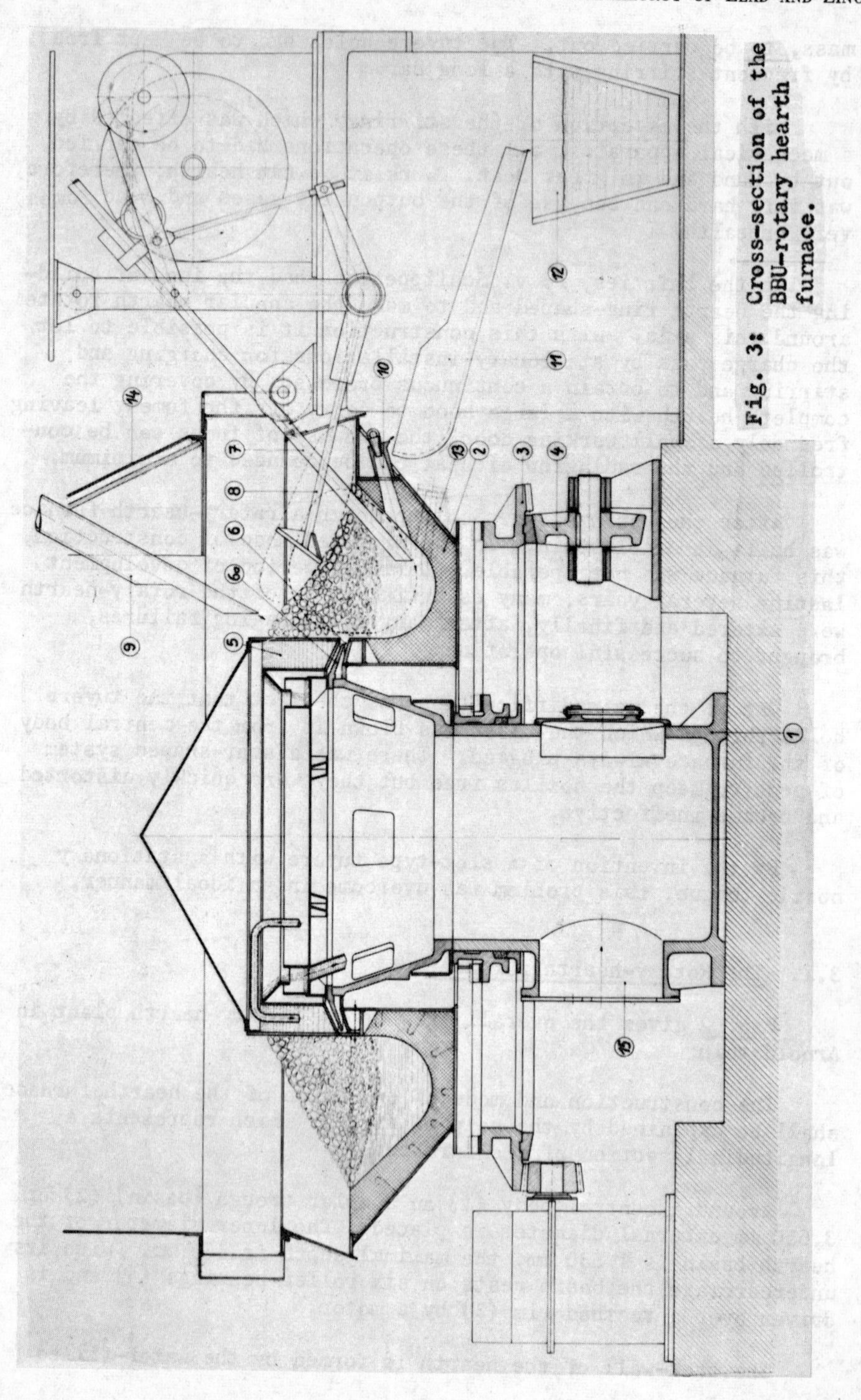

Fig. 3: Cross-section of the BBU-rotary hearth furnace.

cooler (5) which is fixed by four small bars on the top of the back of the basin.

The gap between the cylindrical cooler and the top of the basin forms the tuyere slot (6) through which the blast is blown into the reacting mass.

The interior space of the central body of the furnace thus serves as blast-box and is furnished by a fan with 3,000 Nm^3 air per hour through flange (15).

In state of operation the tuyere slot lies about 4 cm above the level of the lead bath. It must not be placed lower because of the danger of liquid lead entering the slot and plugging it. In this respect the tuyere tongue (6a) plays a very important role: While the cooler is fixedly connected with the basin and therefore rotates synchronously with it, the tuyere-tongue is a stationary ring. Thus a relative motion between the tongue and the tuyere slot is obtained which gives a self-cleaning effect of the tuyere. Any material that enters the slot is crushed and blown out by the blast.

Ore-pellets and coal are charged onto the hearth from two separate hoppers by a feeding device through chutes (9).

The mass is continuously rabbled with a poker (7). The poker bar is eccentrically fixed to a rotating disk and bedded onto a roll in such a way that the point of the bar follows the dotted oval line indicated in the figure. The tip of the poker moves upwards vertically and very closely to the tuyere slot so that eventual accretions are dislodged from the slot.

The poker bar is made from heat-resisting steel and is water-cooled to keep abrasion low.

Beside the poker a mechanical shovel (backing device) is installed which throws the broken-up mass back against the wall of the cooler.

The produced lead is discontinually tapped at the upper tap hole (10) of the basin and runs over a spout(11) into water-cooled moulds (12).

The bottom taphole (13) is only opened if all the lead of the basin has to be let off. This may be necessary if the trough has to be repaired or replaced.

A hood (14) is suspended above the hearth by which fumes and dust are collected and carried away to a baghouse.

In the range of the mechanical shovel the hearth is provided with a small opening through which the hearth attendant can supervise the process. Through this opening the hearth slags are removed from the furnace by a stripper plate.

The hearth trough consists of a steel casing which is tamped with a refractory ramming mixture.

The life of a lining is two or more years. The replacing of the complete basin takes only two to three days. The long life of the lining is assured by the fact that shortly after the starting of the furnace a thick and strongly adhering layer of PbS precipitates on the surface of the basin and safeguards it. An undesired extensive closing up of the basin is hindered by a small cutting tooth underneath the front part of the poker bar.

3.2. Mode of operation of the process.

While until recently coarse ore (jig concentrates) was treated to some extent, today exclusively flotation concentrates are smelted in the hearth furnace.

The scheme of the process can be seen from the flow sheet in Fig. 4.

The flotation concentrates cannot be charged directly onto the hearth as they would impede the penetration of the blast through the mass because of their high density. Therefore, to loosen up the burden, the ore is first blended with return dust, lime hydrate and coal breeze and then pelletized in a granulating saucer. If present, refinery dross, lead slimes and skimmings are also added, the proportions of these, however, not exceeding 20% of the charge as a rule.

The quantity of flue dust added depends on the daily amount of dust collected in the baghouse and the wetness of the flotation concentrates. Usually 16% of the burden consists of dust, but occasionally the ore is pelletized with higher portions of it or, on the other hand, without any dust at all.

With too high portions of fumes and dust the output of the hearth is cut down mainly because of the fact that the lead content of the charge is reduced. The baghouse dust contains only about 67% of lead, mostly as lead sulfate. The addition of lime hydrate (about 1%) is only for the purpose of increasing the consistency of the pellets by hardening during storage.

The coal breeze (about 2%), of grain size range 0 to 3 mm diameter, is not only added as a reducing agent but also to

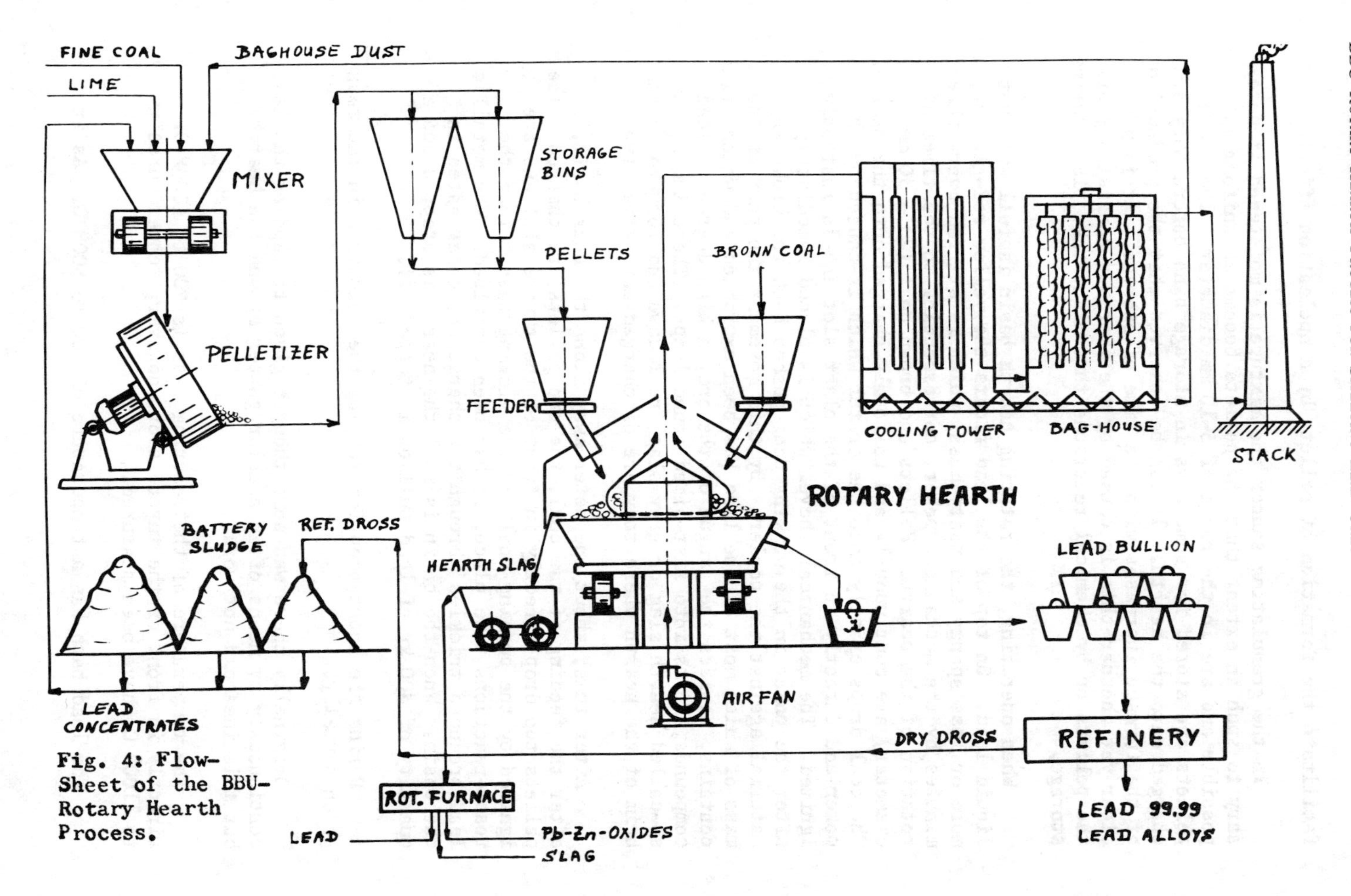

Fig. 4: Flow-Sheet of the BBU-Rotary Hearth Process.

facilitate the formation of pellets by a nucleation effect.

In the granulating saucer the mixture is moistened if necessary to such an extent that the pellets become as uniform as possible and are in the range of 5-10 mm diameter. The fresh pellets are stored for some days in storage bins before they are charged onto the hearth. It can be observed that the production of the furnace increases with the time of storage. It is not clear yet whether this is caused by the improved consistency of the pellets or by chemical reactions that might take place during storage.

When operating, the rotating hearth basin is full with hot liquid lead. On top of the lead floats the yellow-red-glowing, more or less spongy and pasty mass, which is stirred every three minutes by the mechanical poker, corresponding to the times of rotation of the hearth. Pellets and brown coal (20 - 30 mm diameter) are continuously and uniformly charged onto the hearth. The coal drops exactly into the crater which is caused by the poker and directly in front of the blast slot and is instantly ignited. The mechanical shovel which is placed immediately after the poker in the working door pushes back the broken-up material against the cooler. By this movement the part of the mass of which most of the lead has been extracted and which still contains, besides the gangue of the ore, a high degree of lead compounds, forms into fist-sized round lumps. These lumps, the so-called hearth slag or grey slag, roll down and forward to the brim of the hearth where they are discharged automatically.

After this, about one meter away along the hearth rim, after the feeding of the coal, the ore pellets are charged. The pellets too drop directly in front of the tuyere slot and are ignited by the burning coal and the glowing mass. Then the roast-reactions take place, as has been described. The metallic lead produced trickles through the charge and congregates in the basin. When the basin is full the hearth is stopped and a quantity of 400 kg of lead bullion is tapped off.

During the short stop for tapping the reactions in the mass go on normally.

Originally there was some thought given to tapping the lead continuously by means of an annular gutter around the hearth, but this idea did not work.

The temperature of the reacting mass is 700 to 1000° C. Directly in front of the tuyere slot, however, temperatures up to 1100° C. have been measured.

The lead bath has a temperature of 700 to 800° C. As it

serves as heat reservoir for the process, the temperature of the bath should not be lower because of the danger that the furnace will become too cold. Higher temperatures, however, are not favorable because then too much PbS is dissolved in the lead bath.

The regulation of the temperature of the hearth can be easily carried out by the operator by altering the quantities of blast and coal. The feeding rate of pellets, coal and blast can be regulated steplessly by the hearth attendant.

One of the biggest disadvantages of the hearth process always has been the high amount of fumes and dust because of the vaporization of lead and lead compounds and the blowing off of fine particles of the charge by the blast. With the BBU process the baghouse dust is no particular burden but its recycling is an absolutely necessary factor.

Only by returning baghouse dust does the pelletizing of the ore become possible, and the costly sintering of the ore thereby avoided.

The baghouse dust is very fine and absolutely dry and is transported by a tight conveying device to the dust silo of the pelletizing installation. Some 15 per cent of the lead content of the pellets is in steady circulation with the baghouse dust. The daily production of dust is just adequate for the pelletizing of the flotation concentrate.

The waste gases contain about 1 per cent SO_2 leaving the baghouse and, after dilution with the air, pass into the 70 meter high stack. The lead bullion is transported in form of 2 ton ingots to the refinery where 99.99% lead and different lead alloys are made from it.

10 to 15 per cent of the bullion weight returns as dry refinery dross, consisting mainly of lead sulfide, back to the smelting plant and is added to the ore before pelletizing. Because of its high lead content, about 80 per cent, this dross is a material very well suited for the hearth furnace.

In Table 1 the balances of material and metal are given for the typical ore concentrates smelted in Arnoldstein, containing on the average, 74% lead. The metal balance of the hearth furnace, as well as the daily production, depends principally upon lead content of the charged material. This dependance is approximately linear.

With a lead content of the charge of 70% the daily output per hearth is about 20 tons of bullion; with pellets containing 80% lead daily productions of 30 tons of lead bullion can be reached.

As the hearth slags contain on the average 39 per cent of lead, independently from the lead content of the charge, it is clear that high-grade lead concentrates give better yields than poor concentrates.

Table 1: Balance of material and metal of the BBU-process.

	Ratio of Material %	Lead Content %Pb	Distribution of Lead
Input			
Lead concentrate	73	74	75.7
Circulating fume	16	67	15.0
Refinery dross	8	83	9.3
Fine coal	2	--	--
Lime hydrate	1	--	--
Pellets	100	71	100.0
Output			
Lead bullion	63.7	98	76.0
Circulating fume	18.4	67	15.0
Hearth slag	17.9	39	8.5
Losses	--	--	0.5
	100.0		100.0

The fumes are in continuous circulation. As its quantity is constant, it is not necessary to take them into account in the metal balance.

The direct recovery of lead in terms of new material smelted is, therefore, not 76% but 89 per cent, and the amount of lead in the hearth slag about 10 per cent.

The assayed content of the slag is 35 to 42 per cent lead. At present the hearth slags are processed in the blast furnace of a foreign smelter. There is, however, the possibility of treating the hearth slag in the rotary furnace of our own zinc smelter.

Investigations have shown, that in this rotary furnace of the type "Dorschel" (Klockner-Humboldt-Deutz A.G.), which is in use for the processing of leaching residues, the grey slag can be smelted with good results. Approximately 10 percent coke breeze and 5 per cent of quartzite must be added. More than 60% of the lead content of the hearth slag can thus be obtained as lead bullion, the remainder together with zinc, reports to the fumes and, to a small extent, forms lead matte. The zinc content of the fumes can be extracted by leaching and bears an essential part of the smelting costs of the grey slag.

The rotary-hearth furnace can stay in operation without any interruption for one month and even longer; then it must be stopped for one or two days for the cleaning of the flues and for smaller repairs.

The shut down of the furnace is very simple. The feed of ore pellets and coal is stopped and two hours later the then burnt-out mass is removed from the hearth while it is still hot. The lead bath is let solidify; only in case the basin itself has to be repaired is the lead tapped through the bottom spout. Some hours later the hearth is cold.

The starting of the furnace is just as simple. Within the empty or partly filled with lead basin of the hearth, a coke fire is kindled and an amount of molten lead scrap is ladled in, such that the trough is half-filled with liquid lead. Then, in thin layers, hearth mass from the previous operation is charged until the coke bed is completely covered. About four hours after the start ore pellets can be fed and the hearth is set on blast. When the coke is burnt out and the newly formed mass has reached a certain height the mechanical poker and the backing shovel are set into operation. Starting with a period of restricted production, the feed is increased until the furnace is in full operation within 24 hours.

3.3. Main data of operation of the Arnoldstein Rotary-hearth smelter.

3.3.1. Ore analysis

In Table 2 the assays of different lead concentrates are given, which have been treated by the BBU-process. The ore types Bleiberg and Raibl are the standard lead concentrates of our smelter. These ores are very pure and contain only traces of silver and bismuth, so that a simple thermal refining of the crude bullion (drossing, decopperising and Harris process) is sufficient.

The ore types Salafossa and Sletovo hitherto have been

processed in the hearth furnace only for short periods on experimental scale. Their analyses are of interest as they indicated which types of lead ores are best suited for the BBU-process.

Influence of the accompanying elements:

Closer details on the admissible contents of the gangue components can not be given from Arnoldstein experience, as up to now only the four brands of lead concentrates presented in Table 2 have been at our disposal.

In the literature, the opinion on the admissible contents of the accompanying elements is not uniform [8, 9, 10]. This is understandable as not only the individual values of

Table 2 : Assays of various ore types

	Bleiberg %	Raibl %	Salafossa %	Sletovo %
Pb	76.7	71.3	71.6	71.6
Zn	3.3	6.1	4.6	7.2
Fe	1.1	2.1	2.4	3.5
Cu	< 0.001	0.001	0.002	0.26
CaO	1.37	0.7	0.7	0.32
MgO	0.5	0.1	0.6	0.1
SiO_2	0.25	0.15	0.07	1.1
Al_2O_3	< 0.01	< 0.01	0.015	0.55
$BaSO_4$	0.15	1.8	n.o.*	n.o.*
S_{total}	14.3	15.4	15.2	15.5
Sb	< 0.01	0.05	0.1	0.15
Sn	< 0.001	< 0.01	n.o.	n.o.
As	< 0.002	0.32	0.13	n.o.
Ag	0.0002	0.0002	< 0.001	0.046
Bi	< 0.001	< 0.001	< 0.001	0.044

*n.o. - "not observed"

the gangue components but also their relation to each other is of importance.

CaO and MgO are favorable for the hearth process as they raise the melting point of the charge and bind sulfur. Too high proportions of them, however, have an undesirable effect as the percentage of lead in the charge is reduced.

SiO_2: Because of its slag-forming character, SiO_2 is deleterious for the hearth process. Lead silicates are formed which cannot be decomposed in the hearth. Besides, particles of the charge are enveloped by the low-melting phase with a non-reacting skin layer and thus the reaction is strongly impeded. After Buck [10] the content of silica must not exceed 2 per cent, other authors [8, 9] admit 4 to 6 per cent SiO_2. Our own values were not higher than 1.1% SiO_2. Troubles, therefore, did not occur.

Zinc: Zinc also raises the melting point of the charge and is, therefore, favorable. Too high zinc contents, however, may present difficulties with the smelting of the hearth slag in the blast furnace.

With the Sletovo ore we had no trouble in hearth operation although the Zn content was as high as 7.2 per cent.

Iron: Iron forms with SiO_2 low-melting point lead compounds and, therefore, impairs the hearth process if too high contents of it are present in the charge. Generally 4% of Fe are indicated as upper limit. From our own experience the admissible value must lie somewhat lower because the Salafossa ore gave us difficulties.

With this ore, apparently because of the low melting point of the charge, the hearth slag does not ball, the hearth mass remains fine and burns out as the slag cannot be discharged. In a mixture 1 : 1 with concentrate type Bleiberg, however, the Salafossa ore can be processed with good results.

It is of interest that the Sletovo ore gave no trouble in this regard in spite of its high Fe-content of 3.5 per cent. It must be supposed that in this case the particularly high zinc content compensates for the effect of the iron.

From this it may be seen how important it is to consider the combined effects of all the accompanying elements when the qualification of an ore for the hearth process is discussed. Clear statements in this regard can only be obtained when the ore is tested in a trial in the hearth furnace.

Copper: The effect of copper has been closely investigated by Jovanovic[11] in the Newnam hearth. By the formation of matte the hearth mass becomes sticky even with relatively small amounts of copper and accretions are formed which cause mechanical troubles. Copper contents as low as 1% can cause this adverse effect.

Buck[10] indicates an admissible content of copper of the charge of 2 per cent.

Fluor spar can, under certain conditions, exclude the ore from the hearth process on account of its fluxing properties [10].

3.3.2 Composition of the hearth slag

The average lead content of the hearth slag is 39% with scattering values from 32 to 42 per cent. The distribution of the lead in the different lead compounds of the slag varies strongly as can be seen from some arbitrary examples in Table 3.

The zinc contents average 15 to 20%. The composition of the remainder corresponds to the proportion of the different gangue components of the ore.

Table 3: Distribution (mode of occurance) of lead in the hearth slag.

Hearth slag	No.	I	II	III	IV	V
Lead as metal	%	3.6	3.5	2.9	4.1	4.2
Lead as sulfate	%	8.6	9.6	10.3	6.7	12.2
Lead as oxide and silicate	%	5.8	7.2	11.3	16.8	3.6
Lead as sulfide, ferrite etc.	%	16.5	14.6	13.4	13.1	21.8
Lead total		34.5	34.9	37.9	40.7	41.8

On the average the hearth slag contains 7.6% Fe, 8.4% CaO and 5.7% SiO_2 when Bleiberg type ore is treated. Most of the silica content of the slag originates in the ash of the brown coal which is added in the process.

If antimony, silver or bismuth are present in the ore these

metals, for the most part, pass into the bullion; copper is mostly scorified.

3.3.3 Data of operation

Manpower requirements: The hearth furnace plant of Arnoldstein which produces 48 tons of hearth bullion per day with two furnaces needs 24 men who work as follows (Table 4):

Table 4: Personnel requirements for two hearth furnaces

Title	number of men per shift	shifts 8 hours	Total Men
Pelletizer	3	1	3
Smelter	4	3	12
Crane driver and helper	2	3	6
Baghouse attendant	1	3	3
Total			24

The main data of consumption of the BBU-process with the production of crude bullion in the hearth-furnace are given in Table 5.

Table 5:

Brown coal	174 kg /t
Coke	5 kg /t
Lime hydrate	12 kg /t
Current	93.6 MJ (26 k Wh) /t
Man-hours	4 hours /t
Maintenance man-hours	0.3 hours /t

The costs for the smelting of the hearth slag are borne to a considerable extent by the gain of zinc.

3.4 The smelting of battery scrap in the BBU-hearth furnace

At first it had not been expected that the BBU-rotary hearth could also be used for processing battery scrap. Until five years ago the supply of used batteries was so small that the paste of the battery plates could be added to the ore mix, and the lattice material melted down in a kettle. Today more than one third of the raw material of our smelter consists of battery scrap.

As this material introduced silver into the process, only very small quantities of it could be added to the silver-free ore if lead of standard quality had to be produced. As the desilverizing of all the hearth bullion was out of the question because of higher costs, it became necessary to look for another method.

Today all the battery scrap is processed with good results in the BBU-hearth furnace as follows:

The battery scrap is freed of its boxes, and then is separated into lattice material and fine paste material. The fine material consists mainly of the paste of the battery plate and is treated in the hearth in the same way as ore concentrates, only a somewhat greater amount (4%) of fine coal is added before pelletizing.

The hearth mass is in this case not as bright and spongy as with the working of ore but is more dark-red and pasty. Nevertheless the daily production of bullion is even better than with the usual ore charge. The production of residues is also smaller, because there is no gangue.

The crude bullion contains 1.5 to 2.5% antimony and about 30 g of silver per ton that comes from broken lattice particles in the fine material.

The metallurgy of this process might be, that either the lead oxide of the paste is directly reduced to metal or that lead sulfate, which is always present in large quantities, is reduced to lead sulfide. Then the usual roast-reactions can take place.

The lattice material is also treated on the rotary hearth: It is charged by a special feeding device from the pellets bin. In the hearth basin, half-filled with lead, a coke fire is kindled using the rotating hearth, but without use of the rabbler and the mechanical shovel, the lattice material is charged onto it in uniform layers and melts down. When the basin is full with lead, a 2 - ton ingot of lead bullion is tapped. Then the rabbler is put into operation and the residues, consisting of agglomerated organic substances, lead compounds and half-burnt coke are discharged. After that a new bed of coke is charged and the process goes on.

The residues from the lattice material contain from 40 to 50 per cent lead. They can be easily smelted in a rotary furnace, the remaining half-burnt coke serving as reducing agent.

The proportion of the charged lead in the residues is relatively small which indicates that this process is not only a simple melting down of the material. Rather, a certain degree of reaction and reduction of the paste, which is always left in the lattice after crushing, also takes place.

4. Economic features of the BBU-process

For small lead smelters and a raw material situation like that of the BBU works at Arnoldstein, the rotary-hearth process represents the most economic way of lead smelting.

W. Schwartz[12] shows in his article, that with high-grade lead concentrates, and with annual productions of 50,000 tons of bullion, the BBU-process is able to work at lower smelting costs than the blast furnace or the self-fluxing lead smelting of Lurgi[13].

The former disadvantages of the hearth smelting, such as strenuous labour and unhealthy working conditions, have been completely overcome by the particular construction of the rotary hearth.

The fundamental disadvantages of the hearth process, namely that it is restricted to high-grade ores, that it utilizes relatively small equipment and that 10 per cent of the lead content of the raw material passes into the hearth slag, are offset by several important advantages.

They are listed below.

Advantages of the BBU-process:

A. Low costs of installation. Three BBU-hearth furnaces plus a baghouse plant and a pelletizing drum are sufficient for an annual production of 20,000 tons of crude bullion.

B. The ore concentrate can be charged onto the hearth in raw state; the high costs for sintering of the ore can be avoided.

C. Low expenditure for fuel: The process works with cheap brown coal and needs coke only for the starting of the furnace.

D. No fluxes and diluting materials are necessary.

E. The operation of the process is very flexible. Starting

and stopping of the furnace only takes a few hours.

F. Beside ore, the BBU-rotary hearth furnace can treat battery scrap, lead sludges and ashes. According to the situation of raw material, and of orders, the hearth furnace can be changed over from ore processing to battery scrap at any time.

G. Small metal stock. The BBU-process can work with a very small metal stock. If the raw material becomes scarce one single hearth can be stopped without shutting down the whole production.

H. Low personnel requirements. The need of personnel is low compared to other processes within the range of annual bullion production that is of interest for the BBU-process, i.e. 10,000 to 20,000 tons of lead bullion per year. With higher annual productions however no pronounced reduction of personnel expenditure appears, as is the case with the blast furnace, because the rotary-hearth cannot be built much larger.

The BBU- process demonstrates that the long-known hearth smelting still can justify its existence today and under certain conditions, as are given for example, in Arnoldstein, can even be superior to all other processes of lead smelting.

References.

1. Schenck, R., "Experimentelle und theoretische Untersuchungen uber die Rostgleichgewichte beim Blei," Metall und Erz, Vol. 23 (1926), pp. 407-420.

2. Kohlmeyer, E. J., and Monzer, W., "Uber die Reaktionen von Bleisulfid mit Bleioxid bzw. -sulfat; das System Blei -Sauerstoff - Schwefel," Zeitschrift fur anorg. allgem. Chemie, Vol. 252, (1943-44), pp. 74-85.

3. Kellogg, H. H., and Basu, S. K., "Thermodynamic Properties of the System Pb - S - O to 1100° K," Trans. Met. Soc. AIME, Vol. 218 (1960), pp. 70-81.

4. Tuffley, J. R., and Russell, B., "Sulfate Formation During the Roasting of Lead Sulfide," Trans. Met. Soc. AIME, Vol. 230 (1964), pp. 950-956.

5. Fischer, G., "Uber die Moglichkeiten und Grenzen der chemischen Thermodynamic bei der Bearbeitung pyrometallurgischer Probleme," Freiberger Forschungshefte No. B 112, (1965), pp. 59-94.

6. Melin, A., und Winterhager, H., "Beitrag zu den physikalischen Grundlagen der Rostung von Bleiglanz," Erzmetall Vol. 20, (1967), pp. 561-569.

7. Yazawa, A., und Gubcova, A., "Diagramatic Representation of Equilibrium Relations in the Pb - S - O System," Bull. Res. Inst. Mineral Dressing and Metallurgy, Tohoku Univ., Vol. 22 (1966), pp. 127-132.

8. Tafel, V., "Lehrbuch der Metallhuttenkunde," 2. Auflage, Vol. 2, S. Hirzel Verlag, Leipzig, 1953.

9. Prost, E., "Metallurgie des Metaux," 2nd ed., Librairie Polytechnique Ch. Beranger, Paris & Liege, 1924.

10. Buck, L. J., "Lead Smelting in the Federal Improved Mechanical Ore Hearth," Trans. Met. Soc. AIME, Vol. 121 (1936) pp. 106-117.

11. Jovanovic, M., and Kohlmeyer, E. J., "Untersuchungen zum HerdofenprozeB," Erzmetall, Vol. 10, (1957), pp. 273-284.

12. Schwartz, W., "Gegenuberstellung moderner Bleigewinnungsverfahren," Erzmetall, Vol. 18, (1965), pp. 570-577.

13. Schwartz, W., und Haase, W., "Self-Fluxing Lead Smelting," Trans. Met. Soc. AIME, Vol. 224, (1962), pp. 939-944.

Chapter 34

TREATMENT OF LEAD BATTERY SCRAP AT STOLBERGER ZINK A.G.
Aachen, West Germany

Dr. Reinhard Fischer
Manager

Abstract

The consumption of lead for batteries in some western countries and Japan amounts to 870,000 T. annually. Battery life is 2-3 years. Therefore after a short time a considerable quantity of lead flows back to smelters.

The production of lead from scrap batteries is discussed from the following points of view:

1. Separation of the acid contained in the batteries.
2. Separation of the components which are free of lead from the components containing lead, e.g. cases, separators.
3. Separation of metallic lead from lead compounds.
4. Avoidance of manual-work.

A process has been developed and perfected at a plant, which began operation in 1965. The procedure consists essentially of the following steps:

1. Breaking the cases and removing the acid.
2. Crushing the batteries in an impact mill.
3. Screening off separators.
4. Separation of slurry.
5. Gravity separation of metal and organic material.

The plant has a one-shift capacity of 24,000 T. batteries/year.

Plant Description

The lead smelter Binsfeldhammer of Messrs. Stolberger Zink AG was founded in 1846 and is situated at Stolberg (Rhld.), 20 km from Aachen. The smelter was originally built to process lead ore found in the neighborhood. These deposits are exhausted, so that the smelter is now treating German lead ores and ores which are imported from other countries. In 1969 the smelter produced 72,000 T. of lead, of which approximately 40% was manufactured from ore; the remainder was produced from foreign bullion, lead residues, and scrap.

The picture shows an aerial view of the lead battery scrap treatment plant, which is situated in the area of the lead smelter.

Lead Battery Scrap Treatment Plant

Introduction

The use of lead for the production of batteries in the whole world has been increasing. Table 1 shows the consumption of lead for batteries in some western countries and Japan.

Table 1 Consumption of Lead for Batteries

	1966 T	1967 T	1968 T
USA	429.000	423.000	454.000
Japan	76.000	102.000	117.000
UK	89.000	87.000	96.000
Germany	82.000	82.000	96.000
France	54.000	56.000	63.000
Italy	33.000	38.000	42.000
	763.000	788.000	868.000

Provided a life of 2-3 years for the batteries, respective amounts of lead in form of scrap return to smelters after this time.

The processing of such a large quantity of uniform scrap is a problem. Resolving the technical and economical aspects is nearly as interesting as optimizing processes for treatment of lead ores.

Lead batteries consist essentially of the following parts:

1. A container of vulcanite plastic or similar material, partly provided with iron grips or handles
2. Grid plates and pole bridges of lead and lead alloys generally containing up to 9% Sb
3. The filling mass of the grids, which is practically free from antimony, and which, according to the degree of the battery, consists of lead oxide or lead sulphate
4. Separators, preferably of plastic
5. The filling of accumulator acid.

Methods for Scrap Battery Treatment

Much effort has gone into providing advantageous ways of making the recovery of the metal content possible.

In one known method the upper part of the battery with the connectors is removed by means of a guillotine, the housing is separated from the grid plates, and the acid is recovered at the same time. The housing is washed to removed any active material adhering to it and is thereupon discarded. The grid plates are melted in a reverberatory furnace. The separated battery heads are fragmentized, whereupon their metallic fragments are separated from their non-metallic fragments, e.g. by air separation, and the metallic fragments are then melted.

This recovery method yields metals having a relatively low antimony content by melting down of the pole pieces and battery heads, and lead having only a medium antimony content by melting down of the grid metal and active material. Thus, this particular method requires not only an obviously considerable expenditure in terms of labor, but it yields lead having overall only a relatively low antimony content. Furthermore, processing the lead obtained with this method to produce either soft lead or a normal battery alloy is particularly complicated and rather expensive.

In another known method of recovering the lead, the housing of the battery is removed by breaking it manually and by melting the bridges, connectors, grid plates, and other components of the battery in a shaft-or reverberatory furnace.

In another process the battery scrap without housings and preferably dry is fed into an impact crusher in which it is broken up to thereby separate the active material from grid plate fragments. Subsequently, the active material is screened from the grid plate fragments and from the separators. The separators are manually removed. Proposals to use air separation for this latter purpose have in practice not been found satisfactory.

Stolberger Zink Process

The object of the battery scrap treatment process of Stolberger Zink AG is mainly:

1. Separation of the acid contained in the batteries
2. Separation of the components which are free of lead from the components containing lead, e.g. cases, separators
3. Separation of metallic from non-metallic lead, i.e. separation of the grid from the active mass and, therefore, separation of high-antimonial material from low antimonial material
4. Avoidance of manual-work.

A modern process must also be able to treat batteries which may be developed in the near future, e.g., batteries with fiber glass reinforced plastic casings. A modern plant must also be satisfactory from the hygienic point of view.

The development of our process started in 1953 and in 1965 the plant was commissioned. The process comprises the following main steps:

1. Breaking the cases and removing of the acid
2. Crushing the batteries in an impact mill
3. Screening off separators
4. Separation of slurry
5. Gravity separation of metal and organic material

The apparatus for carrying out this method comprises crushing equipment in which the cells are treated so as to obtain a mass of fragments; primary separating equipment for dividing this mass into one fraction which comprises the separators and a second fraction which comprises at least the major part of the housing and also the metallic fragments; and secondary separating equipment for segregating the second fraction by weight into metallic and non-metallic fragments.

Description of Process

The recovery process proceeds as follows: The cells are delivered to a storage area which, in view of the fact that the cells are still acid-filled, must be constructed so as to be acid resistant. For instance, the floor of the storage area may be acid resistant and is provided with a drainage mean for the acid. Figure I shows the flowsheet of the scrap battery treatment plant.

Fig. I - Flowsheet of Scrap Battery Treatment Plant

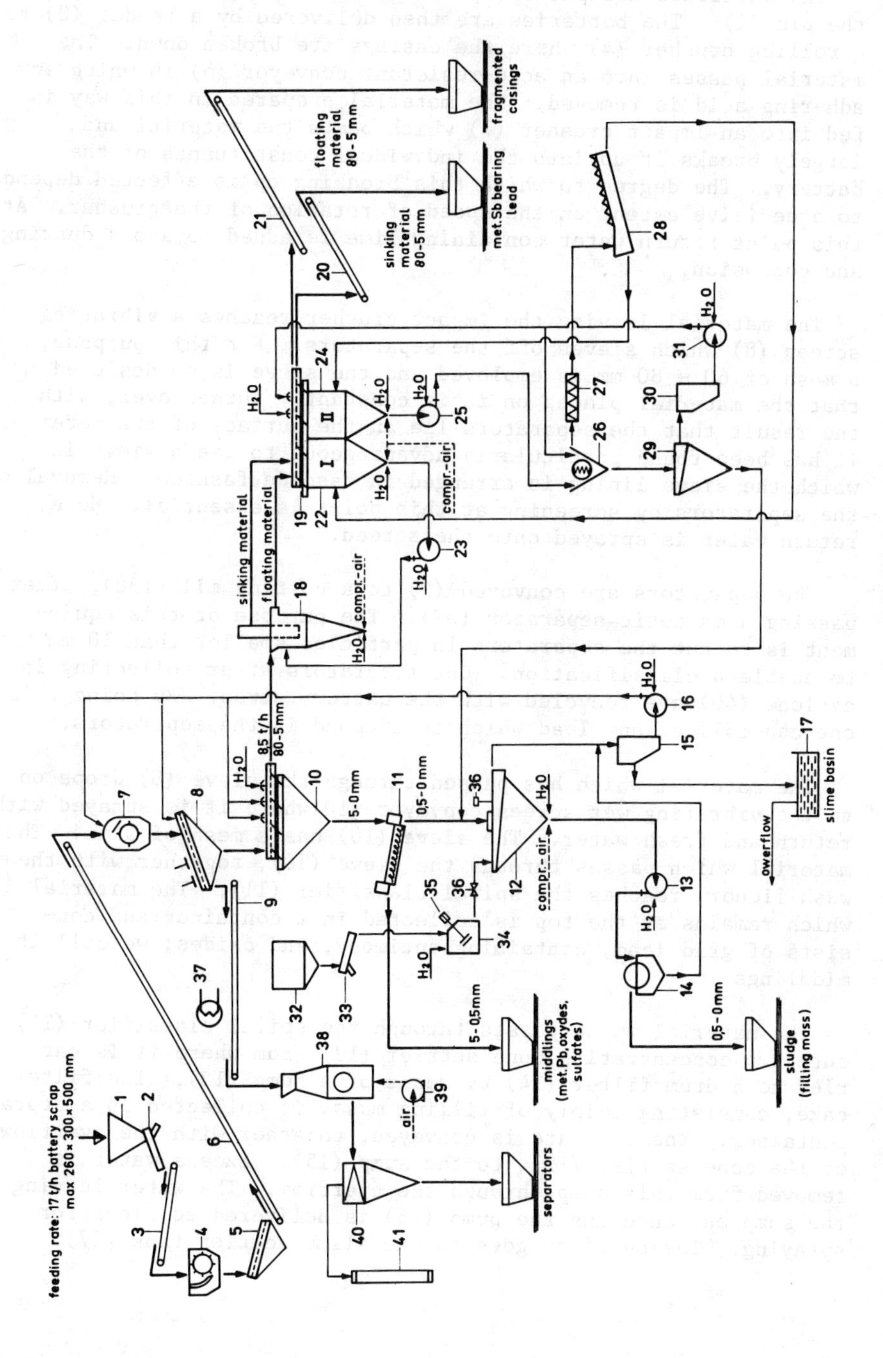

The batteries are picked up by a shovel loader and fed into the bin (1). The batteries are then delivered by a feeder (2) to a rolling crusher (4) where the casings are broken down. The material passes into an acid-resistant conveyor (5) in which any adhering acid is removed. The material prepared in this way is fed into an impact crusher (7) which beats the material and largely breaks it up into the individual constituents of the battery. The degree to which this breaking up is effected depends to a decisive extent on the speed of rotation of the crusher. At this point return water containing lime is added to avoid dusting and corrosion.

The material leaving the impact crusher reaches a vibrating screen (8) which sieves off the separators. For this purpose, a mesh of 60 - 80 mm is employed and the sieve is so designed that the material placed on it is constantly turned over, with the result that the separators lie on the surface of the material. It has been found particularly advantageous to use a sieve in which the sieve lining is arranged in cascade fashion. Removal of the separators by screening at this point is essential. Here, return water is sprayed onto the screen.

The separators are conveyed (9) to a cutting mill (38), after passing a magnetic separator (37). The purpose of this equipment is to cut the separators in particles smaller than 10 mm to enable a classification. Cut separators after collecting in cyclone (40) are recycled with the battery scrap. By doing this one can collect any lead which is trapped in the separators.

The material which has passed through the sieve (8) drops on to the vibrating wet screen conveyor (10)where it is sprayed with return and fresh water. The sieve (10) has a mesh of 5 mm. The material which passes through the sieve (10), together with the wash liquor, reaches the spiral classifier (11). The material which remains at the top is collected in a container and consists of grid lead, containing antimony, and oxides; we call it middlings.

The material which passes through the spiral classifier (11) enters a concentrating cone settler (12) from where it is carried to a drum filter (14) by means of a pump (13). The filter cake, consisting mainly of filling mass, is collected in a storage container. The filtrate is conveyed, together with the overflow of the cone settler (12), to the sump (15). Excess water is removed from this sump through the overflow. The water leaving the sump and entering the pump (16) is delivered to pipes for spraying. The overflow goes to the slime settler tank (17).

Neutralizing solution for maintaining a certain pH in the spray liquid and avoiding acid corrosion in the plant is delivered to the cone settler (12) by means of a pH metering and control device (36). The neutralizing solution is prepared by the addition of lime from the storage bin (32), by a feeder (33) to a mixer tank (34) with stirrer (35), and is delivered to the cone settler (12).

The material which has remained at the top of the vibrating wet screen conveyor (10) is conveyed to a lifting wheel separator (18) where separation into a sink fraction, consisting mainly of grid metal, pole bridges and other metallic parts, and a float fraction, consisting of fragments of casing, takes place. The float and sink materials are both conveyed to one sieve (19) on which they are transported separately.

In the first part of the sieve (19) the slurry flows down into the cone settler I (22) below it and is returned to the lifting wheel separator (18) by a pump (23). On the rear part of the sieve (19) the material is sprayed with fresh water and return water, and the washing liquor is collected in the cone settler II (24) below it.

By means of the pump (25) this thin slurry is delivered for regeneration to a magnetic separator (26) where the magnetite is separated from the liquid. The overflow from the magnetic separator (26) is concentrated in a cone settler (29).

The overflow from the magnetic separator (26) is delivered to the spiral classifier (28), after passing through the demagnetizing coil (27) and it is fed into the cone settler I to maintain the necessary pulp density in the lifting wheel separator (18). The overflow from the thickening cone settler (29) flows into a sump (30) and from there into a pump (31) and is then delivered as spray water to the sieve (19).

The underflow of the cone settler (29) is combined with the lead slurry containing liquor of classifier (11).

The washed float material (fragmented casings) and sink material (grid lead) are conveyed separately via the conveyor belts (20) and (21) to the containers.

Analysis of Products and Process Data

Table 2 shows the analysis and the ratio of the different products.

Table 2 Analysis of Products

	ratio %	Pb %	Pb met %	Sb %	b.l. %	H_2O %
grid metal	25	93	9,8	6,8	–	1,5
middlings	35	75	14,5	1,5	3,3	12
slurry	19	65	3	0,7	8,7	18
plastic	20	< 0,5	–	–	–	–
separators	1	< 0,5	–	–	–	–

The quantity of the middlings depends on the age of batteries. In very old batteries the grids are strongly corroded and break more easily.

More than 65% of the antimony content of the batteries is recovered with the grid metal.

Table 3 Process Data

capacity	20000 T/yr 1 shift
operating labor	
incl. transportation	7 men/shift
throughput	16,4 T/h
consumption per ton of scrap treated	
manpower operation	0,65 h
manpower repair	0,09 h
power	5,73 kwh
lime	4,42 kg
magnetite	1,2 kg
fuel	0,51 kg
water	10,4 m^3

The capacity of the plant is determined by the size of the lift wheel separator. This is the smallest unit, which can treat material of the size of broken batteries. Therefore, it is not possible to build a smaller plant using this process.

The operating crew includes the two drivers of the shovel loader and of the truck, called "Robuster," which transport the products into the smelter and the non-metallic matter to dump.

Treatment of the Products

We get three metal-containing products: grid metal, middlings, and slurry.

The grid metal is melted in a normal steel refinery kettle and directly used to make antimonial alloys.

The middlings are fed into the blast furnace together with the normal lead sinter.

The slurry goes onto the sinter machine because of its fineness and sulphur content.

We think this the most economic way in our case, because the scrap battery treatment plant is linked with a standard lead smelter.

Chapter 35

THE ELECTROTHERMAL PROCESS FOR ZINC DUST PRODUCTION AT IMPERIAL SMELTING CORPORATION (ALLOYS) LTD.

Avonmouth, England

D. S. Newton, Technical Manager

Introduction

Historically the production of zinc dust has been based upon residual and secondary zinc. Using horizontal retorts filled with diecasting scrap, galvanizers drosses and sweater billets, dust has been produced by condensation into static condensers on a 24 hour cycle. Although fairly flexible as regards input materials the process is not amenable to close control of the product, is labour intensive and unless carefully run can cause fume problems.

With a steadily increasing demand for zinc dust of consistent properties and higher quality there is a demand for an improved method of manufacture in which dust can be produced continuously and which is capable of close control thus ensuring a minimum amount of oversize or unsaleable material. The Process in use in the works of Imperial Smelting Corporation (Alloys) Ltd. in England, and in Canada and Holland, satisfies the criteria stated above, and has proved to be easy to control with a minimum labour demand.

The Electrothermal Zinc Dust Plant : Refs 1-4

The plant consists of three main units, the Furnace, the Condenser and the Classifier, the latter being a conventional Alpine Mikroplex air classifier with a capacity matching the output of the furnace and condenser.

Electrothermal Furnace : Figure 1.

The furnace consists of a column of sized metallurgical coke (- 3cm - +2cm) contained in a 52cm. square furnace (1) with a wall thickness of 22.5cm. having on its outside a thickness of insulation bricks with a sheet of heat resistant micanite (2) sandwiched tightly between the common faces. The micanite is used here to restrict metal penetration in the refractory brickwork courses. The brickwork is supported in an angle and flat iron framework also insulated with micanite at the brick metal surfaces.

The coke column is supported at the bottom of the furnace on two graphite slabs (6), which are themselves supported on insulation and refractory brickwork. The two slabs are fitted with copper electrodes, the external ends of which are water cooled, and drilled for connection to the power source.

The electrode at the top of the furnace is immersed approximately 90cms. below the top of the coke column, i.e. approximately 255 cms. above the graphite slabs. This top electrode is a graphite rod, the upper extremity of which is fitted with a water cooled copper clamp arrangement suitable for connecting to the power source. This electrode is housed in a salamander tube where it passes through the furnace walls (5) at an angle of 30° and is sealed in position.

The liquid metal is fed to the shaft via a metering pot system, the bottom pots (Salamander) being carried on a cast refractory slab (3) whilst they support the crucibles fitted with metering jets

The furnace run off at the base of the furnace is tapped through a run off block (7) which is sealed between taps with a clay dolly.

The zinc vapour produced by the shaft furnace is carried through a crossover tube (4) supported by refractory tiles between the furna and the condenser. The crossover trough is made from insulating brickwork whilst the top cover is tiled. The crossover tube has part of its top face cut away, the hole so formed being covered with a section of the same material similar in size and shape.

This hole in the crossover enables a seal to be quickly made when starting up or shutting down the furnace.

FIGURE 1

CROSS SECTION OF FURNACE

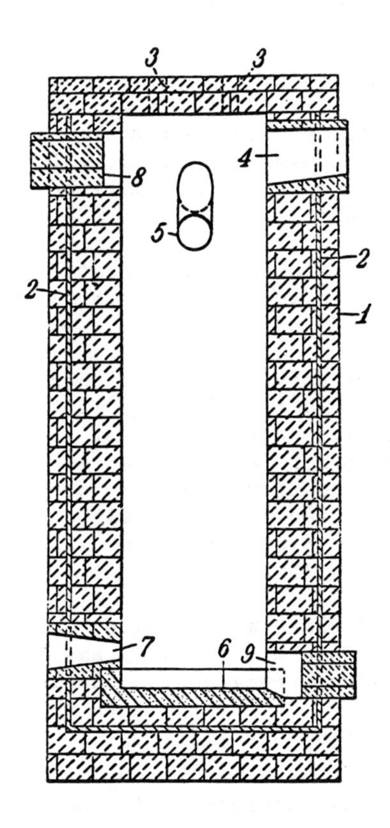

On the front or operating side of the furnace is a panel (8), inserted at a suitable height enabling rodding or cleaning of the crossover to take place as and when necessary. For easy removal of the coke change when necessary, a panel of high temperature insulation brickwork is situated at the bottom of the furnace, just above the level of the bottom electrode (9).

Power Supply :

The power for the furnace is obtained from a single phase transformer/transductor system. The transformer is double wound, and has a capacity of 360KVA with a secondary output no load voltage of 159.6. The primary winding is designed to suit the customer's own distribution system. Tapping for low voltage variation is normally provided on the primary winding, selected by an external handwheel 'offload', as are tappings for supply voltage variations.

The equipment when used in conjunction with a transductor should have the capability of giving a controlled variable output from 0-360KVA. The transductor design is such that with an input of ≈ 134 volts single phase the output voltage is 120v; the current rating of the transductor should be 3,000 amps maximum (360KVA) feeding a resisting load.

Normal indicator instruments and safety controls are, of course, fitted, including power factor meter and earth leakage ammeter.

The steel framework previously mentioned is designed in two sections, top and bottom, electrically separated by means of a high temperature insulation bolt system. For safety reasons the top section of steelwork is earthed, as is the top electrode of the furnace system. The bottom section of steelwork is left earth free and is shielded from possible contact with any operator by means of either high temperature insulation or encased in timber to a suitable height.

The whole of the furnace and furnace casing arrangement is supported on four courses of brickwork having air spaces to ensure that the bottom steelwork remains cool during operation.

Condenser System : Figures 2 & 3

The condenser system consists of two main tanks (1) (2) having a surface area of approximately $65m^2$, and one auxiliary tank (3) having a surface area of $37m^2$. The condenser system is electrically continuous and is connected to earth through the earth leakage meter. Each condenser tank is fitted with a hopper bottom (4), inspection

FIGURE 2

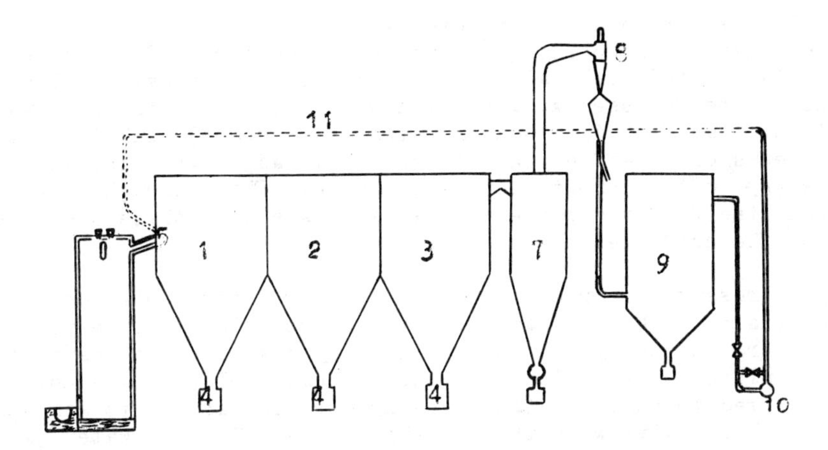

ELEVATION OF ZINC DUST FURNACE

FIGURE 3

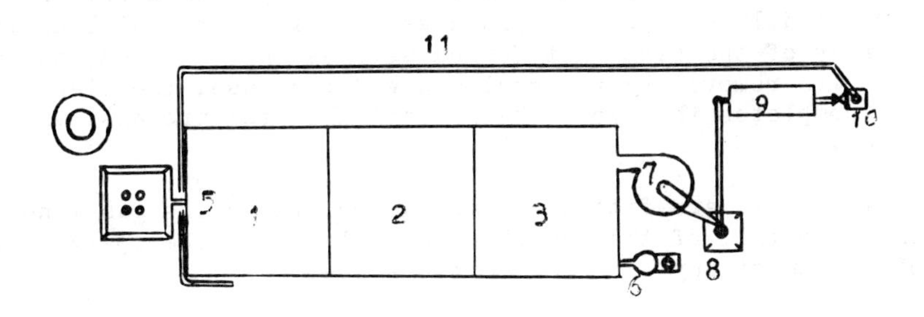

PLAN OF ZINC DUST FURNACE

door and explosion vent. Number 1 tank is also fitted with a grid and shaker designed to catch candles which may form under the condenser end lip of the vapour crossover tube.

The vapour tube is connected into the side of number 1 condenser via an opening (5) which has on three of its sides nozzles fitted with ball joints and locking pieces, enabling them to be focussed at any point with respect to the zinc vapour plume. Gas flow from number 2 tank to number 3 tank is restricted by means of a baffle plate fitted as an adjustable throat plate, the gap in the throat being adjustable. Flow through number 3 tank itself is restricted by means of a second plate suspended from the condenser top.

A pressure recorder is fitted to tank 3 to enable continuous records to be kept of any variations occurring. Since this pressure in the system is continuously changing, to ensure that only nitrogen is pulled into the system, a plastic gas holder (6) is fitted to number 3 tank, the holder discharging to atmosphere via a ball valve when the pressure exceeds 7.5 cm. water gauge pressure.

A gas take off from the end of number 3 tank leads to a gas cyclone cooler (7), followed by a high efficiency cyclone (8) which removes the majority of the very fine dust from the gas. A pipe from the cyclone then leads into the filter bag inlet. The bag filter (9) carried approximately 0.93cm^2 of bag area per cubic foot of gas handled. A rocking mechanism is fitted to the bags to ensure no blockage occurs.

Circulation of the gas through the system is provided by a 9.9m^3/174cm. (10) water gauge blower. Inert gas is fed by the blower to the jets around the crossover pipe via a return pipe (11) where it dilutes the zinc plume as well as shock chilling it. The majority of the zinc dust formed settles in tanks 1-3, whilst any fines are removed by the cyclones and baghouse, the cleaned gas then completes the cycle, being cooled in the process, via the blower.

Manometers are fitted at various points in the gas line to permit control of the gas flow, and also give the operator an indication of any blockage in the system.

Operation of the Furnace :

Before start up the cover on the crossover (5) is removed and both ends plugged. Start up procedure begins by ensuring that the entire system is airtight. Power is then switched on at a low level (40kw) and increased slowly to 80kw, whilst at the same time the melting pot is charged and brought to a temperature of ~ 550°C.

By visual inspection of the coke bed through the vent hole the point at which low red heat is reached is noted and at this point the power input is increased to 100kw. A slow bleed of nitrogen is then run into the condenser system.

Test pours commence when the top of the coke bed shows a bright red heat. A small quantity of liquid metal is run into one of the loading pots and the zinc flame observed at the central vent hole, when a vigorous flame is obtained the furnace is ready to go on line.

At this point power is switched off, the crossover plugs removed and the cover sealed. Power is then switched on at ~ 120kw, the feed pots are filled slowly. When a slight positive pressure is present in the condenser system the nitrogen is switched off. When run off is established, power and metal feed are increased stepwise until the desired targets are achieved.

The recycle gas blower is then started and adjusted to give ~ 20cfm delivery to the jets, this is steadily increased until the target figure is achieved, depending on the type of dust required. The air bleed is also adjusted to give dust of the required metallic content.

Run off is tapped hourly, and when such quality metal as 'Severn' grade is employed this run off should not exceed 5%.

The crossover tube is cleaned out at regular intervals the power being shut off and care being taken that the condenser is under slight positive pressure to reduce the chance of air being sucked in so reducing the metallic content of the dust.

Dust is removed from the condensers at regular intervals making sure that a seal of dust remains in the base of the condenser.

Plant Flexibility :

The fact that the upper electrode is approximately 90cms. below the level of the surface of the coke enables a limited amount of refluxing to take place, this together with the ability to vary the rate of feed and run off gives the plant a certain amount of flexibility in feed for producing a zinc dust of given purity.

Moreover the adjustment of the recycle rate can have a marked effect on the particle size distribution of the raw dusts in the various parts of the system.

TABLE I

EFFECT OF RUN OFF RATE
(6.5 tons per day)

Analysis of Input Zinc	Pb 1.27%	Fe 0.11%	Cd < 0.02%
	Sn 0.0017%	Cu>0.040%	
Run Off	10.5%		
Analysis of Zinc Dust	Total Zinc 99.04%	Metallic Zinc 96.0%	
	Pb 0.087%	Cd 0.070%	

TABLE II

TYPICAL PRODUCTION FIGURES
& PRODUCT PROPERTIES

Total Input		58,500Kg	100%
Output	Raw Dust	50,420Kg	86.3%
	Run Off	7,070Kg	12.0%
	Dross	710Kg	1.21%
	Loss	300Kg	0.50%
		58,500Kg	100%

Power Consumption of Furnace	962KW hr/tonne
Fuel Consumed	25 litres/ton
Metallic Content of Zinc Dust	96.0% - 96.1%
Coke Losses	2.00Kg/tonne.

TABLE III

Recirculation Effects :

DISTRIBUTION OF ZINC DUST IN PLANT

Dilution	Condenser I	Condenser II	Condenser III	Cyclone	Bag-house	Total
8.5m^3/min	29.6%	30.0%	14.7%	15.3%	10.4%	100%
5.66m^2/min	32.1%	34.0%	12.5%	11.3%	10.1%	100%
4.25m^2/min	32.4%	35.6%	17.5%	9.3%	5.2%	100%

TABLE IV

PARTICLE SIZE DISTRIBUTION OF ABOVE DUSTS

SEDIMENTATION BALANCE

Distribution by Wt%

	MPS µ	3µ	3-5µ	5-7µ	7-10µ	10-20µ	20-30µ	30-40µ	40-50µ	>300u	Max P.Sµ
8.5m^3/min											
Cond.I	3.9	16.5	18.0	15.7	19.8	30.0					19.3
Cond.II	3.4	14.9	21.2	19.7	20.3	23.9					15.8
Cond.III	3.0	22.1	27.1	21.0	18.0	11.8					16.7
Cyclone	2.6	37.5	34.9	18.2	9.4						8.5
B/H	2.3	41.8	46.6	11.6							
5.66m^2/min											
Cond.I	4.9	3.6	13.1	14.0	20.4	39.9	9.0			8.3	30.0
Cond.II	5.3	3.5	12.8	13.2	19.4	41.2	7.6	2.3		8.8	37.4
Cond.III	3.4	15.1	18.2	16.2	39.1	10.6	0.8			1.1	21.0
Cyclone	2.7	12.2	24.4	31.4	32.0					NIL	9.3
B/H	2.5	45.8	46.5	7.7						NIL	6.0
4.25m^2/min											
Cond.I	5.7	3.2	11.1	14.8	22.2	37.0	8.2	3.1	0.4	4.4	42.3
Cond.II	5.8	3.0	10.1	12.6	20.7	40.0	6.6	5.4	1.6	5.0	53.0µ
Cond.III	4.0	5.3	12.6	14.1	25.3	18.0	16.4	7.3	1.0	2.0	45µ
Cyclone	3.9	21.0	24.0	31.0	16.0	8.0				NIL	18.0
B/H	2.4	56.7	34.4	8.9						NIL	6.8

To give some idea of the classification effect on dusts produced from the E.T.F. the product obtained by 8.5m^3/minute recycle was classified to give a standard (European) paint grade dust :-

TABLE V

Input 100%	Output		
at 250Kg/hour vane setting 14°	Paint Grade Dust	75%	MPS = 3.1 μ
	Reject	14.9%	MPS = 9.5 μ
	Baghouse (Classifier)	9.4%	MPS = ~ 1.5μ
	Screen Oversize (> 1mm)	0.7%	

Labour Requirements and Operating Schedules :

Excluding labour requirements for classification and packing the plant can be satisfactorily operated by two men per shift, one being responsible for melting the slab zinc and feeding the zinc to the furnace, whilst the second man empties the condensers, attends to the run off, and ensures that supplies of slab zinc are readily available.

On an average annual production of 2,000 tons per year (6 tons per 24 hours 340 day operating year) the cost of labour equates to ~ 35 man hours/tonne.

Shut down occurs once every 12 months for shaft rebuilding although the life of the shaft has been known to exceed 18 months. A partial coke change takes place at 14 day intervals, replacing the top electrode at 3 monthly intervals, whilst the zinc melting pot is replaced every 6-7 weeks. Maintenance of the oil and water systems takes place as and when necessary. Coke usage works out at 2Kg per tonne.

The shaft rebuild takes 14 days and on a 50 week per year basis 10.5 days are needed for the previously mentioned repairs thus the total downtime is 24½ days.

Costs of maintenance over a period of 5 years have been approximately £1.9 per ton.

Power Requirements :

The overall power requirements on continuous running is approximately 1,000Kwhrs/ton of zinc dust.

Gas is used to heat the melting bath, preheating and drying the ingots, also for heating the run off ladle and basin.

The consumption of gas (500 B.T.U.) is about 530cu. ft/ton of zinc dust produced.

Thanks are due to the Board of I.S.C. (Alloys) Ltd. for permission to publish this paper.

References :

1. U.S.P. 3,448,972
2. U.S.P. 3,448,973
3. U.S.P. 3,449,116
4. U.S.P. 3,449,117

SECTION VIII

PROCESS RESEARCH AND USES OF LEAD AND ZINC

Chapter 36

PROCESS RESEARCH ON LEAD AND ZINC EXTRACTION

T. R. A. DAVEY
Professor of Metallurgical Engineering,
Colorado School of Mines, Golden, Colorado

W. R. BULL
Associate Professor of Metallurgical Engineering,
Colorado School of Mines, Golden, Colorado

Abstract

A Survey of current and recent research and developmental work is supplemented by predictions for processes which should be developed over the remainder of this century.

Introduction

The object of this contribution is to discuss present research and to make some predictions as to what may develop over the rest of the century. This may seem presumptuous - indeed it is - but we may first look at developments in the art and science of making lead and zinc since the first Rocky Mountain Fund Lead - Zinc volume in 1936, and see what lessons the past contains, which may be of some use in charting the future. It has been said that all we can learn from history is that we can learn nothing from history. Nevertheless, in certain well-established human activities (such as the extraction of metals which have been known for a long time) it is not too much to expect that certain patterns will be apparent, which have predictive value.

Over the past 34 years, there has been a great deal of progress in the extractive metallurgy of lead and zinc, and extraction efficiencies have improved greatly, while many ores are now treated quite satisfactorily which would not have been commercially treated at all 34 years ago. But there is no single case that we know of where any process used today utilizes a technology that was unknown in 1936. Advances have come about by the utilization of well-known techniques, establishment of better methods of control, and in many cases a new look at old techniques which were discarded previously, only to be revived under changed economic circumstances.

Mineral Processing

Research and development in mineral processing cannot be considered in the restricted context of the treatment of lead and zinc ores. Advances in the field are, in general, of importance to engineers no matter what ores they treat, and advances achieved in the milling of one type of ore have been quickly adapted for others.

Perhaps the most noticeable change in mining and mineral processing since 1936 has been the general increase in the scale of individual operations and the consequent increase in the capacity of individual machines. But the basic unit operations are still carried out in machines that work in the same way - coarse breakage by the application of gradual pressure, fine breakage by the almost random application of impact and attrition, fine sizing on the basis of settling velocities in water, concentration almost universally by flotation (here there is a difference, but only in the relative importance of the process), and dewatering by sedimentation and filtration.

In detail, however, these machines have become more reliable mechanically, and the life of wearing parts has increased, largely due to the development and use of more wear- and corrosion-resistant materials.

Comminution and Sizing

In 1936, rod mills, hydrocyclones and autogenous mills of high diameter-to-length ratio were virtually unknown. Rod-mills are, at present, practically standard primary units in multi-stage grinding circuits, but their days seem to be numbered, since about four-fifths of the new plants in North America use autogenous mills,[1] some up to 10 m in diameter, for primary grinding. Most of these mills treat a wet feed pulp but, elsewhere, dry autogenous mills of the Aerofall type are becoming more widely used, particularly when the ground ore is not subsequently treated by flotation. It is generally recognised, however, that some ores are not amenable at all to autogenous or semi-autogenous grinding, and that conventional regrinding is usually essential.

Small-scale vibration mills are gradually finding their way into laboratories and pilot plants, and extensive tests in South Africa[2] showed that the power consumption of a closed circuit operation compares well with that of conventional milling, with expected savings in ball and liner costs. There is little reason to doubt that the use of autogenous and vibration milling will continue to increase at the expense of conventional rod- and ball-milling.

Hydrocyclones have also become a standard part of the conventional multi-stage grinding circuit, because they almost invariably surpass the tank-type classifier in efficiency or cost or both. Even so, any conventional classifier sand product contains a significant proportion of misplaced slimes which, by returning to a grinding unit, or for some other reason, eventually suffer overgrinding and/or inefficient concentration. This can be particularly true of minerals of high specific gravity like galena. The future will no doubt see continued attempts to improve the efficiency of fine sizing operations, since a process like flotation has a very high efficiency only within a limited size range, and only more accurate sizing can ensure a feed within these limits. It has been shown by simulation[3] that the incorporation of several cyclone classifiers into counter-current circuit can sharpen the size separation significantly, particularly with respect to the amount of fine material in the coarse product. Where it can be shown that inefficient sizing causes significant losses (and it can be difficult to demonstrate this quantitatively), classification circuits may become more common. More likely, however, will be a continuation of the current trend towards the use of screens of various types for finer and finer sizing. It is claimed that the D.S.M. Rapifine screen[4] can be used for separations down to 325 mesh.

Concentration

It seems most likely that the flotation process will remain the work-horse of the industry in the near future, but preconcentration, when mineralogical conditions permit, will remain attractive. A considerable amount of effort is being put into the use of heavy liquids rather than heavy media suspensions for use in the sink-float process, as the cost of suitable heavy organic liquids is reduced. One recent case reports "considerable economic advantages".[5] The use of cyclones for treating fine material, as well as the more conventional bath separators, should expand with the use of these organic liquids.

Flotation, however, will carry most of the load and provide the bulk of the feed for the production of metallic lead and zinc. Excellent research into the fundamental surface chemistry of flotation continues, resulting in a better understanding of the action of conventional reagents and in the development of new ones. Recent Russian work[6], on relatively simple lead-zinc ores, demonstrated the superiority of a bulk- followed by a selective-flotation step over conventional selective flotation. Better recoveries of both lead and zinc in their respective concentrates, and reduced cyanide consumption, were reported.

The most significant change in recent years has been in the size of flotation machines and the speed with which they have been accepted in the industry[7]. Neverthless, however large they may be, it is generally accepted that, for reasons of pulp mixing patterns, a rougher-scavenger bank will still have to contain the usual number of cells in series to ensure good recovery. Two radically different types of flotation unit have appeared in recent years, both with what appear to be intrinsic merits. The DAVCRA cell [8] features intense mixing of pulp and air by nozzle injection, and extremely rapid flotation rates are reported. The flotation column[9] works on the principle of counter-current flow of pulp and air bubbles and a very deep froth layer, which is washed by a spray of water, resulting in a high grade concentrate in a single unit, and good recoveries. Both approaches seem to deserve further development in the future.

Analysis and Control

Without doubt the most active research in the industry is being carried out in fields that have led, or will lead, to improved process design and control. This falls into two main categories, namely, the on-stream measurement of the relevant properties of materials, and the development of suitable mathematical models that can be used to incorporate these measurements in control systems, or to assist in process design. Of both of these fields, little was known in 1936. Measurement of percent solids in a pulp and of volume flow rate (and hence, by computation, the solids and water flow rates) are standard practice using gamma gages and magnetic flowmeters. Continuous multi-channel on-stream X-ray analysis is becoming more widespread, and applied widely to iron, lead, zinc, copper, silver and nickel. Detectors for fluoride and sulfide have recently been reported[10]. Read-outs from such units are being used by operations to assist in manual control and to control reagent flow rates automatically. Lake Dufault has developed a simple model that, from recovery and grade figures obtained from on-line assay data, calculates an economic efficiency of the operation. The most important remaining on-line measurement to be accomplished is that of size distribution, and this is close to realization[11]. A method using the operating data of a hydrocyclone to infer empirically the percent minus 200 mesh in the cyclone overflow has also been reported[12].

However accurate, such data are of limited use until they can be incorporated in automatic control systems which rely upon mathematical models of the processes. The development of such models will no doubt continue for many years. Already models of autogenous-, ball- and rod-grinding mills, and cyclone and rake classifiers, have been developed and used for circuit simulation and control[13],[14]. Modelling of the flotation process is a much more complex business, but a useful model of flotation of a relatively simple feed in a single cell has appeared[15]. Adaptation of such a model to a bank of cells appears to present some complications[16],[17], but work in the field is progressing fairly rapidly and is attracting extremely capable men from outside the metallurgical profession.

Digital computers are being used increasingly to operate checking, alarm and sequential starting systems and data logging, etc., but the time of completely automatic control of comminution and concentration operations still lies in the future. Some individual operations have come under automatic control (including, for example, counter-current thickening[18], but fully integrated control is some distance ahead.

The need for control would be virtually eliminated if the feed to a mill were constant in quality. If decreased fluctuation could improve recovery by 1% in a mill treating 10,000 tons/day of a 3% lead ore, the saving would be of the order of $300,000 per year. Feed blending procedures, which are fairly common in iron ore treatment, may well become much more important in non-ferrous milling.

Environmental Control

In the coming years, control of the disposal of the waste products from milling will probably be uppermost in the superintendent's mind. Even if a high proportion of the tailing can be returned underground, there will still remain the problem of disposal of some finely ground material, and the solution seems to lie in the confinement of this material in as small an area as possible, and the eventual reclamation of the land by re-vegetation. The subject is well reviewed elsewhere[19], and it is clear that increased efforts will be needed to find more suitable ways to dispose of the tailings underground, to re-vegetate the tailings ponds, and even to find uses for the tailings. Some tailings have been shown to be suitable for brick manufacture[20], but this obviusly cannot be a universal solution.

Extractive Metallurgy of Lead

Sintering and Smelting

Turning now to the extraction of lead, we find simultaneous developments in the theory and practice of blast furnacing, tending towards ever higher lead tenors in sinter, giving increased smelting rates, reduced coke consumptions, and lowered lead losses in slag. It is now recognized that the form of lead in sinter is very important. Reduced metallic lead gets an almost "free ride" through the furnace, being merely melted, whereas the combined lead must be reduced, and its proportion in the charge must not exceed a certain amount, or during the course of its reduction the charge becomes sticky, causing "hot-top", increased fume losses, reduced smelting rates, high slag losses, and even a "lost" furnace. The increase in total lead content, without increasing the combined lead content, has been made quite practicable by the development of updraft sintering, which was a revival from 40 or 50 years previously - an excellent example of the utilization of principles which had been discarded under different circumstances decades before. It was to obtain a steadier source of higher SO_2-tenor gas, for sulphuric acid manufacture, that updrafting was developed, and the improved blast furnace performance was a bonus which was at first incidental, but now becomes the main reason for adopting updrafting.

It is probably not too much to claim that the successful development of the lead-zinc blast furnace would scarcely have been possible without the technology of updraft sintering. This Imperial Smelting Process will be discussed further below.

Although Paschen[21] erroneously states that the object of preparing lead sulphide concentrates for the blast furnace is to burn the sulphur as far as possible to SO_2, and transform the PbS to PbO, this otherwise masterly evaluation of the literature from 1959-68 should be consulted for a listing of the practical innovations and theoretical and experimental publications relating to roasting and sintering in this period.

Lead blast furnace research and development is progressing actively at many centers today, and it is not difficult to predict the fields in which progress will occur for the remainder of the century. This will come almost entirely from the application of better methods of measurement and control, plus use of oxygen[22] and fuel oil.[23] The cost of fluctuations in blast furnace performance is fantastic, and justifies almost any expense to obtain uniform operations. The scientific view of the universe is that the same result is obtained if the same material is treated in the same way (provided we are speaking on the macroscale, where the uncertainty principle is ineffective). Hence, if the charge to the sinter plant can be prepared in such a way that a finely mixed, homogeneous feed of controlled composition is produced, it can be sintered and then smelted under standard conditions so that all units run smoothly and yield constant results. Just over a decade ago, it was calculated that the difference between average and best weekly blast furnace performance at Port Pirie was costing nearly $500,000 per year. Since the best weekly performance is itself an average of fluctuating conditions, this amount greatly underestimates the economic savings to be achieved if completely uniform conditions could be maintained.

Uniformity of furnace operation has also been greatly aided by the development, by J. Roy of ASARCO, of the continuous tapper,[24] which has found world-wide application. The improved performance of blast furnaces continuously tapped has been of even greater economic value than the savings in labor and materials achieved.

Present research and development (which will undoubtedly continue into the 21st century) is aimed chiefly towards achieving controlled steady operating conditions - obtaining a fine, intimate mixture of all components, as perfectly mixed as possible, and uniform in time as well as spatially, its chemical composition controlled in advance. Rapid and accurate chemical analyses, preferably on-line, are replacing or will replace methods which tell the sintering and blast furnace superintendents what they had yesterday, so that the best they can hope to do is to make alterations to the charge which will be smelted tomorrow.

The use of oxygen-enriched blast will become commonplace, instead of the exception it still is today, and the more expensive coke will be more and more replaced by tuyere injection of fuel oil or natural gas. The simultaneous injection of water vapor, as recommended by Lumsden,[25] will permit preheating of air blast, and much higher lead tenors of sinter to be smelted, when control of charge composition is so uniform that there is no longer a fear that minor fluctuations in slag constituents will cause a major change in furnace conditions, because the slag constituents are such a small fraction of the burden. The direct coupling of computers to blast furnaces to effect instant correction of any departure from the intended conditions will gradually become standard practice.

The use of computers to perform multiple regression analyses on plant performance is becoming common, and successful models of performance are a necessary prerequisite for the application of direct computer control of furnaces. Port Pirie operate a pilot blast furnace (24" x 18" Shaft) for variation of experimental conditions. Mt. Isa report remarkable throughput figures by experimenting with different furnace configurations. There is still no measure of agreement as to whether the Port Pirie furnace,[26] with two rows of tuyeres, really is superior to standard designs. No doubt there will still be arguments in 30 years time as to the best shape for a blast furnace, but one hopes that by then there will be rather more definite data than at present as to the effect of various configurations.

Direct Reduction Processes

While the blast furnace is unlikely ever to be replaced entirely by any alternative, it seems certain that the direct methods of lead production will find increasing application to rich concentrates, particularly for small producers. It has long been recognized that it makes little sense to take a 75% Pb concentrate and dilute it to less than 40% Pb in order that it may be treated in a blast furnace, with a considerable carbon and oil consumption.

Theoretically, the reaction:

$$PbS + O_2 \rightarrow Pb + SO_2$$

can proceed with little supply of energy - mainly to supply heat losses to the surroundings - and should any PbO be formed by local over-supply of oxygen, then it can be returned for the roast reaction:

$$2PbO + PbS \rightarrow 3Pb + SO_2.$$

The Boliden[27], Outokumpu[28] and St. Joseph[29] direct methods seem likely to find application on a wider scale, and in addition it is possible that a further process could be developed at lower temperature, reacting oxygen and sulphur dissolved in lead:

$$2(O)_{\text{in Pb}} + (S)_{\text{in Pb}} \rightarrow SO_2 \uparrow.$$

High-grade galena concentrate would be dissolved in lead, and oxygen dissolved from air (possibly oxygen-enriched) at a temperature high enough to permit rapid reaction, but low enough to keep fume generation very low. The lead would be intensely stirred by a presently known technique.

The Halkyn process[30], whereby PbS is electrolysed in a $PbCl_2$ electrolyte, yielding Pb and S liquids directly, awaits only the right set of economic conditions for application. The economics depend upon cheap power, plus a blast furnace for eventual treatment of the impurity skimmings, after leaching of electrolyte. Make-up electrolyte is quite simply made by chlorinating galena.

Refining

By whatever process it is made, the lead, being an almost universal solvent, contains many impurities, and lead refining is a major part of the production of market lead. Since 1936 we have seen the introduction of vacuum treatment for recovery of zinc from desilverized lead[31] and from silver-lead-zinc crusts,[32] of a tellurium removal process, of preliminary drossing of blast furnace lead to remove oxides before copper drossing, and of two new continuous processes at Port Pirie, namely continuous copper drossing[33] and continuous vacuum dezincing.[34] Experimental work has also been performed on continuous Harris-type softening processes.[35][36] We have also seen the development of a rival (sulphamate) process[37] to the Betts (silico-fluoride) electrolytic process which, however, after four years of operation at San Gavino, was replaced in 1961 by the classical Betts process, resulting in lower current consumption, reagent costs and labour costs, and increased (doubled) production per cell. Also the Jollivet-Penarroya continuous debismuthizing process[38] was developed and practised for about a decade at Noyelles-Godault, utilizing potassium and magnesium additions instead of the Kroll-Betterton calcium and magnesium reagents. It was abandoned in favor of the latter when the refinery capacity was greatly enlarged, because of the comparatively large capital cost of plant required. The Jollivet-Penarroya process is capable of debismuthizing to very low levels (theoretically to less than 1 ppm, and less than 10 ppm have been produced in practice industrially) and if an economic method can be developed for the generation and recovery of potassium, the process may well be resurrected. This is presently being investigated, and it seems quite feasible that an electrolytic process for recovery and production of potassium can be developed.

It seems reasonably certain also that further alternatives to the Betts electrolyte will be proposed, and it is entirely conceivable that one day a better one will be found. Automation of the electrolytic process will also undoubtedly be introduced in the near future.

Reverting to pyrometallurgical refining, it seems highly desirable that a continuous variation of the Colcord process[39] (sulfur-decoppering of lead) be developed, but it is possible that this must await a better understanding of the mechanism of this reaction, which proceeds away from the thermodynamic equilibrium, and the obvious method for making the process continuous does not work. Sulfur-decoppering is still under investigation at several centers at present. It is also desirable that better methods of continuous softening and desilverizing be developed, as the methods now in use at Port Pirie, although a great advance in their day, are now too expensive to be adopted at other locations. Low-temperature processes for softening are entirely feasible, based either on the Harris-type process, or on a modified Harris process consuming much less caustic soda or nitre, and producing solid granules of dross instead of a melt from which soda must be regenerated. A similar type of continuous final refining process is also feasible, and has been conducted with at least partial success for some time industrially.

A completely automated continuous lead refinery is thus technically feasible today, and its introduction seems to be merely a matter of time, when the right set of economic circumstances occur. Continuous copper drossing will almost certainly become standard practice, in order to meet the stricter anti-pollution standards coming into force, since it is not possible in practice to prevent the massive generation of fume when conducting copper drossing in open kettles. A summary of the present position in lead refining has recently been given by Kleinert.[40]

It is possible that the application of vacuum to hot blast furnace bullion could be developed, with or without reagent additions (oxygen, sulphur or chlorine), where the high temperature available without energy cost offers the possibility of some new separations not otherwise possible.

Lead Quality

Over the past 34 years the quality of the cast product has been improved in three ways: elimination of cavities in cast pigs by controlled cooling, so that solidification proceeds from the bottom upwards; reduction of oxygen content (both suspended and dissolved) giving a much cleaner product on remelting; and reduction of antimony content to less than 1 ppm, resulting in a lead of low-drossing characteristics. The latter two improvements have been effected by giving the lead, just before casting, a final stir with caustic soda. The lead so treated actually has an oxygen content well below saturation, so that its surface remains "blank" for an appreciable time in contact with air, as any oxygen combining with it does not form PbO, but diffuses into the lead. It does not seem likely that any more stringent requirements will be placed on lead quality in the near future, and in fact it would be rational for some to be relaxed - for example the bismuth specifications are much lower than actually needed for most purposes. The successful development in recent years, by the Bunker Hill Company, of a completely automatic casting machine, has already been taken up by one Continental refinery, and can be expected to find wide acceptance in the coming years. The direct casting of lead or lead alloy sheets has been successfully developed by Semmens and coworkers at the Broken Hill Associated Smelters,[41] and is in commercial use in several continents, reducing very considerably the cost of producing similar sheets by rolling.

Aqueous Processes

Although there is no immediate prospect of a commercial application, mention must be made of leaching processes which are being investigated in a variety of plants. Peters at U. B. C. is investigating the galvanic leaching of galena. PbS, nitric acid and PbO_2 are reacted to give elemental sulphur and $PbNO_3$ solution. This latter is purified, and electrolysed to give Pb, and PbO_2 for re-use. Several variations on this procedure are currently being tested, using other media besides nitric acid. Pressure leaching with oxygen in alkaline solutions was extensively studied in the 1950's,[42] and in acid solutions from the 1950's through to the present day,[43] whereby PbS is converted to $PbSO_4$, which can be leached with ethylene diamine to yield a very pure lead, as patented by Forward and Sherritt-Gordon. Björling considers that a necessary future development is a suitable and regenerable reagent for in situ leaching of lead and zinc minerals in mines, and is presently studying the use of ferric chloride to attack sphalerite. Recent Russian investigations in similar vein concern bacterial leaching methods.[44]

Extractive Metallurgy of Zinc

The extractive metallurgy of zinc has seen a more spectacular development than any in lead, over the past 34 years (although it affects lead as well) in that a completely new method of zinc production has come into being, and with each passing year increases its share of the world's total zinc production - the Imperial Smelting Process. As a combined producer of zinc, lead and copper, it seems certain to gain ever wider acceptance.

Slag Fuming Processes

Trail's slag fuming process, a novelty in 1936, has spread all over the globe, and is applied to copper smelting slags as well as lead blast furnace slags[45]. Kellogg's fundamental examination of the process[46] is being developed and applied with success to practical operations, although an alternative approach to the subject has been argued[47].

The St. Joseph electrothermic slag dezincing process was developed as a technical success but was not economically viable.[48] It is possible that under particular economic circumstances electrical energy may again be tried for slag dezincing. It is likely that liquid or gaseous fuel will be substituted for coal, at least in part. The Kolodin process for fuming tin from slags employs liquid fuel, and it is understood that Technoimpex (Bulgaria) claim to have developed a continuous slag fuming process employing oil fuel. Recent developments in the standard process have been towards the use of preheated blast.[45]

The zinc fume produced is deleaded by a mild reduction in a kiln at American plants, whereas at San Gavino and Port Pirie it is given a similar treatment for the removal of halogens. The chemistry is not straightforward, but a mass spectrometric investigation recently carried out has thrown light on the subject.

Pyrometallurgical Processes

Among zinc refining processes must be mentioned the conduct of sintering processes so as to eliminate, at least partially, cadmium and lead in the roasting process; the use of sodium to precipitate arsenic from liquid zinc, followed by oxidation to remove the residual sodium, just prior to casting; and the use of sodium in rather higher concentrations to delead zinc by a precipitation process[49].

As with lead sulphide, so the oxidation of zinc sulphide continues to attract attention, both experimentally[50] and from the mathematical viewpoint[51].

For recovery of zinc from leach residues a plant built recently by Cerro de Pasco and Lurgi at La Oroya, Peru, utilizes an externally-heated rotary kiln, from which zinc, lead and sodium are fumed by reduction with coal, while sponge iron containing copper and precious metals is also formed, and constitutes an ideal feed for cementation of copper-containing solutions.

A further means of recovering zinc from drosses and residues (such as those from vertical or horizontal retorts) is the Lange-Barthel flash smelting furnace, which however has too-great refractory lining wear to permit of reasonable length campaigns. Lurgi and Babcock and Wilcox have had very promising experimental results with a smelting cyclone, and claim extraordinarily high zinc volatilization rates with low fuel consumption. Work has also been conducted at Port Pirie with a cyclone fuming furnace[52] on pilot plant scale, with results comparable to those of the standard fuming process.

Although horizontal retort plants are very nearly extinct, a few remain in existence with mechanized feeding and discharging, and a common condenser replacing individual prolongs on each retort.

An innovation on vertical retorts is the introduction of partial condensation technique to separate higher- and lower-lead fractions of condensate[53].

Leaching Processes

The most significant break-through in electrolytic zinc technology is undoubtedly the development of a low-cost method for extracting zinc from leach residues. A Jarosite method of precipitating iron in easily filterable form out of solutions from hot-acid digestion of the residues has been developed simultaneously in Australia[54], Norway[55] and Japan. A further process, successfully operated in the laboratory by Vieille-Montagne, reduces trivalent iron by the addition of non-calcined zinc concentrate.

Considerable work is also in progress on the leaching of other "difficult" materials, which may be low-grade, mixed, or siliceous. The Sherritt-Gordon technique of reacting an acidic pulp with oxygen under pressure serves as the basis for most procedures to deal with sulphide materials. The British Columbia Research Council have also had some limited success with bacterial leaching, whereby the sulphides are converted to sulphates. The E. Z. Company of Australia has developed a simple method for leaching reasonably high-grade zinc silicates with subsequent electrolytic recovery.

Solution Purification and Electrolysis

Previous comments, on the advantages being achieved and still to be achieved by the introduction of automatic controls, apply as much to zinc production as to lead. Research continues in many fields as required to provide the background data necessary for understanding the phenomena, preliminary to the working out of detailed models as the basis for controls.

For the purification of zinc sulphate solutions, prior to electrolysis, a mass of work appears to be still in progress. Recent publications include the automatic control of copper content during copper-cadmium precipitation, reported by Rannev _et al._[56], which has been adopted in modified form at Port Pirie, resulting in a substantial improvement in plant capacity; investigations of the cementation process by Lange[57], and of ion-exchange processes by Krüger and Winterhager[58]. The latter also investigated electrorefining of zinc, and concluded that separate anode and cathode compartments are necessary in order to obtain very pure zinc, that purification of the electrolyte by cementation and ion-exchange is necessary, and that additions such as potassium fluoride are advantageous; further reduction in the lead content is also possible, using strontium carbonate and carefully avoiding stirring of the bath. Ingraham and Kerby[59], in a careful investigation of the rate of cadmium cementation on zinc, found that this is a function of the diffusion layer thickness (and hence is increased by stirring) and of other impurity ions (such as copper, arsenic, cobalt or tellurium), whose effect is largely due to their influence on the hydrogen overvoltage, and hence on the physical nature of the deposit, or to alloy formation reducing the available surface area by blocking off pores.

Since zinc electrolysis is extraordinarily sensitive to foreign ions in the electrolyte, investigations continue in many parts of the world into the influence of the many ions which may be present -

for example, in the school of Lange[57], by Maja[60] in Italy (effect of nickel and cobalt), and by Hierzyk[61] in Poland. To facilitate the production of special high grade zinc, lead alloy anodes may be pretreated by electrolyzing an electrolyte containing fluoride, which increases their life. This method, developed by Gaunce [62][63] at Trail, has also been adopted elsewhere.

The next major break-through in electrolytic zinc processing is expected to be the successful development of automatic cathode stripping. Development of systems for existing cells is proceeding at Monteponi-Montevecchio, Mitsui Mining and Smelting[64], and the Bunker Hill Company, whereas a new type of cell and cathode, with allied stripping and handling equipment, are believed to be under development at Vieille Montagne.

An alkaline process, for which commercial potential is claimed for treating zinc ores high in iron, has been described by Meek[65]. A zinc sponge is obtained by electrolysis of the solution obtained after 2-stage roasting, 2-stage leaching, oxidation by aeration and electrolyte purification by cementation.

Imperial Smelting Process

Developments on the Imperial Smelting process continue apace in several fields - concerned with adaptations to ever lower grade concentrates, widening its scope to recover more metals than at present, improving existing designs of furnace or ancillary equipment, and developing new equipment or subsidiary processes. Developmental work is now proceeding not only at Avonmouth, but also at the other dozen Imperial Smelting installations throughout the world, and presently active projects include the use of coked bricquettes to avoid dependance on the use of metallurgical coke, and the use of fuel of lower reactivity towards CO_2, to improve the thermal economy of the furnace. Mechanical developments include improved charge distribution through the use of special bell gear, and an irrigated condenser to replace rotors, which consume appreciable energy and require frequent maintenance. Attention is now being paid to the recovery of copper and tin from the bullion. The vacuum dezincing unit, now in commercial operation at Swansea, is being exploited to give a grade of zinc primarily for the continuous galvanising market.

Fundamental data on phase relations of relevance to this process continue to be obtained, as for example on the distribution of arsenic and antimony between zinc and zinc chloride flux,[66] or the activity of zinc oxide in slags[67].

Work is in progress at many centers on improvements in the extraction of metal values from flue dusts, residues and sundry by-product materials. Aqueous methods commend themselves for use with such materials in small quantities, and solvent extraction(68) or ion exchange(69) processes are being investigated to improve selectivities.

Conclusions

It is difficult to escape the conclusion that the major developments over the rest of this century will be improvements in the performance of existing processes and equipment, through the application of process controls (on - line analytical procedures, and direct digital control) much greater use of computers, and more complete mathematical modelling than is used today.

There are no obvious applications of such recently developed techniques as lasers, plasma reactions, or atomic energy - except insofar as isotopes have found application in determining the charge height in a blast furnace, or in tagging charge constituents to determine residence times in furnaces.

Further application of oxygen-enrichment, preheating of blast, liquid or gaseous fuel replacement of coke, or flash smelting techniques can be foreseen, and replacement of the classical or standard techniques by variations especially tailored to local conditions, where certain supplies or commodities are unusually cheap or dear by world standards. (These apply particularly to the production of lead from sulphide concentrates.) Increased use of caustic soda or chlorine, in places where one or other of these is in excess supply, can be envisaged - the former is particularly useful for forming low-melting slags. A lower temperature of operation not only means fuel economy, but also improves separation factors between metal and slag phases, giving greater selectivity, whether of reduction or oxidation.

Increased application of aqueous methods can also be predicted for treatments of small throughputs of ores, concentrates, or by-products: leaching, simple or under pressure, or by bacterial agents; and concentrations or separations by solvent extraction or ion-exchange methods.

It seems reasonably clear that increased application of vacuum techniques can also be expected, and some additional applications of increased pressure may also be possible.

The industries have certain particular desires at present, which are worthy of mention:

(1) Clean-up procedures for gaseous or liquid effluents, improved plant hygiene and health supervision.

(2) Improved methods for recovery of lead and zinc from unusual fumes and residues (for example, from iron and steel-making).

(3) Lower blast furnace operating temperatures.

(4) An improved bebismuthizing process for lead, yielding better separation.

(5) A better grade of copper matte from continuous copper drossing of lead.

(6) A better process for treatment of Parkes process crust.

(7) Truly continuous processes for lead refining - decoppering, vacuum dezincing, and final refining.

(8) A better slag dezincing process, especially one capable of treating lower tonnages, with higher recoveries, or lower capital costs.

(9) A process for flash smelting of oxidized zinc ores.

(10) A process for direct electrolytic production of zinc and sulphur from ZnS.

(11) A better zinc refining process - either cheaper refluxing, or a partial freezing process.

Kuxmann[70] has discussed the desirability for new techniques for the mutual treatment of lead <u>and</u> zinc ores, concentrates and by-products.

Work can be expected to be done on all or most of these projects over the next thirty years. Development of new materials of construction, or cheapening of materials whose cost now excludes their large-scale use, will undoubtedly occur, enabling processes which have previously failed, to be re-tackled successfully in some cases. Possible examples would be the use of pure alumina refractories, or nitrides of iron and iron-alloys.

This account is inevitably incomplete, unbalanced and insufficiently critical. Particularly in areas outside those of the authors' immediate competence, errors of judgement will have been made as to what to include and what to leave out. Recognizing these shortcomings, the authors nonetheless hope that the compilation may be of some use to those engaged in research and development, in directing attention to some areas where more effort is called for, or in presenting challenges worthy of being taken up in the near future.

Acknowledgements

Rather than specify "personal communication" as references throughout the text, grateful acknowledgement is made here to suggestions, information and references contributed by Prof. G. Björling, Technical University, Stockholm; Prof. Dr.-Ing. J. Feiser, Goslar; Dr. H. Fritsche, Stolberger Zink, Aachen; Dr. J. Hamdorf, Electrolytic Zinc Co., Risdon; Mr. R. F. Lambert, ASARCO, Omaha; Mr. R. E. Lund, St. Joseph Lead Co., Zinc Division, Monaca; Mr. S. W. K. Morgan, Imperial Smelting Processes Ltd., Avonmouth; Dr.-Ing. W. Schwarz, Lurgi Gesellschaft, Frankfurt; Mr. J. W. Sherman, St. Joseph Lead Co., Lead Division, Herculaneum; and Mr. D. Ward, The B.H.A.S. Pty. Ltd., Port Pirie.

References

1. Robinson, B., Minerals benefication in '69 steps up tonnage, engineering, environmental control & automation. Mining Engineering, Vol. 22, No. 2, p. 99-101.

2. Echalaz, A. J., Vibration milling tests at Durban Roodepoort Deep, Limited. J.S. Afr. Inst. Min. Metall. June 1968, 68 (II), Pt. 1, p. 501-510.

3. Oxenford, R. J. and W. R. Bull, Colorado School of MInes, Unpublished data, 1970.

4. Anon., Wedge bar screen. Mining Engineering, March 1968, 20 (3) p. 87.

5. Trojan, R. and W. Zwerdling, Economic effectiveness of preliminary zinc/lead ore enrichment with the aid of dense liquid media. Rudy Metale Niezelazne (Poland), May 1969, 14 (5), p. 291-292.

6. Nekrasov, B. D. and Y. P. Sulina, Selective and collective-selective flotation of lead-zinc ores of the Khanikomsk deposit. Tsvetn. Met. (U.S.S.R.), 1968, No. 4, p. 6-10. (In Russian).

7. Arbiter, N, and N. L. Weiss, Trends in flotation machines and circuits. A.I.M.E. Annual Meeting, 1970.

8. Cusak, B. L., The development of the Davcra flotation cell. Australas. Inst. Min. Metall. Monogr., Ser. No. 3, Melbourne, 1968, p. 481-487.

9. Boutin, P. and D. A. Wheeler, Column flotation development using an 18 inch pilot unit. Canadian Mining Journal, 88 (3), 1967, p.94.

10. Moir, D. N., Annual Review - Mineral Processing, World Mining, June 1969, p. 42-50.

11. Randolph, A. D., Continuous particle-size measurement in liquid slurries. State Technical Services, University of Arizona, Special Report, 1970.

12. Lynch, A. J., T. C. Rao, and W. J. Whiten, Technical note on on-stream sizing analysis in closed grinding circuits. Proc. Australas. Inst. Min. Metall., 223, 1967, p. 71.

13. Volin, M. E., R. A. Campbell and T. P. Volin, Computer simulation of autogenous grinding. S.M.E. Fall Meeting, 1968.

14. Lynch, A. J., Automatic control systems for the mineral industry. Australian Mining, 1968, 60 (6), p. 37.

15. Colborn, R. P., Ph.D. Thesis, Univ. of Natal, 1969 (Unpublished).

16. Bull, W. R. and D. J. Spottiswood, The effect of baffle design on mixing in a bank of flotation cells. A.I.M.E. Annual Meeting, 1970. (To be published).

17. Niemi, A., A study of dynamic and control properties of industrial flotation processes. Acta Polytech. Scan., 48, 1966.

18. Johnson, W., Automatic thickener control at Atlas Minerals. Eng. and Min, Jnl., 167, No. 10, p. 92-93.

19. Anon., Mines preserve the environment World Mining, Dec. 1968, p. 18-22.

20. Roos, J. R., M. S. Thesis, Colorado School of Mines, 1968. (Unpublished).

21. Paschen, P., "Sintering roasting in lead metallurgy", Erzmetall, Vol. 22, Nov., Dec. 1969, pp. 553-559, 606-609.

22. Hase, E. A., "Oxygen enriched blast at Asarco's lead smelter", Journal of Metals, Vol. 17, No. 12, Dec. 1965, pp. 1334-1337.

23. Anon., Journal of Metals, Vol. 17, No. 7, July 1965, p. 690.

24. Roy, J. T. and J. R. Stone, "Continuous tapping of a lead blast furnace", Transactions of the Metallurgical Society of the AIME, Vol. 227, Feb. 1963, pp. 177-179.

25. Lumsden, J., "Physical chemistry of the lead blast furnace", Erzmetall, Vol. 17, July 1964, pp. 398-399.

26. White, L. A. "The development of the lead blast furnace at Port Pirie", Transactions AIME, Vol. 188, 1950, pp. 1221-1228.

27. Elvander, H. I., "The Boliden lead process", Symposium "Pyrometallurgical Processes in Non-Ferrous Metallurgy", AIME, 1967, pp. 225-245.

28. Bryk, P. R. Malmstrom and E. Nyholm, "Flash smelting of lead concentrates", Journal of Metals, Vol. 18, No. 12, Dec. 1966, pp. 1298-1302.

29. Fuller, F. T., "Process for direct smelting of lead concentrates", Journal of Metals, Vol. 20, No. 12, Dec. 1968, pp. 26-30.

30. Winterhager, H., "The electrochemical bases of the electrolysis of lead sulfide in molten salt mixtures with lead chloride", Forschungsberichte des Wirtschafts - und Verkehrsministeriums Nordrhein - Westfalen, No. 134, 1955.

31. Isbell, W. T., "Vacuum dezincing in lead refining", Transactions AIME, Vol. 182, 1949, pp. 186-190.

32. Leferrer, V. F., "Vacuum dezincing of Parkes' process zinc crusts", Transactions of the Metallurgical Society of the AIME, Vol. 209, Nov. 1957, pp. 1459-1460.

33. Davey, T.R.A. and H. T. Webster, assigned to B.H.A.S. Pty, Ltd., "Copper Drossing of lead bullion", Australian Patent 256, 553, 1965.

34. Davey, T.R.A. and K. C. Williams, "Vacuum Dezincing plant at the B.H.A.S., Pty. Ltd., Port Pirie", Proceedings Australasian Institute of Mining and Metallurgy, No. 180, 1956, pp. 207-217.

35. Paschen, P. and H. Winterhager, "Refining of lead with caustic soda", Erzmetall, Vol. 21, Jan. 1968, pp.14-20.

36. Smirnov, M. P., Y. Z. Malkin, V. Y. Sergienko and N. G. Tarkhov, "A Continuous alkaline softening process for lead under pilot conditions", Tsvetnye Metalli, (Eng. translation) Vol. 4, Aug. 1963, pp. 40-44.

37. Freni, E. R., "Electrolytic lead refining at the San Gavino Monreale plant of Monteponi and Montevecchio", Hydrometallurgy Symposium, Koln, June 1969, Erzmetall Supplementary Volume, pp. B128-132.

38. Jollivet, L., "Debismuthizing lead by the Jollivet-Penarroya process", Erzmetall, Vol. 13, Dec. 1960, p. 578.

39. Davey, T. R. A., "Decoppering lead with sulphur", Symposium "Research in Chemical and Extraction Metallurgy", Australasian Institute of Mining and Metallurgy, 1967, pp. 121-129.

40. Kleinert, R., "Present state of the Lead refining processes", Erzmetall, Vol. 22, No. 7, July 1969, pp. 327-338.

41. Goff, L. I. and G. Hewish, "Creep resistant lead sheet by the D. M. Process", 3rd International Conference on Lead, Venice Sept. 1968.

42. Mackiw, V. N., "Current trends in chemical metallurgy", The Canadian Journal of Chemical Engineering, Vol. 46, Feb. 1968, pp. 3-15.

43. Exner, F., J. Gerlach and F. Pawlek, "Contribution to the pressure leaching of galena", Erzmetall, Vol. 22, No. 8, Aug. 1969, pp. 379-381.

44. Golbraikht, A.I., "Effect of pyrite on the bacterial oxidation of chalcopyrite and sphalerite", Vestn. Akad. Nauk. Kaz. S.S.R. (U.S.S.R.), Vol. 24, Dec. 1968, pp. 61-62.

45. Sundstrom, J., "The slag fuming plant at the Rönnskär works of the Boliden Aktiebolag, Skelleftehamn, Sweden", Journal of Metals, Vol. 21, June 1969, pp. 15-21.

46. Kellogg, H. H., "Computer model of the slag fuming process for recovery of zinc oxide", Transactions of the Metallurgical Society of the AIME, Vol. 239, Sept. 1967, pp. 1439-1449.

47. Quarm, T. A. A., "Slag fuming - kinetic or thermodynamic?" Engineering and Mining Journal, Vol. 169, Jan. 1968, pp. 92-93.

48. Isbell, W. T. and C. C. Long, "Direct production of metallic zinc from lead blast furnace slag", Transactions AIME, Vol. 159, 1944, pp. 176-181.

49. Pelzel, E., "A new zinc refining process", Erzmetall, Vol. 17, Jan. 1964, pp. 19-24.

50. Dimitrov, R., G. Bakalov and I. Vasilev, "Oxidation fo zinc sulphide", Rubidov, Met. (Sofia) Vol. 23, July 1968, pp. 46-51.

51. Nateson, K. and W. L. Philbrook, "Mathematical model for temperature variation within a particle undergoing reaction, with application for roasting of zinc sulfide", Transactions of the Metallurgical Society of the AIME, Vol. 245, July 1969, pp. 1417-1425.

52. Blanks, R. F. and D. H. Ward, "Development of a cyclone furnace process for slag fuming", Symposium: "Advances in Extractive Metallurgy", Insitution of Mining and Metallurgy, London, 1967, pp. 224-244.

53. Clifton, V. E., "The condensation in stages of metal from zinc retorts", Transactions (British) Institution of Mining and Metallurgy, Vol. 74, 1964-5, pp. 861-867.

54. See article in this volume.

55. See article in this volume.

56. Rannev, G. G., I. M. Kogol, A. A. Salin, N. A. Pilipchuk and N. A. Laptev, "Automatic control of copper content during copper-cadmium purification of zinc solutions", Tsvetnye Metalli (English translation), Vol. 8, Apr. 1967, pp. 33-36.

57. Lange, A. "Investigations into hydro- and electro-chemical zinc and cadmium production", Erzmetall, Vol. 18, May 1965, pp. 242-25

58. Kruger, J. and H. Winterhager, "Contribution to the question of electrolytic refining of zinc", Erzmetall, Vol. 18, Nov. 1965, pp. 564-570.

59. Ingraham, T. R. and R. Kerby, "Kinetics of cadmium cementation on zinc in buffered sulfate solutions", Transactions of Metallurgical Society of the AIME, Vol. 245, Jan. 1969, pp. 17-21.

60. Maja, M. "Infuence of some impurities on the electrodeposition of certain metals", Electrochim. Metal (Italy) Vol. 2, Oct-Dec. 1967, pp. 469-472.

61. Hierzyk, R., D. Krupkowa and E. Lach, "Studies on the behaviour of chloride ions during the electrolysis of zinc", Rudy Metale Niezelazne (Poland), Vol. 14, April 1969, pp. 197-199.

62. Gaunce, F. F., assigned to COMINCO: French Pat. 1,419,356, Nov. 26, 1965.

63. Farmer, R. H., "Anode pre-conditioning and other changes in Cominco's electrolytic zinc cells", AIME Symposium: "Electrometallurgy", 2 Dec. 1968.

64. Mitsui Mining and Smelting Co., Japanese Patent App. 21735/64.

65. Meek, R. L., "Alkaline process for electrolytic zinc", AIME Symposium: "Electrometallurgy", 2 Dec. 1968.

66. Fray, D. J. and I. Imris, "Distribution of arsenic between zinc and zinc chloride", Hutnicke Listy (Czech.), Vol. 24, July 1969, pp. 530-532.

67. Lange, A., and H. J. Lange, "Practical importance of the knowledge of the activity of the mixed phase components, as illustrated for the case of zinc oxide dissolved in metallurgical slags", Sb. Ved. Praci Vysoke Skoly Banske Ostrave (Czech.), Vol. 13, 1967, pp. 191-202.

68. Imperial Smelting Corp. (N. S. C.) Ltd., U.S. Patent 3,441,372, 24 Jan. 1966, "Solvent extraction process for separation of zinc from cadmium".

69. Mokryshev, A. I., et. al., "Use of ion exchange resins for recovery of zinc and cadmium from solutions in fast dust collectors at the Chimkentsk lead works", Tsvetnye Metalli, Vol. 10, Feb. 1969, pp. 36-37.

70. Kuxmann, U., "Metallurgical problems associated with the production of lead and zinc from their common sulphide ores", Erzmetall, Vol. 22, Jan. 1969, pp. 15-22.

Chapter 37

LEAD AND ZINC - A LONG-TERM VIEW OF PROPERTIES, MARKETS AND RESEARCH

By S. F. Radtke
Executive Vice President & Director of Research
International Lead Zinc Research Organization, Inc.
New York, N.Y.

Abstract

The properties and characteristics of lead and zinc have made these metals useful to man in many ways since the days of antiquity. Despite their long history of use, however, these metals have proved to be extremely resilient and responsive to modern needs. New alloys and compounds continue to be developed, adding to the growth of these metals. Consumption data is given for 1969 and compared with one and two decades ago. Trends in major markets also are cited and explained. Uses for lead and zinc which have come into prominence within the past few years are described and explained, with emphasis on the role played by the industry's cooperative research program. Current efforts in the research phase are discussed, with details given on major efforts for both metals, including new alloys, process developments, applications research, finishes, coating, paints and pigments, batteries and fundamental research. A forecast is given of promising new areas and a projection made on a longer term of new applications that may emerge from current research.

Introduction

Both lead and zinc have histories going back to antiquity. The hanging gardens of Babylon, one of the wonders of the ancient world, were lined with lead sheet soldered together to provide a water-tight container so that the moisture required for the plantings would not be lost by seepage. The Egyptians of the early dynasties used lead to glaze pottery, to make solder and decorative ornaments. The Chinese minted lead coins around 3 000 BC and the Romans employed the metal widely for plumbing and roofing, some of which survive to this very day in excellent condition.

Zinc's history has not been traced as far as lead's, yet it has its own exotic past. Zinc jewelry dating to 500 BC has been found on the famed island of Rhodes, one of the Dodecanese Islands off Greece. Idols fashioned from zinc have been uncovered in Dorian settlements in what is now Romania. Fountains of zinc in Pompeii indicated some of the metal's architectural capabilities. And like lead, it was used for coins (as well as mirrors) by the Chinese in the 7th century.

Curiously enough, many of these applications are still to be found in the modern world, including the various architectural uses of lead. Of more significance, however, is the fact that literally hundreds of new applications have been found for both metals so that they are more widely used today than ever before.

Zinc Properties

Zinc ores are commonly found in association with other metals, notably lead throughout the world, including the United States, Canada, Mexico, Peru, several countries in Europe, Japan, and Australia. Since shortly before World War II, the United States has become a large net importer of zinc, both in the form of concentrate and slab. Beginning in the late 1960's such importation has exceeded domestic mine production.

This wide availability of the metal plus its many advantageous properties have helped zinc to hold its own in traditional applications and to gain entry into new markets, in some cases being substituted for other materials. This expansion of zinc into new markets has been greatly facilitated through increased research by the zinc industry companies on an individual basis and through a cooperative international research venture conducted by the International Lead Zinc Research Organization Inc. (ILZRO).

These efforts and zinc's properties have enabled zinc to make a heavy impact on modern technology, as evidenced by its steep increase in consumption in recent years and its successful projection as a modern, versatile material. It now ranks only behind aluminum and copper in order of consumption among the non-ferrous metals.

Some of the more important properties of this blue-gray metal are its relatively low melting point, good resistance to atmospheric corrosion, ability to alloy readily with copper (to make brass), inherent ductility and malleability, and sacrificial protection of steel (e.g., galvanizing). In oxide form, zinc finds wide use in rubber, pigments and many chemical uses. Table I lists some of the basic properties of this metal.

Zinc's many applications are so often disguised by the nature of the application that its role is never fully appreciated by the layman. For example, its alloying with copper to produce brass: its use as a coating to protect steel in metallic form, as with galvanizing, or as a dust in zinc paints; under the chromium in plated zinc die castings, and as zinc oxide in rubber, medical ointments, and other products.

Table I. Basic Zinc Properties

General	
Atomic Number	30
Atomic Weight	65.38
Density at 20°C	7130 kg/m^3
Specific Volume at 20°C	0.140 cm^3/g
Thermal Properties	
Melting Point	419.5°C
Boiling Point	906°C
Specific Heat	0.0915 cal/g/°C
Coefficient of Linear Thermal Expansion 20-250°C	39.7 x 10^{-6} cm/cm/°C
Thermal Conductivity 25°C	0.27 cal/sq. cm/cm/sec/°C
Electrical Properties	
Per cent Electrical Conductivity (Copper = 100%) 20°C	28.5
Resistivity (microhm-cm) (Solid Zinc-Special High Grade) 20°C	5.916

Zinc Alloys

The die casting process permits high speed production of complex parts to close limits of accuracy and with exceptionally smooth finishes requiring little or no further machining. Zinc alloys have for many years been the most widely used metal for die casting, due to their combination of favorable properties, adaptability to the process, and low cost, including longer life for the dies used due to the low melting point of zinc.

The development of the modern zinc die casting alloys has been based on (1) the use of Special High Grade Zinc (99.99% pure); (2) the addition of alloying constituents which are held within close limits; and (3) the control of impurities.

The great bulk of zinc die casting currently is carried out with two alloys, commonly identified as alloys 3 and 5 which have been in use for several decades. In recent years a third alloy has been added and commonly designated as alloy 7. The entire group is often spoken of by its original trade name as Zamak alloys, and in England as the Mazak alloys. The composition, mechanical, and other properties of these alloys are given in Table II, along with corresponding ASTM (American Society for Testing Materials) and SAE (Society of Automotive Engineers) designations.

Aluminum, the major alloying constituent in alloys 3 and 5, is added in amounts of around 4%, which has proved to be the optimum composition from the standpoint of strength, ductility and stability. Loss of strength and stability may be as high as 50% of the original values if the aluminum content is reduced to 2%. The aluminum content also has the important capability of sharply reducing the rate of attack of molten zinc on iron. Aluminum also avoids "soldering", or sticking of the casting to the die. This permits the casting of these zinc alloys in the more productive hot chamber (plunger) type of die casting machine. This type of machine injects the molten metal into the die cavity automatically, unlike the cold chamber machine, which requires the molten metal to be poured manually, by lading, into the cylinder.

Alloys 3 and 5 differ primarily in their copper content. Copper additions increase its strength and hardness and improve corrosion resistance. The copper content is held to a specified maximum of 1.25% (in alloy 5) to avoid making the alloy unstable due to ageing and to avoid reducing the impact strength to a very low value. Dimensional stability also is affected by high levels of copper, so a 1% maximum is usually recommended for alloy 5 despite the prescribed limit of 1.25%. Changes in casting dimensions however, are minimal and always occur within a few weeks after

Table II. Composition and Properties of Zinc Alloy Die Castings

DESIGNATION	ASTM Designation B86-64	AG40A	AC41A	
	SAE	903	925	903
	General Designation	3	5	ZAMAK 7
COMPOSITION % BY WEIGHT	Copper	.25 Max.	.75 to 1.25	.25 Max.
	Aluminum	3.5 to 4.3	3.5 to 4.3	3.5 to 4.3
	Magnesium	.020 to .05	.03 to .08	.005 to .02
	Iron Max.	.100	.100	.075
	Lead Max.	.005	.005	.0030
	Cadmium Max.	.004	.004	.0020
	Tin Max.	.003	.003	.0010
	Nickel	--	--	.005 to .020
	Titanium	--	--	--
	Zinc (99.99 + % purity)	Remainder	Remainder	Remainder

MECHANICAL PROPERTIES	Charpy Impact Strength, .635cm x .635 cm (1/4 in. x 1/4 in.) bar, as cast, Nm/m	2295	2562	2135
	(ft lb/in)	(43)	(48)	(40)
	Charpy Impact Strength, .635cm x .635cm (1/4 in. x 1/4 in.) bar, after 10 yrs indoor aging, Nm/m	2189	2135	2189
	(ft lb/in)	(41)	(40)	(41)
	Tensile Strength, as cast, MN/m^2	282.7	328.2	282.7
	(psi)	(41,000)	(47,600)	(41,000)
	Tensile Strength, after 10 yrs indoor aging, MN/m^2	241.3	271.0	241.3
	(psi)	(35,000)	(39,300)	(35,000)
	Elongation, as cast, % in 5.08 cm (2 in.)	10	7	10
	Elongation, after 10 yrs indoor aging, % in 5.08cm (2in.)	16	13	16
	Expansion (growth), after 10 yrs indoor aging, cm/cm	.0001	.0001	.0001
OTHER PROPERTIES	Compression Strength-MN/m^2	413.7	599.8	413.7
	(psi)	(60,000)	(87,000)	(60,000)
	Modulus of Rupture-MN/m^2	655.0	724.0	655.0
	(psi)	(95,000)	(105,000)	(95,000)
	Shear Strength-MN/m^2	213.7	262.0	213.7
	(psi)	(31,000)	(38,000)	(31,000)
	Solidification Shrinkage- m/m	.0117	.0117	.0117
	Thermal Expansion-cm/cm/^oC	.0000274	.0000274	.0000274
	Transverse Deflection-cm	.686	.406	.686
	Specific Weight-kg/m^3	6643	6643	6643

casting; consequently, unless the castings are large or require very close tolerances, the dimensional changes can usually be considered insignificant. In those cases where very high dimensional accuracy is required, alloy 3 is usually recommended.

Alloy7 is considered a modification of alloy 3. It has a lower magnesium content and iron, lead, tin, and cadmium are held to lower levels. Also, a small amount of nickel is added. This alloy has a slightly lower melting point than alloy 3 and improved casting properties, making it easier to secure high quality surfaces for finishing (mostly chromium plating) and to obtain higher production rates. The improved castability is due primarily to the low level of magnesium.

A relatively high copper content, (1.0-1.5%) a small amount of titanium (0.25-0.30%) and low aluminum addition (0.01-0.03%) gives ILZRO 14 zinc die casting alloy improved creep resistance and good physical properties along with superior castability. In addition it has the usual inherent advantages of conventional zinc die casting alloys. Its use so far has been confined to cold chamber die casting machines , generally used for aluminum, copper or magnesium base alloys.

In the wrought zinc area, numerous compositions and alloys are used, depending on ultimate product requirements. Alloying metals can be used to improve various properties, such as stiffness, for special applications. The zinc-copper-titanium alloy has become the dominant wrought zinc alloy for applications demanding superior performance. Composition of this alloy is 0.4-0.8% copper, 0.08-0.16% titanium, less than 0.4% of lead, iron, manganese, cadmium, and chromium, and the balance Special High Grade Zinc.

The conventional grades of slab or ingot zinc are rolled into sheet, strip, ribbon, foil, plates or rod for a wide variety of uses. The zinc alloy also may be continuous cast into rod or bar. Because of its properties rolled zinc can be easily worked into various shapes and forms by common fabricating methods, including stamping, forming and spinning. It can be polished and lacquered to retain its natural bright luster, or it can be plated or painted for other finishing effects. It can also be left to weather naturally, in which case it forms a very attractive, non-staining patina, making it especially suited for architectural applications.

The zinc-copper-titanium wrought zinc alloy has all of these properties and on a comparative basis is stronger and more dent resistant than some other metals of the same thickness. It is easily soldered, is non-magnetic and has an electrical conductivity equal to that of brass. It is produced in coils ranging in thickness from 0.076 mm to 6.35 mm and in widths from 6.35 mm to 482.6 mm in sheets from 0.508 mm to 3.175 mm thick, widths from 508 to 1524 mm, and lengths to 3 meters. Physical and mechanical properties are shown in Table III.

Lead Properties

Lead occurs in nature principally in the form of galena, which is usually associated with other metals, notably silver and zinc. The metal is mined throughout the world, with major areas yielding over 100 000 metric tons per year being the United States, Canada, Mexico, Peru, Yugoslavia, Australia, the USSR, Bulgaria, and China.

Among lead's many unique properties are its weight, softness, and corrosion resistance. Because it is so dense and because of its inherent limpness, lead is ideal for sound control and for damping applications. Leads softness makes it valuable as a calking material and in part for bearings, gaskets, washers, and lead-healed nails. Its density also makes it especially suitable for shielding against x-rays and gamma rays. Major physical and other properties are listed in Table IV.

Lead's inertness to corrosive chemicals makes it especially suited

Table III. Properties of Zn-Cu-Ti Alloy

PHYSICAL	Zinc-Copper-Titanium	
Density - G/cc	7.18 at 21 °C (70 °F)	
Liquidus Temp.	422 (792)	
Solidus Temp.	419 (786)	
Thermal Conductivity - calories per sq. cm. per cm. per °C	.25	
Electrical Conductivity - referred to standard copper - % IACS	27	
Coefficient of Thermal Expansion cm/cm/oC Max	.0000234	
MECHANICAL	**With Grain**	**Across Grain**
Tensile Strength-MN/M^2 (psi) (.635 cm/min (1/4 in./min) free running head speed for Ti-Zinc)	199.95 (29,000)	275.79 (40,000)
Elogation in 5.08 cm (2 in.) - %	26	14
Hardness Shore Scleroscope	19-25	
Rockwell Hardness - 15T	60-76	

for lining chemical tanks, ducts, and the like. Its corrosion resistance under varying atmospheric conditions recommends its use for various automotive components, for roofing, decorative panels, facades, and many other uses. It is a standard material for producing, transporting, storing, and using many of the acids employed in various manufacturing processes.

As a coating metal, lead has the advantage of ductility. Lead-coated sheet (terne) may be seriously deformed without having the coating strip off and crack. Lead's resistance to corrosion in the atmosphere is due to the formation of a superficial oxide film, relatively impervious in character, which preserves the metal.

Table IV. Properties of Lead

General	
Atomic Number	82
Atomic Weight	207.21
Density:	
Cast Lead, 20°C	11.34 g/cm^3
Rolled, 20°C	11.35 - 11.37 g/cm^3
Weight:	
Cast Lead, 20°C, calculated at	6.555 kg/m^3
equivalent to	12.326 kg/m^3
Sheet Lead, 0.304 m^2 x 0.397 mm thick (1 ft^2 x 1/64 in thick)	4.53 kg/ (1 lb)
Thermal Properties	
Melting Point, common lead	327.4°C
chemical lead	325.6°C
Casting Temperature	421-443°
Thermal Conductivity, 0°C	0.083 $cal/cm^2/cm/sec/°C$
Coefficient of Expansion, Linear (-190 to 19°C)	0.0000265 per °C
Mechanical Properties	
Hardness, Brinell number 1 cm ball, 30 sec., 100 kg load:	
Common Lead	3.2 to 4.5
Chemical Lead	4.5 to 6.0
Modulus of Elasticity	140 - 614 kg/m^2 (2-million psi)
Electrical Properties	
Resistivity, 20°C	20.648 $micro-ohms/cm^3$

When left to weather in its natural state, lead takes on an attractive silvery gray patina that is esthetically pleasing. It is also an excellent base for paint if that is desired as part of a total design concept.

Because of its malleability, lead and lead alloys are readily rolled to any desired thickness down to around 0.0127 mm. In sheet form, lead or lead alloys can be cut easily to desired size and fabricated by welding or soldering. These and other properties enable lead to be used in more diverse applications than any other metal. This wide use is augmented by lead's ready availability and supply, and its low cost.

A major area of lead use is in the form of chemical compounds. Nearly one-half of the lead consumed in the United States, and perhaps a third of world consumption, is in chemical applications. Most important of these are the lead alkyls (i.e., the anti-knock additive in gasoline) and oxides (the active material in lead-acid storage batteries). Other important uses of oxides are in ceramics, glass, colors, and paints. Leaded glass windows can have a lead content as high as 90% and still retain crystal clarity, which is particularly useful in windows of hospital x-ray rooms.

Lead's lubricating properties are exploited in coatings on wire and on sheet metal, with lead acting as a drawing lubricant. In powder or wire form, lead imparts lubricity to friction material, like brake linings. It is also used in lubricating greases and in pipe joint compounds.

Lead also is a durable and salvageable metal. These are factors which play important roles in such applications as batteries, where the lead grids are salvaged and reused over and over again, with only a slight loss of metal per battery.

Lead Composition and Alloys

The metal is offered in several grades, distinguished by their composition. The commerical grades available are corroding lead, chemical lead, acid-copper lead, common desilverized lead and antimonial lead. Corroding lead describes lead which has been refined to a high degree of purity. It has a silver plus copper maximum of 0.0025% and a minimum lead content of 99.94%. Chemical lead, which derived its name from the ores of southeastern Missouri, contains from 0.040 to 0.080% copper and 0.002 to 0.020% silver. The copper content makes it particularly suitable for chemical industry uses.

Antimonial lead contains from 1 to 25% antimony, with the average around 4–7%. Since it provides greater strength and rigidity, it is commonly known as hard lead. Antimony and tin are the alloying metals most commonly used with lead. The added hardness and strength of lead-antimony alloys are major reasons for its principal use as storage battery plates, sheet, for construction, pipe and and castings.

Tin also increases hardness and strength, but the lead-tin alloys are most commonly used for their melting characteristics, as in solder. In solder, terne metal and other lead alloy coatings, tin also imparts the ability to bond with metals like steel and copper. High-purity lead has very slight bonding ability. Terne metal which generally contains from 15 to 20 % tin, protects steel in a wide range of applications, including roofing, automobile fuel, tanks and packaging.

Both tin and antimony improve the casting qualities of lead. Bismuth and tin are often alloyed with lead to obtain extremely low melting alloys. Although lead does not alloy readily with copper, it is combined in relatively high percentages with copper in bearing alloys and is used in smaller percentages in bronzes and free-machining brasses. Similarly, though lead is difficult to alloy with steel, fractional percentages of lead are used in the production of free-machining steel. Traditional type metal consists of lead alloyed with antimony and tin, and sometimes copper. Calcium, magnesium and sodium in fractional percentages are sometimes alloyed with lead in special bearing alloys and cable sheathing. Cadmium additions prove helpful in coating copper wires with lead. Lead-silver alloy anodes containing around 2% silver, are employed to provide cathodic protection to steel structures exposed to salt water.

Zinc Consumption Patterns

On a world basis, excluding the Soviet block of nations, consumption of zinc increased at an average yearly rate of 3.1% during the 1950's, according to the International Lead and Zinc Study Group. This average increased to over 6% in the first half of the 1960's then leveled out at around 4% in the second half of the decade, with some countries, such as Japan, having much higher averages. A graph showing zinc and lead consumption in the Free World from 1954 through 1969 is shown in Figure 1.

Figures from Metallgesellschaft A. G. show that Russia, Poland, and other Soviet group nations, as well as China and North Korea, increased their consumption at slightly more than 7.5% during the 1950's and at about half that rate during the 1960's. Actual consumption of zinc in 1949 for these countries was 230 000 metric tons. In 1960, the total had jumped to 640 000 metric tons, and in 1968, the latest year for which figures are presently available, the total was 922 700 metric tons of zinc.

The Free World consumed 1 494 800 metric tons of zinc in 1949, 2 441 800 metric tons in 1960, and 3 694 900 metric tons in 1968.

The United States has remained the largest single consumer, accounting for roughly one-third of the non-Soviet group of nations. In 1969, preliminary estimates by the United States Bureau of Mines showed approximately 1 271 000 metric tons of zinc consumed, up around 5% over the 1968 figures. In 1949, United States consumption of zinc totaled 675 000 metric tons.

A rather unusual aspect of zinc consumption is that there is rather wide divergence in consumption patterns by countries. In the United States, the largest use of zinc is for die casting alloys, with galvanizing in second place and brass a distant third, at approximately one-third the die casting alloy total.

On a world basis, however, galvanizing is the leading end use for zinc, being especially so in Japan, and in Australia, where it surpasses all the other zinc markets combined. In Europe, galvanizing also tops the list, but brass is a strong second, followed by rolled zinc and die casting.

Galvanizing is the most rapidly expanding use of zinc in the developing countries of the world. According to the International Lead and Zinc Study Group, these nations consumed over 372 000 metric tons of zinc in 1968, versus 350 390 metric tons in 1968 and 297 758 metric tons in 1964. Patterns of consumption in India, South Africa, Mexico, Brazil and Argentina follow closely those of the United States and Europe, undoubtedly due to their long industrial connections with these areas. In the past few years, rate of growth has been most rapid in the Southeast Asian countries. Deterrent local economic conditions have hindered growth in India, Argentina and Mexico, though India seemed to have returned to the growth path in 1968.

Since zinc is so closely allied to markets which strongly reflect the economic strength of a country, annual consumption can swing quite widely from year to year. In the United States, for example, the automotive industry is the largest single consumer of zinc, taking about one-third of the total, most of it in die casting alloys. Thus the economic health of the automotive industry has a direct and immediate effect on the health of the zinc industry in the United States. Similarly, Japan's heavy industrial expansion in the past two decades has placed a heavy demand on galvanized steel, with a large share of it in recent years being exported to countries in Asia and in Africa. This level of exports could be difficult to maintain in the face of national restraints imposed because of international monetary problems.

Lead Consumption

Lead consumption in the Free World grew at an average rate 1.8% per year during the 1950's, and at around 3.5% in the 1960's with higher averages in the first part of the decade and again in the latter part of the decade. A graph of refined lead consumption in the Free World from 1954 through 1969 is seen in Figure 1.

Total world consumption of refined lead according to Metallgesellschaft, amounted to 1 398 000 metric tons in 1949, with the Free World nations accounting for 1 250 000 metric tons and the Soviet group of nations, China, and North Korea accounting for the rest. Metallgesellschaft reported total world consumption of refined lead in 1960 as 2 617 000 metric tons, with the Free World consuming 2 042 500 metric tons. In 1968, the Free World consumed 2 630 000 metric tons, and the Soviet Union, China, and the other nations in this group consumed 859 900 metric tons for a combined world total of 3 489 900 metric tons, 7% above the 1967 total, which itself was slightly below the 1966 figure.

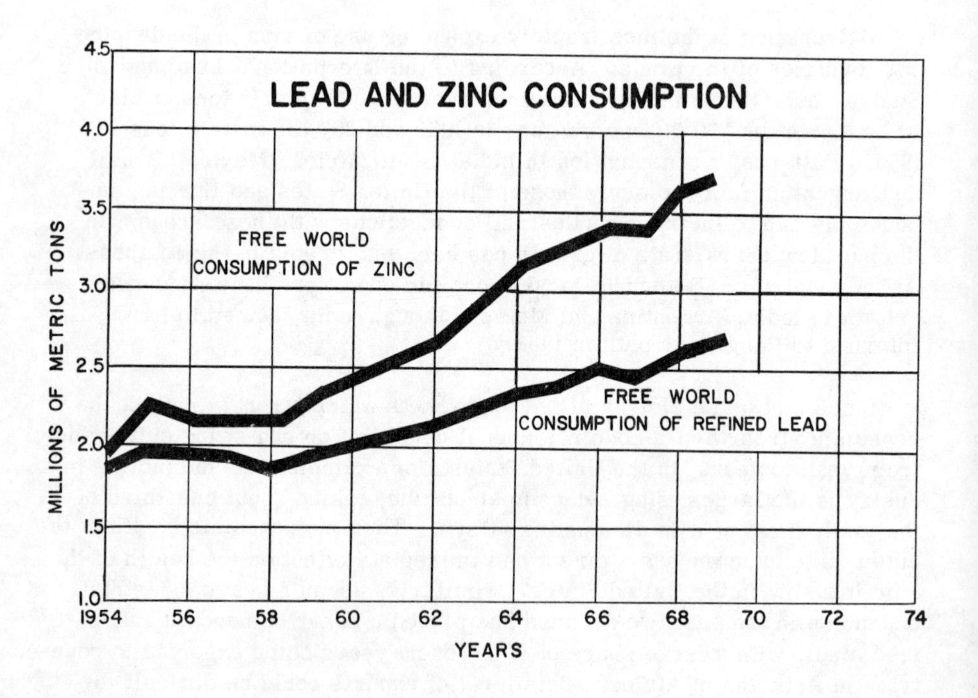

Fig. 1-- Consumption of Lead and Zinc in the Free World, 1954-1969.

Again, the United States is by far the largest single consumer of lead, though its share of the world total may be expected to decline as industrial activity in Europe, Japan, and other areas continues to expand at a higher average annual rate, particularly in automotive applications. In 1949, the United States took roughly 45% of the total world consumption. By 1960, the United States share had dropped to less than 30% a percentage which held fairly steady through the 1960's. Preliminary estimates by the United States Bureau of Mines placed lead consumption in the United States in 1969 at 1 247 600 metric tons, versus 1 205 500 metric tons in 1968. These figures include both refined and secondary lead, which the Metallgesellschaft figures do not.

The United States has major secondary smelters, reflecting the large number of lead acid batteries replaced each year. The secondary lead supply is not so important as yet in Europe, relative to total consumption, but is expected to grow swiftly in the 1970's as the automobile population increases. The United Kingdom is another area where the secondary lead supply is a major factor in total consumption. Japan is another country in which the number of secondary smelters is going up, again reflecting the large increase in automobiles.

Due to the weight of salvage batteries, the smelters are built close to the sources of supply; that is, near or in large cities. This minimizes haulage distance for discarded batteries to the secondary smelter for refining into new plates.

As with zinc, consumption patterns vary from area to area, and even from country to country. Since 1950, several major trends have been evident. The first of these is the growing strength of lead's largest market, storage batteries. Closely associated with this and also the direct result of the growth in automobile use throughout the world is the growth on consumption of tetraethyl and tetramethyl lead as gasoline antiknock additives.

In the United States, batteries accounted for an estimated 500 000 metric tons in 1969, versus 464 000 metric tons in 1968, the previous peak. The total includes both lead metal, used for grids and posts, and lead oxide, for battery pastes. The 1969 increase reflects a record shipment of over 36.5 million replacement batteries during the year.

In Europe, substantial increases in lead consumption for batteries in the latter part of the 1960's helped to offset a continuing drop in use of lead for cable sheathing, due to competitive pressures of other materials. The United States cable sheathing market was affected sooner by competitive materials so that such countries as the United Kingdom and West Germany have had larger consumption in this market than the United States has had for several years. It may be expected, however, that the same use patterns will evolve in Europe, Japan, and elsewhere, before cable sheathing finds its stable level.

The drop in lead use for cable sheathing in the United States appeared to have halted, or even reversed itself, in 1966, when the figure stood at about 60 000 metric tons. However, it dropped again in 1967 and 1968, and stood at 49 000 metric tons in 1969. This compares with 78 000 metric tons consumed for this purpose by the United States in 1945 immediately after the end of World War II.

Recent Developments - Zinc

Galvanizing

Virtually all of today's newer uses of zinc alloys relate to the traditional advantages of zinc - its corrosion protection, its alloying capability with copper (to make brass), its ready castability, and its many compounds. The versatility of this metal, however, has enabled engineers and designers to adapt its properties to new products and processes as they emerge.

Galvanizing, for example, traces its history back some 130 years. In this period it has demonstrated that it can provide effective and economical protection from rust for countless steel products -- bridges, railroads, automotive vehicles, ships, wire, pipe, hardware, roofing, and many more. The fight against corrosion is so important that galvanizing ranks as the largest market outlet for zinc in the world, as it has for many years.

Still, important new uses for galvanizing continue to emerge. At the same time, continued improvements in the process and related areas have significantly increased consumption totals for conventional applications. In the late 1930's, for example, the introduction of the continuous hot-dip galvanizing line led to wide introduction of such lines around the world, turning out millions of tons of galvanized sheet and strip. On the other hand, the traditional method of dipping a steel product into a bath of molten zinc is still widely employed, particularly for parts already fabricated and for very large parts, such as bridge girders.

The galvanizing process itself has been the focus of considerable research directed to improving ultimate performance of the zinc coating and to a better understanding of the process itself. One research program, for example, has involved the addition of alloying elements to the galvanizing bath to control iron-zinc alloy growth on reactive steels. The results obtained with additions of 0.1% vanadium have demonstrated beneficial effects in eliminating gray surfaces and producing compact iron-zinc layers when galvanizing reactive silicon-containing steels, amony other benefits.

It should be remembered that while hot-dip galvanizing is the most widely used method for protecting steel against corrosion, metallic zinc can be applied to steel in four other ways by electrodeposition (electrogalvanizing): metallizing, or spraying of molten metal, sheradizing or cementation, and by painting. This flexibility of zinc coatings broadens its applicability and design potential which, when added to zinc's corrosion resistance capabilities, makes it a preferred coating for many applications, such as the galvanized cable employed in constructing the Verranzo Narrows bridge in New York Harbor, the world's longest suspension span as shown in Figure 2.

Fig. 2 - Steel cable on the Verranzo-Narrows bridge, world's longest suspension bridge, is galvanized for corrosion protection.

Galvanized Sheet

Research in the field of continuous sheet galvanizing has resulted in a wide range of galvanized coatings. Each of these offers improvements in the characteristics which enhance welding, painting, forming, and surface appearance. New technique s, for instance, eliminate or reduce zinc spangle formation on sheet steel and also provide for a thinner, fully alloyed coating. The minimum spangle sheet is mostly used for applications where a medium quality painted finish is required.

One recent innovation has been the painting of galvanized sheet. Painted galvanized sheets find many uses by virtue of their high corrosion resistance in severe environments, combined with excellent appearance and decorative appeal. Such sheets are formed and their used for profiled roofing, simulated clapboard siding, external building facades, gutters, downspouts, flexible blinds, and doors is larely established in the United States and has begun to develop in Europe.

So-called pre-engineered buildings, consisting of pre-painted galvanized steel sections erected almost any design specification, have won increasing acceptance from builders and buyers in the past five years. The new emphasis on pre-built buildings points to large growth in this area, along with the more conventional galvanized steel roofing and siding. Lower construction and maintenance costs are other advantages of the pre-painted galvanized sheet in such use.

Other construction areas that have taken a growing share of galvanized sheet steel production in the past decade are highway guard rails, culvert stock, and highway signs. Engineers are finding that the higher initial cost of the galvanized steel is more than offset by the greatly reduced painting and other maintenance required as compared with painted black steel. Related to these growing markets is the research effort that produced paints with greatly improved service life. "Wipe-coated" galvanized sheets also have been developed to give good paintability combined with the atmospheric corrosion resistance of the original zinc-iron alloy layer. The coating is produced by wiping the surface of the sheet as it leaves the galvanizing bath.

The availability of a growing range of galvanized steel sheets, combined with improvements in manufacturing and painting techniques, has helped to accelerate their growth in several other key markets.

One of the major new uses of galvanized sheet is in automotive productions specifically, for underbodies. Despite zinc's known capabilities in the corrosion area, virtually no zinc coating was employed on

United States cars for this purpose as recently as 1955. Since that time, however, this market (aided by the ever-increasing use of salt to melt snow on streets and highways) has grown so rapidly that it is now perhaps the largest single outlet for galvanized sheet in the United States, taking nearly one-fifth of the total. Today, virtually every United States automobile contains some galvanized and or zinc-rich painted steel members.

The automotive market was further aided by development of differentially coated galvanized sheets. These were developed for automotive applications requiring one surface to have high paintability and the other surface to have high corrosion resistance. By applying a wiping technique to the galvanized sheet as it leaves the galvanizing bath, differentially coated sheets meeting the requirements are produced. Similarly, extra-smooth finishes are produced for exposed auto parts and for other products where especially smooth finishes are desirable after painting.

In the past few years, other important markets in the automotive and transportation industry began to develop. These include galvanized steel containers for movement of cargo from trucks to rail to ship without removal from the containers. Truck bodies and the school bus market also emerged as good markets for galvanized sheet, primarily to reduce operating and maintenance costs.

Some indication of the growth of galvanized steel sheet in the United States can be seen by comparing a few figures. In 1942, shipments of such steel totaled 881 980 metric tons. In 1968, rated capacity of 58 continuing galvanizing lines topped 6-million metric tons. In addition to the automotive market, continuously galvanized sheet is widely used in appliances, construction, and agriculture.

Welding Galvanized Steel

In the late 1950's, research sponsored by ILZRO led to development of welding schedules and practices that enable quality resistance welds to be produced consistently to the sharp rise in use of galvanized sheet steel in the automotive market. These schedules are now included in standard references and are being widely used in production in various industries.

A subsequent program led to establishment in the late 1960's of procedures for arc welding galvanized mild and low-alloy steel in thickness from 1.6 mm to 50.8 mm so that the joint properties were equivalent to those on uncoated steel. The research also led to suitable procedures for the shielded metal-arc welding of butt joints in galvanized steel up to 44.4 mm thick and joints up to 12.7 mm thick. The surface appearance of welds made with a short-circuiting arc using CO_2 shielding are satisfactory, as is shown by the horizontal-vertical weld in 1.6 mm galvanized steel in Figure 3.

An important by-product in this work was the development of a fume extractor nozzle (Figure 4) that effectively removes welding fumes without affecting the shielding gas. Figure 5 shows fumes formed

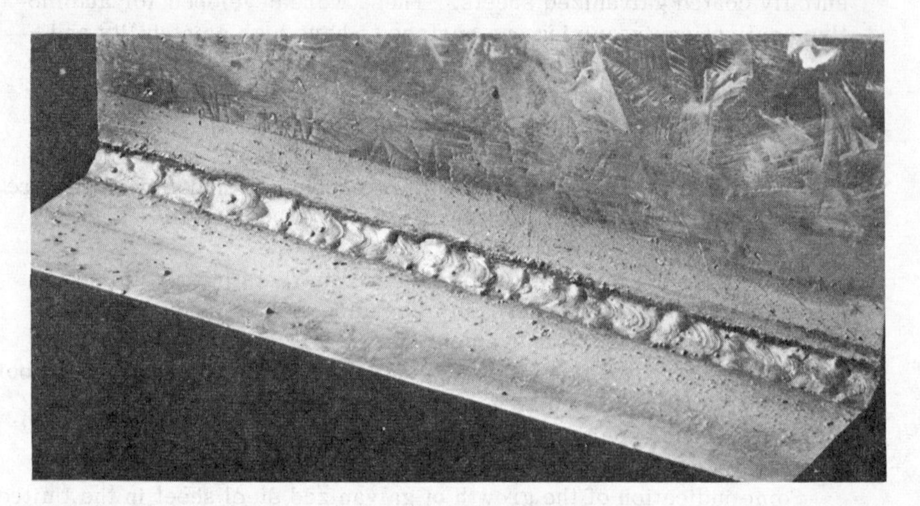

Fig. 3 - Horizontal-vertical fillet weld in 1.6-mm galvanized steel made with CO_2 shielded short-circuiting arc process.

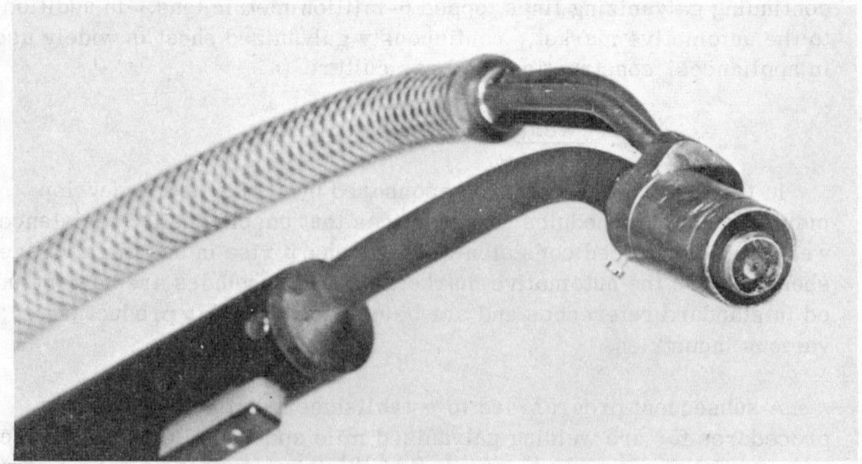

Fig. 4 - Fume extractor nozzle for welding of galvanized steel is fitted around welding torch. Hose carries fumes away.

when welding galvanized steel without a fume extractor and Figure 6 shows the same type of welding with the fume extractor attached to the electrode holder.

Fig. 5 - Fumes formed when welding galvanized steel, without extractor.

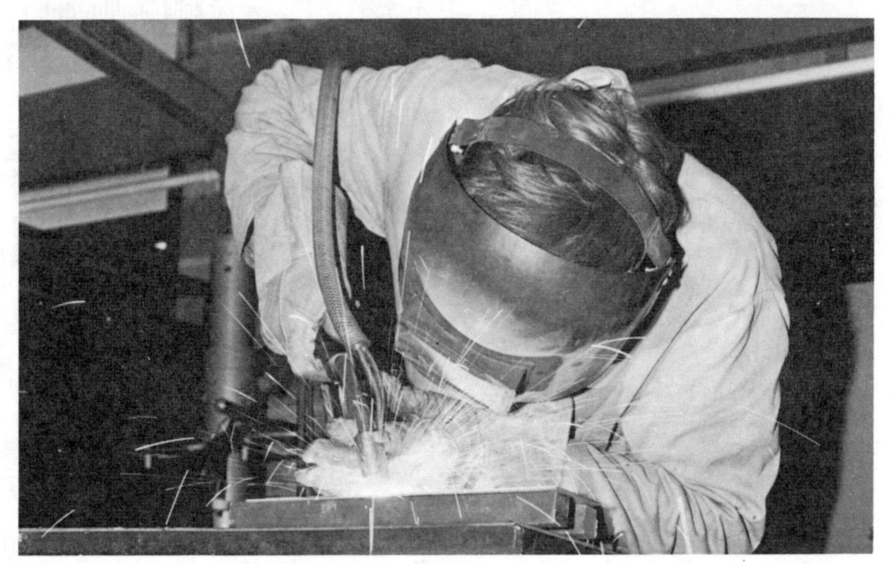

Fig. 6 - Welding galvanized steel with fume extractor on nozzle.

Bolted, Galvanized Connections

The galvanizing of bridges has emerged within the past five years as another major outlet for galvaning. Yet the first all-galvanized and bolted bridge, shown in Figure 7, was opened to traffic only in December, 1963, at Pont Lizotte, Quebec, Canada. This was followed in less than two years by the Stearns-Bayou Bridge in Michigan, the first all-galvanized bridge in the United States. A closeup of one of the galvanized girders used in constructing the Stearns-Bayou bridge is seen in Figure 8. Both this and the Pont Lizotte bridge were on the surfaces of friction-type bolted joints. Within three more years, more than 60 smaller all-galvanized bridges were built in the United States Midwest.

The adoption of galvanized members for bridges reflected efforts to keep maintenance costs under control, and to do so economically. For example, when the Stearns-Bayou bridge was designed, it was estimated that painting the 128-m structure to specifications would cost approximately \$33 per metric ton of steel. Maintenance painting, including sand blasting to near-white finish and a four-coat system (two red lead and two aluminum coats) was contracting at that time for approximately \$100 per metric ton. The cost of hot-dip galvanizing worked out to less than \$72 per metric ton. The first repaint job, therefore, for the

Fig. 7 - The Pont Lizotte bridge, Quebec, Canada-world's first all-galvanized bridge - was opened to traffic in December, 1963.

bridge would cost more than 2 1/2 times the extra investment required for galvanizing, without assuming any increase in painting cost by the time it would be required, usually before the bridge was a decade old.

This new market was augmented by research which provided documented data to design engineers concerning the strength of galvanized connections in structures subject to dynamic loading, such as bridges. Research conducted by the University of Illinois, under ILZRO sponship, demonstrated that such connections attain fatigue strength equivalent to similar but ungalvanized steel in bolted connections. A secondary but almost equally important finding is that galvanized high-strength bolts, nuts and washers can be installed by conventional techniques, provided a suitable lubricant is used on the threaded part of the fastner.

Galvanized Reinforcement

The use of galvanized steel reinforcement for concrete has grown considerably in the past few years. Applications include churches in Holland and Norway, government buildings in the United States and in South Africa, chemical plants, storage tanks, a parking structure, and

Fig. 8 - Galvanized girder used in constructing the Stearns-Bayou bridge in Michigan, first all-galvanized bridge in the United States.

many private and institutional type buildings. The Civic Center in Pine Bluff, Arkansas, is seen during construction in Figure 9, along with the Vimont Overpass near Montreal, Canada. Both involved galvanized reinforcement in their construction.

Up through the mid-1960's, there has been resistance to this application on the belief that the bond strength of galvanized steel was not equal to that of black steel reinforcement. However, ILZRO research conducted at the University of California during most of the 1960's demonstrated that the galvanized rebars have equal or better bond strength with concrete than black bars and that they also have greatly improved corrosion resistance. This has led to its use in buildings where rust staining from black steel reinforcement would be highly undesirable from an esthetic as well as maintenance stand point. Many of these structures, such as the Staten Island Community College in New York or the Bank of Hawaii building in Honolulu, are constructed of highly stylized precast concrete units. Since appearance is an important design factor in these structive galvanized reinforcement is particularly advantageous.

In countries where freezing and thawing cycles crack concrete, the exposed black steel reinforcement rusts, thereby accelerating deterioration of the concrete due to pressure of the corrosion product built up under the concrete. Cracking then becomes more serious and spalling of concrete may occur. The Vimont Overpass was constructed of galvanized reinforcement in an effort to counteract the effects of freezing and thawing cycles.

Galvanized reinforcement also is employed, as in the John F. Kennedy Garage in Detroit, where de-icing salts are a problem. The de-icing

Fig. 9 - Civic Center in Pine Bluff, Ark. and Vimont Overpass.

salts are picked up by vehicles traveling over roads where such salts are used and so garage structures are particularly vulnerable to damage from chlorides. Chlorides break down the passivity of steel in concrete, cause rapid deterioration, and so lead to frequent and extensive maintenance of structures. In marine atmospheres, it is estimated that a 75-mm thickness of good, high-quality concrete is needed to protect steel against corrosion. This was another reason why galvanized reinforcement was employed in the Bank of Hawaii building.

In Bermuda, the warm and humid marine exposure causes so rapid a rusting of steel that it often was necessary to wire brush or other wise remove the rust before the concrete could be poured. It is now routine to use galvanized reinforcement in many structures to avoid a problem which actually precedes the pouring of concrete. Some chemical plants in the United States have also used galvanized reinforcement for this reason.

Zinc-Rich Paints

One of the fastest growing new markets for zinc has been in zinc-rich paints, which are now being used to supplement galvanized steel for automotive underbody protection against corrosion, for bridges and other structures, for ships hulls, and various types of buildings. The Vertical Assembly Building at Cape Kennedy, considered the world's largest building, is maintenance coated with zinc-rich paint. San Francisco's Golden Gate bridge is kept corrosion-free with zinc-rich paint. The world's largest radar-telescope-the Aercibo Ionospheric Observatory in Puerto Rico - has a disc-type reflector consisting of galvanized steel cable which is maintained with zinc-rich paint to ward off the effects of a jungle climate.

Zinc-rich paint provides sacrificial galvanic protection of steel similar to galvanized coatings and is recommended wherever economics, or size and shape of products make galvanizing impracticable. The zinc-rich paints consist of zinc dust pigmented in high concentrations from 85 to 95% - by weight in organic or inorganic binders. Considerable research involving long-term exposure tests is being conducted in efforts to determine effects of particle size, amounts and types of extenders that can be used, and similar basic questions concerning ultimate performance. Previous work led to development of a zinc-rich primer which can be spot welded, an advance of particular interest to the automotive industry.

Die Casting-Finishes

Zinc die castings hold a stronger position in many markets today, particularly in the automotive industry, due to the many advances in finishing developed in the past decade. Whereas in the late 1950's a blemish-free service life of six months could be expected, new plating systems developed in research now offer up to five years of required performance in aggressive environments.

The bright and satin-finished duplex-nickel or microcracked chromium plating systems that improve durability by as much as 500% over previous systems have now been adopted in whole or in part by major automobile manufacturers throughout the world and undoubtedly have been major factors in once again making zinc the superior trim material for automobiles.

Zinc's potential in the automotive area is underscored by the Zn 75, a demonstration vehicle built for ILZRO by the Lamborghini-Bertone team in Italy. The highly stylized vehicle was designed to demonstrate the many old and new applications for zinc and lead in decorative, decorative-functional and functional components. These include new plating systems and other finishes for zinc, as well as new zinc casting alloys.

The use of auxiliary anodes for improving thickness uniformity of nickel and chromium has been widely adopted by electroplaters to conserve nickel and to upgrade the durability of finishes on complex shapes.

Finishing plated and unplated die castings through various paint sys-

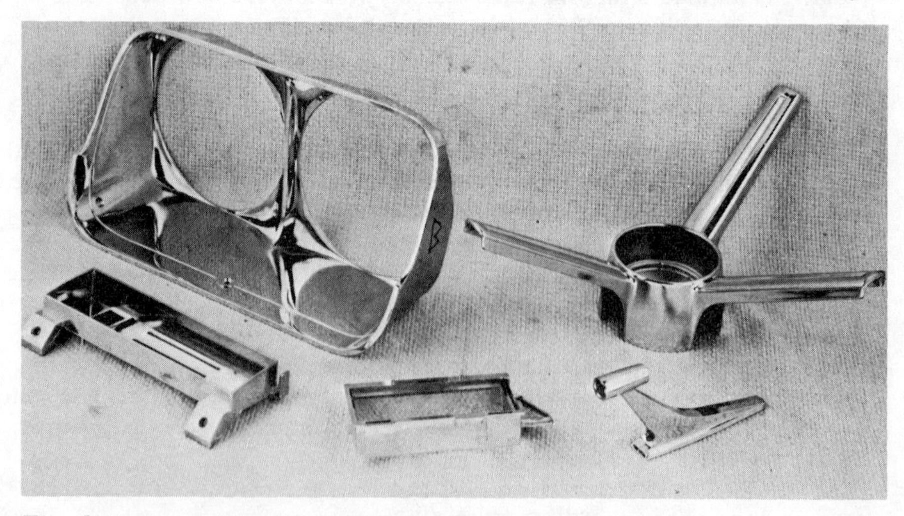

Fig. 10 - Die castings finished in a vibratory mill and strike plate acid copper.

tems also is possible as a result of ILZRO research findings, such castings also can be finished with a variety of other decorative finishes, such as textured surfaces or clear organic coatings. The paint research led to establishment of a practical procedure for obtaining good adherence of decorative paint on chrome-plated zinc.

In the search for decorative finishes to provide additional flexibility to stylists and improved protective coatings for the design engineer, research led to introduction about four years ago of an anodizing process which provides a tough and attractive finish having improved abrasion and corrosion resistance. The process, which is licensed by ILZRO, has been adopted commercially for pump impeller parts in a major washing machine and for components in a lock.

In one of the industry's newer plating developments, buffing is eliminated in a finishing and plating cycle that includes bright leveling copper plated in copper-sulfuric acid solutions. Polishing scratches and other kinds of surface roughness are effectively leveled with the bright acid copper. Data developed in the ILZRO research showed that the cost of mechanical smoothing by buffing ranges from 20 to 40% of the total cost of a casting, including material, casting, finishing, and plating. Later research demonstrated that the quality of plated zinc die castings was improved and finishing costs reduced by more than 50% with the vibratory finishing technique, coupled with the leveling acid copper bath. Figure 10 shows various die castings finished in a vibratory mill and strike plated in a pyrophosphate solution before plating with leveling acid copper and nickel.

Die Castings - Process

While zinc die casting is far superior to any other available process, or material for the high speed production of complex parts, research to improve both continues at an increasing pace, spurred by competitive pressures and the demands of new products and technologies.

One of the earlier ILZRO programs, conducted cooperatively with several other industry associations, consisted of an investigation into the flow and gating of die casting dies. The results proved extremely valuable to die designers and die casters.

In another area, ILZRO completed a project which resulted in use of computers to estimate fabrication costs of die cast parts within hours instead of days. Known as DIECAP (for Die Casting Cost Analysis Program) the program has been made available to designers and users of die castings throughout the world.

Die Casting - Alloys

The zinc industry devoted considerable effort in the 1960's to development of new zinc alloys, both for die casting and for other zinc applications. Among the successful results of this effort are ILZRO 14 creep-resistant die casting alloy, ILZRO 16, a still experimental but improved type of creep-resistant die casting alloy, and ILZRO 12, a primarily foundry alloy.

ILZRO 14 is still so new that it is largely in the evaluation stage. The composition range of ILZRO 14 is 1.0-1.5% copper, 0.25-0.30% titanium, 0.01-0.03% aluminum, and the remainder zinc. The first commercial use of this alloy which is suitable for cold chamber machines, was announced in mid-1970. This application consists of a housing used in an automatic load leveler, a device that keeps an automobile level in a horizontal plane when a heavy load is applied to the rear. A photograph of the housing, which looks like a finned pipe on a circular base, is shown in Figure 11.

The fabricator turned to ILZRO 14 because this componentis subject to elevated temperatures (93°C) and high differential pressures. The casting is designed to withstand 2.07 MN/m^2 (300 psi) internal air pressure without leakage. Before accepting the new alloy, the fabricator subjected ILZRO 14 parts to 1.38 MN/m^2 (200 psi) at 107°C for 7 days. At the end of the test, the ILZRO 14 housing exhibited no measurable creep.

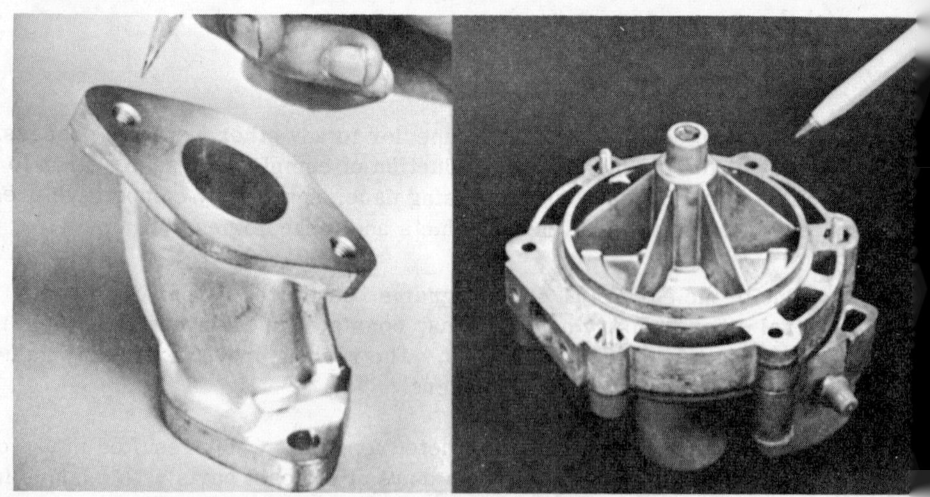

Fig. 11 - ILZRO 14 die casting zinc alloy housing in automatic load leveller (right) combats creep at high temperature. ILZRO 12 carburetor elbow casting has dense, porosity-free structure.

ILZRO 12 became commercial in 1966, when it was used in the gravity casting of prototype auto body parts, primarily because this alloy's properties closely approximate those of a subsequently die cast part using conventional zinc alloys. Its composition range is 0.5-1.25% copper, 0.01-0.013% magnesium, 11.0-13.0% aluminum and the balance zinc. However, the alloy also was quickly found to be especially suited for foundry applications. Several applications in its first and second years resulted because of its advantages in short production runs, which would make costs of die casting dies prohibitive.

The more recent stage of development has seen spreading use of the alloy for various foundry production run parts used in appliances, industrial machines, and vending machines. Of further significance is the fact that

ILZRO 12 has supplanted copper-base or ferrous alloys in some of these applications. It is now being used on a widening scale throughout the world. A photograph of a carburetor elbow cast of ILZRO 12 in a plaster mold, is seen in Figure 11. The machined flange, where the outer layer of the casting was milled away, reveals a very uniform and porosity-free surface. This ILZRO 12 casting is one of several employed on the Zn 75 vehicle.

Wrought Zinc

The unique combination of properties offered by wrought zinc has made it an ideal material for a variety of industrial and commerical applications for nearly a century. Some of the more important advantages include fabricability, design flexibility, corrosion resistance, and uniformity of appearance, regardless of the manufacturing process used. Among established applications are photo-engraver's plates, lithographic plates, building and architectural uses, and dry cell batteries.

Around the mid-1960's a new wrought zinc alloy, containing zinc-copper-titanium, was developed to provide improved creep-resistant properties for applications where stresses are involved. This alloy has now demonstrated its capability in complete rainwater systems, including gutters and downspouts. The alloy also is being used increasingly for many electronic components; automotive parts; various decorative products, such as medallions, jewelry, belt buckles, etc.; general manufacturing, including toys, furniture knobs, bezels, and many other products; and in other construction components, including roll-formed trim, and decorative panels. The Zn 75 vehicle had several innovative wrought zinc trim parts, such as the front and rear bumpers, front grille, and spun wheel covers - the first time such parts were so fabricated for any automobile.

A "superplastic" wrought zinc alloy introduced about three years ago and still largely in the evaluation stage for many applications may well become a major outlet for zinc in a few years, especially in the automotive industry. The product is being seriously considered as a possible replacement material for steel in many automotive products, including the basic car body.

Among the advantages cited for this wrought zinc are its capacity to be formed to a far greater extent than is possible with steel. In some cases it is reported that the superplastic zinc can achieve more than 1000 % elongation, compared to 50 to 60% with deep drawing steel. This characteristic undoubtedly is due to the approximately 22% aluminum content in its composition. The key characteristics is that this formability can be achieved with low-cost tooling.

Zinc Chemicals

Zinc and its compounds are used in growing amounts in the chemical, metallurgical, ceramic, fertilizer, paint, paper, plastics, rubber, textile, electronics, and other industries. Zinc oxide is by far the most important zinc chemical, with its most important use being as a reinforcing pigment in rubber, where it provides good heat conductivity and resistance to aging by sunlight, among other advantages.

In recent years, one of the more interesting new uses has involved the use of zinc as a supplement in plant and animal feed. Tests have shown that zinc in certain trace quantities is highly essential for the growth and development of plants and animals.

Zinc oxide has played a leading role in the copying industry, which has grown from a multi-million-dollar industry to a multi-billion-dollar industry in the past few years. Zinc oxide is used as a thin electrostatic coating material. Despite this thin micron-size layer of zinc, estimates of zinc oxide used by the copying field run to around 45,000 metric tons in North America as of early 1969.

A successful ILZRO research program demonstrated in the late 60's that zinc oxide has greater ultraviolet absorption in polypropylene than any other commercial inorganic pigment. This has led to a significant new market potential that began to manifest itself by the turn of the decade. Zinc oxide's potential as a UV stabilizer in other volume plastics is being developed further by study of synergistic combinations with other types of additives.

Zinc Anodes

Large-scale applications research a decade ago on zinc anode systems for marine tanker use showed zinc to be superior to magnesium anodes in performance and economy. The non-sparking property of zinc because a significant advantage, from a safety standpoint, and now zinc anodes are the preferred sacrificial anode for corrosion protection in this application.

Related efforts led to development a few years later of zinc anode systems for galvanized hot-water storage tanks as well as for glass-lined tanks, providing superior service life at an economic price. Consumption of zinc for this application, however, has yet to develop significantly. Still another interesting offshoot was the development of protective zinc anodes for crab pots.

Recent Developments - Lead

Architectural Applications

Research to develop effective methods of using lead sheet to attenuate sound contributed materially to one of the most promising new architectural markets to emerge in the past few years. The study was aimed at two prime commercial areas- (1) movable partitions, and (2) blocking of over-the-ceiling noise in offices. Both types of applications are illustrated in Figure 12. The approach for correcting ceiling noises, now extensively used in North America, consists of erecting a lead plenum barrier. Another approach, involving the laying of a blanket of lead sheet on a suspended ceiling, is favored and widely used in Australia. With respect to movable partitions, laboratory data established guide lines for the use of lead with a wide group of common building materials and framing systems.

While metallic lead is an excellent material for sound attenuation purposes, combinations of lead with other materials have provided solutions to problems of noise transmission in a more concealed way. Examples are decorative wood veneers laminated with 1/16" thick lead sheets, leaded cloth which can also be used as decorative wall paper, curtains of plastic loaded with metallic lead powder and lead laminates, with aluminum to achieve a combination of strength and lightness, used as enclosures to noisy machinery. An exciting application is leaded plastic sheets to reduce the noise of jet aircraft engines. A modern passenger aircraft may carry as much as 700 lbs of such sheets.

A corollary development of extreme importance to the wide acceptance of lead sheet for sound attenuation was the successful industry development a little more than a decade ago of DM (Direct Machine) lead sheet required for acoustical and other building applications. The range of weights and other characteristics of lead sheet directly castable in sheet form by the machine at a cost around one-fifth that of conventional fabricating technique lend themselves to these applications.

Economical DM lead sheet, plus lead's long service life, attractive patina, and other favorable properties were exploited in another major ILZRO architectural program - composite lead roofing. This effort has had encouraging results to date, including development of composite shingles superior in tests to high-quality asphalt shingles. Various types of patterned lead sheet shingles bonded to asphalt-saturated paper also performed well in tests. Some examples of the "dimpled" surfaces tested are shown in Figure 13.

The roofing, acoustical and other lead-sheet markets were aided by the industry sponsored research into adhesive joining of lead to lead and to other substrates. The number of applications involving adhesive bonding of lead continues to grow, including lead sheet on plywood for building fascia, lining of petroleum, storage tanks, and many more.

The advantageous combination of weight and limpness in lead also comes in useful in the field of vibration control. Lead-asbestos pads have been used for over 50 years to control the transmission of vibrations from the ground to building foundations. The elimination of troublesome vibrations in railroad tracks, subways, locations carrying a heavy traffic load, etc. has been rendered possible by the incorporation of lead-asbestos pads in the foundation design. More recently, smaller parts have been successful to isolate rooftop cooling towers from the steelwork of buildings, and also for printing presses, commercial laundry machines and other equipment.

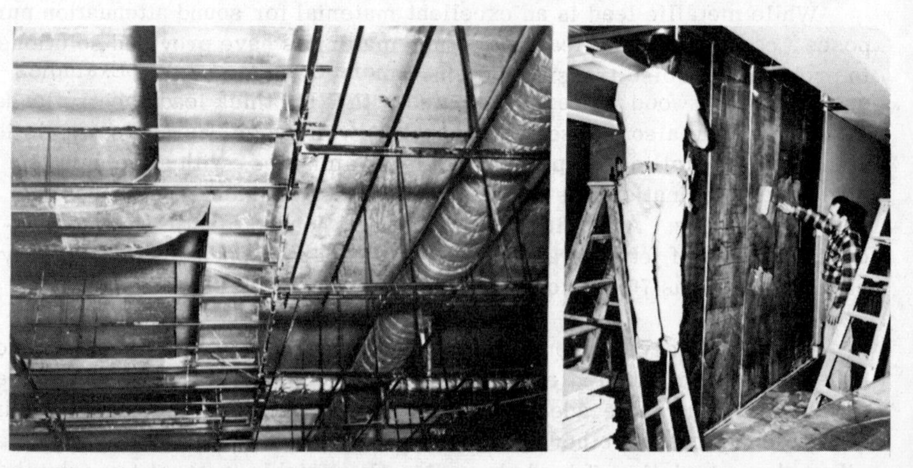

Fig. 12 - Lead sheet hung in space over suspended ceilings (left) to attenuate sound. It is also used in wall partitions.

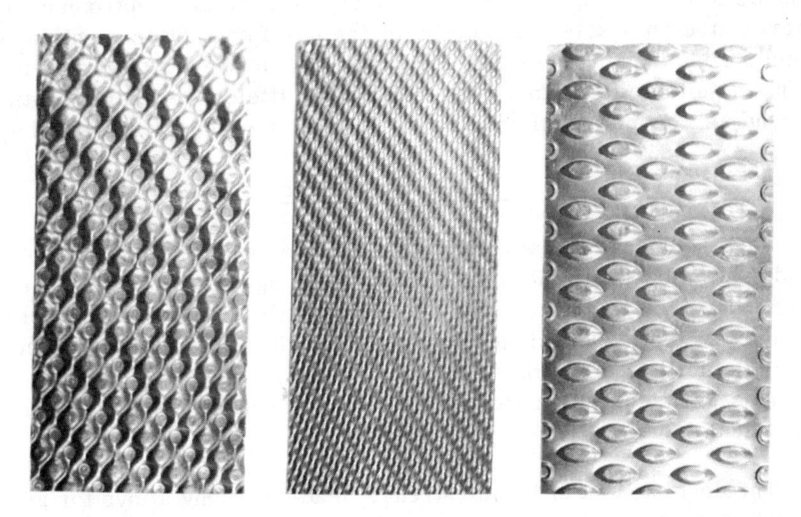

Fig. 13 - Dimpled patterns on lead-asphalt paper laminate roofing shingles.

Paints and Pigments

The two primary functions of a paint are to provide adequate corrosion protection and enhance the aesthetic appeal. Experience over the years has established that lead in the form of pigment contributes more beneficial properties to paint than any other single ingredient. Lead pigments satisfy all the requirements of a good paint, i. e. adhesion, flexibility, distensibility, etc. Most important of all the characteristics of lead pigmented paints is the high resistance to water. Lead paints absorb only a fraction of as much water as non-lead paints.

The two most widely used general purpose lead paints are the white lead paints and red lead paints. In addition to these, many other lead pigments are used for specialized requirements. Some of these are basic lead sulphate, basic lead chromate and metallic lead.

Several ILZRO programs were conducted (1) to determine which lead pigments and vehicles are best in water-thinned primers, both of the air dried and baked types, to inhibit corrosion of steel; (2) to study the beneficial stain-inhibiting properties of lead pigments in water-thinned paints for wood; and (3) to study the electrophoretic deposition of lead-pigmented water-reducible paint formulations onto metal substrates.

Promising lead-pigmented paint systems have been developed in the first two projects and some have withstood outdoor weathering tests for as long as seven years, with outstanding results. In the electrophoretic research, the emphasis has been in testing new formulations containing experimental resins and cross-linking agents. The lead industry wants to be sure it has a suitable lead paint system available if electro-coating continues to expand as a commercial process for coating steel components and structures.

Lead Acid Batteries

The use of lead in batteries, which started with the invention of the lead-acid system by Gaston Plante over 100 years ago, has increased to such an extent that today batteries form the major outlet for lead. Characteristic features of the lead-acid battery, like its high energy storage capacity, economy, flexibility, reliability and good overall efficiency combine to make it the most efficient and economical system for converting chemical energy into electrical energy.

The development of higher strength lead-antimony alloys for grid construction went a long way in minimizing problems of premature failure and helped to bring about a significant improvement in the performance of lead acid batteries. The higher mechanical strength of these alloys has also rendered possible the use of thinner grids, thus achieving a cost reduction as well as making the batteries lighter, thereby facilitating handling and increasing the efficiency of the system.

The search for a still stronger lead material with improved properties led to development of dispersion strengthened (DS) lead. While battery grids manufactured of DS lead may initially have value principally for specialty batteries, the method of manufacture ultimately may offer significant economies because of thinner grids and automated nanufacturing methods. The fabrication of polypropylene cases contributed significantly to reduction of overall battery weight and size in the past few years. Other improvements include development of over-the-wall or over partition connectors which reduce internal resistance and permit the clean, easily maintained one-piece top. A lead-acid semi-sealed cell is now widely used for portable tools, TV acts, and other appliances.

Another important on-going research program that is continuing and alreac has had major effect on battery manufacturers concerns the evaluation and standardization of battery paste composition and production techniques in manufacturing pasted grids. One of the practical objectives of this research is the development of paste preparation and plate processing methods to achieve optimum performance from the active material in the batteries now being produced and to obtain as good active material adhesion to grids of pure lead, DS lead, or calcium lead as can be obtained on grids of antimonial lead.

Dispersion-Strengthened Lead

Attention has been focussed in recent years on dispersion strengthened lead as one approach in overcoming the mechanical weakness of lead without causing a deterioration in its other properties. DS lead has excellent mechanical properties in such areas as. tensile strength, ductility, creep resistance, thermal stability, and hardness. It also has good fatigue strength, electrical properties and corrosion resistance. DS lead can be readily formed, fabricated and machined, and is available in a variety of forms, including sheet, strip, foil, pipe, and the like.

The superior properties of DS lead have made it readily acceptable in many existing applications of lead and its alloys, including - in addition to battery grids -- cable sheathing, chemical industry equipment, radiation shielding, sound attenuation, and architectural applications, among others. The fuel line on the Zn 75 was fabricated of DS lead. Its properties point to improved performance at elevated temperatures and pressures and its rigidity makes feasible piping systems for corrosive materials or in corrosive environments. Such pipe system can have mechanical connections and fittings, thereby adding the benefits of more economic installation. Extruded rigid tubing for such applications is illustrated in Figure 14.

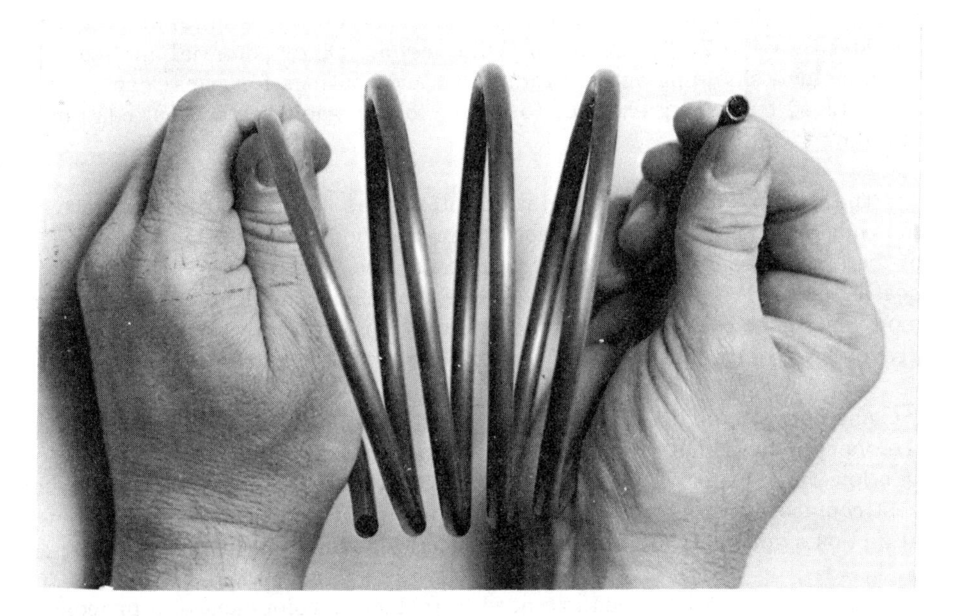

Fig. 14 - Dispersion strengthened lead tubing for chemical applications.

Radiation Shielding

The constant quest for new uses and improved properties have led to the development of several materials to provide shielding from x-rays and nuclear sources. Some of these materials, which have now become virtually standard for these applications, include metallic lead powder mixed with polyethylene in cast rigid sheets up to several inches thick. Lead powder also is mixed with polyvinyl chloride for the manufacture of protective gloves, aprons, and flexible sheet.

The development of these and similar lead materials has contributed to a steady increase in the amount of lead used for radiation shielding in recent times, particularly in hospitals and laboratories. Since there is no other material which can successfully compete with lead in this particular application, lead's role will continue to gain in importance in the nuclear field.

High-Speed Lead Plating

A low-cost method for electrodepositing lead and lead-tin alloy coatings on steel is another promising development of the past decade. The economics of this system are favorable, particularly in view of the high speed with which the coatings can be deposited on steel strip and its compatibility with existing electrolytic tin coating lines. Among evaluations already completed are those on hydraulic brake tubing, similar to that employed for the Zn 75, as shown in Figure 15. Other potential applications include shielding against radiation, and coatings for cans especially those containing shellac, to insure longer shelf life without contamination.

The process has also raised wide interest as a high quality alternative to producing terne plate by the hot dipping method. A significant feature of the electroterne coating is the uniformity and pore-free nature of the coating as well as the reduced thickness required to achieve equivalent corrosion resistance. This has been achieved by an additive which effectively prevents porosity in a range of coating thickness.

Another related program was initiated in the past year or so to study the operating parameters influencing the production of lead-coated steel in a low-tin or tin-free lead alloy bath. This objective would permit lower cost replacement for terne plate in such applications as automotive gasoline tanks, oil pans, fire doors, air conditioners, etc.

Research work has been extended to include development of a process for high-speed plating of low-tin (5 to 20%) terne alloys for can stock and other applications.

The research goal is to lower or eliminate the tin content of terne through substitution by other alloying elements. Tin is required for wetting, since pure lead does not wet steel satisfactorily. The high cost of tin, however, makes it necessary to reduce or eliminate it from terne-coated steel. Various coatings employing such alloying elements as zinc, nickel and copper are being evaluated for porosity and corrosion resistance.

Lead in Ceramics

Lead-in the form of lead oxide-is used in a great variety of ceramic products and for a great number of reasons, such as lower melting range, wider softening range, and higher index of refraction. Lead oxide is one of the very few materials which can be used in almost unlimited proportion in glass.

In efforts to produce a lead-bearing enamel with improved properties of opacification, adherence and durability when applied on aluminum, a series of low-melting leaded frits were developed through ILZRO research. These were white, chemically durable and self-opacified, and were formulated to minimize the reduction in strength of Type 61S aluminum alloys during porcelain enamelling at elevated temperatures.

Another ILZRO program was directed to a study of light dispersion in high-lead porcelain enamel systems with the addition of conventional opacifiers, thus permitting maximum opacity to be developed in the thinnest

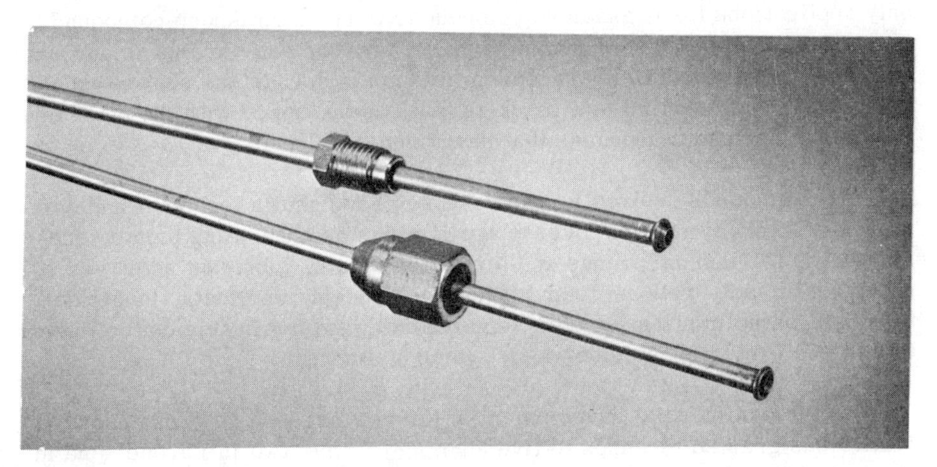

Fig. 15 - Terne-coated brake line tubing fabricated for the Zn 75 show car.

possible layer on various metal substrates.

A program was initiated to develop materials and techniques for manufacturing oriented lead-based magnetically hard ferrite bodies having properties superior to the presently used barium and strontium ferrites. Initially, it was discovered how to make high-lead ferrites in the isotropic (unoriented) form with magnetic properties approximately 40% greater than those of conventional unoriented barium and strontium ferrites. But since the largest potential market exists in the field of oriented lead ferrites, additional research was directed towards the development of orientation techniques, using the best compositions found in the earlier isotropic lead ferrite work. Oriented lead ferrites are expected to have a maximum energy product, approximately four times greater than the oriented type. Applications of such ferrites include powered accessories in automobiles speakers for radio and television, and various home and shop appliances. Other markets for ferrite materials are inductors for filter circuits and various high frequency electronic devices.

Another successful ceramic study proved the technical feasibility of flame-spraying lead-bearing ceramic coatings onto concrete block surfaces. The research showed that these coatings can be applied in assembly line production to steel, glass, and other substrates. An improved flame-spray gun also was developed as part of this program.

Organoleads

ILZRO's synthesis of organolead compounds has been one of most productive of all its programs and one that reflects lead's adaptability to changing time and changing needs. Prior to ILZRO's research in this area, the only applications for organolead compounds were as antiknock compounds in gasoline. While this is a major market for lead and one that is currently being threatened, ILZRO research in the past decade has shown that there are large potential new markets that can be tapped with the new families of organolead compounds that have been developed.

The compounds evolved in this research have shown technical and commercial capability in such diverse applications as antifouling paints, preservatives for marine pilings and for cottons cloth, lubricant additives, catalysts for polyurethane foam production, rodent repellents, fungicides, biocides, anthelmintics for tapeworm control, and molluscicides in the control of snail fever (schistosomiasis), among others.

For the commercial development of the new organolead compounds, ILZRO has granted licenses to five chemical firms (two in Europe, one in the United Kingdom, and two in the United States) to make use, and sell the new compounds under the ILZRO patents. Of all the compounds developed to date, those being used as antifouling agents in marine paints have been most commercialized.

A comparison test on a large British cruise ship which was painted with various antifouling paint formulation, including an ILZRO organolead system, indicate that the organolead system is more effective in antifouling capability than other standard formulation. This shipboard test is now in its second year. Another significant development is the use of organoleads as wood impregnants to repel marine borers. These compounds may use creosote as a carrier to provide outstanding protection against limnorial and teredine borers, which cause millions of dollars damage each year to wood pilings in seawater. Ironically, these borers will become a bigger problem as water pollution control measures enable them to return to formerly polluted waters. The wood preserving capability of organolead compounds is demonstrated in Figure 16.

New research will explore the effectiveness of the organolead compounds against termites and fungal attack in terrestial applications.

Totally unexpected lubricant properties were obtained when certain new organolead compounds were added to conventional lubricating oils. The antiwear properties imparted to rubbing steel surfaces, by oils containing organ-

Fig. 16 - Organolead preservative protected test panels from marine borers which destroyed untreated panels.

lead additives were found to be durable and far superior to these obtained with the commonly used materials. Several large U. S. oil companies have requested organolead samples for evaluation in automotive applications.

Lead Bearings

Lead's natural qualities of lubricity and softness have made it a leading material for automotive bearings, all kinds of electric motors, railroad car journal bearings, and similar applications. In the past few years, several new lead materials have been developed which have expanded the metal's use in these applications.

One of these consists of lead-tin alloy impregnated into a highly porous sheet of fibrous steel. The matrix provides strength and creep resistance to the infiltrated lead, which remains in the matrix when heated above its melting point. A typical composite sheet is 0.8-mm thick. It is being used for home or industrial solder repair work and for various hobbies, including jewelry, stabiles, and other art objects.

Another composite material developed in Japan consists of a lead-impregnated, sintered ferrous alloy which combines the inherent lubricity of lead with the strength of steel. Lubricity is provided by the lead at the material's surface. If the friction surface becomes dry and hot due to starved lubrication, lead in the surface pores melts, absorbs heat as latent heat of fusion, and keeps the composite surface temperature at the melting point of lead. The material thus provides a self-regulating supply of lubricating lead to the surface to achieve outstanding wear resistance. The composite was successfully used for the bar sliders on Japan National Railways new Tokaido line, which travels up to 210 km. and where the high-speed friction creates critical material requirements.

A Look Ahead for Zinc

Many of the more promising growth areas over the near term for zinc, as well as for lead, are already taking shape. Going 20 years ahead or even up to the next century, however, involves more risk and even some conjecture, but the main outlines can be fairly well determined.

In galvanizing, for instance, the simple fact that the United States and Canada steel industry have increased their galvanizing capacity by 25% over the past two years points to a continuation of the sharp growth of galvanizing in North America for the next few years, at the very least. The new galvanizing lines are automated and computerized so that the product is more uniform, more precisely coated, and more adjustable to consumer demands.

The major potentials of galvanizing in bridges and other large structures, aided by improved bolting and welding procedures, will be an important factor in this growth. Looking beyond the next five years or so, there is every reason to believe that all steelwork on bridges, towers, off shore structures, and the like will be protected by zinc coatings, mostly hot-dip galvanizing. Economics will be a prime consideration in the switch to zinc coatings as engineers seek every means to reduce long-term maintenance costs.

The use of galvanized reinforcement is another new application which is likely to be a prime growth market. Growth is likely to accelerate as the history of successful existing applications becomes more widely known and the advantage of galvanized rebar are made known to more builders and architects. Use of galvanized rebar also is likely to be given further impetus by the trend to more highly-stylized precast concrete buildings in which prevention of rust staining is highly desirable. The long-term advantage of reduced maintenance, due to less cracking and spalling of the concrete, also will be a big inducement to wider use of galvanized reinforcement.

Pre-painted galvanized steel sideing is estimated to have a potential running up to one-half million metric tons a year in North America alone compared with only a few thousand metric tons today. The trend to prefabricated housing units will be an important factor in helping galvanized to reach a good part of its ultimate potential before the next decade rolls around. The United States Federal Government's "operation breakthrough" is an indication of the industrialized approach this industry will take.

The growth in the coil coating industry provides another basis for increased use of galvanized steel. This market increased more than four-fold during the 1960's -- from around 250 000 metric tons in 1962, the first year for which figures were compiled, to over 1-million metric tons in 1969, according to the National Coil Coaters Association--and the trend is for a continuation of the sharp percentage increases through the 1970's. Coil-coated stock is used for a wide variety of products, including cans, house siding, appliances, and others.

Other markets that can be expected to become stronger include highway guard rails and signs.

Continued research to improve the galvanizing process will contribute to the growth. It is also likely that techniques will be developed for proper galvanizing of all types of steels with coatings that will provide equally good service life.

Die Casting

It is possible that by 1980 a fully automated die casting plant will be in operation. Die castings produced in this plant will be more consistent and of a higher quality than is now possible. Scrap will be reduced substantially, as will labor costs, while performance will be improved.

ILZRO presently is conducting two vital programs that can help make that prediction come true. Both are designed to establish computer control of all major parameters in the die casting process. The basic aim is to eliminate errors due to faults in human judgment, thereby improving the control over casting conditions and raising the quality and consistency of the castings and their rate of production. Several significant process improvements and instrumentation have already emerged from the first program, including a die temperature-cycle time controller.

The second program has been concentrated initially on thin-wall die castings which are likely to play a more important role in the years ahead. The die castings machine in this study also will be instrumented for fully automatic operation.

In the area of zinc casting alloys, increasing use can be expected of the new creep-resistant alloys, ILZRO 14 and ILZRO 16. Much heavier consumption can be expected of ILZRO 12, particularly in foundry applications, in the next decade. The potential in such applications is great enough to make this as large as die casting, especially in view of the increasing cost of copper-base alloys, one of the materials currently used.

Use of zinc for die casting, meanwhile, will continue to rely most heavily on the automotive industry, at least through the 1970's. Automobile production is projected to increase from its current 8-million units to somewhere around 11-million units in 1975. Research to improve product performance, for example, through thinner-walled castings, improved alloys and processes, and reduced costs should be sufficient to withstand further encroachment from competitive materials, particularly plastics, and may even regain some markets already lost. The proportionately higher increase in automotive production in Europe will help raise die casting consumption levels in that continent sufficiently that it may challenge galvanizing for the number one position in consumption before 1980.

Plating

The impact of new plating systems developed in the past few years can be expected to be even more widely adopted in the immediate years ahead. And several newer systems should accelerate the process even more, thereby helping zinc die castings and wrought zinc to hold present markets and capture many new ones.

The new vibratory finishing method previously described can be expected to play a significant role in the plating of die castings for the immediate years ahead, due to the reduced costs and improved performance.

Another plating program, involving a study of the plating characteristics of a decorative chromium plating bath based on dimethyl-formamide-water as solvent and chromic trichloride as the plating salt. This trivalent plating systems has produced an attractive chromium plate which is somewhat darker than normal. More importantly, it is deposited at a rate some six times faster than that of conventional baths, has some - what improved throwing and covering power and gives microporous deposits of inherently great corrosion resistance. This system, which is now in the pilot plant evaluation stage, can have an important bearing on the finishing aspects of zinc die castings by the mid-1970's, if not sooner.

Wrought Zinc

Roll-formed zinc may possibly hold the largest potential of all for zinc in the next decade, boosted by the introduction of new alloys and improved manufacturing techniques, particularly in the United States, where a new mill has greatly expanded availability of the material in long coil form. The longer coils make the material suitable for high production operations and also reduce the costs. In Europe, which has long been a heavy user of wrought zinc for roofing and many other applications, similar advances are likely to assure steady growth of markets in that area.

Among research programs which could have large impact on future markets is the development of a screw-machine alloy by adding free-machining additives to a modified zinc-copper-titanium system. Results have been very promising and such an alloy could be commercially significant by 1975.

Another very significant research effort now in the pilot production stage is the production of Zn-Cu-Ti tubing by conventional fabricating techniques now employed for other metals. High frequency resistance welding is being used in the production of the tubing, which is already being considered for such applications as tower bars, air conditioners, refrigeration cooling coils, radiator tube construction, and mechanical tubing applications.

Research also is continuing on a zinc-finned automotive radiator. Results of tests conducted on a first series of such radiators have been sufficiently encouraging to merit continuation of the program. The market potential is tremendous, of course, so success in the research could well be translated into large consumption.

ILZRO has conducted environmental testing of wrought zinc gutters and downspouts and found such installations in excellent condition after five years of service in severely corrosive atmospheres. An unpainted installation developed a pleasing patina and there was no evidence of the staining which takes place in copper systems. In addition, such systems are solderable and considerably less expensive than copper.

The many potentials of wrought zinc in automotive production, as demonstrated on the Zn 75, point to an increase in this area in the next year or two. Some of the wrought zinc components of the Zn 75 are seen in Figure 17. They demonstrate how wrought zinc could become an important outlet by the mid-1970's. If 22%-aluminum "superplastic" zinc is considered in the projection, the automotive consumption figures rise significantly. However, superplastic zinc is likely to be used initially for smaller components, though it is aimed primarily at the car body.

Other Zinc Growth Areas

The rise in consumption of zinc-rich paints during the last half of the previous decade should continue at least through the first half of the 1970's

Fig. 17 - Wrought zinc was widely used on the Zn 75 demonstration vehicle, including front grille, extruded rocker panel, wheel covers, window and wheel-opening trim, and the head lamp assembly.

and probably on to 1980. Research programs in progress will aid materially in the growth by providing data for improved systems.

Good growth in the next few years can also be anticipated in the use of zinc compounds in agricultural applications, particularly as a supplement in plant and animal feed.

The research on zinc oxide in plastics has taken on a new urgency due to the rapid growth of some plastics in construction, particularly rigid polyvinyl chloride (PVC) for house siding. One market estimate indicates that 86-million kg (190-million lbs) of PVC will be used for housing by 1975. ILZRO research on use of zinc oxide as an ultraviolet light (UV) stabilizer has shown encouraging results at zinc oxide additions of up to 30 parts per hundred of resin. The effectiveness of zinc oxide as a UV stabilizer in polypropylene has already been demonstrated and could become an important outlet for zinc oxide in the years ahead. Favorable results also have been obtained in research on other large volume plastics.

The entirely new area of organozinc compounds also is likely to have some impact on consumption in the years ahead. Work to date points to the general field of catalysts in polymerization of various intermediates as a major application outlet in the next few years. The organozincs can be expected to play much larger roles in the later years of this century.

A Look Ahead For Lead

Lead-Acid Batteries

The new world awareness of the effect of pollution on ecological balances and the critical need for remedial action to restore these balances will create tremendous opportunity for the lead-acid battery in the next decade and beyond.

It is probable that much of the world will rely on a vehicle powered by a lead-acid battery system for at least part of its traveling requirements, particularly within urban areas. For long distance journeys, the battery-powered vehicle is likely to be driven to an automated "dual mode" highway where electricity, probably through some third-rail systems, will provide the motive power. When the traveler reaches his objective on the automated highway, he will be shunted to an exit track at the end of which he will switch back to his vehicle battery to complete the trip under his own power. Electric vehicles operating on a prototype test track of this type are shown in Figure 18.

The electric vehicle already is an important element in such applications as industrial trucks, fork-lift trucks, garden tractors, and golf carts, among others. There are an estimated 60 000 delivery vans presently in service in England with one dairy company alone having around 3 000 such vans in service in London. Of the 200 000 in-plant trucks in service in the United States in 1969, roughly one-third were estimated to be electric.

The lead industry has been keenly aware of the increasing need for such vehicles and so has been conducting considerable research to improve the lead-acid battery, with the result that the lead-acid battery of today is so far improved over the battery of even 10 years ago as to virtually constitute a new type of energy source.

ILZRO also conducted a program to determine the optimum power system for vehicle propulsion, using either a simple lead-acid battery system or a so-called "hybrid" system combining lead-acid batteries with an engine-generator. It was found, in brief, that the lead-acid battery powered van of limited mission constitutes the best present opportunity for the lead-acid battery.

This conclusion led ILZRO to launch a new program, now under way, to test the battery-powered delivery van concept in greater detail. ILZRO plans to construct four prototype trucks whose design will stress lightweight construction and generally conform to United States Post Office and electrical utility specifications. It is anticipated that these vehciles will have a top speed of around 56 km per hour and have a 50 km range, assuming 350 stops per charge. The lead-acid battery would be of 60-96 volts and have sufficient capacity to meet design criteria of 180 to 225 ampere hours.

Before the next century arrives, however, it is likely that we will have battery powered cars capable of a top speed of around 150 km/hour and a range of at least 250 km.

On the subject of lead consumption, if we assume that 10-million electric vehicles are built by 1980, and each is powered by a 450-kg (1000 lbs) battery pack, we see the potential for lead is roughly 4.5-million metric tons of lead. In 1969, a good year for batteries in the United States, an estimated total of 240 000 metric tons of lead was required.

Another research program that could bear importantly on this market in the years ahead has as its objectives (1) evaluation of lead-air system capabilities; (2) the development of methods for improving the design and fabrication of the cells and batteries; and (3) an analysis of the battery system.

Fig. 18 - Prototype electric vehicles on a test electric track system.

A fully sealed battery, or batteries having a gelled or solid electrolytes, could have heavy impact on the portable hand tool market and similar battery powered applications. ILZRO is conducting research to resolve the problems of gas evolution and recombination to make the sealed battery a reality, hopefully well before 1980.

TEL and other Organoleads

An increase in the number of electric vehicles at the expense of gasoline-powered vehicles will bring a corresponding decrease in the consumption of tetraethylead for gasoline. However, the internal combustion engine will remain the dominant motive power for at least the decade ahead, and probably longer, especially if suitable controls are devised for the control of toxic and annoying emissions, such as hydrocarbons, oxides of nitrogen, carbon monoxide, and particulates. And while political action is always difficult to forecast, the odds are that TEL will not be banned as a gasoline additive, at least through the next five years. If satisfactory controls compatible with lead are developed in the interim, then TEL's future is as secure as that of gasoline itself.

Meanwhile, the many new organolead compounds that have emerged from ILZRO research should begin to make their presence known within the next few years. The first volume markets are likely to be in antifouling paints, wood preservatives, lubricants and catalysts. These and other organolead markets when combined, may have the potential of TEL and so could help offset any loss of consumption in that area.

Particulate Metallurgy

One of the newer technologies to emerge from lead research concerns the production of sheet and strip by the direct conversion of rice-grain size particles. This material has opened many interesting possibilities because of the new alloys that can be created by the compaction and rolling of such particles. The particles are produced as miniature ingots by casting from a spinning cup with annular orifices. The rapid chill effect permits the retention of alloying constituents in solution at levels that would normally precipitate out in conventional bulk casting techniques.

Alloys produced by the particulate metallurgy approach show promise of exhibiting improved tensile, creep, and fatigue properties. These alloys are being considered for such applications as battery grids, cable sheathing, roofing, and other application where outstanding corrosion resistance and mechanical properties are required. Particulate lead has also been successfully extruded into rod, thereby indicating the possibility of this fabrication technique for producing cable sheathing. Extruded particulate lead cable sheathing would have more uniform composition and greater strength.

Similar research is being conducted in zinc, with much the same potential. Further work is required before either metal can go commercial, but this could be the case within a few years. Since there are so many possibilities, due to the range of alloys that can be produced, the impact of this technology on future consumption of both zinc and lead can be very significant, and probably more so in the decade of the 1980's and beyond than in the 1970's.

Lead-Plastics Composites

Cable sheathing , one of the major and traditional uses for lead, has been under severe pressure in recent years due to the inroads of plastics and other materials. These inroads have been made at the expense of quality in exchange for lighter weight and less bulk, which permits longer cable lengths to be coiled on reels. This has led to ILZRO research to develop a composite material combining the beneficial properties of its constituents-lead and a plastic and overcoming their disadvantages.

This composite combines the impermeability and corrosion resistance of lead with the low cost and light weight strength of plastics. The composite would function as a single system enabling a combination of the outstanding advantages of lead with the overall improved mechanical properties. With such composites, the ductility and toughness of lead are improved to an extent that makes the use of thinner lead sheaths practicable, thus improving the technical and economical position of lead in the field of cable sheathing.

Research has demonstrated that it is possible to achieve composites in which the polyethylene under tensile stresses will support the lead portion of the composite to offer high values of elongation before failure becomes evident in the lead. In fact, an elongation of 500% has been achieved before perforation of the lead.

Somewhat along the same line, another program is seeking to develop lead-plastic laminates for such applications as hermetic sealing and packaging and as moisture and gas barriers in industrial and architectural uses. The impermeability of lead plus its great ductility are key properties in these applications. This program differs from the previous in that the superplasticity required does not involve return after extensibility, and the forming temperature may be higher. Several plastic-lead-plastic combinations have shown excellent properties and current efforts are aimed at determining optimum thicknesses of the plastic and the lead, including lead foil (.127 mm thick or less).

Reinforced Lead

In addition to the good market potential for the lead composite roofing shingles previously described, another research effort is directed to development of a lead sheet reinforced with metallic screen materials to improve the mechanical properties of lead for roofing and other applications The leaded screen composite appears well-suited to continuous production techniques. This would make possible applications of lead as roll roofing from long coils which also could be blanked into standard shingle configuration. It is estimated that such a system would cost more than 10 percent less than such traditional roofing materials as aluminum shake, various slate systems, and Spanish tile. Final success will mean that architects and builders will have a new, long-lasting material for roofs, facades, and similar applications.

Other Potentials

In addition to the impact of high-speed electroplating of lead on steel, already described, another research program involving lead coatings could have significance in such markets as storage tanks for petroleum and chemicals. This second program is a truly explosive one -- research to determine the feasibility of explosively welding lead to steel.

The research to date has shown that lead can be explosively clad to steel and that high-quality bonds can be achieved. Other factors have yet to be resolved or determined, but this work again demonstrates some of the many new approaches being taken to expand the untility of lead, even on traditional applications.

Lead is so chemically inert that it can resist corrosion well beyond the life of most buildings. What little oxidation does take place in time gives the lead a self-preserving patina that adds to the visual appeal. In an effort to capitalize on this feature of lead, ILZRO is conducting a program to develop a chemical or mechanical method for creating a quick and uniform decorative patina on the surfaces of lead and lead alloy products, thereby enhancing their marketability for architectural purposes.

Conclusion

The details of the research programs discussed give a broad picture of the tremendous efforts that have been directed toward support of traditional applications of lead and zinc and the opening of new markets. The properties of both metals are such that they will continue to be the ideal choices in many applications, despite the severe competition that can be expected from other materials. As this review emphasizes, both metals are extremely versatile and despite their long histories of useful application, they are modern metals entirely capable of meeting the changing needs of a changing world.

CONVERSION TABLE FOR METRIC TO ENGLISH SYSTEM

Quantity	Metric Unit	Conversion Factor	U.S. or Br. Unit
Area	square meter (m^2)	x 2.471×10^{-4}	= acre
		x 10.7638	= square foot
		x 3.861×10^{-7}	= square mile
Density	kilogram/cubic meter (kg/m^3)	x 3.613×10^{-5}	= pound/cubic inch
Energy	joule (J)	x 2.778×10^{-7}	= kilowatt-hour
Heat	joule (J)	x 9.480×10^{-4}	= British thermal unit
		x 2.3889×10^{-4}	= kilogram-calorie
Length	meter (m)	x 3.2808	= foot
		x 39.37	= inch
Mass	kilogram (kg)	x 2.2046	= pound
		x 9.842×10^{-4}	= ton (long)
		x 1.1023×10^{-3}	= ton (short)
	ton (metric)	x 0.9842	= ton (long)
		x 1.1023	= ton (short)
Power	watt	x 1.341×10^{-3}	= horsepower
Pressure	newton/square meter (N/m^2)	x 9.809×10^{-6}	= atmosphere
		x 7.501×10^{-3}	= millimeters of mercury
Temperature	degree Kelvin (°K)	x 1.8 - 460	= degree Fahrenheit
	degree Celsius (°C)	x 1.8 + 32	= degree Fahrenheit

Quantity	Metric Unit	Conversion Factor	U.S. or Br. Unit
Volume	cubic meter (m^3)	x 35.314	= cubic foot
		x 6.102 x 10^4	= cubic inch
		x 220.1	= gallon (Br.)
		x 264.17	= gallon (U.S.)
	liter (1)	x 0.0353	= cubic foot
		x 0.2201	= gallon (Br.)
		x 0.2642	= gallon (U.S.)
Work	joule (J)	x 0.7375	= foot-pound

MULTIPLE AND SUBMULTIPLE UNITS

Multiplication Factor	Prefix	Metric Symbol
1 000 000 000 000	tera	T
1 000 000 000	giga	G
1 000 000	mega	M
1 000	kilo	k
100	hecto	h
10	deka	da
0.1	deci	d
0.01	centi	c
0.001	milli	m
0.000 001	micro	μ
0.000 000 001	nano	n

INDEX

Authors, Session Chairmen, and Committees

SUBJECT INDEX

EXTRACTIVE METALLURGY OF LEAD

EXTRACTIVE METALLURGY OF ZINC